Stoichiometry
Fifth Edition

ABOUT THE AUTHORS

Bharat I Bhatt is currently a Consultant to Chemical Industries and is based at Ahmedabad. He provides consultancy services in energy conservation, solvent-loss reduction, product improvement, debottlenecking in industry and related fields. He has a service experience of nearly 35 years in various chemical industries. His industrial experience covered the areas of project execution, process engineering, troubleshooting, debottlenecking, production management, management reporting, etc. He served the Indian Farmers Fertiliser Cooperative Limited (IFFCO), Kalol Unit, for nearly 18 years in various capacities. Prior to joining the industry, he worked in a textile research institute (ATIRA) for nearly 5 years where he was involved in industrial research and consultation to member textile units. Besides, he has also worked in a fine chemical unit, an edible-oil processing unit, a bulk drug unit and a carbon-black unit.

Mr Bhatt carried out unit conversion work from FPS units to SI units of the *Introduction to Chemical Engineering Thermodynamics,* 6th and 7th editions by Smith, Van Ness and Abbott, a publication of McGraw-Hill Education, USA. He authored a book titled *Introduction to Process Engineering and Design* with Mr S B Thakore, also published by Tata McGraw Hill Education, New Delhi. Besides these, he also has a book named *Design Data Book* to his credit.

Mr Bhatt graduated in Chemical Engineering from the Institute of Chemical Technology, Mumbai.

Shuchen B Thakore is Assistant Professor of Chemical Engineering at L D College of Engineering, Ahmedabad, Gujarat. He has been teaching undergraduate and postgraduate students of chemical engineering for more than 15 years. Besides teaching, he also undertakes consulting assignments in process and mechanical designs of heat exchangers, scrubbers, distillation columns, multiple effect evaporators, storage tanks, pressure vessels, etc., and environmental audit for various chemical industries.

Prior to joining the academic institute, he worked in the industry for about 6 years. He worked in Alembic Chemical Works (ACW), Gujarat Alcohol and Allied Chemicals (GAAC) Ltd and Indian Engineering Software Co.

He earlier jointly authored two books on the subjects of chemical engineering; one titled *Introduction to Process Engineering and Design* with Mr B I Bhatt, published by Tata McGraw Hill Education, New Delhi, and another titled *Illustrated Process Equipment Design*.

Mr Thakore graduated in Chemical Engineering from the Gujarat University and did his ME in Chemical Engineering from M S University.

Stoichiometry
Fifth Edition

Bharat I Bhatt
Consulting Engineer
Aavishkar Consultancy Services
Ahmedabad, Gujarat

Shuchen B Thakore
Assistant Professor
Department of Chemical Engineering
L D College of Engineering
Ahmedabad

Tata McGraw Hill Education Private Limited
NEW DELHI

McGraw-Hill Offices
New Delhi New York St Louis San Francisco Auckland Bogotá Caracas
Kuala Lumpur Lisbon London Madrid Mexico City Milan Montreal
San Juan Santiago Singapore Sydney Tokyo Toronto

Tata McGraw Hill

Published by the Tata McGraw Hill Education Private Limited,
7 West Patel Nagar, New Delhi 110 008.

This edition can be exported from India only by the publishers,
Tata McGraw Hill Education Private Limited

ISBN (13): 978-0-07-070468-8
ISBN (10): 0-07-070468-6

Managing Director: *Ajay Shukla*

Head—Higher Education Publishing: *Vibha Mahajan*
Manager—Sponsoring SEM & Tech. Ed.: *Shalini Jha*
Assoc. Sponsoring Editor: *Suman Sen*
Asst. Development Editor: *Devshree Lohchab*
Executive—Editorial Services: *Sohini Mukherjee*
Senior Production Manager: *P L Pandita*

General Manager: Marketing—Higher Education: *Michael J Cruz*
Product Manager: SEM & Tech Ed: *Biju Ganesan*
Asst. Product Manager: *Amit Paranjpe*

General Manager—Production: *Rajender P Ghansela*
Asst. General Manager—Production: *B L Dogra*

Typeset at The Composers, 260, C. A. Apt., Paschim Vihar, New Delhi 110 063 and printed at Adarsh Printers, C-50/51, Mohan Park, Naveen Shahdara, Delhi 110 032

Cover: SDR

RCZDCRDZDDDZLX

The McGraw·Hill Companies

Dedicated to our Parents

Contents

Preface

The prime objective of this book is to present fundamentals of chemical engineering in a simple and forthright manner and provide the broad background for applying these principles to industrial and theoretical problems. The importance of stoichiometry—material and energy balances—is widely known and accepted in the chemical industry in analyzing a particular process in whole or in part and also in evaluating the economics of the various processes. Basically, stoichiometry deals with the laws of conservation of mass and energy. With this, if the principles of unit operations and chemical reaction engineering are carefully bridged, the subject becomes extremely valuable to chemical engineers who apply these principles in solving process engineering problems. These have been our main considerations in selecting and preparing the material for this book.

Detailed discussions on material and energy balances of unsteady state operation will be of special interest as the topic is of significant industrial importance. In addition to these, extra care has been taken to include the most reliable thermodynamic and other useful data so that the book can serve as a standard text for students and as a reference book for practising engineers. The material has been so organized that the subject can easily be grasped by undergraduate students, nevertheless inclusion of many advanced problems makes the text quite appropriate for postgraduate students and process and design engineers.

Process engineering has been gaining greater importance in chemical industry. Optimization of the design, evaluation of alternatives, troubleshooting in the running plants, design of environmental friendly plants, and similar topics have become part of process calculations. These calculations lead to the development of process diagrams that convey a wealth of information to practicing/production engineers. Stoichiometric calculations assume a first step in these process calculations. With this chief objective in mind, the present edition has been thoroughly revised.

Emphasis on basic principles is continued with more clarity on non-ideal systems that have become now a part and parcel of the chemical industry. Many problems are drawn from industry that can be classified in this category. Recycling operations have also been considered important for a variety of reasons. New problems on recycling are added to cover few other industries such as gas processing, effluent treatment, etc. New problems on energy conservation involving stoichiometric calculations might be well appreciated by the practicing engineers. Excess enthalpies of inorganic and organic solutions change results in stoichiometric calculations significantly in many instances. This aspect is highlighted in this edition.

Thermodynamic data have been undergone thorough revision in light of up-dated data published by NIST, IUPAC, ACS, JSME and other institutes of repute in the last decade. The idea is to present the most authentic recent data which can be used by practicing engineers for their process designs. New concept of linear modeling in solving multivariable material balance problems is introduced which facilitates the use of mathematical software in solving such problems.

The book is organized in nine chapters. **Chapter 1** on Units is revised in light of the NIST Publication No. 330 (2008 edition) so that the current version of SI Units can be well understood. Conversion factors are corrected to reflect those mentioned in the NIST publication. **Chapter 2** is on Basic Chemical Calculations. Although major sections of previous edition are retained, more clarity on pure component pressure will be appreciated by the reader. **Chapter 3** on Material Balances without Chemical Reaction introduces the process flow sheet, material balances, graphical solution of problems and recycling and bypassing of operations. Introduction to linear modeling is intended to introduce generalized approach to the material balance problems. Material Balances Involving Chemical Reactions are explained in **Chapter 4**.

Chapter 5 discusses Energy Balances with an emphasis on topics on thermochemistry, heat capacity, enthalpy and heat of mixing. **Chapter 6** on Stoichiometry and Unit Operations discusses distillation, absorption, stripping, ex-traction, leaching, crystallization, psychrometry, drying, adsorption and evaporation. **Chapter 7** on Combustion discusses different types of fuels and their combustion characteristics. **Chapter 8** is on Stoichiometry and Industrial Problems. Several new problems of industrial importance are included in this edition. Finally, **Chapter 9** on Stoichiometry and Digital Computation deals with the use of programming lan-guages like FORTRAN, use of spreadsheet programs and specialized software (like Mathcad®) in solving industrial problems. Besides these, there are five **Appendices** which list important tables used in stoichiometric calculations.

The book is accompanied by an exhaustive website which can be accessed at http://www.mhhe.com/bhatt/s5e. It contains the following material:

For Instructors
- Solution Manual
- PowerPoint Slides

For Students
- Interactive Objective Type Questions (approx. 200)
- Sample chapter

The main advantages of the book that can be mentioned are a simple introduc-tion of chemical engineering fundamentals, a careful and proper organization of the subject that allows the student a great deal of self-progress, and a treasure of examples and exercises of advanced levels enveloping a wide range of subjects for students of all levels and practising engineers.

The style of presentation in earlier editions is well appreciated by the faculty and students and hence pedagogy is unchanged. Simple presentation of principles, followed by problems in order of increasing difficulty is maintained. Use of Mathcad® is increasingly adopted in solving problems. Nearly 20% more solved and exercise problems are added to make the book richer and more diversified.

Chapters 6 and 8 have been loaded with many new problems making it a more industry oriented edition.

Continued patronage of faculty in Chemical Engineering, Industrial Chemistry, Process Engineering, Environmental Engineering, Biotechnology and others of various universities in India is acknowledged with gratitude. Their valuable suggestions and comments have been an inspiration for us to revise the edition with current syllabi of different universities.

We are grateful to Prof. (Dr.) M M Sharma, Padma Vibhushan and Former Director of Institute of Chemical Technology, Mumbai, for the continued encouragement. Also, we are thankful to the Director of Technical Education, Gujarat, and the Principal, L D College of Engineering for granting us the permission to publish this edition. We would also like to mention the names of all those reviewers whose inputs were useful while updating the book.

Ashish M Gujrathi
Birla Institute of Technology and Science (BITS), Pilani, Rajasthan

Amalesh Sirkar
Haldia Institute of Technology (HIT), Haldia, West Bengal

Alpana Mahapatra
D J Sanghvi College of Engineering, Mumbai

Ashish M. Desai
Sarvajanik College of Engineering & Technology, Surat, Gujarat

P Sivashanmugam
National Institute of Technology (NIT), Tiruchirapalli, Tamil Nadu

Jayasankar E Variyar
Vellore Institute of Technology, Tamil Nadu

P Ravichandran
St. Joseph's College of Engineering
Jeppiaar Educational Trust, Chennai

A V N Swamy
Jawaharlal Nehru Technological University (JNTU), College of Engineering, Pulivendula.

We are also thankful to Ms Vibha Mahajan and other colleagues of Tata Mc-Graw Hill, New Delhi, for their sincere efforts in bringing out this edition in a short period and in an attractive format.

We are sure our continued efforts in updating the edition will be appreciated by all our colleagues in academia and industry at large. We welcome suggestions from all for making a better and more useful publication.

B I Bhatt
aavishkar.consultancy@gmail.com

S B Thakore
sbthakore@yahoo.co.in

Dimensions and Units

Physical theories gain their definiteness from the mathematical form in which they are expressed. The function of numbering and measuring is indispensable even in order to reproduce the raw material of facts that are to be reproduced and unified in a theory.

Dr E A Cassirer[1]
German Philosopher

No better introduction can be given than the above quotes of Dr Cassirer which clearly indicate that a thorough knowledge of dimensions and the various systems of units is not only essential but a must for a logical understanding of the subject. Mathematics and technology are international languages. Engineers converse effectively in formulae and units. To understand one another, communication is required in commonly accepted units. The expression of results of measurements and/or of calculations in a symbolic and numerical form is essential for the development of physics, chemistry and technology. The study of stoichiometry is no different than that of the other sciences and one must start with the understanding of fundamental quantities, namely, dimensions. This will facilitate appropriate and consistent units in solving stoichiometric problems. This chapter not only deals with these fundamentals but also with the methods of conversion of the units from one system to another.

1.1   DIMENSIONS AND SYSTEMS OF UNITS

According to Maxwell, every physical quantity can be expressed as a product of a pure number and a unit, where the unit is a selected reference quantity in terms of which all quantities of the same kind can be expressed. Physical entities are defined by means of certain quantities, such as mass, length, pressure, energy, etc. While defining a particular physical quantity, two questions need to be answered; (i) What would be the most convenient unit? (ii) What would be the best form and material for the standard, physically representing that unit? Physical quantities can be classified as *fundamental* quantities and *derived* quantities. The first group consists of major four important quantities; namely—length, mass, time and thermodynamic temperature. These are called *dimensions* or *base units* and are represented by symbols L, M, θ and T, respectively. The second group consists of quantities derived from the fundamental quantities, such as area, force, pressure, energy, etc. It follows, therefore, that *derived* quantities are represented algebraically in terms of multiplication and division of fundamental quantities.

The fundamental quantities are represented by a system of units according to the system of measurement. Basically, the *standard,* physically representing the base units, differs in different systems of units. In this chapter, three systems of units, viz., FPS, MKS and SI will be discussed.

The FPS system, developed in England, is based on foot, pound and second as standard measurements for length, mass and time, respectively. This is now commonly known as US Customary Units system.

In 1791, in France, a system of units entirely based on the unit of length, the *metre* was created. Because of its foundation being entirely based on the metre, this system got the name *Systèm Metrique* or Metric System (or MKS). The unit of mass in the metric system is kilogram. An important feature of this system was the decimal expression. This system was increasingly adopted in various countries, including India. In India, the MKS system was introduced in 1957.

Another subsidiary system, the cgs system, was derived from the MKS system. The base standards of the cgs system were accepted to be those of the MKS system. In practice, these two systems were used side by side, depending on convenience. For example, it was common to express the density in g/cm^3 rather than in kg/m^3 (or kg/L) in the MKS system.

For better international understanding, in particular in science and technology and in international and trade relations, a need for an international system of units was felt. At the 10th General Conference on Weights and Measures in 1954 at Paris, it was decided to have an international practical system of units, based on six base units, namely, metre, kilogram, second, ampere, kelvin and candela. It may be seen that the first four base units are the same as those in the MKS system. In 1960, the 11th General Conference on Weights and Measures in Paris gave the name *Le Système International d'Unitès* or the International System of Units to the system and it was abbreviated as SI in all languages.

Later it became evident that the quantity mass, although may be an appropriate concept in mechanics, is entirely unsuitable for use in chemistry where the molecular structure and in particular, the number of molecules in a system are much more relevant than its total mass. For this reason, the concept of *amount of substance* was introduced as a base unit by the 14th General Conference on Weights and Measures in 1971, which by definition is the amount of substance in a system containing as many elementary entities as there are atoms in 0.012 kilogram of carbon-12, and this unit of quantity was called a *mole* (abbreviated as mol as unit). The unified scale of mole thus obtained gives a value of the relative atomic mass (m_u). Reference 2 gives the most important aspects of basic meteorology. References 2, 3, 4 and 5 give an excellent account of SI. India adopted SI units through the Standards of Weights and Measures Act, 1976.

1.2   FUNDAMENTAL QUANTITIES

The fundamental quantities in different systems of units are given in Table 1.1.

Table 1.1 Fundamental Quantities[2, 3, 4]

Fundamental Quantity	System of units			Symbolic Abbreviation			Dimensions
	SI	Metric	FPS	SI	Metric	FPS	
Length	Metre	Metre	Foot	m	m	ft	L
Mass	Kilogram	Kilogram	Pound	kg	kg	lb	M
Temperature	Kelvin	Celsius	Fahrenheit	K	°C	°F	T
Time	Second	Second	Second	s	s	s	θ
Electric current	Ampere	Ampere	Ampere	A	A	A	I
Amount of substance	Mole	—	—	mol	—	—	n
Luminous intensity	Candela	—	—	cd	—	—	

The thermodynamic temperature (kelvin), defined in SI, is accepted as the absolute temperature in the metric system. The thermodynamic temperature scale is defined by choosing the triple point of water as the fundamental fixed point, and assigning to it the exact temperature value of 273.16 degrees kelvin. In other words, kelvin, the unit of thermodynamic temperature is 1/273.16 of the thermodynamic temperature of the triple point of water. In the FPS system, the unit of absolute temperature is Rankine.

Degree Kelvin (K) = °C + 273.15*
Degree Rankine (°R) = °F + 459.67

Use of degrees Fahrenheit is not permitted in SI.

For expressing the temperature interval in the absolute temperature scale, the same symbol is used.

$$280 \text{ K} - 235 \text{ K} = 45 \text{ K}$$
$$520°R - 480°R = 40°R$$
$$30°C = 303 \text{ K}$$
$$35°F = 495°R$$

Although the International Organization for Standardization (ISO)[3] has recommended comma (,) as a decimal marker, the current practice of using a point (.) as the decimal marker in India will be followed in this book.

1.3 DERIVED QUANTITIES

There can be any number of derived quantities, and hence, it is difficult to list all of them. However, the commonly used quantities for stoichiometric calculations in SI, mks and cgs systems are listed in Table 1.2. The International Committee for Weights and Measures has considered that, in general, MKS or cgs units should preferably not be used with SI. Considering the increasing adoption of SI in a large number of countries and also in India (particularly in science and technology), SI units will be followed in this book.

---

*The thermodynamic temperature **273.15 K** is by definition **0.01 K** below the thermodynamic temperature of the triple point of water. In the examples in the text, SI and metric units of temperature are given. While giving a conversion of K to °C or vice versa, the difference of 0.15 will be ignored for all practical purposes except for the values of high accuracy.

Table 1.2 Derived Quantities[2,3,4]

Derived Quantity	Units in SI/MKS/cgs System	Abbreviated Units	Recommended Symbol	Dimension
Mass	Kilogram	kg	m	M
	Gram	g		M
Area	Square metres	m^2	$A(S)$	L^2
	Square centimetres	cm^2		L^2
Volume	Cubic metres	m^3	$V(v)$	L^3
	Cubic centimetres	cm^3		L^3
	Cubic decimetres	dm^3		L^3
Capacity	Litres	L	V	L^3
Linear velocity	Metres per second	m/s	u, v, w	$L\theta^{-1}$
Linear acceleration	Metres per second per second	m/s^2	a, g (free fall)	$L\theta^{-2}$
Density	Kilograms per cubic metre	kg/m^3	ρ	ML^{-3}
	Grams per millilitre	g/mL		ML^{-3}
Specific volume	Cubic metres per kilogram	m^3/kg	v	L^3M^{-1}
Molar volume	Cubic metres per kilogram mole	$m^3/kmol$	V	L^3n^{-1}
	Cubic metres per gram mole	cm^3/mol	V	L^3n^{-1}
Force	Newtons	N	F	$ML\theta^{-2}$
	kilograms-force*	kgf		F
	Dynes	dyn		$ML\theta^{-2}$
Pressure	Newtons per square metre (Pascals)	N/m^2 (Pa)	p (P)	$ML^{-1}\theta^{-2}$
	Kilograms-force per square centimetre	kgf/cm^2		FL^{-2}
Work/Energy	Joules	J	W	$ML^2\theta^{-2}$
	Ergs	erg		$ML^2\theta^{-2}$
	Metres kilogram force	m · kgf		MF
Heat/Enthalpy	Joules	J	q, Q, H	$ML^2\,\theta^{-2}$
	Kilocalories	kcal		$ML^2\,\theta^{-2}$
Power	Kilowatts	kW	P	$ML^2\,\theta^{-3}$
	Horsepower	HP		$MF\,\theta^{-1}$
Heat flow	Joules per second	J/s or W	ϕ	$ML^2\,\theta^{-3}$
	kilocalories per hour	kcal/h		$ML^2\,\theta^{-3}$
Specific/ Absolute humidity	Kilograms water per kilogram dry air	kg/kg	H, x	$M°L°\theta°$
Relative humidity	Nil	Nil	RH	$M°L°\theta°$
Saturation ratio	Nil	Nil	ϕ	$M°L°\theta°$
Molar flow rate	Kilogram moles per hour	kmol/h	$q_n, \dot{n}$	$n\,\theta^{-1}$
	gram moles per second	mol/s		

(Contd.)

Table 1.2 (*Contd.*)

Derived Quantity	Units in SI/MKS/cgs System	Abbreviated Units	Recommended Symbol	Dimension
Mass flow rate	Kilograms per second	kg/s	q_m, $\dot{m}$	$M\,\theta^{-1}$
Volumetric flow rate	Cubic metres per second	m³/s	q_v, $\dot{V}$	$L^3\theta^{-1}$
	Litres per second	L/s		$L^3\theta^{-1}$
Heat capacity (also called specific heat)	Joules per kilogram per degree kelvin	J/(kg · K)	C	$ML^2\theta^{-2}T^{-1}$
	Kilocalories per kilogram per degree Celsius	kcal/ (kg · °C)		$ML^2\,\theta^{-2}T^{-1}$
Molar heat capacity	Joules per mole per degree kelvin	J/(mol · K)	C_m	$ML^2\theta^{-2}n^{-1}T^{-1}$
	Kilocalories per kilogram mole per degree Celsius	kcal/ (kmol · °C)		$ML^2\theta^{-2}n^{-1}T^{-1}$

1.3.1 Force

The definition of force follows from Newton's second law of motion, which states that force is proportional to the product of mass and acceleration.

$$F \propto m \times a \tag{1.1}$$

Introducing a proportionality constant K,

$$F = K\,m\,a \tag{1.2}$$

Force and acceleration are both vector quantities and hence they should act in the same direction. There are two ways of selecting the constant K. In one case, K is selected as unity (dimensionless), and with this value, the units newton (SI) and dyne are defined.

The newton (N) is the force which when applied to a body having a mass of one kilogram gives it an acceleration of one m/s².

The dyne (dyn) is the force which when applied to a body having a mass of one gram gives it an acceleration of one cm/s².

Based on these definitions,

$$1\text{ N} = 10^5 \text{ dyn}$$

A similar unit in the FPS system is the poundal which is the force, when applied to a body having a mass of one pound gives it an acceleration of one ft/s².

$$1 \text{ pdl} = 30.48 \times 453.5924 = 13\,825.5 \text{ dyn} = 0.138\,255 \text{ N}$$

Another choice of the constant K yields the technical unit of force and is defined as a *fundamental* quantity. Thus, the constant K becomes a dimensional quantity. Its numerical value is not unity but fixed at $1/g_c$.

$$F = \left(\frac{1}{g_c}\right) m\,a \tag{1.3}$$

$$g_c = 9.806\,65 \text{ (kg · m)/(kgf · s}^2) = 32.174 \text{ (1b · ft)/(1bf · s}^2)$$

g_c is called the *Newton's law conversion factor*. Its value corresponds to the acceleration due to gravity (g) at the mean sea level (9.806 65 m/s^2 or 32.174 ft/s^2). It should be clearly noted that g_c does not vary even though g varies from place to place. In ordinary calculations, however, g/g_c is taken as 1.0 kgf/kg. By definition, g_c has the units of 1 (kg · m)/(N · s^2) in SI.

The technical units of force in MKS and FPS systems are kilogram-force and pound-force, respectively.

The kilogram-force (kgf) is the force which when applied to a body having a mass of one kilogram gives it an acceleration of 9.806 65 m/s^2.

The pound force (1bf) is the force which when applied to a body having a mass of one pound gives it an acceleration of 32.174 ft/s^2.

The force becomes weight when the body acts under gravitational acceleration (g), i.e., when $a = g$ in Eq. (1.2).

$$\text{Weight, } G = \left(\frac{1}{g_c}\right) m\, g \tag{1.4}$$

Since g and g_c are assumed equal for all practical purposes,

$$G = m \tag{1.5}$$

Thus, the values of weight and mass become practically equal in MKS and FPS systems.

In order to differentiate between the terms mass and force, their units are distinguished by writing 'f' at the end of the fundamental unit of force in MKS and FPS systems.

The measurement of force, pressure, mass and weight have in the past been conveniently made through the use of gravitational acceleration without taking into account the variation of this acceleration from one location to another, which was normally insignificant in the applications. However, as process industries have spread geographically and as the processes involved require more sophisticated control, the difference between the points of calibration and use of an instrument has become more significant. Also, the practice of ignoring the difference was fundamentally wrong. Both these reasons have necessitated the use of SI in the current practice and the term 'weight' is discarded for use with SI.

1.3.2   Pressure

Pressure is defined as the force acting on unit area exposed to the pressure

$$p = \frac{F}{A} \tag{1.6}$$

The common units of pressure in SI, MKS and FPS units are N/m^2 (known as Pascal, symbol Pa), kgf/cm^2 and 1bf/in^2 (commonly known as psi), respectively.

Pressure is normally measured with the help of a gauge which registers the difference between the pressure in vessel and the local atmospheric pressure. This is known as the over pressure/gauge pressure (p_e) and the letter 'g' follows the unit. The gauge pressure does not indicate the true total pressure. In order to obtain the true pressure or pressure above reference zero, it is necessary to add the local atmospheric or barometric pressure expressed in coherent units to the gauge pressure. This sum is called the absolute pressure and the letter 'a' follows the units. In general, if no letter follows the pressure units, it is taken as absolute pressure in this book.

$$\text{Absolute pressure} = \text{gauge pressure} + \text{atmospheric pressure} \qquad (1.7)$$

Although the actual atmospheric pressure varies from one locality to another, its value at the mean sea level is 101 325 N/m^2 or Pa (= 1.033 kgf/cm^2) and is called the *standard* atmosphere (symbol 'atm'). In SI, the standard atmosphere and bar are accepted as the practical units.

$$1 \text{ atm} = 101\ 325 \text{ Pa} \quad (\text{exact})$$
$$1 \text{ bar} = 10^5 \text{ Pa} = 1.019\ 716 \text{ kgf/cm}^2 = 0.986\ 923 \text{ atm}$$

Quite often, the pressure is expressed in pressure heads.

$$\text{Pressure head} = \text{absolute pressure/density} \qquad (1.8)$$

The more commonly used pressure heads are in terms of mercury and water columns.

$$1 \text{ atm} = 760 \text{ Torr (or mmHg at } 0°C \text{ or } 273.15 \text{ K)}$$
$$= 10.33 \text{ mH}_2\text{O at } 0°C \text{ or } 273.15 \text{ K}$$

Vacuum refers to sub-atmospheric pressure.

$$\text{Absolute pressure} = \text{atmospheric pressure} - \text{vacuum} \qquad (1.9)$$

Vacuum is usually expressed in Torr (mmHg) or Pa or mbar.

1.3.3   Volume

Volume is measured in cubic metres and litres (SI) and in gallons (FPS).

A litre is the volume occupied by a mass of one kilogram of pure air free water at the temperature of its maximum density (4°C or 277.15 K) and under standard atmospheric pressure. The cubic decimetre and litre are unequal and differ by about 28 parts in 10^6 parts. Hence the word 'litre' can be employed as a special name of the cubic decimetre. However, the name litre should not be employed to give the results of high accuracy volumetric measurements.

$$1 \text{ litre} = 1.000\ 028 \text{ cubic decimetres} \quad (\text{exact})$$

Approximately, 1 cubic metre = 1000 litres = 1 kilolitre

The Imperial and US gallons are different. The former is defined as the volume occupied by a quantity of distilled water, which weighs 10 1b in air at the temperature of 62°F (16.67°C or 289.82 K) and the pressure of 30 inHg (762 Torr). The US gallon is equal to 231 in^3 (3.7854 L).

1.3.4   Work (Energy) and Power

Work (energy) is defined as the product of the force acting on a body and the distance travelled by the body.

$$W = F \times d \qquad (1.10)$$

The units of work (energy) in SI, MKS, **cgs** and FPS systems are joule (J), m · kgf, erg and ft · 1bf, respectively.

Energy is a physical entity which is present in a system in different forms, e.g., mechanical (work), electromagnetic, chemical or thermal. One form of energy is convertible to another from.

One joule is the work done when the point of application of one newton force moves a distance of one metre in the direction of the applied force.

One erg is the work done when the point of application of one dyne force moves a distance of one centimetre in the direction of the applied force.

$$1 \text{ J} = 10^7 \text{ erg}$$

Power P is defined as the work W done per unit time.

$$\text{Power } P = \frac{W}{\theta} \tag{1.11}$$

$$1 \text{ Watt} = 1 \text{ J/s}$$

$$1 \text{ metric horsepower} = 75 \text{ (m} \cdot \text{kgf)/s} = 0.7355 \text{ kW}$$
$$= 0.986\,32 \text{ hp}$$
$$1 \text{ British horsepower} = 550 \text{ (ft} \cdot \text{lbf)/s} = 0.7457 \text{ kW}$$
$$= 1.013\,87 \text{ metric hp}$$

Horsepower units are not recommended for use with SI.

1.3.5 Heat

Heat is one form of energy that flows from higher temperature to lower temperature, i.e., *enthalpy in transit*. The units of heat in SI, MKS, cgs and FPS systems are the joule (J), kilocalorie (kcal), calorie (cal) and British thermal unit (Btu), respectively and are same as those for energy.

There are several definitions of Btu and cal. All are defined in terms of the joule. Each Btu and its corresponding cal are related by a heat capacity equation.

$$1 \text{ calorie (thermochemical)} = 4.184 \text{ J} \qquad \text{(exact)}$$
$$1 \text{ calorie (International Steam Tables, called IT)} = 4.1868 \text{ J} \qquad \text{(exact)}$$
$$1 \text{ Btu (International Steam Tables, called IT)} = 1055.056 \text{ J}$$

The Celsius Heat Unit (CHU) and Therm were also used in the fps system.

$$1 \text{ CHU} = 1.8 \text{ Btu}$$
$$1 \text{ Therm} = 10^5 \text{ Btu}$$

In the SI system, heat flux (i.e., heat flow rate), ϕ, is customarily expressed in unit of power, i.e. watts (W).

1.3.6 Derived Electrical Units

Current is the fundamental quantity in electricity. The volt V is the unit of electromotive force or of potential difference. Resistance (R in ohms) of the conductor is defined as

$$R = \frac{V}{I} \tag{1.12}$$

where R is the resistance in ohms, V is the potential difference in volts and I is the current in amperes.

Coulomb is the unit of quantity of electricity and is defined as the quantity of electricity carried in one second by a current of one ampere across any cross-section

$$1 \text{ Faraday } (F) = 96\,485.3415 \text{ C/mol (based on carbon-12)} \qquad \text{(Ref. 6)}$$

The quantity coulomb (C) is an important quantity in electrochemistry.

1.4   CONVERSIONS

It is often required to convert units of a particular form from one system to another. Table 1.3 gives a brief list of the conversions in common use.

Table 1.3　Condensed Table of Conversion Factors

Length	1 m = 1.093 613 yd
	= 3.280 84 ft
	1 cm = 0.393 701 in
	1 km = 0.621 37 miles
Area	1 m^2 = 10.763 91 ft^2
	= 1.195 99 yd^2
	1 cm^2 = 0.155 in^2
	1 km^2 = 0.386 102 mile^2
	1 ha = 10 000 m^2
	= 2.471 05 acre
	= 0.003 861 mile^2
Volume	1 m^3 = 1000 dm^3 = 1000 L
	= 35.314 66 ft^3
	= 1.307 95 yd^3
	1 cm^3 = 0.061 024 in^3
Capacity	1 L = 0.219 969 Imperial gal or UK gal
	= 0.264 172 US gal
	= 0.035 3147 ft^3
	1 m^3 = 1000 L = 1 kL
	= 0.000 810 71 acre·ft
Mass	1 kg = 1000 g
	= 2.204 623 lb
Mass	1 t = 1000 kg (metric tonne)
	= 1.102 311 T (short, used in USA)
	= 2204.623 lb
	1 g = 15.4324 grain
Density	1 kg/dm^3 = 1 kg/L
	= 70 156.89 grain/Imperial gal
	= 58 417.834 grain/US gal
	1 g/cm^3 = 62.427 95 lb/ft^3
	= 10.0224 lb/ Imperial gal
	= 8.345 406 lb/US gal
	= 0.036 127 lb/in^3
Specific volume	$1 \text{ m}^3/\text{kg}$ = 16.018 46 ft^3/lb
	= 99.77624 Imperial gal/lb
	= 119.8264 US gal/lb
Force	1 N = 0.101 972 kgf
	= 0.224 809 lbf
Pressure	1 kPa = 0.010 197 kgf/cm^2
	= 0.145 038 lbf/in^2 or psi
	1 bar = 0.1 MPa
	= 1.019 716 kgf/cm^2
	= 14.503 77 lbf/in^2
	1 atm = 101.325 kPa　　　　(defined)

(Contd.)

Table 1.3 (Contd.)

	= 1.013 25 bar	
	= 1.033 227 kgf/cm^2	
	= 14.695 95 lbf/in^2	
1 Torr (1 mmHg)	= 133.3224 Pa	
	= 1.333 224 mbar	
	= 0.039 37 inHg	
1 mbar	= 0.750 06 Torr	
Energy	1 J = 0.238 846 cal (IT)	
	= 2.777 778 $\times$ 10^{-7} kWh	
	= 9.478 17 $\times$ 10^{-4} Btu (IT)	
	= 0.101 972 kgf·m	
	= 0.737 562 lbf·ft	
	= 9.869 233 $\times$ 10^{-3} L·atm	
1 kWh	= 859.8452 kcal (IT)	
	= 3412.142 Btu (IT)	
1 kcal (IT)	= 3.968 32 Btu (IT)	
	= 4.1868 kJ	(defined)
1 kgf · m	= 7.233 014 lbf · ft	
Power	1 kW = 1.359 62 metric hp	
	= 1.341 02 hp (British)	
	= 859.8452 kcal (IT)/h	
	= 3412.142 Btu (IT)/h	
1 (m · kgf)/s	= 7.233 014 (ft · lbf)/s	
Heat capacity	1 J/(g · K) = 0.238 846 kcal (IT)/(kg · °C)	
	= 0.238 846 Btu (IT)/(lb · °F)	
Temperature	°C = 5/9 (°F – 32)	
	°F = (9/5) °C + 32	

Appendix I gives the conversions in a direct usable form.

The precision to which a given conversion factor is known, and its application, determine the number of significant figures which should be used. While comparing the data given in Appendix I with those given in many handbooks and standards, it may be hinted that different sources disagree, in many cases, in the fifth or further figure which indicates that four or five significant figures represent the precision for these factors fairly accurately. At present, the acuracy of process instrumentation, analog or digital, needs only three significant figures. Additional accuracy is only needed in basic fundamental research and could be a waste of time in the industrial practice.

1.5 RECOMMENDATIONS FOR USE OF UNITS

Major recommendations issued by the General Conference on Weight and Measures[2], International Organization for the Standardization[3], for the use of units are summarised as follows.

(i) SI prefixes are given in Table 1.4.

Table 1.4 SI Prefixes

Factor	Prefix	Symbol	Factor	Prefix	Symbol
10^{24}	yotta	Y	10^{-1}	deci	d
10^{21}	zetta	Z	10^{-2}	centi	c
10^{18}	exa	E	10^{-3}	milli	m
10^{15}	peta	P	10^{-6}	micro	μ
10^{12}	tera	T	10^{-9}	nano	n
10^{9}	giga	G	10^{-12}	pico	p
10^{6}	mega	M	10^{-15}	femto	f
10^{3}	kilo	k	10^{-18}	atto	a
10^{2}	hecto	h	10^{-21}	zepto	z
10^{1}	deca	da	10^{-24}	yocto	y

(ii) In the expression of a quantity, the unit symbol is placed after the numberical value and a space is left between the numberical value and the unit symbol.
Examples 10 kg, 5.23 m
This rule implies that the symbol °C for the degree Celsius is to be preceded by a space when one expresses the value of Celsius temperature, i.e., 25 degree Celsius should be written as 25 °C. However, in this book the space is not left between the numerical value and the symbol; °C, as an exception.

(iii) An exponent attached to a compound prefix-unit implies that the exponent refers to the entire compound unit and not just to the base symbol.
1 cm^3 means volume of a cube having one cm side.

(iv) The product of two or more units may be indicated in any one of the following ways.
Correct N · m or N m   *Incorrect* Nm

(v) A solidus (oblique stroke, /), a horizontal line or negative powers may be used to express a derived unit, formed from two others by division, e.g.,
m/s, $\dfrac{m}{s}$, m · s^{-1}, kJ m^{-2} or m s^{-1}

(vi) A solidus must not be repeated on the same line unless ambiguity is avoided by parentheses.

Correct	*Incorrect*
m/s^2 or m · s^{-2} or m s^{-2}	m/s/s
J/(mol · K) or J · mol^{-1} · K^{-1} or J mol^{-1} K^{-1}	J/mol · K or J/mol/K

(vii) Unit symbols do not change in the plural. For example, 5 centimetres should be abbreviated as 5 cm and not as 5 cms.

(viii) Unit symbols are not followed by a full stop (period) except at the end of a sentence.
Correct 8 kg   *Incorrect* 8 kg.

(ix) When numerical values fall outside the range of 0.1 to 1000, it is recommended that the numerals be separated into groups of three with a space replacing the traditional comma.

Recommended	*Not recommended*
3 600 or 3600	3,600
19 625 725	19,625,725
0.001 625	0.001,625 or 0.001625
0.046 89	0.046,89 or 0.004689

In this book, four digits or decimals are grouped.

(x) Prefix symbols are printed without any space between the prefix symbol and unit symbol.

    Correct 10.5 kW or 5 nm   *Incorrect* 10.5 k W or 5 n m

(xi) Compound prefixes formed by the juxtaposition of two or more SI prefixes are not to be used.

    Correct 1 nm   *Incorrect* 1 mμm

(xii) A prefix should never be used alone.

    Correct 5 x 10^6 particels/m^3 air   *Incorrect* 5 M Particles/m^3 air

(xiii) Although kilogram is the base unit in SI units, names of decimal multiples and sub-multiples of mass are formed by attaching prefixes to the word 'gram'.

    Correct 1 mg   *Incorrect* 1 μkg

(xiv) Good practice recommends selection of a prefix which, whenever possible, provides a numerical value between 0.1 and 1000. Prefer expression 10.0 kPa over 0.01 MPa. However, when a group of values is tabulated, they should be expressed in the same unit multiple even though their numerical value lies outside the 0.1 to 1000 range.

    1.2×10^4 N can be written as 12 kN.

    1421 Pa can be written as 1.421 kPa.

(xv) If the magnitude of the number is less than unity, the decimal sign should preferably be preceded by a zero, e.g. .125 should be written as 0.125.

(xvi) The SI prefixes are not to be used with °C or K.

For move recommendations on the use of units, references 2 and 3 should be consulted.

Example 1.1   The volumetric flow rate of kerosene in an 80-mm nominal diameter pipe is 75 Imperial gallons per minute. Taking the density of kerosene as 0.8 kg/dm^3, find the mass flow in kg/s.

Solution   Volumetric-flow rate, $q_v = 75$ (gallon/min) $\times \left(\dfrac{1}{60}\right)$ (min/s)

$$\times \left(\frac{1}{0.219\ 969}\right) (dm^3/gallon)$$

Converting units

$$= 5.683\ dm^3/s$$

Density, $\rho = 0.8$ kg/dm^3

Mass-flow rate, $q_m = q_v \times \rho$

$$= 5.683 \times 0.8 = \textbf{4.546 kg/s}$$

Example 1.2   Steam is flowing at the rate of 2000 kg/h in a 3″ NB 40 schedule pipe at 440 kPa (4.4 bar) absolute and 180°C (453 K). Calculate the velocity of the steam in the pipeline.

Solution   Mass–flow rate, $q_m = 2000$ kg/h

Internal diameter of 3″ NB 40 schedule pipe = 3.068 in = 77.927 mm

Cross-sectional area of the pipe, $A = \left(\dfrac{\pi}{4}\right) (77.927)^2/10^6$

$$= 4.769\ 45 \times 10^{-3}\ m^2$$

Specific volume of the steam at 440 kPa a and 180°C,
$v = 0.461\ 66\ \text{m}^3/\text{kg}$ (ref. Steam Tables; Appendix IV.3)
Volumetric flow rate of

$$\text{steam, } q_v = 2000\ (\text{kg/h}) \times \left(\frac{1}{3600}\right)\ (\text{h/s}) \times 0.461\ 66\ (\text{m}^3/\text{kg})$$
$$= 0.2565\ \text{m}^3/\text{s}$$

Velocity of steam, $v_s = \dfrac{q_v}{A}$

$$= 0.2565\ \text{m}^3/\text{s} \times 1/(4.769\ 45 \times 10^{-3})\ 1/\text{m}^2$$
$$= \textbf{53.77 m/s}$$

Example 1.3 A Ton of Refrigeration (TR) is classically defined as the rate of heat absorption equivalent to the latent heat in a short ton (2000 lb) of ice melted in 24 hours. Latent heat of fusion (λ_f) of ice is 144 thermochemical Btu/lb at 32°F. Calculate energy in kW equivalent to 1 TR.

Solution   Heat-absorption rate, equivalent to 1 TR,

$$\phi = \left(\frac{2000}{24}\right)\ (\text{lb/h}) \times 144\ (\text{therm Btu/lb})$$
$$\times\ 0.251\ 996\ (\text{therm kcal/therm Btu})$$
$$\times\ 4.184\ (\text{kJ/therm kcal}) \times \left(\frac{1}{3600}\right)\ (\text{h/s})$$
$$= \textbf{3.5145 kW}$$

Example 1.4   The conductance of a fluid-flow system is defined as the volumetric flow rate, referred to a pressure of one torr (133.322 Pa). For an orifice, the conductance C can be computed[7] from

$$C = 89.2\ A\ \sqrt{\frac{T}{M}}\ \ \text{ft}^3/\text{s}$$

where A = area of opening, ft^2
T = temperature, °R
M = molar mass
Convert the empirical equation into SI units.

Solution   Let C', A' and T' be the conductance, area of opening and temperature in m^3/s, m^2 and K respectively. Molar mass is unaffected by change of units.

$$C = 35.314\ 67\ C'$$
$$T = 1.8\ T'$$
$$A = 10.763\ 91\ A'$$

On substitution,

$$35.341\ 67\ C' = 89.2 \times 10.763\ 91\ A'\ \sqrt{1.8\frac{T'}{M}}$$

$$C' = \textbf{36.449}\ \sqrt{\frac{T'}{M}}$$

Exercises

1.1 Make the following conversions:

(a) Wavelength 5500 Å to nm

[550 nm]

(b) 175 grain moisture/lb dry air to g moisture/kg dry air

[25 g moisture/kg dry air]

1.2 In a double-effect evaporator plant, the second effect is maintained under vacuum of 475 Torr (mmHg). Find the absolute pressure in kPa, bar and psi.

[38 kPa, 0.38 bar, 5.51 psi]

1.3 A force equal to 192.6 N is applied on a piston with a diameter of 5 cm. Find the pressure exerted on the piston in kPa, bar and psi.

[98.066 kPa, 0.981 bar, 14.227 psi]

1.4 Iron metal weighing 500 lb occupies a volume of 29.25 L. Calculate the density of Fe in kg/dm^3.

[7.754 kg/dm³]

1.5 The diameter and height of a vertical cylindrical tank are 5 ft and 6 ft 6 in respectively. It is full up to 75% height with carbon tetrachloride (CCl_4), the density of which is 1.6 kg/L. Find the mass in kilograms.

[4336 kg]

1.6 A bag filter of 5-micron rating is designed for a pressure drop of 0.05 lbf/in^2 per US gallon per minute of water solution in clean conditions. Calculate the pressure drop in kPa from the filter for water-flow rate of 10 m^3/h.

[15.178 kPa]

1.7 Corrosion rates are normally reported in mills per year (mpy) in the chemical process industry. For the measurement of the rates, a corrosion test coupon is inserted in the process stream for a definite period. The loss of weight is measured during the period of insertion.

In a particular test, a coupon of carbon steel was kept in a cooling water circuit. The dimensions of the coupon were measured to be 7.595 cm × 1.276 cm × 0.1535 cm. Mass of the coupon before insertion in the circuit and after exposure for 50 days were measured to be 14.9412 g and 14.6254 g, respectively. Calculate the rate of corrosion. Take the density of carbon steel to be the same as the one calculated in Exercise 1.4.

Note 1 mil per year (mpy) = 1/1000 in per year

[5.3 mpy]

1.8 Vapour pressure of benzene in the temperature range of 7.5°C (280.65 K) to 104°C (377.15 K) can be calculated using the following Antoine equation.

$$\log_{10} p = 6.9057 - \frac{1211.0}{(t + 220.8)}$$

where p = Vapour pressure in Torr (mmHg), and

t = Temperature in °C

Convert the above equation in SI units.

1.9 Heat capacity of gaseous *n*-butane is given by

$$C_{mp}^{\circ} = 4.429 + 40.159 \times 10^{-3}\, T - 68.562 \times 10^{-7}\, T^2$$

where C_{mp}° = Heat capacity in Btu/(lb mole·°R) and

T = Temperature in °R

Convert the equation in SI units.

1.10 Pressure drop across a venturi scrubber can be calculated using the following Calvert equation[8].

$$\Delta p = (5 \times 10^{-5})\, v^2\, L$$

where Δp = pressure drop, in WC

L = liquid flow rate, US gal/1000 ft^3 gas

v = gas velocity in the venturi throat, ft/s

Convert the equation in SI units.

1.11 In the case of fluids, the local heat-transfer coefficient for long tubes and using bulk-temperature properties is expressed by the empirical equation[9]

$$h = 0.023\, G^{0.8} \times k^{0.67} \times C_p^{0.33}/(D^{0.2} \times \mu^{0.47})$$

where h = heat-transfer coefficient, Btu/(h·ft^2·°F)

G = mass velocity of fluids, lb/(ft^2·s)

C_p = heat capacity of fluid at constant pressure, Btu/(lb·°F)

k = thermal conductivity, Btu/(h·ft·°F)

D = diameter of tube, ft

μ = viscosity of liquid, lb/(ft·s)

Convert the empirical equation into SI units.

Note   Will the above equation change when consistent SI units are used? Why?

References

1. Cassirer, E; *Substance and Function*, Dover Publication, USA, 1953, p. 115.
2. Taylor, B N and Thompson, A; *The International System of Units (SI)*, National Institute of Standards and Technology Special Publication No. 330, 2008 Edition, March 2008, USA.
3. ISO 1000 : 1992/Amd. 1 : 1998(E), *SI Units and Recommendations for the Use of their Multiples and Certain other Units (Amendment 1)*, International Organization for Standards, Switzerland.
4. Thompson, A and Taylor, B N; *Guide for the Use of the International System of Units (SI)*, National Institute of Standards and Technology Special Publication No. 811, 2008 Edition, March 2008, USA.
5. Mills, I, Cvitas, T, Homann, K, Kallay, N, and Kuchitsu, K; *Quantities, Units and Symbols in Physical Chemistry*, 2nd Ed., IUPAC Chemical Data Series, Blackwell Science Ltd., UK, 1993.
6. Mohr, P J and Taylor, B N; *J. Phys. Chem. Ref. Data*, **28**(6), 1999, p. 1713.
7. Green, D W and Malony, J O; *Perry's Chemical Engineers' Handbook*, 6th Ed. McGraw-Hill, New York, 1984, p. 5–33.
8. Doolittle, C, Woodhull, J and Venkatesh, M; *Chem. Engg.*, **109**(13), Dec. 2002, p. 50.
9. McCabe, W L, Smith, J C, and Harriott, P; *Unit Operations of Chemical Engineering*, 7th Ed. McGraw-Hill, New York, 2005, p. 359.

Basic Chemical Calculations

CHAPTER

2

In Chapter 1, an attempt was made to present various systems of units and their conversions from one system of units to another. Before discussing material and energy balances, it is important to understand basic chemical principles.

Matter exists in three different forms, viz., solids, liquids and gases. Most of the elements and compounds can be had in all the three forms except a few, e.g., iodine, ammonium chloride, dry ice, etc., for which the liquid state is not visible and the solid state is sublimated into gaseous state. The easiest way of expressing the quantity of matter is mass. For solids and liquids, this can be done by weighing on a balance. However, a gas occupies the entire volume available to it, and hence it is customary to specify the volume along with its temperature and pressure. Very often, liquid volumes are also specified, in which case, additional information regarding its density is required to compute the mass of the liquid.

2.1 MOLE, ATOMIC MASS AND MOLAR MASS

Although measurement in terms of mass is of direct interest to the engineers, matter is basically made up of atoms and molecules. However, since the discovery of the fundamental laws of chemistry, chemists considered it significant to express the quantity of matter in atoms and molecules rather than in terms of auxiliary properties, such as mass and volume. For instance, 'gram atom' and 'gram mole' have been used to specify amounts of chemical elements or compounds. These units have a direct relationship with 'atomic weights' 'molecular weights' which are, in fact, relative masses.

Originally, the atomic mass of oxygen was taken as a reference base and its numerical value was fixed at 16. However, physicists discovered different isotopes of oxygen which created a conflict between physicists and the chemists. In 1959–60, this controversy came to an end and both the groups of scientists finally agreed on a standard based on carbon-12. The table of elements based on this scale was formulated in which atomic masses (m) were listed. Appendix-II at the end of this book gives values of atomic masses and atomic numbers of naturally occurring isotopes. The amount of substance of a system which contains as many elementary entities as there are atoms in 0.012 kilograms of carbon-12 is defined as a mole. As noted in Chapter 1, a mole is the *base unit* in SI units.

Some elements are monoatomic while others are diatomic. Potassium and sodium are examples of monoatomic elements while chlorine, oxygen, nitrogen, etc., are diatomic elements. In this book, gram mole and kilogram mole will be specified as mol and kmol, respectively.

For chemical compounds, a mole is defined as the amount of substance equal to its formula weight. The formula weight is called the molar mass (M). Based on this understanding, the molecular mass of a monoatomic element is its atomic mass while that of a diatomic element is double that of its atomic mass.

$$1 \text{ atom Al} = 27^* \text{ g Al}$$
$$1 \text{ katom Na} = 23^* \text{ kg Na}$$
$$1 \text{ mol O}_2 = 2 \text{ g atom O}_2 = 32^* \text{ g O}_2$$
$$1 \text{ kmol H}_2 = 2 \text{ kg atom H}_2 = 2^* \text{ kg H}_2$$
$$1 \text{ mol NaCl} = 23 + 35.5 = 58.5^* \text{ g NaCl}$$
$$1 \text{ mol CuSO}_4 = 63.5 + 32 + (4 \times 16) = 159.5^* \text{ kg CuSO}_4$$

From the above discussion, it follows that

$$\frac{(1 \text{ mole of compound X})}{(1 \text{ mole of compound Y})} = \frac{(\text{molar mass of X})}{(\text{molar mass of Y})} \tag{2.1}$$

This expression is of considerable importance in the following chapters where the material and heat balances of chemical reactions are presented. In addition, it is also invaluable in converting the mole composition into mass composition.

Mass of an entity is expressed by the symbol m. Its flow rate is expressed by symbols q_m or $\dot{m}$. For expression of the amount of substance, the symbol n is used. For molar flow rate, the symbol q_n or $\dot{n}$ is used.

The term 'mixture' is used to describe a gaseous, liquid or solid phase containing more than one substance, when the substances are treated in the same way. Air is a special gaseous mixture with constant composition.

Example 2.1   How many grams of NH_4Cl are there in 5 mol?

Solution   Molar mass of NH_4Cl $M = 14 + 4 + 35.5 = 53.5$ g
$$n_{NH_4Cl} = 5 \text{ mol of } NH_4Cl = 5 \times 53.5 = \textbf{267.5 g } NH_4Cl$$

Example 2.2   Convert 499 g $CuSO_4.5H_2O$ into mol. Find equivalent mol of $CuSO_4$ in the crystals.

Solution   Molar mass of $CuSO_4$, $M_1 = 159.5$ g
Molar mass of $CuSO_4.5H_2O$, $M_2 = 159.5 + 5 (1 \times 2 + 16) = 249.5$ g
$$\text{Moles of } CuSO_4.5H_2O, \ n = \frac{499}{249.5} = \textbf{2 mol}$$

In the formula of $CuSO_4.5H_2O$, the moles of $CuSO_4$ are equal (one in each) and hence, the equivalent moles of $CuSO_4$ in the crystals are also 2.0 mol.

Example 2.3   How many moles of K_2CO_3 will contain 117 kg K?

---

* Rounded-off values

Solution   Atomic mass of K, $m_K = 39$

$$\text{Atoms of K} = \frac{117}{39} = 3 \text{ kg atom}$$

Each mole of K_2CO_3 contains 2 atoms of K.

$$2 \text{ atoms of K} \equiv 1 \text{ mole of } K_2CO_3$$

(The sign $\equiv$ refers to 'equivalent to' and not 'equal to')

$$\text{Moles of } K_2CO_3, \, n = \frac{3}{2} = \mathbf{1.5 \, kmol}$$

The number of atoms present in a mole can be obtained from Avogadro's number[1].

$$N_A = 6.022 \; 142 \times 10^{23} \text{ atom/mol}$$

From this relation it is once again clear that the number of atoms present in matter is directly proportional to the number of moles and not the mass.

Example 2.4   How many atoms are present in 416.6 g barium chloride?

Solution

$$\text{Molar mass of } BaCl_2 = 137.3 + 2 \times 35.5 = 208.3$$
$$\text{Moles of } BaCl_2 = 416.6/208.3 = 2 \text{ mol}$$
$$\text{Atoms present in the mass of 416.6 g } BaCl_2 = 2 \times 6.022 \times 10^{23}$$
$$= \mathbf{12.044 \times 10^{23}}$$

2.2   EQUIVALENT MASS

In chemical reactions, one *equivalent mass* of an element or compound has pre-cisely the same power for chemical combination as one equivalent mass of any other element or compound. It depends strictly upon the reaction in which the molecule participates. Consider the reaction:

$$H_2 + \frac{1}{2} O_2 \rightarrow H_2O \tag{2.2}$$

In this reaction, hydrogen is monovalent whereas oxygen is divalent. Two atoms of hydrogen combine with one atom of oxygen to form water.

Again, $$KOH + HNO_3 \rightarrow KNO_3 + H_2O \tag{2.3}$$

In this reaction, one equivalent mass of KOH combines with one equivalent mass of HNO_3 to produce one equivalent mass of KNO_3 and one equivalent mass of H_2O. Thus, it is clear that the reactivity of a molecule in a chemical reaction determines the equivalent mass of the molecule.

In simple terms, the equivalent mass of an element or a compound is equal to the atomic mass or molecular mass divided by the valence. The *valence* of an element or a compound depends on the number of hydrogen ions accepted or the hydroxyl ions donated for each atomic mass or molecular mass.

$$\text{Equivalent mass} = \frac{\text{atomic/molar mass}}{\text{valence}} \tag{2.4}$$

$$1 \text{ g equivalent of hydrogen} = \frac{1}{1} = 1 \text{ g of hydrogen}$$

$$1 \text{ g equivalent of oxygen} = \frac{16}{2} = 8 \text{ g of oxygen}$$

$$1 \text{ g equivalent of Cu} = \frac{63.5}{2} = 31.75 \text{ g Cu}$$

$$1 \text{ g equivalent of } H_3PO_4 = \frac{98.1}{3} = 32.7 \text{ g } H_3PO_4$$

Example 2.5   Find the equivalent mass of (a) PO_4 radical, and (b) Na_3PO_4.

Solution   Molar mass PO_4 radical $= 31 + 4 \times 16 = 95$
Valence of PO_4 radical $= 3$

$$\text{Equivalent mass of } PO_4 \text{ radical} = \frac{95}{3} = \mathbf{31.67}$$

$$\text{Molar mass of } Na_3PO_4 = (3 \times 23) + 95 = 164$$
$$\text{Valence of } Na_3PO_4 = 3$$
$$\text{Equivalent mass of Na/mole} = 3$$

$$\text{Equivalent mass of } Na_3PO_4 = \frac{164}{3} = \mathbf{54.67}$$

Example 2.6   Find the equivalents of 3 kmol of $AlCl_3$.

Solution   Aluminium ion will accept three hydroxyl ions.

$$\text{Equivalents} = (\text{moles}) \times 3 = 3 \times 3 = \mathbf{9 \text{ keq}}$$

2.3   SOLIDS

The composition of solids is chiefly expressed in mass percentages.
In a mixture of two compounds A and B,

$$\text{Mass \% of A} = \left[\frac{\text{mass of A}}{(\text{mass of A + mass of B})} \right] \times 100 \tag{2.5}$$

$$\text{Mass \% of B} = \left[\frac{\text{mass of B}}{(\text{mass of A + mass of B})} \right] \times 100$$

$$= 100 - \text{mass \% A} \tag{2.6}$$

Another way of expressing the composition is in mole %.

$$\text{Moles of A} = \frac{\text{mass of A}}{\text{molar mass of A}} = \frac{m_A}{M_A} \tag{2.7}$$

$$\text{Moles of B} = \frac{\text{mass of B}}{\text{molar mass of B}} = \frac{m_B}{M_B} \tag{2.8}$$

$$\text{Mole \% A} = \left[\frac{\text{moles of A}}{(\text{moles of A + moles of B})} \right] \times 100 \tag{2.9}$$

$$\text{Mole \% B} = \left[\frac{\text{moles of B}}{(\text{moles of A} + \text{moles of B})} \right] \times 100$$

$$= 100 - \text{mole \% A} \qquad (2.10)$$

With the help of Eqs. (2.7) to (2.10), the mass % can be converted into mole %. Whenever no specific mention is made about the composition, i.e., whether it is mass % or mole %, it is taken as mass % for solids.

When the mass % and mole % are expressed as fractions, they are known as mass fraction and mole fraction, respectively. Equations (2.5) to (2.10) are entirely general and can be applied to mixtures of any number of components with appropriate denominators.

Strictly speaking, mole fraction refers to the fraction that the amount of substance contributes to the total amount of the sample. Hence the correct name should be *amount of substance fraction* or *chemical amount fraction*. However, mole fraction term is used by almost everyone without causing any confusion. For condensed phases, (i.e. for solids or liquids) the symbol x is used while for gaseous mixtures, the symbol y is used for expression of fractions. When mass fraction and mole fraction are expressed for the same species in one case (example), they are usually differentiated by symbols w and x for mass fraction and mole fraction respectively, for condensed phases.

Example 2.7   Sodium chloride weighing 600 kg is mixed with 200 kg of potassium chloride. Find the composition of the mixture in (a) mass %, and (b) mole %.

Solution   *Basis*[*] 600 kg NaCl (1) and 200 kg KCl (2)

Mass of NaCl in the mixture, m_1 = 600 kg

Mass of KCl in the mixture, m_2 = 200 kg

Total mass of the mixture m = 600 + 200 = 800 kg

$$\text{Mass \% of NaCl, } w_A = \left(\frac{600}{800} \right) \times 100 = 75$$

Mass fraction of NaCl, x_1 = **0.75**

Mass % of KCl = 100 − 75 = **25**

Mass fraction of KCl, w_2 = **0.25**

Molar mass of NaCl, M_1 = 23 + 35.5 = 58.5

$$\text{Moles of NaCl, } n_1 = \frac{600}{58.5} = 10.26 \text{ kmol}$$

Molar mass of KCl, M_2 = 39 + 35.5 = 74.5

$$\text{Moles of KCl, } n_2 = \frac{200}{74.5} = 2.68 \text{ kmol}$$

Total moles in the mixture, n = 10.26 + 2.68 = 12.94 kmol

$$\text{Mole \% NaCl} = \left(\frac{10.26}{12.94} \right) \times 100 = 79.29$$

Mole fraction of NaCl, x_1 = **0.7929**

---

[*] It is always desirable to start by writing a definite basis which will be used in the example.

$$\text{Mole \% KCl} = 100 - 79.29 = 20.71$$
$$\text{Mole fraction of KCl, } x_2 = \mathbf{0.2071}$$

In material balance calculations involving chemical reactions, mole % is a logical expression of the composition. However, mass % is more practical and convenient in laboratory calculations. Therefore, conversion of mass fraction to mole fraction and vice versa is frequently encountered in stoichiometric calculations. A simple graphical method, presented by Atallah[2], using rectangular graph paper is quite handy for a binary system.

Figure 2.1 is the graphical solution of Example 2.7. On the *y*-axis, points representing molar masses of two components are marked as *P* and *Q*. Draw lines *RP* and *RQ*. Mass fraction $w_A = 0.75$ is marked on the *x*-axis. Draw a vertical line to intersect *RQ* (i.e., line representing molar mass of component 2) at *C*. Join *CE*. This intersects *RP* at *D*. Draw a vertical line passing from *D* which gives the mole fraction of the component 1 (x_A) on the *x*-axis. Similar is the case with component 2. It may be noted that the results tally with the calculated values. For conversion of mole fraction to mass fraction, the procedure is to be reversed.

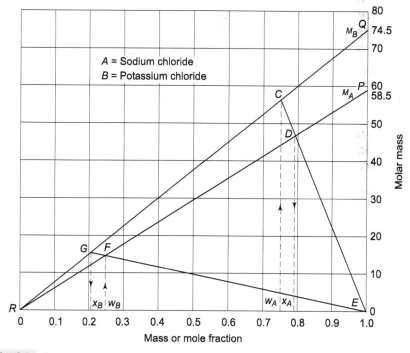

Fig. 2.1   Graphical Solution of Example 2.7

Example 2.8   A carbon–based solid–acid catalyst has the formula $CH_{0.35}O_{0.35}S_{0.14}$. Using atomic mass data listed in Appendix II, calculate its mass % composition and molar mass of the catalyst.

Solution   Formula mass of the catalyst contains 1 atom of carbon, 0.35 atoms of hydrogen, 0.35 atoms of oxygen and 0.14 atoms of sulphur.

Table 2.1   Composition of Solid Acid Catalyst

Element	kg atom	Atomic mass	kg	mass %
Carbon	1.00	12.010 7	12.0107	53.49
Hydrogen	0.35	1.007 94	0.3528	1.57
Oxygen	0.35	15.999 4	5.5998	24.94
Sulphur	0.14	32.065	4.4891	20.00
Total	1.84		22.4524	100.00

$$\text{Molar mass of the catalyst} = \frac{22.4524}{1.84} = \textbf{12.202 kg/kmol}$$

In many instances, indirect reference is made to the composition and/or purity. Examples are, available nitrogen in urea, calcium oxide content of limestone, available phosphorus pentoxide in phosphatic fertilizers, etc. Example 2.9 will be useful in understanding such compositions.

Example 2.9   The available nitrogen in a urea sample is found to be 45% (by mass). Find the actual urea content in the sample.

Solution   Since in the problem, the basis is not defined, a suitable basis will have to be assumed.

Basis 100 kg urea

45 kg nitrogen is present in the sample.

Molar mass of urea (NH_2CONH_2), $M_u = 60$

Nitrogen content in 1 kmol of urea = 28 kg

$$\text{Actual urea present in the sample} = \left(\frac{60}{28}\right) \times 45 = 96.43 \text{ kg}$$

Thus, the sample contains **96.43% urea.**

Very often, the impurities present in solid or liquid compounds are expressed in ppm, i.e., parts per mega (or million*) (i.e., 10^6) parts. This is generally expressed on a mass basis for solids and on a volume basis for liquids.

Example 2.10   Caustic soda flakes obtained from a manufacturer are found to contain 60 ppm silica (SiO_2). Convert this impurity into mass %.

Solution
$$\text{Impurity} = 60 \text{ ppm } SiO_2$$
$$= \frac{60 \text{ g } SiO_2}{1000\,000 \text{ g total solids}}$$
$$\text{Mass \% of } SiO_{2,\,w} = \left(\frac{60}{1000\,000}\right) \times 100$$
$$= \textbf{0.006}$$

Example 2.11   A label of a medicine in the form of a tablet, mentions that there are 800 mg of calcium phosphate, 200 mg of calcium carbonate and 5 mg of calcium fluoride in the tablet. Calculate calcium and fluoride ion contents of the tablet.

---

*term used in the USA.

Solution   Molar mass of calcium phospate, $Ca_3(PO_4)_2$
$$M_1 = 3 \times 40.078 + 2 \ [30.97 \ 762 + 4 \times 15.9994]$$
$$= 310.184$$
Molar mass of calcium carbonate, $CaCO_3$
$$M_2 = 40.078 + 12.0107 + 3 \times 15.9994$$
$$= 100.0869$$
Molar mass of calcuim fluoride, CaF_2
$$M_3 = 40.078 + 2 \times 18.998 \ 4032$$
$$= 78.074 \ 8064$$
Total calcuim ion in the tablet
$$= \frac{120.234}{310.184} \times 800 + \frac{40.078}{100.0869} \times 200 + \frac{40.078}{78.074 \ 8064} \times 5$$
$$= \textbf{392.75 mg}$$
Fluoride ion in the tablet $= \dfrac{18.998 \ 4032}{78.074 \ 8064} \times 2 \times 5$
$$= \textbf{2.433 mg}$$

2.4   LIQUIDS AND SOLUTIONS

As mentioned in the introduction the volumes of pure liquids are usually specified. Along with the volume, the density and temperature of the liquids are also specified.

Regarding the solutions, there are various ways in which they can be expressed. A solution means a solute is dissolved in the solvent. The solute can be a solid, a liquid or a gas. In the case of solids, the solubility is expressed in g/100 g solvent at a definite temperature. This means that the maximum amount of solid which can be dissolved in the solvent will be equal to its solubility at that particular temperature. Solubility data can be found from various sources [3,4]. Mass % and mole % of components are expressed for liquids and solutions, the former being more common. In addition to these two, the volume % of a component is sometimes given, e.g., the alcohol content in wine. Very often, the mass % of the key component or the useful component of the solute present is also expressed, e.g., Na_2O content in caustic soda lye, P_2O_5 content of phosphoric acid, etc.

The trace impurities are either expressed in mg/L or ppm (= mg/kg). When the solution is 'watery' (i.e., its density nearly equals 1.0 kg/L),
$$1 \ mg/L = 1 \ ppm$$
In water treatment and effluent treatment problems, the analysis is given in ppm or mg/L, which are both taken as being similar.

Example 2.12   A saturated solution of salicylic acid in methanol contains 64 kg salicylic acid per 100 kg methanol[3] at 25°C (298.15 K). Find (a) the mass %, and (b) mole % compositions of the solution.

Solution   *Basis* 100 kg methanol (1)
Solution contains 64 kg salicylic acid. (2).

Mass of the solution, $m = 100 + 64 = 164$ kg

$$\text{Mass \% salicylic acid} = \left(\frac{64}{164}\right) \times 100 = \mathbf{39.02}$$

Mass % methanol $= 100 - 39.02 = \mathbf{60.98}$

Molar mass methanol (CH_3OH), $M_1 = 32$

Molar mass of salicylic acid (HOC_6H_4COOH), $M_2 = 138$

$$\text{Moles of methanol, } n_1 = \frac{100}{32} = 3.125 \text{ kmol}$$

$$\text{Moles of salicylic acid, } n_2 = \frac{64}{138} = 0.464 \text{ kmol}$$

$$\text{Total amount, } n = 3.125 + 0.464 = 3.589 \text{ kmol}$$

$$\text{Mole \% methanol} = \left(\frac{3.125}{3.589}\right) \times 100 = \mathbf{87.07}$$

Mole % salicylic acid $= 100 - 87.07 = \mathbf{12.93}$

Example 2.13   A saturated solution of NaCl in aqueons HCl is prepared at 40°C (313.15 K) by dissolving 13.7 g HCl/100 g water and 8.67 g NaCl/100 g water[5]. Caculate mass % and mole % compositions of the solution.

Solution   *Basis* 100 g water

Table 2.2   Compositon of Saturated Solution

Component	mass, m_i	mass %	Molar mass, M_i	mole, n_i	mole %
HCl	13.70	11.20	36.4609	0.3757	6.19
NaCl	8.67	7.88	58.4428	0.1484	2.44
H_2O	100.00	81.72	18.0153	5.5508	91.37
Total	122.37	100.00		6.0749	100.00

Example 2.14   What will be the % Na_2O content of lye containing 73% caustic soda?

Solution   *Basis* 100 kg lye

Caustic soda content of the lye $= 73$ kg

$$2\,NaOH \rightarrow Na_2O + H_2O$$

Molar mass of NaOH $= 40$

Molar mass of $Na_2O = 62$

$$\% \ Na_2O \text{ in the solution} = \frac{62 \times 73}{2 \times 40} = \mathbf{56.58}$$

In water analysis, impurities such as alkalinity, hardness, etc., are expressed in mg/L. In effluent analysis, BOD, COD, TOC, TOD, and ThOD are expressed in mg/L. For definitions of these terms, a standard book on wastewater engineering[6] or on pollution control may be referred. Among these parameters, TOC and ThOD can be theoretically calculated. TOC refers to the total organic carbon present in the solution, while ThOD refers to the theoretical oxygen demand of organic compounds present in the solution.

Example 2.15 Glycerin, weighing 600 mg, is dissolved in pure water to make a final solution of 1 litre. Find the TOC and ThOD of the solution.

Solution *Basis* 1 litre of solution

The structure of glycerin is

CH_2OH

CH_2OH

CH_2OH

1 kmol of glycerin contains 3 atom (or kmol) of carbon.

Molar mass of glycerin, $M = 92$

Glycerin concentration in the solution $= 600$ mg/L

Total carbon present in the solution (TOC) $= \left(\dfrac{3 \times 12}{92}\right) \times 600 =$ **234.8 mg/L**

The oxygen requirement of the compound (for complete combustion) can be determined by writing the combustion reaction as

$$C_3H_8O_3 + 3.5\ O_2 = 3\ CO_2 + 4\ H_2O$$

The O_2 requirement of glycerin present in the solution,

ThOD of solution $= \dfrac{(3.5 \times 32 \times 600)}{92} =$ **730.4 mg/L**

In the case of water analysis, the alkalinity or hardness is expressed in equivalent ppm of $CaCO_3$ although the actual values of alkalinity and hardness in terms of the compounds present will be different.

Example 2.16 By titration, it was found that a sample of water contains hardness equivalent to 500 mg/L (ppm) $CaCO_3$. Assuming that the water contains temporary hardness in 60% $Ca(HCO_3)_2$ form, and 40% $Mg(HCO_3)_2$ form, find the concentrations of both in water.

Solution

Molar mass of $CaCO_3$, $M_1 = 100$

Valence of $CaCO_3 = 2$

Equivalent mass of $CaCO_3 = \dfrac{100}{2} = 50$

Molar mass of $Ca(HCO_3)_2$, $M_2 = 162$

Valence of $Ca(HCO_3)_2 = 2$

Equivalent mass of $Ca(HCO_3)_2 = \dfrac{162}{2} = 81$

Actual concentration of Ca $(HCO_3)_2$ in the sample of water,

$$c_1 = \left(\frac{81}{50}\right) \times 500 \times 0.6 = \textbf{486 mg/L}$$

Molar mass of $Mg(HCO_3)_2$, $M_3 = 146.3$

Valence of $Mg(HCO_3)_2 = 2$

Equivalent mass of Mg $(HCO_3)_2 = \dfrac{146.3}{2} = 73.15$

Actual content of $Mg(HCO_3)_2$ in the sample of water,

$$c_2 = \left(\frac{73.15}{50}\right) \times 500 \times 0.4 = \textbf{292.6 mg/L}$$

Example 2.17   A sample of light diesel oil (LDO) from a refinery is found to contain 0.68 mass% sulphur (as S). Its density is 0.85 kg/L at 30°C (303.15 K). Convert this impurity into ppm.

Solution   Sulphur content = 0.68% by mass

$$= \frac{0.68 \text{ g S}}{100 \text{ g LDO}}$$

$$= \frac{0.68 \text{ g}}{100 \text{ g}} \times \frac{1000 \text{ mg}}{1 \text{ g}} \times \frac{1000 \text{ g}}{1 \text{ kg}} \times \frac{0.85 \text{ kg}}{1 \text{ L}}$$

$$= \textbf{5780 mg/L or ppm}$$

In addition to the concentration units described above, there are three other ways of expressing the concentration of a solution containing either a solid or a liquid solute, namely, molarity (M), normality (N) and molality.

Molarity (M) is defined as the number of mol of solute dissolved in 1 litre or dm^3 of solution.

Normality (N) is defined as the number of gram equivalents dissolved in 1 litre of solution.

Molality ($m^{\ominus}$) is defined as the number of mol of solute dissolved in 1 kilogram of solvent.

From the definition of normality, it is thus possible to find the concentration of solute in g/L (a modified expression of the density).

$$\text{Concentration } C \text{ in g/L} = \text{normality } (N) \times \text{equivalent mass} \qquad (2.11)$$

The terms equivalent, equivalent mass and normality of a solution are now considered outdated as they are ambiguous. Cvitas and Mills[7] have explained in detail that the meaning of 'one equivalent' of a specified chemical depends on the reaction involved. Hence there are no unique definitions of an equivalent nor of a normal solution. A specific ion may have one valency in a solution while it may have a different valency in another soultion. IUPAC therefore recommend use of only molarity and molality as measures of concentration.

Example 2.18   A solution of sodium chloride in water contains 20% NaCl (by mass) at 60°C (333 K). The density of the solution is 1.127 kg/L. Find the molarity, normality and molality of the solution.

Solution   *Basis* 100 kg solution of sodium chloride
The solution contains 20 kg NaCl.

$$\text{Density of the solution, } \rho = 1.127 \text{ kg/L}$$

$$\text{Volume of the solution, } V = \frac{100}{1.127} = 88.73 \text{ L}$$

$$\text{Moles of NaCl in the solution, } n = \frac{20}{58.5} = 0.342 \text{ kmol} \equiv 342 \text{ mol}$$

$$\text{Molarity} = \frac{\text{moles of solute}}{\text{volume of solution}}$$

$$= \frac{342}{88.73} = \textbf{3.85 M}$$

For NaCl, since it is univalent, Molar mass = equivalent mass

Therefore, Normality (N) = molarity (M) = **3.85**

$$\text{Molality, } m^{\ominus} = \frac{\text{moles of solute}}{\text{mass of solution}}$$

$$= \frac{342}{80} = \textbf{4.275 mol/kg}$$

Example 2.19 Aqueous solution of triethanolmine (TEA), i.e., $N(CH_2CH_2OH)_3$, contains 50% TEA by mass. Find the molarity of the solution if the density of the solution is 1.05 kg/L.

Solution *Basis* 100 kg TEA solution
The solution contains 50 kg TEA.

Molar mass of TEA, $M = 149$

Moles of TEA present in the solution, $n = \dfrac{50}{149} = 0.3356$ kmol

Volume of the solution, $V = \dfrac{100}{1.05} = 95.24$ L

Molarity of the solution $= \left(\dfrac{0.3356}{95.24}\right) \times 1000 = \textbf{3.524 M}$

The solubility of a gas in a liquid or solution is expressed in different ways. Some common ways of expression are mass %, mole %, amount of volume dissolved at specific conditions and mole ratio. Any one of them can be converted into another easily.

Example 2.20 The concentration of CO_2 is measured to be 0.206 kmol per kmol monoethanolamine (MEA) in a 20% (by mass) aqueous MEA solution. Assuming the density of the solution to be nearly 1.0 kg/L, find the concentration of CO_2 as mass % and mol % in the solution.

Solution *Basis* 100 kg aqueous MEA solution
The solution contains 20 kg MEA.

Chemical formula of MEA = $NH_2CH_2CH_2OH$

Molar mass of MEA, $M = 61$

Moles of MEA in the solution, $n_1 = \dfrac{20}{61} = 0.3279$ kmol

CO_2 dissolved in the solution = $0.206 \times 0.3279 = 0.0675$ kmol

Mass of CO_2, $m_1 = 0.0675 \times 44 = 2.97$ kg

Moles of water, $n_2 = \left(\dfrac{100 - 22.97}{18}\right) = 4.2794$ kmol

Table 2.3   Composition of Aqueous MEA Solution

Component	kmol n_i	mole %	Molar mass M_i	Mass $(n_i \cdot M_i)$	mass %
Water	4.2794	**91.54**	18	77.029	**77.03**
MEA	0.3279	**7.02**	61	20.0019	**20.00**
CO_2	0.0675	**1.44**	44	2.9700	**2.97**
Total	4.6748	**100.00**		100.00	**100.00**

Quite often, the specific gravities are used for indirect measurements of concentrations of aqueous solutions.

$$\text{Specific gravity } (SG)_{T_1/T_2} = \frac{(\text{Density of solution at } T_1 \text{ K})}{(\text{Denstiry of water at } T_2 \text{ K})} \qquad (2.12)$$

Various hydrometers are used in the industries to measure the specific gravity of a solution. Among them the following scales are commonly used.

(i) $°\text{Twaddell} (°\text{Tw}) = 200(SG_{288.7/288.7} - 1.000)$ $\qquad (2.13)$

(ii) For liquids heavier than water,

$$°\text{Baumè} (°\text{Bè}) = 145 - \left(\frac{145}{SG_{288.7/288.7}}\right) \qquad (2.14.1)$$

For liquids lighter than water,

$$°\text{Baumè} (°\text{Bè}) = \left(\frac{140}{SG_{288.7/288.7}}\right) - 130 \qquad (2.14.2)$$

(iii) For petroleum products, the American Petroleum Institute (API), USA has developed the following scale.

$$°\text{API} = \left(\frac{141.5}{SG_{288.7/288.7}}\right) - 131.5 \qquad (2.15)$$

(iv) For the sugar industry, an arbitrary scale of $°\text{Brix}$ is developed.

$$°\text{Brix} = \left(\frac{400}{SG_{288.7/288.7}}\right) - 400 \qquad (2.16)$$

The last scale is graduated in such a way that $1°\text{Brix} = 1\%$ sugar (by mass) in solution. Hydrometers of the types (i) and (ii) are used to measure the concentration of caustic lye, sulphuric acid strength, hydrochloric acid strength, etc. Table 2.4 gives the relations of $°\text{Bè}/°\text{Tw}$ with concentrations of aqueous sulphuric acid solutions.

Table 2.4   Relationship of Degree Baumè and Degrees Twaddell with the Concentration of Sulphuric Acid[8]

°Bè	°Tw	Specific gravity $SG_{288.7/288.7}$	mass % H_2SO_4	°Bè	°Tw	Specific gravity $SG_{288.7/288.7}$	mass % H_2SO_4
1	1.38	1.0069	1.02	20	32.00	1.1600	22.25
2	2.80	1.0140	2.08	25	41.66	1.2083	28.28
3	4.20	1.0211	3.13	30	52.18	1.2609	34.63
4	5.68	1.0284	4.21	35	63.64	1.3182	41.27
5	7.14	1.0357	5.28	40	76.20	1.3810	48.10
6	8.64	1.0432	6.37	45	90.00	1.4500	55.07
7	10.14	1.0507	7.45	50	105.26	1.5263	62.18
8	11.68	1.0584	8.55	55	122.22	1.6111	69.65
9	13.24	1.0662	9.66	60	141.18	1.7059	77.67
10	14.82	1.0741	10.77	65	162.50	1.8125	88.65
15	23.08	1.1154	16.38	66	167.08	1.8354	93.19

(Reproduced with the permission of Lurgi GmbH, Germany).

An important point to note about the use of these hydrometers is that the measurement of specific gravity should be made at 288.7 K (15.6°C or 60°F). If the hydrometers are used at temperatures other than 288.7 K (15.6°C), a correction should be applied. In India, the Twaddell meters in use are calibrated at 30/30°C (303/303 K). °API is very useful in knowing the nature of a petroleum product, i.e., its properties such as molar mass, viscosity, heating value, etc. The use of such units (based on specific gravity) is common in chemical industries to express concentration of soutions.

2.5 IMPORTANT PHYSICAL PROPERTIES OF SOLUTIONS

The physical properties of a pure solvent and a solution differ depending upon the amount of solute present in it. A commonly known property is pH of the solution. It is defined as

$$pH = - \log (H^+) \tag{2.17}$$

where H^+ = hydrogen ion concentration in geq/L

The property pH is used to express acidity or alkalinity of a solution. A pH of 7 is neutral, decreasing figures below 7 indicate increasing acidity while increasing figures above 7 show increasing alkalinity. The pH of alkaline solutions[9] are plotted in Fig. 2.2.

Strong acids like hydrochloric acid, sulphuric acid or nitric acid completely ionize in dilute solution form. Hence in a dilute solution, concentration of strong acid in geq/L and concentraction of H^+ ions in geq/L are same. For example, pH of 0.098 M HCl solution is $-\log (0.098)$ or 1.0088.

On the other hand, weak acids like acetic acid, hypochlorous acid, citric acid, etc., are not completely ionized in the aqueous form. Therefore, concentration of weak acid in geq/L and concentration of H^+ ions in geq/L are diffrent. Concentration of H^+ ions in aqueous solution of weak acid is given by $\sqrt{M_a \times K_a}$ where M_a is molarity of the weak acid and K_a is the ionization constant.

Example 2.21 Calculate the pH of 0.1 M hypochlorous acid whose ionization constant is 9.6×10^{-7}.

Solution   Concentration of $[H^+] = \sqrt{M_a \times K_a}$

$$= \sqrt{0.1 \times 9.6 \times 10^{-7}}$$
$$= 3.0984 \times 10^{-4}$$
$$pH = - \log [H^+]$$
$$= - \log [3.0984 \times 10^{-4}]$$
$$= \textbf{3.509, say 3.51}$$

A known property of the solvent is the vapour pressure (p_v) of the solvent. The vapour pressure of a liquid is defined as the absolute pressure at which the liquid and its vapour are in equilibrium at a given temperature. Consider the example of pure air-free water. It exerts the vapour pressure of 101.325 kPa (760 Torr) at 100°C (373.15 K). The complete vapour pressure table of water is given in Chapter 6

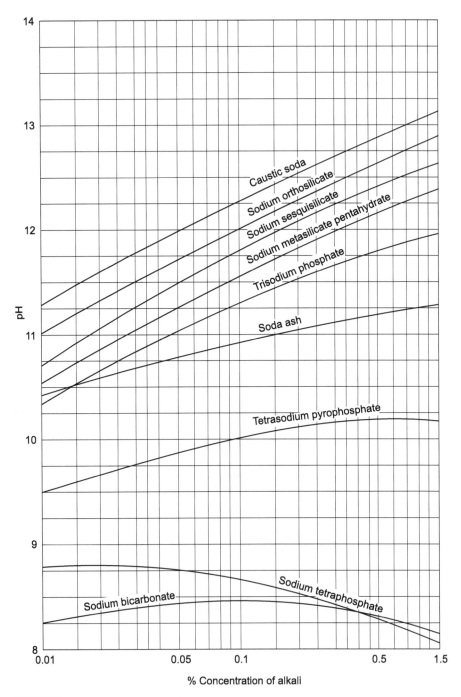

Fig. 2.2   pH of Alkaline Solutions[9]

(refer Table 6.13). Also, Appendix IV gives steam tables in which saturation pressure is vapour pressure at the given temperature.

Normally, a solute dissolved in a solvent depresses the vapour pressure of the solvent. For example, the dissolution of caustic soda, sugar, salt, etc. in water reduces the vapour pressure of water. In Fig. 2.3, the vapour pressure of caustic soda solutions is plotted against temperature[10].

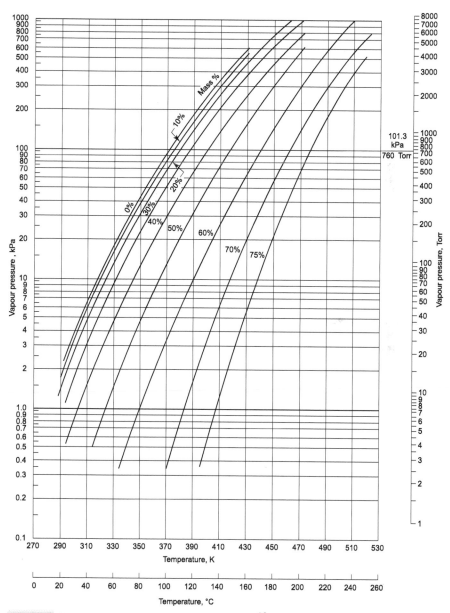

Fig. 2.3   Vapour Pressure of Caustic Soda Solutions[10]

From Fig. 2.3, it is evident that 30% (by mass) caustic soda lye exerts a vapour pressure of 10.666 kPa (80 Torr) at 60°C (333 K), while at the same temperature, the vapour pressure of water is 19.916 kPa (149.38 Torr) (refer Table 6.12). Data on lowering of vapour pressures by a number of inorganic compounds in aqueous solutions is given in the CRC Handbook of Chemistry and Physics[11].

From the above discussion, it is clear that the boiling point of a solution is higher than the boiling point of the solvent. When the temperature of a liquid is plotted against the temperature of the known reference liquid (e.g., water in case of an aqueous solution) at equal vapour pressure, it is called a *Dühring plot.* Also, a line plotting the boiling point of a solution against the boiling point of the solvent is known as *Dühring's line.* Such lines for caustic soda solutions of different concentrations have been given by McCabe[12].

While the elevation of boiling point of a caustic–soda solution calls for heat transfer at higher temperature in a multiple–effect evaporator system, the property of low vapour pressure of a caustic–soda solution can be advantageously used for producing brine at 5°C (278 K), using an absorption refrigeration cycle.

Raoult proposed a law for an ideal solution. It states that the vapour pressure of the solvent in a solution is directly proportional to the mole fraction of the solvent.

Vapour pressure of a solvent in the solution = (vapour pressure of pure solvent) × (mole fraction of the solvent)

$$p_i = p_{vi} \times x_i \qquad (2.18)$$

It was observed later that in most cases, only very dilute solutions obey Raoult's law. However, there are instances in which Raoult's law is applicable over a wide range of concentrations. A mixture of isomers, such as *o-*, *m-* and *p*-xylenes, members of a homologous series, such as benzene/toluene, *n*-hexane/*n*-heptane, etc., are examples for which Raoult's law is applicable over a nearly full range. Aqueous urea solutions are found to obey Raoult's law over a wide range. Hence, an ideal solution may be defined as the one which obeys Raoult's law over the complete range of concentration and at all temperatures. Such solutions are formed by mixing the constituents in the liquid state without heat and volume changes. It is a good approximation to assume that Raoult's law holds good for dilute solutions. To account for the non-ideal behaviour of a solution, a number of corrections have been proposed. The discussion on such correction factor is outside the scope of this book. The reader is advised to refer Reid *et al*[13] and Smith *et al*[14].

Another physical property of the solvent is its freezing point at which the solvent freezes to become a solid. This also results from the lowering of the vapour pressure of the solution by a non-volatile solute. It has been observed that the freezing point of a solution is lower than the freezing point of a pure solvent. In general, equimolar amounts of different solutes when dissolved in the same quantity of water give the same depression of the freezing point. As an approximation, when one kmol of a solute is dissolved in 100 kg water, the freezing point of water will depress by about 18.6°C (18.6 K). This property is used advantageously in making ice-cream or circulating the brine solutions containing calcium chloride for chilling operations (carried out at sub-zero temperatures). Extensive data on freezing point depression of water and other solvents are given in the CRC Handbook of Chemistry and Physics[11]. Freezing points of a number of aqueous brine solutions are presented in the Design Data Book[15].

An interesting and important property of solution is the *osmotic pressure* (π). When a dilute and a concentrated solution are separated from each other by a suitable membrane, the spontaneous flow of water takes place from the dilute solution to the concentrated solution.the essential property of these membranes is that they allow the free passage of water but not of the dissolved substance. A common permeable membrane in industrial use is polyamide. In the real sense, the solute having high molar mass cannot pass through the membrane and as a result, it will exert pressure against the wall of the membrane. The above process is called *osmosis* and the pressure is known as osmotic pressure. It can be determined by the ideal gas as given in Eq. (2.21). The osmotic pressure is the excess pressure which must be applied to the solution to prevent the passage of solvent into the solution when they are separated by a perfectly semipermeable membrane. Rougly, osmotic pressure is equal to 6.86 kPa (51 Torr) for dilute aqueous solution for each 100 mg/L of dissolved inorganic solids.

Reverse osmosis is a process in which the work is done against the osmotic pressure by applying pressure on the side containing the more concentrated solution. As a result, the solution enclosed in the membrane gets concentrated. by permitting permeation of solvent through the membrane. This technique finds application in desalination, effluent disposal, bulk drug manufacturing, dyes manufacturing, etc. Membranes are also developed which permit permeation of vapour of a specific component of the solution (e.g., water from alcohol–water mixture) by pressure diffrence under application of heat and vacuum. This process is known as pervaporation.

2.6   GASES

As discussed in the introduction, the direct weighing of gases is ruled out in practice. The volume of a gas can be conveniently measured and converted into mass from the density of the gas. In order to know the density of a gas, both pressure and temperature should be known. Various equations of state (also known as pVT relations) can be employed for this purpose.

2.6.1   Ideal Gas Law

According to Boyle, for a given mass of an ideal gas, the product of the pressure and volume is constant at a constant temperature, i.e.,

$$p \times V = \text{constant} \quad (T \text{ constant}) \tag{2.19}$$

where, p is the absolute pressure and V is the volume occupied by 1 kmol gas.

Charles proposed the law that for a given mass of an ideal gas, the ratio of the volume to temperature is constant at a given pressure.

$$\frac{V}{T} = \text{constant} \quad (p \text{ constant}) \tag{2.20}$$

where, T is the absolute temperature.

Combining the above two laws, an ideal gas law can be formulated as

$$\frac{(p \times V)}{T} = \text{constant} \tag{2.21}$$

The constant of Eq. (2.21 is designated by the symbol R, known as *universal gas constant*.

Therefore $\qquad\qquad\qquad pV = RT \tag{2.22}$

Equation (2.22) is called **ideal gas law**.

When V' is the volume of a gas in cubic metres of n kmol, Eq. (2.22) gets modified as

$$pV' = nRT \tag{2.23}$$

The value of R is listed in different units in Table 2.5.

Table 2.5   Value of Universal Gas Constant (R) in Different Units

Numerical Value of R	Units
0.083 145	$m^3 \cdot bar/(kmol \cdot K)$
8.314 472	$m^3 \cdot kPa/(kmol \cdot K)$
8.314 472	$J/(mol \cdot K)$
1.987 207	$kcal/(kmol \cdot K)$ or $Btu/(lb \; mol \cdot °R)$
0.082 057	$L \cdot atm/(mol \cdot K)$ or $m^3 \cdot atm/kmol \cdot K)$
62 363.665	$cm^3 \cdot Torr/(mol \cdot K)$
10.731 59	$ft^3 \cdot psia/(lb \; mol \cdot °R)$

[*Updated based on recommendations of CODATA Task Group on Fundamental Constants (2006)*[1]]

In Eq. (2.21), V is called the molar volume. At 273.15 K (0°C or 32°F) and 101.325 kPa a (1 atm a or 14.696 psia or 760 Torr), V = 22.413 996 (rounded value 22.414) m^3/kmol or L/mol. These conditions will be termed as normal temperature and pressure (NTP) in this book. In the FPS system, the molar volume at NTP equals 359.038 ft^3/lb mol.

Local conditions vary from place to place and, therefore, if reference temperature and standard atrmospheric pressure (STP) are considered, the molar volume at STP will differ at different places. In the USA, 14.7 $1bf/cm^2$ a (101.353 kPa a) and 288.7 K (15.55°C or 60°F) are considered in the natural gas industry to be STP. IUPAC recommend[16] 1 bar and 273.15 K (0°C) as **standard temperature and pressure (STP)** at which molar volume, V = 22.710 981 (rounded value 22.711) m^3/kmol.

Knowing the values of p and T, it is easy to calculate the molar volume ussing Eq. (2.22).

If p_1, V_1 and T_1 are the conditions of an ideal gas under one situation, and if p_2, V_2, T_2 are the conditions of the gas under another situation, from Eq.(2.21), it follows that

$$\frac{p_1 V_1}{T_1} = \frac{p_2 V_2}{T_2} \tag{2.24}$$

If Eq. (2.24) is utilised instead of Eq. (2.22), one situation may be taken as NTP, i.e., p_1 = 101.325 kPa, V_1 = 22.414 m^3/kmol and t_1/T_1 = 0°C/273.15 K or p_1 = 100 kPa, V_1 = 22.711 m^3/kmol and t_1/T_1 = 0°C/273.15 K.

2.6.2 Other Equations of State

According to Boyle's law, the volume occupied by a gas is inversely proportional to its pressure. However, real gases exhibit considerable deviation from ideal behaviour. For every gas, the ratio pV/RT is constant over only a definite range of pressure. Within this range, Boyle's law is obeyed. In general, the extent of the deviation from Boyle's law is small at low pressures, expecially when the temperature is relatively high.

In order to account for non-ideal behaviour of the gases, J D van der Waals proposed another equation of state in 1873 as follows:

$$\left(p + \frac{a}{V^2} \right)(V - b) = RT \tag{2.25}$$

In Eq. (2.25), a and b are constants depending on the gas. The values of a and b can be evaluated using the following equations.

$$a = 27 \, \frac{R^2 \, T_c^2}{64 p_c} \, \text{L}^2 \cdot \text{MPa/mol}^2 \text{ or } (\text{m}^3)^2 \cdot \text{MPa/(kmol)}^2 \tag{2.26}$$

$$\text{or } \text{J} \cdot \text{m}^3/\text{mol}^2$$

and

$$b = \frac{RT_c}{8 p_c} \, \text{L/mol or } \text{m}^3/\text{kmol} \tag{2.27}$$

where, p_c and T_c are the critical pressure and the critical temperature of the gas, respectively.

The critical temperature (T_c) is the maximum temperature at which a gas can be liquefied. The critical pressure (p_c) is the saturation pressure corresponding to the critial temperature. Above the critical temperature, a gas cannot be liquefied regardless of the pressure. The volume occupied by a gas under critical conditions is called the critical volume (V_c). At the critical point, the densities of coexisting liquid and gaseous phases are identical. Appendix III gives the critical constants of various compounds.

There are other equations of state, e.g., Beattie Bridgeman equation, Berthelot equation, Benedict, Webb and Rubin equation, three parameter corresponding states priniciple (CSP) of Pitzer and co-workers, etc. The discussion of these equations is beyond the scope of this book. For further study of these equations, reference 14 can be consulted.

In various equations of state, the constants for different compounds are required to be calculated from other properties. Calculations of the constants involve quite complex formulae and may require use of a programmable calculator or a computer. The advantage of the complex equations is the accuracy of the results. However, for quick estimations, non-ideality of a gas can be expressed by the *compressibility factor Z* where,

$$Z = \frac{pV}{RT} \tag{2.28}$$

For an ideal gas $Z = 1.0$. For real gases, values of Z can be obtained from the Nelson–Obert generalised compressibility charts and acentric factor (ω) [13,14].

In order to convert the molar volume into density, molar mass (M) should be employed.

$$\text{Density of gas, } \rho_g = \frac{\text{Molar mass } (M)}{\text{Molar volume } (V)} \tag{2.29}$$

Another important parameter, used in the gas industry, is the *specific gravity* of a gas. Unlike liquids, it is defined in this book as

$$\text{Specific gravity of a gas} = \frac{\text{Molar mass of the gas } (M)}{\text{Molar mass of air } (M_a)} \tag{2.30}$$

Specific gravity of a gas indicates the heavines of a gas as compared to that of air.

2.6.3 Gas Mixtures

In industries, very often, mixtures of various gases are handled. The analysis of the components present in the mixture is usually given on a volume basis. Take an example of air in which the oxygen and nitrogen are present nearly in 21% and 79% proportions on a volume basis, respectively.

If V_i is the volume of pure component i, present in the mixture, the total volume of 1 mol gas

$$V = \Sigma \, V_i \tag{2.31}$$

This is known as Amagat's laws.

Actually, all the components of a gas mixture occupy the total volume, and hence V_i is truly speaking that volume which would be occupied by the component i, if it alone is present at system pressure p and temperature T of the mixture.

$$V_i = \frac{n_i RT}{p} \tag{2.32}$$

where, n_i is the number of moles of component i.

From Eq. (2.32), it is clear that V_i is proportional to n_i. In other words, the volume % of a component in a gas mixture equals to mole % of it. This is strictly true for ideal gases. For non-ideal gases, the compressibility factor Z_i of the component should be considered for each gas present in the mixture. In the chapters that follow, volume % would be considered to be equal to mole % which is an accepted practice for stoichiometric calculations.

In the foregoing discussions, the volume V_i occupied by a component i in the gas mixture seemed to be a hypothetical proposition. However, it is logical to follow that in a gas mixture, each component exerts a different pressure, depending on the mole fraction of that component. This pressure exerted by each component is called the *partial pressure*. As recommended by IUPAC, it is defined as

$$p_i = p \cdot y_i \tag{2.33}$$

where, p_i is the partial pressure of the ith component, p is the total pressure and y_i is the mole fraction of the ith component in the gas mixture.

Equation (2.33) is valid for any gas mixture (ideal or real).

$$\Sigma p_i = p \cdot \Sigma y_i \tag{2.34}$$

Since $\Sigma \, y_i = 1.0$,

$$p = \Sigma \, p_i \tag{2.35}$$

Equation (2.35) is one form of Dalton's law, which states that in a gas mixture, the total pressure is the sum of the partial pressures exerted by each component. In this definition, it is assumed that the component i fills up the entire volume available to it. In other words,

$$p_i = \frac{n_i RT}{V} \tag{2.36}$$

From Eq. (2.32) and (2.36), it is clear that **for an ideal gas mixture,**

$$\textbf{volume \% = mole \% = pressure \%} \tag{2.37}$$

Equation (2.37) is a very important relationship in stoichiometry. The density and specific gravity of a gas mixture can be evaluated using Eq. (2.29) and Eq. (2.30) in which average molar mass of the gas mixture should be taken into account. Mathematically, the average (or mean) molar mass M is defined as

$$M = \Sigma\,(M_i \cdot y_i) \tag{2.38}$$

where, M_i is the molar mass of the ith component.

From Eq. (2.38), it can be deduced that the mass of a gas mixture equivalent to its average molar mass will occupy molar volume.

Pure component pressure (P_i) of the ith component (species) is defined as the pressure exerted by n_i moles of the pure ith component in a real gas mxiture at T and mixture volume V. In other words, it is the pressure that the ith component would exert at given T if it alone occupied the mixture voulme (V).

$$P_i = \frac{Z_i\,n_i\,R\,T}{V} \tag{2.39}$$

In Eq . (2.39), Z_i is evaluted at P_i and T for a real gas. Dalton's law of additive pressures states that the total pressure (p) exerted by a gas miture is equal to the sum of the *pure component pressures* of the components (of the gas mixture of n moles). Since $n_i = y_i \cdot n$

$$p = \Sigma\,P_i = \Sigma\,\left(\frac{Z_i\,n_i\,R\,T}{V}\right) = \frac{n\,R\,T}{V}(\Sigma Z_i\,y_i) \tag{2.40}$$

For the real gas mixture,

$$p = \frac{Z\,R\,T}{V} \tag{2.28}$$

Combining Eq. (2.40) and Eq. (2.28),

$$Z = \Sigma\,Z_i\,y_i \tag{2.41}$$

Since $Z = 1.0$ for an ideal gas mixture, p_i and P_i are same for the species in the ideal gas mixture. For a mixture of real gases (or *non-ideal* gas mixture), pure component pressure can be calculated by an iterative procedure, recommended by Missen and Smith[17]. In this procedure, first iteration commences with partial pressures [Eq. (2.33)]. Z_i obtained from charts, available in literature, or calculated by a representative equation of state (for the component) or calculated by 3-parameter corresposing states principle (CSP) developed by Pitzer and co-workers, involving the acentric factor (ω). $\Sigma\,Z_i\,y_i$ yields the compressibility of the gas mixture (Z). P_i is then calculated by

$$P_i(1) = \left(\frac{Z_i}{Z}\right)p_i \tag{2.42}$$

The second iteration is performed with $P_i(1)$ and fresh Z [say $Z(1)$] is calculated. Iterations are continued till Z converges. Final P_i values are the pure component pressures. During each iteration, V is also calculated for each component and the for the gas mixture at given T. All V values should be same. Alternately, V/RT should be constant for each component and for the gas mixture at the end of iterations.

In this book, calculations are restricted to ideal gas mixtures. However, calculations for real gas mixtures are demonstrated in Examples 5.39 and 8.11. Evalution of P_i is required for calculating real gas enthalpy and entropy of the component. Tabular charts are available for a number of gases in literature listing pressure, temperature, enthalpy and entropy. Alternatively, use of the respresentative equation of state or CSP may be made for calculation of enthalpy or entropy values with pure component pressure (P_i) and T as known parameters.

When trace quantities of a particular component are present in a gaseous mixture, it is expressed either as ppm (v/v) or mg/m^3; e.g., traces of SO_2 in flue gases or in vent gases from sulphuric acid plant, traces of NO_x in tail gas from nitric acid plant or adipic acid plant, etc.

2.6.4   Joule–Thomson Effect

Throttling of gases is often encountered in the industry. In such a process, when a gas is passed through an orifice, a nozzle or a throttling valve, its pressure is reduced. This process essentially takes place at constant enthalpy; also called *isenthalp*. For an ideal gas, throttling should not change the temperature of the gas. However, for most real gases, throttling results in a decrease in temperature. This is known as Joule–Thomson effect. Ratio of the change in temperature to respective pressure reduction is defined as Joule–Thomson coefficient (μ).

Throttling of compressed air, refrigerant gases, steam, etc., are experienced in industry. In cryogenic separation of gases, the Joule–Thomson effect has an important role. It is advantageously used in supplying relatively cold air in air breathing apparatus, commonly known as pressure suits, worn by a person, working in an hazardous environment.

2.6.5   Gas–Liquid Mixtures

It has been seen in Sec. 2.5 that an ideal liquid–liquid mixture obeys Raoult's law. The same law also applies to a gas-liquid mixture, i.e., the partial pressure of a pure component in a gas mixture at equilibrium at a given temperature equals the mole fraction of the component in a liquid mixture multiplied by the vapour pressure of pure liquid at the same temperature.

Mathematically,

$$y_i \cdot p = x_i \cdot p_{vi} \tag{2.43}$$

Left term of the equation is the partial pressure as defined in Eq. (2.33).

At low concentrations of a gas in the liquid, Raoult's law does not hold good. For such non-ideal behaviour, Henry's law is found to be useful. If p_i is the partial pressure of the solute gas i,

$$p_i = y_i\, p = H_i \cdot x_i \tag{2.44}$$

where, x_i is the mole fraction of the ith component in the solution and H_i is the Henry's law constant. Note that according to Raoult's law, H_i should be equal to the vapour pressure p_{vi} for an ideal solution. Although Henry's law was proposed for low concentraions of gas in the liquid, it is one of the most used principles of physical chemistry because of its simplicity. Henry's law may lead to erroneous results if appropriate assumptions are not made.

Example 2.22   Calculate the average molar mass and composition by mass of air.

Solution   An average composition of air at sea level by volume is given in Table 2.6.

Table 2.6   Composition of Air at Mean Seal Level[18]

Gas	mole %
Nitrogen	78.084
Oxygen	20.946
Argon	0.934
Carbon dioxide	0.033
Neon	18×10^{-4}
Helium	5.24×10^{-4}
Methane	1.6×10^{-4}
Krypton	1.14×10^{-4}
Hydrogen	0.5×10^{-4}
Nitrous Oxide	0.3×10^{-4}
Xenon	0.87×10^{-5}

In general, it can be taken that oxygen, nitrogen and argon are present to the extent of 21%, 78% and 1%, respectively (on volume basis). For combustion calculations, air with average composition of 21% oxygen and 79% nitrogen (by volume) is considered for most cases.

Basis 100 kmol air

Table 2.7   Composition of Air without Trace/Noble Gases

Gas	Formula	Molar mass, M_i	n_i kmol	Mass, m_i, kg	mass %
Oxygen	O_2	31.9988	21	671.975	23.19
Nitrogen	N_2	28.0134	78	2185.045	75.43
Argon	Ar	39.948	1	39.948	1.38
Total			100	2896.968	100.00

Average molar mass of air, $M_a = \dfrac{2897}{100} = \mathbf{28.97}$

Note   Molar mass of each gas component is calculated using atomic masses, given in Appendix-II. The average molar mass of air, used at various places in later chapters, will be taken approximately as 29.

Example 2.23   Cracked gas from a petroleum refinery has the following composition by volume: 45% methane, 10% ethane, 25% ethylene, 7% propane, 8% propylene, 5% n-butane.

Find (a) the average molar mass of the gas mixture, (b) the composition by mass, and (c) specific gravity of the gas mixture.

Solution   In this type of problem, it is convenient to assume the basis of 100 kmol of cracked gas.

Since volume % equals mole %, methane present in the mixture is equal to 45 kmol.

Molar mass of methane, $M_1 = 12 + 4 = 16$

Mass of methane, $m_1 = 45 \times 16 = 720$ kg

In a similar way, for all the components of the mixture, masses can be calculated. These calculations are summarized in Table 2.8.

Table 2.8   Composition of Refinery Gas

Gas	Formula	Molar mass, M	kmol	Mass kg, m	mass %
Methane	CH_4	16	45	720	**27.13**
Ethane	C_2H_6	30	10	300	**11.30**
Ethylene	C_2H_4	28	25	700	**26.37**
Propane	C_3H_8	44	7	308	**11.61**
Propylene	C_3H_6	42	8	336	**12.66**
n-Butane	C_4H_{10}	58	5	290	**10.93**
Total	—	—	100	2654	**100.00**

Average molar mass of gas mixture, $M = \dfrac{2654}{100} = \mathbf{26.54}$

Specific gravity of gas mixture $= \dfrac{26.54}{28.97} = \mathbf{0.9161}$

Example 2.24   Calculate the specific volume of superheated steam at 100 bar a and 350°C (623.15 K) using (a) the ideal gas law, and (b) the van der Waals equation.

If the actual specific volume* of steam at the above conditions is 0.022 42 m³/kg, find the percentage error in the above cases.

Solution   Molar mass of steam (water), $M_w = 18.0153$

Ideal gas law states

$$pV = RT$$

$$p = 100 \text{ bar a}, \ T = 623.15 \text{ K}$$

Molar volume $V = \dfrac{RT}{p}$

$$= \frac{0.083\,145 \times 623.15}{100} = 0.5181 \text{ m}^3/\text{kmol}$$

Specific volume $v = \dfrac{V}{M}$

$$= 0.5181/18.0153 \ (\text{m}^3/\text{kmol}) \ (\text{kmol/kg})$$

$$= \mathbf{0.0288 \ m^3/kg}$$

---

*from Appendix IV.3

Evaluation of van der Waals constants

$$\left(P + \frac{a}{V^2}\right)(V - b) = RT$$

where $a = \dfrac{27\,R^2\,T_c^2}{64\,p_c}$ $(m^3)^2$. bar/(kmol)^2 and $b = \dfrac{RT_c}{8p_c}$ m^3/kmol

$p_c = 221.20$ bar, $T_c = 647.30$ K for water,

$$a = \frac{[27 \times (0.083\,145)^2 \times (647.30)^2]}{(64 \times 221.2)}$$

$$= 5.5244 \text{ m}^6.\text{ bar/(kmol)}^2$$

$$b = \frac{(0.083\,145 \times 647.30)}{(8 \times 221.2)}$$

$$= 0.030\ 41 \text{ m}^3\text{/kmol}$$

Substituting the value of a and b in van der Waals equation.

$$\left(100 + \frac{5.5244}{V^2}\right)(V - 0.030\ 41) = 0.083\ 14\ 5 \times 623.15$$

Simplifying,

$$10\ V^3 - 5.4853V^2 + 0.5524\ V - 0.0168 = 0$$

Such equations can be solved by using a numerical method such as the Newton–Raphson method. According to this method, if $F(V) = 0$ then

$$V_{n+1} = V_n - \frac{F(V_n)}{F'(V_n)} \tag{2.45}$$

where, V_n is the starting root and V_{n+1} is the corrected root. To start with, V_1 may be taken as 0.5181 m^3/kmol which is the value obtained with the help of the ideal gas law. Using V_1, calculate V_2. Compare V_1 and V_2. If they are close enough, V_2 is the final root. If they are quite different, evaluate V_3, and so on. Within four or five iterations, it is possible to get the exact root. Using this method,

$$V = 0.428\ 85 \text{ m}^3\text{/kmol}$$

Specific volume, $v = \dfrac{0.428\ 85}{18.0153} = \mathbf{0.0238\ m^3/kg}$

Such equations can be readily solved by specialised mathematical software like Mathcad$^®$.

Given

$$F(V) := \left(100 + \frac{5.5244}{V^2}\right) \cdot (V - 0.03041) - 0.083145(623.15)$$

Guess $\qquad V := 0.518$

$V := \text{root}(F(V), V)$

$$V = 0.42884 \quad \frac{m^3}{kmol}$$

or $\qquad v = \dfrac{0.428\,84}{18.0153} = \textbf{0.0238 m}^3\textbf{/kg}$

Correct value = $0.022\,42$ m^3/kg

% Error by using ideal gas law = $\left[\dfrac{(0.0288 - 0.022\,42)}{0.022\,42} \right] \times 100 = \textbf{28.46}$

% Error by using van der Waals equation = $\left[\dfrac{(0.0238 - 0.022\,42)}{0.022\,42} \right] \times 100$

$\qquad\qquad = \textbf{6.16}$

Example 2.25 Carburetted water gas has the following composition by volume: 35.2% Hydrogen, 14.8% Methane, 12.8% Ethylene, 1.5% Carbon dioxide, 33.9% Carbon monoxide and 1.8% Nitrogen

The gas is available at 500°C (773.15 K) and 4 bar a. Find the molar volume of the mixture using (a) the ideal gas law, and (b) the van der Waals equation.

Solution   *Ideal gas law* $pV = RT$

$\qquad\qquad p = 4$ bar a

$\qquad\qquad T = 773.15$ K

$$V = \frac{RT}{p} = 0.083\,145 \times \frac{773.15}{4} = 16.0709 \text{ L/mol}$$

Evaluation of van der Waals constants

For a gas mixture, a single value of the critical pressure or critical temperature cannot be used, and hence, *pseudo*-critical properties are evaluated using Kay's additive rule as shown in Table 2.9. However, this rule leads to significant errors, particularly when widely boiling components are present in the mixture. Lee and Kesler[19] have presented a set of mixing rules to find the critical properties of the mixtures based on a 3-parameter corresponding states principle that are claimed to give the best results. The discussion on the complex rules is outside the scope of this book. According to Kay's rule,

Psuedo–critical property of a component in the mixture = (mole fraction of the component) × (critical property of the component)   (2.46)

Table 2.9 Composition of Carburetted Water Gas

Component	Formula	Mole fraction y_i	Critical temp., K T_{ci}^*	$y_i \cdot T_{ci}$	Critical pressure, bar a p_{ci}^*	$y \cdot p_{ci}$
Hydrogen	H_2	0.352	32.20	11.334	12.97	4.57
Methane	CH_4	0.148	190.56	28.203	45.99	6.81
Ethylene	C_2H_4	0.128	282.34	36.140	50.41	6.45
Carbon monoxide	CO	0.339	132.91	45.056	34.99	11.86
Carbon dioxide	CO_2	0.015	304.10	4.562	73.75	1.11
Nitrogen	N_2	0.018	126.09	2.270	33.94	0.61
Total		1.000		127.565		31.41

* Ref. Appendix III

$$a = \frac{27R^2T_c^2}{64p_c}$$

$$= \frac{[27(0.083\ 145)^2 \times (127.565)^2]}{(64 \times 31.41)} = 1.511\ \text{L}^2 \cdot \text{bar/(mol)}^2$$

$$b = \frac{RT_c}{8p_c}$$

$$= 0.083\ 145 \times \frac{127.565}{(8 \times 31.41)} = 0.042\ 21\ \text{L/mol}$$

Substituting these values,

$$\left(4 + \frac{1.511}{V^2}\right)(V - 0.042\ 21) = 0.083\ 145 \times 773.15$$

$$= 64.283\ 557$$

Solving the equation by the Newton–Raphson method,

$$V = 15.74\ \text{L/mol}$$

Mathcad solution

Given

$$F(V) := \left(4 + \frac{1.511}{V^2}\right) \cdot (V - 0.0422\ 1) - 0.083145(773.15)$$

Guess $V := 16.0709$

$V := \text{root}(F(V), V)$

$$V = 16.0897\ \frac{\text{L}}{\text{mol}}$$

Example 2.26 A ternary mixture of n-butane, 1-butene and furfural is analysed to find the content of each in it[20]. The mixture is stripped off with the help of carbon dioxide without appreciable entrainment of furfural due to its very low vapour pressure. The stripped gases are passed through an absorber column in which CO_2 is absorbed in 25% (by mass) KOH solution. The mixture of hydrocarbons, saturated with water vapour, is collected in a measuring burette.

The test data are as follows:

Sample mass = 6.5065 g

Volume of saturated gases collected at 23.25°C (296.4 K) and 102.5 kPa (769 Torr) = 415.1 ml

n-Butane present in the hydrocarbons (dry) in the burette = 43.1 mol %.

Find the analysis of the liquid mixture (both on mole and mass basis).

Data Vapour pressure of water over

25% KOH solution at 296.4 K = 2.175 kPa

Solution   *Basis* 6.5065 g furfural-*n* butane-1-butene mixture

Vapour pressure of water over KOH solution = 2.175 kPa

Partial pressure of *n*-butane and 1-butene (*p*) = 102.5 − 2.175

$$= 100.325\ \text{kPa}$$

If n is the total number of mol of n-butane and 1-butene, then according to Eq. (2.23),

$$n = \frac{pV}{RT}$$

$$= \frac{100.325 \times 415.1}{8.314\,472 \times 296.4 \times 1000}$$

$$= 0.0169 \text{ mol}$$

n-Butane in the hydrocarbon mixture $= 0.0169 \times 0.431 = 0.007\,284$ mol

Mass of n-butane in the mixture $= 0.007\,284 \times 58 = 0.422$ g

1-Butene in the hydrocarbon mixture $= 0.0169 - 0.007\,284 = 0.009\,616$ mol

Mass of 1-butene in the mixture $= 0.009\,616 \times 56 = 0.5385$ g

Mass of furfural in the liquid mixture $= 6.5065 - 0.422 - 0.5385 = 5.546$ g

Moles of furfural in the liquid mixture $= \dfrac{5.546}{96} = 0.057\,77$ mol

The result are summarized in Table 2.10.

Table 2.10 Composition of Ternary Mixture

Component	Formula	Molar mass, M_i	n_i mol	mole %	Mass g	mass %
n-Butane	C_4H_{10}	58	0.007 284	**9.75**	0.4225	**6.49**
1-Butene	C_4H_8	56	0.009 616	**12.88**	0.5385	**8.27**
Furfural	$C_5H_4O_2$	96	0.057 778	**77.37**	5.5467	**85.24**
Total			0.074 678	**100.00**	6.5077	**100.00**

Example 2.27 The liquid mixture cited in the above example is boiled at 65°C (338.15 K) and 5.7 bar g. The mole fraction of n-butane in the ternary vapour mixture in equilibrium with the liquid is found to be 49.1 volume %. Assuming ideal behaviour of the liquid and vapour mixture, find the composition of the vapour mixture.

Data Vapour pressure of furtural at 338.15 K = 3.293 kPa = 24.7 Torr

Solution Absolute total pressure $= 5.7 + 1.01 = 6.71$ bar

According to Raoult's law,

Actual vapour pressure of

the furtural $=$ (vapour pressure of pure furfural at 338.15 K) $\times$ (mol fraction of furfural in the liquid mixture)

$= 3.293 \times 0.7737 = 2.548$ kPa

According to Dalton's law of partial pressures,

Mole fraction of furfural in the vapour mixture $= \dfrac{2.548}{6.71 \times 100}$

$$= 0.0038$$

Mole fraction of 1-butene

in the vapour mixture $= 1.0000 - 0.0038 - 0.491 = \mathbf{0.5052}$

Example 2.28 Ambient air on a particular day in Ahmadabad recorded the following conditions.

Total pressure = 100 kPa (750 Torr)

Dry bulb temperature $= 35°C$ (308.15 K)

Dew point $= 21.3°C$ (294.45 K)

Find the absolute humidity of the air.

Data: Vapour pressure of water at 294.45 K $= 2.5326$ kPa $= 19$ Torr (Ref. Table 6.12)

Solution Partial pressure of water

vapour in the air, p_w = vapour pressure for water at dew point
$$= 2.5326 \text{ kPa}$$

Now, according to Dalton's law,

$$\frac{\text{(Moles of water vapour)}}{\text{(Moles of dry air)}} = \frac{\text{(Partial pressure of water vapour)}}{\text{(Partial pressure of dry air)}}$$

$$= \frac{2.5326}{(100 - 2.5326)} = \frac{2.5326}{97.4674} = 0.025\,98$$

$$\frac{\text{(Mass of water vapour)}}{\text{(Mass of dry air)}} = \frac{2.5326}{97.4674} \times \frac{\text{(Molar mass of water)}}{\text{(Molar mass of air)}}$$

$$= \frac{2.5326}{97.4674} \times \frac{18.0153}{28.9697}$$

$$= 0.016\,16 \text{ kg/kg}$$

$$\equiv \mathbf{16.16} \; \frac{\textbf{g water vapour}}{\textbf{kg dry air}}$$

Example 2.29 Refrigerant 12 is expanded through a nozzle from 20.7 bar a and 82°C (355.15 K) to 8.7 bar a. If the average Joule–Thomson coefficient (μ) for R-12 is 1.616 K/bar, calculate the outlet temperature of the gas from the nozzle.

Solution $T_i - T_f = \mu \, (p_i - p_f)$

p_i = initial pressure, 20.7 bar a

p_f = final pressure, 8.7 bar a

$\mu = 1.616$ K/bar

$T_i = 355.15$ K

$T_f = T_i - \mu \, (p_i - p_f)$

$\quad = 355.15 - 1.616(20.7 - 8.7)$

$\quad = \mathbf{335.76 \text{ K or } 62.61°C}$

Note From enthalpy–pressure–temperature data of R-12 (REFPROP - Ver. 8)[21], the outlet temperature of the gas is interpolated to be 60.3°C (333.45 K).

2.7 CONCLUSION

The chapters that follow will require the use of the principles outlined in this chapter. Hence, it is needless to stress upon the importance of understanding these fundamentals. The discussion on the principles is limited to the extent that it is useful in the later chapters. For greater knowledge of basic chemical principles, standard textbooks should be referred [14, 22].

Exercises

2.1 Find the moles of oxygen present in 500 g.   [15.625 mol]

2.2 How many grams of carbon are present in 600 g $CaCO_3$?   [72 g]

2.3 Find the molar mass of $KMnO_4$.   [158]

2.4 A mass of 100 g each of HNO_3 and H_2SO_4 is filled in two separate bottles. Which bottle contains more atoms? How many more?

[**Bottle containing HNO_3 will have 0.567 mol or**
3.415×10^{23} atoms more than the other bottle.]

2.5 How many kilograms of carbon disulphide will contain 3.5 kmol carbon?   [**266 kg**]

2.6 What is the equivalent mass of $Al_2(SO_4)_3$?   [**57**]

2.7 How many equivalents are there in 500 g $KMnO_4$?   [**15.82 g eq**]

2.8 The analysis of magnesite ore obtained from Chalk Hill area, Salem district, yields 81% $MgCO_3$. 14% SiO_2 and 5% H_2O (by mass): Convert the analysis into mole %.

[**65.3% $MgCO_3$, 15.8% SiO_2, 18.9% H_2O (mole basis)**]

2.9 The analysis of a sample of glass yields 7.8% Na_2O, 7.0% MgO, 9.7% ZnO, 2.0% Al_2O_3, 8.5% B_2O_3 and 65.0% SiO_2 (by mass). Convert this composition into mole%

[**7.65% Na_2O, 10.57% MgO, 7.25% ZnO, 1.19% Al_2O_3,**
7.43% B_2O_3 and 65.91% SiO_2 (mole basis)]

2.10 A sample of sea water contains 35 000 ppm solids. Express the concentration of the solids as mass percentage.   [**3.5% (mass)**]

2.11 A sample of milliolite limestone, obtained from Porbandar, Gujarat, is found to contain 54.5% CaO (by mass). If this CaO is present as $CaCO_3$ in the limestone, find the content of $CaCO_3$ in the limestone.   [**97.32 mass %**]

2.12 Calculate the available nitrogen in the following:
(a) Commercial ammonium sulphate (96% pure)
(b) Pure sodium nitrate (100%)

[**(a) 20.36%; (b) 16.47% (mass basis)**]

2.13 A sample of caustic soda flakes contains 74.6% Na_2O (by mass). Find the purity of the flakes.   [**96.26% NaOH**]

2.14 Nitric acid and water forms a maximum boiling azeotrope containing 62.2 mole % water [boiling temperature = 130.6°C (403.75 K)]. Find the composition of the azeotrope by mass.   [**68.02% HNO_3 (mass)**]

2.15 An aqueous solution of common salt (NaCl) contains 25% salt (by mass) at 25°C (298.15 K). Find the mole % of NaCl in the solution.   [**9.3 mole % NaCl**]

2.16 A saturated solution of KCl in aqueous HCl is prepared at 25°C (298.15 K) by dissolving 4.0 g HCl/100 g water and 19.61 g KCl/100 g water[5]. Calculate mass % amd mole % compositions of the solution.

Table 2.11   Composition of Solution

Component	mass %	mole %
HCl	3.24	1.85
KCl	15.86	4.44
H_2O	80.90	93.71
Total	100.00	100.00

2.17 An aqueous solution contains 19.0% NH_3, 65.6% NH_4NO_3 and 6.0% urea (by mass). Calculate the available nitrogen content solution.   [**41.41% nitrogen**]

2.18 Ethanol is present in the aqueous solution to the extent of 1000 mg/L. Find TOC and ThOD of the solution in mg/L.   [**TOC = 522 mg/L; ThOD = 2087 mg/L**]

2.19 The strength of a phosphoric acid sample is found to be 35% P_2O_5 (by mass). Find out the actual concentration of H_3PO_4 (by mass) in the acid   [**48.31% H_3PO_4 (by mass)**]

2.20 Spent acid from a fertiliser unit has the following composition by mass; H_2SO_4: 20%, NH_4HSO_4: 45%, H_2O: 30% and organic compounds: 5%. Calculate the total acid content of the spent acid in terms of H_2SO_4 after adding the acid content, chemically bound in ammonium hydrogen sulphate.   [**58.35% (mass)**]

2.21 A sample of aqueous triethanolamine (TEA) solution contains 47% TEA (on volume basis). If the density of pure TEA is 1125 kg/m^3, find the mass % of TEA in the solution, considering it as an ideal solution.   [**49.94% (mass)**]

2.22 A sample of wine contains 20% alcohol (ethanol) on volume basis. Find the mass % of a alcohol in the wine. Assume the densities of alcohol and alcohol–free liquid (essentially water) to be 0.79 kg/L and 1.0 kg/L, respectively. Consider wine to be an ideal solution.   [**16.49% alcohol**]

2.23 Convert the following into equivalent ppm $CaCO_3$:
(a)   800 ppm Na_2CO_3 in water
(b)   85 ppm $MgSO_4$ in water
   [**(a) 754.7 ppm $CaCO_3$ (b) 70.7 ppm $CaCO_3$**]

2.24 Make the following conversions:
(a)   294 g/L H_2SO_4 to normality (N)
(b)   4.8 mg/mL $CaCl_2$ to normality (N)
(c)   5 N H_3PO_4 to g/L
(d)   54.75 g/L HCl to molarity (M)
(e)   3 M K_2SO_4 to g/L
   [**(a) 6 N; (b) 0.0865 N; (c) 163.35 g/L (d) 1.5 M (e) 522 g/L**]

2.25 An aqueous solution of acetic acid of 35% concentration (by mass) has a density of 1.04 kg/L at 25°C (298.15 K). Find the molarity, normality and molality of the solution.   [**6.066 M; 6.066 N; 8.974 Molality**]

2.26 An aqueous solution of monoethanolamine contains 20% MEA (by mass). It is utilised for the absorption of CO_2. Rich solution from the absorber contains 40 volume CO_2. Calculate CO_2 loading in term of moles of CO_2 dissolved per mole MEA assuming that the density of the solution is 1.011 kg/L.
Hint: 40 volumes CO_2 concentration means that a litre solution will liberate 40 L CO_2 at 101.325 kPa a and 0°C (273.15 K).   [**0.5385 mol CO_2/mol MEA**]

2.27 The strength of an aqueous hydrogen peroxide solution is 60 volumes. Its density is measured to be 1.075 kg/L at 20°C (293.15 K). Find the mass % of H_2O_2 in the solution.
Hint: A quantity of 1 L of 60 volume hydrogen peroxide will liberate 60 L oxygen at 101.325 kPa a and 15.6°C (288.75 K).   [**16.02 mass %**]

2.28 Calculate the elevation in the boiling point of a 40% (by mass) caustic–soda solution over pure water (at standard atmospheric pressure) using Fig. 2.3.   [**29°C (29 K)**]

2.29 An equimolar mixture of benzene and toluene is heated to 50°C (323.45 K). If the mixture is considered to be an ideal solution, calculate its vapour pressure.
Data Vapour pressure of benzene and toluene are 37.2 kPa and 12.3 kPa, respectively at 50°C (323.15 K). [Ref. Table 5.4]   [**24.75 kPa**]

2.30 An aqueous solution contains 25% urea (by mass). Assume that the soultion follows Raoult's law. Calculate the vapour pressure of the solution at 60°C (333.15 K).
Data Vapour pressure of H_2O at 60°C (333.15 K) = 19.92 kPa   [Ref. Table 6.13]
   [**18.11 kPa**]

2.31 Deep water (well below 1000 m under sea) divers use a cylinder containing helium and oxygen for breathing instead of a cylinder containing normal air. Why?
Data Henry's constants[14] (H_i) for helium and nitrogen at 25°C (298.15 K) are 126 600 bar and 87 650 bar, respectively.

2.32 An aqueons solution of 2 mole % NH_3 is in equilibrium with atmospheric air at 30°C (303.15 K). Calculate the mole fraction of NH_3 in air in equilibrium using (a) Raoult's law, and (b) Henry's law.
Data 1. Vapour pressure of ammonia at 30°C (303.15 K) = 11.58 bar (Ref. Table 5.4)
2. Henry's constant for ammonia in water at 30°C (303.15 K) = 0.861 bar
(646 Torr)   **[(a) 0.017 (b) 0.2286]**

Note   Ammonia–water system is non-ideal. Hence, Raoult's law gives erroneous results even for low concentration of ammonia in water.

2.33 A gas mixture has the following composition by volume:
Ethylene   30.6%
Benzene   24.5%
Oxygen   1.3%
Methane   15.5%
Ethane   25.0%
Nitrogen   3.1%
Find (a) the average molar mass of the gas mixture, (b) the composition by mass, and (c) the density of the mixture in kg/m^3 at NTP.
     **[(a) 38.94 (b) ethylene 22.0%, benzene 49.07%, oxygen 1.07%,
methane 6.37%, ethane 19.26%, nitrogen 2.23% (by mass) (c) 1.737 kg/m³]**

2.34 The analysis of a sewage gas sample from a municipal sewage treatment plant is given below on a volume basis:
Methane   68%
Carbon dioxide   30%
Ammonia   2%
H_2S, SO_2, etc.   Traces
Find (a) the average molar mass of the gas, and (b) the density of the gas at NTP.
     [(a) 24.42 (b) 1.09 kg/m³]

2.35 A mass of 1.10 kg of carbon dioxide occupies a volume of 33 L at 27°C (300.15 K). Using the van der Waals equation of state, calculate the pressure.
Data For CO_2, take $a = 3.60 \ [(m^3)^2 . kPa]/(kmol)^2]$ and $b = 4.3 \times 10^{-2}$ $m^3/kmol$
     [19.51 bar a]

2.36 Calculate the density of chlorine gas at 230°C (503.15 K) and 152 bar a using (a) the ideal gas law, and (b) the van der Waals equation.
     [(a) 258.0 kg/m³ (b) 464.24 kg/m³]

2.37 Ethane gas is processed at 73 bar a and 150°C (423.15 K). It follows the following Beattie–Bridgeman equation of state, i.e.,

$$p = \left[\frac{RT \, (1-\varepsilon)}{V^2} \right] (V + B) - \frac{A}{V^2}$$

where
$$A = A_0 \left(1 - \frac{a}{V} \right)$$

$$B = B_0 \left(1 - \frac{b}{V} \right)$$

$$\varepsilon = \frac{c}{VT^3}$$

For ethane[23], $A_0 = 5.88$ bar $(m^3)^2/(kmol)^2$, $B_0 = 0.094$ $m^3/kmol$, $a = 0.058\ 61$ $m^3/kmol$, $b = 0.019\ 15$ $m^3/kmol$ and $c = 90 \times 10^4$ $m^3 \cdot (K)^2/kmol$
Find the density of ethane gas at the given conditions using the above equation.
     [75.092 kg/m³]

2.38 The second–order virial equation of state for dimethyl ether (DME) is given by the following equation[24].

$$pV = ZRT$$

where $$Z = 1 - \frac{Bp}{RT}$$

$$B = \frac{RT_c}{p_c} (f^0 + \omega \cdot f^1)$$

ω = acentric factor = 0.192 for DME[23]

$f^0 = 0.1445 - 0.330/T_r - 0.1385/T_r^2$
$\quad - 0.0121/T_r^3 - 0.607 \times 10^{-3}/T_r^8$.

$f^1 = 0.0637 + 0.331/T_r^2 - 0.423/T_r^3 - 0.8 \times 10^{-2}/T_r^8$

T_r = Reduced temperature = T/T_c

Calculate molar volume of DME at 15 bar a and 80°C (353.15 K). [**2.241 m^3/kmol**]

2.39 In the manufacture of nitric acid, initially ammonia and air are mixed at 7.09 bar g and 923 K (650°C). The composition of the gas mixture (by volume) is as follows:

Nitrogen   70.5%
Oxygen   18.8%
Water   1.2%
Ammonia   9.5%

Find (i) the density of the gas mixture using (a) ideal gas law, (b) the van der Waals equation, and (ii) the specific gravity of the gas mixture.

[**(i) (a) 2.912 kg/m^3 (b) 2.9465 kg/m^3 (ii) 0.952**]

2.40 In Exercise 2.39, water vapour is considered as an impurity. Assuming that the gas mixture behaves ideally, find the concentration of water vapour in (a) mg/m^3, and (b) ppm.   [**(a) 23 071 mg/m^3 (b) 7830 ppm (or mg/kg)**]

2.41 A binary mixture of n-butane and furfural is analysed to find the butane content in it[25]. First, the n-butane present in the mixture is stripped off with the help of carbon dioxide with negligible entrainment of furfural. The mixture of carbon dioxide and n-butane is then passed through the solution containing 25% NaOH (by mass) in which carbon dioxide is absorbed. The saturated hydrocarbon is collected over the solution in a burette. The test data on a specific run are given below:

Weight of sample n-butane and furfural) = 9.082 g
Volume of saturated n-butane stripped off at 22.2°C (295.35 K) and
101.75 kPa (763.2 Torr) = 105.7 mL

Find the amount of n-butane present in the liquid mixture on mole and weight basis.
Data Vapour pressure of water over 25% NaOH solution at 295.35 K = 1.666 kPa
(12.5 Torr)   [**4.48 mole % and 2.75 mass % n-butane**]

2.42 The Orsat (dry) analysis of the flue gas from a boiler house is given as (volume basis); CO_2: 10.0%, O_2: 7.96%, N_2: 82.0% and SO_2: 0.04%. The temperature and pressure of flue gases are 190°C (463 K) and 100 kPa (750 Torr), respectively. The dew point of the gas is found to be 47°C (320.15 K). Find the absolute humidity of the flue gases.
Data Vapour pressure of water at 47°C (320.15 K) = 10.612 kPa [Ref. Table 6.13]   [**71.39 g/kg dry flue gas**]

2.43 In Exercise 2.42, SO_2 is undesirable from the point of view of occupational hazards (environmental pollution). Express the concentration of SO_2 in ppm and mg/m^3 on dry basis.   [**855.2 ppm (or mg/kg); 664.7 mg/m^3**]

2.44 In the Monsanto process for the manufacture of formaldehyde, air, methanol and steam are mixed in the proportion 4:2:1.33 (by mass) at 100°C (373.15 K). The total pressure is 68.6 kPa g. Calculate the partial pressure of each of the components present in the mixture.

[**methanol 38.71; steam 45.78; oxygen 17.94; nitrogen 67.49 (kPa)**]

2.45 A domestic liquefied petroleum gas (LPG) cylinder, conforming to IS:4576, is stored at 40°C (313.15 K). It is a mixture of 30% propane, 45% n-butane, and 25% i-butane by volume. Calculate (a) average molar mass of LPG, (b) specific gravity of LPG, and (c) pressure in the cylinder.

Data Vapour pressures of propane, n-butane and i-butane are 13.975, 3.773 and 5.290 bar, respectively at 40°C (313.15 K). [Ref. Table 5.4]

[**(a) 53.91 (b) 1.861 (c) 7.213 bar a**]

2.46 An absorber is utilised to scrub ammonia from the purge gas of an ammonia synthesis loop. The composition of purge gas is H_2: 62.0%, N_2: 20.6%, Ar: 4.1%, CH_4: 11.1% and NH_3: 2.2% (by volume). Ammonia is absorbed in demineralised water and a solution of 3% NH_3 (by mass) strength is produced. The absorber operates at 6.77 MPa g and the solution leaves the absorber at 32.6°C (305.75 K).

Calculate the quantity of the gas mixture dissolved in 5 m^3 solution. Use the data given in Table 2.12.

Table 2.12   Solubility of Gases in Aqueous Ammonia

Gas	Solubility at 101.325 kPa a and 32.6°C (305.75 K), $Nm^3/100 \ m^3$ 3% NH_3 soln.
Nitrogen	1.35
Hydrogen	1.60
Argon	2.75
Methane	2.80

Hint   At higher pressure, solubilities can be taken proportional to partial pressures.

[**5.873 Nm^3/5 m^3 solution**]

2.47 A breathing apparatus (pressure suit) is supplied with compressed air at 7 bar g and 40°C (313.15 K). Its pressure is reduced to near atmospheric in the apparatus. If the overall Joule–Thomson coefficient[3] in this pressure range is 0.21 K/bar, calculate the air temperature after the letdown.   [**38.53°C (311.68 K)**]

2.48 A nitrogen cylinder is filled with nitrogen at 100 atm and 35°C (308.15 K). Gas is throttled from the cylinder to atmosphere. If the Joule–Thomson coefficient[3] in this pressure range is 0.169 K/atm, calculate nitrogen temperature after throttling.

[**18.1°C (291.25 K)**]

Note   From enthalpy–pressure–temperature data of nitrogen (REFPROP, Ver.8)[20] the outlet temperature is calculated to be 17.3°C (290.45 K).

2.49 A capacity test is conducted of a reciprocating air compressor in which air receiver, located at the downstream of aftercooler, is pressurised from 1 bar g to 7.5 bar g at 40°C (313.15 K) in 4 min. Geometric volume of the air receiver is 2 m^3. Neglect the volume of interconnecting piping. Calculate the capacity of the air compressor.

[**167.9 Nm^3/h**]

2.50 A high vacuum system such as short path distillation (SPD) unit is tested for leaks in the system before putting into service. The leak rate is defined as

$$q_L = \frac{\Delta p}{\theta} \times V$$

where Δp = increase in system pressure, mbar
θ = time elapsed for increase in pressure, s
V = system volume, L
A laboratory SPD unit, having 25 L total volume of the system, is evacuated to 2×10^{-4} mbar. The system is then isolated and it was observed that pressure of the system increased to 1×10^{-3} mbar in 7.5 min. Calculate the leakage rate.

[**4.444 $\times$ 10^{-5} (mbar · L)/s**]

References

1. Mohr, P J, Taylor, B N and Newell D B, *Rev. Mod. Phys.*, **80**(2), April-June 2008, p. 633.
2. Atallah, S I, *Chem Engg.*, **68**(8), April 17, 1961, p. 200.
3. Green, D W and Perry, R H, *Perry's Chemical Engineers' Handbook*, 8th Ed., McGraw-Hill, New York, USA, 2008.
4. Technical Bulletin on *Dow Products and Services*, Dow Chemical Co., USA, 1972.
5. Potter, R W and Clynne, M A; *J. Chem. Engg. Data*, **25**, 1980, p. 50.
6. Tchobanoglous, G and Burton, F L; *Wastewater Engineering; Treatment, Disposal and Reuse*, 3rd Ed., McGraw-Hill, Singapore, 1991.
7. Cvitas, T and Mills, I; *Chemistry International*, **16**(4), 1994, p. 123.
8. H_2SO_4 *Atlas*, Lurgi GmbH, Germany, 1984.
9. Technical Bulletin on *Soda Ash*, Wyandotte Chemicals Corporation, USA, 1955.
10. Technical Bulletin on *Caustic Soda*, Hooker Chemical Corporation, USA, 1966.
11. Weast, R C, *CRC Handbook of Chemistry and Physics*, 64th Ed., CRC Press Inc., USA, 1983, p. E-1.
12. McCabe, W L; Smith, J C and Harriott, P; *Unit Operations of Chemical Engineering*, 7th Ed., McGraw-Hill, New York, 2005, p. 494.
13. Reid, R C, Prausnitz, J M, and Poling, B E, *The Properties of Gases and Liquids*, 4th Ed., McGraw-Hill, USA, 1987.
14. Smith, J M, Van Ness, H C, Abbott, M M, and Bhatt B I, *Introduction to Chemical Engineering. Thermodynamics*, 7th Ed., Tata McGraw-Hill Eduction, New Delhi, 2010.
15. Bhatt, B I; *Design Data Book; Properties of Steam, Selected Refrigerants, n-Hexane and Brines*, CBS Publishers and Distributors, New Delhi, 2007.
16. McNaught, A D and Wilkinson, A, *IUPAC Compendium of Chemical Technology* (also called *Gold Book*), 2nd Ed., 1997.
17. Missen, R W and Smith, W R; *J. Chem. Education*, **82**(8), 2005, p. 1197.
18. Calvert, J G, *Pure & Appl. Chem.*, **62**(11), 1990, p. 2172.
19. Lee, B I and Kesler, M G; *AIChE J.*, **21**(3), May 1975, p. 510.
20. Gerster, J A, Martes, T S; and Colbern, A P; *Ind. Engg. Chem.*, **39**(6), 1947, p. 797.
21. NIST Standard Reference Database 23, Ver. 8, National Institute of Standards and Technology, USA, 2007.
22. Himmelblau, D M and Riggs J B; *Basic Principles and Calculations in Chemical Engineering*, 7th Ed., Pearson Education, Inc., USA, 2004.
23. Beattie, J A, Hadlock, C; and Poffenberger N; *J. Chem. Phys.*, **3**(2), 1935, p. 93.
24. Teng. H, McCandless, J C, and Schneyer J B; *Thermochemical Characteristics of Dimethyl Ether*, a paper presented at SAE World Congress, Detroit, Michigan USA, March 2001.
25. Martes, T S and Colburn, A P; *Ind. Engg. Chem.*, **39**(60), 1947, p. 787.

Material Balances without Chemical Reaction

A process design starts with the development of a *process flow sheet* or *process flow diagram*. For the development of such a diagram, material and energy balance calculations are necessary. These balances follow the *laws of conservation of mass and energy*. The fundamental quantity of mass remains constant regardless of the changes which occur in a physical process or in a chemical reaction. According to the *law of conservation of mass*, the total mass of various compounds remains unchanged during a unit operation or a chemical reaction. Before attempting the study of mass or energy balance, it is necessary to understand the salient aspects of a process diagrams.

3.1 BLOCK DIAGRAMS

A block diagram is a simplified form of a process flow sheet. Such a diagram is useful in estimating feed and product streams along with required utilities. A block diagram is useful at an early stage of the process development.

Figure 3.1 is a block diagram of a batch extraction of a nutraceutical ingredient (sterol) from deodorizer distillate (DO), derived from soybean oil. DO is first esterified with excess methanol in presence of sulphuric acid as a catalyst. Excess methanol is then distilled out under vacuum from the esterified mass. In the subsequent process step, the esterified mass is neutralised (with caustic soda) and washed (twice) with hot water. Decanted esterified mass is dried under vacuum and sent to a crystallizer. Hydrocarbon solvent (such as *n*-hexane) is added to separate out sterol at low temperature. After a specified time, mass from the crystallizer is centrifuged and wet cake (with about 30% hyorocarbon) is sent to a dryer where the solvent is recovered under vacuum. Dried sterol is sent for packaging. Mother liquor from the crystallizer is sent to a distillation unit. The solvent is recovered by batch distillation of the mother liquor. Concentrated DO is a concentrated mass of mixed tocopherols (antioxidant). Figure 3.2 is the water balance for the same batch extraction plant which is yet another block diagram of a utility in a process plant.

In this book, a large number of block diagrams are presented in the various examples that are solved or in the exercises. Such block diagrams can easily be prepared with the help of a spreadsheet program on a personal computer. Such electronic flowsheets are very useful in process development or in answering *what*

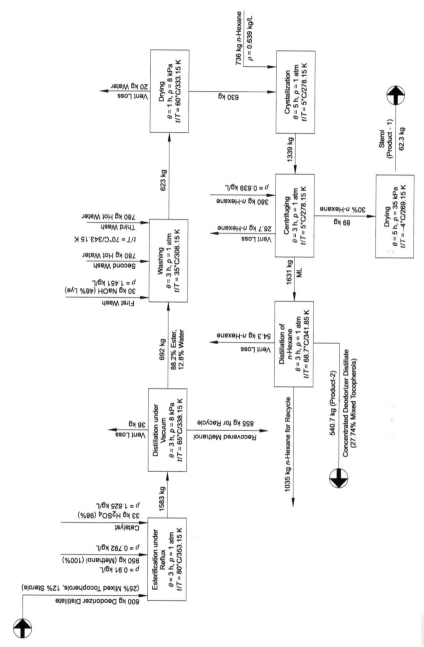

Fig. 3.1 Block Diagram for Batch Extraction of Sterol (a Nutraceutical Product) from Deodorizer Distillate of Soybean Oil

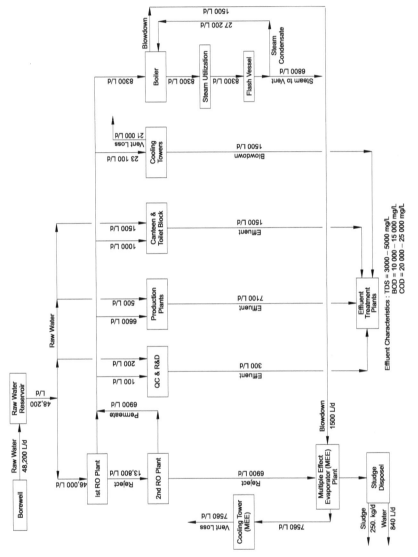

Fig. 3.2 Water Balance in a Nutraceutical Plant

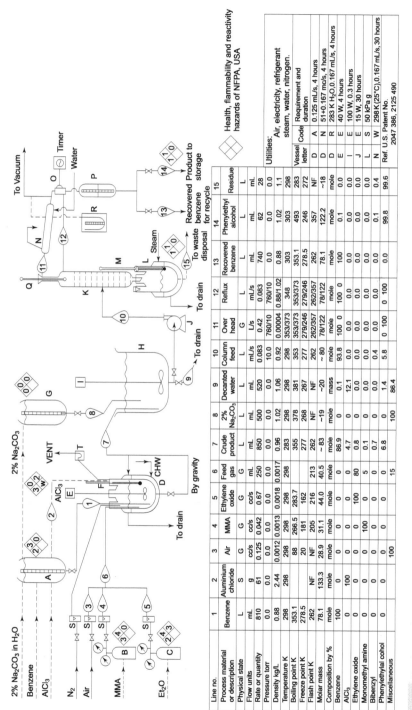

2% Na₂CO₃ in H₂O

To Vacuum

Benzene

AlCl₃

N₂

Air

MMA

Et₂O

2% Na₂CO₃

VENT

By gravity

To drain

Timer · Water · Product to storage · Recovered benzene for recycle · To waste disposal · To drain · Steam

Vessel labels: A, B, C, D, E, F, G, H, I, J, K, L, M, N, O, P, Q, R, T

Line no.	1	2	3	4	5	6	7	8	9	10	11	12	13	14	15
Process material or description	Benzene	Aluminium chloride	Air	MMA	Ethylene oxide	Feed gas	Crude product	2% Na₂CO₃	Decanted water	Column feed	Over head	Reflux	Recovered benzene	Phenylethyl alcohol	Residue
Physical state	L	S	G	G	L	G	L	L	L	L	G	L	L	L	L
Flow units	mL	g	cc/s	cc/s	cc/s	mL	mL	mL	mL	mL/s	L/s	mL/s	mL	mL	mL
Rate or quantity	810	61	0.125	0.042	0.67	250	850	500	520	10.0	0.42	0.083	740	62	28
Pressure torr	0.0	0.0	0.0012	0.0013	0.0018	0.0017	0.0	0.0	0.0	0.083	760/10	760/10	0.0	0.0	0.0
Density kg/l	0.88	2.44	0.0012	0.0013	0.0018	0.0017	0.96	1.02	1.06	0.92	0.00004	0.88/1.02	0.88	1.02	1.1
Temperature K	298	298	298	298	298	298	283	298	298	298	353/373	348	303	303	298
Boiling point K	353.1		88	266.5	283.7		355	378	381	353	353/373	353/373	353.1	493	283
Freeze point K	278.5		20	181	162		277	268	267	277	279/246	279/246	278.5	246	272
Flash point K	262	NF	NF	205	216	213	262	NF	NF	262	262/357	262/357	262	357	NF
Molar mass	78.1	133.3	28.9	31.1	44.0	40.5	~83	~19	~20	~80	78/122	78/122	78.1	122.2	~18
Composition by %	mole	mole	mole	mole	mole	mole	mole	mole	mass	mole	mole	mole	mole	mole	mole
Benzene	100	0	0	0	0	80	86.9	0	0.1	93.8	100 0	100 0	100	0.1	0.0
AlCl₃	0	100	0	0	0	0	4.7	0	12.1	0.0	0.0	0.0	0.0	0.0	0.0
Ethylene oxide	0	0	0	0	100	5	0.8	0	0.0	0.0	0.0	0.0	0.0	0.0	0.0
Monomethyl amine	0	0	0	100	0	0	0.1	0	0.0	0.0	0.0	0.0	0.0	0.0	0.0
Bibenzyl	0	0	0	0	0	0	0.7	0	0.0	0.4	0.0	0.0	0.0	0.0	0.4
Phenylethylal cohol	0	0	0	0	0	0	6.8	0	1.4	5.8	0.0	0.0	0.0	99.8	99.6
Miscellaneous	0	0	100	0	0	15		100	86.4		0 100	0 100	0.0		

Health, flammability and reactivity hazards of NFPA, USA

Utilities:
Air, electricity, refrigerant steam, water, nitrogen.

Vessel letter	Code	Requirement and duration
D	A	0.125 mL/s, 4 hours
D	N	51+0.167 mc/s, 4 hours
D	R	283 K H₂O,0.167 mL/s, 4 hours
E	E	40 W, 4 hours
I	E	100 W, 0.3 hours
J	E	15 W, 30 hours
L	S	50 kPa g
N	W	298 K(25°C),0.167 mL/s, 30 hours

Ref. U.S. Patent No. 2047 386, 2125 490

Fig. 3.3 Manufacture of Phenylethyl Alcohol
(Reproduced with the permission of American Institute of Chemical Engineers, USA.)

if questions relations relating to the material and energy balances. Mathematical software such as Mathcad® also permits development of a process flow sheet. Discussion on the use of a spreadsheet software and Mathcad for stoichiometric calculations is detailed in Chapter 9.

3.2 PROCESS FLOW SHEET

Development of a process flow sheet starts on approval of a project based on the overall information drawn from a block diagram.

A process flow sheet is one in which all incoming and outgoing materials and utilities are shown. It should be clearly understood that such a diagram is different from the piping and instrumentation (P & I) diagram. The latter diagram is not intended to give quantitative picture but is intended to specify the flow sequence, all relevant instrumentation and controls, pipes and fittings, material specifications of pipes and any other specific information for carrying out detailed engineering design. On the other hand, a process flow sheet includes

(i) Flow rate or quantity of each stream; composition of the streams are also recommended

(ii) Operating conditions of each stream, such as pressure and temperature

(iii) Heat added/removed in a particular equipment

(iv) Flow rates of utilities such as steam, cooling water, brine, etc.

(v) Any specific information which is useful in understanding the process

From the above discussion, it is clear that the process flow diagram is a very useful diagram in the chemical process industry. It presents information in a readily understandable form. It helps the operator in adjusting his parameters, the supervisor in checking/controlling the plant operation, the management in discussions across the table and the project engineers in the comparison and evaluation of different processes. If the basic process is simple and involves only a few steps, the P & I diagram and the process flow sheet can be combined into one sheet.

Chemical processes and reactions can be basically divided into two categories, batch and continuous. Batch distillation and extraction, adsorption of solvent on activated carbon and regeneration, and so on are *batch unit operations.* Continuous distillation, drying of cloth, and so on are common examples of unit operations that are continuous in nature. Water treatment by ion exchangers, bulking of effluents and batch production of organic chemicals are examples of batch-type chemical reactions. The manufacture of ammonia, urea, methanol, petrochemicals, and so on, fall under the category of continuous chemical reactions. Continuous ion exchange columns have also been developed. Batch as well as continuous deodorizers are common in refining edible oils. Thus, it may be seen that whether a particular process is batch or continuous purely depends on the scale of economics. Practically, any batch process can be converted to a continuous one.

For more discussion on process flow sheet, please refer Ref. 1.

Figures 3.3 to 3.8 give typical flow sheets of batch and continuous processes. Figure 3.3 gives a flow sheet of the bench-scale production of phenylethyl alcohol as developed by Prugh[2]. This alcohol is produced by a typical Friedel-Crafts reaction. Ethylene oxide is reacted with excess benzene in the presence of anhydrous aluminum chloride. The alcohol yield is increased by diluting the ethylene oxide with air and methylamine is added to neutralise the hydrogen chloride generated during the reaction. The product is washed with sodium carbonate solution and is distilled to recover excess benzene and remove the byproduct biphenyl. It may be seen that the diagram provides nearly complete information on the process. Each of the streams is numbered, illustrating the sequence in batch operations and the stream details are given in a tabular form. To highlight the hazards of the reactants, small diamond markers are shown on the flow sheet and the numbers in the diamonds refer to the health, flammability and reactivity hazards as defined in the Standard 704 of the National Fire Protection Association, USA. The seriousness of hazards is shown by numbers on a scale from 0 to 4, with number 4 indicating 'most serious'.

Figure 3.4 gives the process details of a softening process using ion-exchange technology (see Exercise 4.18). This is a cyclic process in which the service cycle and regeneration cycle are repeated alternatively. It may be noted that tabular data on regeneration steps help in understanding the process. Since this is nearly an isothermal process, temperatures are not indicated on the diagram.

Figures 3.5 to 3.7 give process flow diagrams of continuous processes. Acid gas removal has great importance in the process industry and a variety of processes have been developed by a number of companies. Figure 3.5 represents acid gas removal in a SNG plant (see Example 8.6). Dealkylation of toluene to benzene (Fig. 3.6) is an important unit process in organic industry (see Exercise 8.13). Figure 3.7 represents hydrogenation of benzene to cyclohexane[3] (Exercise 4.41). The reaction takes place in a fixed–bed catalytic reactor. Exothermic heat of reaction is removed by boiling water outside the tubes which contain a catalyst. It is desired that the mole ratio of hydrogen to benzene be maintained as 3.3 kmol/kmol at the reactor inlet. In all these diagrams, operating conditions change during each process step. Material balance at each point can be given in a separate table as can be seen in Tables 8.23 and 8.55 or can be given at the bottom of the diagram as shown in Figs 3.3 and 3.7.

Figure 3.8 depicts continuous atmospheric distillation of crude oil. It is designed for a throughput of Indonesian crude at the rate of 0.226 m^3/s (120 000 US barrels per day). Product summary of Fig. 3.8 is a useful table for discussions across the table for product planning.

It is interesting to note that each flow sheet is presented in a different form. One process engineer may wish to give the component balance on the flow diagram while another may prefer to give it in a tabular form at the bottom. Some flow sheets may include safety aspects, such as explosibility, flammability, toxicity, corrosivity, radioactivity hazards and so on, while others may have the sequence of flow of a batch process in a tabular form. The extent to which information is required to be given in a process flow sheet also depends on the type of flow sheet. For example, a process flow sheet prepared on the basis of laboratory or pilot plant studies (Fig. 3.3) may include more information on safety aspects for safe

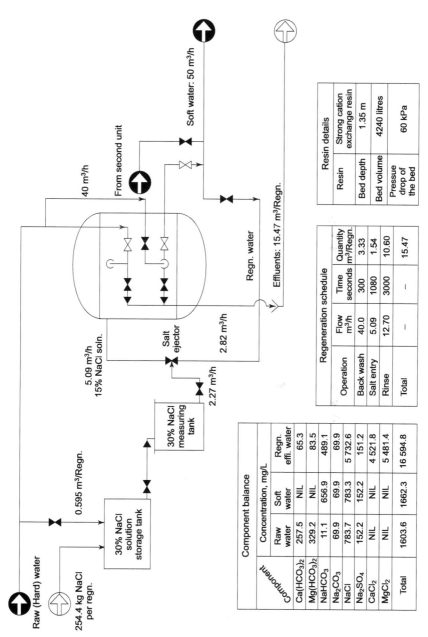

Resin details

Resin	Strong cation exchange resin
Bed depth	1.35 m
Bed volume	4240 litres
Pressure drop of the bed	60 kPa

Regeneration schedule

Operation	Flow m³/h	Time seconds	Quantity m³/Regn.
Back wash	40.0	300	3.33
Salt entry	5.09	1080	1.54
Rinse	12.70	3000	10.60
Total	–	–	15.47

Component balance

Component	Concentration, mg/L			
	Raw water	Soft water	Regn. effl. water	
Ca(HCO₃)₂	257.5	NIL	65.3	
Mg(HCO₃)₂	329.2	NIL	83.5	
NaHCO₃	11.1	656.9	489.1	
Na₂CO₃	69.9	69.9	69.9	
NaCl	783.7	783.3	5 732.6	
Na₂SO₄	152.2	152.2	151.2	
CaCl₂	NIL	NIL	4 521.8	
MgCl₂	NIL	NIL	5 481.4	
Total	1603.6	1662.3	16 594.8	

Soft water: 50 m³/h

40 m³/h

From second unit

Regn. water

Effluents: 15.47 m³/Regn.

5.09 m³/h
15% NaCl soln.

Salt ejector

2.82 m³/h

30% NaCl measuring tank

2.27 m³/h

0.595 m³/Regn.

30% NaCl solution storage tank

Raw (Hard) water

254.4 kg NaCl per regn.

Fig. 3.4 Water Softening by Ion Exchange

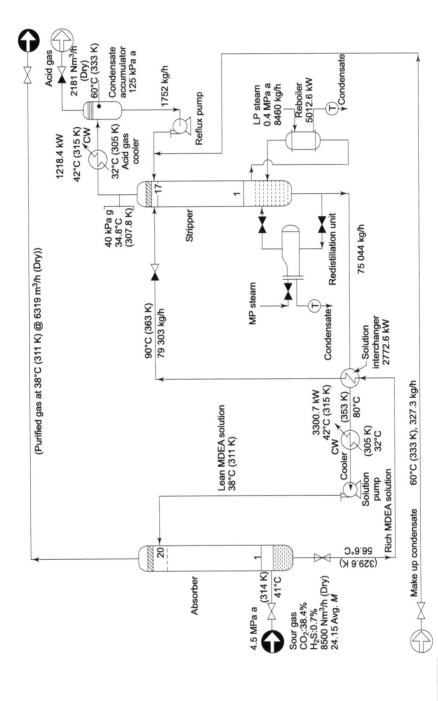

Fig. 3.5 Acid Gas Removal in a Synthetic Natural Gas Plant

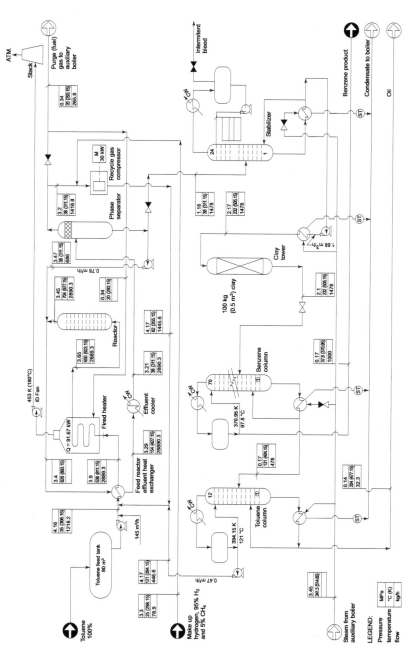

Fig. 3.6 Dealkylation of Toluene to Benzene

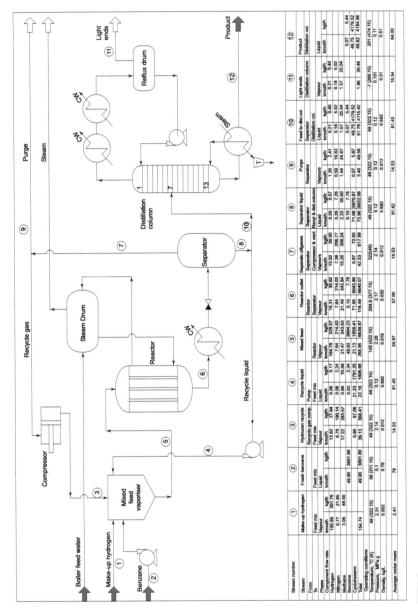

Boiler feed water

Make-up hydrogen ①

Benzene ②

Compressor

Mixed feed vaporiser

Recycle gas

Purge ⑨

Steam

Steam Drum

Reactor

Recycle liquid

Separator

Light ends ⑪

Reflux drum

Distillation column

Product ⑫

Stream number	①	②	③	④	⑤	⑥	⑦	⑧	⑨	⑩	⑪	⑫
Stream	Make-up hydrogen	Fresh benzene	Hydrogen recycle	Recycle liquid	Mixed feed	Reactor outlet	Separator offgases	Separator liquid	Purge	Feed to dist.col	Light ends	Product
From	Feed mix	Feed mix	Recycle gas comp.	Pump	Reactor	Reactor	Separator	Recycl & dist column	Separator	Separator	Distillation column	Distillation col
To	Feed mix	Feed mix	Feed mix	Feed mix	Reactor	Separator	Compressor & vent	Separator	Separator	Distillation col	Distillation column	Distillation col
Phase	Vapour	Liquid	Vapour	Liquid	Vapour	Vapour	Vapours	Liquid	Vapours	Liquid	Vapour	Liquid
Component flow rate (kmol/h / kg/h)												
Hydrogen	150.88 / 301.76		13.82 / 27.64	0.08 / 0.17	164.78 / 329.57	15.31 / 30.62	15.02 / 30.05	0.29 / 0.57	1.20 / 2.41	0.21 / 0.40	0.21 / 0.40	
Nitrogen	0.77 / 21.65		6.79 / 190.14	0.08 / 2.24	7.64 / 214.03	7.64 / 214.03	7.38 / 206.77	0.26 / 7.26	0.59 / 16.63	0.18 / 5.02	0.19 / 5.02	
Methane	3.09 / 49.50		17.22 / 283.57	0.66 / 10.56	21.47 / 343.63	21.49 / 343.84	19.26 / 308.24	2.23 / 35.60	1.54 / 24.67	1.57 / 25.04	1.57 / 25.04	
Benzene		49.90 / 3891.89		0.03 / 2.34	49.93 / 3894.23	0.10 / 7.78		0.10 / 7.78		0.07 / 5.44		0.07 / 5.44
Cyclohexane			0.80 / 67.06	21.33 / 1791.35	21.13 / 1858.41	71.95 / 6043.80	0.87 / 72.93	71.08 / 5970.87	0.07 / 5.87	49.75 / 4179.52		49.75 / 4179.52
Total	154.74 /	49.90 / 3891.89	39.13 / 568.41	22.18 / 1806.66	265.95 / 6639.87	116.49 / 6640.07	42.53 / 617.99	73.96 / 6022.08	3.40 / 49.58	51.78 / 4115.42	1.96 / 30.46	49.82 / 4184.96
Operating conditions												
Temperature, °C (K)	49 (322.15)	38 (311.15)	49 (322.15)	49 (322.15)	149 (422.15)	204.6 (477.15)	49 (322.15)	49 (322.15)	49 (322.15)	49 (322.15)	-7 (266.15)	201 (474.15)
Pressure, MPa g	2.31	0.1	2.14	0.12	2.28	2.17	2.14	0.12	0.12	0.12	0.101	0.11
Density, kg/L	0.002	0.78	0.012	0.692	0.016	0.035	0.012	0.692	0.012	0.692	0.01	0.51
Average molar mass	2.41	78	14.53	81.45	24.97	57.00	14.53	81.42	14.53	81.45	15.54	84.00

Fig. 3.7 Hydrogenation of Benzene to Cyclohexane
(Reproduced with the permission of Aspen Technology, Inc., USA.)

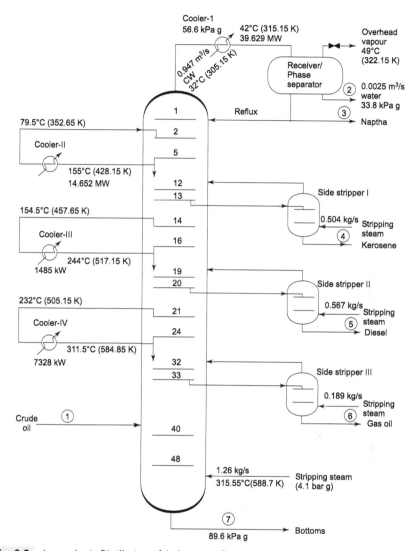

Fig. 3.8 Atmospheric Distillation of Indonesian Crude Oil

Summary of Products

Stream No.	Product	Flow rate		°API	Temperature
		mol/s	m³/s		°C (K)
1.	Crude oil	0.825	0.221	29.4	232°C (505.15 K)
2.	Water	0.136	0.0025	—	49°C (322.15 K)
3.	Naphtha	0.362	0.048	61.5	49°C (322.15 K)
4.	Kerosene	0.127	0.027	40.7	80.6°C (353.75 K)
5.	Diesel	0.081	0.023	31.2	262.2°C (535.35 K)
6.	Gas oil	0.087	0.031	25.2	334°C (607.15 K)
7.	Bottoms	0.171	0.091	14.1	362.5°C (635.65 K)

scale-up and for speedy transition of a bench-scale process. However, ultimately the person who prepares the flow sheet is the best judge to decide the extent of information to be covered by his flow sheet. At times, one does not wish to give patented information on the flow sheet. Also, many vendors do not give complete information at the quotation stage but would like to give adequate information at the contract stage. In summary, a process flow sheet can be an important aid between the process design engineer and the contractor. In fact, process design starts with the preparation of a process flow sheet.

3·3 MATERIAL BALANCES

Material balance problems can be classified as follows.

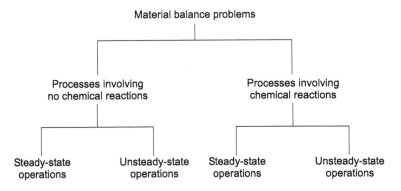

It is proposed to cover the processes involving no chemical reactions in this chapter. Chapter 4 will deal with steady-state processes involving chemical reactions. For unsteady-state material and energy balances, any standard textbook on reaction engineering or kinetics may be referred[4].

From the law of conservation of mass outlined in the introduction, it follows that for any process,

$$\text{Input} - \text{accumulation} = \text{output or disappearance}$$

This equation should be clearly understood. In any flow or batch process, a definite mass of material is charged into the equipment. When the accumulation of the material is constant or nil,

$$\text{Input} = \text{Output}$$

This is usually the case with steady processes. Consider that in a boiler, m_s kg of water is fed per hour. Barring the boiler blow-down, the steam production per hour will also be m_s kg/h. Similarly, in a continuous nitration plant producing nitrobenzene, the feed will consist of benzene, nitric acid, sulphuric acid and water. Let the mass of the feed be m_n kg. At the end of nitration reaction, the total mass will also be m_n kg, although the proportion of each of the components would have changed as per the chemical conversion. In this reaction also, there is no accumulation or loss from the system.

There are certain processes in which accumulation takes place. Consider the example of a storage tank of drinking water. The input into the tank may be q_a m^3/h, while the draw from the tank may be q_b m^3/h ($q_a > q_b$). Under these circumstances, the input does not equal to the output, and the accumulation in the tank amounts to ($q_a - q_b$) m^3/h.

In a kiln treating magnesium hydroxide, the feed is moist magnesium hydroxide. The heat is supplied directly to the kiln. As a result, the magnesium hydroxide decomposes into magnesium oxide and water. From the stack, water escapes. In such a system, input equals the output plus the evaporated moisture.

3.3.1 Material Balances Without Chemical Reactions

There are three general methods of solving material balance problems for systems involving no chemical reactions.

(i) Make the balance of a *tie* material, the quantity of which does not change during the particular operation. The examples falling under this category include concentration of a solution in an evaporator in which the dissolved solids do not change which is a *tie* material for the material balance. While drying the material, bone dry material is unchanged and only the solvent is evaporated.

(ii) Very often, one or several *inert* chemical species which do not take part in the operation are involved in the system. By making balance of this *inert* species, the material balance calculations can be simplified. Examples of this type of problems include leaching of solids, ash present in coal, nitrogen in combustion air entering a furnace, and so on. While leaching copper from the ore, the gangue is unaffected and acts as an inert material. During the combustion of coal, ash is left out on the grate and it does not take part in the combustion process. Extraction of oils from various seeds is carried out using supercritical carbon dioxide, leaving behind deoiled cake (DOC).

(iii) When two or more compounds are present in the system and if all the compounds are affected simultaneously, it is required that the material balance equations be solved by satisfying simultaneous equations. Fortifying spent acids with strong acids (Example 3.8) and material balances of distillation and extraction of liquids (Examples 3.5, 6.1 and 6.5), establishing a cascade–type steam balance (Example 8.7), solving a material balance problem of competitive chemical reactions in series, and so on fall under this category.

3.3.2 Degrees of Freedom

The concept of *degrees of freedom* is well known to chemical engineers. This concept is useful in physical chemistry/thermodynamics to define a system in equilibrium having more than one phase. The same concept is also useful in stoichiometry in solving the problems of a multi-variable system. This is an index which fixes the number of independent equations that are required to be solved for finding the specified number of unknowns. If the number of independent equations are less than the number of unknowns, the system is considered under-defined. In such a case, an optimum solution can be found by fixing some unknowns based on a judgement. In Chapter 8, steam balance calculations (Example 8.7) are given in which certain assumptions are made to arrive at an optimum steam balance. In simulation studies (Chapter 9), a specific parameter is varied and other parameters are calculated, and thereby a trend analysis is generated. For such systems, the degree of freedom is positive.

In certain systems, the degree of freedom is negative which indicates that the system is over-defined. For such calculations, redundant information should be discarded to obtain an unique solution. For example, when a quadratic equation is solved, two values of a parameter—usually positive and negative figures—are obtained. The negative value is discarded thereby increasing the degree of freedom. In another case, there may be contradictory demands of the variables. Consider the dilution of a hazardous gas by an inert gas. If the limiting concentration of the hazardous gas and available quantum of the inert gas are specified, it may not be possible to match them. Under such circumstances, inconsistency has to be removed by fixing one of the variables.

For a balanced system, the degree of freedom is zero.

3.3.3 Solving Material Balance Problems

In any given problem, one has to first determine the particular class under which the problem falls. Then a definite basis is assumed. Often, the basis is defined in the statement of the problem itself. If this basis is convenient, it may be adopted, otherwise, a new, more convenient basis can be selected. Using this basis, the problem must be solved with consistent units.

In the case of gaseous systems, the temperature and pressure are often specified in the statement of the problem. As discussed in Chapter 2, these two parameters are needed to evaluate the density of the gas. With the help of density calculations, the conversion of volume to mass or *vice versa* is possible.

The following illustrative examples will give an idea of the different types of problems.

Example 3.1   A Lancashire boiler is fed with soft water containing 1200 mg/L dissolved solids. IS: 10 392-1982 specifies that the maximum dissolved solids in the boiler water should not exceed 3500 mg/L for boilers, operating up to 20 bar g. In order to maintain the specified level, a continuous blow-down system is adopted. Find the percentage of the feed water which will have to be blown down, assuming that no carryover is observed.

Solution   In this example, the basis is not defined. Therefore, assume a basis of 1 kg of feed water. During evaporation of water in the boiler, the dissolved solids are unaffected and hence the balance of dissolved solids (a tie material) in the feed water and boiler water will provide the clue to the problem. Thus, the example is of type (i).

1 kg of feed water will contain 1200 mg of dissolved solids. Let x kg be the amount of feed water that will be blown down. This blow-down will contain dissolved solids to the extent of 3500 mg (same as boiler water).

Therefore, $x \times 3500 = 1200 \times 1$ or $x = 0.343$ kg

$$\% \text{ Blow-down} = (0.343/1) \times 100 = \mathbf{34.3}$$

Note Density of feed water and boiler water is assumed to be 1.0 kg/L. This blow-down rate is too high, and therefore improvement in feed-water quality is recommended.

Example 3.2 In a textile mill, a double-effect evaporator system concentrates weak liquor containing 4% (by mass) caustic soda to produce a lye containing 25% solids (by mass). Calculate the evaporation of water per 100 kg feed in the evaporator.

Solution   In this problem, the basis is defined.

Basis 100 kg of weak liquor (feed)

It contains 4 kg of caustic soda (the tie material).

Let the quantity of the lye be x kg.

Caustic soda in the lye = $0.25\,x$

However, the caustic soda does not take part in the evaporation.

$$0.25\,x = 4$$
$$x = 4/0.25 = 16 \text{ kg}$$
$$\text{Evaporation} = 100 - 16 = \mathbf{84\ kg}$$

Example 3.3 The analysis of a sample of *babul bark* (of northern India) yields 5.8% moisture, 12.6% tannin, 8.3% soluble non-tannin organic matter and the rest, lignin. In order to extract tannin out of the bark, a counter-current extraction process is employed. The residue from the extraction process is analysed and found to contain 0.92% tannin and 0.65% solute non-tannin organic matter on a dry basis. Find the percentage of tannin recovered on the basis of the original tannin present in the bark. All analyses are given on mass basis.

Solution   *Basis* 100 kg of *babul bark*

It contains 5.8 kg of moisture, 12.6 kg of tannin and 8.3 kg of soluble non-tannin organic material.

Lignin in the bark = $100 - 5.8 - 12.6 - 8.3 = 73.3$ kg

In this leaching process, it is evident that lignin is unaffected. Therefore, it will be considered inert. Thus, the example is of type (ii).

Since the analysis of the residue is given on a dry basis, its lignin content will be given by

Lignin content = $100 - 0.92 - 0.65 = 98.43$ kg/100 kg dry residue

If the final mass of the dry residue is x kg,

$$x \times 0.9843 = 73.3$$

$$x = \frac{73.3}{0.9843} = 74.47 \text{ kg}$$

Tannin present in the residue = $74.47 \times 0.0092 = 0.685$ kg

Tannin recovered = $[12.6 - 0.685)/12.6] \times 100 = \textbf{94.56 \%}$

Example 3.4   Dry neem leaves were subjected to extraction with supercritical carbon dioxide at 200 bar and 60°C (333 K). Dry leaves are analysed to contain 0.46% α-tocopherol and 0.01% β-carotene[5]. The extract is found to contain 15.5% α-tocopherol and 0.41% β-carotene. All percentages are by mass. If β-carotene content of the leached residue is nil, calculate (a) the mass of extract phase per kg of dry leaves, and (b) % recovery of α-tocopherol.

Solution

Basis 1 kg of dry neem leaves

β-carotene content of the leaves = $0.01/100 = 0.0001$ kg

Extract contains 0.41% β-carotene.

$$\text{Extract quantity} = \frac{0.0001}{0.41} \times 100$$

$$= 0.0244 \text{ kg}$$

$$\alpha\text{-tocopherol in the extract} = 0.0244 \times 0.155$$

$$= 0.003\ 78 \text{ kg}$$

$$\alpha\text{-tocopherol in the neem leaves} = 0.46/100 = 0.0046 \text{ kg}$$

$$\text{Recovery of } \alpha\text{-tocopherol} = \frac{0.003\ 78}{0.0046} \times 100$$

$$= \textbf{82.2\%}$$

Example 3.5   A 100–kg mixture of 27.8% of acetone (A) and 72.2% of chloroform (B) by mass is to be batch-extracted with a mixed solvent at 25°C (298 K). The mixed solvent of an unknown composition is known to contain water (S_1) and acetic acid (S_2). The mixture of the original mixture and the mixed solvent is shaken well, allowed to attain equilibrium, and separated into two layers. The compositions of the two layers are given below[6].

Table 3.1   Composition of Immiscible Layers

Layer	Composition, mass %			
	A	B	S_1	S_2
Upper layer	7.5	3.5	57.4	31.6
Lower layer	20.3	67.3	2.8	9.6

Find (a) the quantities of the two layers, (b) the mass-ratio of the mixed solvent to the original mixture, and (c) the composition of the mixed solvent (mass basis).

Solution

Basis 100 kg of original mixture

The mixture contains 27.8 kg of A and 72.2 kg of B.

This problem is of type (iii) because here the system contains more than one component, and the balance of each of the components will yield the complete material balance.

Let x and y be the amount of upper and lower layers, respectively. According to the principle of degrees of freedom, two equations are required to find the unknowns.

$$\text{Total mixture} = (x + y)\text{ kg}$$

Balance of A: $0.075x + 0.203y = 27.8$ (i)

Balance of B: $0.035x + 0.673y = 72.2$ (ii)

Solving Eqs (i) and (ii) by elimination,

$$x = \textbf{93.42 kg and } y = \textbf{102.42 kg}$$
$$\text{Total mixture} = 93.42 + 102.42 = 195.84\text{ kg}$$
$$\text{Mixed solvent} = 195.84 - 100 = 95.84\text{ kg}$$

Mass-ratio of mixed solvent to the original mixture = $95.84/100 =$ **0.9584**

Balance of water (S_1)

Total S_1 in the system = $93.42 \times 0.574 + 102.42 \times 0.028 = 56.49$ kg

Balance of acetic acid (S_2)

Total S_2 in the system = $93.42 \times 0.316 + 102.42 \times 0.096 = 39.35$ kg

Quantity of the solvent = $56.49 + 39.35 = 95.84$ kg

% S_1 in the mixed solvent = $(56.49/95.84) \times 100 =$ **58.94**

% S_2 in the mixed solvent = $100 - 58.94 =$ **41.06**

Example 3.6 A pressure swing adsorption (PSA) unit produces nitrogen for inerting purpose. It is fed with compressed air at 7 bar g and 40°C (313 K) at the rate of 170 Nm^3/h. The unit consists of carbon molecular sieves which adsorbs nitrogen under pressure. Nitrogen is produced from the unit at the rate of 50 Nm^3/h having 99% purity (by volume). Calculate the average composition of the reject stream.

Solution

Basis 170 Nm^3/h air having 79% N_2 and 21% O_2 by volume.

Nitrogen stream has 99% N_2 and 1% O_2 by volume.

Nitrogen content of the nitrogen stream = $50 \times 0.99 = 49.5$ Nm^3/h

Oxygen content of the nitrogen stream = $50 \times 0.01 = 0.5$ Nm^3/h

Table 3.2 Reject Stream Composition

Component	Flow q_{vi}, Nm^3/h	Vol. %
Nitrogen	$170 \times 0.79 - 49.5 = 84.8$	**70.67**
Oxygen	$170 \times 0.21 - 0.5 = 35.2$	**29.33**
Total	120.0	**100.00**

Example 3.7   A sample of mixed acid contains 55% HNO_3 and 48% H_2SO_4 with 3% negative water (mass) basis[7]. Find the actual constituents present in it.

The above mixed acid is prepared by mixing 100% HNO_3 and oleum. Find the required strength of oleum and the proportions of the two acids in which they should be mixed.

Solution   The mixed acid contains 55% HNO_3 and 48% H_2SO_4 which is theoretically impossible as the total of the percentages comes to 103. The real meaning of the expression is that SO_3 dissolved in 100 kg of mixed acid of composition 55% HNO_3 + 45% H_2SO_4 which requires 3 kg water to convert dissolved SO_3 into H_2SO_4.
Basis 100 kg SO_3-free mixed acid
It contains 55 kg HNO_3 and 45 kg H_2SO_4.
The basic reaction with SO_3 and water is

$$SO_3 + H_2O \rightarrow H_2SO_4$$

Thus, 1 kmol $H_2O \equiv$ 1 kmol SO_3
SO_3 equivalent to 3 kg water = $(80/18) \times 3$ = 13.33 kg
Thus, 113.33 kg mixed acid contains 55 kg HNO_3, 45 kg H_2SO_4 and 13.33 kg SO_3. Since the available HNO_3 for mixing is of 100% strength, 55 kg of it will be required.
Quantity of oleum required to be mixed = 45 + 13.33 = 58.33 kg

$$\text{Strength of oleum} = \left(\frac{13.33}{58.33}\right) \times 100 = 22.85\% \text{ free } SO_3$$

$$\text{Ratio of } HNO_3/\text{oleum} = \frac{55}{58.33} = 0.943$$

Hence, HNO_3 and oleum are required to be mixed in the proportion of 0.943:1 (by mass)

Example 3.8   It is required to make 1000 kg of mixed acid containing 60% H_2SO_4, 32% HNO_3 and 8% water by blending (i) the spent acid containing 11.3% HNO_3, 44.4% H_2SO_4 and 44.3% H_2O, (ii) aqueous 90% HNO_3, and (iii) aqueous 98% H_2SO_4. All percentages are by mass. Calculate the quantities of each of the three acids required for blending.

Solution   *Basis* 1000 kg of mixed acid
It contains 600 kg of H_2SO_4, 320 kg of HNO_3 and 80 kg of water. Let x, y and z be the quantities of spent, aqueous nitric and aqueous sulphuric acids, respectively, required for blending
Overall material balance
$$x + y + z = 1000 \tag{i}$$
Balance of sulphuric acid
$$0.444\,x + 0.98\,z = 600 \tag{ii}$$
Balance of nitric acid
$$0.113\,x + 0.9\,y = 320 \tag{iii}$$

Solving Eqs (i), (ii) and (iii), by elimanation method,
$$x = 76.3 \text{ kg} \quad y = 346.0 \text{ kg} \quad z = 577.7 \text{ kg}$$

Example 3.9   An analysis of a sample of borewell near Ahmadabad is given in Table 3.3.

Table 3.3 Analysis of Raw Water Sample

1. Solids, mg/L	
Total solids	1845
Dissolved solids	1625
Supended solids (by difference)	220
2. Alkalinity, expressed as $CaCO_3$, mg/L	
Total alkalinity	456.5
Total carbonates	65.9
Total bicarbonates	390.6
3. Hardness, expressed as $CaCO_3$ mg/L	
Temporary hardness	384.0
Permanent hardness	Nil
Total hardness	384.0
Magnesium hardness	225.0
4. pH	8.7
5. Chlorides as Cl, mg/L	475.6
6. Sulphates as SO_4, mg/L	102.9

Find the actual analysis of the water and check whether the reported analysis is correct.

Solution   *Basis* 1 litre of water

The water contains only temporary hardness and hence it is due to bicarbonates of calcium and magnesium (alkaline hardness). Thus, chlorides and sulphates present in the water are of sodium (neglecting potassium).

$$\text{Chlorides as Cl} = 475.6 \text{ mg}$$
$$58.5 \text{ mg of NaCl} \equiv 23 \text{ mg of Na} \equiv 35.5 \text{ mg of Cl}$$
$$\text{NaCl present in the water} = (58.5/35.5) \times 475.6 = 783.7 \text{ mg}$$
$$\text{Sulphates as } SO_4 = 102.9 \text{ mg}$$
$$142 \text{ mg of } Na_2SO_4 \equiv 46 \text{ mg of Na} \equiv 96 \text{ mg of } SO_4$$

$$Na_2SO_4 \text{ present in the water} = \left(\frac{142}{96}\right) \times 102.9 = 152.2 \text{ mg}$$

Carbonates presents in the water can be only due to Na_2CO_3.

$$\text{Equivalent mass of } CaCO_3 = \frac{100}{2} = 50$$

$$\text{Equivalent mass of } Na_2CO_3 = \frac{106}{2} = 53$$

$$Na_2CO_3 \text{ present in the water} = \left(\frac{53}{50}\right) \times 65.9$$

$$= 69.9 \text{ mg}$$

NaHCO$_3$ present in the water = total bicarbonates – temporary hardness
$$= 390.6 - 384 = 6.6 \text{ mg as CaCO}_3$$

Equivalent mass of NaHCO$_3$ = 84

$$\text{NaHCO}_3 \text{ present in the water} = \left(\frac{84}{50}\right) \times 6.6 = 11.1 \text{ mg}$$

$$\text{Equivalent mass of Mg(HCO}_3)_2 = \frac{146.3}{2} = 73.15$$

$$\text{Mg(HCO}_3)_2 \text{ present in the water} = \left(\frac{73.15}{50}\right) \times 225 = 329.2 \text{ mg}$$

$$\text{Hardness due to Ca(HCO}_3)_2 = 384 - 225 = 159 \text{ mg as CaCO}_3$$

$$\text{Equivalent mass of Ca(HCO}_3)_2 = \frac{162}{2} = 81$$

$$\text{Ca(HCO}_3)_2 \text{ present in the water} = \left(\frac{81}{50}\right) \times 159 = 257.6 \text{ mg}$$

Thus, the water sample contains the compounds given in Table 3.4.

Table 3.4   Component Analysis of Raw Water

Compound	mg/L
Ca(HCO$_3$)$_2$	257.6
Mg(HCO$_3$)$_2$	329.2
NaHCO$_3$	11.1
Na$_2$CO$_3$	69.9
NaCl	783.7
Na$_2$SO$_4$	152.2
Total	1603.7

This total corresponds to dissolved solids. To this, add 220 mg/L of suspended solids, which brings the total solids to 1823.6 mg/L. By actual test, total solids were found to be 1845 mg/L. The calculated and experimental values are not very different and hence, the reported analysis is correct. The difference between the two values can be attributed to experimental errors.

3.4   USE OF LINEAR MODEL AND MATRIX METHOD IN SOLVING MATERIAL BALANCE PROBLEMS

Steady-state material balance equations are linear equations as seen in Examples 3.1 to 3.8. These linear equations express the outlet flows from unit processes or from unit operations as a linear function of inlet flows and other performance variables. A group of linear equations is defined as a *linear model*. The matrix method is useful in solving a linear set of equations. When the inlet flows and performance variables are known, outlet flows can be calculated by writing the data in matrix forms. Unsteady state processes, however, cannot be modeled by linear equations.

The linear model method can be seen as a systematic approach for solving steady-state material balance equations. A generalized computer program can be developed for the pupose. Solution of linear equations up to three variables can be conveniently found by elimination methods or by use of determinants. However, when linear equations with four or more variables are to be solved, matrices can be written which can be solved with the help of a mathematical software, such as Mathcad[R]', Maple[R], Matlab[R], Mathematica[R], etc. A set of linear equations can be written in the following general form.

$$a_{11} x_1 + a_{12} x_2 + a_{13} x_3 + \dots\dots\dots + a_{1n} x_n = y_1$$
$$a_{21} x_1 + a_{22} x_2 + a_{23} x_3 + \dots\dots\dots + a_{2n} x_n = y_2$$

$$\dots\dots\dots\dots\dots\dots\dots\dots\dots\dots\dots\dots\dots\dots\dots\dots$$

$$a_{n1} x_1 + a_{n2} x_2 + a_{n3} x_3 + \dots\dots\dots + a_{nn} x_n = y_n$$

In the above equations $x_1, x_2, \dots\dots\dots, x_n$ are the unknown variables to be determined. $a_{11}, a_{12}, \dots\dots\dots, a_{nn}$ are determined by the performance variables y_1, $y_2, \dots\dots\dots, y_n$ and are the variables determined based on input flows. The above equations can be represented in the matrix form as shown below.

$$
\begin{bmatrix}
a_{11} & a_{12} & a_{13} & \dots\dots & a_{11} \\
a_{21} & a_{22} & a_{23} & \dots\dots & a_{2n} \\
\multicolumn{5}{c}{\dots\dots\dots\dots\dots\dots\dots\dots} \\
\multicolumn{5}{c}{\dots\dots\dots\dots\dots\dots\dots\dots} \\
a_{n1} & a_{n2} & a_{n3} & \dots\dots & a_{nn}
\end{bmatrix}
\begin{bmatrix}
x_1 \\
x_2 \\
\dots \\
\dots \\
x_n
\end{bmatrix}
=
\begin{bmatrix}
y_1 \\
y_2 \\
\dots \\
\dots \\
y_n
\end{bmatrix}
$$

The first matrix A is an (n, n) matrix while the second and third matrices; X and Y, are $(1, n)$ matrices.

$$AX = Y$$
$$A^{-1}(AX) = A^{-1}(Y)$$
$$(AA^{-1})X = A^{-1}Y$$
$$IX = A^{-1}Y$$

or
$$X = A^{-1}(Y)$$

A^{-1} represents inverse of the matrix A and can be determined by the equation:

$$A^{-1} = \frac{\text{adj } A}{|A|}$$

where adj A is the adjoint of the matrix A and $|A|$ is a determinant of matrix A. In this book, Mathcad is used for solving matrices. The following examples will be useful in demonstrating the use of the linear model.

Example 3.10   Using matrices, solve linear equations of (a) Example 3.5, and (b) Example 3.8.

Solution   (a)

$$M := \begin{pmatrix} 0.075 & 0.203 \\ 0.035 & 0.673 \end{pmatrix} \qquad\qquad v := \begin{pmatrix} 27.8 \\ 72.2 \end{pmatrix}$$

$$\text{soln} := M^{-1} v$$

$$\text{soln} = \begin{pmatrix} 93.447 \\ 102.421 \end{pmatrix} \quad \text{kg}$$

(b)

$$M := \begin{pmatrix} 1 & 1 & 1 \\ 0.444 & 0 & 0.98 \\ 0.113 & 0.9 & 0 \end{pmatrix} \qquad v := \begin{pmatrix} 1000 \\ 600 \\ 320 \end{pmatrix}$$

$$\text{soln} := M^{-1} v$$

$$\text{soln} = \begin{pmatrix} 76.414 \\ 345.961 \\ 577.625 \end{pmatrix} \quad \text{kg}$$

Example: 3.11   A spent acid solution from a nitration plant contains 40% H_2SO_4, 10% HNO_3 and 50% H_2O by mass. It is fed to a distillation system at the rate of 1000 kg/h to separate into three fractions; A, B and C. 94% of HNO_3 in the feed is recovered in the fraction A while 6% is recovered in the fraction B. 80% of water in the feed is recovered in the fraction B and 12% is recovered in the fration A. 95% of H_2SO_4 is recovered in fraction C and 4% is recovered in fraction B. Calculate flow rates of the three fractions using the linear model method.

Solution   *Basis* 1000 kg/h of feed to distillation system

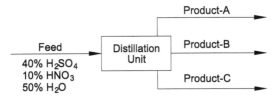

Fig. 3.9 Fractionation of Mixed Acid

Let fractioncal recovery of component i in the fraction j,

$$f_{Rij} = \frac{\text{mass of } i \text{ leaving in fraction } j}{\text{mass of } i \text{ fed to distillation unit}}$$

$$= \frac{\dot{m}_{ij,\,out}}{\dot{m}_{ij,\,in}}$$

Material balance equations
Balance of H_2SO_4

$$\dot{m}_{S,\,A} + \dot{m}_{S,\,B} + \dot{m}_{S,\,C} = \dot{m}_{S,\,F} \qquad (1)$$

Balance of HNO₃

$$\dot{m}_{N,A} + \dot{m}_{N,B} + \dot{m}_{N,C} = \dot{m}_{N,F} \qquad (2)$$

Balance of H₂O

$$\dot{m}_{W,A} + \dot{m}_{W,B} + \dot{m}_{W,C} = \dot{m}_{W,F} \qquad (3)$$

$$\dot{m}_{S,A} = f_{RSA} \times \dot{m}_{s,F} \qquad (4)$$

$$\dot{m}_{N,A} = f_{RNA} \times \dot{m}_{N,F} \qquad (5)$$

$$\dot{m}_{W,A} = f_{RWA} \times \dot{m}_{W,F} \qquad (6)$$

$$\dot{m}_{S,B} = f_{RSB} \times \dot{m}_{S,F} \qquad (7)$$

$$\dot{m}_{N,B} = f_{RNB} \times \dot{m}_{N,F} \qquad (8)$$

$$\dot{m}_{W,B} = f_{RWB} \times \dot{m}_{N,F} \qquad (9)$$

Nine equations are to be solved to determine nine variables. These equations can be represented in matrix form as under.

$$
\begin{bmatrix}
1 & 0 & 0 & 1 & 0 & 0 & 1 & 0 & 0 \\
0 & 1 & 0 & 0 & 1 & 0 & 0 & 1 & 0 \\
0 & 0 & 1 & 0 & 0 & 1 & 0 & 0 & 1 \\
1 & 0 & 0 & 0 & 0 & 0 & 0 & 0 & 0 \\
0 & 1 & 0 & 0 & 0 & 0 & 0 & 0 & 0 \\
0 & 0 & 1 & 0 & 0 & 0 & 0 & 0 & 0 \\
0 & 0 & 0 & 1 & 0 & 0 & 0 & 0 & 0 \\
0 & 0 & 0 & 0 & 1 & 0 & 0 & 0 & 0 \\
0 & 0 & 0 & 0 & 0 & 1 & 0 & 0 & 0
\end{bmatrix}
\begin{bmatrix}
\dot{m}_{S,A} \\
\dot{m}_{N,A} \\
\dot{m}_{W,A} \\
\dot{m}_{S,B} \\
\dot{m}_{N,B} \\
\dot{m}_{W,B} \\
\dot{m}_{S,C} \\
\dot{m}_{N,C} \\
\dot{m}_{W,C}
\end{bmatrix}
=
\begin{bmatrix}
\dot{m}_{S,F} \\
\dot{m}_{N,F} \\
\dot{m}_{W,F} \\
f_{RSA} \cdot \dot{m}_{S,F} \\
f_{RNA} \cdot \dot{m}_{N,F} \\
f_{RWA} \cdot \dot{m}_{W,F} \\
f_{RSB} \cdot \dot{m}_{S,F} \\
f_{RNB} \cdot \dot{m}_{N,F} \\
f_{RWB} \cdot \dot{m}_{W,F}
\end{bmatrix}
$$

Mathcad Solution

$$
M := \begin{pmatrix}
1 & 0 & 0 & 1 & 0 & 0 & 1 & 0 & 0 \\
0 & 1 & 0 & 0 & 1 & 0 & 0 & 1 & 0 \\
0 & 0 & 1 & 0 & 0 & 1 & 0 & 0 & 1 \\
1 & 0 & 0 & 0 & 0 & 0 & 0 & 0 & 0 \\
0 & 1 & 0 & 0 & 0 & 0 & 0 & 0 & 0 \\
0 & 0 & 1 & 0 & 0 & 0 & 0 & 0 & 0 \\
0 & 0 & 0 & 1 & 0 & 0 & 0 & 0 & 0 \\
0 & 0 & 0 & 0 & 1 & 0 & 0 & 0 & 0 \\
0 & 0 & 0 & 0 & 0 & 1 & 0 & 0 & 0
\end{pmatrix}
\qquad
v := \begin{pmatrix}
400 \\
100 \\
500 \\
4 \\
94 \\
60 \\
16 \\
6 \\
400
\end{pmatrix}
$$

$$\text{soln} := M^{-1}v$$

$$\text{soln} = \begin{pmatrix} 4 \\ 94 \\ 60 \\ 16 \\ 6 \\ 400 \\ 380 \\ 0 \\ 40 \end{pmatrix} \text{ kg}$$

Total flow rates of A, B and C are

$$\dot{m}_A = 4 + 94 + 60 = 158 \text{ kg/h}$$

$$\dot{m}_B = 16 + 6 + 400 = 422 \text{ kg/h}$$

$$\dot{m}_C = 380 + 40 = 420 \text{ kg/h}$$

3·5   GRAPHICAL SOLUTION OF PROBLEMS

In a number of cases, graphical methods offer the solution to the problems. An attempt is made here to review two such methods of solving material balance problems. A well-known method of solving simultaneous equations with the coordinate plots can be used for solving Examples 3.5 and 3.8.

Example 3.12   Solve Example 3.5 with the help of geometric plots.

Solution   Balance of acetone (A) and chloroform (B) yielded the following two simultaneous equations.

$$0.075\ x + 0.203\ y = 27.8 \tag{1}$$
$$0.035\ x + 0.673\ y = 72.2 \tag{2}$$

It is necessary to tabulate values of y for different values of x.

Table 3.5   Coordinate Values of Linear Equation

	Value of y				
$x =$	70	80	90	100	110
Equation (1)	111.1	107.4	103.7	100	96.3
Equation (2)	103.6	103.1	102.6	102.1	101.6

Based on the values tabulated above, straight lines are plotted for both the equations in Fig 3.10.

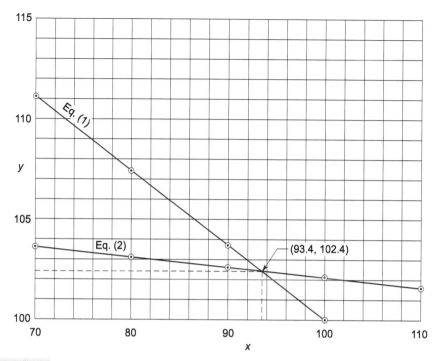

Fig. 3.10   Solution of Simultaneous Equations with the Help of a Coordinate Plot

The intersection point of these two lines represents coordinates x = **93.4 kg** and y = **102.4 kg.**

In Example 3.8, three unknowns are to be evaluated. It is therefore necessary to reduce three equations to two equations by substituting the values of z from Eq. (1) in terms of x and y in Eq. (2) and then a graph, similar to Fig. 3.10, can be plotted to evaluate x and y. Alternatively, a triangular chart may be used for solving the three equations.

Example 3.13   Solve Example 3.8 with the help of a triangular plot.

Solution   Figure 3.11 is a triangular chart in which spent acid, aqueous 90% HNO_3 and aqueous 98% H_2SO_4 are represented by points A, B and C, respectively. Point F represents the mixed acid to be obtained by blending the three acids.

Join points A and B. Also join CF and extend it to cut the line AB at the point M. The following equations can be written with the help of geometric principles.

$$\frac{\text{Amount of aqueous 90\% } HNO_3 \text{ (B)}}{\text{Amount of spent acid (A)}} = \frac{AM}{MB} = \frac{8.64 \text{ units}}{1.19 \text{ units}}$$

$$\frac{\text{Amount of the blend of A and B (point M)}}{\text{Amount of aqueous 98\% } H_2SO_4 \text{ (C)}} = \frac{CF}{FM} = \frac{5.45 \text{ units}}{7.45 \text{ units}}$$

$$CF + FM = 5.45 + 7.45 = 12.90 \text{ units of blend F.}$$

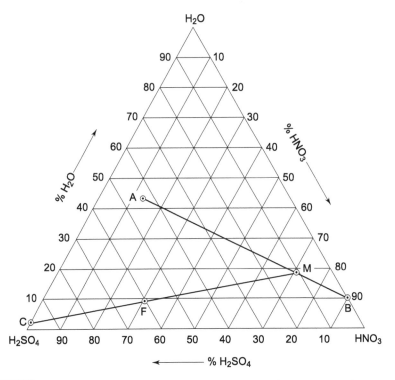

Fig. 3.11 Solution of Simultaneous Equations with the Help of a Triangular Plot

Thus, 12.90 kg of the final blend (F) will consist of 7.45 kg of 98% H_2SO_4 and 5.45 of the blend M.

$$90\% \text{ HNO}_3 \text{ required} = \frac{8.64 \times 5.45}{(8.64 + 1.19)} = 4.46 \text{ kg}$$

Spent acid required = $5.45 - 4.46 = 0.99$ kg

Basis 1000 kg of final mixed acid (F)

$$\text{Amount of spent acid} = \left(\frac{0.99}{12.90}\right) \times 1000 = \textbf{76.7 kg}$$

$$\text{Amount of 90\% HNO}_3 = \left(\frac{4.45}{12.90}\right) \times 1000 = \textbf{345.7 kg}$$

$$\text{Amount of 98\% H}_2\text{SO}_4 = \left(\frac{7.45}{12.90}\right) \times 1000 = \textbf{577.6 kg}$$

In certain cases, experimental data are to be processed for making material balance calculations. It may not be possible to fit these data in a simple equation such as those obtained in Examples 3.5 and 3.8. For such cases, graphical plots are quite handly and permit easy evaluations. In particular, where cyclic or curved plots are obtained, this method is very useful. Ion exchange and adsorption/desorption operations are examples which fall under this category. This method is well illustrated by the following example.

Example 3.14   The ion-exclusion process is a unit operation which utilises ion-exchange resins to separate solutes without the use of chemical reagents. It permits separation of ionised materials from non-ionised or slightly ionised or inorganic substances. In this process, when an aqueous solutions of two or more solutes is percolated through an ion-exchage column, a separation of solutes occurs and they appear in separate fractions in the effluent. Crude glycerine, obtained by saponification of vegetable oils or animal fats can be commercially purified by this technique [8,9,10]. Sodium chloride is the chief solute which can be separated based on the distribution coefficient.

In a pilot plant, a column is first filled to a depth with the ion–exchange resin and flooded with water. A volume of the feed solution considerably less than the bulk resin volume is then added with proper distribution at the top of the resin bed. After the feed solution has passed down the column at a constant flow rate and approximately all of the feed has entered the top of the resin bed, a gradual separation of the solutes occurs and they are eluted from the column with the help of water (as a regenerant), and appear in separate fractions.

In a batch recycle technique, concentration and volume data were collected during elution. These data are presented in Table 3.6 where

C_e = concentration of solute in effluent
C_f = concentration of solute in feed solution
V_e = effluent volume
V_T = bulk volume of resin bed

Table 3.6   Elution Data during Ion-exclusion Process

θ Time from start, min	C_e / C_f of NaCl	of Glycerine	$\dfrac{V_e}{V_T}$
2	0.0	0.0	0.325
5	0.105	0.0	0.35
10	0.465	0.0	0.40
15	0.865	0.0	0.45
20	0.93	0.0	0.50
25	0.94	0.09	0.55
30	0.925	0.335	0.60
35	0.140	0.655	0.65
40	0.0	0.945	0.68
45	0.0	0.850	0.75
50	0.0	0.655	0.80
55	0.0	0.495	0.85
60	0.0	0.340	0.90
65	0.0	0.210	0.95
70	0.0	0.110	1.0
75	0.0	0.045	1.05
80	0.0	0.000	1.10

Data of Table 3.6 are also plotted in Fig. 3.12.

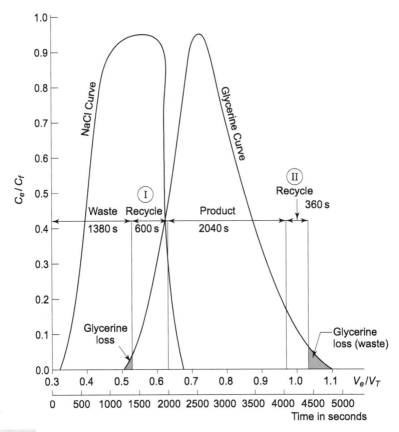

Fig. 3.12 Plot of an Ion-exclusion Process

The effluent, represented by the area of cross-contamination under the elution curves and a portion of the area under the trailing edge of the non-ionic curve is recycled to a recycle tank. A quantity of crude glycerine is then added to the recycled material. This mixture in turn becomes the feed for the second cycle. A complete cycle would then consist of feeding crude glycerine, followed by a water rinse. The effluent would contain cuts designated as waste, Recycle I or the cross-contaminated area product, Recycle II, or the dilute portion of the trailing edge and waste (glycerine loss).

Assuming that C_f (glycerine) $= 12 C_f$ (salt), calculate (a) % recovery of glycerine based on the mixed feed, (b) % loss of glycerine based on the mixed feed, and (c) product contamination with respect of salt content.

Soultion This type of problem can be conveniently solved by calculating the area under the curves.

$$\text{Recovery of glycerine} = \frac{8124 \text{ sq. units}}{9448 \text{ sq. units}} \times 100 = \textbf{85.99\%}$$

Table 3.7 Areas under the Curves

Effluent cut	Area under salt curve, square units	Area under glycerine curve, square units
Waste	4942	16
Recycle I	3436	959
Product	238	8124
Recycle II	Nil	266
Waste	Nil	83
Total	8616	9448

$$\text{Loss of glycerine in waste} = \frac{(16 + 83)}{9448} \times 100 = \mathbf{1.05\%}$$

$$\text{Recycle of glycerine} = 100 - 85.99 - 1.05 = 12.96\%$$

$$\text{NaCl recycled} = \frac{3436}{8616} \times 100 = 39.88\%$$

$$\text{NaCl in product as contaminant of total NaCl fed} = \frac{238}{8124} \times 100 = 2.93\%$$

Let C_f (salt) concentration $= x$

C_f (glycerine) concentration $= 12\,x$

NaCl in the product $= 0.0293\,x$

Glycerine in the product $= 0.8599 \times 12\,x = 10.3188\,x$

Total solute $= (0.0293 + 10.3188)\,x = 10.3481x$

$$\text{NaCl of total solutes in product} = \frac{0.0293\,x}{10.3481x} \times 100$$

$$= \mathbf{0.28\%}$$

Note It may be interesting to note that the NaCl recycled is substantial (in Recycle I) as compared to the glycerine recycle. For example, if fresh crude glycerine contains 30% glycerine and 2.5% salt (by mass) after five batches of recycle, glycerine and salt concentrations will be 55.3% and 13.5%, respectively, based on the above recoveries. Hence, a stage will come when Recycle I will be required to be discarded to maintain low salt concentration in the mixed feed.

3.6 RECYCLING AND BYPASSING OPERATIONS

Recycling and bypassing operations are commonly encountered in unit operations as well as in chemical reactions. These operations are performed for a variety of reasons. A few important ones are listed below.

(i) To utilise the valuable component reactant to their maximum and avoid wastage. For example, CO_2 sublimed during manufacture of dry ice is recycled for reprocessing. Hydrogen and nitrogen are recycled in ammonia synthesis for maximizing ammonia production. During such a recycle, a purge is bled to control undesired species in the mixture.

(ii) To utilise the heat being lost in the outgoing stream, for example, hot-air dryers, calcining the lime in a kiln, and so on.

(iii) To improve the performance of the equipment. For example, SO_3 cannot be easily dissolved in oleum. Oleum is recirculated after cooling to improve absorption.

(iv) To control the operating variable in a reaction, namely, pressure, temperature, and so on. For example, in ammonia synthesis, quenching (bypass) is carried out to control the reactor-bed temperature. While demineralizing water with high dissolved solids, a portion of raw water is bypassed through reverse osmosis plant to reduce salinity of the effluents.

(v) To improve the selectivity of a product, for example, in the manufacture of chlormethanes, methyl choride is recycled to increase production of other chloromethanes.

(vi) To improve the safety of the chemical process, for example, in manufacture of formaldehyde, tail gas is recycled to reduce oxygen concentration in feed gas mixture below flammability limit.

(vii) To minimize waste generation, for example, reverse osmosis technology is widely used for treatment of aqueous effluents. Thereby good quality permeate (a major portion of effluents) is recycled for reprocessing.

In almost all recycling operations, a definite stream has to be removed/purged to control the concentration of a particular component. In this chapter only unit operations with recycling operations will be considered. In Chapter 4, chemical reactions with recycling will be discussed. In Example 3.14 it was noted that Recycle I will have to be discarded at some stage to maintain low salt concentration in the mixed feed to the ion-exchange column. This can be considered intermittent purging to control the mixed-feed composition.

Example 3.15 An air-conditioning plant is employed to maintain 27°C (300 K) dry bulb (*DB*) temperature and 50% relative humidity (*RH*) in an auditorium. The air–flow rate to the auditorium is measured to be 5.806 m³/s at 17°C (290 K) *DB* and 83.5% *RH*. The effluent air from the auditorium is partially recycled and mixed with the incoming fresh air due to economic reasons. The fresh ambient air is fed at the rate of 1.25 m³/s at 35°C (308 K) *DB* and 70% *RH*. The mixed air is found to have 29.5°C (302.5 K) *DB* and 54% *RH* and is passed through the air-conditioning plant to make it suitable for feeding to the auditorium. For all practical purposes, the total pressure can be assumed constant at 101.3 kPa a (760 Torr). Table 3.8 gives the molar humidity. (Refer Fig. 6.11 for data on absolute humidity values for various air conditions.)

Table 3.8 Data on Molar Humidity

Stream	Dry bulb temperature °C (K)	Absolute molar humidity, kmol/ kmol dry air	Relative humidity, % (*RH*)
Fresh ambient air	35 (308)	0.0405	70
Mixed air	29.5 (302.5)	0.0225	54
Air entering the auditorium	17 (290)	0.0163	83.5
Air leaving the auditorium	27 (300)	0.0181	50

Figure 3.13 shows the flow diagram of the above air-conditioning plant.

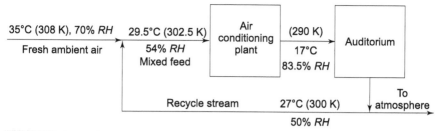

Fig. 3.13   Air-conditioning System of an Auditorium

(a) Calculate the moisture removed in the air-conditioning plant.
(b) Calculate the moisture added in the auditorium.
(c) Calculate the recycle ratio as moles of air recycled per mole of fresh ambient air input.

Solution   *Basis* 1.25 m^3/s of fresh ambient air feed and 5.806 m^3/s of air entering into the auditorium

Specific volume of moist air at 290 K and 101.3 kPa a, V_{a1} = 8.314 × 290/101.3
$$= 23.80 \text{ m}^3/\text{kmol}$$

Molar flow rate of air entering the auditorium, $\dot{n}_{a1} = \left(\dfrac{5.806}{23.8} \right) 1000$

$$= 243.95 \text{ mol/s}$$

Moisture accompanying the air, $\dot{n}_{w1} = \dfrac{243.95 \times 0.0163}{1.0163} = 3.91$ mol/s

Dry air flow, $\dot{n}_{a2}$ = 243.95 – 3.91 = 240.04 mol/s

Moisture in air entering air-conditioning plant,
$$\dot{n}_{w2} = 240.04 \times 0.0225$$
$$= 5.4 \text{ mol/s}$$

In the air-conditioning plant, the moisture is removed as is evident from Table 3.8. However, the flow rate of dry air remains unchanged.

Moisture removed in the air-conditioning plant = 5.4 – 3.91 = 1.49 mol/s
$$\equiv 26.84 \text{ g/s} \equiv \textbf{96.63 kg/h}$$

In the auditorium, the air picks up moisture. Here also, the flow rate of dry air is unchanged.

Moisture in the air leaving the auditorium, $\dot{m}_{m2}$ = 240.04 × 0.0181
$$= 4.345 \text{ mol/s}$$

Moisture added in the auditorium = 4.345 – 3.91 = 0.435 mol/s
$$\equiv 7.83 \text{ g/s} \equiv \textbf{28.2 kg/h}$$

Specific volume of the fresh air, V_{m2} = 8.314 × 308/101.3 = 25.28 m^3/kmol
Molar flow rate of the fresh air, $\dot{n}_{a3}$ = (1.25/25.28) 1000 = 49.45 mol/s
Moisture in the fresh air, $\dot{n}_{m3}$ = (0.0405/1.0405) × 49.45 = 1.925 mol/s
Dry air flow in the fresh air, $\dot{n}_{a4}$ = 49.45 – 1.925 = 47.525 mol/s
Moisture in the recycle stream, $\dot{n}_{m4}$ = moisture in the mixed feed
$$\qquad\qquad - \text{ moisture in the fresh ambient air}$$
$$= 5.40 - 1.925 = 3.475 \text{ mol/s}$$

Dry air flow in the recycled stream = 240.04 – 47.525 = 192.515 mol/s
Molar flow rate of wet recycled stream = 192.515 + 3.475 = 195.99 mol/s

Recycle ratio = 195.99/49.45
= **3.96 kmol of recycle stream/kmol of fresh feed**

Example 3.16 In a pulp mill, a three-stage cascade screening system, shown in Fig. 3.11, is employed to remove the oversize foreign particles from dilute slurries[11]. If E_1, E_2 and E_3 are the fractions of foreign particles (i.e., efficiency of each screen/100) removed in the three screens, respectively, develop a general relationship for the overall efficiency of the system.

Definition: Efficiency of a screen = (foreign material rejected/foreign material entering) × 100

Solution
Basis Let N kg be the amount of foreign material entering the screen 1.
Material balance of foreign materials
Screen 1   Feed = N kg
Oversize particles = NE_1 kg
Undersize particles = $N - NE_1$
= $N(1 - E_1)$ kg
Screen 2 In this screen, the feed is the mixture of oversize particles form Screen 1 and the recycled undersize particles from Screen 3. Let the recycled undersized particles from Screen 3 be X kg.
Feed = $NE_1 + X$ kg
Oversize particles = $(NE_1 + X) E_2$ kg
Undersize particles = $(NE_1 + X) (1 - E_2)$ kg

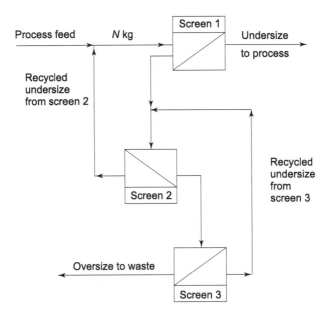

Fig. 3.14 Three Stage Cascade Screening System

The undersize particles from Screen 2 are recycled and mixed with process feed to give N kg particles in the mixed feed to Screen 1.
Fresh particles in the process feed = $N - (NE_1 + X) (1 - E_2)$ kg
Screen 3 The feed to Screen 3 consists of oversized particles from Screen 2.

Feed = $(NE_1 + X) E_2$ kg
Oversize particles = $(NE_1 + X) E_2 E_3$ kg - waste stream
Undersize particles = $(NE_1 + X) E_2 (1 - E_3)$ kg

However, it is assumed that undersize particles from Screen 3 are X kg.

$$(NE_1 + X) E_2(1 - E_3) = X \quad \text{or} \quad X = NE_1E_2 \frac{(1 - E_3)}{[1 - E_2(1 - E_3)]}$$

Overall efficiency of the system = $\left(\dfrac{\text{Oversize particales from screen 3}}{\text{Particles in process feed}} \right) \times 100$

$$= \frac{(NE_1 + X) E_2 E_3}{[N - (NE_1 + X) (1 - E_2)]} \times 100$$

Substituting for X and simplifying,

$$\text{Overall efficiency} = \frac{E_1 E_2 E_3}{[(1 - E_1)(1 - E_2) + E_2 E_3]} \times 100$$

Example 3.17 Polysulphone members are used in industry for recovery of a specific gas component from a gas mixture[12]. A 2-stage membrane process is designed for separation of carbon monoxide from a mixture of carbon monoxide (47.0 mole %) and rest hydrogen. The process is shown schematically in Fig. 3.15.

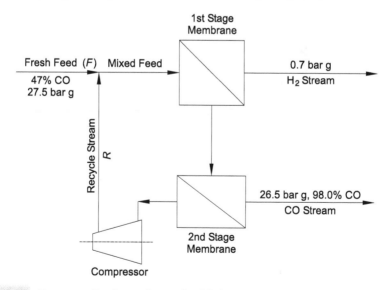

Fig. 3.15 Two-stage Membrane System for CO Separation

The system is designed to recover 93.2% CO with 98.0 mole % purity. Recycle stream is kept at 3000 kmol/h for a fresh feed rate of 5000 kmol/h.

This requirement is stipulted to achieve 1.1 mole ratio of H_2/CO in the feed to the second stage.

(a) Calculte the flow rates of product carbon monoxide stream.

(b) Calculate the composition of the product hydrogen stream.

(c) Calculate the composition the mixed feed to the first stage membrance.

Solution   *Basis* Fresh feed, $F = 5000$ kmol/h

$$CO \text{ in } F = 5000 \times 0.47 = 2350 \text{ kmol/h}$$
$$H_2 \text{ in } F = 5000 - 2350 = 2650 \text{ kmol/h}$$

Product (CO) stream from 2nd–stage membrane:

$$CO \text{ recovery} = 93.2\% \text{ (overall)}$$
$$CO \text{ in product CO stream} = 2350 \times 0.932$$
$$= 2190.2 \text{ kmol/h}$$
$$\text{Product (CO) stream, } \dot{n}_2 = 2190.2 / 0.98$$
$$= \textbf{2234.9 kmol/h}$$
$$H_2 \text{ in CO stream} = 2234.9 - 2190.2$$
$$= 44.7 \text{ kmol/h}$$

Table 3.9 Composition of H_2 Stream from 1st-stage Membrane

Component	Flow rate ($\dot{n}_i$), kmol/h	mole %
H_2	2650 – 44.7 = 2605.3	**94.22**
CO	2350 – 2190.2 = 159.8	**5.78**
Total	2765.1	**100.00**

Let $\dot{n}_{H_2}$ kmol/h of H_2 and $\dot{n}_{CO}$ kmol/h of CO are present in the recycle stream.

$$\dot{n}_{H_2} + \dot{n}_{CO} = 3000 = R \qquad \text{(i)}$$

Feed to 2nd stage

$$CO \text{ in the feed} = 2190.2 + \dot{n}_{CO} \text{ kmol/h}$$
$$H_2 \text{ in the feed} = 44.7 + \dot{n}_{H_2} \text{ kmol/h}$$

$$\frac{44.7 + \dot{n}_{H_2}}{2190.2 + \dot{n}_{CO}} = 1.1 \qquad \text{(ii)}$$

Solving Eq. (i) and Eq. (ii),

$$\dot{n}_{H_2} = 2697.39 \text{ kmol/h}$$
$$\dot{n}_{CO} = 3000 - 2697.39 = 302.61 \text{ kmol/h}$$

Table 3.10 Composition of Mixed Feed

Component	Flow rate ($\dot{n}_i$), kmol/h	mole %
H_2	2650 + 2697.39 = 5347.39	**66.84**
CO	2350 + 302.61 = 2652.61	**33.16**
Total	8000.00	**100.00**

Example 3.18   Production of treated water is required at the rate of 5 m³/h with 5 mg/L (max.) dissolved solids (i.e., < 10 μS/cm conductivity) in a bulk drug plant. Raw water with 4200 mg/L dissolved solids (DS) is available for the purpose. For the treatment of raw water, two-stage reverse osmosis (RO) plant is designed as shown in Fig. 3.16. RO Module I is designed for 66% recovery of the feed to the module while RO Module II is designed for 80% recovery. Rejection of 98.5% salts is achieved from the RO Module II. While reject stream R_1 from Module I will be discarded as effuents, reject stream from Module II (R_2) will be recycled and mixed with the incoming raw water (F). Based on RO membrane characteristics, both feed pumps are designed to feed the modules at 12 bar g.

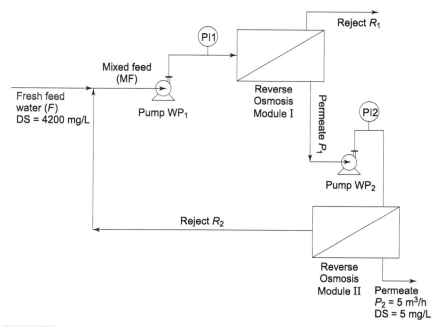

Fig. 3.16   Two-stage Reverse Osmosis Plant

Make complete material balance of the system and calculate F, R_1, P, R_2, recycle ratio, defined as R_2/F, and rejection of salt from Module I.

Solution
Overall Balance

$$F = R_1 + P_2 \qquad \text{(i)}$$

Balance across Module I

$$F + R_2 = R_1 + P_1 \qquad \text{(ii)}$$

Substitute value of F from Eq. (i).

$$R_1 + P_2 + R_2 = R_1 + P_1$$

or $P_1 = P_2 + R_2$ which represents material balance across Module II.

$$P_2 = 5 \text{ m}^3/\text{h}, \qquad P_2/P_1 = 0.8 \quad \text{or} \quad P_1 = 5/0.8 = \mathbf{6.25 \text{ m}^3/\text{h}}$$
$$R_2 = P_1 - P_2 = 6.25 - 5 = \mathbf{1.25 \text{ m}^3/\text{h}}$$

$$\frac{P_1}{F + R_2} = 0.66$$

$$P_1 = 0.66 \, (F + R_2)$$
$$6.25 = 0.66(F + 1.25)$$

or
$$F = \mathbf{8.22 \text{ m}^3/\text{h}}$$
$$R_1 = F - P_2 = 8.22 - 5 = \mathbf{3.22 \text{ m}^3/\text{h}}$$

Balance of DS

Let x represent concentration of DS in water in mg/L (i.e., same as g/m^3).

Overall material balance of DS

$$F x_F = R_1 \, x_{R_1} + P_2 \, x_{P_2}$$
$$8.22 \times 4200 = 3.22 \times x_{R_1} + 5 \times 5$$

or
$$x_{R_1} = 10714 \text{ mg/L or g/m}^3$$

Since rejection in Module II is 98.5%, DS in P_2 will be 1.5% of that in P_1

$$\text{DS in } P_1, x_{P_1} = \frac{5 \times 5}{0.015 \times 6.25} = 267 \text{ g/m}^3 \text{ or mg/L}$$

$$P_1 \, x_{P_1} = P_2 \, x_{P_2} + R_2 \, x_{R_2}$$
$$6.25 \times 267 = 5 \times 5 + 1.25 \times x_{R_2}$$

or
$$x_{R_2} = 1315 \text{ g/m}^3 \text{ or mg/L}$$

$$\text{DS in mixed feed (MF)} = F x_F + R_2 \, x_{R_2}$$
$$= 8.22 \times 4200 + 1.25 \times 1315$$
$$= 36168 \text{ g}$$

$$\text{Concentration of DS in MF} = \frac{36168}{(8.22 + 1.25)} = 3819 \text{ g/m}^3 \text{ or mg/L}$$

$$\text{DS in } R_1 = 3.22 \times 10714 = 34499 \text{ g}$$

$$\text{Rejection in Module I} = \frac{34499}{36168} \times 100$$

$$= 95.4\%$$

$$\text{DS in } P_1 = 36168 - 34499 = 1669 \text{ g}$$

$$\text{Concentration of DS in } P_1 = \frac{1669}{6.25} = 267 \text{ g/m}^3 \text{ or mg/L} \quad \text{Check!}$$

$$\text{Recycle ratio } \frac{R_2}{F} = \frac{1.25}{8.22} = \mathbf{0.152 \text{ m}^3 \text{ reject recycle/m}^3 \text{ fresh feed}}$$

$$\text{Overall recovery} = \frac{P_2}{F} \times 100 = \frac{5}{8.22} \times 100$$
$$= \mathbf{60.83\%}$$

Note If R_2 stream is not recycled, overall recovery would be $0.66 \times 0.8 = 0.528$ or 52.8%.

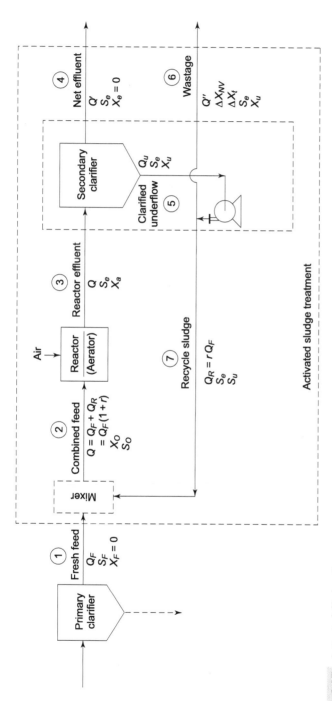

Fig. 3.17 Activated Sludge Process

Example 3.19 An activated sludge process has been developed as a continuous operation by recycling biological sludge. This process uses microorganisms in suspension to oxidise soluble (and colloidal) organics, also known as volatile organic compounds (VOC), to CO_2 and H_2O in the presence of molecular oxygen. In the process, an industrial waste water stream is treated with air to convert BOD into suspended solids which is subsequently removed in the clarifier[13]. The process is illustrated in Fig. 3.17. Waste water (Stream 1) enters the process having a soluble BOD content S_F. The purpose of the treatment is to reduce this value to S_e (final effluent BOD content, i.e., that of stream 4) by oxidation through aerobic biological degradation. Usually, BOD removal efficiency of such a process varies from 90 to 95%. Fresh feed is combined with recycled sludge (stream 7) and enters the aeration tank. Biological sludge is continuously formed in the aeration tank which is usually operated under steady-state conditions with complete mixing. The reaction kinetics of such processes is normally represented by a first-order reaction. The concentration of soluble BOD in streams 3 and 5 is the same as that of the stream 4. The secondary clarifier underflow (Stream 5) is split into two streams—waste sludge and recycle studge.

The kinetic model of the process can be established by setting up a relation between the BOD concentration and the suspended solids that enter the aeration tank. This relation can be varied by varying the recycle ratio.

Establish a mathematical model for such a process. For calculating the recycle ratio, assume that the overflow from the secondary clarifier does not contain any solids and the quantity of air absorbed in the tank is negligible as compared to the feed steam.

Solution *Basis* Feed flow rate of Q_F L/s having no suspended solids (i.e., $X_F = 0$) and BOD concentration equal to S_F kg/L

$$X_e = 0$$

Overall material balance

$$Q_F = Q' + Q'' \qquad \text{(i)}$$

Combined feed $\quad Q = Q_F + Q_R$

$$\text{Recycle ratio, } r = \frac{Q_R}{Q_F}$$

$$Q = Q_F \, (1 + r) \qquad \text{(ii)}$$

BOD balance across the aeration tank

$$Q_F S_F - Q \, (S_O - S_e) = Q_F S_e$$
$$Q_F (S_F - S_e) = Q \, (S_O - S_e)$$
$$S_F - S_e = (1 + r) \, (S_O - S_e)$$

Simplifying, $\qquad r = \dfrac{S_F - S_O}{S_O - S_C}$ $\qquad$ (iii)

Suspended solids balance across the aeration tank

$$Q_F \, X_F + (X_a - X_O) \, Q = Q' \, X_e + Q'' \, X_u$$
$$\text{But } X_F = X_e = 0$$

Using Eqs (i) and (ii)

$$(X_a - X_O)(Q_r + Q_F) = (Q_F - Q')X_u$$

$$(1 + r)(X_a - X_O) = \left(1 - \frac{Q'}{Q_F}\right) X_u \qquad \text{(iv)}$$

Suspended solids balance across secondary clarifier

$$QX_a = Q'X_e + Q''X_u + Q_R X_u$$

Since

$$X_e = 0$$

$$QX_a = (Q'' + Q_R) X_u$$

Using Eq. (ii),

$$(1 + r) = (1 + r) X_u - \frac{Q'}{Q_F} X_u \qquad \text{(v)}$$

Eliminating Q'/Q_F from Eqs (iv) and (v),

$$(X_u - X_o) = \frac{X_u}{(1 + r)}$$

Solving for r,

$$r = \frac{X_O}{X_u - X_O} \qquad \text{(vi)}$$

By comparing Eqs (3) and (6), a relation between BOD concentration and suspended solids can be obtained.

3.7   MATERIAL BALANCES OF UNSTEADY-STATE OPERATIONS

Very often, the operating conditions are not steady. In unsteady-state conditions, input and output parameters change with respect to time. In certain batch operations, at the end of each of the batch, the material balance changes with respect to a particular component, thereby putting the system in an unsteady state. A number of examples can be cited, such as purging of a vessel, batch distillation, sudden change in input or output streams with respect to quantity and/or composition, and so on. In most cases, material balance calculations are made by considering small time intervals ($\Delta\theta$) and finding the change in the parameter taking place during the period $\Delta\theta$. Thus, integral calculus is very useful in solving such problems. Often, the functions are difficult to integrate directly and under such circumstances numerical integration is adopted. The number of iterations to be performed during numerical integration depends on how small the time interval ($\Delta\theta$) is assumed for the iteration to be performed. The smaller the time interval, the better is the accuracy of the final answer. In case the interval is not sufficiently small, it may lead to a complicated or erroneous solution. This selection of time interval is mathematically defined as stability of the solution. In computer-aided material balances, iterations are performed with small time intervals and quite accurate answers are obtained.

Example 3.20 Tanks, gas holders and pipelines are purged with an inert gas to prevent fire or explosion. The inert gas may be nitrogen, argon, helium or any rare gas. They are purged on two occasions, that is, when the equipment is being put into operation with inflammable materials or when the equipment is purged before air is admitted for inspection and maintenance work. There are numerous ways of purging a system[14, 15]. One such method is the atmospheric pressure method. In this method the inert gas is passed continuously into the vessel or system from one point while the purge leaves from another point. The inert gas performs its functions by displacement and/or dilution. In a long narrow vessel such as a small pipe, the purge can take place almost entirely by displacement. In such a case, the amount of inert gas required to sweep out virtually all the gas contained in the pipe, is the same as the volume of the pipe. In more general cases, some mixing of the inert gas and vessel atmosphere occurs and a reduction of the concentration of any component in the vessel takes places by dilution. Assuming that the mixing of the inert gas within the vessel atmosphere is complete throughout the purging operation, prove that the concentration of any component of the original vessel atmosphere will be 1/e times the original concentration after passing one vessel volume of the inert gas for purging.

Solution   Let the initial concentration of a component in the vessel atmosphere be C_0 kmol/L at atmospheric pressure and the vessel volume be V L. Introduce a small volume v L of inert gas into the vessel and allow it to mix well. As a result of the introduction of a small volume of inert gas, pressure will be slightly increased, which will be released.

Concentration of the component after introduction of v volume of inert gas,

$$C_1 = \frac{VC_0}{V + v} = \frac{C_0}{\left(1 + \dfrac{v}{V}\right)}$$

After the introduction of an additional v volume of inert gas, concentration

$$C_2 = \frac{C_1}{\left(1 + \dfrac{v}{V}\right)} = \frac{C_0}{\left(1 + \dfrac{v}{V}\right)^2}$$

Similarly,

$$C_n = \frac{C_0}{\left(1 + \dfrac{v}{V}\right)^n}$$

When the volume of the inert gas used for purging reaches V, i.e., $n = V/v$ and the concentration of the component after purging by one vessel volume,

$$C_V = \frac{C_0}{\left(1 + \dfrac{1}{n}\right)^n}$$

Continuous purging operation will mean that the volume v is very small. Mathematically,

$$\lim_{n \to \infty} \left(1 + \frac{1}{n}\right)^n = e$$

Therefore,

$$C_V = \frac{C_0}{e}$$

If two vessel volumes of inert gas is used for purging,

$$C_{2V} = \frac{C_0}{e^2}, \text{ and so on.}$$

Example 3.21 A storage tank of a demineralised (DM) water has a holding capacity of 1500 m³ up to an overflow point. The inflow of DM water to the tank is 25 L/s having silica (as SiO_2) content of 0.005 mg/L. The supply of DM water to the high pressure boilers from the tank amount to 25 dm³/s. With time, the DM water quality deteriorates and the silica content in the feed DM water increases to 0.02 mg/L. Assume that the inflow into and the outflow from the tank remains constant at 25 L/s. Calculate the time for the silica content in the storage tank to increase to 0.01 mg/L.

Solution *Basis* Inflow of DM water to the tank = 25 L/s

When the inflow DM water and the outflow DM water contain the same silica level (0.005 mg/L), the system is defined as steady, which is shown in Fig. 3.18. The upset in the inflow of DM water creates the unsteady-state conditions. Figure 3.19 represents the upset in silica concentration of make-up.

Total water in the tank = 1500 m³ = 1500 000 L

Let c be the concentration of silica in the tank in mg/L at any time θ, $\Delta\theta$ be the time interval during which the change in the concentration is observed, and Δe be the change in the concentration during the time interval $\Delta\theta$. Consider $\theta = 0$ when the silica level in the incoming DM water increases to 0.02 mg/L.

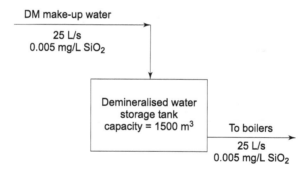

Fig. 3.18 Steady-state Conditions of a Demineralised Water Storage Tank

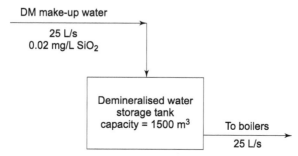

Fig. 3.19 Unsteady-state Conditions of a Demineralised Water Storage Tank

Silica balance

Input into the tank in $\Delta\theta$ s $= 25 \times 0.02 \times \Delta\theta$
$$= 0.5 \ \Delta\theta \ \text{mg}$$
Output from the tank in $\Delta\theta$ s $= 25 \times c \times \Delta\theta$ mg
Accumulation of silica in the tank in $\Delta\theta$ s $= 1500\ 000 \ \Delta \ c$ mg

Input – Output = Accumulation
$$0.5 \ \Delta\theta - 25 \ c \ \Delta\theta = 1500\ 000 \ \Delta c$$
$$\Delta\theta \ (1 - 50c) = \ 3000\ 000 \ \Delta c$$

Converting into the differential form and integrating,

$$d\theta = 3000\ 000 \times \left[\frac{dc}{1 - 50\text{c}} \right]$$

$$= 3000\ 000 \ \int_{c_1}^{c_2} \frac{dc}{(1 - 50\text{c})}$$

$$\theta = \frac{-3000\ 000}{50} \left[\text{In} \ \frac{(1 - 50c_2)}{(1 - 50c_1)} \right]$$

Now when
$$\theta = 0, \quad c_1 = \ 0.005 \ \text{mg/L}$$
$$\theta = \theta, \quad c_2 = \ 0.01 \ \text{mg/L}$$
$$\theta = (-60\ 000) \times \text{In} \ [(1 - 50c_2)/ \ (1 - 50c_1)]$$
$$\theta = (60\ 000) \times 0.4055 = \mathbf{24\ 330 \ s} \equiv \mathbf{6.76 \ h}$$

Example 3.22 In Example 3.21, assume that the inflow to the tank was reduced to 14 L/s as soon as the silica concentration was noticed to be 0.02 mg/L. The outflow from the tank remains constant at 25 L/s. Calculate the time required to increase the silica content in the storage tank to 0.008 mg/L. Also calculate the hold-up of the tank at the time when the silica concentration is 0.008 mg/L.

Solution The unsteady-state flow process is shown in Fig. 3.20. Using the same nomenclature as in Example 3.21, the silica balance may be considered.

Input to the tank $= 14 \times 0.02 \times \Delta\theta = 0.28 \ \Delta\theta$ mg
Output from the tank $= 25 \ c \ \Delta\theta$ mg
Accumulation in the tank $= [1500\ 000 \ - \ (25 - 14) \ \Delta\theta]\Delta c$
$$= (1500\ 000 \ - \ 11 \ \Delta\theta) \ \Delta c \ \text{mg}$$
Input – Output = Accumulation
$$0.28 \ \Delta\theta - 25 \ c \ \Delta\theta = (1500\ 000 - 11 \ \Delta\theta) \ \Delta c$$
$$\Delta\theta \ (1 - 89.3c) = (5357\ 143 - 39.3 \ \Delta\theta) \ \Delta c \qquad \text{(i)}$$

The above equation requires double integration. It can be solved by numerical integration, performing the iterations.

Let $\Delta\theta = 1000$ s

$c = c_1$, i.e., the concentration of silica in the tank at the start of the period
$\Delta c = c_2 - c_1$

Iteration 1
$$1000 \ (1 - 89.3 \ c_1) = (5357\ 149 \ - 39.3 \times 1000) \ (c_2 - \ c_1)$$
Simplifying
$$10\ 000 \ c_2 = 9832 \ c_1 + 1.88$$
$$c_1 = 0.005 \ \text{mg/L to start with}$$
$$c_2 = 0.005\ 104 \ \text{mg/L at the end}$$

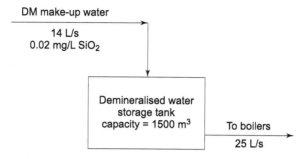

Fig. 3.20 Unsteady-state Conditions of a Demineralized Water Storage Tank with Reduced Inflow

Iteration 2
In this case
$$c_1 = 0.005\ 104 \text{ mg/L}$$
$$c_2 = 0.005\ 206 \text{ mg/L}$$
Similar iterations can be performed. At the end of the 36th iteration,
$$c_2 = 0.00\ 799 \text{ mg/L} \approx 0.008 \text{ mg/L}$$
$$\text{Total time} = \Sigma\ \Delta\theta_i$$
$$= 36 \times 1000 = 36\ 000 \text{ s} \approx \textbf{10 h}$$
Hold-up of the tank

$$\text{at the end of 10 h} = 1500 - \left(\frac{14 \times 36\ 000}{1000}\right) = \textbf{996 m}^3$$

Alternate integral method
Equation (i) can be converted to differential form,

$$\frac{dc}{(1 - 89.3\ c)} = \frac{d\theta}{(5357\ 143 - 39.3\theta)}$$

Integrating the above differential between $c = 0.\ 005$, and $c = 0.008$,

$$\int_{0.005}^{0.008} \frac{dc}{(1 - 89.3\ c)} = \int_{0}^{\theta} \frac{d\theta}{(5357\ 143 - 39.3\theta)}$$

$$\frac{1}{89.3} \ln \frac{89.3 \times 0.008 - 1}{89.3 \times 0.005 - 1} = \frac{1}{39.3} \ln \frac{5357\ 143 - 39.3\theta}{5357\ 143}$$

$$\boldsymbol{\theta = 34\ 437 \text{ s} \equiv 9.57 \text{ h}}$$

Hold-up of the tank at the end of 9.57 h,

$$V = 1500 - \left(14 \times \frac{34\ 437}{1000}\right) = \textbf{1017.88 m}^3$$

Example 3.23 In a batch process, the reaction takes place in the presence of an acid medium. The process is illustrated in Fig. 3.21. The acid is drained from the reaction vessel at the rate of 15 mL/s as a result of the density difference of the acid from the reacting component. To avoid wastage of acid, it is recycled to an acid tank which has 1000 L capacity. The acid, drained from the reaction vessel, picks up 50 g/L of solids from the reactor. Acid is fed once again to the process from the acid tank. When the batch is started, the acid is almost pure in the tank as a result of filtration. As the reaction proceeds, acid in the tank gets more and more contaminated with the solids. The concentration of the solids should not exceed 100 g/L from the process point of view. The batch time is 16 h. Check whether the concentration of the solids will exceed 100 g/L during the batch reaction.

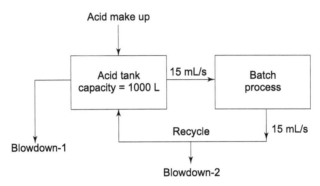

Fig. 3.21   Batch Reaction in an Acid Medium

Solution   Consider the material balance of the solids across the acid tank. Let the acid concentration of the solids be c in the tank at any time θ. Consider a time interval of $\Delta\theta$ during which concentraion of the solids changes by Δc.

$$\text{Input of solids to the tank} = 15 \ (c + 50) \ \frac{\Delta\theta}{1000} \ \text{g}$$

Output of solids from the tank $= 15 \ c \ \Delta\theta/1000\text{g}$
Accumulation in the tank $= 1000 \ (c + \Delta c) - 1000c$
$$= 1000 \ \Delta c \ \text{g}$$
Input $-$ Output $=$ Accumulation
$$\frac{1}{1000} \ [15 \ (c + 50) \ \Delta\theta - 15 \ c \ \Delta\theta] = 1000 \ \Delta c$$
$$750 \ \Delta\theta = 1000 \ 000 \ \Delta c$$
Converting into differential from, $d\theta = 1333.33 \ dc$, when
$\theta = 0$ and $c = 0$. Integration therefore yields
$\theta = 1333.33 \ c$
$c = 100$ g/L is the limit
$\theta = 100 \times 1333.33$
$= \mathbf{133 \ 333 \ s}$
$\equiv \mathbf{37.04 \ h}$

Since this period is higher than batch period, solid concentration will not exceed 100 g/L during the batch.
The above answer can be also obtained by simple material balance.

Total solid pick-up permitted $= 1000 \times 100$
$$= 100\ 000 \text{ g}$$

Total solid pick-up $= 15 \times \dfrac{50}{1000} = 0.75$ g/s

Time reqired to attain 100 g/L solids concentration,

$$\theta = \frac{1000}{0.75}$$
$$= \mathbf{133\ 333\ s}$$
$$\equiv \mathbf{37.04\ h}$$

Example 3.24 In Example 3.23 above, it is assumed that acid is filtered before each batch is started and the concentration of the solids is brought to nearly zero. This filtration can be avoided by blowing down a known quantity of acid from either the tank (Case 1) or the recycle stream (Case 2) such that the concentration of solids in the acid fed to the process vessel is controlled. For both the above cases, draw the plots of solids concentration in the tank versus time for different blow-down rates.

Solution

Case 1 Blow-down is maintained from the acid tank at a constant rate of B mL/s.

Output of solids from the tank $= \left[\dfrac{15c\Delta\theta}{1000} \right] + \left[\dfrac{Bc\Delta\theta}{1000} \right]$ g

$$= (15\ c\ \Delta\theta + B\ c\ \Delta\theta)\ 10^{-3}\,\text{g}$$

Material balance therefore yields,

$$\frac{[15(c + 50)\Delta\theta]}{1000} - \frac{(15\ c\ \Delta\theta + B\ c\ \Delta\theta)}{1000} = 1000\ \Delta\theta$$

$$75\ \Delta\theta - B\ c\ \Delta\theta = 1000\ 000\ \Delta c$$

Converting into differential form,

$$d\theta = 10^6 \left(\frac{dc}{750 - B\ c} \right)$$

when $\theta = 0$, $c = 0$. Therefore, integration yields

$$\theta = \frac{10^6}{B} \ln\left(\frac{750}{750 - B\ c} \right) \text{ or } c = \frac{750}{B}\,(1 - e^{-B\theta/10^6})$$

The above equation permits computation of c by assuming values of B and θ. Therse data are presented in Table 3.11 and Fig. 3.22.

Table 3.11 Concentration of Solids with Blow-down from Acid Tank, g/L

B, mL/s	Time (θ) in seconds				
	18×10^3	36×10^3	90×10^3	180×10^3	360×10^3
1	13.379	26.520	64.552	123.547	226.743
3	13.142	25.593	59.155	104.313	165.101
5	12.910	24.709	54.356	89.015	125.205
7	12.684	23.867	50.079	76.751	98.522

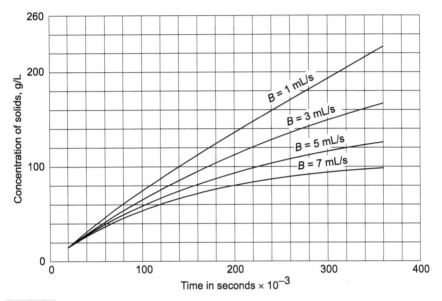

Fig. 3.22 Concentration of Solids vs Time for a Specified Blow-down Rate from the Acid Tank

It can be seen from Fig. 3.22 that for each blow-down rate, the graph converges as the time elapses. Therefore, at infinite time, the concentration of solids will become constant for each of the blow-down rates.

$$\text{When } \theta \to \infty, \ e^{-B\theta/10^6} \to 0, \ c = \frac{750}{B}$$

For a limited concentration of $c = 100$ g/L,

$$B = \frac{750}{100} = 7.5 \text{ mL/s}$$

Case 2 Blow–down is maintained from the recycle stream at a constant rate of B ml/s

$$\text{Input of solids to the tank} = \frac{(15 - B)(c + 50)\Delta\theta}{1000} \text{ g}$$

Material balance therefore yields,

$$\left(\frac{(15 - B)(c + 50)\Delta\theta}{1000}\right) - \left(\frac{15c\,\Delta\theta}{1000}\right) = 1000\,\Delta c$$

Converting into differential form,

$$\frac{10^6\,dc}{750 - 50\,B - B\,c} = d\theta$$

Integration yields,

$$\frac{10^6}{B}\,\ln\left(\frac{50\,B - 750}{B\,c + 50\,B - 750}\right) = \theta$$

Simplifying,

$$\frac{B\,c}{750 - 50\,B} = 1 - e^{-B\theta/10^6}$$

or

$$c = \left(\frac{750 - 50\,B}{B}\right)(1 - e^{-B\theta/10^6})$$

Based on the above equation, Table 3.10 is prepared and the same data are plotted in Fig. 3.23.

Table 3.12 Concentration of Solids with Blow-down from Recycle Stream, g/L

B, mL/s	\multicolumn{5}{c}{Time (θ) in seconds}
	18×10^3	36×10^3	90×10^3	180×10^3	360×10^3
1	12.487	24.752	60.248	115.311	211.627
3	10.514	20.474	47.324	83.450	132.081
5	8.607	16.473	36.237	59.343	66.040
7	6.765	12.729	26.709	40.934	52.545

When $\theta \to \infty$, $e^{-B\theta/10^6} \to 0$, $c = \dfrac{750}{B} - 50$

For

$$c = 100 \text{ g/L}$$

$$B = \frac{750}{150} = 5 \text{ mL/s}$$

Note It can be observed that blow-down from recycle stream results in a lower concentration of solids in the acid fed to the process vessel.

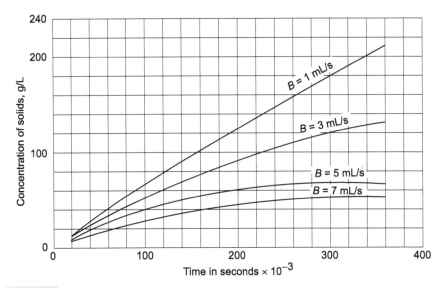

Fig. 3.23   Concentration of Solids vs Time for a Specified Blow-down Rate from the Recycle Stream

Exercises

3.1 The feed water to the reverse osmosis plant has dissoved solids to the extent of 5000 mg/L[16]. The feed-to-product ratio (on mass basis) is 4:3. The treated water (product) from the plant contains 600 mg/L of solids. Find the dissolved solids in the reject stream. **[18 200 mg/L]**

3.2 In a hybrid system for dehydration of ethanol, atmospheric distillation column is coupled with a pervaporation unit[17]. Vapour from the top of the distillation column is divided in two streams. One stream is condensed and totally refluxed at the top of the column. Balance vapour stream is taken to a pervaporation unit at 81°C (354 K), comprising of specially developed zeolite membranes. Water vapour comes out as a permeate at 0.13 bar a and 50°C (323 K) which is condensed and refluxed back to the column at the appropriate stage. The permeate stream is analysed to contain 2.9% ethanol. Non-permeate stream at about 82°C (355 K) is condensed and recovered as anhydrous ethanol having 99.7% strength. For a feed (containing 78% ethanol) at the rate of 20 000 kg/h vapour to the pervaporation unit, calculate the flow rates of permeate and non-permeate streams. Bottom product from the distillation column may be assumed water with negligible ethanol impurity. All compositions are mass %. **[Permeate = 5274.7 kg/h, Non-permeate = 18 254.8 kg/h]**

3.3 A multiple-effect evaporator system has a capacity of processing one tonne per day of solid caustic soda when it concentrates weak liquor from 4 to 25% (both on mass basis). When the plant is fed with 5% weak liquor and if it is concentrated to 50% (both on mass basis), find the capacity of the plant in terms of solid caustic soda, assuming the water-evaporating capacity to be the same in both cases. **[1.167 t/d]**

3.4 A sample of coal from Andrew Yules colliery, West Bengal, is found to contain 67.2% carbon and 22.3% ash (mass basis). The refuse obtained at the end of combustion is analysed to contain 7.1% carbon and the rest ash. Compute the % of the original carbon remaining unbrunt in the refuse. **[2.53%]**

3.5 Soybean seeds are extracted with *n*-hexane in batch extractors. The flaked seeds contain 18.6% oil, 69.0% solids and 12.4% moisture. At the end of the extraction process, de-oiled cake (DOC) is separated from the *n*-hexane-oil mixture. DOC analysis yields 0.8% oil, 87.7% solids and 11.5% moisture. Find the percentage recovery of oil. All percentage are by mass. **[96.6% recovery]**

3.6 A vent stream from an ethylbenzene plant has a composition: 66% H_2, 33% CH_4 and 1% other components (CO + C_2H_6 + C_2H_4 etc.). It is passed through a Pressure Swing Adsorption (PSA) Unit where hydrogen is recovered as 98% pure stream with 2% CH_4 as an impurity. Recovery of hydrogen is 85% at a feed pressure of 50 bar. Calculate the composition of reject stream.

[Composition of reject stream: 23.15% H_2, 74.51% CH_4 and 2.34% other components (on mole basis)]

3.7 Composition of soybean oil deodorizer distillate[5] is C_{16}-fatty acids 19.8%, C_{18}-fatty acids 56.1%, monoglycerides 9.2%, squalene 0.12%, mixed tocopherols 11.23%, sterols 0.15%, diglycerides 1.7% and triglycerides 1.7%. High vacuum distillation in a short path distillation unit is carried out at 5 m bar a and 190°C (463 K) to recover a stream consisting of 95% fatty acids, 0.25% mixed tocopherols and balance other components. Bottom residue is found to contain 10% fatty acids. All percentages are by mass. Calculate the mass ratio of overhead product to bottom residue. **[3.45:1]**

3.8 Crystals of $MgCl_2.6H_2O$ have a solubility[18] of 190 g per 100 g ethanol at 25°C (298.15 K). It is desired to make 1000 kg of saturated solution. Calculate the quantities of the crystals and ethanol required to make the above solution. Also, find the composition of the saturated solution by mass.

[Crystals = 655.5 kg, ethanol = 344.5 kg, Composition: $MgCl_2$ = 30.73%, H_2O = 34.82%, C_2H_2OH = 34.45% (mass basis)]

3.9 A spent solution of chloroacetic acid in ether contains 20 mole % chloroacetic acid. It is desired to make 500 kg of a saturated solution at 25°C (298.15 K). Find the quantities of spent solution and chloroacetic acid required to make the above solution.

Data The solubility of chloroacetic acid in ether[18] is 190 g/100 g ether at 25°C (298.15 K).

[272.6 kg of chloroacetic acid and 227.4 kg of spent solution]

3.10 A mixture of $CuSO_4.5 H_2O$ and $FeSO_4.7 H_2O$ weighs 100 g. It is heated in an oven at 105°C (378 K) to evaporate the water of hydration. The mass of mixture after removal of water is 59.78 g. Calculate the mass ratio of $CuSO_4$ to $FeSO_4$ in the mixture. **[1.23:1]**

3.11 The average molar mass of a flue gas sample is calculated by two different engineers. One engineer uses the correct molar mass of 28 for N_2 and determines the average molar mass to be 30.08. The other engineer, using an incorrect value of 14, calculates the average molar mass to be 18.74.

(a) Calculate the volume % of N_2 in the flue gases.

(b) If the remaining components of the flue gases are CO_2 and O_2, calculate the volume% of each of them.

[(a) N_2 = 81%; (b) CO_2 = 11.0% and O_2 = 8% (by volume)]

3.12 In a batch reactor, esterification of ethanol is carried out with lactic acid. Benzene is added (in small eqantity) in the vessel to distil out water from the reactor, produced during the reaction. Vapour mixture from the reactor at about 100°C (373 K) contains 6.5 % H_2O, 74% C_6H_6 and 19.5% C_2H_5OH by mass. Vapour passing through an overhead condenser is collected in a separator and allowed to separate in two layers at 30°C (303 K). The top layer is analyzed to contain 81% C_6H_6, 15.6% C_2H_5OH and 3.4% H_2O while the bottom layer is analyzed to contain 10% C_6H_6 (by mass). Calculate the mass ratio of the top layer to the bottom layer in the separator.

[**Top layer/bottom layers 9.142:1**]

3.13 In refining mineral oils, a technique of mixed solvent extraction is employed. In a particular method, acetic acid is used as principal solvent and chloroform as an auxiliary solvent. A particular oil having a viscosity gravity constant (VGC) of 0.8553 is first treated with acetic acid. The acetic acid–oil mixture (a complex) has a composition 63.4% acetic acid and 36.6% oil. At 25°C (298.15 K) the complex separated into two coexisting liquid phases having the compositions shown in Table 3.13.

Table 3.13 Composition of an Acetic Acid–oil Mixture

| | Composition, mass % | | VGC of solvent |
	acetic acid	oil	free oil
Complex	63.4	36.6	0.8553
Upper layer	9.62	90.38	0.8418
Lower layer	93.03	6.97	0.9532

To the above complex, chloroform is added. The resultant mixture (a new complex) is separated again in two at 25°C (298.15 K), having the compositions given in Table 3.14.

Table 3.14 Composition of the Complex (see Table 3.11) Plus Chloroform

| | Composition, mass % | | | VGC of solvent |
	acetic acid	chloroform	oil	free oil
New complex	57.8	9.7	Balance	0.8553
Upper layer	14.5	18.93	Balance	0.8424
Lower layer	87.5	3.62	Balance	0.9210

Calculate: (a) the mass ratio of two layers given in Table 3.13, (b) the mass ratio of two layers given in Table 3.14, and (c) the amount of chloroform added to the original complex. Also solve the problem by graphical method.

[(**a) 0.55:1, (b) 0.686:1 and (c) 9.7 kg chloroform per 100 kg original complex**]

3.14 A spent lye sample obtained from a soap-making unit contains 9.6% glycerol and 10.3% salt (NaCl). It is concentrated at the rate of 5000 kg/h in a double-effect evaporator until the final solution contains 80% glycerol and 6% salt. Assume that about 4.5% glycerol is lost by entrainment. All percentages are by mass.

Find (a) the evaporation taken place in the system, and (b) the amount of salt crystallised out in the salt box of the evaporator. [(**a) 3946.5 kg/h, (b) 480.5 kg/h**]

3.15 A mixed fertiliser, having the NPK composition 10:26:26 as % N, % P_2O_5 and % K_2O by mass, respectively, is to be formulated by mixing ammonia, phosphoric acid, potassium chloride and/or urea.

(a) If anhydrous ammonia, anhydrous phosphoric acid and 100% pure potassium chloride are used for mixing, calculate the amount of each of them required for formulating 100 kg of mixed fertiliser.

Assume that the filler will make up the balance.

(b) If 100% pure urea is used in place of anhydrous ammonia, calculate the amount of urea required for formulating 100 kg of mixed fertiliser.

(c) If anhydrous ammonia and 98% potassium chloride (mass %) are available, calculate the strength of H_3PO_4 required for making the required mixed fertiliser.

Note This example can be worked out with the help of a simple nomograph such as the one proposed by Sisson[19].

[(a) 12.14 kg NH_3, 35.89 kg H_3PO_4 and 41.18 kg KCl
(b) 21.43 kg urea (c) 78.09% H_3PO_4 (mass)]

3.16 For carrying out nitration reaction, it is desired to have a mixed acid containing 39% HNO_3, 42% H_2SO_4 (mass). Nitric acid of 68.3% (mass) is readily available (azeotropic composition). Calculate the required strength of sulphuric acid to obtain the above mixed acid. Also solve the problem using a triangular chart.

[(a) 97.9% (mass), 1.33:1]

3.17 In Example 3.8, aqueous 98% H_2SO_4 is used for blending. If, instead of this, 10% oleum is used, find the quantities of each of the three acids required to be blended. Which blending should be preferred? How can a triangular chart be used for this problem?

[128.6 kg spent acid, 339.4 kg 90% HNO_3 and 532.0 kg 10% oleum]

3.18 A mixed acid is to be prepared from spent acid, 99% H_2SO_4, 95% HNO_3 and water, if necessary. Determine the following graphically.

(a) The mass of sulphuric acid, nitric acid and water necessary to convert 1000 kg of spent acid containing 40% H_2SO_4, 20% HNO_3 40% H_2O to a mixed acid containing 50% H_2SO_4, 40% HNO_3 and 10% H_2O.

(b) The mass of water that must be evaporated from 1000 kg of spent acid to produce a mixed acid containing 66% H_2SO_4, 33% HNO_3; and 1% H_2O.

All percentages are on mass basis.

[(a) 1000 kg spent acid, 2267.0 kg 99% H_2SO_4 and 2013.0 kg 95% HNO_3
(b) 393.4 kg water to be evaporated]

3.19 Benzene and cyclohexane form a positive azeotrope which boils at 77.4°C (350.55 K) containing 54 mole % benzene. Acetone is used as an entrainer for separation of the azeotrope. Acetone forms an azeotrope only with cyclohexane that boils at 53.1°C (326.25 K) containing 74.6 mole % acetone. Assume that a mixture of benzene and cyclohexane containing 38.2 mass % benzene is to be azeotropically distilled with the addition of acetone. Calculate the mass of acetone required per 100 kg of feed using a triangular plot such that the distillate is the acetone–cyclohexane azeotrope and the bottom product is pure benzene. Also read the composition of the ternary mixture. [127.9 kg acetone]

3.20 Slabs of building boards contain 16% moisture. They are dried to a water content of 0.5% by circulating hot air over them. The outgoing air contains 0.09 kg water vapour per kg dry air. Calculate the quantity of fresh air required per 1000 kg/h net dry board, if the fresh air is supplied at 28°C (301 K) and 101.325 kPa containing 0.02 kg/kg dry air humidity. [2337.3 m^3/h]

3.21 The component triglycerides present in lard [20] are given in Table 3.15.

Table 3.15   Composition of Lard[20]

No.	Triglyceride	Formula	Mass %
1.	Palmitodistearin	C_3H_5 $\diagup$ $(OOCH_{31}C_{15})$ $\diagdown$ $(OOCH_{35}C_{17})_2$	3
2.	Stearodipalmitin	C_3H_5 $\diagup$ $(OOCH_{31}C_{15})_2$ $\diagdown$ $(OOCH_{35}C_{17})$	2
3.	Oleopalmitostearin	C_3H_5 $\diagup$ $(OOCH_{31}C_{15})$ $(OOCH_{35}C_{17})$ $\diagdown$ $(OOCH_{33}C_{17})$	11
4.	Oleodistearin	C_3H_5 $\diagup$ $(OOCH_{35}C_{17})_2$ $\diagdown$ $(OOCH_{33}C_{17})$	2
5.	Palmitodiolein	C_3H_5 $\diagup$ $(OOCH_{31}C_{15})$ $\diagdown$ $(OOCH_{33}C_{17})_2$	82

Compute the composition of lard in terms of fatty acids.

[Palmitic acid: 31.24%; stearic acid: 7.92%;
and oleic acid: 60.84% (mass basis)]

3.22 The analysis of the water obtained from an underground source is given in Table 3.16.

Table 3.16   Analysis of Raw Water Sample

a. Solids, mg/L.	
Total solids	2688.0
Dissolved solids	2510.0
Suspended solids (by difference)	178.0
b. Alkalinity, expressed as $CaCO_3$, mg/L	
Total alkalinity	572.6
Total carbonates	80.5
Total bicarbonates	492.1
c. Hardness, expressed as $CaCO_3$, mg/L	
Temporary hardness	284.0
Permanent hardness	Nil
Total hardness	284.0
Magnesium hardness	194.0
d. pH	
e. Chlorides as Cl, mg/L	775.6
f. Sulphates as SO_4, mg/L	230.4

Find (a) the actual analysis of water, and (b) % Na of total cations (based on milliequivalents).

[(a) Analysis in mg/L; Ca(HCO$_3$)$_2$ 145.8; Mg(HCO$_3$)$_2$ 283.8; NaHCO$_3$ 349.6; Na$_2$CO$_3$ 85.3; NaCl 1278.1; Na$_2$SO$_4$ 340.8 Dissolved solids 2483.4 (b) 85% Na of total cations]

3.23 A dyehouse effluent is found to contain sodium (as Na) and calcium (as Ca) to the extent of 245.7 mg/L and 37.6 mg/L, respectively. This effluent is to be discharged on the land used for irrigation purposes. According to IS: 2490, the tolerance limit for % Na of total cations (on equivalent basis) is 60. In order to bring the sodium level down to 60%, how much gypsum (essentially CaSO$_4$) is to be dissolved in the effluent. Also, calculate the % Na of total cations as such in the effluents.

[% Na in the effluent = 85.04; Dosage of CaSO$_4$ required = 356.3 mg/L]

3.24 Coking of catalyst is a common phenomenon in the process industry. Masking of active pores by coke results in reduction of catalytic activity, therfore decoking of catalyst is carried out periodically.

Decoking with air from the beginning means supply of excess oxygen; thereby combustion reaction can 'run away' which can result in hot spots in the catalyst bed. Such a phenomenon can destroy the catalyst and may result in explosion if temperature control is not exercised.

To control the catalyst bed temperature effectively, oxygen concentration in the feed stream is to be regulated. This will impart heat, generated by combustion, to the flowing gaseous stream as fast as generated. Laboratory experimentation for fixing various parameters proves useful.

In one experiment[21], 0.1 kg coked catalyst is charged in the laboratory reactor. Ultimate analysis of the coke suggests its average composition to be CH$_{0.6}$. A temperature-sensing element is provided in the catalyst bed. Analyzers for oxygen at inlet and outlet are also provided.

Initially, the reactor is purged with pure nitrogen for about 900 s at a flow rate of 0.025 L/s at NTP to achieve bed temperature of 450°C (723 K). Keeping N$_2$ flow-rate constant, air is introduced in it so that feed stream contains 5% oxygen (by vol.). Decoking (combustion) reaction consumes oxygen from the stream. Bed temperature is controlled around 450°C (723 K). After 1800 s, flow of nitrogen is stopped and only air is allowed to flow at 0.025 L/s at NTP. Oxygen concentration was measured at the exit of reactor at different time intervals. Results are as under.

Table 3.17 Oxygen Concentration Data of Decoking Experiment

Time from start, s	Oxygen concentration at the exit of reactor, vol. %
300	0
600	0
775	0
900	0.17
1200	0.86
1500	1.46
1800	2.15
1950	2.59
2000	2.75
2100	10.34
2250	17.24
2400	20.30
2550	20.52
2700	21.0 – same as air

After 3600 s, air stream is stopped. Reactor is then purged with pure nitrogen for about 600 s and cooled.
Calculate total oxygen consumption during the experiment.

[**0.128 mol or 4.096 $\times$ 10^{-3} kg**]

3.25 In a particular drying operation, it is necessary to hold the moisture content of feed to a calciner to 15% (mass) to prevent lumping and sticking. This is accomplished by mixing the feed having 30% moisture (mass) with a recycle stream of dried material having 3% moisture (mass). The drying operation is shown in Fig. 3.24. What fraction of the dried product must be recycled? [**63.4%**]

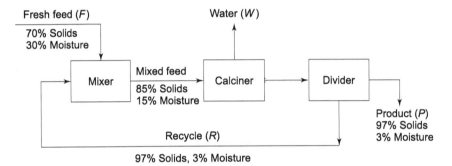

Fig. 3.24 Drying of Solids

3.26 Cloth is dried in a stenter (hot-air dryer) in a texile mill. In this machine, fresh air first mixes with recirculated air. The mixture then passes through a heater. Hot air is jetted over the cloth to evaporate the mixture. A major portion of the jetted air is recirculated while the remaining small portion is exhausted out. The operation is shown schematically in Fig. 3.25.

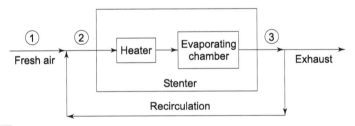

Fig. 3.25 Cloth Drying in Stenter

Test data on particular run of a stenter are given below:
Cloth details: Width = 90 cm; Density = 90 g/m^2; Speed = 1 m/s
Inlet moisture regain = 80% and Outlet moisture regain = 8%
Air conditions
Moisture of air at point (1) = 0.015 kg/kg dry air
Moisture of air at point (2) = 0.095 kg/kg dry air
Moisture of air at point (3) = 0.10 kg/kg dry air
Calculate (a) the rate of evaporation in the stenter, (b) the mass–flow rate of fresh air, (c) the volumetric flow rate of fresh air, if it is supplied at 30°C (303 K) and 100 kPa (755 Torr), and (d) the mass-flow rate of recirculating dry air.

Note (i) Moisture regain of cloth = (kg moisture in cloth/kg dry cloth) × 100   (ii) Use the ideal gas law.

$$[\text{(a) 210 kg/h (b) 2470.6 kg/h (c) 2146.2 m}^3\text{/h (d) 39 530 kg/h}]$$

3.27 A demineralisation (DM) plant employs ion-exchange system for production of high purity water with conductivity of 0.5 μS/cm (max.). Feed water to the plant contains 2500 mg/L dissolved solids (DS) and DM water flow rate is 10 m³/h, net of regeneration. During regeneration of the DM plant, 20% DM water of net production is consumed. Since disposal of highly saline effluents, generated during regeneration of the DM plant, pose a serious problem, a new system, shown in Fig. 3.26, is considered in which major flow of the incoming feed water is passed through a reverse osmosis (RO) module in which 95% DS are rejected and the permeate recovery of 80% is achieved. A small portion of feed water is bypassed and mixed with the permeate to maintain DS concentration of 500 mg/L at the inlet of the ion-exchange system. In this system, DM water requirement for regeneration DM plant is 10% of the net production.

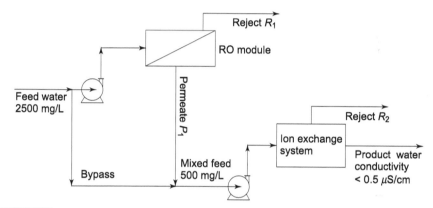

Fig. 3.26   Two-stage Demineralisation Plant

Make complete material balance of the proposed system and compare feed-water requirements in both cases. Also, calculate the ratio of the permeate to bypass feed-water flow rate and concentration of DS in the reject water.

[**Feed water to ion exchange = 12 m³/h**
Feed water to new system = 13.347 m³/h
Ratio of permeate to bypass = 5.82 m³/m³
Concentration of DS in reject = 11 875 mg/L]

3.28 In Example 3.18, recovery of permeate in RO Module I is taken as 66%. Rework material balance with recoveries of 60% and 70% of RO Module I.

[**Table 3.18 Material balance with different recoveries**]

Recovery, %	Reject R_1 flow rate m³/h	Recycle ratio, R_2/F, m³/m³	DS concentration in R_1, mg/L	Rejection of DS in RO module I, %
60	4.17	0.136	9 230	95.84
70	2.68	0.163	12 026	95.07

3.29 In a textile industry, it is desired to make a 24% solution (by mass) of caustic soda for a mercerisation process. Due to the very high heat of dissolution of caustic soda in water, the above solution is prepared by a two-step process.

First, in a dissolution tank, caustic soda is dissolved in the correct quantity of water to produce 50% (by mass) solution. After complete dissolution and cooling, the solution is taken to dilution tank where some more water is added to produce 24% solution. The two-step process is shown in Fig. 3.27.

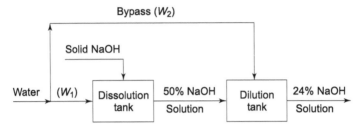

Fig. 3.27 Dissolution of Caustic Soda in Water

Assuming no evaporation loss in the dissolution and dilution tanks, calculate mass ratio W_1/W_2. **[$W_1/W_2 = 0.462$]**

3.30 A 2-compression stage Permselective® memberane system[22] is employed to separate a mixture consisting of 21% CO_2 and 88% CH_4 by mole.These membranes selectively permeate carbon dioxide from the mixture. Feed gas miture at the rate of 3000 Nm^3/h is fed at 41.5 bar and 35°C (308 K). It is mixed with two recycle streams as shown in Fig. 3.28.

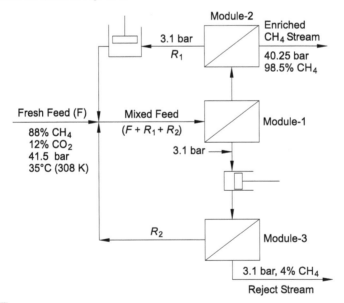

Fig. 3.28 Two-compression Stage Permselective Membrane System

Mixed feed is fed to Module-1. Permeate recovered from the module is 80% and its CO_2 content is analysed to be 60.2 mole %. Non-permeate is analysed to contain 4.25 mole % CO_2.

Non-permeate from Module-1 is fed to Module-2 from which enriched CH_4 stream is obtained as non-permeate at 40.25 bar, containing 98.5 mole % CH_4. Permeate recovery from Module-2 is 12% and is recycled as stream R_1 after compression to 42.5 bar and cooling it to 35°C (308 K).

Pemeate from Module-1 is compressed, cooled to 35°C (308 K) and fed to Module-3. Permeate recovery is 44% which is the reject stream. Non-permeate stream is recycled as steam R_2.

(a) Calculate flow rates of enriched CH_4 and reject streams.

(b) Calculate flow rates of R_1 amd R_2 streams.

(c) Calculate compositions of mixed feed, R_1 and R_2.

[(a) Enriched CH_4 = 2666.67 Nm^3/h and Reject stream = 333.33 Nm^3/h

(b) R_1 = 363.64 and R_2 = 424.24 Nm^3/h

(c) CH_4 contents (mole basis) in mixed feed = 84.56%,

in R_1 = 75.58% and in R_3 = 67.93%]

3.31 In the preparation of cooking liquor for a sulphite pulp mill, an absorption column is used to absorb SO_2 in a weak liquor[23]. The weak liquor enters the top of the column at the rate of 20 L/s with SO_2 concentration of 0.5% (by mass) and leaves with SO_2 concentration of 1.0% (by mass). The gas steam entering the bottom of the column passing in the counter-current direction to the liquor stream contains 17.0% (by volume) SO_2. When the gas leaves the top of the column, 75% of SO_2 gets absorbed. The pressure in the column becomes 50 kPa g and operates isothermally at 35°C (308 K). Assuming that the liquor has a specific gravity of 1.0, calculate (a) the molar flow rate of entering gas, and (b) the volumetric flow rate of entering gas.

[(a) 12.26 × 10^{-3} kmol/s (b) 207.43 dm^3/s]

3.32 An effluent sample from a formaldehyde plant is found to contain methanol and formaldehyde. The analysis of the solution indicated that TOC and ThOD are 258.3 mg/L and 956.5 mg/L, respectively. Find the concentration of each of the compounds in the sample. [Methanol: 535 mg/L, formaldehyde: 144 mg/L]

3.33 Hot acid gases from a calciner are fed to a venturi scrubber[24] at 370°C (643 K) as shown in Fig. 3.29. The volumetric flow rate of the moist gases is 16.5 Nm^3/s which contain 4.2 Nm^3/s of water vapours, 1600 mg SO_3/Nm^3 of dry gas and 9000 mg solids/Nm^3 dry gas of which chlorides (as Cl) amount to 1.5 g/s. After scrubbing the gases in the venturi scrubber, the exit gases from the separator are saturated at 75°C (348 K). Eighty percent of SO_3, entering the scrubber, is scrubbed in the circulating liquor. Solid concentration in the exit gas mixture is found to be 120 mg/Nm^3 dry gas. Practically, all chlorides in the incoming gases are scrubbed. The make-up water which is added to the circulating liquor contains 50 mg/L chlorides (as Cl). The scrubber, separator and other parts of the system are made of stainless steel. At low pH (because of SO_3 dissolution), the concentration of chlorides is limited to 200 mg/L in the circulating liquor to prevent corrosive attack.

For this purpose, a continuous bleed is maintained from the circulating system. Calculate the purge rate, concentration of solids and sulphuric acid in it and make-up water requirement.

Note Humidity of exit gases from separator = 0.614 kmol/kmol dry gas.

[Purge rate = 10.9 kg/s; Solid concn. = 1.00%, H_2SO_4 concn. = 0.18 % (by mass); Make-up water rate = 13.6 kg/s]

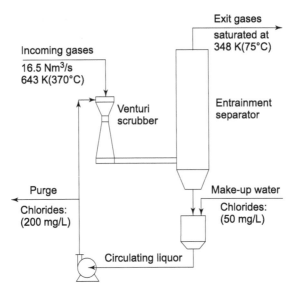

Exit gases
saturated at
348 K(75°C)

Incoming gases
16.5 Nm³/s
643 K(370°C)

Venturi
scrubber

Entrainment
separator

Purge
Chlorides:
(200 mg/L)

Make-up water
Chlorides:
(50 mg/L)

Circulating liquor

Fig. 3.29 Scrubbing of Acid Gases in a Venturi Scrubber

3.34 Waste water from the rice-processing industry is required to be treated in an activated sludge plant before being discharged in a public sewer owing to high BOD
loading (~12 500 mg/L). Waste steam contains 485 mg/L suspended solids which
are non-bacterial in nature. The process flow diagram is similar to the one shown in
Fig. 3.17, except that a primary clarifier is not employed. After aeration in the
aeration tank, all the suspended solids are separated in the secondary clarifier. The
sludge (underflow) from the clarifier is partially recycled. From kinetic considerations
of the aeration tank and design considerations of the clarifier, the minimum recycle
ratio leading to minimum sludge waste can be achieved when the bacterial suspended
solid concentration in the recycle stream is five times[25] higher than that in the total
combined feed entering the aeration tank. Prove that the minimum recycle ratio r
(= Q_r/Q_F) is exactly $1/4$ assuming that suspended solids concentration in the total
combined feed is 2% (mass). The wastage amount can be neglected for calculation
purposes.

Note It may be noted that X_F = 485 mg/L in this problem which was assumed to be zero
in Example 3.19 as the effluents passed through a primary clarifier.

3.35 In Example 3.20, the atmospheric pressure method of purging is described. There are
two more methods of purging.
(a) *Pressure Cycle Method* In this method, the equipment to be purged is pressurised
with inert gas and on complete mixing of the inert gas with vessel atmosphere,
the pressure is released to the initial pressure. Assume that the initial pressure
is p_1 kPa a in the vessel. It is pressurised with inert gas to p_2 kPa a and then
depressurised to p_1. Prove that the concentration of the component will be p_1/p_2
times the initial concentration (c_0) after one cycle of pressurisation/depressurisa-
tion. Also, prove that the number of vessel volumes of inert gas required per
cycle will be $(p_2 - p_1)/p_1$.

(b) *Vacuum Cycle Method* This method is similar to the pressure cycle method except that sub-atmospheric pressure is used. In this method, the vessel is evacuated to p kPa a and then it is refilled with inert gas to the normal atmospheric pressure (i.e., 101.3 kPa a). Prove that the concentration of the component will reduce to $c_0 \, (p/101.3)$ after one cycle and $c_0 (p/101.3)^n$ after n cycles of evacuation/refilling. Also prove that the amount of inert gas required for purging per cycle will be $(1 - p/101.3)$ vessel volumes.

Note It is assumed in all the cases that temperature changes taking place in the system are negligible. Ideal gas law applies.

3.36 An isotank is used for long-distance transportation of an oxygen-sensitive liquid organic product. It is a horizontal pressure vessel having 2.5 m diameter and 6 m length. It is normally filled up to 85% height. Empty volume above the liquid has to have inert atmosphere with oxygen concentration less than 1% (v/v).

Initially, the empty space is occupied by atmospheric air. It is pressure purged with pure nitrogen (containing less than 0.1% O_2) at 35°C (308.15 K). from cylinders. Considering design limitations of the isotank, it is pressurised up to 2 bar g each time with nitrogen and depressurised to near atmospheric (1.0197 bar a) pressure.

Neglecting oxygen in nitrogen, and negligible solubility of nitrogen in the organic liquid, calculate

(a) number of cycles required to achieve desired oxygen concentration in the empty space,

(b) final concentration of oxygen in the empty space, and

(c) total requirement of pure nitrogen for purging.

[(a) 3 cycles (b) 0.8% (v/v) (c) 14.54 Nm³]

3.37 A gas mixture leaving high-temperature shift converter in a typical natural-gas based ammonia plant, has the following compositions on dry basis: H_2: 56%, CO: 15%, CO_2: 7%, N_2: 21.7% and Ar: 0.3%. Steam (essentially in the gas form) to dry gas ratio in the feed is 1.2 kmol/kmol (ref. Exercise 5.37). The converter is normally operated under pressure (around 25 bar g) and 345°C (618.15 K). The shift reaction is exothermic in nature.

Reaction $CO + H_2O \rightarrow CO_2 + H_2$

During a shutdown of the ammonia plant, the converter must be pressure purged after isolation to limit the concentration of steam in it so that the reaction is practically stopped and chances of hot-spot formation in the catalytic bed are eliminated. Pure nitrogen (< 1% O_2 by vol.) is available at 35°C (308.15 K) at 6 bar g. At first, the converter is depressurised to low pressure (to 0.25 bar g). Subsequently, it is pressurised with pure nitrogen to 5 bag g and depressurised again to 0.25 bar g.

(a) Assuming converter's void and empty volume of 40 m³, calculate the number of cycles required to achieve steam concentration below 1% (by vol.) on wet basis.

(b) Calculate final concentration of steam and carbon monoxide at the end of purging on wet basis.

(c) Calculate total requirement of nitrogen at NTP.

[(a) 3 cycles (b) H₂O: 0.5%, CO: 0.06% (c) 498.6 Nm³]

3.38 Combustion can occur when a flammable vapour is mixed with oxygen (or air) within certain concentration ranges. This concentration range is known as flammability envelope (limit). The minimum fuel content requirement to support combustion is called the lower flammability limit and the maximum is called the upper flammability limit. An ignition source is required to cause combustion of the mixture within the flammability limits which is also a function of pressure and temperature.

In a number of gas (vapour) phase oxidation processes, the mixture of gases may be within the flammability limits. To ensure the intrinsic safety of the process, operating conditions must be established in such a way that the process vapours remain outside the flammability envelope at all times or oxygen content does not exceed a certain percentage. Often, it is not possible to operate the process with altered composition of the flammable material and oxygen (or air) content to be away from the flammable limits due to desired process conditions. For such a case, two alternatives are available[26].

In one alternative, addition of an inert gas (such as nitrogen, argon, carbon dioxide, superheated steam, etc.) is practiced such that oxygen content can be brought down to a safe level. In the second alternative, addition of another flammable gas can be considered, the amount of which can be calculated using the Le Châtelier's relationship:

$$\frac{n_1}{N_1} + \frac{n_2}{N_2} + \frac{n_3}{N_3} \cdots\cdots = 1$$

where $\quad n_i$ = mole % of ith flammable gas
and $\quad N_i$ = lower or upper flammability limit of ith gas

In reactor, 100 kmol of hydrogen and 100 kmol of air are present at 101.325 kPa a and 20°C (293.15 K). As such this mixture is to be made non-flammable by addition of (a) nitrogen, and (b) methane. Calculate the minimum requirements of nitrogen and methane in the two cases.

Data

(i) Hydrogen–air mixture is non-flammable when oxygen is less than 5 mole %.
(ii) Flammability data

Table 3.19 Flammability Data

Gas	Flammability limits (vol.%) in air at 101.325 kPa and 20°C (293.15 K)	
	Upper limit	Lower limit
Hydrogen	75 %	4 %
Methane	14 %	5 %

[(a) 219 kmol nitrogen (b) 10.85 kmol methane]

Note It is interesting to note that a flammable gas mixture can be readily made non-flammable by a small amount of another flammable gas than a substantial amount of an inert gas.

3.39 An average astronaut inhales 123 kg of air and exhales 112 kg air, 1.8 kg water vapour and 8.8 kg carbon dioxide every day. He can safely breathe in gases containing 100% to 20% oxygen (v/v). The cabin of a spaceship has a free volume of 4500 L and is filled with pure oxygen at a pressure 154.6 kPa a and a temperature of 293.15 K(20°C). In flight. the temperature is held at 20°C (293.15 K) and the water is absorbed by a desiccant.

(a) How long can a mission astronaut sustain, without an external oxygen supply?

(b) What will be the total pressure and partial pressures of carbon dioxide and oxygen at the end of the mission?

[(a) 26 h 16 min (i.e., 94 560 s)
(b) Total pressure = 147.5 kPa a p_{O_2} = 29.5 kPa; p_{CO_2} = 118 kPa]

3.40 In a continuous kraft pulp bleaching, caustic soda is required at a concentration of 10% NaOH (by mass) and a flow rate of 1.65 kg/s. This solution is prepared by introducing 50% caustic lye (by mass) and diluted with water continuously in a 1900 L tank, equipped with an agitator, and withdrawing the 10% solution continuously at the desired rate. During the operation, the inflow of 50% caustic lye suddenly fails while the dilution water continues to enter the tank. Assuming that a perfect mixing takes place in the tank and the volume is constant (1900 L), calculate the time required for the effluent concentration to fall to 8% NaOH by mass[11].

Data Take the specific gravity of NaOH solution in the range of 10% to 8% concentration to be constant at 1.10. [2827 s]

3.41 Compressed air at 710 kPa g and 45°C (318.15 K) (fully saturated) is dried in a silica gel column. It is desired to dry air at the rate of 150 Sm^3/h [(measured at 101.325 kPa and 15°C (288.15 K)] to use it in pneumatic instruments. The maximum permissible moisture content of the instrument air is 25 mg/m^3 [(approximate atmospheric dew point = −32°C (241.15 K)]. The air passes through a column in which 220 kg bone-dry silica gel is packed. The regenerated silica contains 2.5 kg moisture per 100 kg bone-dry desiccant. The laboratory experiment reveals the following performance of the silica gel.

Table 3.20 Dehydration of Air with Silica Gel[27]

Moisture in silica gel kg moisture/100 kg dry desiccant	Residual water in mg/Sm^3 in air
2.500	5.0
3.750	10.0
5.625	15.0
6.563	20.0
7.344	25.0

Calculate the expected service time of the bed, after which it is required to be regenerated.

Data Moisture of fully saturated air at 710 kPa g and 318.15 K (45°C) = 0.011 95 kmol/kmol dry air. [7.935 h (i.e. 28 566 s)]

3.42 A cooling water system comprises of a cooling tower and a cooling water circuit through various heat exchangers. It has a total hold up of 3000 m^3. On a particular day, the suspended solids were measured to be 50 mg/L. A side-stream sand filter is installed to reduce the turbidity in the cooling water. The filter is fed with cooling water at the rate of 100 m^3/h. The performance of the filter is expected to be as given in Table 3.21.

Assuming that there is no addition of suspended solids from the surroundings, calculate the time required to bring down the suspended solids in the cooling water to 10 mg/L. Refer Fig. 3.30 for the flow diagram.

[68 h]

Table 3.21   Performance of a Side Stream Filter

Suspended solids in the ingoing cooling water, mg/L	Suspended solids in the outcoming cooling water, mg/L
50–40	10
40–30	9
30–27.5	8
27.5–25	7
25–20	6
20–10	5

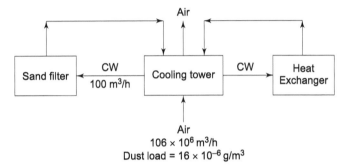

Fig. 3.30   Performance of a Side Stream Filter in a Cooling Water System

3.43   In Exercise 3.42, it was assumed that there is no addition of dust from the atmosphere. However, in actual practice, the dust amounts to a sizeable turbidity in the cooling water. Assume that incoming air at the rate of 106×10^6 m³/h brings in the dust at a rate of 16×10^{-6} g/m³. Calculate the time required to bring down the suspended solids of the cooling water to 25 mg/L based on the filter performance outlined in Table 3.21.   **[109 h]**

3.44   In the exponential dilution technique for preparation of calibration gas mixture, a bottle fitted with a magnetic stirrer, is filled with a gas mixture, having the concentration of component A as C_{A0}. The volume of the bottle is V mL. Inert gas, free from A, is introduced at a rate of F mL/s into the bottle, thoroughly mixed with the content, and the dilute gas mixture is drawn from the bottle at the rate of F mL/s. Prove that the concentration of A in the bottle at time θ (in s) from the start of introducing gas is given by

$$C_A = C_{A0} \times e^{-(F\theta/V)}$$

Note   This is basically a mixing model in which the dependency of the concentration of the component A in the exit stream with time θ is expressed. Fowler[28] has presented a mixing model for dilution of a solution or purging a vessel on the same principle.

3.45   A single-stage, single-acting reciprocating compressor is used to fill a receiver having the volume V m³. The compressor operates as s strokes/s, has the geometric volume v_0 m³ of the cylinder and the clearance c. It is required to increase the absolute pressure in the receiver from p_0 to p_1. The volumetric efficiency of the compressor is defined as

$$\eta_v = 1 + c - \frac{p}{100\,p_0} - c\left(\frac{p}{p_0}\right)^{1/\gamma}$$

where p = discharge pressure after time θ (in s) and γ = ratio of heat capacities of the gas = C_p/C_v.
Prove that the time required to fill the receiver is given by

$$\theta = \frac{V}{(3600\,s\,v_0)} \int_0^{R_1} \frac{dr}{\left[1 + c - \dfrac{r}{100} - c\,(r)^{1/\gamma}\right]}$$

where $r = p/p_0$ and $R_1 = p_1/p_0$.

3.46 A two-stage, double-acting reciprocating compressor is used to fill up a receiver of 60 m^3 capacity with air for use with pneumatic instruments. The inside bore and the stroke length are 310 mm and 150 mm, respectively. The clearance in the cylinder is 7%. The compressor operates at a speed of 9.2 s^{-1}. It is designed for equal compression ratio in each stage. Calculate the time required to pressurise the receiver from normal atmospheric conditions to 7 bar g.
Data γ for air = 1.4. **[555.3 s]**

References

1. Thakore, S B and Bhatt B I; *Introduction to Preocess Engineering and Design*, Tata Mc-Graw Hill Education, New Delhi, 2007.
2. Prugh, R W; *Chem. Engg. Prog.*, **70**(11): 1974, p. 72.
3. Private Communication with Aspen Technology, Inc., USA.
4. Levenspiel, O; *Chemical Reaction Engineering*, 3rd Ed., John Wiley & Sons, Inc., USA, 2000.
5. Mukhopadhyay, M; *Natural Extracts using Supercritical Carbon Dioxide*, CRC Press LLC, USA, 2000, p. 238.
6. Hunter, T G; *Ind. Engg. Chem.*, **34**(8): 1942, p. 963.
7. Kirk, R E and Othmer, D F; *Encyclopedia of Chemical Technology*, 1st Ed., Vol. 9, The Interscience Encyclopedia, Inc., USA, 1952, p. 315.
8. Prielipp, G E and Keller, H W; *J. of the American Oil Chemists' Soc.*, **XXXIII**(3): 1956, p. 103.
9. US Patent No. 3078 140, 1963.
10. *Chemical Processing by Ion Exchange*, Dow Chemical Co., USA.
11. *Chemical Engineering Problems in Pulp and Paper Industry*, Technical Association of the Pulp and Paper Industry (TAPPI), USA, 1965.
12. Kesting, R E and Fritzsche, A K; *Polymeric Gas Separation Membranes*. John Wiley & Sons, USA, 1993, p. 367.
13. Ramalho, R S; *Hydrocarbon Processing*, **57**(10): 1978, p. 112.
14. Saigal, R S; *Gas News*, **1**(12): 1978, p. 3.
15. Kinsley, G R; *Chem. Engg. Prog.*, **97**(2), 2001, p. 57.
16. Chadodkar, M V and Mehta, D J; *Chemical Age of India*, **24**(5): 1973, p. 302.
17. *Chem. Engg.* **115**(2), 2008, p. 11.
18. Technical Bulletin on *Dow Products and Services* Dow Chemical Co., USA, 1972.
19. Sisson, B; *Chem. Engg.*, **84**(6),: March 14, 1977, p. 156.
20. Guillaudan, A; *Ind. Engg. Chem.*, **29**(7), 1937, p. 729.

21. Fulton, J W; *Chem. Engg.*, **95**(1), Jan. 18, 1988, p. 111.
22. Chern, R T, Koros, J W and Fedkiw, P S; *Ind. Engg. Chem; Process Des. Dev;* **24**, 1985, p. 1015.
23. *Tappi*, **47**(8), 1964, p. 114a.
24. Gleason, T G; *Chem Engg.*, **84**(23), Oct. 24, p. 146.
25. *AIChE Student Contest Problem*, 1972.
26. Talmage W P; *Chemtech*, Feb. 1971, p. 117.
27. Davis, K G and Manchanda, K D; *Chem. Engg.*, **81**(19), Sept. 16, 1974, p. 102.
28. Fowler, W B; *Chem. Engg.*, **88**(25), Dec. 14, 1981, p. 110.

Material Balances Involving Chemical Reactions

Chemical reactions play a vital role in the manufacturing processes. For the design of a chemical reaction equipment, the operating conditions, such as pressure, temperature, composition and flow rates of the streams should be known. The material and energy balance calculations come to the rescue of the designer and allow him to calculate the various flow rates and temperatures of the streams. Although the rates of reaction, reactor design and other kinetic aspects of reaction engineering do not fall within the scope of this book, a few terms such as limiting component, excess reactant, degree of conversion, yield and selectivity will be defined in order to have a clear understanding of the subject. Assuming that the kinetic data of a reaction are available, the overall material balance of the steady-state conditions will be discussed in this chapter.

4.1 EQUATIONS FOR CHEMICAL REACTIONS

The International Union for Pure and Applied Chemistry (IUPAC) recommend the following symbols, connecting the reactants and products in a chemical equation.

$C_6H_6 + HNO_3 = C_6H_5NO_2 + H_2O$	Stoichiometric relation	(4.1)
$HCl + NaOH \rightarrow NaCl + H_2O$	Net forward reaction	(4.2)
$CO + H_2O \rightleftarrows CO_2 + H_2$	Reactions in both directions	(4.3)
$NH_3 + HCl \rightleftharpoons NH_4Cl$	Equilibrium	(4.4)

4.2 MATERIAL BALANCES INVOLVING CHEMICAL REACTIONS

The law of conservation of mass, stated in Chapter 3, holds good for the material balances involving chemical reactions also.

The general mathematical statement for steady-state reaction can be written as

Total mass entering the chemical reactor = total mass of products leaving the chemical reactor.

Very often, it is convenient to work with moles rather than with mass, particularly in gaseous systems. It should be noted that in chemical reactions, the total mass of the input remains constant, but the total moles may or may not remain constant. This fact can be understood by studying the following two reactions. Consider the shift reaction:

$$CO \quad + \quad H_2O \quad = \quad CO_2 \quad + \quad H_2 \qquad (4.5)$$
$$\text{1 mole} \qquad \text{1 mole} \qquad \text{1 mole} \qquad \text{1 mole}$$

In this, it can be observed that two moles react with each other and also produce two moles. Thus, the number of moles of the reactants entering the reactor equals the number of moles of the products leaving the reactor. The ammonia synthesis reaction can be written as

$$N_2 \quad + \quad 3\,H_2 \quad \rightleftarrows \quad 2\,NH_3 \qquad (4.6)$$
$$\text{1 mole} \qquad \text{3 moles} \qquad \text{2 moles}$$

It can be observed that four moles (of reactants) produce two moles of ammonia in the forward direction. Thus, the number of moles have been reduced, although the total mass of the reactants entering and of the products leaving the reactor are equal. For the Reaction (4.5), one can write

1 mole of $CO \equiv$ 1 mole of $H_2O \equiv$ 1 mole of $H_2 \equiv$ 1 mole of CO_2

Similarly, for the Reaction (4.6),

1 mole of $N_2 \equiv$ 3 moles of $H_2 \equiv$ 2 moles of NH_3

The above equalities decide the stoichiometric requirements of the components. (The sign $\equiv$ represents *equivalent to* from the point of view of the chemical equilibrium, and not *equal to* from the mathematical point of view.)

Equilibrium denotes a static condition in which absense of change is observed on a macroscopic scale. In chemical reactions, equilibrium means no change in reactants and products stoichiometry with respect to time at a given pressure and temperature. A notable principle; namely *Le Châtelier's principle*, relates to the stability conditions of a chemical reaction against external perturbations. According to this principle, a system at equilibrium resists attempts to change its pressure, temperature or concentration of a reagent. For the shift reaction [Eq. (4.5)], since there is no change in the number of moles during the reaction, pressure has no effect on its equilibrium. However, this reaction is usually performed with excess steam (i.e., molar ratio of steam to $CO > 1$) due to kinetic requirements. This change in concentration of reactants (over stoichiometric requirement) pushes the reaction in the forward direction.

In case of ammonia synthesis [Eq. (4.6)], since there is a reduction in the number of moles, increase in pressure has a favourable effect on the conversion. However, kinetic studies have shown that molar ratio of 1:3 of N_2:H_2 is the optimum for chemical equilibrium.

Thermal effects (i.e., dependence of reaction on the temperature) will be discussed in Chapter 5.

4.3 DEFINITIONS OF TERMS

Some of the terms used in chemical reaction engineering will now be defined.

In most chemical reactions, two or more components reacting together are not in stoichiometric proportions due to technical, economic or safety considerations. In such cases, a *limiting component* is defined as one which decides the conversion in the reactions. An *excess reactant* is the one which is in excess amount over the stoichiometric requirement of the reactant as determined by the desired chemical reaction.

Consider the reforming reactions between methane and steam.

$$CH_4 + H_2O \rightarrow CO + 3 H_2 \tag{4.7}$$
$$CH_4 + 2 H_2O \rightarrow CO_2 + 4 H_2 \tag{4.8}$$

In actual practice, steam that is fed to the reformer is usually much in excess of the stoichiometric requirement. Therefore, methane is the limiting component while steam is the excess reactant.

Urea is produced by the reaction of carbon dioxide and ammonia as per the following reaction:

$$CO_2 + 2 NH_3 \rightarrow NH_2CONH_2 + H_2O \tag{4.9}$$

Normally, NH_3 is the excess reactant and CO_2 is the limiting component in the above synthesis. The feed may consist of CO_2 and NH_3 in $1:4.5$ molar ratio in a typical process.

Consider the ammonia synthesis [Eq. (4.6)]. The synthesis gas normally enters the reactor in stoichiometric proportions, i.e., $1:3$ molar ratio of $N_2:H_2$. In this reaction, none is in excess (unlike most chemical reactions).

Chlorination of methane presents an interesting example. The following four reactions take place simultaneously.

$$CH_4 + Cl_2 \rightarrow CH_3Cl + HCl \tag{4.10}$$
$$CH_3Cl + Cl_2 \rightarrow CH_2Cl_2 + HCl \tag{4.11}$$
$$CH_2Cl_2 + Cl_2 \rightarrow CHCl_3 + HCl \tag{4.12}$$
$$CHCl_3 + Cl_2 \rightarrow CCl_4 + HCl \tag{4.13}$$

In a typical vapour-phase chlorination reaction, normally chlorine is completely consumed while a portion of methane may escape unreacted. Since all the reactions take place simultaneously, it is difficult to specify the stoichiometric requirement of chlorine. In fact, the amount of chlorine determines the products pattern. Therefore, in this type of reaction, conversion of chlorine is 100% and it can be termed as a limiting component. However, conversion of methane need not be 100%.

Distinction between *conversion*, *selectivity* and *yield* should be clear before attempting to solve any problem involving a chemical reaction. These terms, however, are not uniformly employed in various scientific publications. Definitions, accepted in most publications, are presented here.

Conversion is defined as the ratio of the reacting amount of a component to its initial amount. The amount can be expressed in moles, masses or volumes. Accordingly, the conversion is also expressed as mole %, mass % or volume %.

In reforming Reactions, (4.7) and (4.8), two parallel reactions are taking place. CO and CO_2 are co-products. In both reactions, H_2 is the common product.

Let a be the kmol of CH_4 fed of which b kmol of CH_4 are reacted by the Reaction (4.7) and c kmol of CH_4 are reacted by the Reaction (4.8)

Total moles of CH_4 reacted = $b + c$ kmol

$$\text{Percentage conversion of } CH_4 = \left[\frac{b+c}{a} \right] 100$$

Unreacted $CH_4 = a - (b + c)$ kmol

Since steam is the excess reactant, conversion is normally not defined on the basis of consumption of steam.

In the manufacture of nitrobenzene, benzene and nitric acid are reacted.

$$C_6H_6 + HNO_3 \rightarrow C_6H_5NO_2 + H_2O \tag{4.14}$$

The chief product is nitrobenzene but in practice, it is observed that some of the nitrobenzene reacts with additional quantity of nitric acid to produce dinitrobenzene.

$$C_6H_5NO_2 + HNO_3 \rightarrow C_6H_4(NO_2)_2 + H_2O \tag{4.15}$$

Thus, it can be seen that the final product mixture will contain nitrobenzene as well as dinitrobenzene. The amount of the latter depends on operating conditions and excess quantity of HNO_3 present in the mixture. Reaction (4.15) can also be written as

$$C_6H_5 + 2\,HNO_3 \rightarrow C_6H_5(NO_3)_2 + 2\,H_2O \tag{4.16}$$

Yield is defined as under:

$$\text{Yield} = \frac{\text{moles of desired product formed} \times \text{stoichiometric factor}}{\text{moles of specific reactant consumed}}$$

where, stoichiometric factor = stoichiometric requirement of the specific reactant (in moles) per mole of the desired product

For the production of nitrobenzene,

$$\text{stoichiometric factor} = 1$$

$$\text{Percentage yield of nitrobenzene} = \frac{\text{moles of nitrobenzene produced}}{\text{moles of benzene consumed}} \times 100$$

Consider the Reactions (4.7) and (4.8). The aim of reforming reactions is to maximise the yield of hydrogen. Calculation of the yield of hydrogen is complex. Stoichiometric factor for the Reaction (4.7) for hydrogen production is 1/3 and that for the Reaction (4.8) is 1/4 based on methane consumption.

Percentage yield of hydrogen = [moles of hydrogen produced by the (4.7)/3 + moles of hydrogen produced by the (4.8)/4]/[moles of methane consumed] × 100

Formation of chloroform [Reaction (4.12)] can be written as

$$CH_4 + 3\,Cl_2 \rightarrow CHCl_3 + 3\,HCl \tag{4.17}$$

$$\text{Percentage yield of chloroform} = \frac{[\text{moles of chloroform formed}]}{[\text{moles of chlorine consumed} \times 3]} \times 100$$

In all the above cases, it is seen that the competitive reactions take place, and hence the yield of the desired product is worked out by finding the moles of specific reactant consumed for the formation of the desired product. Competitive reactions can either be secondary reactions [Eq. (4.14) and (4.15)] or parallel reactions [Eq. (4.7) and (4.8)]. When there are no competitive reactions, yield is 100% at any conversion.

Selectivity is another term which measures the proportion of the total reaction which produces the desired product. Different conventions are used for assigning a numerical value to the selectivity in literature. One definition of selectivity would be the ratio of amount of limiting reactant that reacts to give the desired product to the amount that reacts to give undesirable product(s). The term selectivity is more often used in catalysis where a catalyst is judged by its selectivity. If yield is 100%, then selectivity is 1.

4.4 GENERALIZED APPROACH FOR SOLVING MATERIAL BALANCE PROBLEMS INVOLVING CHEMICAL REACTIONS

In Sec. 3.3, it was seen that the law of conservation of mass can be applied to solve material balance problems of any system. Having understood the definitions of various terms of reaction engineering in the previous section, a generalized approach to solve material balance problems involving chemical reactions can now be studied.

At first, it is important to note that in chemical reactions, moles are important rather than mass. Therefore, for material balance calculations, mass (m) of reactants or products are converted to moles using molar mass (M) values. Data on conversion of a chemical reaction and yield are then used to arrive at moles of products. When consecutive reactions are taking place, conversion of each reaction will have to be considered for finding the quantity of products.

Consider dehydrogenation of methanol to produce formaldehyde using silver catalyst. In this reaction, a mixture of methanol vapour, steam and a small quantity of air are fed to a reactor, packed with a catalyst. The following stoichiometric reactions are known to take place; the first one is the chief one.

$$CH_3OH = HCHO + H_2 \qquad (4.18)$$
$$CH_3OH = CO + 2\,H_2 \qquad (4.19)$$
$$CH_3OH + (1/2)\,O_2 = HCHO + H_2O \qquad (4.20)$$
$$CH_3OH = CH_4 + (1/2)\,O_2 \qquad (4.21)$$

Conversion of methanol will mean total methanol reacted by all four reactions. Yield will determine product quantities.

Reaction (4.20) can also be written as

$$2\,CH_3OH + O_2 = 2\,HCHO + 2\,H_2O$$

Since mathematically both sides of the reaction are multiplied by a common multiplier, material balance (and heat balance) calculations are unaffected.

Consider reforming Reactions (4.7) and (4.8). Actually, production of CO_2 is the result of shift reaction of CO by the following reaction.

$$CO + H_2O = CO_2 + H_2 \qquad (4.5)$$

Thus, there are two consecutive reactions and conversion of each reaction is determined by kinetic considerations at the operating pressure and temperature.

In many cases compositions of reaction mixture and product mixture are given. Reforming reactions and combustion reactions are examples where such compositions are specified. This type of problem is normally solved by taking 100 mol of the outgoing product gas mixture as a basis and back calculating the reactant requirements.

The multiplier of a reactant or a product in a chemical reaction is called the *stoichiometric number* (v_i) when expressed with proper sign. Normal convention is a positive sign for the stoichiometric number of a product and negative sign for the reactant. Sum of all stoichiometric numbers gives change in total number of moles in the reaction. Any change in total number of moles of a gaseous reaction will mean change in extensive property, i.e., volume and/or pressure, but will not mean change in total mass. In case of liquids, change in volume is relatively small.

Many a times inert material (such as nitrogen, steam, etc.) is present in the reaction mixture. It is deliberately introduced either to reduce the concentration of the reactant (to reduce the rate of reaction) and/or to keep the temperature under control of an exothermic reaction. When air is used for combustion, nitrogen does enter with oxygen. The inert component has zero stoichiometric number. Although it increases total number of moles of the reaction mass, it does not take part in the reaction. Stoichiometric equations remain unchanged. Again, total mass of reaction mixture remains constant.

For the Reaction (4.18), $\Sigma v_i = + 1$, for the Reaction (4.19), $\Sigma v_i = + 2$, for the Reaction (4.9), $\Sigma v_i = - 1$ and for Reaction (4.5), $\Sigma v_i = 0$.

The following examples illustrate steady state material balance calculations involving chemical reactions.

Example 4.1 Monochloroacetic acid (MCA) is manufactured in a semibatch reactor by the action of glacial acetic acid with chlorine gas at 100°C (373 K) in the presence of PCl_3 catalyst. MCA thus formed will further react with chlorine to form dichloroacetic acid (DCA). To prevent the formation of DCA, excess acetic acid is used. A small-scale unit which produces 5000 kg/d MCA, requires 4536 kg/d of chlorine gas. Also, 263 kg/d of DCA is separated in the crystalliser to get almost pure MCA product. Find the % conversion, % yield of MCA and selectivity.

Solution   *Basis* One-day operation
Reactions

CH_3COOH	+	Cl_2	=	$CH_2ClCOOH$	+	HCl
Acetic Acid		Chlorine		MCA		Hydrogen Chloride
$CH_2ClCOOH$	+	Cl_2	=	$CHCl_2COOH$	+	HCl
MCA		Chlorine		DCA		Hydrogen Chloride

In this example, the amount of chlorine determines the product distribution while acetic acid is in excess. Hence, chlorine becomes the limiting component.

$$\text{Chlorine charged} = \frac{4536}{71} = 63.89 \text{ kmol}$$

For each mole of MCA production, one mole of chlorine is consumed.

$$\text{Chlorine utilised for MCA production} = \frac{5000}{94.5} = 52.91 \text{ kmol}$$

Similarly, for each mole of DCA production, two moles of chlorine are consumed.

Chlorine utilised for DCA production = $\dfrac{263 \times 2}{129}$ = 4.08 kmol

Total chlorine utilised = 52.91 + 4.08 = 56.99 kmol

$$\text{Conversion} = \frac{(56.99 \times 100)}{63.89} = \textbf{89.2\%}$$

$$\text{Yield of MCA} = \frac{(52.91 \times 100)}{56.99} = \textbf{92.84\%}$$

$$\text{Selectivity of MCA} = \frac{52.91}{4.08} = \textbf{12.97}$$

Example 4.2 The Bechamp process is classically known for reduction of nitro compounds to corresponding primary amino compounds using iron in an acidic medium. Orthotoluidine (OT) is manufactured from ortho-nitro toluene (ONT) by the Bechamp process.

In a batch of 700 kg ONT, 800 kg iron turnings (containing 90% Fe) and 400 kg water are added. The reaction mixture is heated to 60°C (333 K) and formic acid is added (approx. 6 kg) as a catalyst in batches. The mixture is stirred for about 18 h and then total mass is allowed to settle in two layers. The upper layer of OT is sucked out by vacuum in a distillation unit where it is purified by vacuum distillation.

ONT				OT		
4 × 137	9 × 56	16 × 18		4 × 107	3 × 90	6 × 107
3 Fe(OH)$_2$	+ 6 Fe(OH)$_3$		=		3 Fe$_3$O$_4$	+ 12 H$_2$O
3 × 90	3 × 107				3 × 232	12 × 18

At the end of the batch, 505 kg 99% pure OT is obtained. Assuming 98% completion of reduction, calculate (a) the yield of OT, and (b) excess quantity of iron powder.

Solution *Basis* 700 kg of ONT charged to reactor

OT produced = 505 × 0.99 = 500 kg

$$\text{ONT required} = \frac{4 \times 137 \times 500}{4 \times 107} = 640.2 \text{ kg}$$

ONT reacted = 700 × 0.98 = 686 kg

$$\text{Yield of OT} = \frac{640.2 \times 100}{686} = \textbf{93.32\%}$$

$$\text{Theoretical iron requirement} = \frac{9 \times 56 \times 700}{4 \times 137} = 643.8 \text{ kg}$$

$$\text{Iron charged} = 800 \times 0.9 = 720 \text{ kg}$$

$$\text{Excess iron} = \frac{(720 - 643.8)100}{643.8} = \mathbf{11.84\%}$$

Note Many small–scale industries use the Bechamp process for reduction of nitrocompounds. A recent trend is to use hydrogen for reduction which is available as a by-product from chlor-alkali plants.

Example 4.3 Chlorobenzene is nitrated using a mixture of nitric acid and sulphuric acid[1]. During the pilot plant studies, a charge consisted of 100 kg of chlorobenzene (CB), 106.5 kg of 65.5% (by mass) nitric acid, and 108.0 kg of 93.6% (by mass) sulphuric acid. After two hours of operation, the final mixture was analysed. It was found that the final product contained 2% unreacted chlorobenzene. Also, the product distribution was found to be 66% p-nitrochlorobenzene (p-NCB) and 34% o-nitrochlorobenzene (o-NCB).

Calculate (a) the analysis of charge, (b) the percentage conversion of chlorobenzene, and (c) the composition of the product mixture.

Solution *Basis* 100 kg of chlorobenzene
The charge consists of chlorobenzene and mixed acid.
HNO_3 in the charge = $106.5 \times 0.655 = 69.758$ kg
H_2SO_4 in the charge = $108 \times 0.936 = 101.088$ kg
Water in the charge = $106.5 \times 0.345 + 108.0 \times 0.064 = 43.654$ kg
The analysis of the reactants can be tabulated as shown in Table 4.1.

Table 4.1 Composition of Feed

Component	Molar mass	Charge, kg	mass %
Chlorobenzene	112.5	100.000	31.80
HNO_3	63.0	69.758	22.18
H_2SO_4	98.0	101.088	32.14
H_2O	18.0	43.654	13.88
Total		314.500	100.00

The reactions taking place in the reactor are

| chlorobenzene | nitric acid | o-nitrochlorobenzene | water |

| chlorobenzene | nitric acid | p-nitrochlorobenzene | water |

As given in the problem, the yield of p-NCB is 66%. Since the total charge (mass) remains constant,

Unreacted CB in the product = $314.5 \times 0.02 = 6.29$ kg

Amount of CB that has reacted = $100 - 6.29 = 93.71$ kg

$$\text{Conversion of CB} = \left(\frac{93.71}{100}\right) \times 100 = \mathbf{93.71\%}$$

Sulphuric acid remains unreacted.

From the reactions, it is clear that,

$$1 \text{ kmol of CB} \equiv 1 \text{ kmol of HNO}_3$$
$$\equiv 1 \text{ kmol of NCB}$$
$$\equiv 1 \text{ kmol of H}_2\text{O}$$

Thus, 63 kg HNO_3 will be consumed for converting 112.5 kg of CB into NCB (See Table 4.1).

$$\text{Total HNO}_3 \text{ consumed} = \left(\frac{63}{112.5}\right) \times 93.71 = 52.478 \text{ kg}$$

$$\text{Unreacted HNO}_3 = 69.758 - 52.478 = 17.28 \text{ kg}$$

$$\text{Total NCB produced} = \left(\frac{157.5}{112.5}\right) \times 93.71 = 131.194 \text{ kg}$$

$$p\text{-NCB} = 0.66 \times 131.194 = 86.588 \text{ kg}$$
$$o\text{-NCB} = 0.34 \times 131.194 = 44.606 \text{ kg}$$

$$\text{Water produced} = \left(\frac{18}{112.5}\right) \times 93.71 = 14.994 \text{ kg}$$

Total water in the product mixture = $43.654 + 14.994 = 58.648$ kg

The final analysis of the products is given in Table 4.2.

Table 4.2 Composition of Product Stream

Component	Mass, kg	mass %
CB	6.290	2.00
p-NCB	86.588	27.53
o-NCB	44.606	14.18
HNO_3	17.280	5.49
H_2SO_4	101.088	32.15
H_2O	58.648	18.65
Total	314.500	100.00

Example 4.4 Dehydrogenation of ethanol is a commercial process of manufacturing acetaldehyde[2,3]. Ethyl alcohol vapour is preheated and mixed with air in such a proportion that the exothermic heat of oxidation will just exceed the heat of dehydrogenation. This facilitates the reaction to proceed to dehydrogenation without any external application of heat. The reaction temperature is usually around 447°C (720 K).

Pre-mixed ethanol-air mixture was passed over a silver catalyst. The content of ethanol in the mixture was found to be 2.0 kg ethanol per kg air. The different reactions taking place in the reactor are as follows:

$$CH_3CH_2OH = CH_3CHO + H_2 \tag{i}$$
$$2\ CH_3CH_2OH + O_2 = 4\ CO + 6\ H_2 \tag{ii}$$
$$2\ CH_3CH_2OH + 3\ O_2 = 4\ CO_2 + 6\ H_2 \tag{iii}$$
$$2\ CH_3CH_2OH + 2\ H_2 = 4\ CH_4 + O_2 \tag{iv}$$
$$2\ H_2 + O_2 = 2\ H_2O \tag{v}$$

The exit gases from the converter were passed through a scrubber where cold dilute alcohol cools the gases and dissolves both alcohol and acetaldehyde. The stripped gases, leaving the scrubber, were scrubbed again with water in the second scrubber and released from the system. The dilute alcohol–acetaldehyde solution from the bottom of the first scrubber was sent to a distillation tower to produce 99% pure acetaldehyde as the overhead product. The gases leaving the second scrubber were analysed to contain 0.7% CO_2, 2.1% O_2, 2.3% CO, 7.1% H_2, 2.6% CH_4 and 85.2% N_2 on dry basis (by volume). Find (a) the conversion of ethanol in the converter, and (b) the yield of acetaldehyde.

Solution   *Basis* 100 kmol of outgoing gases (from the second scrubber)

N_2 present in the gases $= 100 \times 0.852 = 85.2$ kmol

Nitrogen comes from which remains unchanged during the reactions. For every 79 kmol of N_2, O_2 entering the converter is 21 kmol.

$$O_2 \text{ supplied through air} = \left(\frac{21}{79}\right) \times 85.2 = 22.65 \text{ kmol}$$

The outgoing gases contain 2.1 kmol of O_2.

$$\text{Reacted } O_2 = 22.65 - 2.1 = 20.55 \text{ kmol}$$

Oxygen balance

[Oxygen consumed by Reactions (ii), (iii) and (v)] – [Oxygen produced by Reaction (iv)] = 20.55 kmol

Let a, b and c be the kmol of ethanol reacted by Reactions (ii), (iii) and (iv), respectively, Also, let d be the kmol of H_2 reacted by Reaction (5). Therefore, oxygen balance will yield:

$$\left(\frac{a}{2}\right) + 1.5b + \left(\frac{d}{2}\right) - \left(\frac{c}{2}\right) = 20.55$$

or $\qquad\qquad a + 3b - c + d = 41.10 \qquad\qquad$ (vi)

Balance of carbon monoxide

$2a = 2.3$ [Reaction (ii)] or $a = 1.15$ kmol

Balance of carbon dioxide

$2b = 0.7$ [Reaction (iii)] or $b = 0.35$ kmol

Balance of methane

$2c = 2.6$ [Reaction (iv)] or $c = 1.3$ kmol

Substiuting the values of a, b and c in Eq. (vi),

$$d = 41.1 - 1.15 - 1.05 + 1.3 = 40.2 \text{ kmol}$$

Balance of hydrogen

Total hydrogen produced = Hydrogen is outgoing gases
+ hydrogen reacted by the Reaction (v)
+ hydrogen reacted by the Reaction (iv)

$$= 7.1 + c + d = 7.1 + 1.3 + 40.2$$
$$= 48.6 \text{ kmol}$$

The above hydrogen is produced by Reactions (i), (ii) and (iii).

Therefore, hydrogen produced by the Reaction (i) $= 48.6 - (3 \times 0.35 + 3 \times 1.15)$
$$= 44.1 \text{ kmol}$$

Ethanol reacted by the Reaction (i) $= 44.1$ kmol

Total ethanol reacted $= 44.1 + 1.15 + 0.35 + 1.3$
$$= 46.9 \text{ kmol} \equiv 2157.4 \text{ kg}$$

Total dry air entering the converter $= 85.2 + 22.65$
$$= 107.85 \text{ kmol} \equiv 3127.7 \text{ kg}$$

Total ethanol entering the converter $= 2 \times 3127.7$
$$= 6255.4 \text{ kg} \equiv 135.99 \text{ kmol}$$

$$\text{Conversion of ethanol} = \left(\frac{\text{total ethanol consumed}}{\text{total ethanol chaged}} \right) \times 100$$

$$= \left(\frac{2157.4}{6255.4} \right) \times 100 = \mathbf{34.49\%}$$

$$\text{Yield of acetaldehyde} = \left(\frac{\text{moles acetaldehyde product} \times \text{stoichiometric factor}}{\text{moles of ethanol reacted}} \right) \times 100$$

$$= \left(44.1 \times \frac{1}{46.9} \right) \times 100 = 94.03\%$$

Selectivity of acetaldehyde $= 44.1/2.8 = \mathbf{15.75}$

Example 4.5 The analysis of water (Table 3.3) has been given in Example 3.9. The same water is treated by the lime-soda process. Calculate the theoretical (stoichiometric) amounts of chemicals required for the treatment.

Solution *Basis* 1 L of water

Since the water contains only temporary hardness, only lime addition is required. The reactions of lime with bicarbonates are

$$Ca(HCO_3)_2 + CaO = 2 \ CaCO_3 + H_2O \qquad \text{(i)}$$
$$Mg(HCO_3)_2 + CaO = MgCO_3 + CaCO_3 + H_2O \qquad \text{(ii)}$$
$$2 \ NaHCO_3 + CaO = CaCO_3 + Na_2CO_3 + H_2O \qquad \text{(iii)}$$

From these equations, it is clear that 1 mole of lime is required for each mole of $Ca(HCO_3)_2$ or $Mg(MCO_3)_2$ and for every 2 moles of $NaHCO_3$.

$$56 \text{ mg of } CaO \equiv 162 \text{ mg of } Ca(HCO_3)_2$$
$$\equiv 146.3 \text{ mg of } Mg(HCO_3)_2$$
$$\equiv 2 \times 84 \text{ mg of } NaHCO_3$$

$$\text{Total lime required} = \left(\frac{56}{162} \right) \times 257.6 + \left(\frac{56}{146.3} \right) \times 329.2$$

$$+ \left(\frac{56}{168} \right) \times 11.1 = 218.8 \text{ mg}$$

Thus, theoretically, the lime dosage of the order of 218.8 mg/L is required to treat the water. The dosage can be easily calculated by knowing te bicarbonate alkalinity in terms of equivalent $CaCO_3$.

$$1 \text{ mole of } CaCO_3 \equiv 1 \text{ mole of } CaO$$
$$100 \text{ mg of } CaCO_3 \equiv 56 \text{ mg of } CaO$$
$$\text{Lime required} = \left(\frac{56}{100}\right) \times 390.6 = \textbf{218.7 mg/L}$$

Note   From the above calculations, it may be seen that the lime requirement can be readily calculated by knowing the total bicarbonate alkalinity taken to be entirely as $CaCO_3$ alone. Thus, one reason for expressing alkalinity in terms of $CaCO_3$ is the ease in calculations. In actual practice, lime is added in excess by 10 to 50%, depending on the process (hot or cold).

Example 4.6   A fertiliser plant manufactures ammonia using water gas and producer gas as raw materials[4]. The compositions of the gases are given in Table 4.3.

Table 4.3   Analysis of Gases

	Analysis, % by volume	
Component	Water gas	Producer gas
N_2	2	63
H_2	51	5
CO	43	25
CO_2	4	5
Ar	Nil	2
Total	100	100

Both the gases are mixed in proper proportions to provide a stoichiometric mixture of nitrogen and hydrogen after converting carbon monoxide to carbon dioxide using steam. Calculate: (a) the kmol of water gas and producer gas required to obtain 100 kmol of dry mixed gas, (b) the analysis of dry mixed gas, and (c) the theoretical amount (in kg) of steam required to convert CO to CO_2 per 100 kmol of dry mixed gas.

Solution   *Basis* 100 kmol of dry mixed gas

Let x be the kmol of water gas and y the kmol of producer gas, mixed to obtain 100 kmol of dry mixed gas.

Overall material balance,

$$x + y = 100 \qquad\qquad (i)$$

Total carbon monoxide present in the mixed gas = $0.43x + 0.25y$ kmol

The shift reaction is

$$CO + H_2O = CO_2 + H_2$$

Thus, each kmol of CO will give 1 kmol of CO_2 and H_2 each, when it combines with 1 kmol of steam.

Total H_2 formed due to shift reaction = $0.43x + 0.25y$ kmol

Amount of H_2 entering with water gas and producer gas = $0.51x + 0.05y$ kmol

Total H_2 after shift reaction $= 0.43x + 0.51x + 0.25y + 0.05y$
$$= 0.94x + 0.30y \text{ kmol}$$
Amount of N_2 coming with both the gases $= 0.02x + 0.63y$ kmol
For ammonia synthesis, the stoichiometric N_2 to H_2 ratio requirement is 1:3. Thus, stoichiometrically, 3(moles of N_2) = moles of H_2, obtained after the shift reaction.
$$3.(0.02x + 0.63y) = 0.94x + 0.30y$$
Simplifying,
$$x = 1.807\ y \qquad\qquad \text{(ii)}$$
Solving Eqs (i) and (ii),
$$\boldsymbol{x = 64.37 \text{ kmol of water gas}}$$
$$\boldsymbol{y = 35.63 \text{ kmol of producer gas}}$$
Using the values of x and y, the analysis of the dry mixed gas can be calculated as shown in Table 4.4.

Table 4.4 Analyses of Gases

Component	Water gas vol. %	Water gas kmol	Producer gas vol. %	Producer gas kmol	Mixed gas kmol	Mixed gas vol. %
N_2	2	1.29	63	22.45	23.74	23.74
H_2	51	32.83	5	1.78	34.61	34.61
CO	43	27.68	25	8.91	36.59	36.59
CO_2	4	2.57	5	1.78	4.35	4.35
Ar	—	—	2	0.71	0.71	0.71
Total	100	64.37	100	35.63	100.00	100.00

Amount of steam required = amount of CO converted
$$= 0.43x + 0.25y = 0.43 \times 64.37 + 0.25 \times 35.63$$
$$= \textbf{36.59 kmol or 658.62 kg}$$
As there is no competitive reaction to the shift reaction, the yield of hydrogen is 100%. Also the conversion of CO is assumed to be 100%.

Example 4.7 Tallow is essentially glyceryl tristearate[5]. It is desired to saponify the tallow with caustic soda. For 100 kg of tallow, calculate (a) the theoretical requirement of caustic soda, and (b) the amount of glycerine liberated.

Solution Basis 100 kg of tallow
The saponification reaction is

$$
\begin{array}{c}
\text{CH}_2\text{OOCH}_{35}\text{C}_{17} \\
| \\
\text{CHOOCH}_{35}\text{C}_{17} \\
| \\
\text{CH}_2\text{OOCH}_{35}\text{C}_{17}
\end{array}
\quad + \quad 3\ \text{NaOH} \quad = \quad 3\ \text{C}_{17}\text{CH}_{35}\text{COONa} \quad + \quad
\begin{array}{c}
\text{CH}_2\text{OH} \\
| \\
\text{CHOH} \\
| \\
\text{CH}_2\text{OH}
\end{array}
$$

Glyceryl tristearate	Caustic soda	Sodium stearate	Glycerine
890	3×40	3×306	92

$$\text{Caustic soda required} = \left[\frac{3 \times 40}{890}\right] \times 100 = \textbf{13.48 kg}$$

$$\text{Glycerine liberated} = \left(\frac{92}{890}\right) \times 100 = \textbf{10.34 kg}$$

Example 4.8 Pure sulphur is burnt in a burner[6] at the rate of 0.3 kg/s. Fresh dry air is supplied at 30°C (303 K) and 100 kPa a (750 Torr). The gases from the burner contain 16.5% SO_2, 3% O_2 and rest N_2 on SO_3-free volume basis. The gases leave the burner at 800°C (1073 K) and 101.325 kPa a (760 Torr). Calculate (a) the fraction of sulphur burnt into SO_3, (b) the percentage excess air over the amount required to oxidise the sulphur to SO_2, (c) the volume of dry air in m^3/s, and (d) the volume of burner gases in m^3/s.

Notes (i) The analysis of sulphur burner gases is always given on SO_3-free basis as SO_3 creates interference in the analysis of the gases. Usually, an Orsat apparatus, with mercury as the working fluid, is used in analysing the gases. (ii) In this example, although a basis of 0.3 kg/s sulphur is given, it would be easier to start solving the problem using a basis of 100 kmol of SO_3-free burner gases.

Solution *Basis* 100 kmol of SO_3 free gases
The gases contain 16.5 kmol of SO_2, 3.0 kmol of O_2 and 80.5 kmol of N_2. The reactions taking place in the burner are

$$S + O_2 = SO_2 \tag{i}$$

$$S + \frac{3}{2} O_2 = SO_3 \tag{ii}$$

Based on Eq. (1),
O_2 required to form 16.5 kmol SO_2 = 16.5 kmol

$$\text{Total } O_2 \text{ supplied to the burner} = \left(\frac{21}{79}\right) \times 80.5 = 21.4 \text{ kmol}$$

$$\text{Unaccounted } O_2 = 21.4 - (16.5 + 3.0) = 1.9 \text{ kmol}$$

Thus 1.82 kmol O_2 have been consumed as per Eq. (2).

$$SO_3 \text{ produced} = \left(\frac{2}{3}\right) \times 1.9 = 1.267 \text{ kmol}$$

Sulphur burnt into SO_2 = 16.5 kmol
Sulphur burnt into SO_3 = 1.267 kmol
Total sulphur burnt in the burner = 16.5 + 1.267 = 17.767 kmol
Mass of sulphur burnt = 17.767 × 32 = 568.54 kg

$$\text{Fraction of S burnt to } SO_3 = \frac{1.267}{17.767} = \textbf{0.0713}$$

Now, if all sulphur would have been burnt into SO_2, O_2 requirement would have been 17.767 kmol [Eq. (i)].

$$\text{Excess } O_2 = 21.4 - 17.767 = 3.633 \text{ kmol}$$

$$\text{Percentage excess air} = \left(\frac{3.633}{17.767}\right) \times 100 = \mathbf{20.448}$$

Air supplied to the burner = 21.4 + 80.5 = 101.9 kmol

However, the actual charge to the burner is 0.3 kg/s.

$$\text{Air supply rate} = \left(\frac{101.9}{568.54}\right) \times 0.3 = 0.053\ 77 \text{ kmol/s}$$

Specific volume of incoming fresh air = $22.414 \times \left(\frac{303.15}{273.15}\right) \times \left(\frac{100}{101.325}\right) =$ 24.55 m³/kmol

Volumetric flow rate of fresh air = 0.053 77 × 24.55 = **1.32 m³/s**

For a basis of 100 kmol SO$_3$-free gases,

Total gases from burner = 100 + 1.267 = 101.267 kmol

$$\text{For 0.3 kg/s sulphur charge, Total gas} = \left(\frac{101.267 \times 0.3}{568.54}\right) = 0.0534 \text{ kmol/s}$$

$$\text{Specific volume of burner gases} = 22.414 \times \left(\frac{1073.15}{273.15}\right) = 88.06 \text{ m}^3/\text{kmol}$$

Volumetric flow rate of burner gases = 88.06 × 0.0534 = **4.7024 m³/s**

Example 4.9 Refined soybean oil is hydrogenated at 2 bar g and 180°C (453 K) in an autoclave to produce 'Vanaspati' (hydrogenated fat) in presence of nickel catalyst. The reaction was considered complete when product's slip melting point was recorded 39°C (312 K). Samples of refined soybean oil and hardened (hydrogenated) fat were chromatographically analysed and found to contain the following fatty acids.

Table 4.5 Composition of Edible Oil and Hardened Fat

Fatty acid	Refined Soybean oil mass %	Hardened fat mass %
Palmitic acid	11.1	11.0
Stearic acid	3.8	14.6
Oleic acid	27.3	71.8
Linoleic acid	51.1	2.6
Linolenic acid	6.7	Nil

Calculate (a) theoretical hydrogen requirement for complete saturation, (b) actual hydrogen requirement, and (c) iodine values (IV) of refined oil and hardened fat.

Note Iodine value is defined as kg of iodine absorbed by 100 kg oil or fat.

Solution *Basis* 100 kg of soya fatty acids

Table 4.6 Composition of Soybean (also Called Soya) Fatty Acids

Fatty acid	kg	Formula	Molar mass	kmol
Palmitic acid	11.1	$C_{16}H_{32}O_2$	256.42	0.0433
(Hexadecanoic acid)				
Stearic acid	3.8	$C_{18}H_{36}O_2$	284.48	0.0134
Oleic acid	27.3	$C_{18}H_{34}O_2$	282.46	0.0967
Linoleic acid	51.1	$C_{18}H_{32}O_2$	280.45	0.1822
Linolenic acid	6.7	$C_{18}H_{30}O_2$	278.43	0.0241
Total	100.0			0.3597

$$\text{Average molar mass of soya fatty acids} = \frac{100}{0.3597} = 278.0$$

All the fatty acids are in triglyceride form which is known as oil. When 3 moles of fatty acids react with 1 mole of glycerol (molar mass = 92.09), one mole of triglyceride and three moles of water are produced.

Average molar mass of soybean oil = $278.0 \times 3 + 92.09 - 3 \times 18.02$
$$= 872.03$$

$$\text{Quantity of soybean oil} = \left(\frac{872.03 \times 100}{278.00 \times 3} \right)$$

$$= 104.56 \text{ kg/100 kg of soya fatty acid}$$

In other words, if 104.56 kg of soybean oil is split, 100 kg of fatty acids (of analysis given in Table 4.5) and 11.04 kg of glycerol will be obtained. Palmitic and stearic acids are saturated fatty acids. When oil is hydrogenated, unsaturated fatty acids (oleic, linoleic and linolenic) will be saturated (i.e., double and triple bonds will be opened).

Reactions are as follows.

$CH_3 (CH_2)_7 CH : CH (CH_2)_7 COOH + H_2 = CH_3(CH_2)_{16} COOH$
Oleic acid   Stearic acid
(Z- octadece-9-enoic acid)   (octadecanoic acid)
$CH_3(CH_2)_4 CH : CHCH_2 CH : CH (CH_2)_7COOH + 2 H_2$
$$= CH_3(CH_2)_{16} COOH$$
Linoleic acid   Stearic acid
(*cis, cis*- 9,12 - octadecadienoic acid)   (octadecanoic acid)
$CH_3CH_2CH : CHCH_2 CH : CHCH_2 CH : CH (CH_2)_7 COOH + 3 H_2$
$$= CH_3(CH_2)_{16} COOH$$
Linolenic acid (Aplha form)   Stearic acid
[(Octadecatrienoic acid (9Z, 12Z, 15Z)]   (octadecanoic acid)

Based on above reactions, theoretical H_2 requirement

for full hydrogenation = $0.0967 + (0.1822 \times 2) + (0.0241 \times 3)$
$$= 0.5334 \text{ kmol/100 kg soya fatty acid}$$
$$\equiv 0.5101 \text{ kmol/100 kg soybean oil}$$
$$\equiv \textbf{11.434 Nm}^3\textbf{/100 kg soybean oil}$$

In actual practice, refined oil is partially hydrogenated for edible purpose. Hardened fat does not contain any linolenic acid and hence assume its full conversion to oleic acid. Let x kg linoleic acid get converted to oleic acid and y kg oleic acid get converted to stearic acid.

Oleic–acid production due to conversion of linolenic acid

$$= \frac{282.46}{278.43} \times 6.7 = 6.797 \text{ kg}$$

Oleic–acid production due to conversion of linoleic acid

$$= \frac{282.46}{280.45} \times x = 1.007\ 17\ x \text{ kg}$$

Stearic–acid production due to conversion of oleic acid

$$= \frac{284.48}{282.46} \times y$$

$$= 1.007\ 15\ y \text{ kg}$$

Oleic acid after partial hydrogenation

$$= 27.3 + 6.797 + 1.007\ 17\ x - y$$
$$= 34.097 + 1.007\ 17\ x - y \text{ kg}$$

Fatty acids after partial hydrogenation

Palmitic acid	11.1 kg
Stearic acid	$3.8 + 1.007\ 15\ y$ kg
Oleic acid	$34.097 + 1.007\ 17x - y$ kg
Linoleic acid	$51.1 - x$ kg
Total	$100.097 + 0.007\ 17x + 0.007\ 15\ y$

Based on analysis given in Table 4.5;

Stearic acid balance

$$\frac{3.8 + 1.007\ 15y}{100.097 + 0.007\ 17x + 0.007\ 15y} = 0.146$$

or $\qquad - 0.001\ 05x + 1.006\ 11y = 10.8142 \qquad\qquad$ (i)

Linoleic acid balance

$$\frac{51.1 - x}{100.097 + 0.007\ 17x + 0.007\ 15y} = 0.026$$

or $\qquad 1.000\ 19x + 0.000\ 19\ y = 48.4975 \qquad\qquad$ (ii)

Solving Eqs. (i) and (ii).

$$x = 48.5 \text{ kg}, \quad y = 10.8 \text{ kg}$$

Table 4.7 Composition of Hardened Fat

Fatty acid	kg	mass %	kmol	H_2 requirement, kmol
Palmitic acid	11.10	10.94	0.0433	—
Stearic acid	14.68	14.60	0.0516	—
Oleic acid	72.14	71.77	0.2554	0.2554
Linoleic acid	2.60	2.59	0.0093	0.0186
Total	100.52	100.00	0.3596	0.2740

Average molar mass of fatty acids in hardened fat $= \dfrac{100.52}{0.3596} = 279.53$

Average molar mass of hardened fat $= 279.53 \times 3 + 92.09 - 3 \times 18.02$
$$= 876.63$$

Quantity of hardened fat $= \dfrac{876.63 \times 100.52}{279.53 \times 3}$

$\qquad\qquad = 105.08$ kg/100 kg of soya fatty acids
$\qquad\qquad \equiv 100.5$ kg/100 kg of soybean oil

H_2 requirement of hardened fat $= 0.274$ kmol for full saturation/100.52 kg
$\qquad\qquad$ of hardened fat
$\qquad\qquad = 0.2864$ kmol/100 kg of soya fatty acids

Net hydrogen requirement for partial hydrogenation
$\qquad\qquad = 0.5334 - 0.2864$
$\qquad\qquad = 0.2470$ kmol/100 kg of soya fatty acids
$\qquad\qquad \equiv 0.2362$ kmol/100 kg of soybean oil
$\qquad\qquad \equiv 5.295$ Nm^3/100 kg of soybean oil
$\qquad\qquad \equiv$ **52.95 Nm^3/t soybean oil**

Iodine reacts with unsaturated fatty acids in the same locations as shown for hydrogenation reactions.

Molar mass of iodine $(I_2) = 253.81$

For soybean oil

Iodine consumption $= 0.5334$ kmol I_2/100 kg of soya fatty acids
$\qquad\qquad \equiv 0.5101$ kmol I_2/100 kg of soybean oil
Iodine value (IV) $\equiv$ **129.5 kg I_2/100 kg of soybean oil**

For hardened fat

Iodine consumption $= 0.274$ kmol/100.52 kg of fat
$\qquad\qquad \equiv 0.2726$ kmol/100 kg of fat
Iodine value (IV) $\equiv$ **69.2 kg I_2/100 kg of fat**

Note   Iodine value (IV) is a good indication of unsaturation of fatty acids/oils. It can be determined experimentally easily and hence offers a quick quality check of fatty acids/oils, For the same slip melting point of 39°C (312 K), there can be variation in IV, indicating quality of hydrogenation. For instance, if for the above example, experimentally IV is found higher than 69.2, it indicates presence of more of linoleic or linolenic acid which may not be desirable.

Example 4.10   In the Formox process, a mixture of metal oxides, consisting of Fe, Mo and V, is used as a catalyst for partial oxidation of methanol to formaldehyde[7]. Different reactions taking place in the reactor are as follows.

$$CH_3OH + (1/2)\ O_2 = HCHO + H_2O \qquad\qquad (i)$$
$$CH_3OH + (3/2)\ O_2 = CO_2 + 2\,H_2O \qquad\qquad (ii)$$
$$CH_3OH = CO + 2\,H_2 \qquad\qquad (iii)$$
$$CH_3OH = CH_4 + (1/2)\ O_2 \qquad\qquad (iv)$$
$$2\ CH_3OH = (CH_3)_2O + H_2O \qquad\qquad (v)$$

Methanol feed is passed through a steam-heated evaporator. Ambient air, containing 0.011 kg moisture/kg dry air, is heated by product gas stream, leaving the reactor, and mixed with methanol vapour in a static mixer.

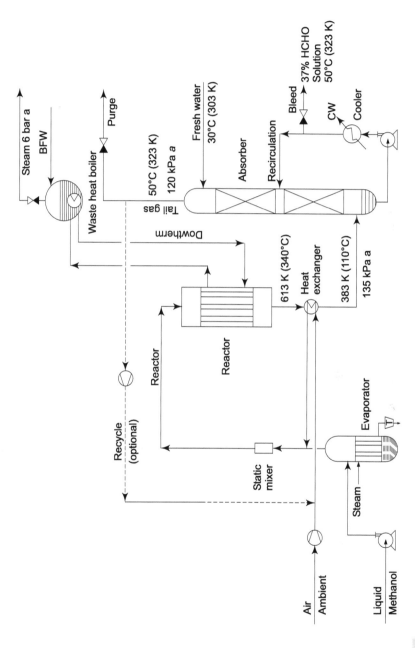

Fig. 4.1 Formaldehyde Production by Formox Process

The gaseous feed, containing 8.4% methanol (by volume on wet basis), employs excess air and is a flammable mixture. It is passed at 170 kPa through catalyst-filled tubes in a heat-exchanging type reactor. Dowtherm-A circulates outside the tubes and removes the heat of reaction. Reactions take place isothermally at 340°C (613 K). Steam is generated at 6 bar a in a waste heat boiler (WHB) by condensing Dowtherm-A vapour. Gas mixture from the reactor is cooled to 110°C (383 K) in a heat exchanger by heating incoming air.

The gas mixture then enters the bottom of the absorber. Formaldehyde concentration at the bottom of the absorber is controlled at 37% (by mass) by fresh water, entering at the top at 30°C (303 K.) A forced circulation cooler for the bottom solution maintains formaldehyde solution at 50°C (323 K). Tail gas leaves the absorber at 120 kPa a and 50°C (323 K) at the top.

Assume 99% conversion of methanol with 90% yield to formalehyde. Based on kinetic considerations, reactions (ii) to (v) consume 71%, 8%, 5% and 16% respectively of 10% methanol yield.

Make complete material balance of the plant for a methanol feed rate of 4000 kg/h. Refer Fig. 4.1 for the process flow diagram.

Solution

Basis Methanol feed rate of 4000 kg/h

Molar feed rate of methanol = $\dfrac{4000}{32}$ = 125 kmol/h

Concentration of methanol in the gaseous mixture to reactor is 8.4% by volume.

Gaseous mixture flow rate = $\dfrac{125}{0.084}$ = 1488.1 kmol/h

Flow of ambient (wet) air = 1488.1 − 125
= 1363.1 kmol/h.

Moisture content of ambient air = 0.011 kg/kg dry air

$\equiv 0.011 \times \dfrac{29}{18} \equiv 0.017\,72$ kmol/kmol dry air.

Dry air flow rate = $\dfrac{1363.1}{(1 + 0.017\,72)}$ = 1339.37 kmol/h

O_2 supply rate = 1339.37 × 0.21 = 281.27 kmol/h
N_2 supply rate = 1339.37 − 281.27 = 1058.10 kmol/h
Moisture, entering with air = 1363.1 − 1339.37 = 23.73 kmol/h

Table 4.8   Composition of Gaseous Mixture Entering Reactor

Component	$\dot{n}_i$ kmol/h	mole %
CH_3OH	125.00	8.40
O_2	281.27	18.90
N_2	1058.10	71.10
H_2O	23.73	1.60
Total	1488.10	100.00

Conversion of methanol = 99%

Total methanol reacted = $125 \times 0.99 = 123.75$ kmol/h

Unreacted methanol = $125.00 - 123.75 = 1.25$ kmol/h

Reaction (i)

Methanol reacted = $123.75 \times 0.9 = 111.375$ kmol/h

HCHO produced = 111.375 kmol/h

O_2 consumed = $111.375/2 = 55.688$ kmol/h

H_2O produced = 111.375 kmol/h.

Reactions (ii) to (v)

Methanol consumed = $123.75 \times 0.1 = 12.375$ kmol/h

Reaction (ii)

CH_3OH reacted = $12.375 \times 0.71 = 8.786$ kmol/h

O_2 consumed = $8.786 \times 1.5 = 13.179$ kmol/h

CO_2 produced = 8.786 kmol/h

H_2O produced = $8.786 \times 2 = 17.572$ kmol/h

Reaction (iii)

CH_3OH reacted = $12.375 \times 0.08 = 0.99$ kmol/h

CO produced = 0.99 kmol/h

H_2 produced = $2 \times 0.99 = 1.98$ kmol/h

Reaction (iv)

CH_3OH reacted = $12.375 \times 0.05 = 0.619$ kmol/h

CH_4 produced = 0.619 kmol/h

O_2 produced = $0.619/2 = 0.309$ kmol/h

Reaction (v)

CH_3OH reacted = $12.375 - (8.786 + 0.99 + 0.619)$

$= 1.98$ kmol/h

DME produced = $1.98/2 = 0.99$ kmol/h

H_2O produced = $1.98/2 = 0.99$ kmol/h

O_2 in reactor exit gas stream = $281.27 - 55.688 - 13.179 + 0.309$

$= 212.712$ kmol/h

H_2O in reactor exit gas stream = $23.73 + 111.375 + 17.572 + 0.99$

$= 153.667$ kmol/h

Table 4.9 Composition of Reactor Exit Gas Stream

Component	$\dot{n}_i$ kmol/h	mole %
CH_3OH	1.25	0.08
HCHO	111.375	7.18
CO_2	8.786	0.57
CO	0.990	0.06
H_2	1.980	0.13
CH_4	0.619	0.04
$(CH_3)_2O$	0.990	0.06
O_2	212.712	13.72
N_2	1058.100	68.25
H_2O	153.667	9.91
Total	1550.469	100.00

In the exit gas stream, CO_2, CO, H_2, CH_4 and $(CH_3)_2O$ are undesired components (UC).

UC in exit gas stream = 8.786 + 0.99 + 1.98 + 0.619 + 0.99
$$= 13.365 \text{ kmol/h}$$

At the top of the absorber, fresh water is introduced and hence it is safe to assume that negligible quantities of methanol and formaldehyde will escape.

p_w at 50°C (323.15 K) = 12.335 kPa (Refer Table 6.14)

$$\text{Moisture content of tail gas} = \frac{12.335}{(120 - 12.335)}$$

$$= 0.1146 \ \frac{\text{kmol}}{\text{kmol dry gas}}$$

Dry tail gas mixture = 1550.469 − (1.25 + 111.375 + 153.667)
$$= 1284.177 \text{ kmol}$$

Moisture in tail gas = 1284.177 × 0.1146 = 147.167 kmol/h
$$\equiv 2649 \text{ kg/h}$$

Table 4.10 Composition of Tail Gas

Component	$\dot{n}_i$ kmol/h		mole %	
	Dry	Wet	Dry	Wet
UC	13.365	13.365	1.04	0.93
O_2	212.712	212.712	16.56	14.86
N_2	1058.100	1058.100	82.40	73.92
H_2O	—	147.167	—	10.29
Total	1284.177	1431.344	100.00	100.00

Material balance across absorber

Bottom solution contains formaldehydehyde and water.

HCHO in bottom solution = 111.375 × 30 = 3341.25 kg/h

Concentration of HCHO = 37% by mass

$$\text{Solution withdrawl rate} = \frac{3341.25}{0.37} = 9030.4 \text{ kg/h}$$

CH_3OH in bottom solution = 1.25 × 32 = 40 kg/h

Water in bottom solution = 9030.4 − (3341.25 + 40) = 5649.15 kg/h

Gases enter the absorber at 135 kPa a and 110°C (383.15 K).

Moisture entering the absorber = 153.667 × 18 = 2766.0 kg/h
(in gas stream)

Fresh water added at the top of the absorber
$$= 2649 + 5649.15 - 2766.0$$
$$= \textbf{5532.15 kg/h} \approx \textbf{5.53 m}^3\textbf{/h}$$

Example 4.11 Pyrites fines are roasted in a chamber plant for making sulphuric acid. The reaction taking place in the burner is

$$4 \ FeS_2 + 11 \ O_2 = 2 \ Fe_2O_3 + 8 \ SO_2$$

The gases leaving the roaster have the composition: 7.12% SO_2, 10.6% O_2 and rest N_2 on SO_3-free volume basis. The temperature and pressure of the gases are 525°C (798 K) and 100 kPa a (750 Torr), respectively. Pyrites contain 42% sulphur and rest inerts (majority Fe and the rest, gangue). The refuse in the roaster (cinder) carried 2.3% S in the form of SO_3. Dry air is supplied for roasting the pyrites at 27°C (300 K) and 100 kPa a (750 Torr).

The gases pass through a catalytic converter where 96% of SO_2 gets converted to SO_3. Gases from the converter are passed through an absorber where 98% SO_3 is absorbed. Based on the charge of 4 kg/s of pyrites, calculate (a) percentage of sulphur that remained in the cinder based on the original charge, (b) percentage of burnt-up sulphur leaving the roaster as SO_3 in the gases, (c) volumetric flow rate of air in m^3/s, (d) volumetirc flow rate of roaster gases in m^3/s, (e) analysis of the gases leaving the SO_3 converter, and (f) amount of sulphuric acid produced per day assuming 98% strength for the acid from the absorber.

Solution *Basis* 100 kg of pyrites
The pyrites contain 42 kg of sulphur and 58 inerts.

It may be noted from the problem statement that during roasting, not only SO_2 is formed but some pyrites get converted to SO_3 also. The reactions are

$$4\ FeS_2 + 11\ O_2 = 2\ Fe_2O_3 + 8\ SO_2 \qquad (i)$$
$$4\ FeS_2 + 15\ O_2 = 2\ Fe_2O_3 + 8\ SO_3 \qquad (ii)$$

Some SO_3 is absorbed in the form of basic sulphur in the cinder and the rest escapes through the roaster exhaust. From the above two reactions, it is clear that

$$8 \text{ moles of } SO_2 \text{ or } SO_3 \equiv 2 \text{ moles of } Fe_2O_3$$
$$8 \text{ moles of } S \equiv 3 \text{ moles of } O_2 \text{ in } Fe_2O_3$$

Thus, the amount of O_2

$$\text{combined to form } Fe_2O_3 = \left[\frac{3 \times 32}{8 \times 32}\right] \times 42 = 15.75 \text{ kg}$$

This O_2 and other inerts will be in the cinder.

Mass of SO_3-free cinder = 58 + 15.75 = 73.75 kg
Now, 100 kg of cinder contains 2.3 kg of sulphur.

$$\text{Equivalent } SO_3 = \left(\frac{2.3}{32}\right) \times 80 = 5.75 \text{ kg}$$

$$SO_3\text{-free cinder} = 100 - 5.75 = 94.25 \text{ kg}$$

Thus for 94.25 kg SO_3-free cinder, 100 kg is the actual amount of cinder. Therefore, for 73.75 kg of SO_3-free cinder,

$$\text{Actual amount of cinder} = \left(\frac{100}{94.25}\right) \times 73.75 = 78.25 \text{ kg}$$

$$\text{Sulphur in cinder} = 78.25 \times 0.023 = 1.8 \text{ kg}$$

Thus, out of 42 kg of S in the pyrites, 1.8 kg of S is retained in the cinder in the form of SO_3.

Percentage of sulphur that remained in the cinder on the basis of

$$\text{orignial charge} = \left(\frac{1.8}{42}\right) \times 100 = \textbf{4.29}$$

For finding out SO_3 content of roaster gas, oxygen balance is required. For these calculations, assume a new basis of 100 kmol of SO_3-free roaster gases.

Amount of SO_2 in the roaster gases = 7.12 kmol

Amount of O_2 present in SO_2 = 7.12 kmol

Amount of O_2 in the gases (as such) = 10.6 kmol

Amount of N_2 in the roaster gases = 100 − (7.12 + 10.6) = 82.28 kmol

Amount of O_2 entering the roaster along with N_2 = $\left(\dfrac{21}{79}\right)$ × 82.28 = 21.87 kmol

With the formation of SO_2, Fe gets converted to Fe_2O_3. Therefore, O_2 in the cinder (in the form of Fe_2O_3) equivalent to

$$SO_2 \text{ of the gases} = \left(\frac{3}{8}\right) \times 7.12 = 2.67 \text{ kmol}$$

Total O_2 accounted for = 7.12 + 10.60 + 2.67 = 20.39 kmol

Unaccounted O_2 = 21.87 − 20.39 = 1.48 kmol

According to Eq. (ii), 8 kmol of SO_3 are formed for 15 kmol of O_2 consumed.

$$SO_3 \text{ formed} = \left(\frac{8}{15}\right) \times 1.48 = 0.789 \text{ kmol}$$

Sulphur in SO_2 = 7.12 kmol

Sulphur in SO_3 = 0.789 kmol

Total sulphur burnt = 7.12 + 0.789 = 7.909 kmol

$$\text{Percentage of S roasted to } SO_3 = \left(\frac{0.789}{7.915}\right) \times 100 = 9.98$$

However, it was found that 4.29% of the sulphur, charged to the roaster, was retained in the cinder.

Hence, Percentage of S going in

the roaster gas as SO_3 = 9.98 − 4.29 = **5.69%**

$$SO_3 \text{ going into the roaster gases} = 0.789 \times \left(\frac{5.69}{9.98}\right) = 0.45 \text{ kmol}$$

The above data are calculated on the basis of the charge of 100 kmol of SO_3-free roaster gases.

Now, again take the original basis of 100 kg of pyrites. Out of 42 kg of S, the roasting of S to SO_2 is 37.81 kg (i.e., 90.02%) and the roasting of S to SO_3 is 4.19 kg (i.e., 9.98%).

$$SO_2 \text{ formed} = \left(\frac{37.81}{32}\right) = 1.181 \text{ kmol}$$

It is known that for 7.12 kmol of SO_2 in the roaster gas,

air supplied = 82.28 + 21.88 = 104.16 kmol

For 1.181 kmol SO_2,

$$\text{air supply} = \left(\frac{104.16}{7.12}\right) \times 1.181 = 17.28 \text{ kmol}$$

However, it is desired to roast 4 kg/s pyrites.

$$\text{Total air supplied} = \left(\frac{17.28 \times 4}{100}\right) = 0.6912 \text{ kmol/s}$$

$$\text{Specific volume of entering air} = 22.414 \times \left(\frac{101.325}{100}\right) \times \left(\frac{300.15}{273.15}\right)$$

$$= 24.957 \text{ m}^3/\text{kmol}$$

Volumetric flow rate of air = $24.957 \times 0.6912 = $ **17.25 m³/s**

Total roaster gases will be 100.455 kmol for 100 kmol of SO_3-free gases or for 104.16 kmol air supply.

Thus, for 0.6912 kmol/s air supply,

$$\text{Roaster gases} = \frac{(100.455 \times 0.6912)}{104.16} = 0.6666 \text{ kmol/s}$$

$$\text{Specific volume of roaster gases} = 22.414 \times \left(\frac{101.325}{100}\right) \times \left(\frac{798.15}{273.15}\right)$$

$$= 66.386 \text{ m}^3/\text{kmol}$$

Volumetric flow rate of roaster gases = $66.386 \times 0.6666 = $ **44.253 m³/s**

In the converter, SO_2 gets converted to SO_3 as per the reaction,

$$2\ SO_2 + O_2 = 2\ SO_3 \tag{iii}$$

$$\text{Total } SO_2 \text{ entering the converter} = \frac{(7.12 \times 0.6666)}{100.455}$$

$$= 4.725 \times 10^{-2} \text{ kmol/s}$$

Since the conversion efficiency is 96%,

$$SO_2 \text{ converted to } SO_3 = 4.725 \times 10^{-2} \times 0.96 = 4.536 \times 10^{-2} \text{ kmol/s}$$

$$\text{Unconverted } SO_2 = (4.725 - 4.536)10^{-2}$$

$$= 1.89 \times 10^{-3} \text{ kmol/s}$$

$$\text{Amount of } O_2 \text{ consumed} = (4.536 \times 10^{-2})/2 = 2.268 \times 10^{-2} \text{ kmol/s}$$

Amount of O_2 in the gases entering the converter

$$= \frac{(0.6666 \times 10.60)}{100.455} = 7.034 \times 10^{-2} \text{ kmol/s}$$

$$\text{Unreacted } O_2 = 7.034 \times 10^{-2} - 2.268 \times 10^{-2}$$

$$= 4.766 \times 10^{-2} \text{ kmol/s}$$

$$SO_3 \text{ formed} = 4.536 \times 10^{-2} \text{ kmol/s}$$

$$SO_3 \text{ entering the converter} = \left(\frac{0.455}{100.455}\right) \times 0.6666 = 3.019 \times 10^{-3} \text{ kmol/s}$$

$$\text{Total } SO_3 \text{ leaving the converter} = 4.536 \times 10^{-2} + 3.019 \times 10^{-3}$$

$$= 4.838 \times 10^{-2} \text{ kmol/s}$$

$$N_2 \text{ in the gases} = \left(\frac{82.28}{100.455}\right) \times 0.6666 = 0.546 \text{ kmol/s}$$

The analysis of the gases is given in Table 4.11.

Table 4.11 Composition of Converter Gases

Component	Inlet gas		Outlet gas	
	kmol/s	Volume %	kmol/s	Volume %
SO_2	4.725×10^{-2}	7.09	1.89×10^{-3}	0.29
O_2	7.034×10^{-2}	10.55	4.766×10^{-2}	7.41
SO_3	3.019×10^{-3}	0.45	4.838×10^{-2}	7.51
N_2	0.546	81.91	0.546	84.79
Total	0.6666	100.00	0.6439	100.00

Amount of SO_3 absorbed in the absorber = $4.838 \times 10^{-2} \times 0.98$
$$= 4.741 \times 10^{-2} \text{ kmol/s}$$

Absorption reaction is
$$SO_3 + H_2O = H_2SO_4 \qquad\qquad (iv)$$
Amount of H_2SO_4 produced = 4.741×10^{-2} kmol/s of 100% strength

Amount of 98% acid strength = $\dfrac{(4.741 \times 10^{-2} \times 98 \times 24 \times 3600)}{(0.98 \times 1000)}$

$$= \textbf{409.64 t/d}$$

Note It may be noted that the bases for calculations were changed thrice in this example. This is required in many problems. However, all the different bases should not be confused with one another. For this reason, the different bases should be clearly underlined while solving such problems.

Example 4.12 A mixture of pyrites and zinc sulphide ore is burnt in a burner. The mixture contains 75% pyrites and 25% zinc sulphide ore. The pyrites yield 92% FeS_2 and the rest, gangue. The zinc sulphide ore contains 68% ZnS and the rest, inerts. A sample of cinder yields 3.5% S. 70% of S in the cinder in the form of SO_3, absorbed in it, and the rest is unoxidised FeS_2. All percentages are by mass. Based on 100 kg of mixed charge, calculate (a) the amount of cinder formed with its analysis, and (b) the percentage of the sulphur left in the cinder based on the total sulphur charged.

Solution *Basis* 100 kg of mixed charge
The charge consists of 75 kg of pyrites and 25 kg of zinc sulphide ore.
Pyrites $\qquad\qquad FeS_2 = 75 \times 0.92 = 69$ kg
$\qquad\qquad\qquad$ Gangue = 75 − 69 = 6 kg
The roasting reactions are
$$4 FeS_2 + 11 O_2 = 2 Fe_2O_3 + 8 SO_2 \qquad\qquad (i)$$
$$4 FeS_2 + 15 O_2 = 2 Fe_2O_3 + 8 SO_3 \qquad\qquad (ii)$$
Zinc ore $\qquad\qquad ZnS = 25 \times 0.68 = 17.0$ kg
$\qquad\qquad\qquad$ Inerts = 25 − 17 = 8 kg
The roasting reaction is
$$2 Zns + 3 O_2 = 2 ZnO + 2 SO_2 \qquad\qquad (iii)$$
$\qquad\qquad$ Total inerts = 8 + 6 = 14 kg

Now assume a new basis of 100 kg of cinder. It contains 3.5% sulphur.
Sulphur in the form of SO_3 = 3.5 × 0.7 = 2.45 kg
Sulphur in the form of FeS_2 = 3.5 − 2.45 = 1.05 kg

$$\text{Amount of } SO_3 \text{ in the cinder} = \left(\frac{2.45}{32}\right) \times 80 = 6.125 \text{ kg}$$

$$\text{Amount of } FeS_2 \text{ in the cinder} = \left(\frac{120}{64}\right) \times 1.05 = 1.969 \text{ kg}$$

Sulphur compound-free cinder = 100 − (6.125 + 1.969) = 91.906 kg
This 91.906 kg comprises Fe_2O_3, ZnO and inerts. Now, for the original charge of 100 kg of mixed feed,

$$\text{ZnO} = \left(\frac{81.4}{97.4}\right) \times 17 = 14.2 \text{ kg}$$

Let x be the mass of FeS_2 reacted.
Unreacted FeS_2 = (69 − x) kg

$$\text{Amount of } Fe_2O_3 \text{ produced} = \frac{x \times 160}{120 \times 2} = 0.667\, x \text{ kg}$$

$$\text{Total S-free cinder} = 14.2 + 0.667\, x + 14$$
$$= 28.2 + 0.667x \text{ kg}$$

Thus, $$\frac{FeS_2 \text{ in cinder}}{\text{S-free cinder}} = \frac{(69 - x)}{(28.2 + 0.667x)}$$

But, this ratio is 1.969/91.906 as calculated before.

$$\frac{(69 - x)}{(28.2 + 0.667x)} = \frac{1.969}{91.906}$$

or $$x = 67.43 \text{ kg}$$

S-free cinder = 14.2 + 0.667 × 67.43 + 14 = 73.18 kg

FeS_2 in the cinder = 69 − 67.43 = 1.57 kg

$$SO_3 \text{ in the cinder} = \left(\frac{6.125}{91.906}\right) 73.18 = 4.88 \text{ kg}$$

Fe_2O_3 produced = 0.667 x = 44.98 kg

The composition of the cinder formed is given in Table 4.12.

Table 4.12 Composition of Cinder

	Cinder	
Component	kg	mass %
ZnO	14.20	17.83
Fe_2O_3	44.98	56.49
S as FeS_2	1.57	1.97
S as SO_3	4.88	6.13
Inerts	14.00	17.58
Total	79.63	100.00

Sulphur charge to the burner = S in FeS_2 + S in Zns

$$= \left(\frac{64}{120}\right) \times 69 + \left(\frac{32}{97.4}\right) \times 17 = 42.385 \text{ kg}$$

Amount of S in the cinder = $0.035 \times 79.63 = 2.787$ kg

Percentage of sulphur left in the cinder with respect to the total sulphur charged

to the burner = $\left(\dfrac{2.787}{42.385}\right) \times 100 = \textbf{6.58}$

Example 4.13 A batch reactor contains 1 200 L of reactants' mass. Density of the mass is 1.2 kg/L and its pH is 6. It is required to raise pH of the reaction mass from 6 to 9 by adding 0.5% (by mass) NaOH solution. Density of the NaOH solution is 1.005 kg/L. Calculate the mass of 0.5% NaOH solution required to be added to raise the pH.

Solution Let m_s be the mass (in g) of 0.5% NaOH solution required and ρ_s be the density of the resulting solution (in kg/L).

Mass of the reactants = $1200 \times 1.2 = 1440$ kg

pOH of the reaction mass = $14 - 6 = 8$

pOH of the final (resulting) mass = $14 - 9 = 5$

pH of 0.5% NaOH solution = 12.85   (Ref. Fig. 2.2)

pOH of 0.5% NaOH solution = $14 - 12.85 = 1.15$

$$\rho_s = \frac{1}{\sum \dfrac{w_i}{\rho_{si}}}$$

where $\qquad w_i$ = mass fraction of ith component in solution

ρ_{si} = density of pure componet i, kg/L

$$\rho_s = \frac{1}{\left(\dfrac{1440 \times 10^3}{(1440 \times 10^3 + m_s)} \times \dfrac{1}{1.2}\right) + \left(\dfrac{m_s}{(1440 \times 10^3 + m_s)} \times \dfrac{1}{1.005}\right)}$$

$$= \frac{1440 \times 10^3 + m_s}{1200 \times 10^3 + 0.995\, m_s} \qquad\qquad \text{(i)}$$

Balance of OH⁻ ions

$$1200 \times 10^{-8} + \left(\frac{m_s}{1.005 \times 10^3}\right) \times 10^{-1.15} = \left(\frac{1200 \times 1.2 \times 10^3 + m_s}{\rho_s \times 10^3}\right) \times 10^{-5}$$

$$(1.2 \times 10^{-5}) + (7.044 \times 10^{-5}\, m_s) = \left(\frac{1440 \times 10^3 + m_s}{\rho_s \times 10^3}\right) \times 10^{-5} \qquad \text{(ii)}$$

Solving Eq. (i) and Eq. (ii),

$$m_s = \textbf{170.21 g}$$
$$\rho_s = \textbf{1.2016 kg/L}$$

4.5 LINEAR MODEL FOR MATERIAL BALANCE PROBLEMS INVOLVING CHEMICAL REACTIONS

Material balance problems around a reactor can be solved by using the linear model method, introduced in Chapter 3. If flow rates of ingoing components to the reactor and performance variables (namely, converison and yield) are known, flow rates of the outcoming components can be calculated by the model. Consider the following steady-state reactor system as under in which multiple reactions are taking place.

$$\dot{n}_{i,\text{out}} = \dot{n}_{i,\text{in}}\,(1 - f_{ci}) \tag{4.22}$$

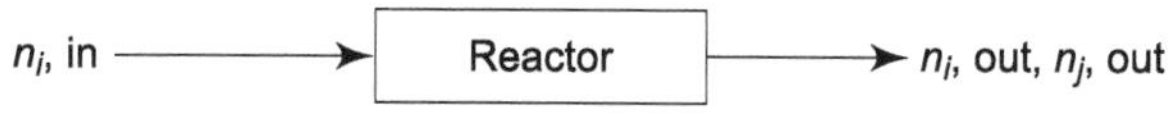

$$n_i, \text{ in} \longrightarrow \boxed{\text{Reactor}} \longrightarrow n_j, \text{ out}, n_j, \text{ out}$$

Fig. 4.2 Schematic Representation of a Steady-state Reactor System

where i = incoming components
j = newly formed products
$i + j$ = total components of outlet stream

where f_{ci} = fractional conversion of reactant i

$$= \frac{\dot{n}_{i,\text{in}} - \dot{n}_{i,\text{out}}}{\dot{n}_{i,\text{in}}} \tag{4.23}$$

where $\dot{n}_{i,\text{in}}$ = molar flow rate of ith component at inlet
$\dot{n}_{i,\text{out}}$ = molar flow rate of ith component at outlet
For an inert component in the ingoing stream,

$$f_{ci} = 0$$

Hence $\dot{n}_{i,\text{in}} = \dot{n}_{i,\text{out}}$ for inert component
If only one reaction is taking place in the reactor, the extent of reaction is defined as

$$\varepsilon = \frac{\text{change in moles of any reaction component}}{\text{stoichiometric coefficient of the component}}$$

$$= \frac{\dot{n}_{i,\text{out}} - \dot{n}_{i,\text{in}}}{v_i} \tag{4.24}$$

where, v_i = stoichiometric coefficient of ith component
In a multiple reaction system, extent of the reaction of any reaction k can be written as

$$\varepsilon_k = \frac{\dot{n}_{i,\text{out},k} - \dot{n}_{i,\text{in},k}}{v_{i,k}} \tag{4.25}$$

For the entire reaction system,

$$\dot{n}_{i,\,out} = \dot{n}_{i,\,in} + \sum_{all\ k} v_{i,\,k} \times \varepsilon_k \qquad (4.26)$$

From Eqs (4.23) and (4.26),

$$f_{ci} = \frac{-\sum v_{i,\,k} \times \varepsilon_k}{n_{i,\,in}} \qquad (4.27)$$

Example 4.14   Solve Example 4.10 by Linear Model Method.

Solution   *Basis* Methanol feed rate of 4000 kg/h
Here, the reaction system involves nine components and total five reactions. Air is used as a source of oxygen, hence nitrogen is an additional inert component. For 10 components, 10 material balance equations [like Eq. (4.26)] can be written:

$$\dot{n}_{N_2,\,out} = \dot{n}_{N_2,\,in} \qquad (i)$$

$$\dot{n}_{CH_3OH,\,out} = \dot{n}_{CH_3OH,\,in} - \varepsilon_1 - \varepsilon_2 - \varepsilon_3 - \varepsilon_4 - 2\varepsilon_5 \qquad (ii)$$

$$\dot{n}_{O_2,\,out} = \dot{n}_{O_2,\,in} - 0.5\,\varepsilon_1 - 1.5\,\varepsilon_2 + 0.5\,\varepsilon_4 \qquad (iii)$$

$$\dot{n}_{H_2O,\,out} = \dot{n}_{H_2O,\,in} + \varepsilon_1 + 2\varepsilon_2 + \varepsilon_5 \qquad (iv)$$

$$\dot{n}_{HCHO,\,out} = \dot{n}_{HCHO,\,in} + \varepsilon_1 \qquad (v)$$

$$\dot{n}_{CO_2,\,out} = \dot{n}_{CO_2,\,in} + \varepsilon_2 \qquad (vi)$$

$$\dot{n}_{CO,\,out} = \dot{n}_{CO,\,in} + \varepsilon_3 \qquad (vii)$$

$$\dot{n}_{H_2,\,out} = \dot{n}_{H_2,\,in} + 2\varepsilon_3 \qquad (viii)$$

$$\dot{n}_{CH_4,\,out} = \dot{n}_{CH_4,\,in} + \varepsilon_4 \qquad (ix)$$

$$\dot{n}_{(CH_3)_2O,\,out} = \dot{n}_{(CH_3)_2O,\,in} + \varepsilon_5 \qquad (x)$$

For 5 reactions, 5 reactor performance equations [like Eq. (4.27)] can be written.

$$f_{c,\,CH_3OH} = \frac{(\varepsilon_1 + \varepsilon_2 + \varepsilon_3 + \varepsilon_4 + 2\varepsilon_5)}{\dot{n}_{CH_3OH,\,in}} \qquad (xi)$$

$$f_{c,\,O_2} = \frac{(0.5\,\varepsilon_1 + 1.5\,\varepsilon_2 - 0.5\,\varepsilon_4)}{\dot{n}_{O_2,\,in}} \qquad (xii)$$

$$f_{c,\,H_2O} = \frac{(-\varepsilon_1 - 2\varepsilon_2 - \varepsilon_5)}{\dot{n}_{H_2O,\,in}} \qquad (xiii)$$

$$f_{c,\,CH_3OH\,(4)} = \frac{\varepsilon_4}{\dot{n}_{CH_3OH,\,in}} \qquad (xiv)$$

$$f_{c,\,CH_3OH\,(5)} = \frac{2\varepsilon_5}{\dot{n}_{CH_3OH,\,in}} \qquad (xiv)$$

The above 15 equations are presented in matrix form as under. All fractional conversions are calcutlated as under and put into matrix Examples of fractional conversion calculation:

$$f_{c,O_2} = \frac{\text{moles of } O_2 \text{ consumed in reactions}}{\text{moles of } O_2 \text{ fed to reactor}}$$

$$= \frac{125 \times 0.99(\ 0.9 \times 0.5 + 0.1 \times 0.71 \times 1.5 - 0.1 \times 0.05 \times 0.5)}{281.27}$$

$$= 0.2437$$

$$f_{c,H_2O} = \frac{-125 \times 0.99[(0.9 + 0.1 \times 0.7)2 + (0.1 \times 0.16 \times 0.5)]}{33.73}$$

$$= -5.47566$$

$$f_{c,CH_3OH(4)} = 0.99 \times 0.1 \times 0.05 = 0.00495$$

$$f_{c,CH_3OH(5)} = 0.99 \times 0.1 \times 0.16 = 0.01584$$

$$f_{c,CH_3OH(4)} \times \dot{n}_{CH_3OH,in} = 0.00495 \times 125 = 0.61875$$

$$f_{c,CH_3OH(5)} \times \dot{n}_{CH_3OH,in} = 0.01584 \times 125 = 1.98$$

$$MX = V$$

$$X = \begin{bmatrix} \dot{n}_{N_2,out} \\ \dot{n}_{CH_3OH,out} \\ \dot{n}_{O_2,out} \\ n_{H_2O,out} \\ \dot{n}_{HCHO,out} \\ \dot{n}_{CO_2,out} \\ \dot{n}_{CO,out} \\ n_{H_2,out} \\ \dot{n}_{CH_4,out} \\ \dot{n}_{(CH_3)_2O,out} \\ \varepsilon_1 \\ \varepsilon_2 \\ \varepsilon_3 \\ \varepsilon_4 \\ \varepsilon_5 \end{bmatrix}$$

Mathcad Solution

$$M := \begin{pmatrix}
1 & 0 & 0 & 0 & 0 & 0 & 0 & 0 & 0 & 0 & 0 & 0 & 0 & 0 & 0 \\
0 & 1 & 0 & 0 & 0 & 0 & 0 & 0 & 0 & 0 & 1 & 1 & 1 & 1 & 2 \\
0 & 0 & 1 & 0 & 0 & 0 & 0 & 0 & 0 & 0 & 0.5 & 1.5 & 0 & -0.5 & 0 \\
0 & 0 & 0 & 1 & 0 & 0 & 0 & 0 & 0 & 0 & -1 & -2 & 0 & 0 & -1 \\
0 & 0 & 0 & 0 & 1 & 0 & 0 & 0 & 0 & 0 & -1 & 0 & 0 & 0 & 0 \\
0 & 0 & 0 & 0 & 0 & 1 & 0 & 0 & 0 & 0 & 0 & -1 & 0 & 0 & 0 \\
0 & 0 & 0 & 0 & 0 & 0 & 1 & 0 & 0 & 0 & 0 & 0 & -1 & 0 & 0 \\
0 & 0 & 0 & 0 & 0 & 0 & 0 & 1 & 0 & 0 & 0 & 0 & -2 & 0 & 0 \\
0 & 0 & 0 & 0 & 0 & 0 & 0 & 0 & 1 & 0 & 0 & 0 & 0 & -1 & 0 \\
0 & 0 & 0 & 0 & 0 & 0 & 0 & 0 & 0 & 1 & 0 & 0 & 0 & 0 & -1 \\
0 & 0 & 0 & 0 & 0 & 0 & 0 & 0 & 0 & 0 & 1 & 1 & 1 & 1 & 2 \\
0 & 0 & 0 & 0 & 0 & 0 & 0 & 0 & 0 & 0 & 0.5 & 1.5 & 0 & -0.5 & 0 \\
0 & 0 & 0 & 0 & 0 & 0 & 0 & 0 & 0 & 0 & -1 & -2 & 0 & 0 & -1 \\
0 & 0 & 0 & 0 & 0 & 0 & 0 & 0 & 0 & 0 & 0 & 0 & 0 & 1 & 0 \\
0 & 0 & 0 & 0 & 0 & 0 & 0 & 0 & 0 & 0 & 0 & 0 & 0 & 0 & 2
\end{pmatrix}$$

$$v := \begin{pmatrix}
1058.1 \\
125 \\
281.27 \\
23.73 \\
0 \\
0 \\
0 \\
0 \\
0 \\
0 \\
0.99 \cdot 125 \\
0.2437 \cdot 281.27 \\
-5.4756 \cdot 23.73 \\
0.61875 \\
1.98
\end{pmatrix}$$

$$\text{soln} := M^{-1}v$$

	0
0	$1.0581 \cdot 10^3$
1	1.25
2	212.7245
3	153.6674
4	111.4227
5	8.7623
6	0.9662
7	1.9323
8	0.6188
9	0.99
10	111.4227
11	8.7623
12	0.9662
13	0.6188
14	0.99

$\text{soln} :=$ $\dfrac{\text{kmol}}{\text{h}}$

4.6   ELECTROCHEMICAL REACTIONS

Electrochemistry is an important branch of chemistry. The chlor–alkali industry, aluminium industry, copper industry, etc. are the typical examples of electrochemical industries.

In an electrochemical cell, the amount of an electrolyte liberated depends on the current and time. Theoretically, the amount of current required to liberate 1 g eq of an electrolyte at each pole is the *faraday* (F), which is equal to 96 485.3399 coulombs/mol.

$$1 \text{ coulomb} = 1 \text{ ampere} \cdot \text{second}$$

In actual practice, 1 faraday will liberate less than 1 g eq electrolyte. The ratio of the theoretical faraday consumption to the actual faraday consumption is defined as the current efficiency of the cell.

It may be noted that in electrochemical reactions, only the current is important for the liberation of the electrolyte. Hence, in most electrolytic cells, for maximum utilisation of the power, the voltage is kept as low as possible while the current is kept to its maximum.

Example 4.15 In an electrochemical cell, the current is passed at the rate of 1130 amperes for 18 000 s through a solution containing copper sulphate. At the end of the process, 1.12 m³ of oxygen (at NTP) is collected. Find (a) amount of copper liberated, and (b) the current efficiency of the cell.

Solution

Basis 1.12 m³ of oxygen at NTP

At NTP, the specific volume of oxygen = 22.4 m³/kmol

$$\text{Oxygen liberated} = 1.12 \text{ m}^3 = 1.12 \times \frac{1}{22.414} \text{ kmol}$$

$$\equiv 50 \text{ mol} \equiv 1600 \text{ g}$$

$$\text{Equivalent mass of oxygen} = \frac{16}{2} = 8$$

$$\text{Oxygen liberated} = \frac{1600}{8} = 200 \text{ g eq}$$

These electrochemical reactions taking place in the cell are:

$$CuSO_4 = Cu^{++} + SO_4^{--}$$

At the cathode $Cu^{++} + 2e = Cu$

At the anode $SO_4^{--} - 2e = SO_4$

$$SO_4^{--} + 2 H_2O = H_2SO_4 + 2 OH^-$$

$$2 OH^- = H_2O + \frac{1}{2} O_2 + 2e$$

Thus,   1 mole of $O_2 \equiv$ 2 moles of $CuSO_4$

$$\text{Equivalent mass of Cu} = \frac{63.5}{2} = 31.75$$

$$\text{Copper deposited} = \frac{(31.75 \times 1600)}{8} = \mathbf{6350 \text{ g}}$$

$$\text{Total energy passed through the solution in the cell} = \frac{(1130 \times 18\,000)}{96\,485} \text{ faradays}$$

$$\text{Theoretical liberation of Cu} = \left(\frac{1130 \times 18\,000 \times 31.75}{96\,485} \right)$$

$$= 6693.2 \text{ g}$$

$$\text{Current efficiency} = \left(\frac{\text{Cu liberated actually}}{\text{theoretical liberation of Cu}} \right) \times 100$$

$$= \left(\frac{6350}{6693.2} \right) \times 100 = \mathbf{94.87\%}$$

Example 4.16 Typical operating data on the Hooker-type diaphragm cell are as follows:

Power characteristics: 3.25 V, 15 000 A

Brine feed = 26.6% NaCl by mass at
65 to 70°C (338 K to 343 K)

NaOH concentration in the cell liquor = 11.0% by mass

Salt/NaOH ratio in the cell liquor = 1.4:1.0 by mass

Temperature of the cell liquor = 87°C (360 K)

Production of NaOH = 514.1 kg/(d · cell)

Based on the above data, find (a) the current efficiency of the cell, (b) the amounts of chlorine and hydrogen produced from the cell, and (c) the evaporation loss (of water) in the cell.

Solution *Basis* 1 day operation of the cell
The reactions taking place in the cell are

$$NaCl = Na^+ + Cl^-$$
$$H_2O = H^+ + OH^-$$
$$Na^+ + OH^- = NaOH$$

$$H^+ + e = \frac{1}{2} H_2$$

$$Cl^- - e = \frac{1}{2} Cl_2$$

Total energy passed through the cell $= \dfrac{(15\ 000 \times 3600 \times 24)}{96\ 485}$

$$= 13\ 432.1 \text{ faraday/d}$$

Theoretical (expected) NaOH formation $= \dfrac{(15\ 000 \times 3600 \times 24 \times 40)}{(96\ 485 \times 1000)}$

$$= 537.3 \text{ kg/d}$$

Current efficiency $= \left(\dfrac{\text{actual NaOH produced}}{\text{theoretical NaOH Production}}\right) \times 100$

$$= \left(\frac{514.1}{537.3}\right) \times 100 = \mathbf{95.7\%}$$

Chlorine produced $= \left(\dfrac{35.5}{40}\right) \times 514.1 = \mathbf{456.3\ kg/d}$

Hydrogen produced $= \dfrac{(456.3 \times 2)}{(35.5 \times 2)} = \mathbf{12.85\ kg/d}$

Now, 40 g NaOH $\equiv$ 58.5 g NaCl

NaCl consumed in the reaction $= \left(\dfrac{58.5}{40}\right) \times 514.1 = 751.9 \text{ kg/d}$

Cell liquor contains 11.0% NaOH.

Total cell liquor $= \dfrac{514.1}{0.11} = 4673.6 \text{ kg/d}$

NaCl that remained in the cell liquor $= 514.1 \times 1.4 = 719.7 \text{ kg/d}$

Total NaCl entering the system $= 751.9 + 719.7 = 1471.6 \text{ kg/d}$

The original feed contains 26.6% NaCl.

Brine feed rate $= \dfrac{1471.6}{0.266} = 5532.3 \text{ kg/d}$

Water consumed in the reaction $= \left(\dfrac{18}{40}\right) \times 514.1 = 231.3 \text{ kg/d}$

Hence,

Loss of water due to evaporation = 5532.3 − (4673.6 + 231.3)
= **627.4 kg/d**

4.7   RECYCLING, PARALLEL AND BYPASSING OPERATIONS

The recycling operation with chemical reactions is common in industrial processes. This is mainly performed to utilise the valuable reactants to their maximum so that the loss of the reactants is minimised. However, various reasons for carrying out these operations are described in detail in Section 3.6. In most cases, the inerts enter with the fresh feed, which need to be limited to a desired level in the so-called *mixed or combined feed* of the fresh feed and recycle feed. For limiting the inerts, a portion of the recycle stream is purged.

For the overall material balance calculations, the recycling stream can be omitted as discussed in Chapter 3. After finding the flow rates of incoming and/or outgoing streams, the recycling ratio can be easily calculated.

Parallel and bypassing operations are often encountered in industry. The materials balances of these operations are easier to evaluate than in the case of recycling operations.

Example 4.17   A fertiliser plant produces ammonia by reforming naphtha with steam. The synthesis gas, obtained from the methanator is passed through the converter after mixing with the recycle stream. Based on the operating parameters of the converter, the conversion per pass is limited to 25%. The composition of the fresh feed (synthesis make-up gas) is CH_4: 0.7%, Ar: 0.3%, H_2: 74.25% and

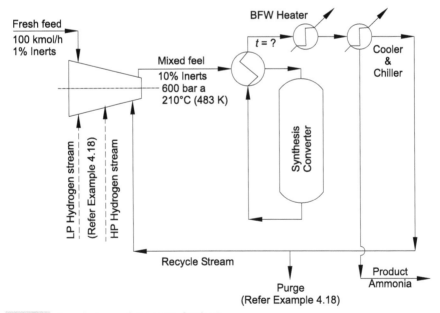

Fig. 4.3   Recycle Loop of Ammonia Synthesis

N_2: 24.75% on mole basis. The converter outlet gases pass through the heat exchanger where it cools down. Later, the gases are passed through a chiller-cum-separator which separates 65% of the ammonia present in the converter outlet gas. Noncondensible gases and uncondensed ammonia are recycled back. In order to limit the concentration of inerts (CH_4 + Ar) to 10 mole % in the mixed feed, a portion of the recycle stream is purged.

Based on a fresh feed rate of 100 kmol/s, calculate (a) the recycle feed rate and recycle ratio, (b) the purge gas rate, (c) the product ammonia rate, and (d) the compositions of various streams.

Solution   The process flow diagram is schematically represented in Fig. 4.3.

Basis 100 kmol/s of fresh feed

Let M, F and R respectively be the kmol/s of the mixed feed to the converter, fresh feed and recycle stream.

Material balance of feed $F + R = M$

$$M = 100 + R \qquad (i)$$

Let a be the kmol/s of N_2 in the mixed feed.

$$H_2 \text{ in the mixed feed} = 3a \text{ kmol/s}$$

$$\text{Inerts } (CH_4 + Ar) \text{ in the mixed feed} = 0.1M$$

$$\text{Ammonia in the mixed feed} = M - a - 3a - 0.1M$$

$$= (0.9M - 4a) \text{ kmol/s}$$

Chemical reaction $N_2 + 3 H_2 = 2 NH_3$

$$\text{Conversion per pass} = 25\%$$

$$N_2 \text{ reacted in the converter} = 0.25a \text{ kmol/s}$$

$$H_2 \text{ reacted in the converter} = 3 \times 0.25a = 0.75a \text{ kmol/s}$$

$$NH_3 \text{ produced in the converter} = 2 \times 0.25a = 0.50a \text{ kmol/s}$$

$$\text{Total gas mixture leaving the converter} = M - 0.25a - 0.75a + 0.5a$$

$$= (M - 0.5a) \text{ kmol/s}$$

$$\text{Total } NH_3 \text{ in the outlet gas} = 0.5a + 0.9M - 4a$$

$$= (0.9M - 3.5a) \text{ kmol/s}$$

$$NH_3 \text{ separated in the separator} = (0.9M - 3.5a) \, 0.65$$

$$= (0.585M - 2.275a) \text{ kmol/s}$$

$$NH_3 \text{ uncondensed} = (0.9M - 3.5a) \, 0.35$$

$$= (0.315M - 1.225 \, a) \text{ kmol/s}$$

The above values are listed in Table 4.13.

Table 4.13   Composition of Gas Mixture Leaving the Separator

Component	kmol/s
N_2	$0.75a$
H_2	$2.25a$
NH_3	$0.315M - 1.225a$
Inerts: (CH_4 + Ar)	$0.1M$
Total	$0.415M + 1.775a$

Let the purge be P kmol/s.

For the inerts level to be maintained in the fresh feed, the inerts exhausted out with the purge should equal the inerts in the fresh feed.

$$\text{Inerts in the purge} = \frac{0.1\,MP}{(0.415\,M + 1.775a)}\ \text{kmol/s}$$

$$\text{Inerts in the fresh feed} = 100 \times 0.01 = 1.0\ \text{kmol/s}$$

Therefore, $0.1MP/(0.415M + 1.775a) = 1.0$ (ii)

$$\text{Recycle stream} = (0.415M + 1.775a - P)\ \text{kmol/s}$$

Substituting this value in Eq. (i),

$$100 + 0.415M - P + 1.775a = M \qquad\qquad \text{(iii)}$$

Balance of nitrogen

$$\text{Nitrogen lost in purge} = \frac{0.75\,aP}{(0.415\,M + 1.775a)}\ \text{kmol/s}$$

N_2 in the recycle stream $= 0.75a - [0.75aP/(0.415M + 1.775a)]$ kmol/s

N_2 in the fresh feed $= 24.75$ kmol/s

Hence, $0.75a - \left[\dfrac{0.75\,aP}{(0.415\,M + 1.775a)}\right] + 24.75 = a$ (iv)

Equations (ii), (iii) and (iv) need to be solved for evaluating a, M and P. Substituting the value of $0.415M + 1.775a = 0.1MP$ [from Eq. (ii)] in Eq. (iv),

$$0.75a - \left[\frac{0.75\,aP}{0.1\,MP}\right] + 24.75 = a$$

$$a = \frac{24.75\,M}{0.25\,M + 7.5} \qquad\qquad \text{(v)}$$

From Eq. (ii), $P = (4.15\,M + 17.75a)/M$

Substituting the value of P in Eq. (iii),

$$0.585M - 1.775a + (4.15M + 17.75a)/M = 100$$

or $0.585M^2 - 1.775aM + 4.15M + 17.75a = 100M$ (vi)

Substituting the value of a from Eq. (v) into Eq. (vi),

$$0.585M^2 - 1.775M\left[\frac{24.75\,M}{0.25\,M + 7.5}\right] - 95.85M + 17.75\left[\frac{24.75\,M}{0.25\,M + 7.5}\right] = 0$$

(vii)

Simplifying Eq. (vii),

$$0.146\,25M^2 - 63.506\,25 - 279.5625 = 0$$

$$M = 438.589\ \text{kmol/s}\ \ \text{(only positive root)}$$

From Eq. (v), $a = \dfrac{24.75 \times 438.589}{(0.25 \times 438.589) + 7.5}$

$$= 92.662\ \text{kmol/s}$$

From Eq. (ii),

$$P = \frac{(4.15 \times 438.589) + (17.75 \times 92.662)}{438.589} = \textbf{7.900 kmol/s}$$

Recycle stream R = 438.589 − 100.0 = **338.589 kmol/s**

$$\text{Recycle ratio} = \frac{338.589}{100} = \textbf{3.386 kmol/kmol fresh feed}$$

$$\text{Product NH}_3 \text{ rate} = 0.585M - 2.275 \ a$$
$$= 0.585 \times 438.589 - 2.275 \times 92.662$$
$$= 45.769 \text{ kmol/s}$$

Mass rate of NH_3 product = 45.769 × 17.0305 = **779.47 kg/s**

The composition of various streams are given in Tables 4.14 and 4.15.

Table 4.14 Composition of Different Streams

Component	Fresh feed (F)		Recycle stream (R)		Mixed feed (M)	
	kmol/s	mole %	kmol/s	mole %	kmol/s	mole %
N_2	24.75	24.75	67.912	20.06	92.662	21.13
H_2	74.25	74.25	203.736	60.17	277.986	63.38
$(CH_4 + Ar)$	1.00	1.00	42.859	12.66	43.859	10.00
NH_3	Nil	Nil	24.082	7.11	24.082	5.49
Total	100.00	100.00	338.589	100.00	438.589	100.00

Table 4.15 Composition of Different Streams (Contd.)

Component	Converter outlet stream		Gas stream after separator	
	kmol/s	mole %	kmol/s	mole %
N_2	69.497	17.72	69.497	20.06
H_2	208.490	53.15	208.490	60.17
$(CH_4 + Ar)$	43.859	11.18	43.859	12.66
NH_3	70.413	17.95	24.644	7.11
Total	392.259	100.00	346.490	100.00

Note The example illustrates the actual design calculations of a recycle loop. However, if it is assumed that the whole of ammonia formed in the converter is condensed and separated in the separator, the material balance calculations become simple. Solution of simultaneous equations can be made easy with Mathcad (refer Chapter 9).

Example 4.18 In Example 4.17, purge stream contains 60 mole % H_2 and more than 7.3 mole % NH_3. Both are valuable constituents and therefore need to be recovered. As an energy conservation program, two-stage membrane separators are employed as shown in Fig. 4.4.

The purge stream is first fed to an absorber to recover as 4% aqueous ammonia solution (refer Example 6.20). Moist gas from the absorber is sent to a drying unit, packed with molecular sieves. Dry gas [having pressure dew point less than −60°C (213 K)] is then fed to two banks of polymeric membranes. Enriched hydrogen stream from the first bank is recycled at 68.5 bar a while that from the second bank is recycled at 24.5 bar a. Both the enriched streams have nearly same compostion; 90% H_2, 5% N_2 and rest inerts by mole. Overall recovery of hydrogen can be taken as 90% based on that contained in the

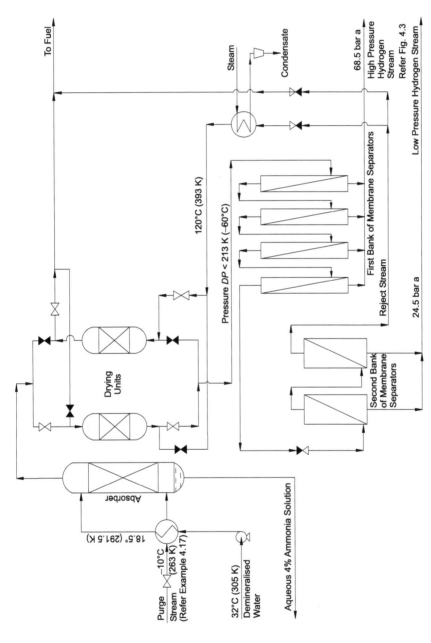

Fig. 4.4 Hydrogen Recovery from Purge Gas by Membrane Modules

feed purge stream. Considering these additional recycles, establish the material balance of the synthesis loop and memberane banks.

Solution The recycle stream, shown in Fig. 4.3, will be redesignated as R_1 kmol/s ($= R$) while recovered hydrogen streams (two together) from the membrane banks will be designated as R_2 kmol/s. Since one more variable (R_2) is introduced, one more equation will be necessary. Since R_2 is rich in H_2 and M has H_2/N_2 ratio equal to 3.0, H_2/N_2 ratio of F will no longer be 3.0. In fact, H_2/N_2 ratio of F will be less than 3.0 to compensate for N_2 requrement of stream M. Table 4.13 will remain unchanged. Purge stream (after ammonia separation) is fed to the membrane banks as shown in Fig. 4.3.

$$H_2 \text{ in } P = \frac{2.25 \, aP}{(0.415 \, M + 1.775 \, a)} \text{ kmol/s}$$

Overall hydrogen recovery is 90% and R_2 contains 5% each of N_2 and inerts.

$$R_2 = \frac{2.25 \, aP \times 0.9}{0.9 \, (0.415 \, M + 1.775 \, a)} = \frac{2.25 \, aP}{(0.415 \, M + 1.775 \, a)} \text{ kmol/s}$$

$$\text{Inerts/N}_2 \text{ in } R_2 = \frac{0.05 \times 2.25 \, aP}{(0.415 \, M + 1.775 \, a)}$$

$$= \frac{0.1125 \, aP}{(0.415 \, M + 1.775 \, a)} \text{ kmol/s} \quad \text{(each)}$$

Inerts in the reject stream from the memberane

$$\text{banks} = \frac{0.1 \, M \, P}{(0.415 \, M + 1.775 \, a)} - \frac{0.1125 \, aP}{(0.415 \, M + 1.775 \, a)} = 1 \qquad \text{(i)}$$

$$\text{Ammonia balance,} \quad \frac{(0.315 \, M - 1.225 \, a) \, R_1}{(0.415 \, M + 1.775 \, a)} = 0.9 \, M - 4a \qquad \text{(ii)}$$

Overall material balance,

$$M = 100 + R_1 + R_2$$

$$= 100 + R_1 + \frac{2.25 \, aP}{(0.415 \, M + 1.775 \, a)} \qquad \text{(iii)}$$

Inerts balance in the loop,

$$\frac{0.1 \, M \, R_1}{(0.415 \, M + 1.775 \, a)} + \frac{0.1125 \, M \, P}{(0.415 \, M + 1.775 \, a)} + 1 = 0.1 \, M \qquad \text{(iv)}$$

Solving above four equations by Mathcad,

Mathcad Solution

Guess Values:

M := 45(R_1 := 35(P := 10.(a := 7(

Given

$$\frac{\left(0.1{\cdot}M{\cdot}R_1\right)}{(0.415\,M + 1.775\,a)} + \frac{(0.1125\,a{\cdot}P)}{(0.415\,M + 1.775\,a)} + 1 = 0.1{\cdot}M$$

$$\frac{R_1 \cdot (0.315M - 1.225a)}{(0.415M + 1.775a)} = (0.9 M - 4 \cdot a)$$

$$M = 100 + R_1 + \frac{(2.25 a \cdot P)}{(0.415M + 1.775a)}$$

$$\frac{0.1 \cdot M P}{(0.415M + 1.775a)} - \frac{(0.1125 a \cdot P)}{(0.415M + 1.775a)} = 1$$

$$\text{vec} := \text{Find}(M, R_1, P, a)$$

$$\text{vec} = \begin{pmatrix} 457.011 \\ 350.771 \\ 10.368 \\ 96.608 \end{pmatrix} \frac{\text{kmol}}{\text{h}}$$

$$M = 457.011 \text{ kmol/s}$$
$$R_1 = 350.771 \text{ kmol/s}$$
$$P = 10.368 \text{ kmol/s}$$
$$a = 96.608 \text{ kmol/s}$$

$$R_2 = \frac{2.25 \times 96.608 \times 10.369}{(0.415 \times 457.011 + 1.775 \times 96.608)}$$

$$= 6.240 \text{ kmol/s}$$

With above flow rates, following tables are prepared.

Table 4.16 Composition of Different Streams

Component	Mixed feed (M)		R_1 Stream		R_2 Stream	
	kmol/s	mole %	kmol/s	mole %	kmol/s	mole %
N_2	96.608	21.14	70.376	20.06	0.311	4.98
H_2	289.824	63.42	211.129	60.19	5.616	90.00
(CH_4 + Ar)	45.701	10.00	44.388	12.66	0.313	5.02
NH_3	24.878	5.44	24.878	7.09	Nil	Nil
Total	457.011	100.00	350.771	100.00	6.240	100.00

Table 4.17 Composition of Different Streams (Contd.)

Component	Fresh feed $F = M - R_1 - R_2$		Purge (P) stream		Reject stream	
	kmol/s	mole %	kmol/s	mole %	kmol/s	mole %
H_2	25.921	25.92	2.081	20.06	1.769	52.14
N_2	73.079	73.08	6.240	60.19	0.624	18.39
(CH_4 + Ar)	1.000	1.00	1.313	12.66	1.000	29.47
NH_3	Nil	Nil	0.735	7.09	Nil	Nil
Total	100.000	100.00	10.368	100.00	3.393	100.00

$$H_2/N_2 \text{ ratio in fresh feed} = \frac{73.079}{25.921} = 2.819 \quad (< 3.0)$$

Ammonia condensed $= 0.585 \, M - 2.275 \, a$

$\qquad\qquad\qquad = 0.585 \times 457.011 - 2.275 \times 96.608$

$\qquad\qquad\qquad = 47.568$ kmol/s

Ammonia recovered as aqueous solution

$\qquad$ from absober $= 0.735$ kmol/s

$\qquad$ Total NH_3 produced $= 47.568 + 0.735 = 48.303$ kmol/s

$\qquad\qquad\qquad\qquad \equiv 822.624$ kg/s

$$\text{Increase in } NH_3 \text{ production} = \frac{(48.303 - 45.769)\,100}{45.769}$$

$$= 5.54 \%$$

$$\text{Recycle ratio} = \frac{R_1 + R_2}{F}$$

$$= \frac{(350.771 + 6.240)}{100}$$

$$= 3.57 \text{ kmol/ kmol fresh feed}$$

Example 4.19   In a partial demineralisation plant (also called a blend process), the raw water is divided into two streams. One stream passes through the sodium ion exchanger while the other stream passes through the hydrogen-ion exchanger. The process is represented in Fig. 4.5

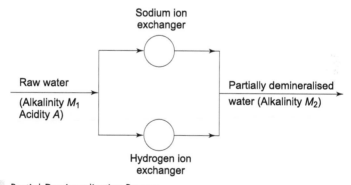

Fig. 4.5   Partial Demineralisation Process

In a particular partial demineraliser, the raw water analysis is observed to be as follows:

Total alkalinity (methyl-orange reading) $= 550$ mg/L as $CaCO_3$

Permanent hardness $=$ Nil

Chlorides as Cl $= 312$ mg/L

Sulphates as $SO_4 = 43.2$ kg/L

The mixed effluents of sodium ion and hydrogen ion exchangers were found to contain a total alkalinity of 50 mg/L as $CaCO_3$. Assume that both the ion exchangers are 100% efficient. Calculate the flow distribution of the water through the ion exchangers.

Solution Since the water does not contain permanent hardness, the chlorides and sulphates are attached to sodium (assuming that the water does not contain potassium). When the raw water passes through the hydrogen ion exchanger, the chlorides and sulphates are converted to the corresponding mineral acids, i.e., HCl and H_2SO_4, respectively. The bicarbonates and carbonates produce weak carbonic acid (H_2CO_3). Thus, the decationated water shows free acidity. When the water passes through the softener (i.e., sodium ion exchanger), the Ca^{++} and Mg^{++} ions are replaced by Na^+ ion. This means that $Ca(HCO_3)_2$ and $Mg(HCO_3)_2$ get converted to $NaHCO_3$. The softened water will have the same total alkalinity when expressed in terms of equivalent $CaCO_3$ (although the actual alkalinity figure will vary).

The reactions taking place in the ion exchangers are summarised below.

Hydrogen ion exchanger

$$NaCl + HRe = HCl + NaRe \qquad \text{(i)}$$
$$Na_2SO_4 + 2\ HRe = H_2SO_4 + 2\ NaRe \qquad \text{(ii)}$$
$$Ca(HCO_3)_2 + 2\ HRe = 2\ H_2CO_3 + Ca(Re)_2 \qquad \text{(iii)}$$
$$Mg(HCO_3) + 2\ HRe = 2\ H_2CO_3 + Mg\ (Re)_2 \qquad \text{(iv)}$$

Sodium ion exchanger

$$Ca(HCO_3)_2 + 2\ NaRe' = 2\ NaHCO_3 + Ca(Re')_2 \qquad \text{(v)}$$
$$Mg\ (HCO_3)_2 + 2\ NaRe' = 2\ NaHCO_3 + Mg(Re')_2 \qquad \text{(vi)}$$

(Re and Re' stand for resins)

$$\text{Chlorides, expressed as equivalent } CaCO_3 = \left(\frac{50}{35.5}\right) \times 312 = 439.44 \text{ mg/L}$$

$$\text{Sulphates, expressed as equivalent } CaCO_3 = \left(\frac{50}{48}\right) \times 43.2 = 45.0 \text{ mg/L}$$

Equivalent mineral acidity (EMA) in raw water, A = 439.44 + 45.0
$$= 484.44 \text{ mg/L as } CaCO_3$$

Let 100 L be the total raw water inlet to both the ion exchangers. Also let x L be the raw water inlet to the hydrogen ion exchanger.

Water input to sodium ion exchanger = $(100 - x)$ L

Free acidity in the demineralised water = $x\ (A + M_1)$ mg

where, M_1 is the total alkalinity of raw water.

Let M_2 be the total alkalinity of blend water.

Total alkalinity removed = $100\ (M_1 - M_2)$ mg

For the neutralisation to be balanced,

$$x\ (A + M_1) = 100\ (M_1 - M_2)$$

$$\frac{x}{100} = \left(\frac{M_1 + M_2}{A + M_1}\right)$$

$$= \left(\frac{550 - 50}{484.44 + 550}\right)$$

$$x = \textbf{48.34}$$

Thus, 48.34 % of the total raw water passes through the hydrogen ion exchanger.

Note This example illustrates the material balance calculations of the parallel flow operations. It may be noted that the final material balance equation could be written because all the values of acidity and alkalinity were expressed in terms of equivalent $CaCO_3$. Consider another operation in which there is no sodium ion exchanger. A part of the raw water, however, passes through the hydrogen ion exchanger and the rest is bypassed to blend with decationated water. Will the flow distribution (i.e., 48.94%) change to attain 50 mg/L of the total alkalinity in the blend water? Why?

Example 4.20   In Example 4.10, single reactor is considered for partial oxidation of methanol. In an innovative approach to boost the capacity of the existing plant, a second reactor is added in series[8] as shown in Fig. 4.6. Additional methanol is fed as bypass between the reactors and mixed with the gas mixture, leaving the first reactor in a static mixer.

Based on safety and catalyst life considerations, methanol concentration is controlled at 6.25% (by volume) at the first reactor inlet while maintaining total wet molar gas mixture flow rate to the first reactor constant. Methanol concentration at the inlet of second reactor is maintained at 8.4% (by volume) on wet basis. Assume that conversion per pass in both the reactors is 99%, yield of formaldehyde is 90% and other secondary reactions are also unchanged. Also assume that the absorber can be revamped to take additional load of formaldehyde to produce bottom solution of 37% (by mass).

Make material balance of the new series reactors scheme. Calculate increase in the capacity achieved and % methanol bypassed to the second reactor.

Solution   *Basis* Gas mixture flow to Reactor I = 1488.1 kmol/h
CH_3OH in the gas mixture = 1488.1 × 0.0625 = 93.0 kmol/h
Ambient (wet) air flow = 1488.1 − 93.0 = 1395.1 kmol/h

Dry air flow rate = $\dfrac{1395.1}{1.017\ 72}$ = 1370.8 kmol/h

Moisture, entering with air = 1395.1 − 1370.8 = 24.3 kmol/h

Table 4.18   Composition of Gas Mixture Entering Reactor-I

Component	$\dot{n}_i$, kmol/h	mole %
CH_3OH	93.00	6.25
O_2	287.87	19.35
N_2	1082.93	72.77
H_2O	24.30	1.63
Total	1488.10	100.00

Conversion of CH_3OH in R–I = 93.0 × 0.99
$= 92.07$ kmol/h
Unreacted CH_3OH = 93.0 − 92.07 = 0.93 kmol/h
Reaction (i)
CH_3OH reacted = 92.07 × 0.9 = 82.863 kmol/h
O_2 consumed = 82.863/2 = 41.43 kmol/h

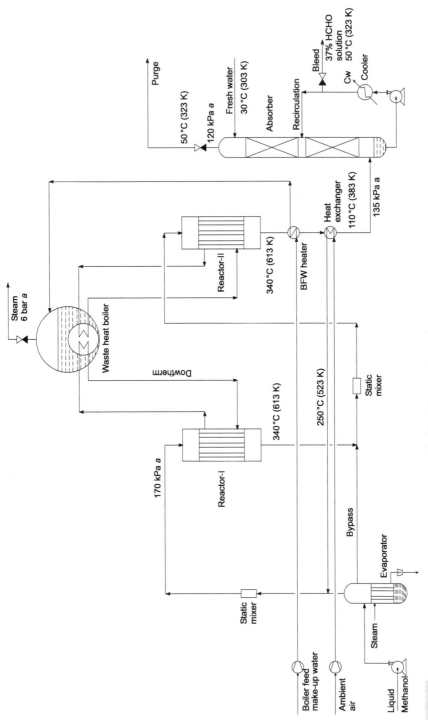

Fig. 4.6 Formaldehyde Production by Topsøe Process (Modified Formox Process)

HCHO produced = 82.863 kmol/h

H_2O produced = 82.863 kmol/h

CH_3OH reacted through reactions (ii) to (v) = 92.07 − 82.863

= 9.207 kmol/h

Reaction (ii)

CH_3OH reacted = 9.207 × 0.71 = 6.537 kmol/h

O_2 consumed = 1.5 × 6.537 = 9.806 kmol/h

CO_2 produced = 6.537 kmol/h

H_2O produced = 2 × 6.537 = 13.074 kmol/h

Reaction (iii)

CH_3OH reacted = 9.207 × 0.08 = 0.737 kmol/h

CO produced = 0.737 kmol/h

H_2 produced = 2 × 0.737 = 1.474 kmol/h

Reaction (iv)

CH_3OH reacted = 9.207 × 0.05 = 0.46 kmol/h

CH_4 produced = 0.46 kmol/h

O_2 produced = 0.46/2 = 0 .23 kmol/h

Reaction (v)

CH_3OH reacted = 9.207 − (6.537 + 0.737 + 0.46) = 1.473 kmol/h

$(CH_3)_2O$ produced = 1.473/2 = 0.737 kmol/h

H_2O produced = 1.473/2 = 0.737 kmol/h

O_2 in R-I exit gas stream = 287.87 − 41.43 − 9.805 + 0.23

= 236.865 kmol/h

H_2O in R-I exit gas stream = 24.3 + 82.863 + 13.074 + 0.737

= 120.974 kmol/h

Table 4.19 Composition of R-I Exit Gas Stream

Component	$\dot{n}_i$, kmol/h	mole %
CH_3OH	0.93	0.06
HCHO	92.07	5.96
CO_2	6.537	0.42
CO	0.737	0.05
H_2	1.474	0.10
CH_4	0.460	0.03
$(CH_3)_2O$	0.737	0.05
O_2	236.865	15.34
N_2	1082.930	70.15
H_2O	120.974	7.84
Total	1543.714	100.00

Let x kmol/h CH_3OH be added in between the reactors.

CH_3OH entering R-II = 0.93 + x kmol/h

$$\frac{0.93 + x}{1543.714 + x} = 0.084$$

or

$$x = 140.548 \text{ kmol/h}$$

CH_3OH entering R–II = 140.548 + 0.93 = 141.478 kmol/h

CH_3OH reacted in R–II = 141.478 × 0.99 = 140.063 kmol/h

Unreacted CH_3OH = 141.478 − 140.063 = 1.415 kmol/h

Reaction (i)

CH_3OH reacted = 140.063 × 0.9 = 126.057 kmol/h

O_2 consumed = 126.057/2 = 63.029 kmol/h

HCHO produced = 126.057 kmol/h

H_2O produced = 126.057 kmol/h

CH_3OH reacted through reaction (ii) to (v) = 140.063 − 126.057

= 14.006 kmol/h

Reaction (ii)

CH_3OH reacted = 14.006 × 0.71 = 9.944 kmol/h

O_2 consumed = 9.944 × 1.5 = 14.916 kmol/h

CO_2 produced = 9.944 kmol/h

H_2O produced = 2 × 9.944 = 19.888 kmol/h

Reaction (iii)

CH_3OH reacted = 14.006 × 0.08 = 1.12 kmol/h

CO produced = 1.12 kmol/h

H_2 produced = 1.12 × 2 = 2.24 kmol/h

Reaction (iv)

CH_3OH reacted = 14.006 × 0.05 = 0.7 kmol/h

CH_4 produced = 0.7 kmol/h

O_2 produced = 0.7/2 = 0.35 kmol/h

Reaction (v)

CH_3OH reacted = 14.006 − (9.944 + 1.12 + 0.7) = 2.242 kmol/h

$(CH_3)_2O$ produced = 2.242/2 = 1.121 kmol/h

H_2O produced = 2.242/2 = 1.121 kmol/h

O_2 in R-II exit gas stream = 236. 865 − (63.029 + 14.916 − 0.35)

= 159.27 kmol/h

H_2O in R-II exit gas stream = 120.974 + 126.057 + 19.888 + 1.121

= 268.04 kmol/h

HCHO in R-II exit gas stream = 92.07 + 126.057 = 218.127 kmol/h

Table 4.20 Composition of R-II Exit Gas Stream

Component	$\dot{n}_i$, kmol/h	mole %
CH_3OH	1.415	0.08
HCHO	218.127	12.43
CO_2	16.481	0.94
CO	1.857	0.11
H_2	3.714	0.21
CH_4	1.160	0.07
$(CH_3)_2O$	1.858	0.11
O_2	159.270	9.07
N_2	1082.930	61.71
H_2O	268.040	15.27
Total	1754.852	100.00

Material balance across absorber

$$\text{Total HCHO produced} = 218.127 \times 30 = 6543.8 \text{ kg/h}$$

$$\text{Total } CH_3OH \text{ fed to both reactors} = 140.548 + 93 = 223.548 \text{ kmol/h}$$

$$CH_3OH \text{ bypassed} = \frac{140.548 \times 100}{223.548} = \mathbf{62.87\%}$$

$$\text{Bottom solution flow rate} = \frac{6543.8}{0.37} = \mathbf{17\ 686.0 \ kg/h}$$

$$CH_3OH \text{ in bottom solution} = 1.415 \times 32 = 45.3 \text{ kg/h}$$

$$H_2O \text{ entering the absorber} = 268.04 \times 18 \quad (\text{in gas stream})$$
$$= 4824.7 \text{ kg/h}$$

$$\text{Dry tail gas flow rate} = 1754.852 - (1.415 + 218.127 + 268.04)$$
$$= 1267.27 \text{ kmol/h}$$

$$\text{Moisture in tail gas} = 1267.27 \times 0.1146$$
$$= 145.229 \text{ kmol/h} \equiv 2614.1 \text{ kg/h}$$

$$\text{Fresh water added} = 17\ 686.0 - (6543.8 + 45.3 + 4824.7)$$
$$+ 2614.1 = 8\ 886 \text{ m}^3/\text{h}$$

$$\text{Increase in capacity} = \frac{(17\ 686.0 - 9030.4)\ 100}{9030.4} = \mathbf{95.85\%}$$

Table 4.21 Composition of Tail (Purge) Gas from Absorber

Component	$\dot{n}_i$, kmol/h		mole %	
	Dry	Wet	Dry	Wet
UC	25.07	25.07	1.98	1.77
O_2	159.27	159.270	12.57	11.28
N_2	1082.93	1082.930	85.45	76.67
H_2O	—	145.229	—	10.28
Total	1267.27	1412.499	100.00	100.00

4.8   **METALLURGICAL APPLICATIONS**

Complex reactions take place in the furnaces where the metal is extracted from the ore. It is difficult to treat individual reactions as seen in various examples cited above. Overall material balances are set for getting the desired information. Example 4.21 will demonstrate the application of stoichiometry in extractive ferrous metallurgy.

Example 4.21 A blast furnace makes pig iron containing 3.6% C, 1.4% Si and 95% Fe. The ore used contains 80% Fe_2O_3, 12% SiO_2 and 8% Al_2O_3. The coke analysis shows the presence of 10% SiO and 90%C. The flux used is pure $CaCO_3$. The exit gases contain 28% CO and 14% CO_2. The coke ratio is 1 kg/kg pig iron. Flux is 0.4 kg/kg pig iron. Calculate per tonne of pig iron; (a) the mass of the slag made, (b) the mass of the ore used, (c) the composition of slag, and (d) the volume of the air required at NTP.

Solution

Basis 1 tonne (= 1000 kg) of pig iron

$$\text{Coke} = 1000 \text{ kg}$$
$$\text{Flux} = 400 \text{ kg}$$
$$\text{Fe in the pig iron} = 0.95 \times 1000 = 950 \text{ kg}$$
$$\text{Fe available per kg of ore} = \left(\frac{112}{160}\right) 0.8 = 0.56 \text{ kg}$$
$$\text{Ore required} = \frac{950}{0.56} = \mathbf{1696.43 \text{ kg}}$$

Silica balance Si in the pig iron = $0.014 \times 1000 = 14$ kg as Si

$$\text{SiO}_2 \text{ present in the pig iron} = \left(\frac{60}{28}\right) \times 14 = 30 \text{ kg}$$
$$\text{SiO}_2 \text{ present in the ore} = 1696.43 \times 0.12 = 203.57 \text{ kg}$$
$$\text{SiO}_2 \text{ present in the coke} = 0.10 \times 1000 = 100 \text{ kg}$$
$$\text{SiO}_2 \text{ present in the slag} = 203.57 + 100 - 30 = 273.57 \text{ kg}$$

Al$_2$O$_3$ balance Al$_2$O$_3$ present in the ore = $1696.43 \times 0.08 = 135.71$ kg

$$\text{Al}_2\text{O}_3 \text{ present in the slag} = 135.71 \text{ kg}$$

CaO balance

CaO comes into the slag due to the decomposition of CaCO$_3$.

$$\text{CaCO}_3 \text{ fed to the furnace} = 400 \text{ kg}$$
$$\text{CaO present in the slag} = \left(\frac{56}{100}\right) \times 400 = 224 \text{ kg}$$

The composition of the slag is given in Table 4.22.

Table 4.22   Composition of Slag

Component	Mass, kg	mass %
SiO$_2$	273.57	**43.20**
Al$_2$O$_3$	135.71	**21.43**
CaO	224.00	**35.37**
Total	**633.28**	**100.00**

Air requirement

Total carbon available = carbon present in the coke
+ carbon present in the CaCO$_3$
− carbon left over in pig iron

$$= 0.90 \times 1000 + \left(\frac{12}{100}\right) \times 400 - 36 = 912 \text{ kg as C}$$

In the blast, the ratio of CO to CO$_2$ is 2:1. Therefore, two-thirds of 912 kg C will be burnt to CO and one-third to CO$_2$

$$\text{Carbon converted to CO}_2 = \left(\frac{1}{3}\right) \times 912 = 304.0 \text{ kg}$$

$$\text{Carbon converted to CO} = \left(\frac{2}{3}\right) \times 912 = 608.0 \text{ kg}$$

Oxygen required to form CO and $CO_2 = 608 \times \left(\dfrac{16}{12}\right) + 304 \times \left(\dfrac{32}{12}\right)$

$$= 810.67 + 810.67 = 1621.34 \text{ kg as } O_2$$

Thus, the total oxygen requirement is 1621.34 kg. However, a part of the oxygen is available from SiO_2, Fe_2O_3 and $CaCO_3$.

$$SiO_2 = Si + O_2$$
$$60 \quad 28 \quad 32$$

Oxygen derived from $SiO_2 = \left(\dfrac{32}{28}\right) \times 14 = 16 \text{ kg}$

$$Fe_2O_3 = 2 \text{ Fe} + 3/2 \text{ } O_2$$
$$160 \quad 112 \quad 48$$

Oxygen derived from $Fe_2O_3 = \dfrac{1696.43 \times 0.8 \times 48}{160} = 407.14 \text{ kg}$

$$CaCO_3 = CaO + CO_2$$
$$100 \quad 56 \quad 44$$
$$CO_2 = C + O_2$$
$$44 \quad 12 \quad 32$$

Oxygen derived form $CaCO_3 = \dfrac{400 \times 32}{100} = 128 \text{ kg}$

Total oxygen available $= 16 + 407.14 + 128 = 551.14 \text{ kg}$

Oxygen to be supplied from air $= 1621.34 - 551.15 = 1070.19 \text{ kg}$

$$\equiv 33.44 \text{ kmol}$$

Air supplied $= \dfrac{33.44}{0.21} = 159.24 \text{ kmol}$

At NTP, specific volume of air $= 22.414 \text{ m}^3/\text{kmol}$

Volume of air supplied at NTP $= 159.24 \times 22.414 = \textbf{3569.2 m}^3$

Exercises

4.1 Methane is used as a raw material for the manufacture of ammonia. Reforming of methane with steam yields hydrogen.

$CH_4 + 2 H_2O = CO_2 + 4 H_2$

(a) Pure nitrogen is mixed with hydrogen to produce ammonia.

$N_2 + 3 H_2 = 2 NH_3$

Consider 100% conversions of both the reactions and calculate theoretical requirement of methane per tonne of ammonia.

(b) Instead of pure nitrogen, ambient air containing 78% N_2, 21% O_2 and 1% Ar (by volume) is mixed with hydrogen in stoichiometric proportion. Oxygen of air reacts with hydrogen as under.

$2 H_2 + O_2 = 2 H_2O$

Consider 100% conversions of all the reactions, 100% removal of ammonia from the reaction mass and venting of pure Ar to atmosphere. Calculate theoretical requirement of methane per tonne of ammonia.

[(a) **493.54 Nm^3/t NH$_3$**, (b) **582.13 Nm^3/t NH$_3$**]

4.2 Methane is used as a raw material for the manufacture of methanol. Reforming of methane with steam yields hydrogen.

$$CH_4 + 2 H_2O = CO_2 + 4 H_2$$

Reaction of hydrogen and carbon dioxide is carried out in a converter at specified conditions to produce methanol.

$$CO_2 + 3 H_2 = CH_3OH + H_2O$$

Consider 100% conversions of both the reactions and calculate theoretical requirement of methane per tonne methanol.   **[699.52 Nm^3/t CH$_3$OH]**

4.3 In Exercise 3.24, decoking of a catalyst is described. Calculate mass % coke on the catalyst, assuming average composition of the coke to be $CH_{0.6}$.   **[1.0%]**

4.4 A pilot plant reactor was charged with 50 kg of naphthalene and 200 kg (98% by mass) of H_2SO_4. The reaction was carried out for 3 hours at 160°C (433 K). The reaction goes to near completion. The product distribution[9] was found to be 18.6% monosulphonate naphthalene and 81.4% disulphonate naphthalene. Calculate (a) the quantities of monosulphonate (MSN) and disulphonate (DSN) products, and (b) the complete analysis of the product.

[(a) 19.53 kg MSN and 85.45 kg DSN
(b) 7.94% MSN, 34.74% DSN, 52.29% H$_2$SO$_4$ and 5.13% H$_2$O]

4.5 Dinitro-o-sec-butyl phenol (DNOSBP) is manufactured by the nitration of sec-butyl phenol (SBP) in presence of zinc chloride and hydrogen chloride.

SBP   **DNOSBP**

SBP   **DNOSBP**

After the reaction is complete, a sample from the reactor is analysed as follows:

Table 4.23   Analysis of Reactor Product

Component	mass %
Nitric acid	15
sec-Butyl phenol	65
4,6 Dinitro-*o-sec*- butyl phenol (DNOSBP)	18
3,6 Dinitro-*p-sec*-butyl phenol (DNPSBP)	2

Calculate (a) conversion, and (b) yield of *ortho* and *para* products.

[(a) Conversion = 41.2% (b) Yield of o-product = 90.04%
and of p-product = 9.96%]

4.6 Ethyl alcohol is industrially produced by fermenation of molasses[10]. A sample of molasses contains 45% (mass) fermentable sugars (in the form of sucrose). The reactions taking place in the fermenter are as follows:

$$C_{12}H_{22}O_{11} \quad + \quad H_2O \quad = \quad C_6H_{12}O_6 \quad + \quad C_6H_{12}O_6$$

Sucrose $\qquad\qquad\qquad\qquad\qquad$ d-Glucose $\qquad$ d-Fructose

$$C_6H_{12}O_6 \quad = \quad 2\ C_2H_5OH \quad + \quad 2\ CO_2$$

Monosaccharide $\qquad$ Alcohol

Calculate the theoretical production of rectified spirit (having density of 0.785 kg/L) in liters per tonne of molasses. **[308.41 L]**

4.7 Selective dehydrogenation of alkanes to alkenes is a well-established process. In this process, dehydrogenation of *i*-butane is carried out on a platinum impregnated catalyst at 50 kPa g and 500°C (773 K). The feed to the reactor is pure *i*-butane alongwith 0.75 kmol H_2 per kmol *i*-butane. Hydrogen stream contains 90% H_2 and 10% methane (by mole). Following reactions are known to take place.

$$i\text{-}C_4H_{10} \quad = \quad i\text{-}C_4H_8 \quad + \quad H_2 \qquad \text{(i)}$$

i-Butane $\qquad$ *i*-Butylene $\qquad$ Hydrogen

$$i\text{-}C_4H_{10} \quad = \quad C_3H_6 \quad + \quad CH_4 \qquad \text{(ii)}$$

i-Butane $\quad = \quad$ Propylene $\qquad$ Methane

Literature reports 50% per pass conversion in a battery of three reactors with 88% yield of *i*-butylene. Calculate the composition of the product stream leaving the final reactor.

[(mole %) *i*-C₄H₁₀: 21.43%, *i*-C₄H₈: 18.86%, C₃H₆: 2.57%, H₂: 51.01% and CH₄: 6.13%]

4.8 In the BASF oil quench process to manufacture acetylene, pure oxygen and pure methane are fed to the acetylene burner[11]. The cracked gas from the burner has the following composition:

H_2: 56.5% CH_4: 5.2%, C_2H_4: 0.3%, C_2H_2: 7.5%, C_3H_6: 0.5%, CO: 25.8%, CO_2: 4.0% and O_2: 0.2% (mole% on dry basis).

Assume that formation of other compounds, such as aromatics, is negligible.

For 100 kmol cracked gas, calculate (a) methane requirement, (b) oxygen requirement, (c) production of water, (d) conversion of methane, and (e) yield of acetylene production.

[(a) 52.1 kmol CH₄, (b) 30.95 kmol O₂ (c) 27.7 kmol H₂O (d) 90.02%, (e) 31.98%]

4.9 The flue gas mixture is known to contain CO_2, O_2 and N_2 along with water vapour. In order to analyse the mixture, the gas is first passed through silica gel which absorbs the moisture. Later, the dry gas is passed through 1 L of caustic potash solution. Thus, CO_2 is preferentially absorbed in it. Finally, the mixture containing O_2 and N_2 is collected in 1 L flask at 101.325 kPa and 25°C (298.15 K). The increase in the mass of the silica gel due to moisture absorption was found to be 0.362 g. The caustic potash solution was analysed for carbonate formation. A volume of 10 mL of the solution was titrated against 0.012 M HCl solution. It was found that the phenolphthalein reading was 35.4 mL, while the total titration reading (with methyl orange indicator) was 38 mL. The increase in the mass of the flask was 1.16 kg. Based on these observations, find (a) the concentration of KOH and K_2CO_3 in the solution, (b) the Orsat analysis of the gas, and (c) the mass percentage composition of the wet gas.

[(a) 2191 mg/L KOH and 447 mg/L K₂CO₃ (b) 7.34% CO₂, 8.78% O₂ and 83.88% N₂ (by volume) (c) 10.65% CO₂, 9.25% O₂, 77.39% N₂ and 2.71% H₂O (by mass)]

4.10 The analysis of limestone gives 60% $CaCO_3$, 33.5% $MgCO_3$ and rest inerts. It is treated with 12% aqueous sulphuric acid (by mass) to obtain pure CO_2. An excess of 15% of the acid over the stoichiometric amount is used to ascertain that the reaction goes to completion. Based on the treatment of 500 kg of limestone, calculate (a) the amount of 100% (by mass) sulphuric acid required, (b) the amount of the residue, (c) the analysis of the residue left in the vessel, and (d) the moles of CO_2 produced.

[(a) 562 kg (b) 4964.2 kg (c) $CaSO_4$: 8.21%, $MgSO_4$: 4.82%, H_2SO_4: 1.48%, H_2O: 84.84%, Inerts 0.65% (by mass); (d) 5 kmol]

4.11 In the Deacon process for manufacturing chlorine, hydrochloric acid gas is oxidized with air. The reaction taking place is

$$4 \; HCl + O_2 = 2 \; Cl_2 + 2 \; H_2O$$

If the air is used in excess of 30% of that theoretically required, and if the oxidation is 80% complete, calculate the composition by volume of dry gases leaving the reaction chamber.

[HCl: 10.27%, O_2: 6.42%, Cl_2: 20.53%, and N_2: 62.78% (by volume)]

4.12 The gaseous reaction A = 2 B + C takes place isothermally in a constant-pressure reactor. Starting with a mixture of 75% A and 25% inerts (by volume), in a specified time the volume double. Calculate the conversion achieved. [66.67%]

4.13 The shift reaction is a very important reaction in the gas processing industry.

$$CO + H_2O = CO_2 + H_2$$

If a and b are the per cent carbon monoxide in the dry inlet and outlet gas mixtures to and from the shift converter respectively, prove that moles of CO converted (n_{co}) per 100 moles of inlet gas mixture can be calculated by using the formula,

$$n_{co} = \frac{100(a - b)}{100 + b}$$

4.14 The analysis of the gas entering the secondary converter in a contact sulphuric acid plant is 4% SO_2, 13% O_2 and 83% N_2 (on volume basis). The gas leaving the converter, contains 0.45% SO_2 on SO_3-free basis (by volume). Calculate the percentage of SO_2 entering the converter getting converted to SO_3. [89.35%]

4.15 A mixture of pure carbon dioxide and hydrogen is passed over a nickel catalyst. The temperature of the catalyst bed is 315°C (588 K) and the reactor pressure is 2 MPa g. The analysis of the gases leaving the reactor showed CO_2: 57.1%, H_2: 41.1%, CH_4: 1.68% and CO: 0.12% (by volume) on a dry basis. The reactions taking place in the reactor are

$$CO_2 + 4 \; H_2 = CH_4 + 2 \; H_2O$$

and $$CO_2 + H_2 = CO + H_2O$$

Find (a) the conversion of CO_2 per pass, (b) yield of CH_4 in terms of CO_2 reacted, and (c) the composition of the feed (volume basis)

[(a) 3.06% (b) 93.33%; (c) CO_2: 55.13%, H_2: 44.87% (volume basis)]

4.16 Acetaldehyde is oxidized over silica gel with the help of air. The mixture is passed over that catalyst at 114°C (387 K). The outgoing dry gases are found to contain 4.85% CO_2, 8.65% acetaldehyde, 14.9% acetic acid, 2.55% O_2 and 69.05% N_2 by volume. For carrying out dry analysis, water was first removed from the mixture. During the water removal, some acetic acid is also condensed.

Calculate (a) the percentage conversion of acetaldehyde, (b) the percentage yield of acetic acid, (c) mass ratio of air to acetaldehyde in incoming feed, (d) the percentage removal of acetic acid during the removal of water, and (e) that actual analysis of the gases leaving the reactor.

[(a) 71.7% (b) 89% (c) 1.884:1 (d) 23.6% (e) CO_2: 4.43%, CH_3CHO: 7.90%, CH_3COOH: 17.82%, O_2: 2.33, N_2: 63.09% H_2O: 4.43% (vol. basis)]

4.17 It is desired to produce hydrogen from methane by partial oxidation in the presence of steam[12]. The reactor is charged with 100 kg of methane at 425°C (698 K), 100 kg of oxygen at 425°C (698 K) and 100 kg of steam at 980°C (1253 K). The product gases are assumed to leave the reactor at 925°C (1198 K) in chemical equilibrium. Based on kinetic considerations at 925°C (1198 K), the equilibrium constant value is 0.7,

i.e., $K_p = \dfrac{(y_{CO_2})\,(y_{H_2})}{(y_{CO})\,(y_{H_2O})} = 0.7$

where y stands for the mole fraction of the component. Calculate the kmol of various components present in the product gas.

[CO$_2$: 1.151, CO: 5.099, H$_2$: 13.651, and H$_2$O: 4.405, all in kmol]

4.18 Exercise 3.22 gives the analysis of water (Table 3.16). If the same water is treated with lime and soda ash, what will be the theoretical requirement of the chemicals?

[159 mg/L of CaO]

4.19 The analysis of the water obtained from an underground source is given in Table 4.24.

Table 4.24 Analysis of Water

(a) Solids, mg/L	
Total solids	3071
Dissolved solids	2946
Suspended solids (by difference)	125
(b) Alkalinity, expressed as CaCO$_3$ mg/L	
Total alkalinity	250
Total carbonates	17.9
Total bicarbonates	232.1
Sodium bicarbonates (by difference)	Nil
(c) Hardness, expressed as CaCO$_3$, mg/L	
Temporary hardness	232.6
Permanent hardness	623.4
Total hardness	856.0
Magnesium hardness	162.0
(d) Chlorides as Cl, mg/L	1070
(e) Sulphates as SO$_4$, mg/L	168.7

If this water is treated by the lime-soda method, calculate the theoretical dosages of chemicals required to be added to the water. Is it possible to give the actual concentrations of all components present in water?

[Requirement of lime = 130.3 mg/L; requirement of soda ash = 660.8 mg/L]

4.20 Raw water, described in Example 3.9, is to be softened in an ion exchange bed containing a strong cation exchange resin. It is proposed to soften raw water at the rate of 50 m^3/h on a continuous basis. This is a batch process in which two ion-exchange beds are utilised. One bed is in normal use for 8 hours (service cycle period) while another bed is under regeneration. Regeneration is carried out with the help of sodium chloride solution. In each of the beds, 4240 litres of resin are loaded. From various considerations[13], the regeneration level is fixed at 60 kg NaCl/m^3 resin. Calculate the % excess NaCl used over the stoichiometric requirement in the softening process.

[41.5% excess NaCl]

Note The process flow sheet of the softening process is given in Fig. 3.4.

4.21 The composition of a sample of cotton seed oil is given in Table 4.25. This oil is saponified with caustic potash. For 100 kg oil, calculate (a) the theoretical amount of KOH required, and (b) the amount of glycerine liberated after 100% saponification.

Table 4.25 Composition of Cotton Seed Oil[14]

Component	Chemical formula	mass %
(i) Oleodipalmitin	$C_3H_5 \Big\langle \begin{matrix} (OOCH_{33}C_{17} \\ (OOCH_{31}C_{15})_2 \end{matrix}$	8
(ii) Oleopalmitostearin	$C_3H_5 \Big\langle \begin{matrix} (OOCH_{33}C_{17}) \\ (OOCH_{35}C_{17}) \\ (OOCH_{31}C_{15}) \end{matrix}$	5
(iii) Palmito-oleolinolein	$C_3H_5 \Big\langle \begin{matrix} (OOCH_{33}C_{17}) \\ (OOCH_{31}C_{15}) \\ (OOCH_{31}C_{17}) \end{matrix}$	41
(iv) Palmitodilinolein	$C_3H_5 \Big\langle \begin{matrix} (OOCH_{31}C_{15}) \\ (OOCH_{31}C_{17})_2 \end{matrix}$	18
(v) Oleodilinolein	$C_3H_5 \Big\langle \begin{matrix} (OOCH_{33}C_{17}) \\ (OOCH_{31}C_{17})_2 \end{matrix}$	28

[**(a) 19.525 kg (b) 10.693 kg**]

4.22 Refined castor oil is analysed to have fatty acid composition (by mass) as under. *Palmitic acid* 1.4%, Stearic acid: 1.2%, Oleic acid: 4.5%, *Linoleic acid* 6.0% Linolenic acid: 0.5% and Ricinoleic acid: 86.4% It is hydrogenated near to full saturation (having less than 3 Iodine value) and slip melting point of 85°C (358 K) for production of hydroxystearic acid. Calculate (a) iodine value, and (b) theoretical hydrogenation requirement.

[**(a) 86.07 (b) 7.601 Nm^3/100 kg oil**]

Note IUPAC Name of Ricinoleic acid is (9Z, 12R) -12-Hydroxyoctadec-9-enoic acid and has a formula $CH_3(CH_2)_5CHOHCH_2CH{:}CH(CH_2)_7COOH$ and molar mass of 298.46 g/mol. Hydroxy stearic acid finds many industrial applications.

4.23 Used vegetable oil can be reacted with methanol to produce methyl esters which can be used as biodiesel in a diesel engine[15]. Used soybean oil is found to contain 46.04% palmitic acid, 5.60% stearic acid, 21.94% oleic acid, 23.22% linoleic acid and 3.20% linolenic acid (by mass). Methyl esters, produced by reaction at 70°C (343 K), can be used as biodiesel which meets requirements of high speed diesel (HSD) oil, conforming to IS:1460. Its gross calorific value is found to be 39 920 kJ/kg at 25°C (298.15 K). Absence of sulphur and reduction of noxious compounds in exhaust gases from the engine makes it a 'green' fuel.

Calculate the stoichiometric requirements of methanol and production of methyl esters per kg soybean oil.

[(a) methanol requirement = 0.1135 kg per kg soybean oil
(b) methyl ester production = 1.005 kg per kg soybean oil]

4.24 Fatty acid methyl esters (FAME) can be hydrogenated to fatty alcohols (FOH) in a homogeneous phase by using propane at supercritical conditions[16]. FAME, derived in Exercise 4.23, are hydrogenerated over a fixed catalyst bed at 150 bar and 280°C (553 K). Reaction mixture contains 1% FAME, 20% H_2 and rest propane (by mole). Reactions go to 100% completion with near 100% selectivity to FOH in less than 800 ms. Calculate the production of FOH per 100 kg FAME.

[90.1 kg FOH/100 kg FAME]

4.25 Sulphamic acid is produced by reaction of urea, sulphuric acid and sulphur trioxide. Technical grade urea (nearly pure), 98 mass % H_2SO_4 solution and pure SO_3 in liquid form are used as reactants. Due to very high heat of reaction, the reaction is carried out in a battery of five continuous stirred tank reactors (CSTR), operated in series. Reactions taking place are

$$NH_2CONH_2(s) + H_2SO_4(l) + SO_3(l) = 2NH_4SO_2OH(l) + CO_2(g)$$
$$SO_3(l) + H_2O(l) = H_2SO_4(l)$$

Each CSTR is operated at 7 bar a and 80°C (353 K). Exothermic heat of reactions is removed with the help of cooling water and refrigeration. Carbon dioxide from all reactors, saturated with SO_3, is taken to a condenser in which SO_3 is liquefied by refrigeration and refluxed at 30°C (303 K). Assume nearly all SO_3 is condensed.

First reactor is charged with 350 kg/h of urea, 25% excess H_2SO_4 and 250% excess SO_3 over stoichiometric requirements. Assume total conversion of urea to sulphamic acid in the battery of CSTRs. Calculate the composition of the solution, leaving the final (5th) reactor. **[H_2SO_4 : 9.05%, SO_3: 44.87%, SA: 46.08% (by mass)]**

4.26 Dodeeyl mercaptan (DDM) is used as a surfactant in detergent industry and as a modifier in rubber polymerization. In Monsanto process[17], propylene tetramer in liquid phase is contacted with hydrogen sulphide to produce DDM as per the following neaction in presence of boron trifluoride as a catalyst.

$$\underset{\text{C-12 olefin}}{C_{12}H_{24}} + H_2S = \underset{\text{DDM}}{C_{12}H_{25}SH}$$

In a lab experimental unit, a packed column-type reactor is used. A 50-mm dia packed column contains glass Berl saddles and has a total packing height of 4.2 m in three sections. Propylene tetramer (liquid mixture), containing 0.8% $C_{10}H_{20}$, 9.9% $C_{11}H_{22}$, 82.2% $C_{12}H_{24}$, 6.7% $C_{13}H_{26}$ and 0.4% $C_{14}H_{28}$ (by mole), is introduced to the reactor at 50° C (323 K) from top at the rate of 6.1 kg/h. Density and boiling range of the tetramer are 0.774 kg/L at 15.6° C (288.75 K) and 175 to 195°C (448 K to 468 K), respectively. Impure hydrogen sulphide stream is available in the plant and has the composition; 96.7% H_2S, 1.3% CO_2 and balance C_2–C_3 hydrocarbons (having average molar mass of 44) on dry basis. It is introduced at the bottom at the rate of 1 Nm^3/h in saturated condition at 0.35 bar g. Boron trifluoride (BF$_3$) gas is fed at the rate of 0.035 Nm^3/h after mixing with the H_2S stream. The reaction is exothermic and hence intermittent cooling is provided in the packed beds to maintain the reaction temperature in the range of 50 to 70°C (323 K to 343 K).

Assume that entire tetramer ($C_{12}H_{24}$) is consumed. Calculate (a) mass % DDM in the outlet solution, (b) composition of dry gas stream, leaving the packed tower, (c) mole ratio of dry gas stream to feed liquid, and (d) conversion of H_2S.

(a) 84.98% DDM by mass

(b) Table 4.26 Composition of Outgoing Dry Gas Stream

Component	mole %
H_2S	76.19
CO_2	4.35
HC	6.65
BF_3	12.81

(c) Dry gas/feed = 1.114 mol/mol

(d) H_2S conversion = 76.34%

4.27 What will be the composition of gases obtained by burning pure FeS_2 with 60% excess air? Assume that the reaction proceeds in the following manner:

$$4\ FeS_2 + 11\ O_2 = 2\ Fe_2O_3 + 8\ SO_2$$

[9.90%, SO_2, 8.17% O_2 and 81.93% N_2 (by volume)]

4.28 Zinc sulphide ore containing 74% ZnS and 26% inerts are roasted in a burner. Assume complete combustion of the ore to SO_2 with dry air at 27°C (300 K) and stoichiometric amount required for complete roasting of the ore. The gases are passed through a V_2O_5 catalyst bed where nearly 98% of SO_2 gets converted to SO_3. The converter gases are passed through an absorption tower where all SO_3 is absorbed in the form of H_2SO_4 of 90% strength. It is desired to produce 1000 kg/h of 90% acid by mass by spraying pure water at the top of the absorption tower. Calculate (a) the analysis of the burner gases, (b) the analysis of the converter exit gases, (c) the quantity of the ore to be roasted per hour, and (d) the volumetric flow rate of air entering the converter in m^3/h.

[(a) 9.46% SO_2, 7.80% O_2, 82.74% N_2 (volume %)
(b) 0.20% SO_2, 9.72% SO_3, 3.32% O_2, 86.76% N_2 (by volume)
(c) 1232.7 kg/h (d) 2587 m^3/h]

4.29 A sample of iron pyrites contain 88% FeS_2 and rest, gangue. It is roasted with air 150% in excess of the theoretical requirement for oxidiation of FeS_2 as per the reactions:

$$4\ FeS_2 + 11\ O_2 = 2\ Fe_2O_3 + 8\ SO_2$$
$$4\ FeS_2 + 15\ O_2 = 2\ Fe_2O_3 + 8\ SO_3$$

The residue of the burner contains 2.6% S. 40% of this sulphur is in the form of FeS_2 while the rest is in the form of SO_3 absorbed in the cinder. Also, assume that 92% of the sulphur burnt produces SO_2 and the rest 8% oxidizes to SO_3. Based on 100 kg of pyrites charged, calculate (a) the mass of the cinder produced, (b) the percentage of the sulphur lost in the cinder, (c) the analysis of the burner gas on SO_3-free basis, and (d) the volume of dry air required in m^3 at 27°C (300 K) and 100 kPa a (750 Torr).

[(a) 74.4 kg (b) 4.11% (c) 5.59% SO_2, 13.03% O_2 and
81.38% N_2 (Volume %) (d) 600 m^3]

4.30 Magnesium ore (chiefly $MgCO_3$), containing 5% moisture is roasted with the help of flue gases in a furnace. The ratio of the dry flue gases to the ore is kept at 1.82 kg/kg. The analysis of the entering flue gases shows a composition of 12.8% CO_2, 6.1% O_2 and rest N_2 (volume % on dry basis). The exit gases from the furnace contain 24% CO_2 (by volume) on a dry basis. Based on the 100 kmol of dry gases entering the furnace, calculate (a) the kmol of CO_2 added to flue gases, (b) the analysis of exit gases on a dry basis, and (c) the average molar mass of dry incoming and outgoing flue gases.

[(a) 14.74 kmol (b) CO_2: 24.0%, O_2: 5.33% and N_2: 70.67%
(c) 30.29 and 32.05, respectively]

4.31 In hydroalkylation process, feed stream to reactor contains 1% benzene, 3.67% toluene, 6% xylene, 7.34% pseudocumene and 81.99 % hydrogen (by mole). Assume a feed flow rate of 100 kmol/h. Following reactions take place in the reactor.

$$C_6H_5CH_3 + H_2 = C_6H_6 + CH_4 \qquad \text{(i)}$$
$$C_6H_4(CH_3)_2 + H_2 = C_6H_5CH_3 + CH_4 \qquad \text{(ii)}$$
$$C_6H_3(CH_3)_3 + H_2 = C_6H_4(CH_3)_2 + CH_4 \qquad \text{(iii)}$$
$$2\ C_6H_6 = C_6H_5C_6H_5 + H_2 \qquad \text{(iv)}$$
$$\text{Diphenyl}$$

Assume that 70% conversion of pseudocumene, 17% conversion of xylene, 75% conversion of toluene and 20% conversion of benzene in the reactor. Set up a linear model of the reactor and find the composition of reactor exit stream by matrix method.

4.32 Potassium iodide is electrolysed in an electrolytic cell. When a definite amount of current is passed through the cell liquor for 10 800 s, it was found that 127 g iodine was liberated at the anode. Calculate the theoretical current passed through the cell.
[8.95 amperes]

4.33 In a silver electroplating plant, silver nitrate is used. When 1130 amperes were passed through $AgNO_3$ solution for 32 400 s, it was found that 2.0 m^3 oxygen (at NTP) was liberated at the anode. Calculate (a) the amount of silver liberated in kg, and (b) the current efficiency of the cell. **[(a) 38.55 kg (b) 94.15%]**

4.34 A batch reactor contains 1500 L reaction mass. Specific gravity and pH of the reaction mass are 1.25 and 9, respectively. It is required to reduce the pH of the mass from 9 to 4 by adding 0.1 M HCl solution having a specific gravity of 1.005. Calculate the mass of 0.1 M HCl to be added to change the pH. **[1509 g]**

4.35 The addition of lime is being extensively used as a means of clarifying waste water. The limed waste water at pH of 11.8 –12.0 is recarbonated by treatment with CO_2 to pH of 9.8–10.0 to remove ions:

$$Ca(OH)_2 + CO_2 = CaCO_3 + H_2O$$

However, this precipitation is rapid and $CaCO_3$ tends to deposit on some parts of the CO_2 absorber, lowering efficiency and causing maintenance problems.

A modified approach to the problem is to put a bypass of limed waste around the absorber to the clarifier[18] as shown in Fig. 4.7. Part of the feed stream goes through this bypass and the pH of the recarbonated stream is brought to 7.0 so that the carbonation forms bicarbonate instead of carbonate

$$Ca(OH)_2 + 2\ CO_2 = Ca(HCO_3)_2$$

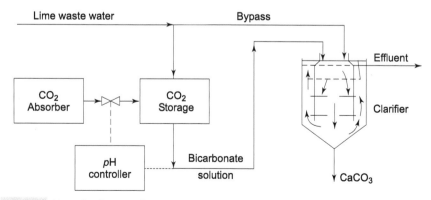

Fig. 4.7 Lime clarification of waste water

Since $Ca(HCO_3)_2$ is soluble in water, it does not precipitate. The bicarbonate solution from the absorber subsequently meets the bypassed limed waste water. As a result, calcium is precipitated in the form of carbonate as per the reaction:

$$Ca(OH)_2 + Ca(HCO_3)_2 = 2\ CaCO_3 + 2\ H_2O$$

This occurs in the clarifier, where $CaCO_3$ is conveniently removed. Assuming that the chemical reactions taking place in the absorber and the clarifier go to 100% completion, calculate the % of the incoming limed waste water flow bypassed to the clarifier.   **[50%]**

4.36   Refer Example 4.17.

(a) If conversion per pass is assumed to be 24% and ammonia separation is taken as 65%, calculate the purge rate.

(b) If conversion per pass is taken as 25% and ammonia separation is assumed to be 70%, calculate the purge rate.   **[(a) 7.971 kmol/s (b) 7.871 kmol/s]**

Note   It may be noted that change in the conversion has a pronounced effect on the purge rate over change in ammonia separation.

4.37   Rework Example 4.18 with

(a) Inerts = 9 mole % in mixed feed and

(b) Inerts = 11 mole % in mixed feed.

[(a) P = 11.951 kmol/s NH$_3$ production = 768.4 kg/s

(b) P = 9.162 kmol/s NH$_3$ Production = 877.4 kg/s]

4.38   A hydrocracker unit in a petroleum refining unit is fed with make-up hydrogen stream at the rate of 45 000 Nm^3/h containing 88.5% H_2 and 11.5% hydrocarbons (HC)[19]. In the reactors, operating at 130 bar g, hydrogen is partially consumed while a definite quantity is dissolved in the product stream along with the light hydrcarbons formed during the reactions. Product stream from the reactors is taken to a high pressure (HP) separator, operating at 124 bar g. Part of the HP separator gas mixture is recycled while another part amounting 4500 Nm^3/h gas, is purged out containing 74.5 % hydrogen and balance HC. Liquid from the HP separator is let down to a low pressure (LP) separator. Flashed gas mixture from the LP separator at the rate of 12 500 Nm^3/h contains 51.7% H_2 and balance HC. Purge stream from the HP separator and flash gas stream from the LP separator are used as a fuel. The process is schematically represented in Fig. 4.8.

(a) Calculate net consumption of hydrogen in the reactor.

(b) As a part of hydrogen conservation program, it is decided to instal a membrane system I for the HP purge gas stream. Permeate-I from the membrance system at 31.0 bar g contains 94.5% H_2. A separator is designed to reject 85% HC in the reject stream-I. Permeate I stream is recycled to the make-up compressor. With this arrangement, calculate reduction in make-up H_2 stream requirement for the same H_2 consumption.

(c) Further improvement is proposed by the way of installation of the separation system-II for LP purge gas. Permeate-II from the system contains 92% H_2. This system is designed to reject 88% HC in reject stream-II. Permeate-II is recycled back to the make-up H_2 stream. Calculate additional reduction in make-up H_2 stream requirement for the same H_2 consumption.

All percentages are mole %.

[(a) Net H$_2$ consumption = 30 010 Nm^3/h

(b) and (c) Reduction in H$_2$ consumption by way of installation of

System-I = 7.43% and System - II = 20.92%]

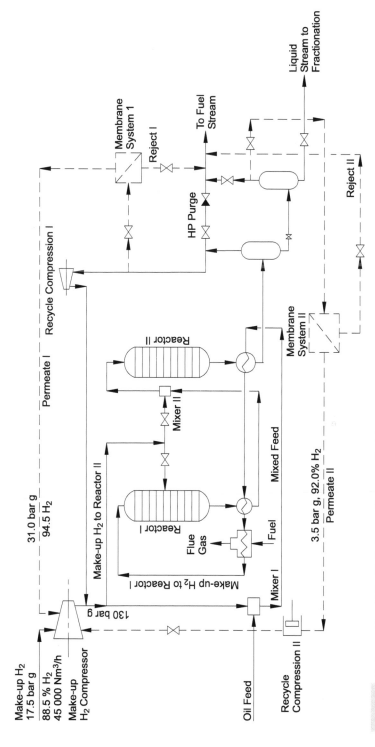

Fig. 4.8 Hydrocracking Unit with Hydrogen Recovery Modules

4.39 The use of weak ion-exchange resins in the desalination processes offer advantages of very high regenation efficiency and lower rinse requirements. On the other hand, the ability of such resins to exchange ions is strongly influenced by the pH of the influents. Based on the buffer capacity of the CO_2/HCO_3 system, a process is developed for the desalination of saline water at the Bary Laboratory of the Water Research Institute, Italy, named as the SIRA process[20,21]. The process is shown in Fig. 4.9.

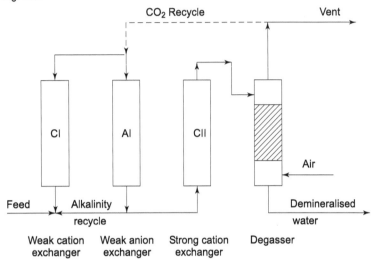

Fig. 4.9   SIRA Process of Desalination

$$2\ RCOOH + Ca^{++}\ (or\ Mg^{++}) + 2\ HCO_3^- = (RCOO)_2Ca + H_2O + CO_2$$
$$or\ (RCOO)_2Mg$$

(b) A recycle of the CO_2 produced in the degasser (if necessary) to convert all the anions in the bicarbonate in the weak anion exchanger as per the reaction.

$$R'OH + NaCl + CO_2 = R'Cl + NaHCO_3$$

A third column, CII, containing strong cations can be used for obtaining complete demineralisation according to the reaction.

$$R''\ SO_3H + NaHCO_3 = R''\ SO_3Na + H_2O + CO_2$$

The effluent from CII flows to degasser where CO_2 is removed and recycled (if necessary). For producing potable water, column CII may not be necessary.

Let, A = feed water strong anions, meg/L

M = feed water alkalinity, meq/L

C = feed water cations, meq/L

H = feed water hardness (total), meq/L

X = alkalinity recyle flow rate from anion section/feed flow ratio

Y = CO_2 recycle to anion section/CO_2 discharged in the product

With the hypothesis that (a) leakage of strong ions (i.e., Ca and Mg from CI and Cl and SO_4 from AI) is nil, (b) cations are exchanged on the cationic column (CI) in quantum equal to the alkalinity contents of the feed water, and (c) CO_2 is fed to the anionic column (AI) in a quantity equal to convert all the anions to bicarbonates, prove that

$$X = \frac{H - M}{C - H}$$

$$Y = \frac{A - M}{M}$$

and,
$$(1 + X)(1 + Y) = \frac{A}{M}$$

Notes 1. SIRA process offers the following advantages.

   (a) Regeneration of CI can be carried out with low concentration of aqueous sulphuric acid solution, obtained by in-line dilution of the concentrated sulphuric acid solution, used for regeneration of CII in sodium from.

   (b) Precipitation of hardness is avoided in the anionic column nearing exhaustion of cation column CI.

   2. When $A = H$, i.e., strong anions and hardness are same, $Y = 0$ or CO_2 recycle is not necessary.

   3. When $M \geq H$, $X = 0$, thereby indicated that when feed water contains only temporary hardness, recycle of alkalinity is not necessary.

4.40 Refer Example 4.10. With a view to improve inherent safety of the plant, it is decided to recycle partially tail gas (shown as 'optional' in Fig. 4.1) from the absorber such that the concentration of oxygen in the feed gas to the reactor does not exceed 10% (by volume). Assume that conversion and yields are unchanged and total wet gas molar flow to the reactor also remains unchanged. Rework the material balance of the plant and calculate

(a) ratio of recycle stream to purge stream,

(b) ratio of recycle stream to fresh air, and

(c) concentration of UC in purge stream on dry gas basis.

          [(a) 2.042 kmol/kmol (b) 1.96 kmol/kmol (c) UC = 3.37% (by volume)]

4.41 Cyclohexane can be produced by hydrogenation of benzene.[22]. The reaction can be written as

$$C_6H_6 + 3 H_2 = C_6H_{12}$$

Fresh benzene, make-up hydrogen stream, recycle hydrogen stream and recycle cyclohexane are mixed (ref. Fig. 3.7) and fed to a fixed-bed catalytic reactor. Assume benzene as 100% pure while the make-up hydrogen stream contains 97.5% H_2 and 2.5% inerts ($N_2 + CH_4$). The reaction is highly exothermic and to have effective control of the reaction temperature of 204.5°C (477.5 K), recycle of a definite amount of cyclohexane is maintained such that benzene concentration is limited at 18.5 mole % in the mixed feed. Also, the mole ratio of hydrogen to benzene in the mixed feed is kept at 3.3. The heat of reaction is removed by boiling water outside the catalyst tubes.

Assume 100% conversion in the reactor. The reactor effluent is cooled and the entire quantity of cyclohexane is condensed. Effluent from the cooler is sent to a separator where cyclohexane is separated from the mixture. A major portion of the gases from the separator will be recycled back to the reactor. A small portion of the offgasses is purged to bleed off the inerts from the recycle stream such that the total inerts are limited to the 10 mole % in the mixed feed.

For 100 kmol of fresh benzene feed, calculate the flows of purge, make-up hydrogen, recycle hydrogen and recycle cyclohexane streams.

          [Purge stream = 12.139 kmol,

Make-up hydrogen stream = 312.139 kmol,

Recycle hydrogen stream = 71.915 kmol and

Recycle cyclohexane stream = 56.49 kmol]

4.42 Refer Exercise 4.41. As an energy conservation measure, it is decided to process the offgases from the separator by a cryogenic route in a cold-box. Product H_2 stream from the cold-box contains 90% of H_2 and 5% of inerts as compared to that contained in the offgases. Tail-gas stream, containing 10% of hydrogen and 95% of inerts (contained in offgases), is purged out. For the revised conditions, calculate the flows of make-up hydrogen stream, recycle hydrogen stream, recycle cyclohexane stream and purge stream. Also, calculate the inerts contents of the mixed feed.

[**Purge stream = 10.769 kmol, Make-up H_2 stream = 303 kmol, Recycle H_2 stream = 27.404 kmol, Recycle cyclohexane stream = 102.236 kmol, Inerts content of mixed feed = 1.51 mole %**]

Note Cryogenic purification of cooler exit gas stream shows all-round improvement in process parameters.

4.43 In the Halcon SD process to manufacture ethylene oxide, ethylene is directly oxidised by oxygen[23]. Ethylene concentration is maintained at 10% at the reactor inlet. Pure ethylene (100%) and oxygen with 97% purity are used as feedstocks. Both the gases are mixed with recycled gas and the mixed gas is then fed to a multi-tube reactor. The process is shown in shown in Fig. 4.10.

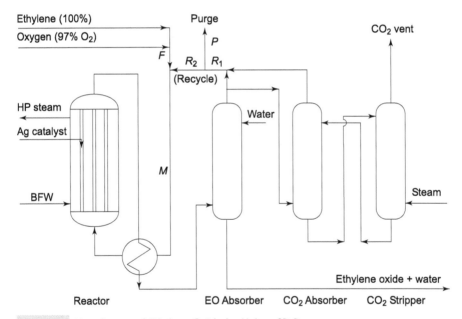

Fig. 4.10 Manufacture of Ethylene Oxide by Halcon SD Process

In the reactor, per pass conversion is 50% while the yield of ethylene glycol is 70%. Carbon dioxide and water are the chief by-products while trace amounts of acetaldehyde and formaldehyde are also formed which may be neglected for stoichiometric calculations. The following reactions are known to take place:

$$CH_2 = CH_2 + \frac{1}{2} O_2 = CH_2 \underset{O}{\diagdown\diagup} CH_2 \qquad \text{(i)}$$

Ethylene Oxide

$$CH_2 = CH_2 + 3 O_2 = 2 CO_2 + 2 H_2 O \qquad \text{(ii)}$$
Ethylene

$$CH_2 \underset{O}{\diagdown\diagup} CH_2 = CH_3CHO \qquad \text{(iii)}$$

Ethylene Oxide   Acetaldehyde

$$CH_2 = CH_2 + O_2 = 2 CH_2O \qquad \text{(iv)}$$
Ethylene   Formaldehyde

The reactor is basically a heat exchanger in which the reaction is carried out at 2 MPa g and 250°C (523 K). Tubes are filled with silver catalyst while the reaction temperature is maintained by boiling water on the shell side, producing high-pressure steam. The reactor effluent gas is cooled in a heat exchanger by exchanging heat with incoming gas mixture and scrubbed with water in an EO absorber to recover ethylene oxide. The scrubber offgases are compressed and recycled back to the reactor. A slip-stream of the recycle gas is first sent to a CO_2-removal section where CO_2 is absorbed in a circulating solution. The CO_2-lean gas from the CO_2 absorber is then returned to the recycle gas stream. CO_2-rich solution is regenerated in CO_2 stripper. To avoid excess build-up of inerts such as nitrogen, argon, etc., a small purge of recycle gas is bled out and used as fuel so that inerts (N_2 + Ar) do not exceed 10% in the mixed feed gas.

For the production rate of 3500 kg/h of ethylene oxide, calculate (a) ethylene feed rate in kg/h, (b) oxygen (97%) feed rate in Nm^3/h, (c) recycle ration in kmol recycle gas per kmol fresh feed, and (d) oxygen concentration of mixed feed, entering the reactor.

**[(a) 3245.66 kg/h ethylene (b) 3277.8 Nm^3/h oxygen stream
(c) 7.114 kmol recycle gas per kmol fresh feed (d) 6.25 mole%]**

4.44 In the shell process for the manufacture of synthetic alcohol[24], hydration of ethylene is carried out at 6.5 MPa g and 300°C (573 K). Fresh ethylene feed contains 96.0 mole % ethylene and 4.0 mole % non-reactive gases (NRG). The ethylene stream is mixed with steam and heated in a preheater. The preheated mixture is fed to a reactor which contains pellets of diatomaceous earth, impregnated with phosphoric acid. The steam input with fresh ethylene stream is so adjusted that the molar ratio of water to ethylene in the combined feed (fresh feed + recycle feed) is 0.65:1. At the operating conditions, the conversion per pass is only 5%, based on ethylene. The reaction taking place in the reactor is

$$C_2H_{4(g)} + H_2O_{(g)} = C_2H_5OH_{(g)} \quad \text{(exothermic)}$$

Side reactions produce diethylether and acetaldehyde, which can be neglected for the purpose of stoinchiometric calculations. The reactor effluents are first passed through the heat exchangers and then through a flash drum and a scrubber where practically all ethanol and water are removed from the gaseous mixture. The offgases from the scrubber are recycled back to the reactor. In order to limit the NRG concentration in the combined feed at 15 mole % based on ethylene plus NRG feed basis (excluding water), a small quantity of recycle stream is purged. The process flow diagram is shown in Fig. 4.11.

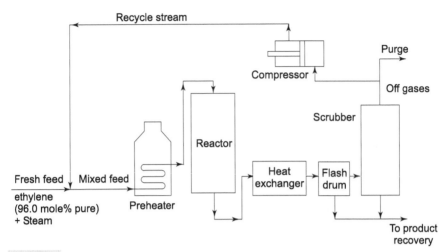

Fig. 4.11   Manufacture of Ethyl Alcohol by Hydration of Ethylene

Compute, (a) the recycle ratio, (b) the purge rate per 100 kmol of fresh ethylene, (c) the percentage loss of ethylene based on unreacted ethylene from the reactor, (d) the composition of the gas mixtures ingoing to and outcoming from the reactor.
[(a) **Recycle ratio = 16.52 kmol per kmol fresh ethylene feed** (b) **Purge = 25.526 kmol, (c) Loss = 1.52%, (d) See Table 4.27**]

Table 4.27   **Composition of Reactor Exit Gases**

Component	Gas mixture, ingoing to reactor		Gas mixture, outcoming from reactor	
	kmol	mole %	kmol	mole %
Ethylene	1489.41	54.83	1414.94	53.56
Water	968.12	35.64	893.65	33.82
NRG	258.92	9.53	258.92	9.80
Ethanol	—	—	74.47	2.82
Total	2716.45	100.00	2641.98	100.00

4.45   A plant produces 1,3-butadiene by dehydrogenation of n-butane using Houdry 'one-step' process[24]. In this process, the heat of reaction is supplied by the burning of coke during the regeneration step of the process. The n-butane feed is preheated to about 595°C (868 K) and is passed through a brick-lined reactor containing a fixed bed of pelletized alumina-chromia catalyst. The absolute pressure in the reactor is maintained at around 20 kPa. The fresh n-butane feed is combined with the recycle feed and passed through the fuel-gas separator system. The effluent gas mixture is then passed through a product separator where the butadiene is separated from the gases. The offgases from the product separator are recycled and mixed with the fresh feed. The simplified block diagram of the flow process is shown in Fig. 4.12. The composition of various gaseous streams are given in Table 4.28.

Calculate (a) the recycle ratio, (b) the composition of recycle stream, and (c) the yield of butadiene based on n-butane consumption.

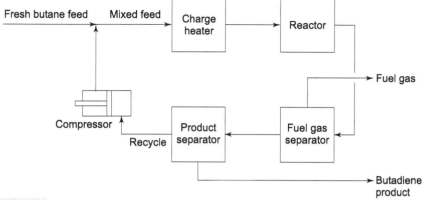

Fig. 4.12 Manufacture of 1,3-butadiene

Table 4.28 Composition of Gaseous Streams

| Component | Composition, mole % | | | | |
	Fresh feed	Mixed feed (fresh + recycle)	Reactor effluent	Fuel gas	Butadiene product mixture
Hydrogen			22.05	73.57	
Methane			3.25	10.86	
Ethylene			1.16	3.83	
Ethane			1.08	3.56	
Propylene			1.32	4.39	
Propane			0.64	2.09	
iso-butane	1.5	3.84	2.50	—	
iso-butylene		6.94	4.93	0.24	
n-butylene		25.29	17.88	0.24	1.69
n-butane	98.5	63.59	30.91	0.45	—
1,3-butadiene	—	0.34	8.78	0.24	98.31
C_5			0.16	0.56	
Coke			5.34	—	

[(a) Recycle ratio = 4.04 kmol per kmol fresh feed (b) *i*-butane: 4.42%, *i*-butylene: 8.66%, *n*-butylene; 31.55%, *n*-butane: 54.95% and 1,3-butadiene: 0.42% (mole %) (c) Yield of butadiene = 63.0%]

4.46 Flue gases from a steam generation plant, firing coal containing 1% (mass) sulphur, amounts to 265 000 m^3/h at 175°C (448 K) and 106.6 kPa a (800 Torr). The gases are found to contain 1160 mg/m^3 SO_2 and 2.11 kg/s water vapour. It is necessary to remove sulphur dioxide from the flue gases by reacting it with aqueous soda-ash solution in an absorber[25].

$$Na_2CO_3 + SO_2 = Na_2SO_3 + CO_2$$

The scrubbing system is shown in Fig. 4.13. At first, the flue gas is spray cooled in the quencher to 50°C (323 K) and directed downward into the circulating liquor. Gas bubbles through the liquor, enters the adjacent absorber and travels upward through two sieve trays. A circulating pump pumps the solution to the absorber after cooling. A purge stream is maintained from the discharge of the pump to limit the solids ($Na_2CO_3 + Na_2SO_3$) concentration to 8% (mass) to avoid any precipitation in the absorber.

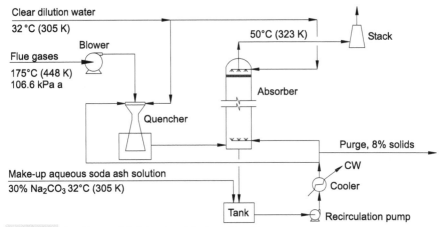

Fig. 4.13 Scrubbing of Sulphur Dioxide from Flue Gases

Soda ash is supplied in the form of aqueous 30% (mass) solution at 32°C (305 K) to the absorber pump. Dilution water is made-up at 32°C (305 K) in the quencher and the absorber as shown in the figure.

Gases leave the absorber at 50°C (323 K) and 101.325 kPa a (760 Torr). Nearly 90% of SO_2 in the inlet gas is removed when 50% excess reactant is used in the system. Make the material balance of the system and calculate the flow rates of the make-up soda-ash solution, dilution water and purge solution.

[Make-up soda solution = 2545.7 kg/h, Dilution water = 17 270.3 kg/h, Purge = 10 626.9 kg/h]

4.47 Phosphoric acid is made by reacting the rock phosphate with hydrochloric acid. It is desired to use the rock phosphate, obtained from hilly areas near Udaipur, Rajasthan. The composition of the rock phosphate[26] is given in Table 4.29.

Table 4.29 Composition of Rock Phosphate of Rajasthan Region

Components	Analysis by mass %
P_2O_5	34.55
CaO	48.62
$Al_2O_3 + Fe_2O_3$	3.76
MgO	1.29
SiO_2	5.58
CaF_2	2.50
CO_2	1.30
SO_3	2.40

The laboratory tests reveal the following data[26].

25% (by mass) HCl used = 3.0 kg per kg rock phosphate
Water retention in the sludge = 0.22 kg water per kg rock phosphate
P_2O_5 retained in the sludge = 2% (by mass)
It is intended to make 2 t/h of phosphoric acid of 80% strength.

Assume (i) 95% of the P_2O_5 present in the rock is reacted, (ii) all CaF_2 takes part in the reaction, and (iii) the recovery of H_3PO_4 is 97% by the leaching process (using butyl alcohol).

The main reaction
$$Ca_3(PO_4)_2 + 6\ HCl = 2\ H_3PO_4 + 3\ CaCl_2$$
The side reactions are:
$$CaF_2 + 2\ HCl = 2\ HF + CaCl_2$$
$$6\ HF + SiO_2 = H_2SiF_6 + 2\ H_2O$$
Calculate: (a) the per cent excess acid used, (b) the quantity of rock phosphate to be treated per hour, and (c) the quantity of $CaCl_2$ formed per hour.

[(a) 40.71% (b) 3.64 t/h (c) 3.49 t/h]

4.48 In the manufacture of nitric acid, ammonia is oxidised to nitric oxide on a catalyst as per the following chemical reactions:

$$4\ NH_3 + 5\ O_2 = 4\ NO + 6\ H_2O \qquad (i)$$
$$4\ NH_3 + 3\ O_2 = 2\ N_2 + 6\ H_2O \qquad (ii)$$

Nitric oxide is further oxidised to nitrogen dioxide which is absorbed in water to yield nitric acid.

$$2\ NO + O_2 = 2\ NO_2 \qquad (iii)$$
$$2\ NO_2 + (1/2)\ O_2 + H_2O = 2\ HNO_3 \qquad (iv)$$

Dry air is first preheated, mixed with superheated ammonia vapours and reacted over a catalyst gauze, composed of 90% Pt and 10% Rh (by mass %), at a temperature of 915°C (1188 K) and 0.75 MPa g. The preheated air temperature is 260°C (533 K). The superheated ammonia enters the burner. The process flow is shown in Fig. 4.14.

Operating data of a plant[27] having a production capacity of 250 t/day of HNO_3 are given below.

Flow of primary air = 29 394 Nm^3/h (dry)
Flow of ammonia = 3266 Nm^3/h
Flow of secondary air = 8145 Nm^3/h (dry)
Vol.% NO in burner outlet gas = 9.27 (wet basis)
Vol.% NO in tail gas = 0.2 (dry basis)

Calculate (a) the combustion efficiency, defined as the moles of ammonia consumed to produce NO to the moles of ammonia fed (can also be termed as the yield of NO), (b) the absorber efficiency, defined as NO consumed to NO fed to the absorber, and (c) the overall efficiency of the system, defined as the product of combustion efficiency and absorber efficiency. [(a) 95.02% (b) 98.0% (c) 93.12%]

4.49 A blast furnace uses ore of the composition, Fe_2O_3: 90% and SiO_2: 10%. The coke fed to the furnace has 90% C and 10% SiO_2. The flux is limestone containing 95% $CaCO_3$, 3% $MgCO_3$ and 2% SiO_2. The coke rate is 1 kg/kg of pig iron. The pig iron contains 4% C, 1% Si and rest Fe. The slag must contain 45% (CaO + MgO). Assume that no FeO is present in the slag. For 1000 kg of pig iron production, calculate the mass of limestone required.

All percentages are by mass. [354.1 kg limestone per tonne of pig iron]

References

1. McCormach, H; *Ind. Engg. Chem.*, **29**(12): 1937, p. 1333.
2. Lowenheim, F A and M K Moran; *Faith, Keys and Clark's Industrial Chemicals*, 4th Ed., John Wiley & Sons, USA, 1975, p. 3.
3. Boffelli, S O; *Ind. Engg. Chem.*, **53**(6): 1961, p. 428.
4. *Wealth of India*, Part I, Council of Scientific and Industrial Research, New Delhi, 1948, p. 89.
5. Levitt, B; *Oil, Fat and Soap*, Chemical Publication Co., USA, 1951, p. 58.

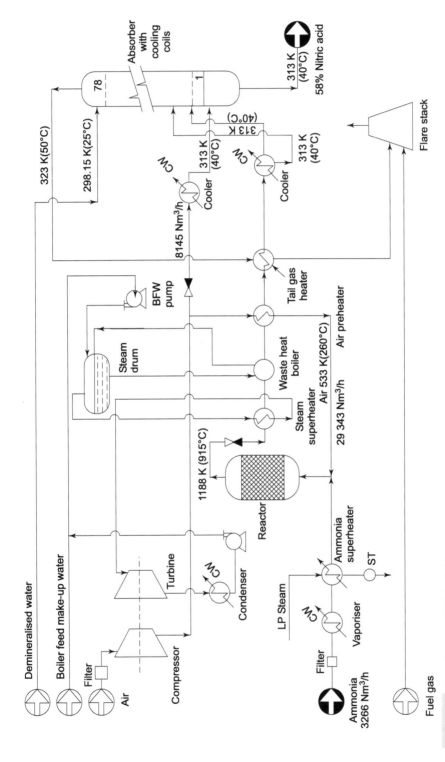

Fig. 4.14 Manufacture of Nitric Acid

6. *Tappi*, **48**(1): 1965, p. 167A.

7. Wolfgang Gerhartz; *Ullmann's Encyclopedia of Industrial Chemistry*, Vol. **A11**, 5th Ed., VCH Verlagsgesellschatt mbH, 1988, p. 625.

8. Private Communication with Haldor Topsoe, Denmark.

9. Simpson, W A, and J C Olsen; *Ind. Engg. Chem.*, **29**(12): 1937, p. 1350.

10. Shreve, R N and J A Brink, Jr; *Chemical Process Industries,* 4th Ed., McGraw-Hill, USA, 1977, p. 530.

11. Wolfgang Gerhartz, *Ullman's Encyclopedia of Industrial Chemistry,* Vol. **A1**, 5th Ed., VCH Verlagsgesellschaft mbH, 1985, p.110.

12. Edmister, W C; *Hydrocarbon Processing,* **53**(8): 1973, p. 109.

13. Product Literature on "INDION 225" of Ion Exchange (India) Ltd., Mumbai.

14. Hilditch, T P; *The Chemical Constitution of Natural Fats*, Chapman & Hall Ltd., UK, 1949, p. 255.

15. Srivastava A and Prasad R; *indian Chemical Engineer*, Section-B, **44**(2), April–June 2002, p. 132.

16. Hark, S van den and Harrord, M; *Ind. Engg. Chem. Research,* **40**, 2001, p. 5052.

17. Frantz, J F and Glass K L; *Chem. Engg. Prog,* **59** (7) 1963, p. 68.

18. Pinto, A P; *Chem. Engg.,* **82**(2): Jan. 20, 1975, p. 125.

19. Bollinger, W A, Long S P; and Motzger T R; *Chem. Engg. Prog.,* **80** (5), 1984, p. 81.

20. Boari, Liberti G L; Merli, C and Passino, R; *Proceedings of the Third International Symposium on Fresh Water from Sea,* **2**: 1970, p. 63.

21. Boari, G Liberti, L; and Passino, R; *Environmental Protection Engg.,* 1(2): 1975.

22. Private Communication with Aspen Technology, Inc., USA.

23. Meyers, R A; *Handbook of Chemicals Production Processes,* McGraw-Hill, USA, 1986, p. 15.

24. Stephenson, R M; *Introduction to the Chemical Process Industries,* Van Nostrand Reinhold Co., USA, 1966.

25. *Power,* **121**(11): 1977, p. 51.

26. Chatterjee, M K; *Chemical Age of India,* **24**(7): 1973, p. 428.

27. Jain, B K; *Indian Chemical Engineer, Transactions,* **16**(3): 1974, p. 44.

Energy Balances

Physical or chemical changes in matter are accompanied by enthalpy changes. Therefore, when a chemical reaction takes place, a change in enthalpy is invariably observed. In Chapters 3 and 4, the material balances with and without chemical reaction were considered. In this chapter, the energy balances related to these operations or reactions will be dealt with. Dilution of acid or alkali solutions, mixing of fluids, crystallization and other unit operations involve thermal changes. These physical processes will also be partly covered in this chapter.

5.1 ENERGY AND THERMOCHEMISTRY

When a definite amount of force is applied over a material object and if it is displaced in the direction of the force, mechanical work is said to be done on the object. This work can produce a property of the matter which is called *energy*. Thus, when a solid is forced upward, it results in an increase in potential energy. Similarly, due to friction between two solids, heat is generated, i.e., the loss of work done on the solid is converted into thermal energy. When a reaction takes place, energy change also takes place which can be termed as 'chemical' energy. Thus, energy can be in different forms, e.g., potential energy, kinetic energy, thermal energy, electrical energy, chemical energy, etc. Conversely, any form of energy can be converted into work, e.g., electricity can run mechanical machinery, potential energy can be utilized to run hydraulic turbines, thermal energy of a fuel can be beneficially utilized in a chemical process, chemical (internal) energy is utilised in softening or demineralisation of water, etc. Thus, basically the units of work and energy are same (refer Chapter 1).

Thermodynamic temperature was introduced as a fundamental quantity in Chapter 1. However, it is also an important thermodynamic state function which is requried in any heat balance calculation. Kuhn and Foresterling[1] have given the definition of thermodynamic temperature as the zeroth law of thermodynamics. It is defined as a state function which has the same value in all systems which are in thermal equilibrium. In other words, when diffrent systems are at same thermal equilibrium, their temperature is same.

In the space of thermodynamic parameters, a surface can be constructed which depicts zones of constant temperature. This imaginary surface is defined as a temperature function which provides a continuous ordering of states. When two systems are in equilibrium, the ideal gas law states that

$$\frac{p_1 V_1}{n_1} = \frac{p_2 V_2}{n_2} = RT \qquad (2.24)$$

where, V_1 and V_2 are total volumes of systems, comprising n_1 and n_2 moles respectively. Hence, the surface represented by pV/n, is the surface of equal temperature. The term *zeroth law* was originally introduced by Fowler in 1920 and is the most fundamental of all the laws of thermodynamics, providing the definition of thermodynamic temperature as a function.

When two substances are at different temperatures, it is known that heat flows from a hot substance to a relatively cold substance (*second law of thermodynamics*). Thus, heat is defined as a form of energy which is in transit between a hot source and a cold receiver and therefore has units of energy. The transmission of heat solely depends on the temperatures of the two substances. In other words, temperature can be termed as the *level* of thermal energy.

A substance possesses a definite quantity of energy due to the never-ending motion of its molecules. This quantity is by virtue of the presence, relative positions and movement of the molecules, and is defined as *internal energy*. The evaluation of internal energy involves the Einstein's theory and is beyond the scope of this book. To differentiate *external energy* from the internal energy, it can be said that the former is by virtue of the position and motion of the *whole* substance. Thus, external energy comprises of all mechanical energies. Since in chemical or physical changes, it is always the difference of the energies of two states which is important, the differential energy is commonly regarded as a useful quantity rather than an absolute value. Enthalpy H of a particular substance is defined as

$$H = E + pV \qquad (5.1)$$

where E is the internal energy, p pressure, and V volume.

Since p and V are the properties of the state of a system, H is again defined by the state only and is the external property or external state function.

In general, enthalpy is the energy possessed by a system due to its molecular arrangement while heat is the energy that flows due to a temperature gradient.

In this book, the terms *energy*, *enthalpy* and *heat* are essentially used for thermal energy.

The science related with changes in energy, associated with a given chemical or physical process is called *thermochemistry*. The ultimate aim of thermochemistry is to determine thermodynamic properties, such as heat of formation, enthalpy, free energy, etc. Although calorimetric measurements form the major activity in thermochemistry, spectroscopic determination of the heats of dissociation of diatomic molecules, measurement of bond dissociation energies in polyatomic molecules by kinetic and electron impact studies, measurement of the equilibrium constant of a chemical reaction, statistical and other methods are also helpful in determining thermodynamic properties.

5.2   ENERGY BALANCES

The energy balance of a particular system can be achieved from the *first law of thermodynamics* which states that the total energy of an isolated system and its surrounding remains constant. The conversion of one form of energy into another is possible. When a system gains or loses energy, it must be exactly equal to the loss from or gain of energy by the surroundings. Thus, the first law of thermodynamics relates to the conservation of energy. This concept can be understood clearly by considering the steady flow process of an incompressible fluid as shown in Fig. 5.1.

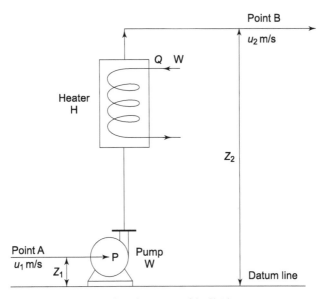

Fig. 5.1   Steady Flow Process of an Incompressible Fluid

In this process, the absolute pressure and velocity of the fluid at the point A are p_1 and u_1 respectively. The fluid is pumped with the help of a pump P which does net work W on the fluid. The fluid receives heat Q in the heater H and comes out at the point B with pressure p_2 and velocity u_2. Let E_1 and E_2 be the internal energies of the fluid at points A and B, respectively.

$$\text{Total energy at point A} = E_1 + q_m \left[Z_1 \left(\frac{g}{g_c} \right) + \frac{u_1^2}{2\alpha_1 g_c} + \frac{p_1}{\rho} \right]$$

where, q_m = mass flow rate, kg/s
   g = acceleration due to free fall (gravity)
      = 9.806 65 m/s^2 at mean sea level
   g_c = gravitational constant = 1 kg · m/(N · s^2)
   u_1 = velocity, m/s
   ρ = density of the fluid, kg/m^3

p_1 = pressure, N/m^2 (or Pa)

Z_1 = elevation from datum level, m

a_1 = kinetic energy correction factor

It is clear from the above equation that the total energy at the point A is made of four different forms of the energy. The parameter E is the internal energy and depends entirely on the state and conditions of the fluid.

The quantity Z stands for potential energy, a form of mechanical energy, $u^2/(2\alpha g_c)$ is kinetic energy, another form of mechanical energy and p/ρ is pressure energy, yet another form of mechanical energy. These three forms of mechanical energy are expressed in pressure head terms (m of the fluid). These values when multiplied by mass-flow rate get converted to work units which can be easily converted to heat units.

Energy added during the transport

= mechanical work done by the pump + heat added by the heater

= $W + Q$

where W represents the mechanical work done by the pump (in J) and Q, the heat added by the heater (in J).

Instead of a pump, if a turbine is present in the system which is driven by the fluid, the mechanical work will be performed by the fluid on the turbine. As a result, W will assume a negative sign.

Similarly, if a cooler is installed in the place of a heater, Q will assume a negative sign.

$$\text{Total energy at point B} = E_2 + q_m \left[Z_2 \left(\frac{g}{g_c} \right) + \frac{u_2^2}{2\alpha_2 g_c} + \frac{p_2}{\rho} \right]$$

According to the first law of thermodynamics,

Total energy in the fluid at A + energy gain during transport = total energy in the fluid at B

$$E_1 + q_m \left[Z_1 \left(\frac{g}{g_c} \right) + \frac{u_1^2}{2\alpha_1 g_c} + \frac{p_1}{\rho} \right] + Q + W$$

$$= E_2 + q_m \left[Z_2 \left(\frac{g}{g_c} \right) + \frac{u_2^2}{2\alpha_2 g_c} + \frac{p_2}{\rho} \right] \tag{5.2}$$

In Eq. (5.2), the friction losses are neglected.

Imagine a reactor R in the place of a heater H in Fig. 5.1. Let the flowing fluid be a mixture of reactants. In the reactor, reaction takes place and as a result, heat is absorbed from, or released to surroundings, depending on whether the reaction is endothermic or exothermic. This heat of reaction (refer Sec. 5.13) will take the place of Q with the proper sign in Eq. (5.2). It is clear that Eq. (5.2) accounts for the transformation of one form of energy into another form.

Often, in industrial chemical processes, changes in mechanical energies are absent or negligible. Under these circumstances, Eq. (5.2) reduces to thermal changes only and is called a *heat balance*. In other words, the change in internal energies amounts to only a thermal change. Thus, a heat balance of a process is a simplified form of the energy balance, dealing with thermal changes only. This is normally a case with energy balances of the process industry.

Example 5.1   Water is pumped from the bottom of a 50 m deep well at the rate of 1 L/s into an atmospheric storage tank that is 10 m above the ground. To prevent freezing in winter, a heater supplies 52 kW into the water during its transfer from the well to the storage tank. Heat is lost from the whole system at the constant rate of 21 kW. A 1.5 BkW pump is used to pump the water. About 55% of the rated power goes into the work of pumping and the rest is dissipated as heat to the atmosphere. Assume the change in kinetic energy to be negligible. Calculate the changes in internal energies between the storage tank and the bottom of the well.

Solution   The flow system is shown in Fig. 5.2.

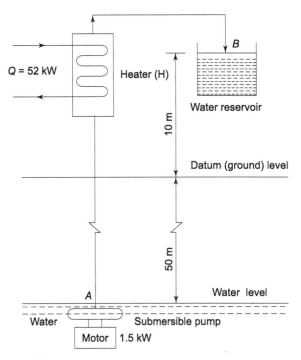

Fig. 5.2   Pumping of Water

Basis Pumping of 1 L/s of water

Heat added in the system = 52 kW

Heat lost to surroundings = 21 kW

Net heat gained by water, ϕ = 52 – 21 = 31 kW

$$p_1 = p_2 = \text{atmospheric pressure} = 101\ 325\ \text{Pa}$$
$$Z_1 = -50\ \text{m}$$

$$Z_2 = 10 \text{ m}$$

$$g = 9.806\ 65 \text{ m/s}^2$$

$$g_c = 1 \text{ kg} \cdot \text{m/(N} \cdot \text{s}^2)$$

Density, $\rho = 1.0$ kg/L

Since the kinetic energy change is negligible, u_1 and u_2 can be neglected.

Net pump work done on the fluid $(W) = 1.5 \times 0.55 = 0.825$ kW

It is required to find $(E_2 - E_1)$.

Writing the energy balance between A and B,

$$E_1 + q_m \left[\frac{p_1}{\rho} + Z_1 \left(\frac{g}{g_c} \right) \right] + W + Q = E_2 + q_m \left[\frac{p_2}{\rho} + Z_2 \left(\frac{g}{g_c} \right) \right]$$

where q_m stands for the mass-flow rate of water (1 kg/s).

Since $p_1 = p_2$

$$(E_2 - E_1) = W + Q + (Z_1 - Z_2) \left(\frac{g}{g_c} \right) q_m$$

$$= (0.825) + 31 + \left[(-50 - 10) \times \frac{9.806\ 65}{1000} \right] \times 1$$

$$= 0.825 + 31 - 0.588 = 31.237 \text{ kW}$$

The increase in internal energy will increase the temperature of water.

Note It may be noted that contribution of the potential energy and mechanical work done by the pump are very small and hence the change in internal energy due to these factors is quite small.

5.3   HEAT CAPACITY

In Chapter 1, the unit of heat (or enthalpy) is given as joule (J) in SI (Section 1.3.4). For any substance, the heat required to raise the temperature by 1 K of 1 kg of it, is defined as *heat capacity*. It is customary to define the heat capacity on a unit mass or on a unit mole basis, the latter being known as *molar* heat capacity. For pure water, heat capacity is 4.1855 kJ/(kg · K) at 15°C (288.15 K). *Specific heat* of a substance is the ratio of the heat capacity of a particular substance to that of water, usually at 4°C (277.15 K). For solids and liquids, heat capacity values on mass basis are normally used. However, molar values are not uncommon.

Consider the heat capacity of a gas. Its numerical value depends on the route followed for attaining a particular temperature. Normally, two routes are chosen, viz., the constant-volume path and the constant-pressure path.

Fundamentally, $\qquad dQ = n \cdot C_m \cdot dT \qquad$ (5.3a)

where dQ is the change in heat, n the number of moles, C_m the molar heat capacity, and dT the change in temperature.

$$\text{For } n = 1 \text{ mol, } Q = C_m \cdot dT \tag{5.3b}$$

For a constant–volume process,

$$dQ = C_{mv} \cdot dT \tag{5.4}$$

where C_{mv} represents the molar heat capacity at constant volume.

Since the volume of the gas remains constant, no work is done on the gas. Hence,

$$dQ = dE \tag{5.5}$$

or $\qquad\qquad dE = C_{mv} \cdot dT \tag{5.6}$

This indicates that the change in internal energy equals the heat added at constant volume.

For a constant–pressure process,

$$dQ = C_{mp} \cdot dT \tag{5.7}$$

In this process, since the volume changes at constant pressure, Q is the total heat content (or enthalpy) H of the gas.

$$dQ = dH$$

$$= dE + pdV \qquad \text{[with the use of Eq. (5.1)]}$$

$$= C_{mp} \cdot dT \tag{5.8}$$

For an ideal gas, it can be proved* that

$$C_{mp} - C_{mv} = R = \text{Gas constant} \tag{5.9}$$

The ratio $\dfrac{C_{mp}}{C_{mv}}$ is denoted by γ and equals 1.4 for an ideal gas. The distinction of constant-volume and constant-pressure processes is not so important in the case of liquids and solids as the liquid or solid expands very little with increase in temperature. Therefore, heating or cooling at constant pressure nearly equals heating or cooling at constant volume for liquids and solids.

5.4 SENSIBLE HEAT CHANGES IN GASES AT CONSTANT PRESSURE

As discussed in Sec. 5.3, the heat capacity at constant pressure is defined as

$$dQ = C_{mp} \cdot dT \tag{5.10}$$

Integrating the above equation between the two temperatures,

$$Q = \int_{T_1}^{T_2} C_{mp} \cdot dT \tag{5.11}$$

---

*For the proof of Eq. (5.9) a standard textbook on thermodynamics or physical chemistry should be referred such as those given in Ref. 2 and 3.

In order to evaluate Eq. (5.11), the value of C_{mp} should be known. For an ideal gas, C_{mp} at 1 bar a is expressed as a function of temperature (T) and is denoted by C_{mp}^o.

Although the calculations of enthalpy changes are accurate at 101.325 kPa a with published C_{mp}^o data, they give fairly accurate enthalpy changes up to about 10 bar a for most of the gases. The effect of temperature on C_{mp}^o can be expressed in graphical or tabular form or in an empirical equation form. Spencer[4] presented empirical equations as far back as 1948 based on the tabulated C_{mp}^o data from API Research Project 44 (through April, 1947). Base data were since then constantly revised by API Research Project. A number of equations are developed on the basis of these data among which the most common form of the equation is the polynomial form.

$$C_{mp}^o = a + bT + cT^2 \qquad (5.12)$$

$$C_{mp}^o = a + bT + cT^2 + dT^3 \qquad (5.13)$$

$$C_{mp}^o = A + BT + CT^2 + DT^{-2} \qquad (5.14)$$

Thinh *et al*[5] utilized data compiled up to 1969 and presented constants of Eq. (5.13) for 408 hydrocarbons and related compounds. Yaws *et al*[6] presented constants of Eq. (5.13) for 700 organic compounds based on various references. Constants for Eq. (5.14) are given in Ref. 2. Physical properties package, called FLOWTRAN[7], developed by the Monsanto Company, USA, proposed a fourth-order polynomial equation, generally valid in the range of 298.15 to 1500 K.

$$C_{mp}^o = a + bT + cT^2 + dT^3 + eT^4 \qquad (5.15)$$

The NIST Chemistry WebBook[8] has proposed Shomate equation for ideal gas heat capacity as under.

$$C_{mp}^o = A' + BT + CT^2 + DT^3 + ET^{-2} \qquad (5.16)$$

The reciprocal term of Eq. (5.14) and Eq. (5.16) is a distinguishing characteristic, claimed to give accuracy over a wider temperature range.

Many other equations have been developed for the estimation of C_{mp}^o. However, the data presented by Thinh *et al*[5] are accurate (up to 1500 K) as they are derived by minimising the sum of squares of percentage deviations.

The truncation of the polynomial equation for a given set of constants is normally not recommended. For example, Eq. (5.13) was truncated[9] to a second-order polynomial and the dT^3 term was omitted. The calculation of C_{mp}^o with the reduced form of the equation and with the same constants were found to result in an error exceeding $2-3\%$ above 500 K for the equation, valid in the range 25°C (298.15 K) to 1500 K.

Extensive data on constants for various equations are listed in Table 5.1. For data on additional compounds, Ref. 10 may be consulted.

Table 5.1 Empirical Heat Capacity Equations for Gases

Form of equation

$$C_{mp}^0 = a + bT + cT^2 + dT^3 + eT^4$$

where C_{mp}^0 = Ideal gas heat capacity at 101.325 kPa a (760 Torr), kJ/(kmol · K)

and T = Absolute temperature, K

Compound	Formula	Molar mass	a	$b \times 10^3$	$c \times 10^6$	$d \times 10^9$	$e \times 10^{12}$	Range, K	Ref.
Inorganic Compounds									
Ammonia	NH_3	17.0305	27.55	25.6278	9.9004	−6.6864			7
			25.6503	33.4806	0.3518	−3.0832		298−1500	9
Argon	Ar	39.948	20.7723						7
Bromine	Br_2	159.808	33.6874	10.2992	−8.9025	2.6792			7
Carbon dioxide	CO_2	44.0095	19.0223	79.6291	−73.7067	37.4572	−8.133		7
			30.664	−48.3885	382.5044	−492.6398		50−298	5
			21.3655	64.2841	−41.0506	9.7999		298−1500	5
			37.174	23.2371	−7.3788	0.8213		1500−4000	5
			19.774	73.375	−56.02	17.155		298−1000	6
Carbon monoxide	CO	28.0101	29.0063	2.4924	−18.644	47.9892	−28.7266		7
			29.1151	0.2456	−2.067	5.9026		50−298	5
			29.0277	−2.8165	11.6437	−4.7063		298−1500	5
			27.4163	8.6192	−2.7046	0.3041		1500−4000	5
			30.842	−12.839	27.877	−12.709		298−1000	6
Chlorine	Cl_2	70.906	28.5463	23.8795	−21.3631	6.4726			7
Fluorine	F_2	37.9968	−24.9539	697.984	−3.2446	−528.857	270.246		7
Hydrogen	H_2	2.0159	17.6386	67.0055	−131.485	105.883	−29.1803		7
			19.6578	9.9027	289.2195	−741.5409		50−298	5
			28.6105	1.0194	−0.1476	0.769		298−1500	5
			25.4233	5.4355	−0.4974	−0.0054		1500−4000	5
Hydrogen chloride	HCl	36.4609	30.3088	−7.609	13.2608	−4.3336			7

(Contd.)

Table 5.1 (Contd.)

Compound	Formula	Molar mass	a	b × 10³	c × 10⁶	d × 10⁹	e × 10¹²	Range, K	Ref.
					Constants				
Hydrogen iodide	HI	127.9124	30.2697	−10.3319	25.946	−15.9529	3.1862		7
Hydrogen sulphide	H₂S	34.0809	34.5234	−17.6481	67.6664	−53.2454	14.0695		7
Oxygen	O₂	31.9988	29.8832	−11.3842	43.3779	−37.0082	10.1006		7
			29.1189	0.9952	−12.2586	40.1241		50–298	5
			26.0257	11.7551	−2.3426	−0.5623		298–1500	5
			18.4331	21.7174	−8.3048	1.1558		1500–4000	5
Ozone	O₃	47.9982	34.089	−23.1418	149.4231	43.8521		50–298	5
			20.5451	80.0947	−62.4369	16.9722		298–1500	5
Neon	Ne	20.1797	20.7723						7
Nitric oxide	NO	30.0061	29.7657	0.976	6.0987	−3.5881	0.5853		7
			29.4867	−2.0524	11.3379	−4.8195		298–1500	9
Nitrogen	N₂	28.0134	29.4119	−3.0068	5.4506	5.1319	−4.2531		7
			29.5909	−5.141	13.1829	−4.968		298–1500	9
			31.1182	3.1969	−0.4052	0.0023		1500–4000	9
Nitrogen dioxide	NO₂	46.0055	25.1165	43.9956	−9.6172	−12.1653	5.4494		7
			23.5804	53.5944	−31.4901	6.5394		298–1500	9
Nitrogen pentoxide	N₂O₅	108.0104	36.8193	259.7005	−215.4134	60.8531		298–1500	9
Nitrogen tetroxide	N₂O₄	92.0110	32.2558	189.6139	−138.303	35.908		298–1500	9
Nitrogen trioxide	N₂O₃	76.0116	37.4964	117.0169	−80.8775	20.137		298–1500	9
Nitrous oxide	N₂O	44.0128	20.5437	81.2993	−82.8968	49.8739	−11.2709		7
Sulphur (diatomic)	S₂	64.131	23.2082	63.6695	−42.3402	10.4061		298–1500	9
Sulphur dioxide	SO₂	64.0638	16.0581	4.7177	−2.9459	0.6668		298–1500	9
			25.7725	57.8938	−38.0844	8.6063		800–1500	7
Sulphur trioxide	SO₃	80.0632	24.7706	62.9481	−44.2582	11.122		298–1500	9
			15.507	145.719	−113.253	32.4046		298–1500	9
			22.0376	121.624	−91.8673	24.3691		298–1500	9

(Contd.)

Table 5.1 (Contd.)

Compound	Formula	Molar mass	Constants					Range, K	Ref.
			a	$b \times 10^3$	$c \times 10^6$	$d \times 10^9$	$e \times 10^{12}$		
Water	H_2O	18.0153	34.0471	-9.6501	32.9983	-20.4467	4.3023	298-1500	7
			32.4921	0.0796	13.2107	-4.5474		298-1000	9
			25.1584	21.2818	-5.34	0.4825		1500-4000	9
Organic Compounds									
Acetaldehyde	CH_3CHO	44.0526	24.5377	76.013	136.254	-199.942	75.9551	298-1500	7
			15.455	144.5	-43.25	-3.9835		298-1000	9
Acetic acid	CH_3COOH	60.0520	6.8995	257.068	-191.771	75.7676	-12.3175	298-1000	7
Acetone	C_3H_6O	58.0791	4.828	254.68	-175.26	49.509		298-1000	6
Acetylene (Ethyne)	C_2H_2	26.0373	20.916	204.056	-62.3	—	—	273-1500	—
			21.8212	92.058	-65.2231	18.1959		298-1500	7
			22.5039	90.1238	-63.7357	17.8644		298-1000	5
			15.812	128.15	-127.85	50.589		298-1000	6
Aniline	$C_6H_5NH_2$	93.1265	-2.2559	307.834	241.742	-537.543	235.694	298-1500	7
			-40.502	637.93	-513.08	163.31		298-1000	6
Benzene	C_6H_6	78.1118	18.5868	-11.7439	1275.14	-2079.84	1053.29	298-1500	7
			-37.9852	490.4208	-321.388	79.3646		298-1000	5
			-43.781	523.29	-376.27	106.61		298-1000	6
Butadiene 1,2	C_4H_6	54.0904	17.2814	224.295	-18.9688	-102.998	44.4247	298-1500	7
			11.1997	272.361	-146.8244	30.891		298-1500	5
			9.802	280.05	-159.68	37.256		298-1000	6
Butadiene 1,3	C_4H_6	54.0904	-5.6322	312.606	-2.8582	-368.547	246.459	298-1500	7
			-5.8354	353.1742	-239.9229	62.5332		298-1500	5
			-16.316	413.47	-342.51	114.98		298-1000	6
iso-Butane (Methyl propane)	C_4H_{10}	58.1222	52.9035	-107.178	1380.44	-2066.67	1008.88	298-1500	7
			-8.9133	419.5341	233.6331	51.0434		298-1500	5
			-10.853	430.53	-251.59	59.455		298-1000	6

(Contd.)

Table 5.1   (Contd.)

Compound	Formula	Molar mass	Constants					Range, K	Ref.
			a	$b \times 10^3$	$c \times 10^6$	$d \times 10^9$	$e \times 10^{12}$		
n-Butane	C_4H_{10}	58.1222	66.7088	−185.523	1528.44	−2187.92	1045.77	298−1500	7
			−2.4511	391.8275	−202.9882	40.7927		298−1000	5
Butene 1	C_4H_8	56.1063	−1.779	386.96	−193.25	34.833		298−1000	6
			9.2323	254.744	73.0443	−265.873	124.165	298−1500	7
			−2.3835	348.8153	−191.4879	41.2491		298−1000	5
cis-Butene 2	C_4H_8	56.1063	−4.02	357.67	−205.85	48.053		298−1500	6
			−7.8425	338.3705	−169.3661	32.239		298−1000	5
$trans$-Butene 2	C_4H_8	56.1063	−5.201	321.93	−139.37	15.605		298−1500	6
			9.2193	303.9495	−143.5319	25.4956		298−1000	6
n-Butyl alcohol (Butanol 1)	C_4H_9OH	74.1407	11.891	287.61	−114.33	9.5977		298−1500	6
			−2.07	429.749	−169.148	−73.744	61.4903	273−1500	7
Carbon disulphide	CS_2	76.141	14.6837	360.4152	−133.0594	1.4778		298−1500	5
			7.913	396.63	−192.66	31.739		298−1000	6
Carbon tetrachloride (Tetrachloromethane)	CCl_4	153.8227	33.0999	10.6167	275.934	−342.168	130.288	298−1000	7
			27.416	81.228	−76.63	26.724		298−1000	6
Chlorobenzene	C_6H_5Cl	112.5569	8.9763	420.036	−751.639	627.332	−199.811	273−1500	7
			50.1106	143.6852	−131.9483	39.3043		298−1000	5
			40.671	204.73	−226.88	88.383		298−1000	6
Chloroform (Trichloromethane)	$CHCl_3$	119.3776	−2.7793	357.786	−23.148	−240.458	125.736	298−1000	7
			−31.032	549.48	−430.53	131.7		298−1000	6
			31.8924	144.743	−111.583	30.721		273−1500	7
Ethane	C_2H_6	30.069	30.2685	151.0778	−118.6769	33.1579		298−1500	5
			23.975	189.18	−183.98	66.542		298−1000	6
			33.8339	−15.5175	376.892	−411.77	138.89	298−1500	7
Ethyl Alcohol (Ethanol)	C_2H_5OH	46.0684	5.4129	178.0872	−67.3749	8.7147		298−1500	5
			−8.181	161.46	−40.071	−6.9421		298−1000	6
			17.6907	149.532	89.4815	−197.384	83.1747	273−1000	7
			10.4197	209.5142	−82.4825	3.9339		298−1500	5
			6.296	231.5	−118.56	22.218		298−1000	6

(Contd.)

Table 5.1   (Contd.)

Compound	Formula	Molar mass	a	$b \times 10^3$	$c \times 10^6$	$d \times 10^9$	$e \times 10^{12}$	Range, K	Ref.
Ethyl benzene	$C_6H_5C_2H_5$	106.165	44.995	−45.8883	1832.28	−2919.74	1463.46	298−1500	7
			−36.7243	671.1231	−422.0211	101.1472		298−1000	5
			−43.087	706.76	−481.03	130.11			6
Ethylene	C_2H_4 (Ethene)	28.0532	16.8346	51.5193	216.352	−345.618	158.794	298−1500	7
			4.1261	155.0213	−81.5455	16.9755		298−1000	5
			3.798	156.5	−83.467	17.562			6
Ethylene glycol	$C_2H_6O_2$	62.0678	35.8417	108.695	290.598	−452.216	186.584	298−1000	7
			29.226	287.87	−224.54	73.835			6
Ethylene oxide (Epoxyethane)	C_2H_4O	44.0526	17.9573	34.3445	351.051	−478.345	190.011	298−1000	7
			−7.52	222.06	−125.6	25.918			6
Ethyl amine	$C_2H_5NH_2$	45.0837	27.5175	62.6593	391.9	−527.782	206.496	298−1000	7
			3.68	274.96	158.26	38.088			6
n-Hexane	C_6H_{14}	86.1754	42.7147	199.102	789.486	−1278.67	591.511	298−1500	7
			−4.4152	581.9233	−311.8584	64.9193		298−1000	5
			−4.738	582.41	−310.64	62.923		298−1200	6
Hydrogen Cyanide	HCN	27.0253	32.693	22.5921	−4.3691	−0.4077			—
Methane	CH_4	16.0425	38.387	−73.6639	290.981	−263.849	80.0679	298−1500	7
			19.2494	52.1135	11.973	−11.3173		298−1000	5
			25.36	16.868	71.312	−40.837			6
Methyl alcohol (Methanol)	CH_3OH	32.0419	34.4925	−29.1887	286.844	−312.501	109.833	273−1000	7
			24.8692	50.8755	58.6274	−45.1266		298−1000	5
			21.137	70.843	25.86	−28.497			6
Methyl amine	CH_3NH_2	31.0571	12.5367	151.044	−68.8093	12.345		298−1000	7
			16.086	121.42	−22.822	−9.0692			6
Methyl chloride (Chloromethane)	CH_3Cl	50.4875	19.4308	59.6368	70.6089	−117.502	46.7507	273−1500	7
			13.5427	105.0548	−47.4009	7.8612		298−1500	5
			13.728	102.3	−40.602	3.442			6

(Contd.)

Table 5.1   (Contd.)

Compound	Formula	Molar mass	a	$b \times 10^3$	$c \times 10^6$	$d \times 10^9$	$e \times 10^{12}$	Range, K	Ref.
Methylene chloride (Dichloromethane)	CH_2Cl_2	84.9326	16.9092	140.4533	-94.028	23.7905		273–1500	5
Methyl formate	$C_2H_4O_2$	60.0520	11.87	172.27	-149.25	52.283		298–1000	6
n-Pentane	C_5H_{12}	72.1488	-1257.0364	45 516.011	-443 651.0	—	1352.76	273–1000	—
			83.1454	-241.925	1946.53	-2807.49		298–1500	7
			-3.6266	487.4859	-258.0312	53.0488		298–1000	5
Phenol	C_6H_5OH	94.1112	-3.411	485.01	-251.94	48.677		298–1000	6
			-36.1498	566.519	-411.357	93.903	18.0687	298–1000	7
Propane	C_3H_8	44.0956	-35.833	597.81	-482.42	152.67		298–1000	6
			47.2659	-131.469	1170.0	-1696.95	818.91	298–1000	7
			-4.2227	306.264	-158.6316	32.1455		298–1000	6
			-5.338	310.24	-164.64	34.691		298–1000	7
Propionic acid	C_2H_5COOH	74.0785	32.217	182.665	160.153	-329.308	141.924	298–1500	5
Propylene (Propene)	C_3H_6	42.0797	24.3657	71.2795	338.448	-515.275	230.475	298–1000	6
			3.7457	234.0107	-115.1278	21.7353		298–1000	7
			5.084	225.64	-99.926	13.311		298–1500	5
Propylene oxide	C_3H_6O	58.0791	-7.868	322.82	-194.98	46.455		298–1000	6
Sytrene	C_8H_8	104.1491	-32.4471	631.898	-398.206	46.5312	36.4421	298–1000	6
			-36.914	665.26	-485.05	140.88		298–1000	7
Toluene	$C_6H_5CH_3$	92.1384	31.82	-16.1654	1444.65	-2289.48	1135.73	298–1000	6
			-35.1932	563.179	-349.7963	82.5884		298–1500	5
			-43.647	603.54	-399.45	104.38		298–1000	6
m-Xylene (Dimethyl benzene 1.3)	C_8H_{10}	106.1650	-27.833	623.1759	-366.4589	-82.2828		298–1500	5
			29.154	629.32	374.51	84.789		298–1000	6
o-Xylene (Dimethyl benzene 1,2)	C_8H_{10}	106.1650	-15.1201	592.8425	-341.4235	75.3348		298–1500	5
			15.859	595.72	-344.22	75.312		298–1000	6
p-Xylene (Dimethyl benzene 1,4)	C_8H_{10}	106.1650	-26.733	609.0789	-349.4772	76.4221		298–1500	5
			-25.088	603.63	-337.23	68.233		298–1000	6

Constants

(Reproduced with the permissions of (i) Monsanto Chemical Co., USA, (ii) Gulf Publishing Co., USA (iii) McGraw-Hill Inc., USA, and (iv) Central Laboratory, Transport Ministry, Quebec, Canada.)

Experimental data are not easily available for a number of substances for heat capacity of gases at high pressures. For this reason, a generalised approach is attempted by Weiss *et al*[11]. A graphical correlation in terms of the difference between the heat capacity under other operating conditions C_{mp} and the isobaric heat capacity in the ideal gas state C_{mp}^0 (at zero absolute pressure) as a function of reduced temperature (T_r) and reduced pressure (p_r) is given in Fig. 5.3. For calculation of $C_{mp}^R = C_{mp} - C_{mp}^0$ values, the Benedict–Webb–Rubin equation of state was used. C_{mp}^R is also known as *residual heat capacity* or excess heat capacity.

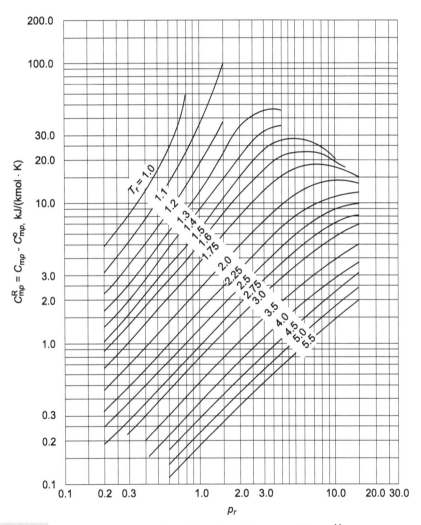

Fig. 5.3 Effects of Pressure on the Isobaric Heat Capacity of Gases[11] (*Reproduced with the permission of the American Chemical Society, USA*).

It may clearly be noted that C^R_{mp} is a point value. For calculating the enthalpy difference between given two temperature values at a given pressure, numerical integration will have to be adopted as a polynomial expression of C^R_{mp} is not available in literature. Another method for evaluation of C^R_{mp} is given by Lee *et al*[12] which is based on a three-parameters corresponding states principle. The values obtained by both the methods are generally in good agreement.

Ideal gas heat capacity C^o_{mp} referred to in Fig. 5.3 is for zero absolute pressure while the one reported in Table 5.1 is for a hypothetical ideal state at 101.325 kPa a. For the purpose of evaluation C_{mp} at high pressure, C^o_{mp} values from the table are not expected to have serious errors.

C^R_{mp} data from Fig. 5.3 are reliable for simple hydrocarbons and permanent light gases. For further discussion on the subject, the reader is advised to refer to Ref. 14.

Substituting C^o_{mp} in Eq. (5.13), for a polynomial equation of third order

$$Q = \int_{T_1}^{T_2} (a + bT + cT^2 + dT^3)\,dT$$

$$= a\,(T_2 - T_1) + \left(\frac{b}{2}\right)(T_2^2 - T_1^2) + \left(\frac{c}{3}\right)(T_2^3 - T_1^3) + \left(\frac{d}{4}\right)(T_2^4 - T_1^4) \quad (5.17)$$

This equation can be solved algebraically or with the help of mathemical software such as Mathcad, Maple, etc.

Example 5.2 Pure methane is heated from 30°C (303.15 K) to 250°C (523.15 K) at atmospheric pressure. Calculate the heat added per kmol methane, using data given in Table 5.1.

Solution *Base* 1 kmol of methane

$T_1 = 303.15$ K and $T_2 = 523.15$ K

(A) Reference 5 Using Eq. (5.17),

$$H = 19.2494\,(523.15 - 303.15) + 52.1135 \times 10^{-3}\,\frac{[523.15^2 - 303.15^2]}{2} + 11.973$$

$$\times 10^{-6}\,\frac{[523.15^3 - 303.15^3]}{3} - 11.3173 \times 10^{-9}\,\frac{[523.15^4 - 303.15^4]}{4}$$

$$= 4234.9 + 4736.8 + 460.24 - 188 = 9243.9 \text{ kJ}$$

Mathcad Solution

$$H := \int_{303.15}^{523.15} \left(19.2494 + 52.1135 \cdot 10^{-3} \cdot T + 11.973 \cdot 10^{-6} \cdot T^2 - 11.3173 \cdot 10^{-9} \cdot T^3\right) dT$$

$$H = 9243.8 \quad \text{kJ}$$

(B) Reference 6

$$H = 25.36\ (523.15 - 303.15) + 16.868 \times 10^{-3}\ \frac{[523.15^2 - 303.15^2]}{2}$$

$$+ 71.312 \times 10^{-6}\ \frac{[523.15^3 - 303.15^3]}{3} - 40.837 \times 10^{-9}\ \frac{[523.15^4 - 303.15^4]}{4}$$

$$= 5579.2 + 1533.2 + 2741.2 - 678.5 = \textbf{9175.1 kJ}$$

Mathcad Solution

$$H := \int_{303.15}^{523.15} \left(25.36 + 16.868 \cdot 10^{-3} \cdot T + 71.312 \cdot 10^{-6} \cdot T^2 - 40.837 \cdot 10^{-9} \cdot T^3\right) dT$$

$$H = 9175.1 \quad kJ$$

(C) Reference 7

$$H = 38.387\ (523.15 - 303.15) - 73.6639 \times 10^{-3}\ \frac{[523.15^2 - 303.15^2]}{2}$$

$$+ 290.981 \times 10^{-6}\ \frac{[523.15^3 - 303.15^3]}{3} - 263.849 \times 10^{-9}$$

$$\frac{[523.15^4 - 303.15^4]}{4} + 80.0679 \times 10^{-12}\ \frac{[523.15^5 - 303.15^5]}{5}$$

$$= 8445.1 - 6695.5 + 11185.2 - 4383.7 + 586.5 = \textbf{9137.6 kJ}$$

Mathcad Solution

$$H := \int_{303.15}^{523.15} \left(38.387 - 73.6639 \cdot 10^{-3} \cdot T + 290.981 \cdot 10^{-6} \cdot T^2 - 263.849 \cdot 10^{-9} \cdot T^3 + 80.0679 \cdot 10^{-12} \cdot T^4\right) dT$$

$$H = 9137.6 \quad kJ$$

Note From the above calculations, it is evident that with different constants, the calculation differs to a certain extent and hence the use of reliable data is must.

Example 5.3 Calculate the heat added per kmol methane when it is heated from 30°C (303.15 K) to 250°C (523.15 K) at 25 bar a.

Solution   1 kmol methane at 25 bar a

For methane, $p_c = 46.04$ bar and $T_c = 190.5$ K   (Ref. Appendix III)

$$p_r = 25/46.04 = 0.543$$

Residual enthalpy $$H - H° = \int_{303.15}^{523.15} C_{mp}^R\ dT$$

Since only point values can be read from Fig. 5.3 for C_{mp}^R, it is necessary to use a numerical method for integration.

The temperature range of 303.15 to 523.15 K can be divided into 4 intervals.

Temperature interval, $\Delta T = (523.15 - 303.15)/4$

$$= 55\ K$$

Table 5.2   Residual Heat Capacity Calculations

Temperature, °C (K)	Reduced temperature, T_r	Residual heat capacity C_{mp}^R, k J/(kmol · K) (read from Fig. 5.3)
30 (303.15)	1.59	2.6
85 (358.15)	1.879	1.5
140 (413.15)	2.168	1.0
195 (468.15)	2.457	0.7
250 (523.15)	2.745	0.52

According to Simpson's one-third rule,

$$H^E = H - H^\circ = \frac{\Delta T}{3} \ (C_{mp1}^R + 4 \ [C_{mp2}^R + C_{mp4}^R] + 2[C_{mp3}^R] + C_{mp5}^R)$$

$$= \frac{55}{3} \ (2.6 + 4 \ [1.5 + 0.7] + 2 \times 1.0 + 0.52) = 255.2 \text{ kJ/kmol}$$

Enthalpy required to be added for raising the temperature of methane from 303.15 to 523.15 K at 25 bar a,

$$H = 9175.1 + 255.2 = \textbf{9430.3 kJ/kmol}$$

Note Difference between the enthalpy values under ideal state conditions and at 2.5 MPa is 255.2 kJ/kmol which is about 2.7% of the correct enthalpy. Error becomes significant for high p_r and low T_r.

In the absence of reliable data on the heat capacity of many organic compounds (vapour/gas phase), various other data for estimation are available in literature[13]. Rihani and Doraiswamy[14] proposed an additive group method which is based on Eq. (5.12) and is applicable to many types of organic compounds. Detailed discussions on the group contribution methods is outside the scope of this book.

5.5   SENSIBLE HEAT CHANGES IN LIQUIDS AND SOLIDS

As mentioned earlier in Sec. 5.3, the heat capacities at constant pressure and constant volume of a liquid are nearly equal. In general, the heat capacity of a liquid increases with an increase in the temperature, although the variation of the heat capacity of a liquid with temperature is considered to be of less importance. This is because the temperature range in which the heating or cooling is performed is usually small.

For liquids, $dH = m \ C_1 \ dT$ (5.18)

where C_1 is the heat capacity of the liquid [kJ/(kg · K)] and m is the mass of the liquid (kg).

In a similar manner, molar heat capacity (C_{ml}) can be used.

$$dH = n \ C_{ml} \ dT \qquad (5.19)$$

The heat capacity of a liquid can be expressed as a function of temperature.

Table 5.3 presents data on molar liquid heat capacity from references 7, 14 and 15. Considering the third-order polynomial equation (similar to Eq. (5.13)).

Table 5.3 Molar Heat Capacity of Liquids

$$C_1 = a + bT + cT^2 + dT^3, \ \text{kJ/(kmol}\cdot\text{K)}, \quad T \text{ in K}$$

Compound	Formula	Molar mass	a	$b \times 10^3$	$c \times 10^6$	$d \times 10^9$	Temp. Range K	Ref.
Acetaldehyde	C_2H_4O	44.0526	16.8842	810.208	− 3080.85	4425.9	150–324	7
			54.7	− 22.0844	147.634			15
Acetic acid	$C_2H_4O_2$	60.0520	− 36.0814	604.681	− 393.957	− 561.602	290–421	7
			155.48	− 326.5951	744.199			15
Acetyl chloride	C_2H_3ClO	78.4976	21.7323	1524.8	− 5449.35	6980.35	160–354	7
			102.94	− 91.5796	446.3516			15
Ammonia	NH_3	17.0305	20.1494	845.765	− 4067.45	6606.87	196–373	7
			− 137.1179	2217.5586	− 7907.6285	9811.4489	196–373	14
Aniline	C_6H_7N	93.1265	− 13.6683	931.971	− 1604.01	1367.15	267–487	7
			206.27	− 211.5065	564.2902			15
Argon	Ar	39.948	− 24.93	1416.64	− 2869.02	− 42 749.6	84–143	7
			− 79.914	3875.2813	− 42566.2	162 688.2		14
Benzene	C_6H_6	78.1118	− 7.2733	770.541	− 1648.18	1897.94	279–523	7
			− 484.365	5056.235	− 14292.204	14 419.754		14
Bromine	Br_2	159.808	21.1979	517.99	− 1759.21	1952.66	266–553	7
			− 266.8805	2980.8129	− 8945.117	8851.3807		14
Butadiene 1,2	C_4H_6	54.0904	6.2582	913.303	− 3101.42	4386.33	164–393	7
Butadiene 1,3	C_4H_6	54.0904	− 16.1777	1085.11	− 3682.61	5410.41	165–4211	7
			85.721	237.573	− 1304.7267	311.7756		14
1-Butanol (n-Butyl alcohol)	$C_4H_{10}O$	74.1216	− 0.5104	1446.97	− 3833.39	4288.49		7
			162.68	− 141.2138	623.2696			15
Carbon dioxide	CO_2	44.0095	11.0417	1159.55	− 7231.3	2075.75	217–259	7
			98.63	− 294.1525	933.0371			15

(Contd.)

Table 5.3 (Contd.)

Compound	Formula	Molar mass	Constants				Temp. Range K	Ref.
			a	$b \times 10^3$	$c \times 10^6$	$d \times 10^9$		
Carbon disulphide	CS_2	76.1407	17.4151	554.537	-1723.46	15 501.9		7
			68.39	-45.6772	243.2064		161–349	15
Carbon monoxide	CO	28.0101	14.9673	2143.97	$-32\ 470.3$	15 804.2		7
			61.53	-176.9687	2054.408		68–112	15
Carbon tetrachloride (Tetrachloromethane)	CCl_4	153.8227	12.2846	1094.75	-3182.55	3425.24		7
			139.73	-204.5003	586.787			15
Chlorine	Cl_2	70.906	15.412	723.104	-3397.26	5262.36	172–353	14
			-39.246	1401.2228	-6047.226	8591.4		7
Chlorobenzene	C_6H_5Cl	112.5569	-11.5494	939.618	-1898.5	1791.89		7
			150.41	-142.546	464.2096		228–435	15
Chloroform (Trichloromethane)	$CHCl_3$	119.3776	23.8419	755.531	-2407.01	2842.62	210–364	15
			110.54	-121.5667	441.0741			7
Ethanol (Ethyl alcohol)	C_2H_6O	40.0684	-325.137	4137.87	-14030.7	17 035.4	159–381	15
			100.92	-111.8386	498.54			7
Ethylene (Ethene)	C_2H_4	28.0532	-39.959	730.3548	-5887.003	14 834.966	104–233	14
Ethyl acetate	$C_4H_8O_2$	88.1051	4.2905	934.378	-2640.0	3342.58		7
Ethylbenzene	C_8H_{10}	106.165	4.3143	900.174	-1450.05	1433.6		7
Ethylene glycol	$C_2H_6O_2$	62.0678	31.0224	1100.34	-2845.71	2889.21		7
			15.3	-114.819	331.6842			15
Ethylene oxide	C_2H_4O	44.0526	7.4126	742.687	-2713.2	3900.92	260–500	15
			79.81	-27.5124	182.2322			7
Formaldehyde	CH_2O	30.0260	25.099	793.671	-3826.91	6104.92	161–314	15
			77.73	-56.6673	323.9887		156–254	7

(Contd.)

Table 5.3   (Contd.)

Compound	Formula	Molar mass	a	$b \times 10^3$	$c \times 10^6$	$d \times 10^9$	Temp. Range K	Ref.
Formic acid	CH_2O_2	46.0254	133.43	−347.5111	785.7561		282–404	15
n-Hexane	C_6H_{14}	86.1754	31.421	976.058	−2353.68	3092.73	273–698	7
Hydrogen peroxide	H_2O_2	34.0147	63.2314	170.7533	−389.9272	372.4104	275–473	14
Hydrazine	N_2H_4	32.0452	−621.733	6574.2164	−20 138.569	20 970.409		14
Methanol (Methyl alcohol)	CH_4O	32.0419	−258.25	3358.2	−11 638.8	14 051.6	176–368	7
			74.86	−102.315	406.6567			15
Methyl chloride	CH_3Cl	50.4875	7.9961	798.5	−3507.58	5515.01	175–279	7
			72.77	−44.0239	229.4864			15
Methylene chloride	CH_2Cl_2	84.9323	117.11	−149.6366	616.2757		178–343	15
Naphthalene	$C_{10}H_8$	128.1735	−63.27	1243.34	−1768.51	1218.97	354–683	7
			−757.746	6230.475	−13 555.71	10 534.386		14
Nitric oxide	NO	30.0061	33.6324	2904.98	−32 658.3	120 828.0	109–138	7
			−2394.499	65 779.627	−591 024.17	1786 075.2		14
Nitrogen	N_2	28.0134	14.7141	2202.57	−35 214.6	179 960.0	63–113	7
			−124.793	6975.028	−90 158.135	393 765.98		14
Nitrogen dioxide	NO_2	46.0055	16.9925	1714.99	−7839.62	12 001.7	262–413	7
			−313.0	3657.775	−11 888.25	13 246.19		14
Nitrous oxide	N_2O	44.0128	8.5894	1051.71	−6392.8	13 326.0	182–303	7
			−537.155	8152.228	36 393.88	55 521.39		14
Oxygen	O_2	31.9988	1105.01	−33 363.6	35 021.1	−1212 620.0	55–143	15
			−61.4532	4332.673	−52 932.565	211 100.59		
Phenol	C_6H_6O	94.1112	−36.1614	1153.54	−2122.91	1741.83	314–485	15
			207.48	−103.7491	274.0052			

(Contd.)

Table 5.3 (Contd.)

Compound	Formula	Molar mass	Constants a	$b \times 10^3$	$c \times 10^6$	$d \times 10^9$	Temp. Range K	Ref.
n-Pentane	C_5H_{12}	72.1488	65.4961	628.628	-1898.8	3186.51		7
1-Propanol	C_3H_8O	60.0950	-488.104	5786.32	$-18\,872.0$	22\,003.5		7
(*n*-Propyl alcohol)		119.39	-100.2081		501.3639		147–400	15
Propionic acid	$C_3H_6O_2$	74.0785	31.7072	930.795	-2330.49	2457.4		7
			-137.5366	2383.124	-6235.805	-6253.25	243–598	14
Propylene (Propene)	C_3H_6	42.0797	82.9137	296.523	-2963.469	7764.571	243–598	14
Styrene	C_8H_8	104.1491	-38.0191	1197.21	-2195.65	1933.12	88–313	7
			-137.5366	2283.124	6235.805	-6253.25	243–598	14
Sulphur dioxide	SO_2	64.0638	19.2884	845.429	-3727.48	5653.65	243–598	14
			-153.877	2773.3755	$-10\,803.826$	14\,175.33	200–423	7
Sulphur trioxide	SO_3	80.0632	16.2291	1374.62	-5177.38	6886.34	290–473	14
			-1333.443	13\,461.809	$-39\,051.315$	39\,554.121		7
Toluene	C_7H_8	92.1384	1.8083	812.223	-1512.67	1630.01	178–583	14
			-56.3627	1768.423	-5192.623	5497.39		7
Water	H_2O	18.0153	18.2964	472.118	-1338.78	1314.24	273–623	14
			50.845	213.08	-631.398	648.746		7
m-Xylene	C_8H_{10}	106.165	14.0673	870.264	-1477.33	1511.93	225–573	14
			-38.846	1699.3	-4753.1	5086.0		7
o-Xylene	C_8H_{10}	106.165	14.8871	903.295	-1550.98	1512.01	248–298	14
			-199.626	3058.7	-8254.7	7926.3		7
p-Xylene	C_8H_{10}	106.165	-22.0553	811.839	-1366.7	1442.16	287–598	14
			-374.08	3976.9	-9524.0	81\,088.12		7

(Reproduced with the permissions of (i) Monsanto Chemical Co., USA and (ii) McGraw-Hill Inc., USA)

$$\int dH = \int_{T_1}^{T_2} C_{ml} \, dT \qquad (5.20)$$

$$H = a(T_2 - T_1) + \left(\frac{b}{2}\right)(T_2^2 - T_1^2) + \left(\frac{c}{3}\right)(T_2^3 - T_1^3) + \left(\frac{d}{4}\right)(T_2^4 - T_1^4) \qquad (5.21)$$

Luria and Benson[13] have proposed an accurate group contribution method for the estimation of the molar heat capacity of liquid hydrocarbons which is applicable below the normal boiling point.

Often, heat capacity data are available in graphical or tabular form. For example, heat capacity plots for a number of aqueous solutions are available in literature. Figures 5.4 and 5.5 give the heat capacity of caustic soda solutions and sulphuric

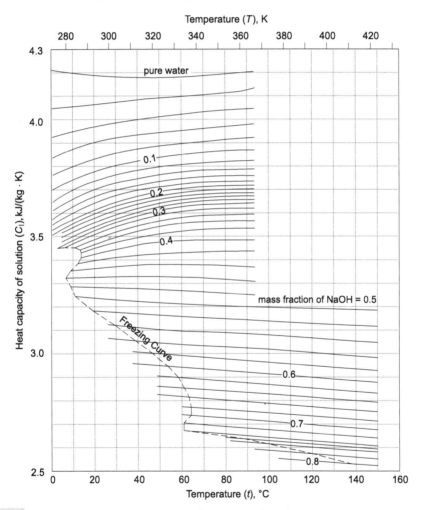

Note The freezing point curve indicates the point at which the crystals exists in contact with solution.

Fig. 5.4 Heat Capacity of Aqueous Caustic Soda Solutions[16, 17, 18]
(Reproduced with the permission of the American Chemical Society, USA).

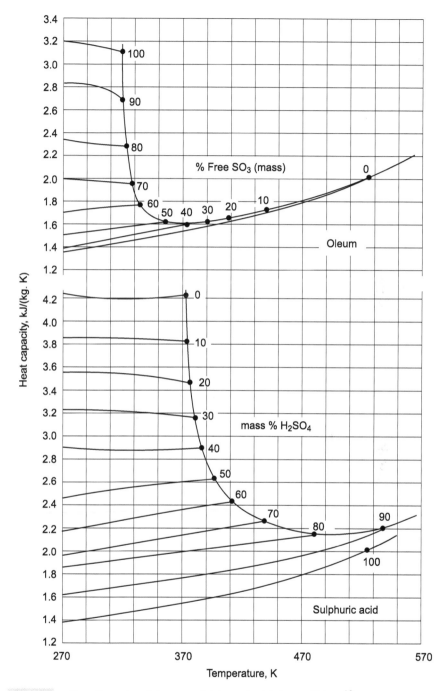

Fig. 5.5 Heat Capacity of Aqueous Sulphuric Acid Solutions/Oleum[19]
(Reproduced with the permission of Lurgi GmbH, Germany).

acid solutions respectively of different concentrations at different temperatures[16,17]. Figure 5.17 is another chart which gives the heat capacity of mixed acids.

Example 5.4   Toluene is heated from 17°C (290.15 K) to 77°C (350.15 K) at the rate of 0.25 kg/s. Calculate the heat required to be added to toluene using constants given in Table 5.3.

Solution   0.25 kg/s toluene heated from 290.15 K to 350.15 K

$$\text{Molar flow rate, } q_m = \frac{0.25}{92} = 2.717 \times 10^{-3} \text{ kmol/s}$$

(A) Reference 7

$$\phi = 2.717 \times 10^{-3} \left[1.8083 \, (350.15 - 290.15) + 812.223 \times 10^{-3} \, \frac{(350.15^2 - 290.15^2)}{2} \right.$$

$$\left. -1512.67 \times 10^{-6} \, \frac{(350.15^3 - 290.15^3)}{3} + 1630.01 \times 10^{-9} \, \frac{(350.15^4 - 290.15^4)}{4} \right]$$

$$= 2.717 \times 10^{-3} \, [108.5 + 15602 - 9329.8 + 3237.4]$$

$$= 2.717 \times 10^{-3} \times 9618.1 \text{ kJ/s} \equiv \mathbf{26.132 \text{ kW}}$$

(B) Reference 14

$$\phi = 2.1717 \times 10^{-3} \left[-56.276 \, (350.15 - 290.15) + 1768.423 \times 10^{-3} \, \frac{(350.15^2 - 290.15^2)}{2} \right.$$

$$\left. -5192.623 \times 10^{-6} \, \frac{(350.15^3 - 290.15^3)}{3} + 5497.39 \times 10^{-9} \, \frac{(350.15^4 - 290.15^4)}{4} \right]$$

$$= 2.717 \times 10^{-3} \, [-3376.6 + 33\,969.6 - 32\,026.9 + 10\,918.6]$$

$$= 2.717 \times 10^{-3} \times 9484.7 \text{ kJ/s} \equiv \mathbf{25.77 \text{ kW}}$$

Both values differ by about 1.4%.
Mathcad can also be used to find ϕ.

Example 5.5   How much heat must be added in order to raise the temperature of a 20% (mass) aqueous caustic soda solution from 7°C (280.15 K) to 87°C (360.15 K).

Solution   *Basis* 1 kg of 20% NaOH Solution
From Fig. 5.4, for 20% caustic soda solution,

$$C_{11} = 3.56 \text{ kJ/(kg} \cdot \text{K) at 280.15 K}$$

and

$$C_{12} = 3.71 \text{ kJ/(kg} \cdot \text{K) at 360.15 K}$$

Mean heat capacity, $C_{1m} = \dfrac{(3.56 + 3.71)}{2} = 3.635$ kJ/(kg × K)

Heat required to raise the temperature

of 1 kg 20% NaOH solution = 1 × 3.635 (360.15 − 280.15)

= **290.8 kJ**

Example 5.6 Chlorinated diphenyl (Diphyl A-30[R]) is heated from 40°C (313.15 K) to 280°C (553.15 K) at the rate of 4000 kg/h in an indirectly fired heater. In this particular temperature range, the heat capacity of the fluid is given by the equation

$$C_l = 0.7511 + 1.465 \times 10^{-3} \, T \text{ kJ/(kg} \cdot \text{K)}$$

where T is in K.

Also, the heat capacity data of Diphyl A-30 at 40°C (313.15 K) and 280°C (553.15 K) are 1.1807 and 1.5198 kJ/(kg · K), respectively[20].

Calculate the heat to be supplied to the fluid in the heater using the heat capacity equation. Also, calculate the % error involved in using the mean heat capacity data for the heat change calculations.

Solution *Basis* 1 kg Diphyl A-30

Sensible heat change,

$$Q = \int_{T_1}^{T_2} C_1 \, dT \ = \ \int_{313.15}^{553.15} (0.7511 + 1.465 \times 10^{-3} \, T) \, dT$$

$$= 0.7511 \, (553.15 - 313.15) + 1.465 \times 10^{-3} \, \frac{(553.15^2 - 313.15^2)}{2}$$

$$= 180.26 + 152.29 = 332.55 \text{ kJ/kg}$$

For the mass-flow rate of 4000 kg/h,

$$\phi = 4000 \times 332.55 = 1330\,200 \times 10^4 \text{ kJ/h} \equiv \textbf{369.5 kW}$$

$$C_{lm} = \frac{(1.1807 + 1.5198)}{2} = 1.3503 \text{ kJ/(kg} \cdot \text{K)}$$

$$\phi' = C_{lm} \, (T_2 - T_1) \cdot 4000$$

$$= 1.3503 \, (553.15 - 313.15) \cdot 4000 = 129.6288 \times 10^4 \text{ kJ/h} \equiv \textbf{360.08 kW}$$

$$\% \text{ error} = \left[\frac{360.08 - 332.55}{332.55} \right] \times 100 = \textbf{8.3}$$

The heat capacity of solids are lower than liquids and increase with the increase in temperature as is the case with liquids or gases. Heat capacity data for number of solids (inorganic and organic) are given in Perry's Chemical Engineer's Handbook[21]. Kelley[22] have presented voluminous heat capacity data for elements and inorganic compounds in different states.

A number of methods are reported in literature for estimation of heat capacity of liquids, solutions and solids. A good summary of the methods can be found in

Ref. 2 and 21. Only in the absence of non-availability of experimental data, these methods may be used with caution.

5.6   HEAT CAPACITY OF GASEOUS MIXTURES

In Sec. 5.4, the sensible heat change of a gas between two temperatures was considered. However, in practice, the mixtures of gases are often heated or cooled. The sensible heat change of an ideal gaseous mixture can be calculated by calculating the mixture properties from the properties of pure gases present in the mixture. For an ideal gas mixture, the molar heat capacity of a gas mixture at a constant pressure is given by

$$C^o_{mp_{mix}} = \sum_{1}^{n} y_i \cdot C^o_{mpi} \qquad (5.22)$$

where y_i is the mole fraction of the ith component and $C^o_{mp_i}$ is the molar heat capacity of the ith component. In this equation $C^o_{mp_{mix}}$ can be expressed as a function of temperature.

For real gas mixtures, Lee et al[12] have proposed an additive rule for estimation of critical properties which can be utilised for evaluation of residual heat capacity. This rule is different from Kay's additive rule for estimation of pseudo-critical properties (refer Example 2.25).

For a limited range of pressure and temperature, enthalpy of a real gas mixture can be represented by a model, incorporating $C^o_{mp_{mix}}$ and pressure parameter p. Exercise 5.35 gives such an equation for a sour gas mixture from a refinery. Such models should not be used beyond the specified range of conditions.

Example 5.7   Pyrites fines are roasted in a chamber plant for making sulphuric acid. The gases leaving the roaster are at 502°C (775.15 K) and have molar composition SO_2 7.09%, O_2 10.55%, SO_3 0.45% and N_2 81.91%. Calculate the heat content of 1 kmol gas mixture over 25°C (298.15 K), using the heat capacity data provided in Table 5.1.

Solution   *Basis* 1 kmol of gas mixture
(a) In the first instance, take the value of $C^0_{mp} = f(T)$ given in Table 5.1.

$$\text{Heat change } Q = \int_{T_1}^{T_2} C^o_{mp_{mix}} \, dT$$

Sulphur dioxide

$$y_{SO_2} \cdot C^o_{mp_{SO_2}} = 0.0709 \, (24.7706 + 62.9481 \times 10^{-3} \, T - 44.2582 \times 10^{-6} \, T^2$$

$$+ \, 11.122 \times 10^{-9} \, T^3)$$

$$= 1.7562 + 4.4630 \times 10^{-3} \, T - 3.1379 \times 10^{-6} \, T^2 + 0.7885 \times 10^{-9} \, T^3$$

Oxygen

$$y_{O_2} \cdot C^o_{mpO_2} = 0.1055 \, (26.0257 + 11.7551 \times 10^{-3} \, T - 2.3426 \times 10^{-6} \, T^2$$
$$- 0.5623 \times 10^{-9} \, T^3)$$
$$= 2.7457 + 1.2402 \times 10^{-3} \, T - 0.2471 \times 10^{-6} \, T^2 - 0.0593 \times 10^{-9} \, T^3$$

Sulphur trioxide

$$y_{SO_3} \cdot C^o_{mpSO_3} = 0.0045 \, (22.0376 + 121.624 \times 10^{-3} \, T - 91.8673 \times 10^{-6} \, T^2$$
$$+ 24.3691 \times 10^{-9} \, T^3)$$
$$= 0.0992 + 0.5473 \times 10^{-3} \, T - 0.4134 \times 10^{-6} \, T^2 + 0.1097 \times 10^{-9} \, T^3$$

Nitrogen

$$y_{N_2} \cdot C^o_{mpN_2} = 0.8191 \, (29.5909 - 5.141 \times 10^{-3} \, T + 13.1829 \times 10^{-6} \, T^2 - 4.968$$
$$\times 10^{-9} \, T^3)$$
$$= 24.2379 - 4.2110 \times 10^{-3} \, T + 10.7891 \times 10^{-6} \, T^2 - 4.0693 \times 10^{-9} \, T^3$$

Summing up,

$$C^o_{mp_{mix}} = \sum y_i \cdot C^o_{mpi} = 28.839 + 2.0395 \times 10^{-3} \, T + 6.9907 \times 10^{-6} \, T^2$$
$$- 3.2304 \times 10^{-9} \, T^3$$
$$T_1 = 298.15 \text{ K} \quad \text{and} \quad T_2 = 775.15 \text{ K}$$

Using Eq. (5.17)

$$Q = 28.839 \, (T_2 - T_1) + 2.0395 \times 10^{-3} \, \frac{(T_2^2 - T_1^2)}{2} + 6.9907 \times 10^{-6}$$

$$\frac{(T_2^3 - T_1^3)}{3} - 3.2304 \times 10^{-9} \, \frac{(T_2^4 - T_1^4)}{4}$$

$$= 13 \, 756.2 + 522.1 + 1023.6 - 285.2 = \textbf{15 016.7 kJ/kmol}$$

5.7 HEAT CAPACITY OF LIQUID MIXTURES

For an immiscible liquid mixture, pure component values are additive and a weighted average is used for calculations. For miscible systems, additivity is not generally true although for similar substances and for systems with small heats of mixing, additivity gives fairly good results. As indicated in Sec. 5.5 earlier, a number of plots are available for aqueous solutions in literature. The heat capacity of mixtures of liquid metals or fused salts can be predicted within about 10% accuracy by the additivity rule.

For petroleum oils, the American Petroleum Institute has compiled extensive data[23]. For a defined liquid hydrocarbon mixture, additivity rule is recommended by API. Thus, for immiscible liquid mixtures and also for liquid hydrocarbon mixtures,

$$C_1 = \Sigma w_i \cdot C_{1i} \tag{5.23}$$

where w_i = mass fraction of ith component, and

C_{li} = heat capacity of ith component.

For petroleum fractions, API gravity is the parameter used to find the heat capacity at atmospheric pressure[2].

Example 5.8   A mixture of aniline and water, containing 11.8 (mass %) aniline, is subcooled in the overhead condenser of the distillation column from 100 to 40°C (373 K to 313 K) with the help of cooling water at the rate 8000 kg/h. Find the heat removal rate of the subcooling zone of the condenser.

Solution   *Basis* 8000 kg/h mixture is to be cooled.
Aniline and water are practically immiscible in each other and hence the additivity rule can be used for calculations.

Aniline in the mixture, q_{n_1} = 0.118 × 8000 = 944 kg/h ≡ 10.137 kmol/h
Water in the mixture, q_{n_2} = 8000 − 944 = 7056 kg/h ≡ 391.67 kmol/h

Use the data provided in Table 5.3 (Ref. 15 for aniline and Ref. 14 for water).

$$T_1 = 373.15 \text{ K} \quad \text{and} \quad T_2 = 313.15 \text{ K}$$

Heat extraction rate,

$$\phi = 10.137 \left[206.27 \, (T_1 - T_2) - 211.5065 \times 10^{-3} \frac{(T_1^2 - T_2^2)}{2} + 564.2902 \times 10^{-6} \right.$$

$$\left. \frac{(T_1^3 - T_2^3)}{3} \right] + 391.67 \left[50.845 \, (T_1 - T_2) + 213.08 \times 10^{-3} \frac{(T_1^2 - T_2^2)}{2} - 631.398 \right.$$

$$\left. \times 10^{-6} \frac{(T_1^3 - T_2^3)}{3} + 648.746 \times 10^{-9} \frac{(T_1^4 - T_2^4)}{4} \right]$$

$= 10.137 \, (12\ 376.2 - 4354.7 + 3996.9) + 391.67 \, (3050.7 + 4387.1 - 4472.3 + 1584.8)$
$= 10.137 \times 12\ 018.4 + 391.67 \times 4550.3$
$= 121\ 830.5 + 1782\ 216 = 190\ 4046.5 \text{ kJ/h} \equiv$ **528.9 kW**

Heat capacity of aniline and water at 25° (298.15 K) are 2.0515 and 4.1868 kJ/(kg × K) respectively[21]. If it is assumed to be constant over the temperature range of 313.15 K to 373.15 K,

$$\phi = (944 \times 2.0515 + 7056 \times 4.1868) \, (373.15 - 313.15)$$

$$= (1936.6 + 29\ 542.1) \, (60) = 1888\ 722 \text{ kJ/h} \equiv \mathbf{524.65 \text{ kW}}$$

$$\text{Error} = (528.9 - 524.65) \, \frac{100}{528.9} = 0.8\%$$

This error is quite low. It indicates that in most cases of liquids, the variation of heat capacity with respect to the temperature is quite small.

5.8 LATENT HEATS

When matter changes from one phase to another, the latent heat is either absorbed or rejected. For example, ice melts at 0°C (273.15 K) by supplying heat to produce water. Similarly, water at 101.325 kPa (760 Torr) and 100°C (373.15 K) produces vapour if heat is continuously supplied to it. The former is called the *latent heat of fusion*, while the latter is called the *latent heat of vaporization*. In some cases, such as iodine crystals, camphor, dry ice, etc., vapour is produced from the solids, the process being called *sublimation*. The heat supplied for such a phase change process is called the *latent heat of sublimation*.

The heat supplied to melt the solid to liquid or removed to convert the liquid into solid per kilogram is called the *latent heat of fusion*, represented by the symbol λ_f.

The heat supplied to convert liquid to vapour at a constant pressure (at the corresponding boiling point) is called the *latent heat of vaporization*, represented by the symbol λ_v.

In the case of liquids/vapours, the boiling/saturation point changes with changes in pressure, and hence the latent heat of vaporization also varies with pressure. From the foregoing discussion, it is clear that the units of latent heat are kJ/kg. As in the case of heat capacity, molar latent heats are expressed in kJ/mol.

The variation of the latent heat of vaporization with pressure/temperature is of considerable interest to the process industry. For this reason, a reliable equation for the correlation of pressure and the corresponding saturation temperature must be available.

An equation proposed by Antoine is as follows:

$$\log_{10} p_v = A - \frac{B}{(T + C)} \quad \text{or} \quad (5.24)$$

where p_v is the vapour pressure in bar, T is the temperature in K and A, B and C are species specific constants.

A graph having $\log p_v$ (or $\ln p_v$) on the y-axis and $1/T$ on the x-axis is called the *Cox chart*. In other words, it is a representation of the Antoine equation in the graphical form.

It is observed that barring some of the compounds (such as organic sulphur compounds), the Antoine equation is proved to give the vapour pressure in the range of 1 to 200 kPa (10 to 1500 Torr) of a variety of compounds well within the experimental uncertainty. Table 5.4 gives values of A, B and C for Eq. (5.24)[8]. The representation of vapour pressure over a wider range of pressure, however, requires the use of a more complex equation of four or more parameters such as the one given by Yaws[14].

Table 5.4   Antoine Constants

A. Inorganic Compounds:

Compound	CAS Reg. No.	Chemical Formula	Molar Mass	Antoine Constants			Temperature Range, K	
				A	B	C	From	To
Ammonia	7664-41-7	NH_3	17.0305	3.187 57	506.713	−80.78	164.0	239.5
				4.868 86	1113.928	−10.409	239.5	371.4
Argon	7440-37-1	Ar	39.948	3.295 55	215.240	−22.233	83.78	150.72
Bromine	7726-95-6	Br_2	159.808	2.945 29	638.258	−115.144	224.4	331.3
				4.708 27	1562.264	0.628	343	383
Carbon Dioxide	124-38-9	CO_2	44.0095	6.812 28	1301.679	−3.494	154.26	195.89
Carbon Disulphide	75-15-0	CS_2	76.1407	4.066 83	1168.620	−31.616	76.74	353.08
Chlorine	7782-50-5	Cl_2	70.906	3.021 30	530.591	−64.639	155	239.3
				4.288 14	969.992	−12.791	239.3	400.2
Hydrazine	302-01-2	N_2H_4	32.0452	5.011 05	1724.782	−41.833	288	343
Hydrogen	1333-74-0	H_2	2.0159	3.543 14	99.395	7.726	21.01	32.27
Hydrogen Bromide	10035-10-6	HBr	80.9119	4.024 19	695.466	−33.542	134.3	206.6
				4.155 85	754.969	−25.086	206.6	343.7
Hydrogen Chloride	7647-01-0	HCl	36.4609	3.607 65	535.172	−39.847	122.3	188.3
				4.573 89	868.358	1.754	188.3	309.3
Hydrogen Iodide	10034-85-2	HI	127.9124	4.268 54	939.994	−18.012	149.8	238.0
Hydrogen Sulphide	7783-06-4	H_2S	34.0809	4.436 81	829.439	−25.412	138.8	212.7
				4.528 87	958.587	−0.539	212.7	349.4
Nitrogen	7727-37-9	N_2	28.0134	3.736 20	264.651	−6.788	63.14	126.0
Nitrogen Dioxide	10102-44-0	NO_2	46.0055	3.352 48	540.635	−131.93	217.5	294
Nitrous Oxide	10024-97-2	N_2O	44.0128	4.377 99	621.077	−44.659	129.7	187.6
Nitric Oxide	10102-43-9	NO	30.0061	3.736 20	264.651	6.788	63.14	126
Oxygen	7782-44-7	O_2	31.9988	3.952 30	340.024	−4.144	54.36	154.33
Sulphur Dioxide	7446-09-5?	SO_2	64.0638	3.485 86	668.225	−72.252	177.6	263
				4.377 98	966.575	−42.071	263	414.8

(Contd.)

Table 5.4 (Contd.)

A. Inorganic Compounds:

Compound	CAS Reg. No.	Chemical Formula	Molar Mass	Antoine Constants			Temperature Range, K	
				A	B	C	From	To
Sulphur Trioxide	7446-11-9	SO_3	80.0632	4.20515	892.175	-103.564	333	483
				5.22279	-1623.87	0	317.7	490.9
Water	7732-18-5	H_2O	18.0153	4.65430	1435.264	-64.848	255.8	373
				3.55959	643.748	-198.043	379	573

B. Organic Compounds

Compound		CAS Reg. No.	Chemical Formula	Molar Mass	Antoine Constants			Temperature Range, K	
Common Name	IUPAC Name				A	B	C	From	To
Acetaldehyde	Ethanal	75-07-0	C_2H_4O	44.0526	3.686 39	822.894	-69.899	293.3	377.4
Acetic Acid	Ethanoic Acid	64-19-7	$C_2H_4O_2$	60.0520	4.682 06	1642.540	-39.764	290.26	391.01
Acetic Acid Anhydride	Ethanoic Anhydride	108-24-7	$C_4H_6O_3$	102.0886	4.246 55	1427.770	-75.113	335.99	412.57
Acetophenone	1-Phenyl-1-ethanone	98-86-2	C_8H_8O	120.1485	4.648 96	2006.397	-43.472	310.2	475.5
Acetone	2-Propanone	67-64-1	C_3H_6O	58.0791	4.424 48	1312.253	-32.445	259.16	507.60
Acetonitrile	Ethanenitrile	75-05-8	C_2H_3N	41.0519	4.278 73	1355.374	-37.853	288.2	362.3
Acetyl Chloride	Ethanoyl Chloride	75-36-5	C_2H_3ClO	78.4976	3.965 68	1062.860	-55.531	266.86	324.20
Acetylene	Ethyne	74-86-2	C_2H_2	26.0373	4.195 98	699.530	-21.470	192.59	206.30
Aniline	Benzenamine	62-53-3	C_6H_7N	93.1265	4.661 41	909.079	7.947	214.64	308.33
					4.345 41	1661.858	-74.048	304	457.00
Benzene	Benzene	71-43-2	C_6H_6	78.1118	4.018 14	1203.835	-53.226	287.70	354.07
					4.725 83	1660.652	-1.461	333.4	373.4
n-Butane	1-Butane	106-97-8	C_4H_{10}	58.1222	4.603 62	1701.073	20.806	421.56	554.70
					4.708 12	1200.475	-13.013	135.42	212.89

(Contd.)

Table 5.4   (Contd.)

B. Organic Compounds

Compound Common Name	IUPAC Name	CAS Reg. No.	Chemical Formula	Molar Mass	Antoine Constants			Temperature Range, K	
					A	B	C	From	To
Isobutane	2-Methylpropane	75-28-5	C_4H_{10}	58.1222	3.850 02	909.650	-36.146	195.11	272.81
					4.355 76	1175.581	-2.071	272.66	425
n-Butanol	1-Butanol	71-36-3	$C_4H_{10}O$	74.1216	3.944 17	912.141	-29.808	188.06	261.54
					4.328 10	1132.108	0.918	261.31	408.12
Isobutanol	2-Methyl-1-Propanol	78-83-1	$C_4H_{10}O$	74.1216	4.546 07	1351.555	-93.340	295.7	390.9
					4.390 31	1254.502	-105.246	391	479
sec-Butanol	2-Butanol	78-92-2	$C_4H_{10}O$	74.1216	4.429 21	1305.001	-94.676	419.34	562.98
					4.431 26	1236.991	-101.528	353.36	388.77
tert-Butanol	1,1-Dimethyl Ethanol	75-65-0	$C_4H_{10}O$	74.1216	4.400 62	1260.453	-92.588	422.64	547.71
					4.329 43	1158.672	-104.683	345.54	380.30
Carbon Tetrachloride	Tetrachloromethane	56-23-5	CCl_4	153.8227	4.198 27	1094.254	-111.603	422.11	535.9
					4.497 74	1174.869	-93.920	312.66	355.56
Chlorobenzene		108-90-7	C_6H_5Cl	112.5569	4.332 58	1095.084	-102.409	333.93	362.71
					4.263 83	1075.578	-102.588	376.42	506
Chloroform	Trichloromethane	67-66-3	$CHCl_3$	119.3776	4.022 91	1221.781	-45.739	293.03	350.86
					4.110 83	1435.675	-55.124	335.19	404.88
Cyclohexane	Hexahydrobenzene	110-82-7	C_6H_{12}	84.1595	4.207 72	1233.129	-40.953	215	334.4
					4.569 92	1486.455	-8.612	334.4	527
Cyclohexanol	Hexahydrophenol	108-93-0	$C_6H_{12}O$	100.1589	3.992 00	1216.930	-48.621	303	343
					4.139 83	1316.554	-35.581	323	523
Cyclohexanone	Cyclohexyl Ketone	108-94-1	$C_6H_{10}O$	98.1430	3.080 77	777.363	-182.037	366.88	433.8
					3.103 30	1495.510	-63.598	362.78	438.9
p-Dichlorobenzene	1,4-Dichlorobenzene	106-46-7	$C_6H_4Cl_2$	147.0020	4.122 90	1575.110	-64.637	341.12	447.21

(Contd.)

Table 5.4 (Contd.)

B. Organic Compounds

Compound Common Name	IUPAC Name	CAS Reg. No.	Chemical Formula	Molar Mass	Antoine Constants A	B	C	Temperature Range, K From	To
m-Dichlorobenzene	1,3-Dichlorobenzene	541-73-1	$C_6H_4Cl_2$	147.0020	4.197 54	1629.812	−57.328	363.87	446
o-Dichlorobenzene	1,2-Dichlorobenzene	95-50-1	$C_6H_4Cl_2$	147.0020	4.195 18	1649.550	−59.836	293.14	453.57
Diethanol Amine		111-42-2	$C_4H_{11}NO_2$	105.1356	5.264 58	2328.560	−98.751	463.9	582.3
Diethyl Amine	N-Ethyl Ethanamine	109-89-7	$C_4H_{11}N$	73.1368	2.861 93	559.071	−132.974	304.60	333.73
Diethyl Ether	1-Ethoxyethane	60-29-7	$C_4H_{10}O$	74.1216	4.133 77	1102.878	−40.460	212.3	293.02
					4.022 00	1062.640	−44.930	250.04	328.57
					4.469 88	1354.913	−5.537	350.14	466.73
(Di)Methyl Amine	N-Methyl Methanamine	124-40-3	C_2H_7N	45.0837	4.293 71	995.445	−47.869	201.38	280.01
Dimethy-lacetamide	N,n-Dimethyl Acetamide	127-19-5	C_4H_9NO	87.1204	6.094 51	2725.960	28.209	303	363
Dimethyl Formamide	N,N-Dimethyl Formamide	68-12-2	C_3H_7NO	73.0938	3.930 68	1337.716	−82.648	303	363
1,4-Dioxane	1,4-Dioxacyclohexane	123-91-1	$C_4H_8O_2$	88.1051	4.581 35	1570.093	−31.297	293	378
Ethane	Ethane	74-84-0	C_2H_6	30.0690	4.507 06	791.300	−6.422	91.33	144.13
					3.938 35	659.739	−16.719	135.74	199.91
Ethyl Acetate	Ethyl Ethanoate	141-78-6	$C_4H_8O_2$	88.1051	4.228 09	1245.702	−55.189	288.73	348.98
Ethyl Alcohol	Ethanol	64-17-5	C_2H_6O	46.0684	5.372 29	1670.409	40.191	273	351.70
					4.925 31	1432.526	−61.819	364.8	513.91
(Mono) Ethanol Amine		141-43-5	C_2H_7NO	61.0831	4.292 52	1408.873	−116.093	338.5	444.0
Ethyl Amine	Aminoethane	75-04-7	C_2H_7N	45.0837	4.455 86	1121.445	−37.854	190.8	289.7
					4.530 13	1203.822	−23.716	289.7	449

(Contd.)

Table 5.4 (Contd.)

B. Organic Compounds

Compound		CAS Reg. No.	Chemical Formula	Molar Mass	Antoine Constants			Temperature Range, K	
Common Name	IUPAC Name				A	B	C	From	To
Ethyl Benzene		100-41-4	C_8H_{10}	106.1650	4.074 88	1419.315	−60.539	329.74	410.27
					4.405 36	1695.026	−23.698	420.00	600.00
Ethyl Chloride	Chloroethane	75-00-3	C_2H_5Cl	64.5141	4.161 81	1052.821	−32.078	217.21	285.66
					4.133 77	1102.878	−40.46	212.3	293.02
(Di)Ethyl Ether	Epoxy Ethane	60-29-7	$C_4H_{10}O$	74.1216	4.022 00	1062.640	−44.93	250.04	328.57
					4.469 88	1354.913	−5.537	350.14	466.73
Ethyl Mercaptan	Ethanethiol	75-08-1	C_2H_6S	62.1340	4.076 96	1084.531	−41.765	273.5	339.26
					4.445 83	1330.977	−8.272	308	493
Ethylene	Ethene	74-85-1	C_2H_4	28.0532	3.872 61	584.146	−18.307	149.37	188.57
Ethylene Dichloride	1,2-Dichloroethane	107-06-2	$C_2H_4Cl_2$	98.9592	4.585 18	1521.789	−24.670	242.33	372.5
Ethylene Glycol	1,2-Ethanediol	107-21-1	$C_2H_6O_2$	62.0678	5.215 70	2088.90	−69.750	323	473
(Di)Ethylene Glycol	2-2'-Oxybisethanol	111-46-6	$C_4H_{10}O_3$	106.1204	6.246 62	3709.672	−1.062	421.6	475.3
Ethylene Oxide	1,2-Epoxyethane	75-21-8	C_2H_4O	44.0526	4.385 90	1115.100	−29.015	182.59	283.59
					5.846 96	2022.830	62.656	273.4	304.9
Ethylidene Chloride	1,1-Dichloroethane	75-34-3	$C_2H_4Cl_2$	98.9592	4.221 53	1229.158	−39.204	212.4	330.5
Formaldehyde	Methanal	50-00-0	CH_2O	30.0260	4.281 76	959.430	−29.758	163.76	250.86
Formic Acid	Methanoic Acid	64-18-6	CH_2O_2	46.0254	2.001 21	515.000	−139.408	273.6	307.3
Furfural	2-Furancarboxaldehyde	98-01-1	$C_5H_4O_2$	96.0841	4.093 55	1430.133	−84.449	329.02	433.90
Glycerine	1,2,3-Propanetriol	56-81-5	$C_3H_8O_3$	92.0938	3.937 37	1411.531	−200.566	456.40	533.5
n-Heptane	1-Heptane	142-82-5	C_7H_{16}	100.2019	4.818 03	1635.409	−27.338	185.29	295.60
					4.028 32	1268.636	−56.199	299.07	372.43

(Contd.)

Table 5.4 (Contd.)

B. Organic Compounds

| Compound | | CAS | Chemical | Molar | Antoine Constants | | | Temperature Range, K | |
Common Name	IUPAC Name	Reg. No.	Formula	Mass	A	B	C	From	To
n-Hexane	1-Hexane	110-54-3	C_6H_{14}	86.1754	3.456 04	1044.038	-53.893	177.70	264.93
					4.002 66	1171.530	-48.784	286.18	342.69
Hydrogen Cyanide		74-90-8	CHN	27.0253	4.674 17	1340.791	-11.592	256.73	319.38
Methane	Methane	74-82-8	CH_4	16.0425	3.989 50	443.028	-0.490	90.99	189.99
Methyl Acetate	Methyl Ethanoate	79-20-9	$C_3H_6O_2$	74.0785	4.203 64	1164.426	-52.690	274.91	328.99
Methyl Alcohol	Methanol	67-56-1	CH_4O	32.0419	5.204 09	1581.341	-33.500	288.0	356.83
					5.158 53	1569.613	-34.846	353.4	512.63
Methyl Amine	Methanamine	74-89-5	CH_5N	31.0571	4.519 90	1034.977	-37.574	190.06	266.92
Methyl Isobutyl Ketone	4-Methyl-2-pentanone	108-10-1	$C_6H_{12}O$	100.1589	3.952 98	1254.095	-71.537	294.8	389.3
Methyl Stearate	Methyl(Z)-9-octade-cenoate	112-61-8	$C_{19}H_{38}O_2$	298.5038	5.881 85	3249.472	-59.659	427.16	484.82
(Di)Methyl Sulphide	2-Thiapropane	75-18-3	C_2H_6S	62.1340	4.287 13	1201.134	-29.906	250.60	293.24
Methyl Bromide	Bromomethane	74-83-9	CH_3Br	94.9385	4.268 74	1069.708	-25.771	203	276.7
Methyl Chloride	Chloromethane	74-87-3	CH_3Cl	50.4875	4.154 54	916.223	-28.466	183	249.3
					4.225 07	951.561	-23.468	198	278
Methyl Chloroform	1,1,1-Trichloroethane	71-55-6	$C_2H_3Cl_3$	133.4042	4.918 58	1427.529	45.137	303	416.2
					5.886 07	2210.179	34.902	267.79	290.07
Methyl Ethyl Ketone	2-Butanone	78-93-3	C_3H_8O	72.1057	3.989 40	1150.207	-63.904	314.5	370.5
Methyl Mercaptan	Methanethiol	74-93-1	CH_4S	48.1075	4.192 01	1031.431	-32.720	221.87	279.13
					4.353 81	1122.494	-21.748	279.9	458

(Contd.)

Table 5.4 (Contd.)

B. Organic Compounds

Compound Common Name	IUPAC Name	CAS Reg. No.	Chemical Formula	Molar Mass	Antoine Constants A	B	C	Temperature Range, K From	To
Methyl Palmitate	Methyl Hexadecanoate	112-39-0	$C_{17}H_{34}O_2$	270.4507	6.246 62	3709.672	-1.062	421.6	475.3
Methylene Chloride	Dichloromethane	75-09-2	CH_2Cl_2	84.9326	4.536 91	1327.016	-20.474	233	313
Methyl Formate	Methyl Methanoate	107-31-3	$C_2H_4O_2$	60.0520	3.973 23	1016.865	-56.623	303.14	313.14
					0.250 97	6.524	-278.540	294	304.8
Methyl Stearate	Methyl(Z)-9-octadecanoate	112-61-8	$C_{19}H_{38}O_2$	298.5038	5.881 85	3249.472	-59.659	427.16	484.82
Naphthalene	Naphthalene	91-20-3	$C_{10}H_8$	128.1705	4.271 17	1831.571	-61.329	353.48	452.30
					3.970 67	1606.529	-85.923	399.47	491.79
β-Naphthol	2-Naphthalenol	135-19-3	$C_{10}H_8O$	144.1699	5.179 07	2771.316	-24.925	417	561
Nitrobenzene	Nitrobenzene	98-95-3	$C_6H_5NO_2$	123.1094	4.215 53	1727.592	-73.438	407.2	483.78
n-Pentane	1-Pentane	109-66-0	C_5H_{12}	72.1488	3.989 20	1070.617	-40.454	268.7	341.37
Propane	Propane	74-98-6	C_3H_8	44.0956	4.011 58	834.260	-22.763	166.02	231.41
					3.982 92	819.296	-24.417	230.5	320.6
Propionic Acid	Propanoic Acid	79-09-4	$C_3H_6O_2$	74.0785	4.745 58	1679.869	-59.832	345.54	401.49
					5.313 84	1690.864	-51.804	292.4	370.4
n-Propanol	1-Propanol	71-23-8	C_3H_8O	60.0950	4.876 01	1441.629	-74.299	333.32	377.72
					4.598 71	1300.491	-86.364	405.46	536.71
Isopropanol	2-Propanol	67-63-0	C_3H_8O	60.0950	4.861 00	1357.427	-75.814	329.92	362.41
					4.577 95	1221.423	-87.474	395.0	508.24
Phenol	Hydroxybenzene	108-95-2	C_6H_6O	94.1112	4.246 88	1509.677	-98.949	380.30	454.90
Propylene	Propene	115-07-1	C_3H_6	42.0797	3.974 88	795.819	-24.884	165.81	225.98
Propylene Oxide	1,2-Epoxypropane	75-56-9	C_3H_6O	58.0791	4.094 87	1065.270	-46.867	199.70	307.38
					3.550 46	802.487	-81.348	292	344.9
Pyridine	Azabenzene	110-86-1	C_5H_5N	79.0999	4.162 72	1371.358	-58.496	340.4	426.04
Styrene	Ethenyl Benzene	100-42-5	C_8H_8	104.1491	4.219 48	1525.059	-56.379	303.07	417.92

(Contd.)

Table 5.4 (Contd.)

B. Organic Compounds

Compound Common Name	IUPAC Name	CAS Reg. No.	Chemical Formula	Molar Mass	Antoine Constants A	Antoine Constants B	Antoine Constants C	Temperature Range, K From	Temperature Range, K To
Tetrachloroethylene	1.1.2.2-Tetrachloroethene	127-18-4	C_2Cl_4	165.8334	4.180 56	1440.819	−49.171	301.03	380.84
Tetrahydrofuran	1,4-Epoxybutane	109-99-9	C_4H_8O	72.1057	4.121 18	1202.942	−46.818	296.29	372.8
Thiophene		110-02-1	C_4H_4S	84.1396	4.073 58	1239.578	−52.585	312.21	392.94
Toluene	Methylbenzene	108-88-3	C_7H_8	92.1384	4.141 57	1377.578	−50.507	273	323
					4.078 27	1343.943	−53.773	308.52	384.66
Trichloroethylene	1,1,2-Trichloroethene	79-01-6	C_2HCl_3	131.3883	4.544 36	1738.123	0.394	420.00	580.00
					3.553 46	974.538	−85.811	290.9	359.62
Triethanol Amine	2,2',2''-Ethanolnitrilotris	102-71-6	$C_6H_{15}O_3N$	149.1882	7.192 51	4543.902	24.749	525.8	578.7
Vinyl Trichloride	1,1,2-Trichloroethane	79-00-5	$C_2H_3Cl_3$	133.4042	4.069 74	1310.297	−64.410	323.12	386.82
o-Xylene	1,2-Dimethylbenzene	95-47-6	C_8H_{10}	106.1650	4.937 55	1901.373	−26.268	273	323
					4.129 28	1478.244	−59.076	336.61	418.52
m-Xylene	1,3-Dimethylbenzene	108-38-3	C_8H_{10}	106.1650	5.091 99	1996.545	−14.772	273	333
					4.136 07	1463.218	−57.991	332.3	413.19
p-Xylene	1,4-Dimethylbenzene	106-42-3	C_8H_{10}	106.1650	4.145 53	1474.403	−55.377	286.43	452.38
Mixed Xylene	Dimethyl Benzenes	1330-20-7	C_8H_{10}	106.1650	4.509 44	1788.910	−13.902	420.00	600.00
					4.990 53	1453.430	−57.840	—	—

Source: NIST Chemistry WebBook, 2008.

Example 5.9 Calculate vapour pressure of (a) *n*-hexane at 32°C (305.15 K), and (b) water at 122°C (395.15 K) using Antoine constants given in Table 5.4.

Solution

(a) Vapour pressure of *n*-hexane, $T = 305.15$ K

Reference 8 gives $\quad \log_{10} p_v = 4.002\ 66 - \left[\dfrac{1171.530}{(305.15 - 48.784)} \right] = -0.5671$

or $\qquad\qquad\qquad p_v = 0.271$ bar

Reference 24 gives $\qquad p_v = 0.267$ bar at 32°C (305.15 K)

(b) Vapour pressure of water, $T = 395.15$ K

$$\log_{10} p_v = 3.559\ 59 - \left[\frac{643.748}{(395.15 - 198.043)} \right] = 0.2936$$

or $\qquad\qquad\qquad p_v = 1.9661$ bar

Steam Tables (Appendix IV.2) gives $p_v = 211.45$ kPa at 122°C (395.15 K).

The latent heat of vaporization can be calculated from the Antoine constants B and C and the second virial coefficient[3]. The reader is advised to Ref. 3 for the correlation. Another method is given in Ref. 3 which also uses Antoine constants for calculation of latent heat of vaporization.

For reliable estimation of latent heat of vaporization, the following equation, proposed by Watson, is recommended.

$$\frac{\lambda_v}{\lambda_{v_1}} = \left[\frac{T_c - T}{T_c - T_1} \right]^n \tag{5.25}$$

where $\quad \lambda_v$ = latent heat of vaporization at T K,

λ_{v_1} = latent heat of vaporization at T_1, K,

T_c = critical temperature, K, and

n = characteristic constant of equation = 0.38.

The Watson equation is simple and reliable. Values of T_c, λ_{v_1} and T_1 are given in Table 5.5. It may be noted that T_1 is usually selected as the normal boiling point T_B in Table 5.5 in most cases as experimental data for many compounds for λ_v at T_B are available. In absence or non-availability of the value of λ_v at T_B, the Riedel equation[3] is useful

$$\frac{\lambda_v}{RT_B} = \frac{1.092\ (\ln p_c - 5.6182)}{0.930 - T_{Br}} \tag{5.26}$$

where $\quad \lambda_v$ = latent heat of vaporization, kJ/kmol

p_c = critical pressure, kPa

T_{Br} = reduced pressure at $T_B = T_B/T_c$

$R = 8.314\ 472$ kJ/(kmol · K)

The Riedel equation is quite accurate and the error rarely exceeds 5%.

Table 5.5 Enthalpy of Vaporization (λ_v) Equation (NIST) Constants for Compounds

Common Name	IUPAC Name	CAS Reg. No.	Chemical Formula	Molar Mass M	Enthalpy of Vaporization Equation Constants				Temperature Range, K		T_B^*, K	λ_v, kJ/mol at T_B^*
					A kJ/mol	α	β	T_c, K	From	To		
Acetaldehyde	Ethanal	75-07-0	C₂H₄O	44.0526	—	—	—	466	—	—	293.3	25.76
Acetic Acid	Ethanoic Acid	64-19-7	C₂H₄O₂	60.0520	22.84	0.0184	-0.0454	590.7	298	392	391.1	23.7
Acetic Anhydride	Ethanoic Anhydride	108-24-7	C₄H₆O₃	102.0886	—	—	—	606	—	—	412.0	40.02
Acetone	2-Propanone	67-64-1	C₃H₆O	58.0791	46.95	—	0.2826	508.1	300	345	329.3	29.1
Acetonitrile		75-05-8	C₂H₃N	41.0519	—	—	—	545	—	—	354.7	29.75
Acetyl Chloride	Ethanoyl Chloride	75-36-5	C₂H₃ClO	78.4976	—	—	—	—	—	—	325	30.1
Acetophenone(Methyl Phenyl Ketone)	Ethanone	98-86-2	C₈H₈O	120.1485	—	—	—	709.6	—	—	475	55.9
Ammonia	Ammonia	7664-41-7	NH₃	17.0305	—	—	—	405.5	—	—	239.82	23.325
Aniline	Benzenamine	62-53-3	C₆H₇N	93.1265	80.66	—	0.3744	705	298	333	457.2	42.44
Benzene	Benzene	71-43-2	C₆H₆	78.1118	47.41	0.1231	0.3602	562.05	293	469	353.3	30.72
Bromine	Bromine	7726-95-6	Br₂	159.808	—	—	—	588.0	—	—	332.0	30.76
n-Butane	Benzene	106-97-8	C₄H₁₀	58.1222	—	—	—	425.12	—	—	272.7	22.44
Isobutane	Benzene	75-28-5	C₄H₁₀	58.1222	—	—	—	407.8	—	—	261.44	21.297
n-Butanol	1-Butanol	71-36-3	C₄H₁₀O	74.1216	62.53	-0.6584	0.696	563.0	298	410	390.9	43.29
Isobutanol	2-Methyl-1-Propanol	78-83-1	C₄H₁₀O	74.1216	49.05	-1.6587	1.1038	547.7	298	381	381.1	41.82
sec-Butanol	2-Butanol	78-92-2	C₄H₁₀O	74.1216	52.6	-1.462	1.0701	536.2	298	372	372.7	40.75
tert-Butanol	2-Methyl-2-Propanol	75-65-0	C₄H₁₀O	74.1216	69.08	-0.3583	0.678	506.2	298	358	355.5	39.07
Carbon Disulphide	Carbon Disulphide	75-15-0	CS₂	76.1407	37.07	—	0.2264	552	282	319	319.4	26.74
Carbon Tetrachloride	Tetrachloromethane	56-23-5	CCl₄	153.8227	45.85	—	0.2656	556.3	298	358	349.9	29.82
Carbon Disulphide	Carbon Bisulphide	75-15-0	CS₂	76.1407	—	—	—	552.0	—	—	319.2	27.65
Chlorine	Chlorine	7782-50-5	Cl₂	70.906	—	—	—	416.9	—	—	239.17	20.43
Chlorobenzene		108-90-7	C₆H₅Cl	112.5569	—	—	—	633	—	—	404.9	35.19
Chloroform	Trichloromethane	67-66-3	CHCl₃	119.3776	—	—	—	536.2	—	—	334.3	29.24
Cyclohexane	Hexahydrobenzene	110-82-7	C₆H₁₂	84.1595	43.32	-0.1437	0.4512	553.8	292	422	353.9	29.97
Cyclohexanol	Hexahydrophenol	108-93-0	C₆H₁₂O	100.1589	—	—	—	645	—	—	431.7	45.44
Cyclohexyl Ketone	Cyclohexyl Ketone	108-94-1	C₆H₁₀O	98.1430	—	—	—	665	—	—	428.8	45.130

*T_B = Normal boiling point

(*Contd.*)

Table 5.5 (Contd.)

| Common Name | IUPAC Name | CAS Reg. No. | Chemical Formula | Molar Mass M | Enthalpy of Vaporization Equation Constants | | | | Temperature Range, K | | T_B, K | λ_v, kJ/mol at T_B |
					A kJ/mol	α	β	T_c, K	From	To		
Diethyl Amine	N-Ethyl Ethanamine	109-89-7	$C_4H_{11}N$	73.1368	51.41	—	0.3266	499.7	298	343	328.7	29.06
Diethyl Ether	1-Ethoxyethane	60-29-7	$C_4H_{10}O$	74.1216	43.01	—	0.2786	466.7	281	313	307.7	26.52
Dimethyl Amine	N-Methylmethanamine	124-40-3	C_2H_7N	45.0837	—	—	—	437.2	—	—	280.03	26.485
Dimethyl Formamide	N-N-Dimethyl Formamide	68-12-2	C_3H_7NO	73.0938	—	—	—	649.6	—	—	426	47.57
Dimethyl Sulphide	2-Thiapropane	75-18-3	C_2H_6S	62.1340	41.54	—	0.2731	503	276	311	310.5	27.0
1,4-Dioxane	1,4-Dioxacyclohexane	123-91-1	$C_4H_8O_2$	88.1051	—	—	—	588	—	—	374.5	34.16
Ethane	Ethane	74-84-0	C_2H_6	30.0690	29.43	—	0.3693	305.32	289	301	184.1	14.703
Ethyl Acetate	Ethyl Ethanoate	141-78-6	$C_4H_8O_2$	88.1051	54.26	—	0.2982	523.3	298	363	350.3	31.94
Ethyl Alcohol	Ethanol	64-17-5	C_2H_6O	46.0684	50.43	-0.4475	0.4989	514.0	298	469	351.4	38.56
Ethyl Benzene	Ethyl Benzene	100-41-4	C_8H_{10}	106.1650	58.32	—	0.2823	617.15	295	437	409.3	35.57
Ethyl Chloride	Chloroethane	75-00-3	C_2H_5Cl	64.5141	—	—	—	460	—	—	285.42	24.652
Ethyl Mercaptan	Ethanethiol	75-08-1	C_2H_6S	62.1340	40.82	—	0.2669	499	281	308	308.2	26.79
Ethyl tert-butyl Ether	2-Ethoxy-2-methyl Propane	637-92-3	$C_6H_{14}O$	102.1748	—	—	—	509.4	—	—	345.6	29.76
Ethylene	Ethene	74-85-1	C_2H_4	28.0532	—	—	—	282.34	—	—	169.40	13.544
Ethylene Glycol	1,2-Ethanediol	107-21-1	$C_2H_6O_2$	62.0678	—	—	—	720	—	—	409.0	65.7
Ethylene Oxide	1,2-Epoxyethane	75-21-8	C_2H_4O	44.0526	—	—	—	469	—	—	283.66	25.527
(Di)Ethylene Glycol	2-2' Oxybisethanol	111-46-6	$C_4H_{10}O_3$	106.1204	—	—	—	—	—	—	523	66.57
Ethylene Dichloride	1,2-Dichloroethane	107-06-2	$C_2H_4Cl_2$	98.9592	—	—	—	561.5	—	—	356.6	31.98
Ethylidene Chloride	1,1-Dichloroethane	75-34-3	$C_2H_4Cl_2$	98.9592	—	—	—	523.4	—	—	293.0	30.62
(Di)Ethyl Ether	Epoxy Ethane	60-29-7	$C_4H_{10}O$	74.1216	43.01	—	0.2786	466.7	281	313	307.6	26.52
Formaldehyde	Methanal	50-00-0	CH_2O	30.0260?	—	—	—	—	—	—	254.05	—
Formic Acid	Methanoic Acid	64-18-6	CH_2O_2	46.0254	23.8	2.1043	-1.2652	588	298	374	373.8	22.69
Furfural	2-Furancarboaldehyde	56-81-5	$C_5H_4O_2$	96.0841	—	—	—	670.0	—	—	434.7	50.63
Glycerine	1,2,3-Propanetriol		$C_3H_8O_3$	92.0938	—	—	—	850.0	—	—	560.0	91.7
n-heptane	1-Heptane	142-82-5	C_7H_{16}	100.2019	53.66	—	0.2831	540.2	298	363	371.6	31.77
n-Hexane	1-Hexane	110-54-3	C_6H_{14}	86.1754	43.85	-0.039	0.397	507.6	298	444	341.9	28.85

(Contd.)

Table 5.5 (Contd.)

Common Name	IUPAC Name	CAS Reg. No.	Chemical Formula	Molar Mass M	Enthalpy of Vaporization Equation Constants				Temperature Range, K		T_B, K	λ_v, kJ/mol at T_B
					A kJ/mol	α	β	T_c, K	From	To		
Hydrogen Cyanide		74-90-8	CHN	27.0253	—	—	—	—	—	—	298.85	25.217
Methane	Methane	74-82-8	CH$_4$	16.0425	10.11	−0.22	0.388	190.564	112	180	111.7	8.17
Methyl Acetate	Methyl Ethanoate	79-20-9	C$_3$H$_6$O$_2$	74.07854	48.51		0.2757	506.5	296	343	330.1	30.32
Methyl Alcohol	Methanol	67-56-1	CH$_4$O	32.0419	45.3	−0.31	0.4241	512.5	298	477	337.7	35.21
Methyl Amine	Methanamine	74-89-5	CH$_5$N	31.0571	—			430.8	—	—	266.8	25.6
Methyl Bromide	Bromomethane	74-83-9	CH$_3$Br	92.9226	—			504	—	—	276.71	23.91
Methyl Chloride	Chloromethane	74-87-3	CH$_3$Cl	50.4875	—			416.25	—	—	248.94	21.535
Methyl Ethyl Ketone	2-Butanone	78-93-3	C$_3$H$_6$O	58.0791	51.87		0.2925	536.7	298	371	352.8	31.3
Methyl Formate	Methyl Methanoate	107-31-3	C$_2$H$_4$O$_2$	60.520	46.09		0.3119	487.2	293	314	304.7	27.92
Methyl Isobutyl Ketone	4-Methyl-2-pentanone	108-10-1	C$_6$H$_{12}$O	100.1589	58.41		0.2883	574.6	298	389	388.9	40.610
Methyl tert-butyl Ether	2-Methoxy-2-methyl Propane	1634-04-4	C$_5$H$_{12}$O	88.1482	46.23		0.2893	497.1	298	343	328.3	27.94
Methyl Mercaptan	Methanethiol	74-93-1	CH$_4$S	48.1075	—			470	—	—	279.12	24.568
Methylene Chloride	Dichloromethane	75-09-2	CH$_2$Cl$_2$	84.9326	—			508	—	—	313	28.06
Naphthalene	Naphthalene	91-20-3	C$_{10}$H$_8$	128.1705	—			748.4	—	—	323	70.85
β-Naphthol	2-Naphthalenol	135-19-3	C$_{10}$H$_8$O	144.1699	—			—	—	—	94.2	558.7
Nitrobenzene		98-95-3	C$_6$H$_5$NO$_2$	123.1094	—			—	—	—	291	56.1
n-Pentane	1-Pentane	109-66-0	C$_5$H$_{12}$	72.1488	37.01	−0.1238	0.4121	469.7	260	428	309.2	25.79
Phenol	Hydroxybenzene	108-95-2	C$_6$H$_6$O	94.1112	—			694.2	—	—	455.0	68.7
n-Propane	1-Propane	74-98-6	C$_3$H$_8$	44.0956	27.9	0.028	0.3766	369.83	278	361	231.1	19.04
n-Propanol	1-Propanol	71-23-8	C$_3$H$_8$O	60.0950	52.06	−0.8386	0.6888	536.8	298	390	370.3	41.44
Isopropanol	2-Propanol	67-63-0	C$_3$H$_8$O	60.0950	53.38	−0.708	0.6538	508.3	298	380	355.4	39.85
Propionic Acid	Propanoic Acid	79-09-4	C$_3$H$_6$O$_2$	74.0785	—			598.5	—	—	414.0	55.0
Propylene	Propene	115-07-1	C$_3$H$_6$	42.0797	—			364.9	—	—	225.5	18.42
Propylene Glycol	1,2-Propanediol	57-55-6	C$_3$H$_8$O$_2$	76.0944	—			676	—	—	353	64
Propylene Oxide	1,2-Epoxypropane	75-56-9	C$_3$H$_6$O	58.0791	—			485	—	—	307.7	27.35

(Contd.)

Table 5.5 (Contd.)

Common Name	IUPAC Name	CAS Reg. No.	Chemical Formula	Molar Mass M	Enthalpy of Vaporization Equation Constants				Temperature Range, K		T_B, K	λ_v, kJ/mol at T_B
					A kJ/mol	α	β	T_c, K	From	To		
Pyridine	Azabenzene	110-86-1	C_5H_5N	79.0999	55.43	—	0.2536	620.0	298	388	388.4	35.09
Styrene	Ethenyl Benzene	100-42-5	C_8H_8	104.1491	—	—	—	—	—	—	419.0	43.5
Tetrachloroethylene	1.1.2.2-Tetrachloroethene	127-18-4	C_2Cl_4	165.8334	—	—	—	611.0	—	—	394.1	34.68
Tetrahydrofuran	1,4-Epoxybutane	109-99-9	C_4H_8O	72.1057	46.11	—	0.2699	540.5	302	339	339.1	29.81
Thiophene	Thiophene	110-02-1	C_4H_4S	84.141?	49.56	—	0.288	580	319	357	357.3	31.48
Toluene	Methylbenzene	108-88-3	C_7H_8	92.1384	53.09	—	0.2774	591.75	298	410	383.8	33.18
1,1,1-Trichloroethane	Methyl Chloroform	71-55-6	$C_2H_3Cl_3$	133.4042	—	—	—	550	—	—	347.2	29.86
1,1,2-Trichloroethane	Vinyl Trichloride	79-00-5	$C_2H_3Cl_3$	133.4042	—	—	—	602	—	—	386.9	34.82
Trichloroethylene	1,1,2-Trichloroethene	79-01-6	C_2HCl_3	131.3874?	—	—	—	571	—	—	360.4	31.4
Triethanolamine	2,2',2''-Ethanolnitrilotris	102-71-6	$C_6H_{15}O_3N$	149.1882	—	—	—	—	—	—	105.9	608.55
o-Xylene	1,2-Dimethylbenzene	95-47-6	C_8H_{10}	106.1650	—	—	—	630.3	—	—	417.6	36.24
m-Xylene	1,3-Dimethylbenzene	108-38-3	C_8H_{10}	106.1650	—	—	—	617.0	—	—	412.3	35.66
p-Xylene	1,4-Dimethylbenzene	106-42-3	C_8H_{10}	106.1650	58.21	—	0.2768	616.2	298	440	411.5	35.67
Mixed Xylenes	Dimethyl Benzenes	1330-20-7	C_8H_{10}	106.1650	—	—	—	623	—	—	409.15	36.39

Source: NIST Chemistry WebBook, 2008.

Example 5.10 For *o*-xylene, calculate (a) latent heat of vaporization at T_B using Riedel equation, and (b) latent heat of vaporization at 25°C (298.15 K) using Watson equation.

Solution

(a) For *o*-xylene, $p_c = 3732$ kPa   and $T_c = 630.3$ K

$$T_B = 417.6 \text{ K}$$

$$T_{Br} = \frac{417.6}{630.3} = 0.6625$$

$$\lambda_v = 8.314\ 472 \times 417.6 \left[\frac{1.092\ (\text{In } 3732 - 5.6182)}{(0.930 - 0.6625)} \right]$$

$$= 36\ 945 \text{ kJ/kmol}$$

Ref. 25 gives $\lambda_v = 36\ 240$ kJ/kmol.   (Table 5.5)

(b) $T_1 = 298.15$ K

$$\lambda_{v1} = 36\ 240 \left[\frac{630.3 - 298.15}{630.3 - 417.6} \right]^{0.38} = 42\ 928 \text{ kJ/kmol}$$

Ref. 25 gives $\lambda = 43\ 450$ kJ/kmol at 25°C (298.15 K).

NIST has developed the following equation[8] for computation of enthalpy of vaporization.

$$\lambda_v = A\ e^{-(\alpha T_r)} (1 - T_r)^\beta \tag{5.27}$$

where *A*, α and β are species specific constants, listed in Table 5.5. Wherever only value of β is given, consider $\alpha = \beta$. This equation is reliable and requires knowledge of T_c only to calculate λ_v.

Example 5.11 For ethanol, calculate (a) latent heat of vaporization at T_B using Riedel equation and NIST equation, and (b) latent heat of vaporization at 25°C (298.15 K) using Watson equation and NIST equation.

Solution

For ethanol, $p_c = 61.37$ bar and $T_c = 514.0$ K

(a) $T_B = 351.4$ K or $t_B = 78.25$°C at $p = 1$ atm

$$T_{Br} = \frac{351.4}{514.0} = 0.6837$$

Riedel Equation

$$\lambda_v = 8.314\ 472 \times 351.4 \left[\frac{1.092(\ln 6137 - 5.6182)}{(0.930 - 0.6837)} \right]$$

$$= 40\ 207 \text{ kJ/kmol}$$

NIST Equation

$$\lambda_v = 50\ 430 \times e^{-(-0.4475 \times 0.6837)}\ (1 - 0.6837)^{0.4989}$$
$$= 38\ 562\ \text{kJ/kmol}$$

Table 5.5 gives $\lambda_v = 38\ 260$ kJ/kmol.

(b) $\qquad T_1 = 298.15$ K

$$T_{\text{Br1}} = \frac{298.15}{514.0} = 0.5801$$

Watson Equation

$$\lambda_{v1} = 38\ 563 \left[\frac{514.0 - 298.15}{514.0 - 351.4} \right]^{0.38} = 42\ 946\ \text{kJ/kmol}$$

NIST Equation

$$\lambda_{v1} = 50\ 430 \times e^{-(-0.4475 \times 0.5801)} (1 - 0.5801)^{0.4969}$$
$$= 42\ 479\ \text{kJ/kmol}$$

Ref. 25 gives $\lambda_{v1} = 42\ 458$ kJ/kmol which is in better agreement with the value, calculated using NIST equation.

Nomographs are available in literature[21] for the estimation of the latent heat of vaporization or fusion.

Some of the compounds are extensively used in industry for heating and cooling. Steam, thermic fluids, refrigerants, chlorine, n-hexane, etc., are commonly used in the process industry. It is rather inconvenient to handle equations for vapour pressure, saturation temperature and latent heat of vaporization calculations for such compounds. Tables are found to be more convenient in practice[24,26]. Such tables also take into account non-ideal behaviour of the fluids, if any.

Steam tables in Appendix IV give the latent heat of water at different temperatures/pressures. In the steam tables, h denotes the sensible heat of water over 0.01°C (273.16 K). The latent heat of vaporization is λ_v and the total heat of steam is given by H or i. For saturated steam,

$$H = h + \lambda_v \tag{5.28}$$

For wet steam having dryness (mass) fraction x [i.e., $(1 - x)$ kg moisture present in 1 kg moist (wet) steam],

$$H' = h + x\ \lambda_v \tag{5.29}$$

In the case of superheated steam, total heat,

$$i = h + \lambda_v + C_{pm}\ (T - T_s) \tag{5.30}$$

where C_{pm} is the mean heat capacity of steam in kJ/(kg · K), T the temperature of superheated steam in K, and T_s the saturation temperature of steam corresponding to pressure in K.

Relationship of saturation vapour pressure (p_v) of a pure liquid at temperature T is not directly proportional as can be seen from Eq. (5.24). Therefore, estimation of saturation vapour pressure at intermediate temperature T can be accurately calculated by

$$\ln \frac{p_s}{p_{s_1}} = \frac{T_2\ (T - T_1)}{T\ (T_2 - T_1)} \ln \frac{p_{s2}}{p_{s1}} \tag{5.31}$$

where p_s = saturation vapour pressure at T

p_{s_1} = saturation vapour pressure at T_1

and p_{s_2} = saturature vapour pressure at T_2

Equation (5.31) could be quite useful in interpolation of steam tables.

For interpolation of enthalpy values, linear relationship with temperature gives satisfactory results.

Example 5.12 Refer Appendix IV and calculate saturation pressure of steam at 292°C (565.15 K).

Solution From Appendix IV.2,

$$p_{s_1} = 75 \text{ bar a} \quad \text{and} \quad T_1 = 563.65 \text{ K } (290.5°C)$$

and $$p_{s_2} = 80 \text{ bar a} \quad \text{and} \quad T_2 = 568.12 \text{ K } (294.97°C)$$

for $$T = 565.15 \text{ K } (292°C),$$

$$\ln \frac{p_s}{75} = \frac{568.12 \, (565.15 - 563.65)}{565.15 \, (568.12 - 563.65)} \ln \frac{80}{75}$$

or $$p_s = 76.65 \text{ bar a}$$

JSME Steam Tables report $p_s = 76.65$ bar a at $T = 565.15$ K (292°C).

Linear interpolation will yield $p_s = 76.68$ bar a.

Heating and cooling are commonly encountered in the process industry. Steam is the most widely used heating medium. Apart from steam, organic heat transfer fluids are also used. Figure 5.6 gives the temperature range for various heat-transfer fluids and electrical heating systems. Diphenyl-diphenyl oxide eutectic is another

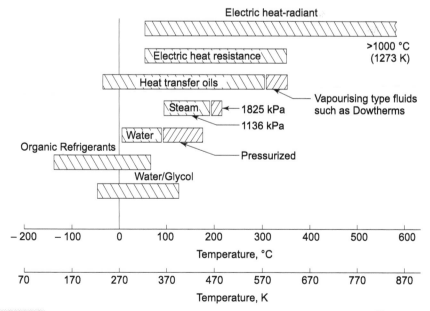

Fig. 5.6 Recommended Temperature Range for Selected Heat-Transfer Media[27]

versatile vapour phase heating medium. Properties of this eutectic mixture are given in Table 5.6.

Table 5.6 Characteristic Data of Eutectic Mixture of Diphenyl (26.5% v/v) and Diphenyl Oxide (73.5% v/v)[27]

Temperature		Saturation pressure, p_s	Density (kg/m³)		Enthalpy, kJ/kg		
°C	K	kPa a	Liquid	Vapour	Sensible h	Latent λ_v	Total H
100	373	0.5	995	0.027	147.3	364.8	512.1
120	393	1.31	978	0.067	184.1	356.1	540.2
140	413	3.09	961	0.151	221.7	347.3	569.0
160	433	6.61	943	0.306	260.7	338.9	599.6
180	453	13.1	925	0.579	300.4	330.1	630.5
200	473	24.9	907	1.025	341.4	321.7	663.1
220	493	41.7	888	1.717	383.3	313.4	696.7
240	513	68.6	869	2.742	426.8	304.2	731.0
257.1	**530.25**	**101.325**	**852**	**3.957**	**464.8**	**296.2**	**761.0**
260	533	107.9	849	4.194	471.1	295.0	766.1
280	553	163.1	828	6.210	516.7	284.9	801.6
300	573	237.9	807	8.911	563.6	274.0	837.6
320	593	336.5	784	12.48	611.7	262.3	874.0
340	613	463.3	761	17.12	660.7	250.2	910.9
360	633	623.0	736	23.10	711.3	236.8	948.1
380	653	820.9	709	30.87	762.7	222.6	985.3
400	673	1063.0	680	40.98	815.5	206.3	1021.8

(Courtesy: The Dow Chemical Company, USA)

Chlorofluorocarbon compounds are common refrigerants in industry. Due to ill environmental effects of these compounds, new compounds are under development. In addition, ammonia, carbon dioxide, ethylene, propane and other compounds are also used as refrigerants in industry. Thermodynamic data in a tabular form and also in a chart form for the refrigerants are available in literature[24,26,28].

Table 5.7 gives thermodynamic data of 1,1,1,2-tetrafluoroethane (refrigerant-134a)[28] which is getting increasingly adopted in the world to replace traditional refrigerant-12 (Dichloro-difluoromethane).

Selection of various heat-transfer fluids requires thorough knowledge of various heat-transfer fluids and process heating/cooling requirements. References 29 and 30 give excellent account on heat-transfer fluids. Figure 5.7 can be useful in selection heating/ cooling medium in general.

Simplest correlation for λ_v of a liquid mixture is given as

$$\lambda_v = \sum \lambda_{vi} \, x_i \qquad (5.32)$$

$$\lambda_v = \sum \lambda_{vi} \, y_i \qquad (5.33)$$

where, liquid fraction x_i and vapour fraction y_i are mass or molar fractions, depending on the units of the component latent heats.

Table 5.7 Thermodynamic Properties of Refrigerant[28] R-134a
Chemical name : 1, 1, 1, 2 - Tetrafluoroethane (CJ_2 FCF_3)

Temperature		Satura-tion pressure,	Liquid density	Specific volume of vapour	Enthalpy kJ/kg		Entropy kJ/(kg · K)	
					liquid	vapour	liquid	vapour
°C	K	p_s bar	ρ_l kg/m³	V_v m³/kg	h	H	S_l	S_v
− 40	233.15	0.512 2	1414.8	0.360 95	148.57	374.16	0.7973	1.7649
− 30	243.15	0.843 6	1385.9	0.225 96	161.10	380.45	0.8498	1.7519
−26.07[b]	**247.08**	**1.013 25**	**1374.3**	**0.190 16**	**166.07**	**382.90**	**0.8701**	**1.7476**
− 24	249.15	1.112 7	1368.2	0.174 10	168.70	384.19	0.8806	1.7455
− 22	251.15	1.216 0	1362.2	0.160 10	171.26	385.43	0.8908	1.7436
− 20	253.15	1.326 8	1356.2	0.147 44	173.82	386.66	0.9009	1.7417
− 18	255.15	1.445 4	1350.2	0.135 97	176.39	387.89	0.9110	1.7399
− 16	257.15	1.572 1	1344.1	0.125 56	178.97	389.11	0.9211	1.7383
− 14	259.15	1.707 4	1338.0	0.116 10	181.56	390.33	0.9311	1.7367
− 12	261.15	1.851 6	1331.8	0.107 49	184.16	391.55	0.9410	1.7351
− 10	263.15	2.005 2	1325.6	0.099 63	186.78	392.75	0.9509	1.7337
− 8	265.15	2.168 4	1319.3	0.092 46	189.40	393.95	0.9608	1.7323
− 6	267.15	2.341 8	1313.0	0.085 91	192.03	395.15	0.9707	1.7310
− 4	269.15	2.525 7	1306.6	0.079 91	194.68	396.33	0.9805	1.7297
− 2	271.15	2.720 6	1300.2	0.074 40	197.33	397.51	0.9903	1.7285
0	273.15	2.926 9	1293.7	0.069 35	200.00	398.68	1.0000	1.7274
2	275.15	3.145 0	1287.1	0.064 70	202.68	399.84	1.0097	1.7263
4	277.15	3.375 5	1280.5	0.060 42	205.37	401.00	1.0194	1.7252
6	279.15	3.618 6	1273.8	0.056 48	208.08	402.14	1.0291	1.7242
8	281.15	3.874 9	1267.0	0.052 84	210.80	403.27	1.0387	1.7233
10	283.15	4.144 9	1260.2	0.049 48	213.53	04.40	1.0483	1.7224
12	285.15	4.428 9	1253.3	0.046 36	216.27	405.51	1.0579	1.7215
14	287.15	4.727 6	1246.3	0.043 48	219.03	406.61	1.0674	1.7207
16	289.15	5.041 3	1239.3	0.040 81	221.80	407.701	1.0770	1.7199
18	291.15	5.370 6	1232.1	0.038 33	224.59	408.78	1.0865	1.7191
20	293.15	5.715 9	1224.9	0.036 03	227.40	409.84	1.0960	1.718
24	397.15	6.456 6	1210.1	0.031 89	233.05	411.93	1.1149	1.7169
28	301.15	7.2676	1194.9	0.028 29	238.77	413.95	1.1338	1.7155
32	305.15	8.1530	1179.3	0.025 16	244.55	415.90	1.1527	1.7142
36	309.15	9.117 2	1163.2	0.022 41	250.41	417.78	1.1715	1.7129
40	313.15	10.165	1146.5	0.019 99	256.35	419.58	1.1903	1.7115
44	317.15	11.300	1129.2	0.017 86	262.38	421.28	1.2091	1.7101
48	321.15	12.527	1111.3	0.015 98	268.49	422.88	1.2279	1.7086
52	325.15	13.852	1092.6	0.014 30	274.71	424.35	1.2468	1.7070
56	329.15	15.280	1073.0	0.012 80	281.04	425.68	1.2657	1.7051
60	333.15	16.815	1052.4	0.011 46	287.49	426.86	1.2847	1.7031
64	337.15	18.464	1030.7	0.010 26	294.08	427.84	1.3039	1.7007
68	341.15	20.234	1007.7	0.009 17	300.84	428.61	1.3234	1.6979
72	345.15	22.130	983.1	0.008 18	307.79	429.10	1.3430	1.6945
76	349.15	24.159	956.5	0.007 28	314.96	429.27	1.3631	1.6905

[b] normal boiling point (T_B)
Reference state: h = 200 kJ/kg and S_l = 1.0000 kJ/(kg · K) at 0°C(273.15 K)
(Reproduced with permission of the American Society of Heating, Refrigerating and Air-Conditioning Engineers, Inc., Atlanta, USA.)

For organic mixtures, the above equations represent the data within 15%. For other mixtures and extreme temperature-pressure conditions the error can be quite high.

For latent heat of fusion, attempts to obtain general correlations have been unsuccessful. Table 5.8 gives the latent heat of fusion of common compounds.

Table 5.8 Melting Point and Enthalpy of Fusion (λ_f) of Organic Compounds

Compound		CAS Reg.	Chemical	Molar	Melting	λ_f kJ/mol
Common Name	IUPAC Name	No.	Formula	Mass	Point, K	at T_F
Acetaldehyde	Ethanal	75-07-0	C_2H_4O	44.0526	149.78	2.310
Acetic Acid	Ethanoic Acid	64-19-7	$C_2H_4O_2$	60.0520	289.9	11.728
Acetone	2-Propanone	67-64-1	C_3H_6O	58.0791	177.6	5.690
Aniline	Benzenamine	62-53-3	C_6H_7N	93.1265	266.8	10.556
Isobuatane	2-Methylpropane	75-28-5	C_4H_{10}	58.1222	113.74	4.540
Benzene	Benzene	71-43-2	C_6H_6	78.1118	279.1	9.300
n-Butanol	1-Butanol	71-36-3	$C_4H_{10}O$	74.1216	184.5	9.372
Isobutanol	2-Methyl-1-Propanol	78-83-1	$C_4H_{10}O$	74.1216	171.18	6.322
sec-Butanol	2-Butanol	78-92-2	$C_4H_{10}O$	74.1216	177.38	6.000
tert-Butanol	1,1-Dimethyl Ethanol	75-65-0	$C_4H_{10}O$	74.1216	298.5	6.782
Carbon Disulphide	Carbon Disulphide	75-15-0	CS_2	76.1407	161.11	4.389
Carbon Tetrachloride	Tetrachloromethane	56-23-5	CCl_4	153.8227	250.53	2.562
Chlorobenzene		108-90-7	C_6H_5Cl	112.5569	227.89	9.556
Cyclohexane	Hexahydrobenzene	110-82-7	C_6H_{12}	84.1595	279.84	9.39
Cyclohexanol	Hexahydrophenol	108-93-0	$C_6H_{12}O$	100.1589	297.92	1.806
p-Dichlorobenzene	1,4-Dichlorobenzene	106-46-7	$C_6H_4Cl_2$	147.0020	326.15	18.050
m-Dichlorobenzene	1,3-Dichlorobenzene	541-73-1	$C_6H_4Cl_2$	147.0020	248.75	12.590
o-Dichlorobenzene	1,2-Dichlorobenzene	95-50-1	$C_6H_4Cl_2$	147.0020	255.65	12.922
Diethyl Ether	1-Ethoxyethane	60-29-7	$C_4H_{10}O$	74.1216	156.8	7.301
Dimethyl Amine	N-Methyl Methanamine	124-40-3	C_2H_7N	45.0837	180.97	5.941
Dimethyl Formamide	N,N-Dimethyl Formamide	68-12-2	C_3H_7NO	73.0938	212.85	8.950
1,4-Dioxane	1,4-Dioxacyclohexane	123-91-1	$C_4H_8O_2$	88.1051	283.2	11.880
1,3-Dinitrobenzene	1,3-Dinitrobenzene	99-65-0	$C_6H_4N_2O_4$	168.1070	363.23	17.350
1,4-Dinitrobenzene	1,4-Dinitrobenzene	100-25-4	$C_6H_4N_2O_4$	168.1070	446.65	28.1
1,2-Dinitrobenzene	1,2-Dinitrobenzene	528-29-0	$C_6H_4N_2O_4$	168.1070	390.05	22.750
Ethane	Ethane	74-84-0	C_2H_6	30.0690	90.341	0.583
Ethyl Acetate	Ethyl Ethanoate	141-78-6	$C_4H_8O_2$	88.1051	189.3	10.481
Ethyl Alcohol	Ethanol	64-17-5	C_2H_6O	46.0684	159	4.973
Ethyl Benzene	Phenylethane	100-41-4	C_8H_{10}	106.1650	178.15	9.1818
Ethyl Chloride	Chloroethane	75-00-3	C_2H_5Cl	64.5141	134.82	4.452
Ethyl Ether	Epoxy Ethane	60-29-7	$C_4H_{10}O$	74.1216	156.8	7.301
Ethylene	Ethene	74-85-1	C_2H_4	28.0532	103.97	3.351
Ethylene Dichloride	1,2-Dichloroethane	107-06-2	$C_2H_4Cl_2$	98.9592	237.2	8.8366
Ethylene Glycol	1,2-Ethanediol	107-21-1	$C_2H_6O_2$	62.0678	260.6	9.958
Ethylene Oxide	1,2-Epoxyethane	75-21-8	C_2H_4O	44.0526	160.65	5.1731
(Di)Ethylene Glycol	2-2'-Oxybisethanol	111-46-6	$C_4H_{10}O_3$	106.1204	302.2	14.971
Ethylidene Chloride	1,1-Dichloroethane	75-34-3	$C_2H_4Cl_2$	98.9592	176.18	7.870
Formic Acid	Methanoic Acid	64-18-6	CH_2O_2	46.0254	281.40	12.678
Furfural	2-Furancarboxaldehyde	98-01-1	$C_5H_4O_2$	96.0841	235.1	14.368
Glycerine	1,2,3-Propanetriol	56-81-5	$C_3H_8O_3$	92.0938	292	18.303
n-heptane	1-Heptane	142-82-5	C_7H_{16}	100.2019	182.57	13.990
n-Hexane	1-Hexane	110-54-3	C_6H_{14}	86.1754	177.84	13.079

(*Contd.*)

Table 5.8 (Contd.)

Compound		CAS Reg.	Chemical	Molar	Melting	λ_{fp} kJ/mol
Common Name	IUPAC Name	No.	Formula	Mass	Point, K	at T_F
Hydrogen Cyanide	Hydrogen Cyanide	74-90-8	CHN	27.0253	259.90	8.406
Methyl Acetate	Methyl Ethanoate	79-20-9	$C_3H_6O_2$	74.0785	175.15	7.486
Methyl Alcohol	Methanol	67-56-1	CH_4O	32.0419	176.1	2.196
Methyl Amine	Methanamine	74-89-5	CH_5N	31.0571	179.70	6.134
Methyl Chloride	Chloromethane	74-87-3	CH_3Cl	50.4875	175.44	6.431
Methyl Chloroform	1,1,1-Trichloroethane	71-55-6	$C_2H_3Cl_3$	133.4042	240.0	1.880
Methyl Ethyl Ketone	2-Butanone	78-93-3	C_3H_6O	58.0791	186.47	8.385
Methyl Palmitate	Methyl Hexadecanoate	112-39-0	$C_{17}H_{34}O_2$	270.4507	302.2	14.971
Methyl Stearate	Methyl(Z)-9-octadecenoate	112-61-8	$C_{19}H_{38}O_2$	298.5038	310.93	19.234
Methylene Chloride	Dichloromethane	75-09-2	CH_2Cl_2	84.9326	178.22	6.160
Naphthalene	Naphthalene	91-20-3	$C_{10}H_8$	128.1705	353.50	19.100
α-Naphthol	1-Naphthalenol	90-15-3	$C_{10}H_8O$	144.1699	369.0	23.220
β-Naphthol	2-Naphthalenol	135-19-3	$C_{10}H_8O$	144.1699	393.60	18.790
Nitrobenzene	Nitrobenzene	98-95-3	$C_6H_5NO_2$	123.1094	278.9	10.815
n-Pentane	1-Pentane	109-66-0	C_5H_{12}	72.1488	143.47	8.401
Phenol	Hydroxybenzene	108-95-2	C_6H_6O	94.1112	314.06	11.514
Propane	Propane	74-98-6	C_3H_8	44.0956	86.05	28.5
Propionaldehyde	Propanal	123-38-6	C_3H_6O	58.0791	171.32	8.590
n-Propanol	1-Propanol	71-23-8	C_3H_8O	60.0950	148.75	5.372
Isopropanol	2-Propanol	67-63-0	C_3H_8O	60.0950	185.20	5.410
Propylene	Propene	115-07-1	C_3H_8	42.0797	87.85	3.003
Propylene Oxide	1,2-Epoxypropane	75-56-9	C_3H_6O	58.0791	161.25	6.569
Pyridine	Azabenzene	110-86-1	C_5H_5N	79.0999	231.49	8.2785
Styrene	Ethenyl Benzene	100-42-5	C_8H_8	104.1491	242.27	10.964
Tetrachloroethylene	1.1.2.2-Tetrachloroethene	127-18-4	C_2Cl_4	165.8334	250.81	10.880
Tetrahydrofuran	1,4-Epoxybutane	109-99-9	C_4H_8O	72.1057	164.76	8.540
Toluene	Methylbenzene	108-88-3	C_7H_8	92.1384	178.15	6.636
Trichloroethylene	1,1,2-Trichloroethene	79-01-6	C_2HCl_3	131.3883	188.5	8.450
Vinyl Trichloride	1,1,2-Trichloroethane	79-00-5	$C_2H_3Cl_3$	133.4042	237.9	10.880
o-Xylene	1,2-Dimethylbenzene	95-47-6	C_8H_{10}	106.1650	247.82	13.598
m-Xylene	1,3-Dimethylbenzene	108-38-3	C_8H_{10}	106.1650	225.27	11.569
p-Xylene	1,4-Dimethylbenzene	106-42-3	C_8H_{10}	106.1650	286.4	17.1175
Water	Water	7732-18-5	H_2O	18.0153	0.0	6.012

Source: NIST Chemistry WebBook, 2008.

The latent heat of sublimation is the sum of the latent heats of vaporization and fusion where both the latent heats are at the same temperature.

The triple point of carbon dioxide is -56.56°C (216.59 K) at 5.18 bar. At this temperature, latent heat of fusion is 8.68 kJ/mol and latent heat of vaporization is 15.42 kJ/mol. Latent heat of sublimation of CO_2 is 24.10 kJ/mol.

5.9 ENTHALPY CHANGES FOR PURE SUBSTANCES AND THEIR MIXTURES IN IDEAL STATES

In chemical plants, different types of mixtures are encountered. Mostly, these are liquid and gaseous mixtures. In this section a general methodology for calculating enthalpies of different types of mixtures is described.

5.9.1 Generalized Procedure

The following steps may be followed when enthalpy of a stream (an ideal fluid or an ideal fluid mixture) is required:

(a) The composition of the stream is fixed from the material balance of the process. Also, the pressure and temperature of the stream are known or can be fixed depending on the process requirements.

(b) Enthalpy of substances are calculated relative to a particular temperature. This temperature, T_0 which can be selected based on convenience is called the *reference temperature*. This may not be the same for all the streams of the plant. Generally, 25°C (298.15 K) is taken as the reference temperature. For calculating the enthalpy of the processes involving steam, use enthalpies given in steam tables (Appendix-A IV) in which 0.01°C (273.16 K) is taken as the reference temperature. In the petroleum industry, 60°F [15.56°C (288.7 K)] is used as the reference temperature for many calculations.

(c) Based on the data available in para (a), fluids can be classified into following categories:
  (i) Pure substances
  (ii) Mixtures

Enthalpies of the process fluids in ideal state can then be calculated as described below.

5.9.2 Pure Substances

If the stream contains a pure substance, the enthalpy depends on the temperature and the state of the substance. As the degree of freedom is only one for a pure substance, only one variable is required to know the state of the substance. Thus, if the pressure or temperature of the substance is known, its state can be found. For the given pressure, the saturation temperature, T_s, of the substance can be found from published data or from correlations like the Antoine equation [Eq. (5.24)].

If the temperature $T < T_s$ then the state of the substance is liquid and if $T > T_s$, the state is superheated vapour (i.e., gas). For example, at atmospheric pressure, water will be liquid at ambient temperature.

After finding the state of the substance, the enthalpy of an ideal substance (in kJ/kg) can be calculated from the following equation:

(i) For liquids, $H_L = \int_{T_o}^{T} C_1 \, dT$ (5.34)

and

(ii) For vapour, $H_V = \int_{T_o}^{T} C_1 \, dT + \lambda_v + \int_{T_o}^{T} C_{pm} \, dT$ (5.35)

where λ_v = Latent heat of vaporization at T_s.

If molar heat capacity data are used, conversion with the help of molar mass will be required.

The integral in the above equations can be solved by using methods described in Sec. 5.4 and 5.5 while the latent heat of vaporization at different temperatures can be evaluated by using methods described in Sec. 5.8. For certain common compounds (e.g., steam, refrigerants, heat transfer fluids, etc.), enthalpy values are read from the tables (as described in Sec. 5.8) and substituted in Eq. (5.34) or Eq. (5.35).

5.9.3 Ideal Mixtures

The mixtures, encountered in the chemical plants, can be divided into three types, with respective criteria for ideality, as follows:

(i) Ideal Gas Mixture   A gas mixture following the ideal-gas law is defined as the *ideal gas mixture*. At low pressure (say, up to 10 bar) a gas mixture may be considered as an ideal gas mixture. For an ideal gas mixture, the mixture enthalpy depends only on the enthalpy of the individual ideal gas which comprises the gas mixture. The enthalpy of the ideal gas mixture can be calculated as described in Sec. 5.6. In other words,

$$H_{mix}^{ig} = \Sigma\, y_i H_i^{ig} \tag{5.36}$$

where H_i^{ig} is the enthalpy of the ith component in ideal state at the prevalent pressure and temperature and y_i is the mole fraction of the ith component in the gas mixture.

(ii) Ideal Liquid Solution   An ideal liquid solution follows Raoult's law (Sec. 2.5). Its heat of mixing (Sec. 5.16) is zero. The enthalpy of the ideal liquid solution is given by

$$H_{sol} = \Sigma\, x_i H_i \tag{5.37}$$

where H_i is the enthalpy of the ith component (in pure state) at the mixture temperature (and pressure) and x_i is the mole fraction of the ith component in the liquid mixture. Usually, the effect of pressure on liquid enthalpy is quite small.

(iii) Ideal Vapour–Liquid Mixture   When the vapour phase is an ideal gas and the liquid phase is an ideal solution, the equilibrium vapour–liquid mixture can be described by the simple and useful Raoult's law (Sec. 2.5). In other words, an equilibrium vapour–liquid mixture which follows Raoult's law is defined as ideal vapour-liquid mixture. When a system consists of saturated liquid and saturated vapour phases co-existing in equilibrium, the enthalpy of the mixture is the sum of the enthalpies of the individual phases.

As the degrees of freedom for a mixture are more than one (depending on the number of components in the mixture), more than one variable is required to be specified for defining the state of the mixture. It can be established by using the composition, pressure and temperature data. From the known composition and pressure, the bubble point (T_{BB}) and dew point (T_{DP}) temperatures can be found by using the methods shown in Sec. 5.9.4. The state of the mixture can then be judged from Table 5.9.

When the temperature is between the bubble point and dew point, the mixture is an equilibrium vapour–liquid mixture. For calculating the enthalpy of such ideal mixtures, the fraction of the total mixture in saturated vapour condition (V), is required to be known. Also, the compositions of the saturated vapour and liquid phases are required. These can be found by the equilibrium $p - T$ (also known as flash) calculations, described in Sec. 5.10.

$$H_{mix}^{VL} = (1 - V)\, H_{sol} + V \cdot H_{mix}^{ig} \tag{5.38}$$

For mixtures which are non-ideal, calculations are complex and the reader is advised to refer any standard textbook on thermodynamics (Ref. 3 and 13).

Table 5.9 State of Vapour–liquid Mixtures at Temperature T

Condition	State of mixture
$T < T_{BB}$	Subcooled liquid mixture
$T = T_{BB}$	Saturated liquid mixture
$T_{BB} < T < T_{DP}$	Equilibrium vapour-liquid mixture
$T = T_{DP}$	Saturated vapour mixture
$T > T_{DP}$	Superheated vapour mixture

5.9.4 Bubble Points and Dew Points of Ideal Mixtures

When a liquid mixture is heated from a subcooled state at a constant pressure, vaporization occurs over a range of temperatures unlike vaporization of a pure substance which occurs at a constant temperature at a given pressure. For any mixture, the two limiting temperatures of the above range are known as *bubble point* and *dew point*.

Figure 5.7 shows T vs. x, y of n-pentane for the n-pentane/n-hexane system at 101.325 kPa (760 Torr) considering the mixture to be an ideal one.

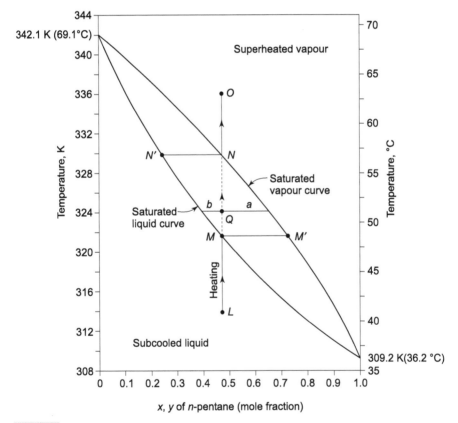

x, y of n-pentane (mole fraction)

Fig. 5.7   Vapour–Liquid Equilibrium Diagram (or T/t – x, y Diagram) for n-pentane/ n-hexane

When the mixture is heated from the point L, the mixture temperature follows the path LM. At M, the liquid mixture is saturated and a slight increase in temperature will form a bubble of vapour. Hence the point M is called the bubble point.

As the heating process continues beyond M, the temperature rises, the amount of vapour increases and the amount of liquid decreases. During this process, the vapour and liquid phase compositions change along the paths $M'N$ and MN', respectively. Finally, as the point N is approached, the liquid phase is reduced to minute drops (called dew) and at the point N, the liquid phase is completely vaporized to a saturated vapour phase. Hence, the point N is called the dew *point*.

Further heating above the point N increases the temperature of the vapour phase and the vapour gets superheated (path NO).

When a vapour–liquid mixture is present, amounts of both phases can be calculated by a tie-line method. A horizontal line at the point Q on Fig. 5.7 is the tie-line. By geometric principles,

$$\frac{\text{Amount of liquid mixture}}{\text{Amount of vapour mixture}} = \frac{a}{b} \tag{5.39}$$

For an ideal mixture, the bubble and dew points can be calculated using Raoult's law. For a given pressure and composition, the bubble point and dew point and the composition at respective points are calculated by the iterative calculations shown below:

(a) Bubble Point

(i) For a liquid mixture of known composition, assume a temperature and find the vapour pressure of all the components present in the mixture (p_{is}) at this temperature.

(ii) Calculate $y_i = x_i \cdot p_{is}/p$
where p is the total pressure.

(iii) Σy_i should be 1. If $\Sigma\, y_i \neq 1$ then a new temperature should be assumed and the above calculations should be repeated.

(iv) The temperature for which $\Sigma\, y_i = 1$ is the bubble point. Also, the vapour composition at the bubble point is given by y_i.

(v) The initial guess value of the temperature can be taken as $T_i = \Sigma\, (x_i \cdot T_{is})$, where T_{is} is the saturation temperature of the ith component at a total pressure p.

(b) Dew Point

(i) For a vapour mixture of known composition, assume a temperature and find the vapour pressures of all components (p_{is}) at this temperature.

(ii) Calculate $x_i = y_i \cdot p/p_{is}$.

(iii) Σx_i should be 1. If $\Sigma\, x_i \neq 1$ then a new temperature should be assumed and the above calculations should be repeated.

(iv) The temperature for which $\Sigma\, x_i = 1$ is the dew point, and the liquid composition at dew point is given by x_i.

(v) The initial guess value of the temperature can be taken as $T_i = \Sigma\, y_i \cdot T_{is}$.

Example 5.13   For an equimolar liquid mixture of *n*-pentane/*n*-hexane, find the bubble and dew point at 101.325 kPa (760 Torr).

Solution

Basis 1 kmol of equimolar mixture

$$n\text{-pentane (1) in mixture} = 0.5 \text{ kmol}$$
$$n\text{-hexane (2) in the mixture} = 0.5 \text{ kmol}$$
$$p = 101.325 \text{ kPa}$$

Use Antoine equation for evaluating saturation pressure for a given temperature.

Bubble point $x_i = x_2 = 0.5$

$$T_{S_1} = 309.2 \text{ K} \quad \text{and} \quad T_{S_2} = 341.9 \text{ K}$$

For the first iteration (for equimolar miture), $T_1 = \dfrac{(309.2 + 341.9)}{2} = 325.55$ K

Table 5.10   Evaluation of Bubble Point

Component		Temperature, K							
		$T_1 = 325.55$		$T_2 = 320$		$T_3 = 322$		$T_4 = 321.6$	
	x_i	p_{is} kPa	y_i	p_{is} kPa	y_i	p_{is} kPa	y_i	p_{is} kPa	y_i
n-pentane (1)	0.5	172.41	0.846	144.71	0.712	154.12	0.758	152.20	0.749
n-hexane (2)	0.5	58.57	0.290	47.82	0.239	51.44	0.256	50.70	0.253
Σy_i			1.136		0.951		1.016		1.002

Bubble point $T_{BB} = 321.6$ K ($t_{BB} = 48.45°C$)

Dew point $y_1 = y_2 = 0.5 \; y_i \cdot p = 50.6625$

For first iteration $T_1 = T_{S_2}$ K

Table 5.11   Evaluation of Dew Point

Component		Temperature, K					
		$T_1 = T_{S_2}$		$T_2 = 328$		$T_3 = 330$	
	y_i	p_{is} kPa	x_i	p_{is} kPa	x_i	p_{is} kPa	x_i
n-pentane (1)	0.5	172.41	0.296	185.228	0.275	196.606	0.258
n-hexane (2)	0.5	58.57	0.861	63.635	0.790	68.177	0.743
Σx_i	1.0		1.157		1.065		1.001

Dew point, $T_{DP} = 329.9$ K ($t_{DP} = 56.75°C$)

Note   For accurate determination of the bubble/dew point for a binary mixture, temperature (T) vs. $\Sigma \; y_i$ or $\Sigma \; x_i$ may be plotted respectively for different iterations. At a unity value of $\Sigma \; y_i$ or $\Sigma \; x_i$, the bubble point or dew point is read. Figure 5.8 is the plot for *n*-pentane and *n*-hexane mixture.

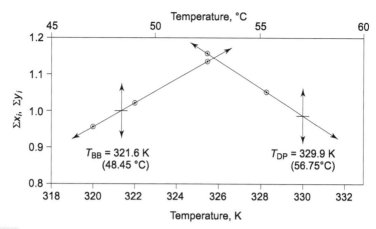

Fig. 5.8 Graphical Determination of Bubble Point and Dew Point

Example 5.14 A hot-air drying machine (called a stenter) in a textile industry uses 8 bar a steam at the rate of 1000 kg/h. The condensate at its saturation temperature is discharged to the atmosphere through a steam trap. Assume that there is no loss of heat to the surroundings. Calculate the quantity of flash steam produced at the atmospheric pressure due to the let down of the pressure.

Solution *Basis* 1000 kg/h of condensate at the saturation temperature corresponding to 8 bar a.

The thermodynamic properties of steam at 101.3 kPa and 8 bar a can be had from the steam table (Appendix IV.2).

The condensate has an enthalpy equal to 720.94 kJ/kg before the trap. After discharge, at atmospheric pressure, it cannot have an enthalpy more than 419.06 kJ/kg. Thus, the additional heat of condensate is converted into the latent heat of vaporization and thereby flashing takes place.

Let x be the quantity in kg of the flash steam produced.

$$\text{Condensate at 101.3 kPa a} = (1000 - x) \text{ kg}$$
$$\text{Total heat of condensate before flashing} = 1000 \times 720.94 = 720\ 940 \text{ kJ/h}$$
$$\text{Total heat of condensate after flashing} = (1000 - x)\ 419.06$$
$$\text{Total heat of flash steam} = x \times 2676.0 \text{ kJ/h}$$
$$2676.0x + (1000 - x)\ 419.06 = 720\ 940$$
$$2256.94\ x = 720\ 940 - 419\ 060 = 301\ 880$$
$$x = \textbf{133.76 kg/h}$$

Note

1. Flashing of the condensate has assumed importance as a result of the energy crisis. In most of the industries, it is now an accepted practice to utilise the flash steam. Boiler blow down is flashed to produce low-pressure steam. Atmospheric pressure steam, produced from flashing of low-pressure condensate, can be compressed in a thermocompressor (see Exercise 5.14) to a sufficiently high pressure for utilisation in

heaters. A simple, nomograph such as the one given by Sisson[30] can be used for quick estimation of the flashed steam from the condensate.

2. In refrigeration, liquid refrigerant at a higher pressure from the receiver is throttled to the chiller, operating at low pressure. In this process, flashing of the refrigerant takes place which results in loss of refrigeration. Measures are available to reduce flashing, thereby improving coefficient of performance (COP) of the refrigeration cycle.

Example 5.15 Aqueous monoethylene glycol (MEG) solution of 50% strength (by mass) is used as brine in a fine chemical plant. Hot brine from the plant enters tubes of a chiller at 50 L/s and is chilled from −10°C (263.15 K) to −15°C (258.15 K). In the shell of the chiller, refrigerant R-134 a evaporates at −24°C (249.15 K) which is supplied from a receiver of a mechanical refrigeration system at 40°C (313.15 K) through an expansion valve. The density and specific heat of aqueous MEG solution are 1.08 kg/L and 3.08 kJ/(kmol · K) respectively in the desired temperature range. Calculate the flow of saturated vapours of R-134a from the evaporator.

Solution

Brine flow, $q_{vl} = 50$ L/s

$$q_m = 50 \times 1.08 = 54 \text{ kg/s}$$

Heat transfer in the chiller, $\phi = 54 \times 3.08 (263.15 - 258.15) = 831.6$ kJ/s or kW

From Table 5.7, latent heat of vaporization at 249.15 K,

$$\lambda_v = 384.19 - 168.70 = 215.49 \text{ kJ/kg}$$

Evaporation rate of R-134a in the chiller,

$$q_{m2} = 831.6/215.49 = 3.859 \text{ kg/s}$$

Enthalpy of liquid

R-134a at 313.15 K = 256.35 kJ/kg

Let x kg/s be flash vapours formed due to isoenthalpic expansion of liquid at 313.15 K to 249.15 K.

$$256.35 (3.859 + x) = 168.7 \times 3.859 + x \times 384.19$$

or $x = 2.646$ kg/s

Total flow of R-134a vapour from the chiller

$$= 3.859 + 2.646 = \textbf{6.505 kg/s}$$

Example 5.16 Compression of chlorine is carried out to liquefy it in the chloralkali industry[31]. The suction temperature of chlorine gas to the compressor plays an important role in determining the size and power requirement of the compressor. In order to keep the ingoing gas temperature low, the dry cellhouse gas (refer Example 6.16) available at 103 kPa a and 40°C (313.15 K) is passed through a wash column in which gas bubbles through liquid chlorine. Saturated gas at 101 kPa a leaves the wash column and is compressed in the first stage of the compressor. Compressed gas at 225 kPa g is discharged from the first stage and is cooled in an intercooler to 40°C (313.15 K) with the help of cooling water. Gas at 215 kPa g enters the second stage of the compressor and is further compressed to 560 kPa g. An aftercooler is provided to cool the gas to 40°C (313.15 K) with the help of cooling water. A chiller provided on the downstream of the aftercooler liquefies the gas at 530 kPa g. A portion of liquid chlorine is recycled to the wash column. Cooling water is supplied at 32° C (305.15 K) and a temperature rise of 8°C (8 K) is permitted in the cooler. Figure 5.9 schematically represents the compression system. For a liquefaction plant having 0.116 kg/s ($\approx$ 10 t/d) capacity, calculate (a) the recycle ratio in terms of the amount of liquid chlorine recycled to the wash column to the fresh chlorine gas, entering the wash column, (b) cooling water requirements of the intercooler and aftercooler, and (c) the refrigeration load of the chiller.

Note Flashing of 2.646 kg/s R-134a liquid represents nearly 40% of total vapour flow.

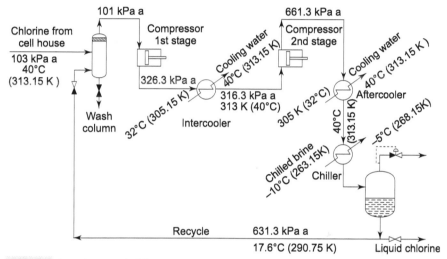

Fig. 5.9 Liquefaction of Chlorine

Solution

Basis Liquefaction capacity = 0.116 kg/s
The final saturated product is withdrawn at 530 kPa g. Similarly, mixed feed is fed to the first stage as saturated vapours. Therefore, saturation temperatures are required to be calculated for both these pressures. Using Eqs (5.24) and (5.26), saturation temperatures and latent heats of vaporization can be calculated.

$$p_1 = 101 \text{ kPa a}$$

Using Antoine equation, $\quad T_{s1} = 239.15 \text{ K } (-34°\text{C})$
$$\lambda_{v_1} = 20\ 430 \text{ kJ/kmol} = 288.13 \text{ kJ/kg}$$
$$p_2 = 530 \text{ kPa g} = 631.3 \text{ kPa a}$$
$$T_{s_2} = 290.75 \text{ K } (17.6°\text{C})$$

Using Watson equation,
$$\lambda_{v2} = 17\ 934 \text{ kJ/kmol} = 252.93 \text{ kJ/kg}$$

Since the lowest temperature in the system is 239.15 K, it can be taken as the base temperature. The sensible heat of saturated chlorine vapours at 101 kPa a and 239.15 K (– 34°C) = 0 kJ/kg. The sensible heat of liquid chlorine at 290.75 K (17.6°C) can be calculated using Eq. (5.21) and Table 5.3.

$$T_1 = 239.15 \text{ K} \qquad T_2 = 290.75 \text{ K}$$

$$H_1 = \int_{T_1}^{T_2} C_{ml} \, dT$$

$$= - 39.246 \, (T_2 - T_1) + 1401.223 \, \frac{(T_2^2 - T_1^2) \, 10^{-3}}{2} - 6047.226$$

$$\frac{(T_2^3 - T_1^3) \, 10^{-6}}{3} + 8591.4 \, \frac{(T_2^4 - T_1^4) \, 10^{-9}}{4}$$

$$= - 2025.1 + 19 \, 156.7 - 21 \, 973.8 + 8323.5 = 3480.7 \text{ kJ/kmol}$$

Let x be the quantity of liquid chlorine which will be flashed per kg of liquid chlorine at 631.3 kPa a.

$$3480.7 = x \times 20 \, 430$$
$$x = 0.17 \quad \text{or} \quad 17\% \text{ flashing}$$

Now the sensible heat to be extracted of the fresh chlorine feed

$$H_2 = \int_{T_1}^{T_3} C_{mp}^o \, dT \qquad\qquad \text{(Ref. Table 5.1)}$$

$$T_3 = 313.15 \text{ K}$$
$$H_2 = 28.5463 \, (T_3 - T_1) + 23.8795 \times 10^{-3} \, \frac{(T_3^2 - T_1^2)}{2} - 21.3631 \times 10^{-6}$$

$$\frac{(T_3^3 - T_1^3)}{3} + 6.4726 \times 10^{-9} \, \frac{(T_3^4 - T_1^4)}{4}$$

$$= 2112.4 + 488.0 - 121.3 + 10.3$$
$$= 2489.4 \text{ kJ/kmol} \equiv 35.11 \text{ kJ/kg}$$

Heat to be extracted from
the incoming fresh feed, $\phi_2 = 0.116 \times 35.11 = 4.073 \text{ kW}$

$$\text{Liquid chlorine evaporated} = \frac{4.073}{288.13} = 0.0141 \text{ kg/s}$$

$$\text{Recycled liquid chlorine} = \frac{0.0141}{(1 - 0.185)} = 0.0173 \text{ kg/s at 290.75 K}$$

$$\text{Recycle ratio} = \frac{0.0173}{0.116}$$

$$= \mathbf{0.149 \text{ kg/kg fresh feed}}$$

Mixed feed, entering 1st stage = 0.116 + 0.0173 = 0.1333 kg/s

First-stage compression
For adiabatic compression,

$$\frac{T_4}{T_1} = \left(\frac{p_2}{p_1} \right)^{(\gamma - 1)/\gamma} \qquad\qquad (5.40)$$

where γ = ratio of heat capacity at constant pressure to that at constant volume

= 1.355 for chlorine   (Ref. 21)

p_2 = 225 kPa g = 326.3 kPa a

p_1 = 101 kPa a

$$T_4 = 239.15 \left(\frac{326.3}{101} \right)^{\frac{(1.355-1)}{1.355}} = 239.15 \, (3.2307)^{0.262}$$

= 325.17 K° t_4 = 52 °C

T_5 = 313.15 K after intercooler

Enthalpy, removed in the intercooler,

$$\phi_3 = \frac{0.1333}{70.906} \int\limits_{T_5}^{T_4} (28.5463 + 23.8795 \times 10^{-3} \, T - 21.3631 \times 10^{-6} \, T^2$$

$$+ \, 6.4726 \times 10^{-9} \, T^3) \, dT$$

$$= 1.88 \times 10^{-3} \, (343.1 + 91.6 - 26.2 + 2.5) = 0.773 \text{ kW}$$

Cooling water flow rate = $\dfrac{0.773}{8 \times 4.1868}$ = **0.023 kg/s**

Second-stage compression

$$\frac{T_6}{T_5} = \left(\frac{p_4}{p_3} \right)^{0.262}$$

p_3 = 215 kPa g = 316.3 kPa a after intercooler

p_4 = 560 kPa g = 661.3 kPa a

$$T_6 = 313.15 \left(\frac{661.3}{316.3} \right)^{0.262}$$

T_6 = 379.9 K t_6 = 106.75°C

This gas is cooled top 313.15 K (40°C) in the aftercooler.

$$\phi_4 = 1.88 \times 10^{-3} \int\limits_{T_5}^{T_6} C_{mp}^0 \, dT$$

$$= 1.88 \times 10^{-3} \, [28.5463 \, (T_6 - T_5) + 23.8795 \times 10^{-3} \, \frac{(T_6^2 - T_5^2)}{2} - 21.3631$$

$$\times 10^{-6} \, \frac{(T_6^3 - T_5^3)}{3} + 6.4726 \times 10^{-9} \, \frac{(T_6^4 - T_5^4)}{4}]$$

$$= 1.88 \times 10^{-3} \, (1905.5 + 552.3 - 171.8 + 18.1) = 4.332 \text{ kW}$$

Cooling water flow rate = $\dfrac{4.332}{8 \times 4.1868}$ = **0.129 kg/s**

Total cooling water requirement = 0.129 + 0.023 = **0.152 kg/s** $\approx$ **0.55 m³/h**

The gas at 313.15 K is to be further cooled to and liquefied at 290.75 K with the help of chilled water.

Heat-removal rate (i.e., refrigeration requirement),

$$\phi_5 = 1.88 \times 10^{-3} \int_{T_2}^{T_5} C_{mp}^0 dT + 0.133 \lambda_{v2}$$

$$= 1.88 \times 10^{-3} \left[28.5463 (T_5 - T_2) + 23.8795 \times 10^{-3} \frac{(T_5^2 - T_2^2)}{2} \right.$$

$$\left. -21.3631 \times 10^{-6} \frac{(T_5^3 - T_2^3)}{3} + 6.4726 \times 10^{-9} \frac{(T_5^4 - T_2^4)}{4} \right] + 0.1333 \times 252.93$$

$$= 1.88 \times 10^{-3} (639.4 + 161.5 - 43.6 + 4.0) + 33.716$$

$$= \mathbf{35.147 \ kW} \equiv \mathbf{10 \ TR}$$

Note In this example, the use of various equations outlined in previous sections was demonstrated. It can be seen that empirical equations lead to tedious calculations. Tabular thermodynamic properties (such as Tables 5.6 and 5.7) based on a definite reference temperature are therefore preferred over empirical equations.

Example 5.17 Tin is melted in an open pan using a jacket. The jacket is fed with the vapour of an eutectic mixture of diphenyl-diphenyl oxide at 171 kPa a. Tin is fed to the pan at 30°C (303.15 K). Calculate the quantity of eutectic mixture of the diphenyl-diphenyl oxide condensed per 100 kg of tin melted at its melting temperature. Assume no subcooling of vapours.

Data for Tin[19]:

$$\text{Molar mass, } M = 118.7$$
$$\text{Melting point} = 505.15 \text{ K}$$
$$\text{Latent heat of fusion, } \lambda_f = 7201 \text{ kJ/kmol}$$
$$\text{Heat capacity of solid tin, } C_{ms} = 21.14 + 0.02T \text{ kJ/(kmol} \cdot \text{K)}$$

where T is in K.

Data on diphenyl-diphenyl oxide are given in Table 5.6.

Solution *Basis* 100 kg of tin

For melting tin, the temperature of tin must be raised from 303.15 K to the melting point (505.15 K). At the melting point, the heat of fusion must be supplied to melt it.

Sensible heat for raising the temperature,

$$Q_1 = n \int_{T_1}^{T_2} C_{ms} \, dT$$

$$n = \frac{100}{118.70} = 0.8425 \text{ kmol}$$

$$T_1 = 303.15 \text{ K}, \quad T_2 = 505.15 \text{ K}$$

$$Q_1 = 0.8425 \int_{T_1}^{T_2} (21.14 + 0.02T) \, dT = 4973.3 \text{ kJ}$$

Latent heat supply

$$Q_2 = n \times \lambda_f$$
$$= 0.8425 \times 7201 = 6066.8 \text{ kJ}$$

Total heat supply

$$Q = Q_1 + Q_2$$
$$= 4973.3 + 6066.8 = 11\,040.1 \text{ kJ}$$

This amount of heat is supplied by condensation of the diphenyl-diphenyl oxide vapours at 171 kPa a. At this pressure, latent heat, $\lambda_v = 278$ kJ/kg. Since no subcooling is allowed, only latent heat transfer takes place.

$$\text{Amount of vapour condensed} = \frac{11\,040.1}{278} = \textbf{39.7 kg}$$

Example 5.18 In a chemical plant, the demand of steam keeps fluctuating. To permit steady operation of the boiler, a steam accumulator of 45 m³ volume is used. Water and steam are present at equilibrium in the accumulator at 6 bar g. When the accumulator is in operation, 85% of the tank volume is filled with water, the remaining being steam. The accumulator is well insulated. During two plant holidays, the accumulator stores steam and water but does not have the incoming and outgoing steam flows. Under these circumstances, the accumulator loses the heat at the rate of

$$Q = 0.045 \, (T_s - T_a) \text{ kW}$$

where, T_s is the temperature of steam inside the accumulator and T_a is the ambient temperature in K.

If the average ambient temperature is 27°C (300 K), calculate the time in hours by which the pressure of steam will be 5 bar g inside the accumulator.

Solution   This illustration is a case of an unsteady-state process, because the rate of heat loss depends on the temperature of the steam inside the accumulator. As soon as some heat is lost, the vapour–liquid equilibrium in the accumulator changes and the pressure is reduced. Correspondingly, the saturation temperature of steam also varies. This, in turn, reduces the heat loss. Such a problem can be solved by numerical integration. For illustration, four different temperatures/pressures are taken. The properties of steam at these four pressures (see Appendix IV.2) are given in Table 5.12.

Table 5.12   Properties of Steam

| Pressure kPa a | Saturation temperature K | Density, kg/m³ | | Enthalpy, kJ/kg | | |
		Liquid ρ_l	Steam ρ_g	Sensible h	Latent λ_v	Total H
701.3	438.2	902.30	3.674	697.38	2064.7	2762.1
666.7	436.0	904.31	3.502	688.53	2071.4	2759.9
634.0	434.0	906.28	3.339	679.82	2078.0	2757.8
601.3	432.1	908.30	3.176	670.78	2084.7	2755.5

I. At 6 bar g (i.e., 701.3 kPa a), the volume occupied by the water is 85%.

Volume of water in the accumulator = $0.85 \times 45 = 38.25$ m^3

Volume occupied by steam in the accumulator = $0.15 \times 45 = 6.75$ m^3

Total weight of both the fluids in the accumulator = $38.25 \times 902.30 + 6.75 \times 3.674$

$= 34\,512.975$ kg water + 24.8 kg steam = 34 537.775 kg

Total thermal energy accumulated in the accumulator,

$H_1 = 34\,512.975 \times 697.38 + 24.800 \times 2762.1$

$= 24\,137\,159$ kJ over 273.16 K

II. Now, when the temperature of the steam–water mixture drops to 436 K, the proportions of steam and water in the accumulator will change. Let x be amount of steam present in the accumulator at 436 K. Since total mass is constant,

Water in the accumulator = $(34\,537.775 - x_1)$ kg

However, the total volume occupied by both the fluids remains unchanged, i.e., 45 m^3.

$$\frac{x_1}{3.502} + \frac{(34.537.775 - x_1)}{904.31} = 45 \quad \text{or} \quad x_1 = 23.93 \text{ kg steam}$$

Quantity of water = 34 537.775 – 23.93

$= 34\,513.85$ kg

Total enthalpy at $H_2 = 34\,513.85 \times 688.53 + 23.93 \times 2759.9$

$= 23\,829\,866$ kJ

Loss in enthalpy between 438.2 K and 436 K, $H_1 - H_2 = 307\,293$ kJ

III. Temperature of fluids in the accumulator = 434 K

$$\frac{x_2}{3.339} + \frac{(34.537.775 - x_2)}{906.28} = 45 \quad \text{or} \quad x_2 = 23.09 \text{ kg steam}$$

Quantity of water = 34 514.685 kg

Total enthalpy at $H_3 = 34\,514.685 \times 679.82 + 23.09 \times 2757.8$

$= 23\,527\,451$ kJ

Loss in enthalpy between 436 K and 434 K, $H_2 - H_3 = 305\,415$ kJ

IV. Temperature of fluids in the accumulator = 432.1 K

$$\frac{x_3}{3.176} + \frac{(34.537.775 - x_3)}{908.30} = 45 \quad \text{or} \quad x_3 = 22.23 \text{ kg steam}$$

Quantity of water = 34 515.545 kg

Total enthalpy at $H_4 = 34\,515.545 \times 670.78 + 22.23 \times 2755.5$

$= 23\,213\,592$ kJ

Change in enthalpy $H_3 - H_4 = 313\,859$ kJ

Temperature fall calculations

I. Average steam temperature in the range 438.2 K and 436 K,

$$T_{s1} = \frac{(438.2 + 436)}{2} = 437.1 \text{ K}$$

$$T_a = 300 \text{ K}$$

$$\phi_1 = 0.045\ (437.1 - 300) = 6.1695\ kW$$
$$\equiv 22\ 210.2\ kJ/h$$
$$\text{Time } \theta_1 = \frac{307\ 293}{22\ 210.2} = 13.836\ h$$

II.
$$T_{s2} = \frac{(436 + 434)}{2} = 435\ K$$
$$\phi_2 = 0.045\ (435 - 300)$$
$$= 6.075\ kW \equiv 21\ 870\ kJ/h$$
$$\text{Time } \theta_2 = \frac{302\ 415}{21\ 870} = 13.828\ h$$

III.
$$T_{s3} = \frac{(434 + 432.1)}{2} = 433.05\ K$$
$$\phi_3 = 0.045\ (433.05 - 300)$$
$$= 5.987\ kW \equiv 21\ 554.1\ kJ/h$$
$$\text{Time } \theta_3 = \frac{313\ 859}{21\ 554.1} = 14.561\ h$$

$$\text{Total time } \theta = \Sigma \theta_i$$
$$= 13.836 + 13.828 + 14.561 = \mathbf{42.225\ h}$$

Without numerical integration, the problem can be solved as follows:

Total enthalpy change between 438.2 K and 432.1 K, $H_1 - H_4 = 923\ 567\ kJ$

$$\text{Average temperature of fluids in the accumulator} = \frac{(438.2 + 432.1)}{2} = 435.15\ K$$

$$\phi = 0.045\ (435.15 - 300) = 6.081\ kW \equiv 21\ 894.3\ kJ/h$$

$$\text{Time } \theta = \frac{923\ 567}{21\ 894.3} = \mathbf{42.183\ h}$$

Example 5.19 High-pressure carbon dioxide, available in the urea plant of a fertilizer factory, is used to manufacture dry ice. Pure carbon dioxide is available at 20 MPa a and 130°C (430.15 K). It is cooled in a cooler with the help of cooling water to 40°C (313.15 K). Cooled gas is throttled to 3.9 MPa a as a result of which a part of the carbon dioxide is liquefied. The mixture of gas and liquid is taken to a carbon dioxide liquefier which utilises ammonia refrigerant at − 5°C (268.15 K). Liquefied carbon dioxide exchanges heat with revert gas and the latter is vented at 0°C (273.15 K). Subcooled liquid is throttled to atmospheric pressure in the snow tower to produce dry ice. Sublimed carbon dioxide gas is reverted through the exchanger and vented to the atmosphere. Figure 5.10 depicts the process schematically. Calculate (a) yield of dry ice, based on carbon dioxide fed to the water cooler, (b) per cent liquefaction, achieved by throtting cooled high pressure gas (at 313.15 K) to 3.9 MPa a, assuming pressure drop in the water cooler to be negligible, and (c) temperature of gas being vented to the atmosphere.

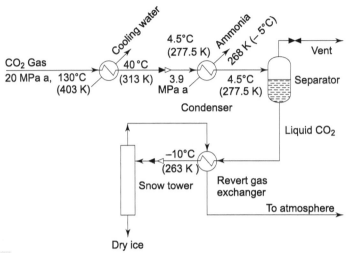

Fig. 5.10 Manufacture of Dry Ice

Solution *Basis* 100 kg/h of feed gas at 20 MPa a and 130°C (430 K).

Since the pressure is quite high, the data given in Table 5.1 can lead to grossly erroneous results. Therefore, real heat capacity data are required. At 20 MPa a, the heat capacity data are as follows:

Use of data, obtained from Ref. 23, is made to evelute properties of carbon dioxide at different pressure and temperature. In Ref. 24, reference state of CO_2 is taken as 0°C (273.15 K) at which enthalpy of saturated liquid CO_2 is 200 kJ/kg.

Enthalpy of CO_2 at 20 MPa a and 403 K = 482.9 kJ/kg

Enthalpy of CO_2 at 20 MPa a and 313 K = 273.4 kJ/kg

Heat removed in water cooler, $\phi_1 = 100 (482.9 - 273.4)$

$$= 21\ 450 \text{ kJ//h} \equiv 5.958 \text{ kW}$$

If C_{mp}^0 data of Table 5.1 (Ref. 5) are used $T_1 = 313.15$ K, $T_2 = 403.15$ K

$$\phi_1' = [21.3655 (403.15 - 313.15) + 64.2841 \times 10^{-3} \frac{(403.15^2 - 313.15^2)}{2} - 41.0506$$

$$\times 10^{-6} \frac{(403.15^3 - 313.15^3)}{3} + 9.7999 \times 10^{-9} \frac{(403.15^4 - 313.15^4)}{4}]$$

$$= 8089.1 \text{ kJ/h} \equiv 2.247 \text{ kW}$$

Because of very high pressure (20 MPa), heat duty of the cooler could have been grossly erroneous (154% underdesign).

When the gas is throttled from 20 MPa a and 313 K to 3.9 MPa a, cooling/liquefaction will take place due to Joule–Thompson effect. At 20 MPa a, $T_s = 277.6$ K (4.6°C), $h_1 = 211.1$ kJ/kg and $H_1 = 427.8$ kJ/kg

Enthalpy of CO_2 gas before throttling = 100×273.4 kJ/h

Let x kg CO_2 is liquefied.

$$x \times 211.1 + (100 - x)\ 427.8 = 100 \times 273.4$$

$$x = 71.25 \text{ kg}$$

Liquefaction due to throttling = **71.25%**

Balance liquefaction is achieved in CO_2 condenser.

Heat duty of condenser, $\varphi_2 = (100 - 71.25)\ (427.8 - 211.1)$

$$= 6230 \text{ kJ/ h} \equiv 1.731 \text{ kW}$$

Liquid CO_2 is throttled to atmospheric pressure at $-78.46°C$ (194.69 K).

Enthalpy of dry ice at 194.69 K, $h_2 = -148.39$ kJ/kg

Enthalpy of CO_2 vapour at 194.69 K, $H_3 = 422.61$ kJ/kg

Assume that y kg of liquid CO_2 at 4.5° C will be converted to dry ice at atmospheric pressure.

Enthalpy of liquid CO_2 at 3.9 MPa a and $-10°C$ (263.15 K), $h_3 = 176.18$ kJ/kg

$$176.18 \times 100 = (100 - y)\ 422.61 + (-148.39 \times y)$$

$$571.0\ y = 24\ 643$$

$$y = 43.16 \text{ kg}$$

Heat carried by CO_2 vapour at 194.69 K $= (100 - 43.16)\ 422.61$

$$= 24\ 021 \text{ kJ/h}$$

Heat transfer in revert gas exchanger, $\varphi_3 = 100\ (211.1 - 176.8)$

$$= 3492 \text{ kJ/h} \equiv 0.97 \text{ kW}$$

Enthalpy of CO_2 gas from revert gas exchanger

$$= 24\ 021 + 3492 = 27\ 513 \text{ kJ/h}$$

Specific enthalpy of CO_2 from revert gas exchanger,

$$H_4 = \frac{27\ 513}{(100 - 43.16)} = 484.04 \text{ kJ/kg}$$

From CO_2 property table (Ref. 23), this enthalpy (H_4) of CO_2 gas at atmospheric pressure corresponds to **262.15 K** or **–11°C**.

Note Use of tabular data are handy in calculating the heat exchangers duties and flashing calculations. While dealing with high pressures, real gas enthalpies are required for accurate heat-transfer duty calculations.

The above example can be easily solved by the pressure–enthalpy $(p–H)$ diagram of CO_2. Refer Fig. 5.11[32]. In this diagram, reference enthalpy of CO_2 is 500 kJ/kg at 0°C (273.15 K). A point representing 3.9 MPa a and $-10°C$ (263 K) is located on it. The constant enthalpy path (i.e., vertical vline) is followed till the horizontal line representing 101.3 kPa a is crossed. This clearly gives 0.56 mass fraction of gaseous CO_2. In other words, dry ice formation is 0.44 kg/kg of liquid CO_2. This agrees well with the calculated yield of 0.4316 kg/kg. Diagrams are thus very useful in finding final conditions under various operating conditions, such as adiabatic letdown, constant enthalpy letdown, etc.

Ref. 25 give tabular properties and graphs for a large number of gases.

Example 5.20 A sulphur burner in a sulphite pump mill burns 200 kg of pure sulphur per hour[33]. The gases leave the burner at 871°C (1144 K) and are cooled before being sent to an absorption tower. As a primary cooler, a waste heat boiler is employed for producing saturated steam at 15 bar a. The temperature of the feed water to the boiler is 15°C (15 K) lower than that of saturated steam at 15 bar a and the temperature of the gas mixture leaving the boiler is 190°C (463 K). Assume

10% excess air, complete combustion, no heat loss to the surroundings and no SO_3 formation. Calculate the amount of steam produced, assuming 90% efficiency.

Solution *Basis* 200 kg/h of sulphur firing

$$\text{Molar feed rate of sulphur} = \frac{200}{32} = 6.25 \text{ kmol/h}$$

The reaction is

$$S + O_2 = SO_2$$

Theoretical oxygen required = 6.25 kmol/h
Actual oxygen supplied = $6.25 \times 1.1 = 6.875$ kmol/h

$$\text{Air supply to the burner} = \frac{6.875}{0.21} = 32.738 \text{ kmol/h}$$

N_2 entering the burner with air = $32.738 - 6.875 = 25.863$ kmol/h
SO_2 formed = 6.25 kmol/h

The burner effluent gases will contain 6.25 kmol/h SO_2, 0.625 kmol/h O_2 and 25.863 kmol/h N_2.

$$T_1 = 1144.15 \text{ K} \quad \text{and} \quad T_2 = 463.15 \text{ K}$$

Assume base temperature to be 298.15 K.

$$\begin{aligned}\Sigma C^o_{m\,pi} &= [6.25 \times 24.7706 + 0.625 \times 26.0257 + 25.863 \times 29.5909] \\ &\quad + [6.25 \times 62.9481 + 0.625 \times 11.7551 - 25.853 \times 5.141]10^{-3}\,T \\ &\quad + [-44.2585 \times 6.25 - 0.625 \times 2.3426 + 25.863 \times 13.1829]10^{-6}\,T^2 \\ &\quad + [6.25 \times 11.122 - 0.625 \times 0.5623 - 25.863 \times 4.968]10^{-9}\,T^3 \\ &= 936.3918 + 267.8623 \times 10^{-3}\,T + 62.8696 \times 10^{-6}\,T^2 - 59.3263 \times 10^{-9}\,T^3 \end{aligned}$$

$$\text{Enthalpy removed in the WHB, } \phi = \int_{T_1}^{T_2} (\Sigma n_i \cdot C^o_{m\,pi})\,dT$$

$$= 788\,852.2 \text{ kJ/h} \equiv 219.13 \text{ kW}$$

Saturation temperature of steam at 15 bar a, $t_s/T_s = 198.29°C/471.44$ K
Feed water temperature to boiler = 198.29 − 15

$$= 183.29°C \quad \text{or} \quad 456.44 \text{ K}$$

Enthalpy to be supplied for steam generation = sensible heat for raising temperature of water by 15 K + latent heat of vaporization at 15 bar

$$H = 15 \times 4.1868 + 1945.2 = 2008 \text{ kJ/kg}$$

Amount of steam generated, $q_m = (\phi/H) \times 0.9$

$$= \frac{788\,852.2}{2008} \times 0.9 = \textbf{353.6 kg/h}$$

Example 5.21 Calculate (a) enthalpy of equimolar liquid mixture of n-pentane and n-hexane, and (b) enthalpy of equimolar vapour mixture of the same components at 101.325 kPa.

Solution Bubble point and dew point of the equimolar liquid and vapour mixture are calculated (in Example 5.13) to be 48.45°C (321.6 K) and 56.75°C (329.9 K), respectively.

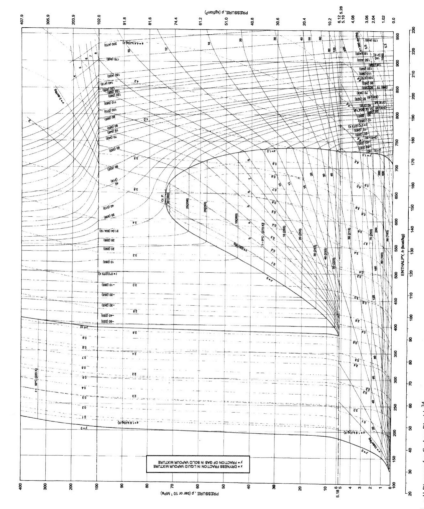

Fig. 5.11 p-H Diagram for Carbon Dioxide[34]
(Reproduced with the permission of BUSE Anlagenbau GmbH, Germany).

Enthalpy of liquid mixture at T_{BB}

Assume a reference temperature (T_0) as 25°C (298.15 K). Table 5.3 give constants of the polynomial equation for liquid heat capacities.

Enthalpy of *n*-pentane at T_{BB},

$$H_1 = 65.4961\ (321.6 - 298.15) + 628.628 \times 10^{-3}\ \frac{(321.6^2 - 298.15^2)}{2}$$

$$- 1898.8 \times 10^{-6}\ \frac{(321.6^3 - 298.15^3)}{3} + 3186.51 \times 10^{-9}\ \frac{(321.6^4 - 298.15^4)}{4}$$

$$= 4052.8\ \text{kJ/kmol}$$

Enthalpy of *n*-hexane at T_{BB},

$$H_2 = 31.421\ (321.6 - 298.15) + 976.058 \times 10^{-3}\ \frac{(321.6^2 - 298.15^2)}{2}$$

$$- 2353.68 \times 10^{-6}\ \frac{(321.6^3 - 298.15^3)}{3} + 3092.73 \times 10^{-9}\ \frac{(321.6^4 - 298.15^4)}{4}$$

$$= 4688.1\ \text{kJ/kmol}$$

$$H_{\text{sol}} = 0.5\ H_1 + 0.5\ H_2$$
$$= 0.5 \times 4052.8 + 0.5 \times 4688.1$$
$$= \textbf{4370.5 kJ/kmol of equimolar mixture}$$

Enthalpy of vapour mixture at T_{DP}

Pure component enthalpy in vapour state comprises sensible enthalpy of liquid from T_0 to T_{DP} and latent heat of vaporization at T_{DP}. For evaluation of the latent heat, the Watson equation (Eq. 5.26) can be used.

Latent heat of vaporization of *n*-pentane,

$$\lambda_{v1} \text{ at } T_{DP} = 25\ 790 \left(\frac{469.7 - 329.9}{469.7 - 309.2} \right)^{0.38} = 24\ 472\ \text{kJ/kmol}$$

Latent heat of vaporization of *n*-hexane,

$$\lambda_{v2} \text{ at } T_{DP} = 28\ 850 \left(\frac{507.6 - 329.9}{507.6 - 341.9} \right)^{0.38}$$

$$= 29\ 627.0\ \text{kJ/kmol}$$

Enthalpy of *n*-pentane vapour at T_{DP}

$$H_2^{ig} = \int_{T_0}^{T_{DP}} C_{11}\ dT + \lambda_{v1}$$

$$= 65.4961\ (329.9 - 298.15) + 628.628 \times 10^{-3}$$

$$\frac{(329.9^2 - 298.15^2)}{2} - 1898.8 \times 10^{-6}\ \frac{(329.9^3 - 298.15^3)}{3}$$

$$+ 3186.51 \times 10^{-9}\ \frac{(329.9^4 - 298.15^4)}{4} + 24\ 472$$

$$= 5537.9 + 24\ 472 = 30\ 009.9\ \text{kJ/kmol}$$

Enthalpy of n-hexane vapour at T_{DP}

$$H_2^{ig} = \int_{T_0}^{T_{DP}} C_{12}\, dT + \lambda_{v2}$$

$$= 31.421\,(329.9 - 298.15) + 976.058 \times 10^{-3}\,\frac{(329.9^2 - 298.15^2)}{2}$$

$$- 2353.68 \times 10^{-6}\,\frac{(329.9^3 - 298.15^3)}{3} + 3092.73 \times 10^{-9}$$

$$\frac{(329.9^4 - 298.15^4)}{4} + 29\,627.0$$

$$= 5802.2 + 29\,627.0 = 35\,429.2 \text{ kJ/kmol}$$

$$H_{mix}^{ig} = 0.5 \times H_1^{ig} + 0.5 \times H_2^{ig}$$

$$= 0.5 \times 30\,009.9 + 0.5 \times 35\,429.2$$

$$= \mathbf{32\,719.6 \text{ kJ/kmol of equimolar mixture}}$$

5.10 EQUILIBRIUM FLASH CALCULATIONS OF A MULTICOMPONENT SYSTEM

A single-component system as well as a binary system were discussed in Sec. 5.9. Calculations of a multicomponent system are quite complex. The amount of each of the several components in the liquid and vapour states in equilibrium are required to be calculated. The cryogenic separation of gases involve such calculations. The separation of hydrogen, helium, argon, etc., are classical examples of the cryogenic process. The liquefaction of natural gas, partial condensation of vapours, depressurisation of a liquid below its vapour pressure, etc., are other operations in which equilibrium flash calculations are involved. Normally, these calculations are done by trial and error. Basic formulae are derived from the material balance and vapour–liquid equilibrium relationships and follow the guidelines given in Sec. 5.9. An important source of vapour–liquid equilibrium data for the hydrocarbons are nomographs by Daduburjor[34] and the *Engineering Data Book*[35] published by the Gas Processors Suppliers Association. References 3 and 36 may also be referred for the vapour–liquid equilibrium calculations.

For 1 kmol of the total fluid (vapour + liquid),

Let N_i = kmol of the ith component in the total fluid

V = kmol of vapours

L = kmol of liquid

x_i = mole fraction of the ith component in the liquid

y_i = mole fraction of the ith component in the vapour

L_i = kmol of the ith component in the liquid

V_i = kmol of the ith component in the vapour

K_i = equilibrium constant

    = y_i/x_i by definition   (5.41)

$N_i = L_i + V_i$ (5.42)

$$= Lx_i + Vy_i$$

$$= Lx_i + VK_ix_i$$

$$= x_i (L + VK_i) \tag{5.43}$$

$$x_i = L_i/L \tag{5.44}$$

$$N_i = \frac{L_i}{L} (L + VK_i) \tag{5.45}$$

$$L_i = \frac{LN_i}{(VK_i + L)} \tag{5.46}$$

$$= \frac{N_i}{\left(\dfrac{V}{L} K_i + 1 \right)} \tag{5.47}$$

$$L_i = \frac{N_i}{\left(\dfrac{1-L}{L} K_i + 1 \right)} \tag{5.48}$$

Degree of freedom for flash calculation is 1 for a single-component system. It can be calculated for a multicomponent system. However, one variable out of two intensive properties; namely pressure and temperature is specified to find the values of other variables. Normally, pressure is specified. For example, a hydrocarbon mixture is flashed from 20 bar a to 2 bar a pressure. In addition to this, molar flow rate of feed F, its composition N_is, its enthalpy H_F, its pressure (for example, 20 bar a in above case) and temperature are known variables.

The method of calculation is a trial-and-error method. For the given pressure of stream after flashing, assume V/L ratio and temperature of stream after flashing. For ideal vapour–liquid equillibrium K_i values can be determined from the values of temperature and pressure. For the hydrocarbon mixtures, K_i values can be determined from the chart available in literature (Ref. 34) for given temperature and pressure. Determine K_is and find L_is from Eq. (5.47). Conditions $\Sigma L_i = L$ and $V + L = F$ give the value of V. Calculate V/L ratio and compare its value with the assumed one. For the second trial, revise the value of V/L ratio. Repeat the calculations till the assumed value of V/L becomes equal to its value abtained after the trial calculations. Finally, to verify the assumed value of the temperature, find the enthalpies of vapour and liquid streams after flashing and carry out the enthalpy balance. Flashing through an expansion (control) valve or an orifice is an adiabatic operation. Hence, enthalpy of feed should be equal to enthalpy of vapour plus enthalpy of liquid after flashing. If enthalpy of the vapour–liquid mixture after flashing is not equal to the enthalpy of feed, the assumed value of temperature is not correct. If so, revise the temperature of streams after flashing and repeat the calculations until enthalpies of feed and that of vapour–liquid stream are same.

If a heat exchanger is placed after the expansion valve, it is possible to specify both pressure and temperature of the liquid–vapour mixture after flashing.

Trial-and-error methods differ slightly in format and presentation. A commonly employed approach is to assume L. Since N_i is known from feed data, L_i can be calculated for each of the components. $\Sigma\, L_i$ is compared with the assumed value of L. Iterations are repeated till the assumed L and calculated $L\, (= \Sigma L_i)$ are in agreement. For ideal fluids, according to Dalton's law,

$$p_i = y_i\, p \qquad (5.49)$$

and according to Raoult's law

$$p_i = x_i\, p_{vi} \qquad (5.50)$$

where p_i = partial pressure of the ith component
  p = total pressure
  p_{vi} = vapour pressure of the ith component

Thus, for an ideal fluid,

$$K_i = \frac{y_i}{x_i} = \frac{p_{vi}}{p} = \frac{\text{vapour pressure of the } i\text{th component}}{\text{total pressure}} \qquad (5.51)$$

Example 5.22 A saturated liquid mixture, containing 45.1% propane, 18.3% iso butane and 36.6% n-butane (by mole), is available at 40.8 bar a and 125.6°C (398.78 K). It is adiabatically flashed at 22 bar a and 93.1°C (366.25 K). At these conditions, K values[37] are 1.42, 0.86 and 0.72, respectively. Calculate the liquid fraction and its composition after flashing.

Solution *Basis* 1 kmol of the mixture

Table 5.13 Flashing of Propane–butane Mixture

Component	N_i kmol	K_i	$L = 0.8$ kmol	0.6 kmol	0.5 kmol	0.4 kmol	mole % in liquid fraction
			Values of L_i for trial values of L				
C_3H_8	0.451	1.42	0.3328	0.2317	0.1864	0.1441	36
iso-C_4H_{10}	0.183	0.86	0.1506	0.1163	0.0984	0.0799	20
n-C_4H_{10}	0.366	0.72	0.3102	0.2476	0.2128	0.1760	44
Total	1.000		0.7936	0.5956	0.4796	0.4000	100

Sample calculations for C_3H_8
  For $L = 0.8$

$$\left(\frac{1-L}{L}\right) K_i + 1 = \left(\frac{1-0.8}{0.8}\right) 1.42 + 1 = 1.355$$

Using Eq. (5.48) $L_i = \dfrac{0.451}{1.355} = 0.3328$

Liquid fraction will contain 36% C_3H_8, 20% iso-C_4H_{10} and 44% n-C_4H_{10} (on mole basis).

From Ref. 26, enthalpy values of all three mixtures are drawn. Reference state was pure component's liquid state enthalpy at NBP of each component equal to 0 kJ/kg.

Enthalpy of original saturated liquid mixture,

$$H_1 = 23\ 549\ kJ/kmol$$

Enthalpy of saturated liquid fraction after flashing, $H_2 = 16\ 325\ kJ/mol$

Enthalpy of vapour mixture in equilibrium with liquid mixture,

$$H_3 = 28\ 332\ kJ/mol$$

Enthalpy of vapour–liquid mixture after flashing,

$$H_4 = 0.4 \times 16\ 325 + 0.6 \times 28\ 332 = 23\ 529\ kJ/mol$$

$$H_1 \approx H_4$$

Note It can be seen that the enthalpy of vapour–liqiud mixture after flashing is in close agreement with that of the original saturated liquid mixture. It is important that these values should also match for ensuring the correctness of the calculations, based on *K*-values.

Example 5.23 A basic flow sheet of the conventional process for cryogenic gas separation from the oil refinery off gas is given in Fig. 5.12. Feed gas contains a number of acid gases, including carbon dioxide and hydrogen sulphide. These impurities are removed by chemical wash process. After the removal of a bulk of the impurities, trace constituents and water are completely eliminated and dried by adsorption. The final cleaned-up feed gas, containing 60% H_2, 20% CH_4 and 20% C_2H_6 (on mole basis) enters the cold box where it is cooled and condensed in

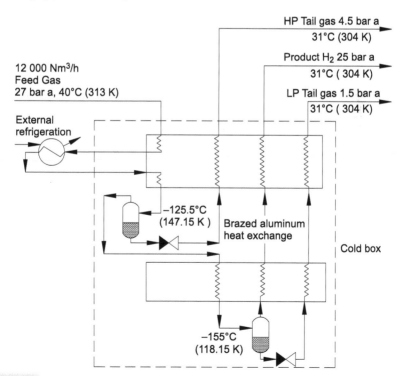

Fig. 5.12 Hydrogen Recovery from Refinery Off-Gases

two plate-and-fin type brazed aluminium heat exchangers. The major portion of the hydrocarbons is liquefied at $-125.5°C$ (147.65 K) in the first heat exchanger and collected in the first separator. The condensate from the first separator is then throttled to 4.5 bar a and evaporated and reverted through the first exchanger.

The gas leaving the first separator is further cooled in the second separator to $-155°C$ (118.15 K). This low temperature makes it necessary that the condensate is throttled to low pressure, say to 1.5 bar a. This mixture is evaporated and reverted through both the heat exchangers while the incoming feed gas is cooled and partially liquefied. Feed gas enters at 27 bar a and at 40°C (313 K) at the rate of 12 000 Nm^3/h and product hydrogen (at 25 bar a) and tail gas streams (at 4.5 bar a and 1.5 bar a) leave the cold box at 31°C (304 K). Calculate the recovery and purity of hydrogen stream. Use the data given in Table 5.14.

Table 5.14   Equilibrium Constants[38] (K) at 27 Bar a

Equation $\log_{10} K = A/T + B$, where T = temperature in K

Component	A	B	Temperature range, K
Methane	-378.9	2.1686	110-200
	-302.2	1.5134	100-110
	-214.5	0.638	90-100
Ethane	-756.0	2.83	157-200
	-752.0	2.75	90-157
Hydrogen	120.5	0.611	90-200
Nitrogen	-257.0	2.379	110-200
	-242.5	2.241	90-110

Solution   *Basis* Feed gas = 12 000 Nm^3/h = 535.4 kmol/h

First gas separator incoming feed gas is cooled to 147.65 K ($-125.5°C$) in the first heat exchanger by exchanging heat with reverted gases and sent to the first gas separator.

$$T_1 = 147.65 \text{ K}$$

Calculate K_i using data given in Table 5.14.

Table 5.15   Flashing in First Gas Separator ($T_1 = 147.65$ K)

Gas	K_i	N_i kmol	$L_1 =$ 0.5	$L_2 =$ 0.3636	$L_3 =$ 0.3285	$L_4 =$ 0.3190	$L_5 =$ 0.3163	V_i kmol	Mole fraction in vapour
				Values of L_i for trial values of L					
H$_2$	26.8	0.6	0.0216	0.0125	0.0108	0.0103	0.0102	0.5898	0.8617
CH$_4$	0.4	0.2	0.1429	0.1176	0.1100	0.1079	0.1073	0.0927	0.1355
C$_2$H$_6$	0.0045	0.2	0.1991	0.1984	0.1982	0.1981	0.1981	0.0019	0.0028
Total		1.0	0.3636	0.3285	0.3190	0.3163	0.3156	0.6844	1.0000

Liquid stream from first separator is revaporized to HP Tail gas stream.

HP Tail gas stream, $\dot{n}_1 = 535.4 \times 0.3156$
$$= 168.97 \text{ kmol/h}$$

Table 5.16 HP Tail Gas Stream

| Gas | HP Tail gas stream (liquid from first gas separator) | | |
	kmol/h	Nm³/h	Vol. %
H_2	5.46	122.4	3.23
CH_4	57.45	1287.7	34.00
C_2H_6	106.06	1377.2	62.77
Total	168.97	3787.3	100.00

Second gas separator Vapours (366.43 kmol/h) under pressure from the first gas separator are taken to the second gas exchanger, cooled to $-155°C$ (118 K) and sent to the second gas separator.

$$T = 118.15 \text{ K}$$

Table 5.17 Flashing in Second Gas Separator

| Gas | K_i | N_i kmol | Values of L_i for trial values of L | | | | V_i kmol |
			$L_1 =$ 0.1	$L_2 =$ 0.0798	$L_3 =$ 0.0709	$L_4 =$ 0.06	
H_2	42.9	0.8617	0.0022	0.0017	0.0015	0.0013	0.8606
CH_4	0.09	0.1355	0.0748	0.0664	0.0621	0.0561	0.0792
C_2H_6	2.38×10^{-4}	0.0028	0.0028	0.0028	0.0028	0.0028	0
Total		1.0000	0.0798	0.0709	0.0664	0.0602	0.9398

Liquid stream from second separator is revaporized to LP Tail gas stream.

LP Tail gas stream, $\dot{n}_2 = (535.4 - 168.97) \, 0.0602$
$$= 22.07 \text{ kmol/h}$$

Product hydrogen stream, $\dot{n}_3 = 535.4 - 168.97 - 22.07$
$$= 344.36 \text{ kmol/h}$$

Table 5.18 Product Hydrogen and LP Tail Gas Streams

| Gas | Product hydrogen stream | | | LP tail gas stream | | |
	kmol/h	Nm³/h	mole %	kmol/h	Nm³/h	mole %
H_2	315.35	7068.3	91.58	0.48	10.8	2.17
CH_4	29.01	650.2	8.42	20.56	460.8	93.16
C_2H_6	0	0	0	1.03	23.1	4.67
Total	344.36	7718.5	100.00	22.07	494.7	100.00

Example 5.24   In Example 5.23, an external refrigeration input is shown in Fig. 5.12.

(a) Calculate refrigeration requirement using ideal-gas heat capacity equation.

(b) In Table 5.19, enthalpies of real gas mixtures are given. Calculate refrigeration requirement based on these values.

Table 5.19   Enthalpies of Gas Mixtures[26]

Gas Mixture	Conditions	Enthalpy, kJ/mol mixture
Feed	27 bar a and 40°C (313.15 K)	12 086
Product hydrogen	25 bar a and 31°C (304.15 K)	8 743.2
HP tail gas	4.5 bar a and 31°C (304.15 K)	18 036
LP tail gas	1.5 bar a and 31°C (304.15 K)	15 892

Reference State   Enthalpy of each saturated liquid component at NBP = 0 kJ/kmol. NBP values are given in Table 5.75 (Exercise 5.26).

Solution

(a) Heat capacity equation constants are listed in Table 5.20.

Table 5.20   Heat Capacity Equation Constants for Feed Gas

Component	$\dot{n}_i$	Heat capacity equation constants			
	kmol/h	$\dot{n}_i \cdot a_i$	$\dot{n}_i \cdot b_i \times 10^3$	$\dot{n}_i \cdot c_i \times 10^6$	$\dot{n}_i \cdot d_i \times 10^9$
H2	321.24	9 190.8	327.5	−47.4	247.0
CH4	107.08	2 061.2	5 580.3	1282.1	−1211.9
C_2H_6	107.08	579.6	19 069.6	−7214.5	933.2
Total	535.40	11 831.6	24 977.4	−5979.8	−31.7

All product streams leave at 31°C (304.15 K). Use of ideal gas heat capcity equation does not involve pressure correction. Hence, refrigeration requirement of the cold box will be the enthalpy diffrence of the feed gas at 40°C (313.15K) and 31°C (304.15 K).

Refrigeration requirement,

$$\phi = \int_{304.15}^{313.15} (11\,831.6 + 24\,997.4 \times 10^{-3}\,T - 5979.8 \times 10^{-6}\,T^2 - 31.7 \times 10^{-9}\,T^3)\,dT$$

$$= \textbf{170 787.7 kJ/h} \equiv \textbf{47.441 kW} \equiv \textbf{13.5 TR}$$

(b) Based on real gas enthalpies,

ϕ = Enthalpy of feed stream − Enthalpy of product streams

= 535.4 × 12 086 − [344.36 × 8743.2 + 168.97 × 18 036 + 22.07 × 15 892]

= **61 756.7 kJ/h** ≡ **17.155 kW** ≡ **4.88 TR**

Note Cryogenic processes use Joule–Thomson effect for achieving desired temperatures in the cold box. Pressure has therefore a significant role to play in achieving the cold state. Calculations, based on real gas enthalpies, indicate only 36.2% refrigeration as compared to that calculated using ideal–gas heat capacity equations.

Example 5.25 Chlorination of benzene is carried out in a single–stage co-current continuous reactor. The reaction pressure and temperature are kept at 150 kPa a and 55°C (328 K). The reactions taking place in the reactor are

| Benzene | Chlorine | MCB | Hydrochloric acid |

| MCB | Chlorine | 1,4-DCB | Hydrochloric acid |

The reactor is supplied with chlorine at the rate of 0.4 kmol Cl_2 per kmol benzene. Chlorine is fully consumed in the reactions. Conversion of benzene in the reactor is 37% while yield of monochlorobenzene (MCB) is 91.89%. Liquid product coming out of the reactor is in equilibrium with the gas mixture leaving the reactor. Establish the material balance.

Solution *Basis* 100 kmol/h of benzene feed rate

$$Cl_2 \text{ feed rate} = 0.4 \times 100 = 40 \text{ kmol/h}$$

From the reactions, it is clear that 1 kmol of chlorine produces 1 kmol of HCl.

HCl production rate = 40 kmol/h

Benzene consumed = 37 kmol/h

MCB production rate = $100 \times 0.37 \times 0.9189 = 34$ kmol/h

1,4-DCB production rate = $37 - 34 = 3$ kmol/h

Unreacted benzene = $100 - 37 = 63$ kmol/h

Overall material balance

If L is the liquid product rate (kmol/h) and V is the vapour flow rate (kmol/h),

$$N_t = L + V = 40 + 34 + 3 + 63 = 140 \text{ kmol/h}$$

Vapours leaving the reactor, will have hydrogen chloride gas (1), benzene (2), MCB (3) and 1,4-DCB (4). Let y_i be the mole fraction of each component in the gaseous mixture and x_i be the mole fraction of each component in the liquid product. Assume ideal behaviour of gas and liquid mixtures.

$$y_i = \frac{p_{vi}}{p_t} \, x_i = K_i \cdot x_i \qquad (5.51)$$

Rearranging Eq. (5.44) and substituting,

$$x_i = \frac{N_i}{L + VK_i}$$

$$= \frac{N_i}{L + (N_t - L) \cdot K_i}$$

$$= \frac{N_i}{L(1 - K_1) + N_t K_i}$$

$$\Sigma \, x_i = 1$$

Since the vapour pressure of hydrogen chloride is very high at 328.15 K, K_i for HCl will be so high that x_i may be taken as nil. Use Antoine constants from Table 5.4 for calculation of vapour pressures of other components. At $p_t = 150$ kPa and 55°C (328.15 K), $K_2 = 0.3114$, $p_{v2} = 43.59$ kPa, $K_3 = 0.0508$, $p_{v3} = 7.12$ kPa, $K_4 = 0.0091$, and $p_{v3} = 1.27$ kPa.

Assume a value of L. Calculate x_2 to x_4. Sum of mole fractions in liquid state should be equal to one. If not unity, iterate L.

$$\frac{63}{(1 - 0.3114)\,L + 140 \times 0.3114} + \frac{34}{(1 - 0.0508)\,L + 140 \times 0.0508}$$

$$+ \frac{3}{(1 - 0.0091)\,L + 140 \times 0.0091} = 1$$

$$\frac{63}{0.6886\,L + 43.596} + \frac{34}{0.9492\,L + 7.112} + \frac{3}{0.9909\,L + 1.274} = 1$$

By trail-and-error or by Mathcad,

$$L = 89.669 \text{ kmol/h}$$
$$V = 140 - 89.669 = 50.331 \text{ kmol/h}$$

Table 5.21 Composition of Liquid and Vapour Mixtures

Component	Product mixture $\dot{n}_i$ kmol/h	Vapour, V		Liquid, L	
		kmol/h	mole %	kmol/h	mole %
Benzene	63.0	9.378	18.63	53.622	59.80
MCB	34.0	0.939	1.87	33.061	36.87
1,4-DCB	3.0	0.014	0.03	2.986	3.33
HCl	40.0	40.000	79.47	—	—
Total	$N_i = 140.0$	50.331	100.00	89.669	100.00

5.11 ENTHALPY CHANGES ACCOMPANYING CHEMICAL REACTIONS

In Secs .5.1 to 5.10, the enthalpy changes of physical processes were considered. However, when chemical reactions take place, either heat is absorbed or evolved. Three types of reactions are of interest, viz., combustion, formation and the reaction of one or more substances to form other compounds. In Chapter 7, the combustion of fuels will be described in detail. In this chapter, the discussion will be restricted to the heat of formation and heat of reaction.

5.11.1 Standard Heat of Formation and Standard Heat of Combustion

Heat of formation is defined as the isothermal enthalpy change in a synthesis reaction from the elements in their standard states. This enthalpy change can be exothermic (i.e., evolution of enthalpy) or can be endothermic (i.e., absorption of enthalpy). Take a look at the synthesis reaction:

$$N_2 + 3\ H_2 \rightarrow 2\ NH_3$$

In this reaction, elements react to form ammonia and, therefore, it is a representation of a formation reaction.

Consider another reaction in which phosphorous pentoxide is dissolved in water to produce phosphoric acid.

$$P_4O_{10} + 6\ H_2O \rightarrow 4\ H_3PO_4$$

This is not the formation reaction for the purpose of calculation of enthalpy of formation.

In reality, only a few formation reactions can be actually carried out (e.g., ammonia synthesis) and, therefore, the enthalpy of formation is usually determined indirectly. Combustion reaction easily lends itself to experimental investigation and the methods are well known for evaluation of heat of combustion.

Data on heat of combustion can be conveniently utilised for the calculation of heat of formation. Due to this reason, often heat of formation and heat of combustion data are tabulated side by side.

For tabulating the data, *standard states* need to be defined. The following standard states represent a normal choice (IUPAC recommendations).

Phase	Reference standard state
Solid	Pure crystalline at 25°C (298.15 K)
Liquid	Pure at 25°C (298.15 K) and 1 bar a
Gas	Pure at 25°C (298.15 K) and 1 bar a
Solution	Solute concentration of 1 mol/kg solvent at 25°C (298.15 K).

In Appendix V, ai represents solution of ionized substance and ao represents unionized substance.

In Appendix V, standard heat of formation (ΔH_f^o) and standard heat of combustion (ΔH_c^o) are tabulated. Units employed are kJ/mol which can be easily converted to other units like kJ/kg, kJ/L, etc. Most data are extracted from the thermodynamic tables, published by the Thermodynamics Research Centre (TRC), USA and the NBS Tables of Chemical Thermodynamics Properties, published by the National Institute of Standards and Technology (NIST), USA. These are considered very reliable data. Although the tabulated data correspond to 25°C (298.15 K), data are also reported in literature corresponding to -273.15°C (0 K), 0°C (273.15 K) and 18°C (291.15 K).

Data on ΔH_f^o are useful in evaluating the heat of reaction as will be discussed in Sec. 5.13.

For hydrocarbons and compounds with oxygen (C–H–O) standard heat of combustion (ΔH_c^o) are obtained by considering that products of combustion are CO_2 and H_2O as per the following reaction eqautions.

$$C_aH_b + (a + b/4)\ O_2(g) = a\ CO_2(g) + (b/2)\ H_2O\ (g\ or\ l) \qquad \text{(HC-1)}$$
$$C_aH_bO_d + [(4a + b - 2d)/4]\ O_2(g) = a\ CO_2(g) + (b/2)\ H_2O\ (g\ or\ l) \qquad \text{(HC-2)}$$

Organic nitrogen (C–H–N) compounds form N_2 as a productin the combustion reaction.

$$C_aH_bN_c + (a + b/4)\, O_2(g) = a\, CO_2(g) + (b/2)\, H_2O\ (g\ or\ l) + (c/2)\, N_2(g) \quad (HC-3)$$

For organic sulphur (C–H–S) compounds product of combustion are CO_2, H_2O and H_2SO_4, 115 H_2O (sol).

For net ΔH_c^0.

$$C_aH_bS_e + [(4a + b + 6e)/4]\, O_2(g) = a\, CO_2(g) + (b/2)\, H_2O\ (g) + e\, SO_2(g) \quad (HC-\ 4)$$

For gross ΔH_c^0:

$$C_aH_bS_e + [(4a + b + 6e)/4]\, O_2(g) + [116e - (b/2)]\, H_2O(l) = a\, CO_2(g) + e\, H_2SO_4,$$
$$115\ H_2O\ (sol) \quad\quad\quad (HC-5)$$

In Eq. (HC-5), production of aqueous sulphuric acid is considered in 115 mol H_2O per mol H_2SO_4. Dilution water includes $[(b/2) - e]$ mol H_2O produced during the reaction which is not specified as discreste product. Hence while calculating gross ΔH_c^0, ΔH_f^0 of $[(b/2) - e]$ mol product H_2O must be taken into consideration. Also ΔH_f^0 of reactant H_2O mol is not to be considered as they are for dilution only.

$$\Delta H_f^0\ of\ H_2SO_4.115\ H_2O(sol) = -887.811\ kJ/mol\ H_2SO_4$$

Example 5.26 Calculate the heat of formation of ethylene gas at 25°C (298.15 K) using the heat of combustion data.

Solution The values of heats of combustion of carbon, hydrogen and ethylene are listed in Appendix V.
The combustion reaction are

$$2\ C(g) + 2\ O_2(g) = 2\ CO_2(g) \quad\quad (A)$$
$$2\ H_2(g) + O_2(g) = 2\ H_2O(g) \quad\quad (B)$$
$$C_2H_4(g) + 3\ O_2(g) = 2\ CO_2(g) + 2\ H_2O(g) \quad\quad (C)$$

Add Eqs. (A) and (B), and from the sum, subtract Eq. (C).

$$2\ C(g) + 2\ O_2(g) + 2\ H_2(g) + O_2(g) - C_2H_4(g) - 3\ O_2(g)$$
$$= 2\ CO_2(g) + 2\ H_2O(g) - 2\ CO_2(g) - 2\ H_2O(g)$$
Simplifying, $\quad 2\ C(g) + 2\ H_2(g) = C_2H_4(g) \quad\quad (D)$

Thus, it is clear that the algebraic sum of relevant heats of combustion (with proper signs) gives the heat of formation of ethylene.

Heat of formation of ethylene gas $(\Delta H_f^0) = 2 \times$ Heat of combustion of C(s) or heat of formation of $CO_{2(g)} + 2 \times$ Heat of combustion of $H_2(g)$ or heat of formation of $H_2O_{(g)}$ – Heat of combustion of $C_2H_4(g)$

$$= -2 \times 393.51 - 2 \times 241.82 + 1323.1 = 52.44\ kJ/mol$$

From Appendix V.2, the standard heat of formation of ethylene gas is **52.5 kJ/mol** which is in close agreement with the calculated figure.

Example 5.27 Calculate standard heat of combustion of ethyl mercaptan; $C_2H_6S(l)$
Use heat of formation data of the sulphur compound and that of CO_2 and H_2O.

Solution

Net ΔH_c^o:

$C_2H_6S(l) + 4.5\ O_2(g) = 2\ CO_2(g) + 3\ H_2O(g) + SO_2(g)$
$\Delta H_c^o = [2\ (-393.51) + 3\ (-241.82) + (-296.83)] - (-73.6 + 0)]$
$\qquad = -1735.71$ kJ/mol

Reported net $\Delta H_c^o = -1735.6$ kJ/mol

Gross ΔH_c^o:

$C_2H_6S(l) + 5\ O_2(g) + \langle 113\ H_2O(l)\rangle = 2\ CO_2(g) + H_2SO_4.\ 115\ H_2O(sol) + \langle 2\ H_2O(l)\rangle$
$\Delta H_c^o = [2\ (-393.51) - 887.811 + 2\ (-285.83)] - (-73.6 + 0)]$
$\qquad = -2172.891$ kJ/mol

Reported gross $\Delta H_c^o = -2173.1$ kJ/mol

Example 5.28   Find the standard heat of formation data of gaseous diethyl ether from Appendix IV.2 and calculate latent heat of vaporization using data from Table 5.4 at 25°C (298.15 K). With these data, calculate the standard heat of formation of liquid diethyl ether.

Solution λ_{v1} at 34.55°C (307.7 K) = 26 694 kJ/kmol Ref. Table 5.5. T_c = 466.74 K

Latent heat of vaporization at 25°C (298.15 K), $\lambda_{v2} = 26\ 694 \left(\dfrac{466.7 - 298.15}{466.7 - 307.7}\right)^{0.38}$

$$= 27\ 292\ \text{kJ/kmol} \equiv 27.292\ \text{kJ/mol}$$

Standard heat of formation of gaseous diethyl ether,

$$\Delta H_f^o(g) = -252.0\ \text{kJ/mol}$$

Therefore, standard heat of formation of liquid diethyl ether,

$$\Delta H_f^o(l) = -252.0 - 27.114 = -279.114\ \text{kJ/kmol}$$

$$\text{Reported } \Delta H_f^o(l) = \mathbf{-279.2\ kJ/mol}$$

Example 5.29   A sample of motor spirit (83 octane) has an API gravity of 64. The net heat of combustion of motor spirit (liquid) is determined to be 44 050 kJ/kg at 288.7 K. Calculate the heat of formation of the motor spirit at 25°C (298.15 K).

Solution   *Basis* 1 kg of motor spirit
The carbon to hydrogen mass ratio of petroleum fraction is given by the following formula[23]

$$\frac{C}{H} = \frac{74 + 15G}{26 - 15G} \tag{5.52}$$

where G = specific gravity of petroleum fraction at 288.7 K (15.55°C or 60°F)

$$= \frac{141.5}{(131.5 + 64)} = 0.724 \quad [\text{Ref. Eq. (2.15)}]$$

$$\frac{C}{H} = \frac{74 + 15 \times 0.724}{26 - 15 \times 0.724} = 5.605\ \text{kg/kg}$$

$$\text{Carbon content of motor spirit} = \frac{5.605}{6.605}$$

$$= 0.8486 \text{ kg} \equiv 0.070\ 72 \text{ kmol}$$

$$\text{Hydrogen content of motor spirit} = 1 - 0.8486$$

$$= 0.1514 \text{ kg} \equiv 0.0757 \text{ kmol}$$

$$\text{Oxygen required for complete combustion} = 0.070\ 72 + \left(\frac{0.0757}{2}\right)$$

$$= 0.108\ 57 \text{ kmol}$$

Motor spirit (l)	$+ O_2(g)$	$=$	$CO_2(g)$	$+$	$H_2O(g)$
1 kg	0.10 857 kmol		0.070 72 kmol		0.0757 kmol
ΔH_{f1}^{o}	$\Delta H_{f2}^{o} = 0$		ΔH_{f3}^{o}		ΔH_{f4}^{o}

Assume net heat of combustion at 288.7 K to be same as the heat of reaction at 298.15 K.

$$\Delta H_c^{o} = \Delta H_r^{o}$$
$$= -44\ 050$$
$$= -0.070\ 72 \times 393.51 \times 1000 - 241.82 \times 0.0757 \times 1000 - \Delta H_{fi}^{o}$$
$$\Delta H_{f1}^{o} = +44\ 050 - 27\ 829 - 18\ 306 = -\textbf{2085 kJ/kg}$$

A number of group contribution methods are available for the estimation of the standard heat of formation and the standard heat of combustion of a compound. These methods are summarised in the literature[13]. Among these, the method proposed by Thinh and coworkers[39] is quite accurate for hydrocarbons.

5.12.2   Effect of Temperature on Heat of Formation

As is the case with heat capacity, heat of formation varies with temperature. A generalised equation for calculation of heat of formation at any temperature T in K is

$$\Delta H_f = \Delta H_f^{o} + \int_{298.15}^{T} \Delta C_{mp}^{o}\, dT \qquad (5.53)$$

where ΔC_{mp}^{o} represents the algebraic sum of the heat capacities of the compound and the constituent elements in their standard states using appropriate stoichiometric coefficients (ref. Sec. 4.3). It may be noted that ΔC_{mp}^{o} is not residual heat capacity (C_{mp}^{R}) as defined in Sec. 5.4. While using appropriate ΔC_{mp}^{o} data for elements, care should be exercised in referring to the standard states of these elements. For example, standard state of carbon, sulphur and iodine is solid while that of bromine is liquid and that of hydrogen and chlorine is gas.

As the method represented by Eq. (5.53) is tedious, attempts are made to represent the relation of the heat of formation with the temperature, in a polynomial form.

Yaws et al[40] have presented data for 700 organic compounds in the second-order polynomial form.

$$\Delta H_f = \alpha + \beta T + \gamma T^2 \qquad (5.54)$$

Species specific constants α, β and γ permit direct calculations of the heat of formation at a given temperature. In most cases, the average deviation of correlation and data is claimed to be less than 0.2 kJ/mol.

5.12 ABSOLUTE ENTHALPY

As such, enthalpy has no absolute value. Only change in enthalpy can be calculated. In order to account for variations of ΔH_f° with temperature, a new function ($H^\circ - H_0^\circ + \Delta H_{f0}^\circ$) is developed. In this function, ΔH_{f0}° stands for heat of formation of the compound from its elements at 101.325 kPa ($\approx$ 1 bar) and 0 K ($-$ 273.15°C), H° for enthalpy of the compound at T K, and ΔH_0° for enthalpy of the compound at 0 K ($-$ 273.15°C). As this new function is the enthalpy of the compound over 0 K (the lowest thermodynamic temperature), it is termed as *absolute enthalpy* in this book.

United Catalyst Inc., USA, have reported the value of ($H^\circ - H_0^\circ + \Delta H_{f0}^\circ$) for various compounds[41] at different temperatures. These data are given in Table 5.22. This new function is extremely useful and allows speedy calculations of enthalpy change during any physical and/or chemical process. This is particularly so in cases where chemical reactions cannot be accurately written. For example, in steam–hydrocarbon reforming reactions, the exact extent of individual reactions taking place in the reformer is not easy to be spelled out. However, the product gas stream analysis is solely determined by the chemical equilibrium. Under such circumstances, the initial and final compositions and conditions (such as pressure and temperature) are well known. With the data on ($H^\circ - H_0^\circ + \Delta H_{f0}^\circ$), the enthalpy changes of such reactions can be easily evaluated. The value of ($H^\circ - H_0^\circ + \Delta H_{f0}^\circ$) can also be converted into mean heat capacity data. For such conversions, a reference temperature is required to be fixed, e.g., 25°C (298.15 K). The difference in the values of ($H^\circ - H_0^\circ + \Delta H_{f0}^\circ$) between the desired temperature and base temperature gives the enthalpy change between the two temperatures. When this enthalpy difference is divided by the temperature difference, the mean heat capacity is evaluated. Mean heat capacity data for combustion gases are given in Table 7.14. Example 5.30 will illustrate the method.

Enthalpy values of various compounds are extensively tabulated in literature at different pressures and temperatures. These data permit calculations of enthalpy changes of processes involving changes in pressure.

($H^\circ - H_0^\circ$) is called (differential) enthalpy above 0 K ($-$ 273.15°C) which can be calculated using ΔC_{mp}° data valid up to 0 K ($-$ 273.15°C), considering ideal gas. However, for evaluation of this function at different pressure and temperature, a generalised correlation based on 3-parameter corresponding states principle is presented by Lee and Kesler[12]. For use of this procedure, the reader is advised to refer the original article or Ref. 3.

Table 5.22 Absolute Enthalpy of Gases in Ideal State Conditions[41]

Temperature		Absolute enthalpy ($H^\circ - H_0^\circ + \Delta H_{f0}^\circ$), kJ/kmol			
K	°C	Nitrogen N_2	Oxygen O_2	Hydrogen H_2	Carbon monoxide CO
273.15	0.00	7 905	7 878	7 683	$-$ 105 978
298.15	25.00	8 613	8 597	8 407	$-$ 105 271

(Contd.)

Table 5.22 (Contd.)

Temperature		Absolute enthalpy $(H° - H_0° + \Delta H_{f0}°)$, kJ/kmol			
K	°C	Nitrogen N_2	Oxygen O_2	Hydrogen H_2	Carbon monoxide CO
400.00	126.85	11 541	11 603	11 363	− 102 340
500.00	226.85	14 479	14 666	14 272	− 99 387
600.00	326.85	17 478	17 830	17 194	− 96 361
700.00	426.85	20 537	21 086	20 131	− 93 267
800.00	526.85	23 656	24 423	23 088	− 90 107
900.00	626.85	26 833	27 833	26 070	− 86 885
1000.00	726.85	30 066	31 305	29 079	− 83 603
1100.00	826.85	33 355	34 830	32 119	− 80 265
1200.00	926.85	36 699	38 399	35 196	− 76 874
1300.00	1026.85	40 096	42 003	38 313	− 73 433
1400.00	1126.85	43 545	45 630	41 473	− 69 946
1500.00	1226.85	47 045	49 273	44 681	− 66 415

Temperature		Absolute enthalpy $(H° - H_0° + \Delta H_{f0}°)$, kJ/kmol			
K	°C	Carbon dioxide CO_2	Water H_2O	Sulphur dioxide SO_2	Sulphur trioxide SO_3
273.15	0.00	− 385 097	− 230 070	− 348 938	− 444 062
298.15	25.00	− 384 158	− 229 252	− 347 992	− 442 759
400.00	126.85	− 380 118	− 225 843	− 343 911	− 437 046
500.00	226.85	− 375 835	− 222 379	− 339 575	− 430 849
600.00	326.85	− 371 268	− 218 799	− 334 953	− 424 131
700.00	426.85	− 366 448	− 215 101	− 330 082	− 416 950
800.00	526.85	− 361 405	− 211 284	− 325 000	− 409 365
900.00	626.85	− 356 167	− 207 346	− 319 746	− 401 437
1000.00	726.85	− 350 766	− 203 286	− 314 357	− 393 224
1100.00	826.85	− 345 231	− 199 103	− 308 873	− 384 785
1200.00	926.85	− 339 593	− 194 796	− 303 331	− 376 180
1300.00	1026.85	− 333 880	− 190 363	− 297 769	− 367 469
1400.00	1126.85	− 328 122	− 185 802	− 292 225	− 358 710
1500.00	1226.85	− 322 351	− 181 113	− 286 738	− 349 962

Temperature		Absolute enthalpy $(H° - H_0° + \Delta H_{f0}°)$, kJ/kmol			
K	°C	Ammonia NH_3	Nitrous oxide N_2O	Nitric oxide NO	Nitrogen dioxide NO_2
273.15	0.00	− 29 616	93 524	98 322	45 856
298.15	25.00	− 28 751	94 505	99 044	46 779
400.00	126.85	− 24 997	98 699	102 042	50 751
500.00	226.85	− 20 962	103 117	105 067	54 954
600.00	326.85	− 16 599	107 817	108 170	59 426
700.00	426.85	− 11.925	112 784	111 345	64 136
800.00	526.85	− 6 958	118 003	114 589	69 054

(Contd.)

Table 5.22 (Contd.)

Temperature		Absolute enthalpy $(H^\circ - H_0^\circ + \Delta H_{f0}^\circ)$, kJ/kmol			
K	°C	Ammonia	Nitrous oxide	Nitric oxide	Nitrogen dioxide
		NH_3	N_2O	NO	NO_2
900.00	626.85	− 1 713	123 459	117 897	74 149
1000.00	726.85	3 792	129 138	121 265	79 389
1100.00	826.85	9 539	135 025	124 688	84 744
1200.00	926.85	15 512	141 105	128 163	90 183
1300.00	1026.85	21 693	147 363	131 686	95 675
1400.00	1126.85	28 066	153 784	135 251	101 190
1500.00	1226.85	34 613	160 354	138 854	106 695

Temperature		Absolute enthalpy $(H^\circ - H_0^\circ + \Delta H_{f0}^\circ)$, kJ/kmol			
K	°C	Hydrogen sulphide	Carbon disulphide	Methane	Ethane
		H_2S	CS_2	CH_4	C_2H_6
273.15	0.00	− 72.670	− 5 844	− 57 770	− 58 620
298.15	25.00	− 71 852	− 4 644	− 56 960	− 57 348
400.00	126.85	− 68 387	378	− 53 206	− 51 315
500.00	226.85	− 64 785	5 509	− 48 845	− 44 137
600.00	326.85	− 60 993	10 818	− 43 863	− 35 813
700.00	426.85	− 57 021	16 286	− 38 305	− 26 441
800.00	526.85	− 52 877	21 893	− 32 219	− 16 115
900.00	626.85	− 48 571	27 620	− 25 650	− 4 934
1000.00	726.85	− 44 111	33 449	− 18 646	7 006
1100.00	826.85	− 39 507	39 358	− 11 252	19 608
1200.00	926.85	− 34 768	45 330	− 3 516	32 775
1300.00	1026.85	− 29 902	51 345	4 517	46 412
1400.00	1126.85	− 24 920	57 383	12 800	60 421
1500.00	1226.85	− 19 829	63 425	21 286	74 705

Temperature		Absolute enthalpy $(H^\circ - H_0^\circ + \Delta H_{f0}^\circ)$, kJ/kmol			
K	°C	Propane C_3H_8	n-Butane $n\text{-}C_4H_{10}$	i-Butane $i\text{-}C_4H_{10}$	n-Pentane $n\text{-}C_5H_{12}$
273.15	0.00	− 68 896	− 80 996	− 87 877	− 93 812
298.15	25.00	− 67 080	− 78 546	− 85 450	− 90 834
400.00	126.85	− 58 434	− 67 003	− 73 961	− 76 755
500.00	226.85	− 48 114	− 53 376	− 60 326	− 60 069
600.00	326.85	− 36 133	− 37 666	− 44 563	− 40 790
700.00	426.85	− 22 644	− 20 062	− 26 871	− 19 161
800.00	526.85	− 7 800	− 756	− 7 452	4 577
900.00	626.85	8 247	20 065	− 13 494	30 183
1000.00	726.85	25 345	42 210	35 764	57 415
1100.00	826.85	43 339	65 489	59 160	86 030
1200.00	926.85	62 078	89 713	83 479	115 789
1300.00	1026.85	81 409	114 693	108 520	146 448
1400.00	1126.85	101 179	140 237	134 083	177 766
1500.00	1226.85	121 235	166 158	159 966	209 502

(Contd.)

Table 5.22 (Contd.)

Temperature		Absolute enthalpy ($H^\circ - H_0^\circ + \Delta H_{f0}^\circ$), kJ/kmol			
K	°C	Ethylene C_2H_4	Propylene C_3H_6	Butadiene 1,2 C_4H_6	Butadiene 1,3 C_4H_6
273.15	0.00	70 158	47 246	189 852	139 270
298.15	25.00	71 239	48 818	191 780	141 345
400.00	126.85	76 268	56 205	200 816	150 892
500.00	226.85	82 119	64 906	211 401	161 862
600.00	326.85	88 800	74 922	223 499	174 267
700.00	426.85	96 235	86 134	236 930	187 962
800.00	526.85	104 348	98 424	251 513	202 802
900.00	626.85	113 066	111 673	267 067	218 641
1000.00	726.85	122 311	125 763	203 410	235 333
1100.00	826.85	132 010	140 575	283 410	252 734
1200.00	926.85	142 085	155 990	300 362	270 698
1300.00	1026.85	152 463	171 891		289 079
1400.00	1126.85	163 068	188 157		307 732
1500.00	1226.85	173 824	204 672		326 511

Temperature		Absolute enthalpy ($H^\circ - H_0^\circ + \Delta H_{f0}^\circ$), kJ/kmol			
K	°C	Acetylene C_2H_2	Methanol CH_3OH	Ethanol C_2H_5OH	n-Propanol C_3H_7OH
273.15	0.00	236 213	− 180 149	− 205 628	− 216 632
298.15	25.00	237 351	− 179 072	− 203 811	− 214 323
400.00	126.85	242 241	− 174 130	− 195 536	− 203 604
500.00	226.85	247 422	− 168 462	− 186 129	− 191 160
600.00	326.85	252 947	− 162 049	− 175 553	− 176 986
700.00	426.85	258 786	− 154 954	− 163 915	− 161 254
800.00	526.85	264 910	− 147 240	− 151 315	− 144 133
900.00	626.85	271 288	− 138 971	− 137 859	− 125 795
1000.00	726.85	277 890	− 130 210	− 123 649	− 106 411
1100.00	826.85	284 685		− 108 789	− 86 150
1200.00	926.85	291 645		− 93 383	− 65 185
1300.00	1026.85	298 738		− 77 534	− 43 686
1400.00	1126.85	305 934		− 61 346	− 21 823
1500.00	1226.85	313 203		− 44 922	

Temperature		Absolute enthalpy ($H^\circ - H_0^\circ + \Delta H_{f0}^\circ$), kJ/kmol			
K	°C	i-Propanol C_3H_7OH	Formaldehyde HCHO	Acetaldehyde CH_3CHO	Acetone CH_3COCH_3
273.15	0.00	− 235 063	− 103 023	− 144 129	− 186 057
298.15	25.00	− 232 733	− 102 193	− 142 835	− 184 142
400.00	126.85	− 221 954	− 98 477	− 136 775	− 175 268
500.00	226.85	− 209.484	− 94 336	− 129 683	− 164 984
600.00	326.85	− 195 310	− 89 742	− 121 580	− 153 279
700.00	426.85	− 179 595	− 84 732	− 112 581	− 140 285
800.00	526.85	− 162 502	− 79 343	− 102 805	− 126 136

(Contd.)

Table 5.22   (Contd.)

Temperature		Absolute enthalpy $(H° - H_0^o + \Delta H_{f0}^o)$, kJ/kmol			
K	°C	*i*-Propanol C_3H_7OH	Formaldehyde HCHO	Acetaldehyde CH_3CHO	Acetone CH_3COCH_3
900.00	626.85	− 144 195	− 73 611	− 92 369	− 110 965
1000.00	726.85	− 124 837	− 67 572	− 81 391	− 94 905
1100.00	826.85	− 104 591	− 61 264		− 78 091
1200.00	926.85	− 83 620	− 54 721		− 60 655
1300.00	1026.85	− 62 088	− 47 981		− 42 731
1400.00	1126.85	− 40 158	− 41 081		− 24 452
1500.00	1226.85	− 17 993	− 34 056		− 5 951

Temperature		Absolute enthalpy $(H° - H_0^o + \Delta H_{f0}^o)$, kJ/kmol			
K	°C	Benzene C_6H_6	Toluene C_7H_8	Ethyl benzene C_8H_{10}	Styrene C_8H_8
273.15	0.00	112 278	88 263	76 827	186 280
298.15	25.00	114 397	90 912	80 119	189 398
400.00	126.85	124 642	103 665	95 830	204 143
500.00	226.85	137 046	119.052	114 612	221 605
600.00	326.85	151 546	137 007	136 405	241 749
700.00	426.85	167 919	157 265	160 899	264 299
800.00	526.85	185 938	179 558	187 781	288 982
900.00	626.85	205 380	203 618	216 741	315 524
1000.00	726.85	226 019	229 179	247 466	343 649
1100.00	826.85	247 630	225 972	279 645	373 084
1200.00	926.85	269 990	283 731	312 967	403 554
1300.00	1026.85	292 872	312 189	347 120	434 786
1400.00	1126.85	316 052	341 077	381 793	466 504
1500.00	1226.85	339 306	370 129	416 674	498 434

(Reproduced with the permission of United Catalysts Inc., USA)

Example 5.30   The values of $(H° - H_0^o + \Delta H_{f0}^o)$ are listed in Table 5.22 for styrene at 298.15 K (25°C) and 600 K (327°C). Calculate the mean heat capacity between the two temperatures.

Solution   *Basis* 1 kmol of styrene
Enthalpy change between 298.15 K and 600 K = 241 749 − 189 398 = 52 351 kJ/mol

$$C_{mpn}^o = \frac{52\ 351}{(600 - 298.15)} = \textbf{173.4 kJ/(kmol · K)}$$

5.13   **STANDARD HEAT OF REACTION**

An understanding of the heat of formation enables one to evaluate the standard heat of a chemical reaction at 25°C (298.15 K). Consider the reaction between A and B to produce C and D.

$$n_a A + n_b B = n_c C + n_d D \qquad (5.55)$$

where n_a, n_b, n_c, and n_d are number of moles of A, B, C and D respectively. For this reaction, the standard heat of reaction, ΔH_r^o is defined as

ΔH_r^o = Enthalpy of products − enthalpy of reactants

$= \Sigma(n_i \cdot \Delta H_f^o)_{\text{Products}} - \Sigma(n_i \cdot \Delta H_f^o)_{\text{Reactants}}$

$= n_c \cdot \Delta H_{fC}^o + n_d \cdot \Delta H_{fD}^o - n_a \cdot \Delta H_{fA}^o - n_b \cdot \Delta H_{fB}^o \qquad (5.56)$

where ΔH_{fi}^o is the standard heat of formation of the ith component. If the values of ΔH_{fi}^o are used at some other temperature (but all values at one particular temperature only), ΔH_r will be available at the corresponding temperature. In general,

$$\Delta H_r = \Sigma(n_i \cdot \Delta H_{fi})_{\text{Products}} - \Sigma(n_i \cdot \Delta H_{fi})_{\text{Reactants}} \qquad (5.57)$$

When ΔH_r is positive, the reaction is said to be endothermic, i.e., it absorbs heat during the course of reaction and, if ΔH_r is negative, the reaction is termed as exothermic, i.e., heat will be evolved during the course of the reaction.

Enthalpy is known to be a state function. Hence change in enthalpy taking place while going from one state to another final state is independent of the pathway. This principle is known as *Hess's law* and can be stated as '*In going from a particular set of reactants to a particular set of products, the change in enthalpy is same whether the reaction takes place in one step or in a series of steps*'. In other words, heat of reaction of an overall reaction involving a set of reactants to specific set of products is independent of number of reactions that determine the overall reaction.

Consider the reforming reaction (1).

$CH_4(g) + 2 H_2O(g) = CO_2(g) + 4 H_2(g) \qquad \Delta H_r^o = + 164.65$ kJ/mol

This reaction can be split in the following two reactions.

$CH_4(g) + H_2O(g) = CO(g) + 3 H_2(g) \qquad$ (2) $\quad \Delta H_r^o = + 205.81$ kJ/mol

$\underline{CO(g) + H_2O(g) = CO_2(g) + H_2(g) \qquad \text{(3)} \quad \Delta H_r^o = -41.16 \text{ kJ/mol}}$

$CH_4(g) + 2 H_2O(g) = CO_2(g) + 4 H_2(g)$

Heat of reaction of overall reaction (1)

= + 205.81 − 41.16

= + 164.65 kJ/ mol CH_4, which proves Hess's law.

The schematic representation of Hess's law is given in Fig. 5.13.

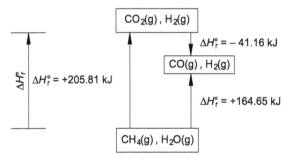

Fig. 5.13   Schematic Representation of Hess's Law

In Example 5.26, Standard heat of formation of ethylene was calculated using standard heats of combustion, described in three reactions. This is yet another illustration of Hess's law.

Example 5.31 In the production of sulphuric acid from anhydrite, gypsum is roasted with clay to obtain sulphur dioxide and cement clinker. The reaction proceeds as follows.

$$3 \, CaSO_4(s) + SiO_2(s) = 3 \, CaO \cdot SiO_2(g) + 3 \, SO_2(g) + (3/2) \, O_2(g)$$

Calculate the heat of reaction at 25°C (298.15 K).

Solution *Basis* 1 mol of $SiO_{2(s)}$ reacted

Table 5.23 Thermodynamic Data

Component	Phase	ΔH_f° at 25°C (298.15 K) kJ/mol
$CaSO_4$	Solid	− 1432.7
SiO_2	Solid (amorphous)	− 903.5
3 $CaO.SiO_2$	Solid (clinker)	− 2879.0
SO_2	Gas	− 296.81
O_2	Gas	0.0

Standard heat of reaction at 298.15 K,

$$\Delta H_f^\circ = \Sigma(n_i \cdot \Delta H_f^\circ)_{Products} - \Sigma(n_i \cdot \Delta H_f^\circ)_{Reactants}$$

$$= \left[-2879.0 + 3\,(-296.81) + \left(\frac{3}{2}\right) \times 0 \right] - [3\,(-1432.7) + 1\,(-903.5)]$$

$$= (- 2879.0 - 890.43) - (-4298.1 - 903.5)$$

$$= 1432.17 \text{ kJ/mol } SiO_2 \equiv 477.39 \text{ kJ/mol } CaSO_4$$

Since ΔH_r° is positive, the reaction is highly endothermic.

Example 5.32 Calculate the standard heat of reaction at 25°C (298.15 K) when gaseous ammonia is dissolved in water to form 2% by mass of its solution for the regeneration of weak anion exchanger of a water treatment plant.

Solution *Basis* 100 kg of 2% ammonia solution
In the solution, 2 kg ammonia (as NH_3) and 98 kg water are present. However, the ammonia is usually present as NH_4OH.

$$NH_3(g) + H_2O(l) = NH_4OH(l)$$

Using data given in Appendix V.1,

$$\Delta H_r^\circ = -361.20 - (- 45.94 - 285.83)$$

$$= -361.20 + 331.77 = - 29.43 \text{ kJ/mol } NH_3 \text{ dissolved}$$

Since ΔH_r° is negative, the dissolution is exothermic.

$$\text{Ammonia present in the solution} = \frac{2}{17.0305} \text{ kmol}$$

$$\text{Heat of dissolution} = \frac{29.43 \times 2 \times 1000}{17.0305}$$

$$= \frac{3456.1 \text{ kJ}}{100 \text{ kg solution}} \text{ at 298.15 K}$$

5.13.1 Effect of Temperature on Heat of Reaction

In Examples 5.31 and 5.32, the heat of reaction is calculated at 25°C (298.15 K) using the data on the standard heat of formation. However, in actual practice, reactants and products are at temperatures other than 25°C (298.15 K). When the heat balance is to be made with reactants and products at 1 bar a pressure but at temperatures other than 25°C (298.15 K), the following procedure is recommended (Fig. 5.14).

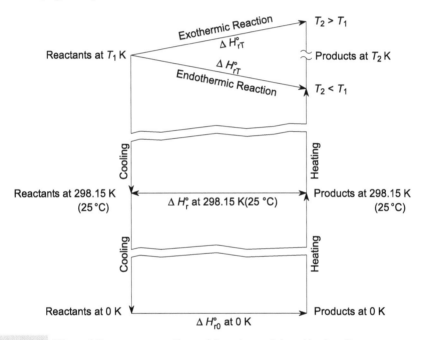

Fig. 5.14 Effect of Temperature on Heat of Reaction at 1 bar Absolute Pressure

Consider again the reaction,

$$n_a \text{ A} + n_b \text{ B} = n_c \text{ C} + n_d \text{ D} \qquad (5.55)$$

There can be two possibilities. In one case, both the reactants and products are at T K, while in another case both are at different temperatures, say the reactants enter the reactor at T_1 K while products leave it at T_2 K. In either case, the method of calculation is essentially the same.

Step 1 Assume that reactants are cooled to 25°C (298.15 K). Calculate the enthalpy of (ΔH_1) of reactants at T_1 K over 25°C (298.15 K).

Step 2 Calculate the standard heat of reaction (ΔH_r^o) using data given in Appendix V. If more than one reaction is taking place, the standard heat of reaction for each of them should be calculated and summed up algebraically.

Step 3 Assume that products are heated from 25°C (298.15 K) to temperature T_2 K. Calculate the enthalpy (ΔH_r^o) of products at T_2 K over 25°C (298.15 K).

The *algebraic* sum of enthalpies of all the three steps yield the heat balance, as enthalpies are point (state) functions.

Case (a): $T_1 = T_2 = T$

For this case, the heat balance yields the heat of reaction at T K. It is possible to develop an empirical relation for the heat of reaction at T K using the empirical equation for heat capacity as described below.

$$\Delta H_1 = \int_{T_0}^{T_1} (\Sigma\, n_i \cdot C_{mpi}^o)_{\text{Reactants}}\, dT \tag{5.58}$$

$$\Delta H_2 = \int_{T_0}^{T_2} (\Sigma\, n_i \cdot C_{mpi}^o)_{\text{Products}}\, dT \tag{5.59}$$

Now at constant pressure (at 1 bar),

$$\Delta H_{rT}^o = \Delta H_r^o - \Delta H_1 + \Delta H_2 \tag{5.60}$$

where ΔH_{rT}^o is the heat of reaction at reference temperature.

$$\Delta H_2 - \Delta H_1 = \int_{T_0}^{T_2} (\Sigma\, n_i \cdot C_{mpi}^o)_{\text{Products}}\, dT - \int_{T_0}^{T_1} (\Sigma\, n_i \cdot C_{mpi}^o)_{\text{Reactants}}\, dT \tag{5.61}$$

When $T_1 = T_2 = 298.15$ K and $T_0 = 0$ K, (refer Fig. 5.14)

ΔH_{r0}^o = Standard heat of reaction at 0 K

$\quad = \Delta H_r^o + (\Delta H_2 - \Delta H_1)$ (based on Eq. (5.60))

$$= \Delta H_r^o + \int_{298.15}^{0} (\Delta a + \Delta b\, T + \Delta c\, T^2 + \Delta d\, T^3)\, dT \tag{5.62}$$

Where $\Delta a = \Sigma v_i\, a_i$, $\Delta b = \Sigma v_i\, b_i$, $\Delta c = \Sigma v_i\, c_i$ and $\Delta d = \Sigma v_i\, d_i$, v_i is a stoichiometric number of reaction component i and it is positive for product and negative for reactant.

When $T_0 = 0$ K and $T_1 = T_2 = T$,

$$\Delta H_{rT}^o = \Delta H_{r0}^o + \int_{0}^{T} (\Delta a + \Delta b\, T + \Delta c\, T^2 + \Delta d\, T^3)\, dT$$

or $$\Delta H_{rT}^o = \Delta H_{r0}^o + \Delta a + \left(\frac{\Delta b}{2}\right) T^2 + \left(\frac{\Delta c}{3}\right) T^3 + \left(\frac{\Delta d}{4}\right) T^4 \tag{5.63}$$

Equations (5.58) to (5.62) are entirely general and can be used for any chemical reaction (in ideal state). For finding ΔH_r^o use data of the standard heat of formation [Appendix V] and substitute in Eq. (5.56). Care must be taken to use correct data, taking into account phase changes, if any.

Example 5.33 Obtain an expression relating the heat of reaction and the temperature of the reaction

$$SO_2(g) + (1/2) O_2(g) = SO_3(g)$$

Using the same expression, calculate the heat of reaction at 502°C (775 K).

Solution *Basis* 1 kmol of SO_2 reacted

$\Delta a = 22.036 - 24.771 - 0.5(26.026) = -15.748$

$\Delta b \times 10^3 = 121.624 - 62.948 - 0.5(11.755) = 52.799$

$\Delta c \times 10^6 = -91.867 - (-44.258) - 0.5(-2.343) = -46.438$

$\Delta d \times 10^9 = 24.369 - 11.122 - 0.5(-0.562) = 13.528$

$\Delta H_r^0 = -395\ 720 - (-296\ 810) = -98\ 910$ kJ/kmol

$$\Delta H_{r0}^0 = \Delta H_r^0 + \int_{298.15}^{0} (-15.748 + 52.799 \times 10^{-3}\ T - 46.438 \times 10^{-6}\ T^2$$

$$+ 13.528 \times 10^{-9}\ T^3)\ dT$$

$$= -98\ 910 + 15.748 \times 298.15 - 52.799 \times 10^{-3}\ \frac{(298.15)^2}{2} + 46.438$$

$$\times 10^{-6}\ \frac{(298.15)^3}{3} - 13.528 \times 10^{-9}\ \frac{(298.15)^4}{4}$$

$$= -98\ 910 + 4695 - 2347 + 410 - 27 = -\mathbf{96\ 179\ kJ/kmol}$$

$\Delta H_{rT} = 96\ 179 - 15.748\ T + 26.4 \times 10^{-3}\ T^2 - 15.48 \times 10^{-6}\ T^3 + 3.382 \times 10^{-9}\ T^4$

Substituting $T = 778.15$ K

$\Delta H_r = -96\ 179 - 12\ 254 + 15\ 985 - 7293 + 1240 = \mathbf{-98\ 501\ kJ/kmol}$

Example 5.34 Acetic acid is esterified in the liquid phase with ethanol at 100°C (373 K) and atmospheric pressure to produce ethyl acetate and water.

$$CH_3COOH(l) + C_2H_5OH(l) = CH_3COOC_2H_5(l) + H_2O(l)$$

(a) Calculate the heat of reaction at 100°C (373 K) using heat capacity of reactants and products at mean temperature.

Table 5.24 Mean Heat Capacity Data

Component	Mean heat capacity, C_{lmi} at 62.5°C (335.65 K), kJ/(kmol · K)
Ethylacetate	146.89
Water	75.76
Ethanol	119.55
Acetic acid	129.70

(b) Develop an expression of calculation of heat capacity equation constants, given in Table 5.3 as a function of temperature.

Solution In this reaction, all stoichiometric coefficients (v_i) are unity.

$$\Delta H_r^o = \Sigma(v_i \cdot \Delta H_{fi}^o)_{\text{Products}} - \Sigma(v_i \cdot \Delta H_{fi}^o)_{\text{Reactants}}$$

$$= -480 - 285.83 + 277.2 + 484.2$$

$$= -4.43 \text{ kJ/mol reactants (exothermic)}$$

$$\Delta H_{rT}^o = \Delta H_{rT} = \Delta H_r^o + (\Sigma(v_i \cdot C_{\text{lm}i})_{\text{Products}} - \Sigma(v_i \cdot C_{\text{lm}i})_{\text{Reactions}}) (373.15 - 298.15)$$

$$= -4.43 \times 1000 + [146.89 + 75.76 - 119.55 - 129.70] (75)$$

$$= -6425 \text{ kJ/kmol}$$

$$\equiv -6.425 \text{ kJ/mol reactant at } 100^{\circ}\text{C (373 K)}$$

$$\Delta H_r = \Delta H_{r0}^o + \Delta a\,T + \frac{\Delta b}{2}\,T^2 + \frac{\Delta c}{3}\,T^3 + \frac{\Delta d}{4}\,T^4$$

From Table 5.3,

$$\Delta a = 4.2905 + 50.845 - 100.92 - 155.48 = -201.2645$$

$$\Delta b \times 10^3 = 934.378 + 213.08 - [-111.83\ 86 - 326.5951] = 1585.8917$$

$$\Delta c \times 10^6 = -2640.0 - 631.398 - 498.54 - 744.199 = -4514.137$$

$$\Delta d \times 10^9 = 3342.58 + 648.746 - 0 - 0 = 3991.326$$

$$\Delta H_{r0} = \Delta H_r^o + \int\limits_{298.15}^{0} (\Delta a + \Delta b \times 10^3\,T + \Delta c \times 10^6\,T^2 + \Delta d \times 10^9\,T^3)\,dT$$

$$= -4.43 \times 1000 - 201.2645\,(0 - 298.15) + 1585.897 \times 10^{-3}\,(0 - 298.15^2)/2$$
$$-4514.137 \times 10^{-6}\,(0 - 298.15^3)/3 + 3991.326 \times 10^{-9}\,(0 - 298.15^4)/4$$

$$= 17\ 084.4 \text{ kJ/kmol}$$

$$\Delta H_{rT} = 17\ 084.4 - 201.2645\,T + 792.949 \times 10^{-3}\,T^2 - 1504.712 \times 10^{-6}\,T^3$$
$$+ 997.832 \times 10^{-9}\,T^4$$

For $T = 373.15$ K

$$\Delta H_{rT} = 17\ 084.4 - 75\ 101.8 + 110\ 410.9 - 78\ 181.5 + 19\ 346$$

$$= -6442 \text{ kJ/kmol} \equiv -6.442 \text{ kJ/mol reactant}$$

Note For liquids, it can be concluded that if the reaction temperature is not very far from 25°C (298.15 K), use of mean heat capacity values of liquids provide sufficiently accurate result of heat of reaction.

Case (b): $T_1 \neq T_2$ For this case, the heat balance calculations are best illustrated by the following example.

Example 5.35 In Table 5.25, the compositions of the incoming and outgoing gas mixtures to and from a converter are given. Assume that the sulphur burner gases enter the converter at 800 K (527°C) and the outgoing gases leave it at 875 K (602°C). Intercoolers are installed in the catalyst beds of the converter.

Table 5.25 Composition of Converter Gases

Components	Inlet gas, kmol/h	Outlet gas, kmol/h
SO_2	8.851	0.351
O_2	13.200	8.950
SO_3	0.984	9.484
N_2	102.400	102.400
Total	125.435	121.185

Calculate the heat transfer taking place in the intercoolers, using (a) heat capacity data, and (b) the data of $(H° - H_0° + \Delta H_{f0}°)$ from Table 5.22.

Solution   *Basis* 125.435 kmol/h of inlet gas mixture (n_1)

Table 5.26   Heat Capacity Equation Constants for Incoming Gas Mixture

Component	$\dot{n}_i$ kmol/h	$a_i \cdot n_i$	$b_i \cdot n_i \times 10^3$	$c_i \cdot n_i \times 10^6$	$d_i \cdot n_i \times 10^9$
SO_2	8.851	219.245	557.154	− 391.729	98.441
O_2	13.200	343.539	155.167	− 30.922	− 7.422
SO_3	0.948	21.685	119.678	− 90.397	23.997
N_2	102.400	3030.108	− 526.438	1349.929	− 508.723
Total	125.435	3614.577	305.561	836.881	− 393.707

Enthalpy of ingoing gas mixture at 800 K over 298.15 K,

$$\phi_1 = 3614.577 \, (800 - 298.15) + 305.561 \times 10^{-3} \, \frac{(800^2 - 298.15^2)}{2} + 836.881$$

$$\times 10^{-6} \, \frac{(800^3 - 298.15^3)}{3} - 393.707 \times 10^{-9} \, \frac{(800^4 - 298.15^4)}{4}$$

$$= 1813\,976 + 84\,198 + 135\,434 - 39\,538 = 1994\,070 \text{ kJ/h} \equiv 553.91 \text{ kW}$$

Table 5.27   Heat Capacity Equation Constants for Outgoing Gas Mixture

Component	$\dot{n}_i$ kmol/h	$a_i \cdot n_i$	$b_i \cdot n_i \times 10^3$	$c_i \cdot n_i \times 10^6$	$d_i \cdot n_i \times 10^9$
SO_2	0.351	8.694	22.095	− 15.535	3.904
O_2	8.950	232.930	105.208	− 20.966	− 5.033
SO_3	9.484	209.005	1153.482	− 871.269	231.117
N_2	102.400	3030.108	− 526.438	1349.929	− 508.723
Total	121.185	3480.737	754.347	442.159	− 278.735

Enthalpy of outgoing gas mixture at 875 K over 298.15 K,

$$\phi_2 = 3480.737 \, (875 - 298.15) + 754.347 \times 10^{-3} \frac{(875^2 - 298.15^2)}{2}$$
$$+ 442.159 \times 10^{-6}$$

$$\frac{(875^3 - 298.15^3)}{3} - 278.735 \times 10^{-9} \frac{(875^4 - 298.15^4)}{4}$$

$$= 2007\,863 + 255\,245 + 94\,831 - 40\,297$$
$$= 2317\,642 \text{ kJ/h} \equiv 643.79 \text{ kW}$$

$\Delta H_r° = -98\,910$ kJ/kmol SO_2 reacted (Ref. Example 5.33)

Total heat of reaction at 298.15 K,

$$\phi_3 = \dot{n}_{SO_2} \, (\text{reacted}) \times \Delta H_r°$$

$$= (8.8511 - 0.351) \, \frac{(-98\,910)}{3600} = - 233.54 \text{ kW}$$

Net enthalpy change = $\phi_2 + \phi_3 - \phi_1$
$$= 643.79 - 233.54 - 553.91 = -143.66 \text{ kW (exothermic)}$$

Thus, during the reaction, enthalpy equivalent to 143.66 kW is to be removed from the system in order to maintain the temperature of the outgoing gas mixture at 875 K (602°C).

Table 5.28 Absolute Enthalpy Data

Com-ponent	Ingoing gas mixture mixture at 800 K		Outgoing gas mixture at 875 K	
	$\dot{n}_i$ kmol/h	$n_i \cdot (H^\circ - H_0^\circ + \Delta H_{f0}^\circ)$ kW	$\dot{n}_i$ kmol/h	$\dot{n}_i \cdot (H^\circ - H_0^\circ + \Delta H_{f0}^\circ)$ kW
SO_2	8.851	-799.05	0.351	-31.30
O_2	13.200	89.55	8.950	67.08
SO_3	0.984	-111.89	9.484	-1067.78
N_2	102.400	672.88	102.400	740.66
Total	125.435	-148.51	121.185	-286.35

Enthalpy change = $-286.34 - (-148.51) = -137.83 \text{ kW}$
Error between two answers is 4.23%.

Example 5.36 Refer Example 4.4. Assume that the moisture in ingoing ambient air is 0.015 kg/kg dry air. The mixture of ethanol–air is fed to the reactor at 62°C (335 K). Make enthalpy balance across the reactor.

Solution *Basis* 100 kmol outgoing gas mixture from scrubber
Moisture entering with ambient air = $3127.7 \times 0.015 = 46.92$ kg $\equiv 2.61$ kmol
Total water in the reactor effluent = $40.2 + 2.61 = 42.81$ kmol

$$\Delta H_r = \Sigma n_i \cdot (H^\circ - H_0^\circ + \Delta H_{f0}^\circ)_{\text{Products}} - \Sigma n_i \cdot (H^\circ - H_0^\circ + \Delta H_{f0}^\circ)_{\text{Reactants}}$$

Table 5.29 Enthalpy of Reactants at 62°C (335 K)

Component	n_i kmol	$(H^\circ - H_0^\circ + \Delta H_{f0}^\circ)$, kJ/kmol	$n_i \cdot (H^\circ - H_0^\circ + \Delta H_{f0}^\circ)$ kJ
C_2H_5OH	135.99	$-200\ 817$	$-27\ 309\ 104$
N_2	85.2	$9\ 672$	$824\ 054$
O_2	22.65	$9\ 685$	$218\ 881$
H_2O	2.61	$-224\ 977$	$-587\ 190$
Total	246.45		$-26\ 853\ 359$

Table 5.30 Enthalpy of Products at 447°C (720 K)

Component	n_i kmol	$(H^\circ - H_0^\circ + \Delta H_{f0}^\circ)$, kJ/kmol	$n_i \cdot (H^\circ - H_0^\circ + \Delta H_{f0}^\circ)$ kJ
C_2H_5OH	89.09	$-161\ 395$	$-14\ 378\ 681$
N_2	85.2	$21\ 161$	$1\ 802\ 900$
O_2	2.1	$21\ 753$	$45\ 682$
CO_2	0.7	$-365\ 439$	$-255\ 808$

(Contd.)

Table 5.30   (Contd.)

Component	n_i kmol	$(H° - H°_0 + \Delta H°_{f0})$, kJ/kmol	$n_i \cdot (H° - H°_0 + \Delta H°_{f0})$ kJ
CO	2.3	$-$ 92 635	$-$ 213 061
H_2	7.1	20 722	147 129
CH_4	2.6	$-$ 37 088	$-$ 96 428
CH_3CHO	44.1	$-$ 110 626	$-$ 4 878 598
H_2O	42.81	$-$ 214 338	$-$ 9 175 793
Total	276.00		$-$ 27 002 658

From Tables 5.29 and 5.30,

Net heat of reaction, ΔH_R = -27 002 658 $-$ (-26 853 359) = -149 299 kJ

$\equiv$ 605.8 kJ/kmol total reactants (exothermic)

$\equiv$ **3183.3 kJ/kmol C_2H_5OH reacted (exothermic)**

Note   The net heat of reaction (exothermic) is quite small and it can be attributed to heat losses from the system. Hence, the reaction can be termed as near isenthalpic or adiabatic.

Example 5.37   Refer Example 4.10. Make heat balance of the system and calculate saturated steam generation at 6 bar a assuming that the boiler is fed with water at 30°C (303 K). Also assume constant molar heat capacity (at constant pressure) as 65.1 and 48.2 kJ/(kmol · K) for gaseous dimethyl ether and formaldehyde, respectively. If the Dowtherm circuit operates at atmospheric pressure, calculate its circulation rate.

Solution   Calculate standard heat of reaction using standard heat of formation (Appendix-V) for all five reactions.

$\Delta H°_{r1}$ = $-241.82 - 108.6 - (-200.94)$ = -149.48 kJ/mol CH_3OH

$\Delta H°_{r2}$ = $-393.51 - 241.82 - (-200.94)$ = -434.39 kJ/mol CH_3OH

$\Delta H°_{r3}$ = $-110.53 - (-200.94)$ = $+90.41$ kJ/mol CH_3OH

$\Delta H°_{r4}$ = $-74.52 - (-200.94)$ = $+126.42$ kJ/mol CH_3OH

$\Delta H°_{r5}$ = $-184.0 - 241.82 - (-2 \times 200.94)$

= -23.94 kJ/2 mol $CH_3OH \equiv -11.97$ kJ/mol CH_3OH

Total heat of reaction at 298.15 K,

$\Delta H°_r$ = 111.375 (-149 480) + 8.786 ($-$ 434 390) + 0.99 ($+99$ 410) + 0.610 ($+126$ 420) + 1.98 (-11 970)

= -20 313 054 kJ/h $\equiv -5642.52$ kW (exothermic)

For evaluation of enthalpy of ingoing gas mixture to the reactor, heat capacity data are tabulated below.

Table 5.31   Heat Capacity Data of Reactor Inlet Gas Mixture

Component	$\dot{n}_i$ kmol/h	Heat capacity $(C°_{mpi})$ equation constants			
		$\dot{n}_i \cdot a_i$	$\dot{n}_i \cdot b_i \times 10^3$	$\dot{n}_i \cdot c_i \times 10^6$	$\dot{n}_i \cdot d_i \times 10^9$
CH_3OH	125.00	3 108.7	6359.4	7 328.4	$-$ 5640.8
O_2	281.27	7320.2	3306.4	$-$ 658.9	$-$ 158.2
N_2	1058.10	31310.1	$-$ 5439.7	13 948.8	$-$ 5256.6
H_2O	23.73	771.0	1.9	313.5	$-$ 107.9
Total	1488.10	42510.0	4228.0	20 931.8	$-$ 1163.6

From the above Table 5.31, heat capacity of input air,

$C_{mpa}^o = 39\,401.3 - 2131.4 \times 10^{-3}\,T + 13\,603.4 \times 10^{-6}\,T^2 - 5522.7 \times 10^{-9}\,T^3$

and, heat capacity of input methanol,

$C_{mpme}^o = 3108.7 + 6359.4 \times 10^{-3}\,T + 7328.4 \times 10^{-6}\,T^2 - 5640.8 \times 10^{-9}\,T^3$

In similar fashion, heat capacity data of reaction exit gas stream are given in Table 5.32.

Table 5.32 Heat Capacity Data of Reactor Exit Gas Stream

Component	$\dot{n}_i$, kmol/h	Heat capacity (C_{mpi}^o) equation constants			
		$\dot{n}_i \cdot a_i$	$\dot{n}_i \cdot b_i \times 10^3$	$\dot{n}_i \cdot c_i \times 10^6$	$\dot{n}_i \cdot d_i \times 10^9$
CH_3OH	1.25	31.1	63.6	73.3	– 56.4
HCHO	111.375	5 368.3	—	—	—
CO_2	8.786	187.7	564.8	– 360.7	86.1
CO	0.99	28.7	– 2.8	11.5	– 4.7
H_2	1.98	56.6	2.0	– 0.3	1.5
CH_4	0.619	11.9	32.3	7.4	– 7.0
$(CH_3)_2O$	0.99	65.1	—	—	—
O_2	212.712	5 536.0	2500.5	– 498.3	119.6
N_2	1058.100	31 310.1	– 5439.7	13 948.8	– 5256.6
H_2O	153.667	4 993.0	12.2	2 030.0	– 698.8
Total	1550.469	47 588.5	– 2267.1	15 211.7	– 5816.3

Reactor exit gas stream is cooled from 340°C (613.15 K) to 110°C (383.15 K), preheating ingoing air.

Heat duty of heat exchanger, $\phi_4 = \displaystyle\int_{383.15}^{613.15} C_{mpa}^o\,dT$

$= 11\,395\,056$ kJ/h $\equiv 3165.29$ kW

Air enters the heat exchanger at 35°C (308.15 K) and leaves it at T_1 K.

$\displaystyle\int_{308.15}^{T_1} C_{mpa}^o\,dt = 11\,395\,056$

Solving by Mathcad, $T_1 = 588$ K or $t_1 = 314.85°C$

Evaporator heat duty

Liquid methanol enters evaporator at 35°C (308.15 K) and at 170 kPa a. Using Antoine equation (Eq. 5.24),

$$\log 1.70 = 5.204\,09 - \frac{1581.341}{T - 33.500}$$

or $\qquad T_s = 351.45$ K $\quad$ or $\quad t_s = 78.3°C$

Using Watson equation (Eq. 5.25) and data of Table 5.5,

$$\frac{\lambda_v}{35210} = \left(\frac{512.5 - 351.45}{512.5 - 337.7}\right)^{0.38}$$

$\lambda_v = 34\,131$ kJ/kmol at 351.45 K

Thus, liquid methanol will have to be first heated from 308.15 K to 351.45 K and then supplied λ_v for evaporation. Heat capacity data of liquid methanol can be taken from Table 5.3.

Heat duty of evaporator,

$$\phi_1 = 125 \int_{308.15}^{351.45_1} C_{ml}^o \, dT + 125 \times 34 \, 131$$

$$= 462 \, 513 + 4266 \, 250 = 4728 \, 888 \text{ kJ/h} \equiv 1313.58 \text{ kW}$$

Assume use of saturated steam at 4.5 bar a.

λ_v of steam = 2119.7 kJ/kg (Refer Appendix V.2)

$$\text{Steam consumption in evaporator} = \frac{4728 \, 888}{2119.7} = 2230.9 \text{ kg/h}$$

Methanol vapours at 351.45 K and hot air at 588 K mix in a static mixer. Let the temperature of mixed stream be T_2.

$$\int_{351.45}^{T_2} C_{mpme}^o \, dT = \int_{T_2}^{588} C_{mpa}^o \, dT$$

Use heat capacity data of Table 5.32.

Solving by Mathcad $T_2 = 554.05$ K or $t_2 = 545.97°$C

Assume reference temperature, $T_0 = 298.15$ K

Enthalpy of reactor input gas stream,

$$\phi_2 = \int_{298.15}^{554.05} C_{mpa}^o \, dT$$

$$\phi_2 = 12 \, 316 \, 119 \text{ kJ/h} \equiv 3421.144 \text{ kW}$$

Enthalpy of reactor exit gas stream,

$$\phi_3 = \int_{298.15}^{613.15} C_{mpi}^o \, dT$$

$$= 15 \, 505 \, 407 \text{ kJ/h} \equiv 4307.058 \text{ kW}$$

Heat transfer in reactor = 4758.764 + 20 320 839 − 15 505 407

$$= 17 \, 131 \, 551 \text{ kJ/h} \equiv 4758.764 \text{ kW}$$

From Table 5.6, λ_v of Dowtherm-A at 101.325 kPa a = 296.2 kJ/kg

$$\text{Dowtherm circulation rate} = \frac{17 \, 131 \, 551}{296.2} = 57 \, 838 \text{ kg/h}$$

This heat is picked up by Dowtherm-A and used in generation of saturated steam at 6 bar a.

Enthalpy required for steam generation = 2755.3 − 126   (Appendix IV.2)

$$= 2629.3 \text{ kJ/kg}$$

$$\text{Steam generated, } \dot{m}_s = \frac{17 \, 131 \, 551}{2629.3} = \textbf{6515.6 kg/h}$$

Example 5.38 Chlorination of ethylene to ethylene dichloride (EDC) is carried out in a loop reactor as shown in Fig. 5.15.

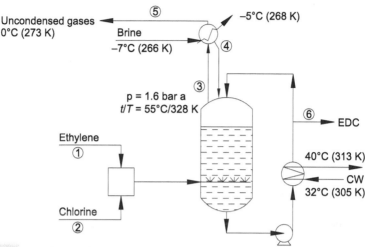

Fig. 5.15 Loop Reactor for EDC Manufacture

Reaction can be written as
$$C_2H_4(g) + Cl_2(g) = C_2H_4Cl_2(l) \qquad (i)$$
Side reaction produces 1,1,2 - trichloroethane (TCE) as per the reaction
$$C_2H_4(g) + 2\ Cl_2(g) = C_2H_3Cl_3(l) + HCl(g) \qquad (ii)$$
In the reactor, EDC itself is used as a solvent. Ethylene is the limiting reactant and its conversion is 99%. Chlorine to ethylene molar ratio is kept 1.1. Yield of EDC, based on ethylene, is 99.8%. Reactions are carried out at 1.6 bar a and 55°C (328.15 K). Exothermic heat of reactions is removed in an external cooler by exchanging heat with cooling water, available at 32°C (305 K). Cooling water leaves at 40°C (313K).

Unconverted gases, saturated with organic vapours at 55°C (328 K), are taken to an overhead condenser. Gases are cooled to 0°C (273 K) by exchanging heat with aqueous ethylene glycol (40% concentration by mass) brine which heats from −7°C (266.15 K) to −5°C (268.15 K) in the condenser. Condensed organic vapours are returned to the reactor.

For ethylene feed rate of 100 kmol/h to the reaction, calculate
(a) Compositions of various streams,
(b) Heat duty of the overhead condenser and required flow rate of brine, and
(c) Heat duty of external condenser and required cooling water flow rate.

Solution
Basis   Feed rate of ethylene = 100 kmol/h
Ethlene consmed in the reactor = 100 × 0.99 = 99 kmol/h
Ethylene consumed as per reaction (i) = 99 × 0.998 = 98.802 kmol/h

Ethylene consumed as per reaction (ii) = 99 − 98.802 = 0.198 kmol/h

Total chlorine consumed = 98.802 + 2 × 0.198 = 99.198 kmol/h

Cholrine fed to the reactor = 100 × 1.1 = 110 kmol/h

Cholrine in stream 3 = 110 − 99.198 = 10.802 kmol/h

HCl in stream 3 = 0.198 kmol/h

TCE production = 0.198 kmol/h

EDC produced = 98.802 kmol/h

Mixture of HCl and (unconverted) Cl_2 leaves from top at 1.6 bar a saturated with EDC and TCE vapours.

Antoine equations

For EDC, $\log p_{v1} = 4.585\ 18 - \dfrac{1521.789}{(T - 24.67)}$

For TCE, $\log p_{v2} = 4.069\ 74 - \dfrac{1310.297}{(T - 64.41)}$

At $t_1 = 55°$ C or $T_1 = 328.15$ K,

$p_{v1} = 0.3722$ bar $p_{v2} = 0.1264$ bar

At top of the loop reactor,

$$P_t = p_{HCl} + p_{C_2H_4} + p_{EDC} + p_{TCE}$$

where p_i indicates partical pressure of ith component. The loop reactor is essentially an ideal mixed flow reactor where liquid composition is constant throughout the reactor.

$$x_{EDC} = \frac{98.802}{98.802 + 0.198} = 0.998$$

$x_{TEC} = 1 - 0.998 = 0.002$

$p_{EDC} = 37.22 × 0.998 = 37.146$ kPa

$p_{TCE} = 12.64 × 0.002 = 0.0253$ kPa

$p_{Cl_2} + p_{HCl} + p_{C_2H_4} + 37.164 + 0.0253 = 1.6 × 100 = 160$

$p_{Cl_2} + p_{HCl} + p_{C_2H_4} = 122.8107$

Partial pressures are proportional to molar quatities for an ideal gas.

$$\frac{\dot{n}_{Cl_2} + \dot{n}_{HCl} + \dot{n}_{C_2H_4}}{\dot{n}_t} = \frac{p_{Cl_2} + p_{HCl} + p_{C_2H_4}}{p_t}$$

$$\frac{10.802 + 0.198 + 1}{\dot{n}_t} = \frac{122.8107}{160} = 0.767\ 57$$

$\dot{n}_t = 15.6338$ kmol/h

$$y_{EDC} = \frac{37.146}{160} = 0.2322$$

$$y_{TEC} = \frac{0.0253}{160} = 1.581 × 10^{-4}$$

$\dot{n}_{EDC} = 0.2322 × 15.6338 = 3.6302$ kmol/h

$$\dot{n}_{TEC} = 1.581 \times 10^{-4} \times 15.6338 = 0.0025 \text{ kmol/h}$$

Gas and vapours are cooled to 0°C (273.15° K).

At $t_2 = 0°C$ or $T_2 = 273.15$ K,

$$p'_{v1} = 2.896 \text{ kPa} \quad \text{and} \quad p'_{v2} = 6.2025 \times 10^{-3} \text{ kPa}$$

Since p'_{v2} is very low, it can be safely assumed that all TCE will condense. In the gas mixture, leaving the chiller.

$$y'_{TEC} \approx 0$$

Also, $x'_{EDC} \approx 1.0$

Assume a pressure drop of 10 kPa in the overhead condenser

At $t_2, p_{Cl_2} + p_{HCl} + p_{C_2H_4} + p_{EDC} = 160 - 10 = 150 \text{ kPa}$

$$p_{Cl_2} + p_{HCl} + p_{C_2H_4} = 150 - 2.89 = 147.11$$

$$\frac{\dot{n}_{Cl_2} + \dot{n}_{HCl} + \dot{n}_{C_2H_4}}{\dot{n}'} = \frac{147.11}{150} = 0.9807$$

$$\dot{n}' = 12.2207$$

$$y'_{EDC} = \frac{2.89}{150} = 0.01927$$

$$\dot{n}'_{EDC} = 0.019\ 27 \times 12.2207 = 0.2355 \text{ kmol/h}$$

Revised composition of liquid,

$$x''_{EDC} = \frac{(98.566 - 0.2355)}{(98.566 - 0.2355) + 0.198} = 0.998$$

Since there is hardly any change in the liquid composition, no additional trial is neccessary.

Table 5.33 Compostions of Gas Streams 3 and 5

Component	Stream 3		Stream 5	
	kmol/h	mole %	kmol/h	mole %
Cl_2	10.8020	69.10	10.8020	88.28
HCl	0.1980	1.27	0.1980	1.62
C_2H_4	1.0000	6.40	1.0000	8.17
EDC	3.6302	23.22	0.2355	1.93
TCE	0.0025	0.01	Nil	—
Total	15.6327	100.00	12.2355	100.00

Table 5.34 Compositions of Liquid Streams 4 and 6

Component	Stream 4		Stream 6	
	kmol/h	mole %	kmol/h	mole %
EDC	3.3947	99.93	98.5665	99.80
TCE	0.0025	0.07	0.1988	0.20
Total	3.3972	100.00	98.7645	100.00

Table 5.35 Heat Capacity Data

Component	Phase	Heat capacity at 25°C (298.15K) kJ/(kmol · K)
Cl_2	Gas	33.9
HCl	Gas	29.1
C_2H_4	Gas	43.6
EDC	Gas	17.4
EDC	Liquid	129.4
TCE	Gas	85.3
TCE	Liquid	144.4

Heat capacity values of Table 5.35 will be used for enthalpy calculations as maximum and minimum temperature are 55°C (328.15) K and 0°C (273.15 K), respectively.

$$\text{Reference temperature, } T_o = 273.15 \text{ K}$$

Enthalpy of gas stream at 55°C (328.15 K) entering overhead condenser, $\phi_1 = (10.802 \times 33.9 + 0.198 \times 29.1 + 1 \times 43.6 + 3.6302 \times 17.4$
$+ 0.0025 \times 85.3) (328.15 - 273.15)$
$= 26\,341$ kJ/h $\equiv 7.317$ kW

EDC and TCE are condensed. Assume average temperature for the condensation.

$$t_{avg} = \frac{0 + 55}{2} = 27.5°C$$

$$T_{avg} = 27.5 + 273.15 = 300.65 \text{ K}$$

Using Watson equation and data contained in Table 5.5, enthalpy of vaporizations are calculated as follows.

Table 5.36 Enthalpy of Vaporization

Component	λ_v kJ/mol	
	27.5°C (300.65 K)	55°C (328.15 K)
EDC	35.053	33.6
TCE	39.58	38.166

Condensation heat duty,
$\phi_2 = 35.053 \times 1000 \times 3.3947 + 39.58 \times 1000 \times 0.0025$
$= 119\,093$ kJ/h $\equiv 33.081$ kW

Since gases and EDC vapour leave at 0°C (273.15 K) from the condenser, enthalpy of the stream is zero.

Organic vapour starts condensing as soon as the vapour starts cooling and hence average temperature can be taken for subcooling duty.

Subcoolling heat duty,
$\phi_3 = (3.3947 \times 129.4 + 0.0025 \times 144.4) (55/2)$
$= 12\,090$ kJ/h $\equiv 3.358$ kW

Total heat exchange in overhead condenser,

$$\phi_c = \phi_1 + \phi_2 + \phi_3$$
$$= 157\ 524 \text{ kJ/h} \equiv 43.757 \text{ kW} \equiv 12.44 \text{ TR}$$

Specific heat and density of aqueous 40% ethylene glycol solution[24] are 3.38 kJ/(kg · K) and 1.034 kg/h, respectively at $-6°C$ (267.15 K).

$$\text{Mass-flow rate of brine} = \frac{157\ 524}{3.38 \times 2}$$

$$= 23\ 302 \text{ kg/h} \equiv 21\ 963 \text{ L/h} \approx 22 \text{ m}^3/\text{h}$$

Enthalpy of feed, $\phi_5 = (100 \times 43.6 + 110 \times 33.9)\ (328.15 - 273.15)$
$$= 444\ 895 \text{ kJ/h} \equiv 123.58 \text{ kW}$$

Consider energy balance of the reactor.

Enthalpy of gas stream, $\phi_1 = 26\ 341$ kJ/h $\equiv 7.317$ kW

Evaporation duty of organic vapours at 55°C (328.15 K),

$$\phi_6 = 3.6302 \times 1000 \times 33.6 + 0.0025 \times 1000 \times 38.166$$
$$= 122\ 010 \text{ kJ/h} \equiv 33.892 \text{ kW}$$

Enthalpy of liquid product stream

$$\phi_7 = (98.5665 \times 129.4 + 0.1988 \times 144.4)\ (328.15 - 273.15)$$
$$= 703\ 077 \text{ kJ/h}$$

Heats of reactions

For reaction (i),

$$\Delta H_{r1}^o = -167.2 - 52.50$$
$$= -219.7 \text{ kJ/ mol ethylene}$$

ΔH_{r1} at 55°C (328.15 K) $= -219.7 \times 1000 + (129.4 - 43.6 - 33.9)\ (328.15 - 273.15)$
$$= -216\ 845.5 \text{ kJ/kmol ethylene}$$

For reaction (ii),

$$\Delta H_{r2} = -188.0 + (-92.31) - (52.50)$$
$$= -332.81 \text{ kJ/ mol ethylene}$$

ΔH_{r2} at 55°C (328.15 K) $= -332.81 \times 1000 + (144.4 + 29.1 - 43.6 \times -2 \times 33.9)$
$$(328.15 - 273.15)$$
$$= -329\ 394.5 \text{ kJ/kmol ethylene}$$

Total heat generated,

$$\phi_8 = 216\ 845.5 \times 98.802 + 329\ 394.5 \times 0.198$$
$$= 21\ 489\ 989.2 \text{ kJ/h} \equiv 5969.44 \text{ kW}$$

Liquid stream (4), leaving the condenser is at 0°C (273.15 K) and hence its enthalpy is zero.

Heat duty of external cooler,

$$\phi_{col} = \phi_5 + \phi_8 - \phi_1 - \phi_6 - \phi_7$$
$$= 444\ 895 + 21\ 489\ 989.2 - 26\ 341 - 122\ 010 - 703\ 077$$
$$= 21\ 083\ 456.2 \equiv 5856.5 \text{ kW}$$

$$\text{Cooling water-flow rate} = \frac{21\ 083\ 456.2}{8 \times 4.1868}$$

$$= 629\ 462 \text{ kg/h} \equiv 629.5 \text{ m}^3/\text{h}$$

5.13.2 Effect of Pressure on Heat of Reaction

In Sec. 5.13.1, the effect of temperature on the heat of reaction at 1 bar pressure is described. Usually, the effect of pressure on the heat of a reaction is insignificant at relatively low pressures. However, a number of reactions take place at very high pressures, such as ammonia synthesis, methanol synthesis, etc. For such reactions, correction needs to be applied. The following example will illustrate the correction procedure.

Example 5.39 Refer Example 4.17. Assume that mixed feed enters the adiabatic converter at 600 bar a and 210°C (483 K). Gas mixture leaves the converter at 580 bar a. Calculate the temperature of the gas mixture leaving the reactor, considering (a) ideal gas mixtures, and (b) real gas behavior of the gas mixture.

Solution

(a) *Ideal-Gas Law* No pressure correction is considered.

Table 5.37 Heat Capacity Equation Constants for Ingoing Gas Mixture

Component	kmol/h	Heat capacity equation constants			
	$\dot{n}_i$	$\dot{n}_i \cdot a_i$	$\dot{n}_i \cdot b_i \times 10^3$	$\dot{n}_i \cdot c_i \times 10^6$	$\dot{n}_i \cdot d_i \times 10^9$
N_2	92.674	2742.3	–476.4	1221.7	–460.4
H_2	278.022	7954.3	283.4	–41.0	213.8
Ar	12.184	273.9	—	—	—
CH_4	30.763	592.2	1603.2	368.3	–348.2
NH_3	24.825	636.8	831.2	8.7	–76.5
Total	439.468	12 199.5	2241.4	1557.7	–671.3

Refrence temperature, $\quad t_0 = 25°C \quad$ or $\quad T_0 = 298.15$ K

$$t_1 = 210°C \quad \text{or} \quad T_1 = 483.15 \text{ K}$$

Enthalpy of ingoing gas mixture,

$$\phi_1 = \int_{298.15}^{483.15} (12\,199.5 + 2241.4 \times 10^{-3}\, T + 1557.7 \times 10^{-6}\, T^2 - 671.3 \times 10^{-9}\, T^3)\ dT$$

$$= 2256\,907.5 + 161\,986.5 + 44\,799.5 - 7818.9$$

$$= 2455\,874.6 \text{ kJ/h} \equiv 682.187 \text{ kW}$$

$\Delta H_r^o = 2\,(-45.94) - [0 + 3(0)]$

$\quad = -91.88$ kJ/mol N_2 reacted

N_2 recated in the converter $= 92.674 - 69.506 = 23.168$ kmol/h

Heat produced, $\phi_2 = 91.88 \times 1000 \times 23.168$

$$= 2128\,675.8 \text{ kJ/h} \equiv 591.299 \text{ kW}$$

Enthalpy of outcoming gas mixture.

$$\phi_3 = \phi_1 + \phi_2$$

$$= 2455\,874.6 + 2128\,675.8$$

$$= 4584\,550.4 \text{ kJ/h} \equiv 1273.486 \text{ kW}$$

Table 5.38 Heat Capcity Equation Constants for Outcoming Gas Mixture

Component	kmol/h	Heat capacity equation constants			
	$\dot{n}_i$	$\dot{n}_i \cdot a_i$	$\dot{n}_i \cdot b_i \times 10^3$	$\dot{n}_i \cdot c_i \times 10^6$	$\dot{n}_i \cdot d_i \times 10^9$
N_2	69.506	2056.7	−357.3	916.3	−345.3
H_2	208.517	5965.8	212.6	−30.8	160.3
Ar	13.184	273.9	—	—	—
CH_4	30.763	592.2	1603.2	368.3	−348.2
NH_3	71.162	1825.3	2382.5	25.0	−219.4
Total	393.132	10 713.9	3841.0	1278.8	−752.6

Let temperature of outcoming gas mixture = T_2 K

$$\varphi_3 = \int_{298.15}^{T_2} (10\,713.9 + 3841.0 \times 10^{-3}\, T + 1278.8 \times 10^{-6}\, T^2 - 752.6 \times 10^{-9}\, T^3)\, dT$$

$$= 4584\,550.4 \text{ kJ/h}$$

Solving the equation by Mathcad,

$$T_2 = 657.41 \text{ K} \quad \text{or} \quad t_2 = 384.26^{\circ}\text{C}$$

(b) High-Pressure Correction

One method, described in Sec. 5.4, is to find residual heat capacity C_{mp}^R for each of the gas components at the respective pure component pressure and 210°C (483.15 K). Another more versatile method is to calculate residual enthalpy (H^R) of the gas mixture based on the 3-parameter corresponding states principle (CSP). This method was proposed by Lee and Kester[12].

$$H^R = H - H^{ig} \text{ kJ/kmol} \tag{5.64}$$

where H = enthalpy of real gas at given pressure and temperature, kJ/kmol

H^{ig} = enthalpy of gas as an ideal gas and at given temperature, kJ/kmol

Lee and Kesler[12] defined H^R for real gas as

$$\left(\frac{H^R}{RT_c}\right) = \left(\frac{H^R}{RT_c}\right)^0 + \omega \left(\frac{H^R}{RT_c}\right)^1 \tag{5.65}$$

where, $(H^R)^0$ is the function for the simple fluid and $(H^R)^1$ is the deviation function, based on the compressiblity factor of the real fluid.

ω = Acentric factior

$$= -1.0 - \log (p_{rs})_{T_r=0.7} \qquad \text{(as defined by Pitzer[3])} \tag{5.66}$$

For a gas mixture, the above equation holds good when T_c is replaced by T_{pc} (pseudo-critical temperature) which is calculated by Kay's additive rule (see Example 2.25). Also, $\omega = \Sigma y_i\, \omega_i$ However, for a quantum gas like H_2, effective critical parameters are to be used with a condition that $\omega = 0$. For H_2,

$$T_{ec} = \frac{43.6}{1 + \dfrac{21.8}{2.016\,T}}\text{K} \qquad p_{ec} = \frac{20.5}{1 + \dfrac{44.2}{2.016\,T}}\text{bar}$$

The values of $(H^R/RT_c)^0$ and $(H^R/RT_c)^1$ are listed by Lee and Kesler for different p_r and T_r parameters.

Converter Ingoing Gas Stream

$$T_1 = 483.15 \text{ K}$$

For H_2,

$$T_{ec1} = \frac{43.6}{1 + \dfrac{21.8}{(2.016 \times 483.15)}} = 42.65 \text{ K}$$

$$P_{ec1} = \frac{20.5}{1 + \dfrac{44.2}{(2.016 \times 483.15)}} = 19.61 \text{ bar}$$

$$\omega = 0$$

Note that actual T_c, and p_c for hydrogen are 33.20 K and 12.97 bar, respectively (ref. Appendix III). Also, ω for H_2 is reported to be -0.216 in Ref. 3.

Table 5.39 Pseudo-critical Properties of Ingoing Gas Mixture

Component	y_i	ω_i	$y_i \cdot \omega_i$	p_{ci}, bar	$y_i \cdot p_{ci}$	T_{ci}, K	$y_i \cdot T_{ci}$
N_2	0.2109	0.038	0.0080	33.94	7.158	126.09	26.592
H_2	0.6326	0	0	19.610	12.405	42.65	26.980
Ar	0.0300	0	0	48.630	1.459	150.69	4.521
CH_4	0.0700	0.012	0.0008	45.99	3.219	190.56	13.339
NH_3	0.0565	0.253	0.0143	113.50	6.413	405.50	22.911
Total	1.0000		0.0231		30.654		94.343

At converter inlet pressure, $p = 600$ bar, $T_1 = 483.15$ K

$$p_{r1} = \frac{600}{30.654} = 19.573 \qquad T_{r1} = \frac{483.15}{94.343} = 5.121$$

The values of $(H^R/RT_c)^0$ and $(H^R/RT_c)^1$ are presented for minimum $p_r = 10.0$ and maximum $T_r = 4.0$ by Lee and Kesler. Above these ranges,

$$\left(\frac{H^R}{RT_{pc}}\right)^0 = 0 \quad \text{and} \quad \left(\frac{H^R}{RT_{pc}}\right)^1 = 1.0 \text{ are assumed}$$

$$\left(\frac{H^R}{RT_{pc}}\right) = 0 + 0.0231 \times 1.0 = 0.0231$$

$$H_r^R = 0.0231 \times 8.314\,472 \times 94.343 = 18.12 \text{ kJ/kmol}$$

Corrected $\phi_{\text{inlet}} = \phi^{\text{ig}} + \phi^R = 2455\,874.6 + 18.12 \times 439.468$

$$= 2463\,837.8 \text{ kJ/h} \equiv 684.4 \text{ kW}$$

Corrected $\phi_{\text{outlet}} = \phi_{\text{inlet}} + \phi_2$

$$= 2463\,837.8 + 2128\,675.8 = 4592\,513.6 \text{ kJ/h} \equiv 1275.7 \text{ kW}$$

Converter Outcoming Gas Stream

Temperature of the outgoing gas mixture is unknown. Hence assume that temperature of $T_2 = 657.41$ K, obtained with ideal gas conditions, is valid.

For H_2,

$$T_{ec2} = \frac{43.6}{1 + \dfrac{21.8}{(2.016 + 657.41)}} = 42.89 \text{ K}$$

$$p_{ec2} = \cfrac{20.5}{1 + \cfrac{44.2}{(2.016 + 657.41)}} = 19.838 \text{ bar}$$

Table 5.40 Pseudo-critical Properties of Outcoming Gas Mixture

Component	y_i	ω_i	$y_i \cdot \omega_i$	p_{ci}, bar	$y_i \cdot p_{ci}$	T_{ci}, K	$y_i \cdot T_{ci}$
N_2	0.1768	0.038	0.0067	33.94	6.001	126.09	22.293
H_2	0.5304	0	0	19.838	10.522	42.89	22.749
Ar	0.0335	0	0	46.630	1.629	150.65	5.047
CH_4	0.0783	0.012	0.0009	45.990	3.601	190.56	14.928
NH_3	0.1810	0.253	0.0458	113.50	20.544	405.50	73.396
Total	1.0000		0.0534		42.297		138.413

$$p_{r2} = \frac{580}{42.297} = 13.713 \qquad T_{r2} = \frac{657.41}{138.413} = 4.75$$

Again both p_r and T_r, are out of range.

$$\left(\frac{H^R}{RT_{pc}} \right)^0 = 0 \quad \text{and} \quad \left(\frac{H^R}{RT_{pc}} \right)^1 = 1.0 \text{ are assumed.}$$

$$\left(\frac{H^R}{RT_{pc}} \right) = 0 + 0.0534 \times 1 = 0.0534$$

$H_2^R = 0.0534 \times 8.314\,472 \times 138.413 = 61.454 \text{ kJ/kmol}$

$\phi_{outlet}^{ig} = \phi_{outlet}^{ig} - H_2^R \times \dot{n}_i$

$\qquad = 4592\,513.6 - 61.454 \times 393.132 = 4568\,354.5 \text{ kJ/h} \equiv 1269 \text{ kW}$

$$\int\limits_{298.15}^{T_2} (10713.9 + 3841.0 \times 10^{-3}\,T + 1278.8 \times 10^{-6}\,T^2 - 752.6 \times 10^{-9}\,T^3)dT$$

$$= 4568\,354$$

Solving by Mathcad, **T_2 = 656.21 K or t_2 = 383.06°C**

The calculated T_2 is very close to assumed T_2.

Difference in calculated outlet temperature = 656.21 − 657.41 = −1.2 K or °C

In yet another method, enthalpies of individual gas components are required to be calculated at pure component pressure and actual gas stream temperatures. Since heat of reaction is calculated at 1 bar and 25°C (298.15 K), reference state should be taken same as 1 bar and 25°C (298.15K). The following calculations will demostrate the method.

In the first step, pure component pressures (refer Sec. 2.6.3) of the components in both gas streams are to be calculated. Lee and Kesler[12] proposed that

$$Z = Z^0 + \omega Z^1 \tag{5.67}$$

Values of Z^0 and Z^1 are calculated by 3-parameter CSP. Knowledge of p_r, T_r and ω gives values of Z^0 and Z^1.

Iteration 1   For evaluation of p_r, pure component pressures (p_i) are required. However, these values are unknown and hence an iterative procedure is to be adopted. For the first iteration, P_i may be taken as partial pressure.

$$P_i = y_i \cdot p \qquad p = 600 \text{ bar} \qquad T_1 = 483.15 \text{ K}$$

Compressibility factors (Z_i) are availabe in literature in tabular form at different pressures and temperatures (e.g., Perry's *Chemical Engineers' Handbook*[21]) for a number of compounds. It is recommended that values from the tables be extracted for available components and used to calculate Z for the gas mixture. Only when tabulated values are not available, Eq. (5.67) may be used. Z^0 and Z^1 are extracted from Ref. 3.

Table 5.41   Calculation of Compressibility Factor for Converter Ingoing Gas Mixture

Component	y_i	$p_i = Pi(1)$ $= y_i . 600$	p_c, bar	$p_{ri} = \dfrac{p_i}{p_{ci}}$	T_c, K	$T_{ri} = \dfrac{T_1}{T_{ci}}$
N_2	0.2109	126.54	33.94	3.7283	126.09	3.8318
H_2	0.6326	379.56	19.61	19.3554	42.65	11.3283
Ar	0.0300	18.00	48.63	0.3701	150.65	3.2063
CH_4	0.0700	42.00	45.99	0.9132	190.56	2.5354
NH_3	0.0565	33.90	113.50	0.2987	405.50	1.1915
Total	1.0000	600.00	—	—	—	—

Table 5.42   Calculation of Compressibility Factor (Continuation of Table 5.41)

Component	ω_i	Z^0	Z^1	Z_i	$Z_i \cdot y_i$
N_2	—	—	—	1.0586*	0.2233
H_2	−0.216	1.1773	0.2994	1.1126	0.7038
Ar	—	—	—	1.0030*	0.0301
CH_4	—	—	—	0.9986*	0.0699
NH_3	0.253	0.9408	0.0137	0.9443	0.0534
Total					1.0805 (Z_1)

*From *Perry's Chemical Engineers' Handbook* (Ref. 21)

Iteration 2

Revised $\qquad\qquad P_i(2) = \dfrac{P_i(1) \times Z_i}{Z}$ $\qquad\qquad$ (5.68)

Table 5.43   Calculation of Compressibility Factor for Converter Ingoing Gas Mixture

Component	y_i	$P_i(2)$ Eq. (5.68)	p_c, bar	$p_{ri} = \dfrac{p_i}{p_{ci}}$	T_c, K	$T_{ri} = \dfrac{T_1}{T_{ci}}$
N_2	0.2109	123.9752	33.94	3.6529	126.09	3.8318
H2	0.6326	390.8361	19.61	19.9319	42.65	11.3283
Ar	0.0300	16.7089	48.63	0.3436	150.69	3.2063
CH_4	0.0700	38.8165	45.99	0.8441	190.56	2.5354
NH_3	0.0565	29.6268	113.50	0.2610	405.50	1.1915
Total	1.0000	600.0000	—	—	—	—

Table 5.44 Claculated Compressibility Factor (Continuation of Table 5.43)

Component	ω_i^*	Z^0	Z^1	Z_i	$Z_i \cdot y_i$	$\dfrac{V_i}{RT} = \dfrac{Z_i \cdot y_i}{P_i(2)}$
N_2	—	—	—	1.0573	0.2230	0.001 799
H_2	−0.216	1.1773	0.2994	1.1126	0.7038	0.001 801
Ar	—	—	—	1.0028	0.0301	0.001 800
CH_4	—	—	—	0.9986	0.0699	0.001 801
NH_3	0.253	0.9358	0.0117	0.9388	0.0530	0.001 800
Total					1.0798 (Z_2)	0.001 800

Compressibility factor (Z_i) calculated in Iteration 2, is in close agreement (within 0.05%) of that calculated in Iteration 1. Also, $V_i = V_1$ which satisfies Dalton's law. Hence, $P_i(2)$ values can be considered as pure component pressures of the converter ingoing gas mixture.

$$V_1 = 0.0018 \times 0.083\ 14 \times 483.15 = 0.0723 \text{ m}^3/\text{kmol}$$

Converter outgoing gas mixture

$$T_2 = 674 \text{ K (assumed)} \qquad p_2 = 580 \text{ bar}$$

Iteration 1

Table 5.45 Calculation of Compressibility Factor for Converter Outgoing Gas Mixture

Component	y_i	$\begin{array}{c}p_i = P_i(1)\\= y_i \cdot 580\end{array}$	p_c, bar	$p_{ri} = \dfrac{p_i}{p_{ci}}$	Tc, K	$T_{ri} = \dfrac{T_1}{T_{ci}}$
N_2	0.1768	102.544	33.94	3.0213	126.09	5.3454
H2	0.5304	307.632	19.838	15.6875	42.89	15.8031
Ar	0.0335	19.430	48.63	0.3995	150.65	4.4728
CH_4	0.0783	45.414	45.99	0.9875	190.56	3.5369
NH_3	0.1810	104.980	113.50	0.9249	405.50	1.6621
Total	1.0000	580.000	—	—	—	—

Table 5.46 Calculation of Compressibity Factor (Continuation of Table 5.45)

Component	ω_i	Z^0	Z^1	Z_i	$Z_i \cdot y_i$
N_2	—	—	—	1.0442	0.1846
H_2	−0.216	1.1773	0.2994	1.1126	0.5901
Ar	—	—	—	1.0054	0.0337
CH_4	—	—	—	0.0122	0.0793
NH_3	0.253	0.9469	0.0751	0.9659	0.1748
Total					1.0625 (Z_2)

Iteration 2

Table 5.47 Calculation of Compressibility Factor for Outcoming Gas Mixture

Component	y_i	$\begin{array}{c}P_i(2)\\ \text{Eq. (5.68)}\end{array}$	p_c, bar	$p_{ri} = \dfrac{p_i}{p_{ci}}$	Tc, K	$T_{ri} = \dfrac{T_1}{T_{ci}}$
N_2	0.1768	100.7778	33.94	2.9692	126.09	5.3454

(*Contd.*)

Table 5.47 (Contd.)

Component	y_i	$P_i(2)$ Eq. (5.68)	p_c, bar	$p_{ri} = \dfrac{p_i}{p_{ci}}$	Tc, K	$T_{ri} = \dfrac{T_1}{T_{ci}}$
H_2	0.5304	322.1377	19.838	16.4274	42.89	15.8031
Ar	0.0335	18.3855	48.63	0.3781	150.65	4.4728
CH_4	0.0783	43.2634	45.99	0.9407	190.56	3.5369
NH_3	0.1810	96.4339	113.50	0.8408	405.50	1.6621
Total	1.0000	580.0000	—	—	—	—

Table 5.48 Calculated Compressibility Factor (Continuation of Table 5.47)

Component	ω_i^*	Z^0	Z^1	Z_i	$Z_i \cdot y_i$	$\dfrac{V_i}{RT} = \dfrac{Z_i \cdot y_i}{P_i(2)}$
N_2	—	—	—	1.0430	0.1844	0.001 830
H_2	−0.216	1.1773	0.2994	1.1126	0.5901	0.001 832
Ar	—	—	—	1.0051	0.0337	0.001 831
CH_4	—	—	—	0.0113	0.0792	0.001 830
NH_3	0.253	0.9499	0.0705	0.9677	0.1752	0.001 835
Total					1.0626 (Z_2)	0.001 832

Z_2 of Iteration 2 is in close agreement with Z_2 of Iteration 1. Also, $V_i = V_2$ which satisfies Dalton's law. Hence, $P_i(2)$ values are pure component pressures of components of the converter outgoing gas mixture.

Enthalpies of pure gases at P_i and T are required for the heat balance. The following reference states are valid for the respective (gas) component.

Table 5.49 Reference States[26]

Component	Reference enthalpy (kJ/kmol) and state
N_2	Enthalpy of saturated at liquid NBP* (77.36 K)
H_2	Enthalpy of saturated at liquid NBP* (20.37 K)
Ar	Enthalpy of saturated liquid = 0 at NBP (87.30 K)
CH_4	Enthalpy of saturated liquid = 0 at NBP (111.67 K)
NH_3	Enthalpy of saturated liquid = 200 at 0°C (273.15 K)

Table 5.50 Enthalpy of Converter Ingoing Gas Mixture

Component	$\dot{n}_i$ kmol/h	Enthalpy[26] at 1 bar and 25°C (298.15 K) H_1, kJ/kmol	Enthalpy[26] at P_i bar and 210°C (483.15 K) H_2, kJ/kmol	$(H_2 - H_1) \cdot \dot{n}_i$ kJ/h
N_2	92.674	12082	17381	491 079
H_2	278.022	7926	13909	1663 406
Ar	13.184	10 884	14695	50 244
CH_4	30.763	14598	21829	222 447
NH_3	24.825	26 341	32767	159 525
Total	439.468	—	—	2586 701

$$\phi_1 = 2586\ 701\ \text{kJ/h} = 718.528\ \text{kW}$$
$$\phi_3 = \phi_1 + \phi_2 = 2586\ 701 + 2128\ 676$$
$$= 4715\ 377\ \text{kJ/h} \equiv 1309.827\ \text{kW}$$

Table 5.51 Enthalpy of Converter Outcoming Gas Mixture

Compo-nent	$\dot{n}_i$ kmol/h	Enthalpy[26] at 1 bar and 25°C (298.15 K) H_3, kJ/kmol	Enthalpy[26] at P_i bar and 660 K H_4 kJ/kmol	670 K H_5 kJ/kmol	$(H_4-H_3)\cdot\dot{n}_i$ kJ/h	$(H_5-H_3)\cdot\dot{n}_i$ kJ/h
N_2	69.506	12 082	22 862	23 174	749 275	770 961
H_2	208.517	7926	19 033	19 329	2315 998	2377 714
Ar	13.184	10 884	18 402	18 611	99 117	101 873
CH_4	30.763	14 598	30 929	31498	502 391	519 895
NH_3	71.162	26 341	40 330	40 858	995 485	1033 059
Total	393.132	—	—	—	4662 266	4803 507

Temperature of outcoming gas mixture

$$T_2 = \left(\frac{4715\ 377 - 4662\ 266}{4803\ 507 - 4662\ 266} \right) 10 + 660$$

$$= \textbf{663.76 K or 390.61°C}$$

The calculated outlet temperature (663.76 K) is not very different from the assumed value of 674 K and hence no further calculations are necessary.

Difference in calculated outlet temperature = 663.76 – 657.41 = 6.35 K or °C

$$V_2 = 0.001\ 832 \times 0.083\ 14 \times 663.76 = 0.1011\ \text{m}^3/\text{kmol}$$

Note The second method, based on actual gas enthalpy values at pure component pressure and system temperature, is a recommended method over the method, based on 3-parameter CSP. However, actual enthalpy values of all gases are not easily available in literature and hence the method based on 3-parameter CSP, is accepted in practice.

Residual enthalpy of the real gas can also be calculated by numerical integration of residual heat capacity values as described in Sec. 5.3.

5.14 ADIABATIC REACTIONS

When a system does not give heat to the surroundings nor does it receive from the surroundings, it is called an *adiabatic* process or operation. More correctly speaking, the system is called *isenthalp*, as reversible adiabatic processes also obey constant entropy criterion. In this book, adiabatic process will be considered as the one in which the heat is contained within a system without loss or addition of heat to or from the outside source.

When adiabatic reactions take place, two observations can be made.

(a) If the reaction is exothermic, the temperature of the product stream rises. In this case, total heat content of the product stream equals total heat content of reactants plus the heat of reaction.

All oxidation reactions are exothermic. Similarly, the dilution of sulphuric acid or caustic soda solution is exothermic.

(b) If the reaction is endothermic, the temperature of the product stream decreases. In this case, total enthalpy of the product stream equals total enthalpy of reactants minus the heat of reaction.

Industrially important reactions like steam–hydrocarbon reforming reaction, thermal reduction of hydrogen sulphide to sulphur, dehydrogenation of ethyl-benzene, etc., are endothermic. The dissolution of common salt in water is also endothermic.

The temperature of products under adiabatic conditions of the reaction is called the *adiabatic reaction temperature.*

In actual industrial practice, except for a few reactions, the reaction temperatures are controlled either by the addition or removal of heat as the case may be. This is because of conflicting demands from kinetic and thermodynamic considerations. When such a temperature control is provided, the reaction becomes non-adiabatic. Oxidation reactions are practically irreversible and hence they can be carried out without the control of temperature. When the fuel is burnt (i.e. combustion reaction), the adiabatic reaction temperature is called the *adiabatic flame temperature* because it represents the flame temperature. Even in well-insulated furnaces and boilers, the heat is lost due to radiation from the surface. Hence, the *actual flame temperature* is less than the adiabatic flame temperature. Chapter 7 gives calculations of flame temperatures.

In Sec. 4.2, the Le Châtelier principle was discussed in which effect of pressure on the reaction kinetics was considered. When the same principle is applied with consideration of heat of reaction, it can be concluded that exothermic reactions are preferred to be controlled to a lower temperature while enothermic reactions are preferred to be controlled at a higher temperature for better conversions/ yields. However, kinetic considerations (such as rate of reaction) may override temperature control strategy in the actural plants. Actual reaction temperature is controlled by optimum balance of two.

Example 5.40   In a commercial process, chlorine is manufactured by burning hydrogen chloride gas using air. The reaction taking place in the burner is

$$4 \text{ HCl(g)} + O_2(g) = 2 \text{ H}_2O(g) + 2 \text{ Cl}_2(g)$$

For good conversion, air is used in 35% excess of that theoretically (stoichio-metrically) required. Assume that the oxidation is 80% complete and the dry air and hydrogen chloride gas enter the burner at 25°C (298.15 K). Calculate (a) the composition of dry gases leaving the burner, and (b) the adiabatic reaction temperature of the product gas steam.

Solution   *Basis* 4 kmol of hydrogen chloride gas

Theoretical O_2 requirement = 1 kmol

Actual O_2 supply = 1 × 1.35 = 1.35 kmol

Nitrogen supply through air = $\left(\dfrac{79}{21}\right)$ × 1.35 = 5.08 kmol

Total air supply = 1.35 + 5.08 = 6.43 kmol
Conversion in the burner is 80%.
HCl burnt = 0.8 × 4 = 3.2 kmol

Table 5.52 Composition of Product Gas Stream

Component	Product gas stream, kmol		Composition on dry basis (mole %)
	Wet (n_i)	Dry	
HCl	4 − 3.2 = 0.8	0.8	9.96
O_2	1.35 − 0.8 = 0.55	0.55	6.85
Cl_2	0.8 × 2 = 1.6	1.60	19.93
H_2O	0.8 × 2 = 1.6	—	—
N_2	5.08	5.08	63.26
Total	9.63	8.03	100.00

Now assume base temperature to be 25°C (298.15 K).
Enthalpy of the reactants at 25°C (298.15 K), $\Delta H_1 = 0$ kJ
Standard heat of reaction at 25°C (298.15 K), $\Delta H_r^o = -241.82 \times 2 - 4.0 (-92.31)$

$$= -114.4 \text{ kJ/mol } O_2 \text{ consumed}$$

This represents the exothermic nature of the reaction.
Total heat liberated = 114.4 × 1000 × 0.8 = 91 520 kJ
Total enthalpy of product stream $\Delta H_2 = 0 + 91\ 520 = 91\ 520$ kJ

Table 5.53 Heat Capacity Equation Constants for Product Gas Stream

Component	n_i	Heat capacity equation constants			
	kmol	$a_i \cdot n_i$	$b_i \cdot n_i \times 10^3$	$c_i \cdot n_i \times 10^6$	$d_i \cdot n_i \times 10^9$
HCl	0.8	24.247	− 6.087	10.609	− 3.467
O_2	0.55	14.314	6.465	− 1.288	− 0.309
Cl_2	1.6	45.674	38.207	− 34.181	10.356
H_2O	1.6	51.987	0.127	21.137	− 7.276
N_2	5.08	150.322	− 26.116	66.969	− 25.237
Total	9.63	286.544	12.596	63.246	− 25.933

Enthalpy of product stream

over 25°C (298.15 K), $\Delta H_2 = \displaystyle\int_{298.15}^{T} (286.544 + 12.596 \times 10^{-3}\, T + 63.246 \times 10^{-6}$

$$T^2 - 25.933 \times 10^{-9}\, T^3)\, dT$$
$$= 91\ 520$$

Solving by Mathcad

T = Adiabatic reaction temperature
= 599.5 K or 326.35°C

Note The product gas stream contains HCl and H_2O which condense when cooled. Acid gas dew point can be calculated by a method, given by Ganapathy[42]. At atmospheric pressure (101.325 kPa), this dew point is calculated to be 73.5°C (346.5 K). For more discussion on the acid dew point, refer Sec. 7.6.

Example 5.41 Dehydrogenation of ethylbenzene (EB) is commercially employed to manufacture styrene. The reaction is carried out in the gas phase with steam over a catalyst[43], consisting primarily of iron oxide with potassium as a promoter. The reaction is endothermic and is carried out adiabatically at near atmospheric pressure.

Main reaction $C_6H_5CH_2CH_3 = C_6H_5CH{:}CH_2 + H_2$ (A)

Competing reactions $C_6H_5CH_2CH_3 = C_6H_6 + C_2H_4$ (B)

                      $C_6H_5CH_2CH_3 = 8\ C + 5\ H_2$ (C)

                      $C_6H_5CHCH_2 + 2\ H_2 = C_6H_5CH_3 + CH_4$ (D)

Fresh EB is mixed with recycled EB, vaporized and superheated to 538°C (811 K). To prevent coke formation [reaction (C)], one mole of EB is mixed with 15 moles of superheated steam at 705°C (978 K). Large dilution of steam also supplies necessary heat of reaction.

Overall conversion is 35%. Net yield of styrene is 90%. Yields of benzene and toluene are 3% and 6%, respectively. Assume that 1% of EB converted forms coke by reaction (C). Calculate the adiabatic reaction temperature at the outlet of the reactor.

Solution   *Basis* 1 kmol of EB vapours entering the reactor at 508°C (811.15 K)

Steam mixed with EB = 15 kmol

Table 5.54 Heat Capacity Equation Constants for Reactants

Component	n_i kmol	Heat capacity (C_{mpl}^0) equation constants			
		$n_i \cdot a_i$	$n_i \cdot b_i \times 10^3$	$n_i \cdot c_i \times 10^6$	$n_i \cdot d_i \times 10^9$
EB	1.0	-36.72	671.12	-422.02	101.15
H_2O	15.0	487.38	1.19	198.16	-68.21
Total	16.0	450.66	672.31	-223.86	32.94

Let T_1 K be the temperature of reactant gas stream.

$$\int_{811.15}^{T_1} (-36.72 + 671.12 \times 10^{-3}\ T - 422.02 \times 10^{-6}\ T^2 + 101.15 \times 10^{-9}\ T^3)\ dT$$

$$= \int_{T_1}^{978.15} (487.38 + 1.19 \times 10^{-3}\ T + 198.16 \times 10^{-6}\ T^2 - 68.21 \times 10^{-9}\ T^3)\ dT$$

Solving by Mathcad, $T_1 = 929.72$ K or 656.57°C

Reference temperature, $T_0 = 298.15$ K

Enthalpy of reactants at 929.72 K over 298.15 K,

$$H_1 = \int_{298.15}^{929.72} C_{mpl}^0\ dT = 493\ 405\ kJ$$

EB reacted = 0.35 kmol

Styrene in product stream = 0.35 × 0.9 = 0.315 kmol

Benzene produced by reaction (B) = 0.35 × 0.03 = 0.0105 kmol

Ethylene produced by reaction (B) = 0.0105 kmol = EB reacted by reaction (B)
Carbon formation by reaction (C) = 0.35 × 0.01 = 0.0035 kmol
Carbon will deposit on the catalyst and will not appear in the product gas mixture stream.

Toluene produced by reaction (D) = 0.35 × 0.06 = 0.021 kmol
$$= CH_4 \text{ produced} = \text{styrene reacted by reaction (D)}$$
$$= \text{EB reacted by reaction (A)}$$
Total EB reactected by reaction (A) = 0.315 + 0.021 = 0.336 kmol
Total hydrogen produced = 0.315 + 0.021 + 0.0035 × 5 − 0.021 × 2
$$= 0.3115 \text{ kmol}$$

Heat of reactions at 298.15 K

Reaction (A) $\Delta H^o_{r1} = 147.36 - 29.92 = 117.44$ kJ/mol EB
Reaction (B) $\Delta H^o_{r2} = 82.93 + 52.50 - 29.92 = 105.51$ kJ/mol EB
Reaction (C) $\Delta H^o_{r3} = -29.92$ kJ/mol EB
Reaction (D) $\Delta H^o_{r4} = 50.17 - 74.52 - 147.36 = -171.71$ kJ/mol styrene

Total heat of reaction,
$$\Delta H^o_r = 1000 \, [117.44 \, (0.315 + 0.021) + 105.51 \times 0.0105 - 29.92$$
$$\times \, 0.0035 - 171.71 \times 0.021]$$
$$= 36 \, 857 \text{ kJ (endothermic)}$$

Table 5.55 Heat Capacity Equation Constants for Products

Component	n_i kmol	Heat capacity (C^0_{mp2}) equation constants			
		$n_i \cdot a_i$	$n_i \cdot b_i \times 10^3$	$n_i \cdot c_i \times 10^6$	$n_i \cdot d_i \times 10^9$
EB	0.6500	− 23.87	436.23	− 274.31	65.75
Styrene	0.3150	− 11.63	209.56	− 152.79	44.38
C_6H_6	0.0105	− 0.40	5.15	− 3.37	0.83
C_7H_8	0.0210	− 0.74	11.83	− 7.35	1.73
H_2	0.3115	8.91	0.32	− 0.05	0.24
CH_4	0.0210	0.40	1.09	0.25	− 0.24
C_2H_4	0.0105	0.04	1.63	− 0.86	0.18
H_2O	15.0000	487.38	1.19	198.16	− 68.21
Total	16.3395	460.09	667.00	240.32	44.66

Let T_2 be the temperature of product gas stream, leaving the reactor.

$$\text{Enthalpy of products } H_2 = \int_{298.15}^{T_2} C^o_{mp2} \, dT$$
$$= 493 \, 405 - 36 \, 857 = 456 \, 548 \text{ kJ}$$

Solving by Mathcad,
$$T_2 = \textbf{798.79 K} \quad \textbf{or} \quad \textbf{525.64°C}$$

5.15 **THERMOCHEMISTRY OF MIXING PROCESSES**

It is a common experience that when a solute (either solid, liquid or gas) is dissolved in a solvent to make its solution, enthalpy change takes place. When a solid or gas is dissolved in the solvent (liquid), the heat evolved or absorbed is called the *heat of solution*, more correctly, the *heat of dissolution*. When two liquids are mixed, the heat effect is termed as the *heat of mixing*. Both are also known as *excess enthalpy*. These heat changes are measured at constant temperature usually at 18°C (291.15 K) or 25°C (298.15 K) and at atmospheric pressure or at 1 bar. It is expressed in different forms, e.g., kJ/kmol solution, kJ/kg solution, kJ/kmol solute, kJ/kg solute, etc. The heat of solution of an ideal solution is zero.

Basically, the heat of solution is defined as the heat change associated with the system when one mole of solute is dissolved in a definite number of moles of solvent, keeping the temperature constant and the pressure at 100 kPa a. The number of moles of solvent vary from 100 to 1800 and even more. When the number of moles is very high, the heat of solution at infinite dilution is obtained. Since the measurement of the heat of solution is made in a calorimeter, practical difficulty is observed in measuring the temperature changes when a large number of moles of the solvent are present. Therefore, from the practical point of view, the number of moles is usually restricted to about 200.

The heat effect can be exothermic (realized by the evolution of heat) or endothermic (realized by the absorption of heat).

The common nomenclature, internationally accepted, is as under.

When a solid or gas is dissolved in a solvent (such as water) or liquid is mixed with another liquid (e.g., mixing of two organic liquids) and heat is liberated, the dissolution or mixing is termed exothermic*. Heat effect of dissolution/mixing is endothermic when heat is absorbed. In other words, when a mixing process is exothermic, enthalpy of the mixture, so formed is less than that of the sum of enthalpies of consitituent components in ideal state. Similarly, for the endothermic mixing process, enthalpy of the mixture is higher than the sum of enthalpies of the constituent components in pure state.

The above convention will be followed in this book.

Let H_1 and H_2 be the enthalpies of two pure components mixed together. Let H_n^E represent the total heat of solution (of n moles) while the total enthalpy of the final solution is assumed to be H_m.

$$H_n^E = H_m (n_1 + n_2) - (n_1 H_1 + n_2 H_2) \tag{5.69}$$

where n_1 and n_2 are the number of moles of the two components mixed together. Consistent units need to be employed in the above equation.

Different systems will now be considered in the light of the above equation.

5.16   DISSOLUTION OF SOLIDS

Dissolution of solids in water is a very common process in the industry, the well-known examples being the dissolution of caustic soda, common salt, etc. Data are reported in Ref. 21 of the heat of solution of solids in water at 18°C (291.15 K).

Crystallization is the reverse process of dissolution. For all practical purposes, the heat of solution with a reverse sign is taken as heat of crystallization. Most data on the heat of crystallization indicate exothermic operation.

---

*This convention is reverse for dissolution of solids in water for the data, presented in *Perry's Chemical Engineer's Handbook* (8th edition, Ref. 21).

Heat of dissolution of solids can also be calculated using standard heat of formation data of crystalline solids and their solutions. Extensive data on heat of formation of inorganic compounds are available in Ref. 44. Heat of formaiton data for selected inorganic compounds are extracted from Ref. 44 and given in Appendix V.1.

Example 5.42 The heat absorbed when $Na_2CO_3.10 \ H_2O$ (hydrated crystals) is dissolved isothermally at 291.15 K (18°C) in a large quantity of water is 62.86 kJ per mol solute[21]. Calculate the heat of crystallization of 1 kg $Na_2CO_3.10H_2O$.

Solution   As indicated earlier, the heat of crystallization is just the opposite of the heat of solution.
Heat of solution of $Na_2CO_3.10 \ H_2O$ at 291.15 K = 62.86 kJ/mol solute (endothermic)
Molar mass of $Na_2CO_3.10 \ H_2O$ = 286.1414

$$\text{Heat of crystallization} = \frac{62.86 \times 1000}{286.1414}$$

$$= \textbf{219.68 kJ/kg solute (exothermic)}$$

Example 5.43   Calculate the heat of crystallization of $Na_2SO_4.10 \ H_2O$ using the data of heat of formation. Standard heat of formation of $Na_2SO_4(c)$ and $Na_2SO_4.10 \ H_2O(c)$ are − 1387.08 and − 4327.26 kJ/mol respectively.

Solution   From Appendix IV, ΔH_f° of $H_2O(1) = -285.82$ kJ/mol
The crystallization reaction can be written as
$$Na_2SO_4(c) + 10 \ H_2O(1) = Na_2SO_4.10 \ H_2O(c)$$
Using the thermodynamic laws of the heat of reaction,
Heat of crystallization = −4327.26 − (−1387.08 − 10 × 285.82)
$$= -81.98 \text{ kJ/mol (exothermic)}$$
The above heat of crystallization is also called the heat of hydration.

Note   The heat of solution of $Na_2SO_4.10 \ H_2O$ is reported[21] to be 78.461 kJ/mol (endothermic). Therefore, the heat of crystallization is −78.461 kJ/mol (exothermic). This value is lower than the value obtained in Example 5.43. Such a discrepancy is due to the neglect of the heat of dilution in the calculation of the heat of crystallization.

Example 5.44   Making use of heat of formation data (Ref. 44), calculate the heat of solution of boric acid.

Solution ΔH_f° of $H_2BO_3(s) = -1094.33$ kJ/mol at 25°C (298.15 K)
ΔH_f° of $H_2BO_3(ao) = -1072.32$ kJ/mol at 25°C (298.15 K)
Heat of soliution of $H_2BO_3 = -1072.32 - (-1094.33)$
$$= \textbf{+22.01 kJ/mol } \textbf{H}_2\textbf{BO}_3 \textbf{ (endothermic)}$$
Ref. 21 reports heat of soluiton of H_2BO_3 as 22.6 kJ/mol at 18°C (291.15 K). Both vlaues are in good agrement.

Example 5.45   (a) Making use of heat of formation data, calculate the heat of soluiton of $ZnSO_4$ in 15 H_2O by dissolving crystals of $ZnSO_4$ in water at 25°C (298.15 K). (b) Instead of $ZnSO_4$ crystals, if $ZnSO_4.7 \ H_2O$ (hydrated crystals) is used to prepare that same solution, what would be the heat of solution at 25°C (298.15 K)?

Solution   It is desired to prepate an aqueous solution of 1 mol of $ZnSO_4$ in 15 mol H_2O. The solution will have 37.40 mass % strength of $ZnSO_4$.
(a) Standard heat of formation data:

ΔH_f^o of $ZnSO_4(c) = -982.8$ kJ/mol   (Ref. Appendix V.1)

ΔH_f^o of $ZnSO_4$. 15 $H_2O = -1053.904$ kJ/mol   (Ref. 44)

$ZnSO_4(c) + [15\ H_2O(l)] = ZnSO_4$. 15 H_2O (sol)

Note that in the above equation, liquid water is neither formed nor destroyed in the dissolution process. Hence ΔH_f^o of $H_2O(l)$ is *not to be used* in calculation of heat of dissolution.

Heat of dissoluiton $= -1053.904 - (-982.8)$

$= \mathbf{-71.104\ kJ/mol\ ZnSO_4\ (exothermic)}$

(b) In this case, crystals of heptahydrate are used. The dissoultion process can be written as

$ZnSO_4$. 7 $H_2O(c) + [8\ H_2O(l)] = ZnSO_4$, 15 H_2O (sol) $+ 7\ H_2O(l)$

In this process, 7 mol H_2O, associated in the hydrate are separated as liquid.

ΔH_f^o of $ZnSO_4$. 7 $H_2O = -3077.75$ kJ/mol   (Ref. 44)

Heat of solutuon $= -1053.904 + 7\ (-285.83) - (-3077.75)$

$= \mathbf{23.036\ kJ/kmol\ (endothermic)}$

5.16.1   Enthalpy–Concentration Diagrams

In Sec. 2.5, properties of the solutions were discussed. It is known that the boiling point of a solution is higher than the boiling point of the solvent at a given pressure. Such a chart for NaOH–H_2O system (called Dühring lines) was presented by McCabe in 1935. The elevation of boiling point is attributed to the effect of heat of dissolution of the solute into the solvent and of the different heat capacity of the solution as compared to the solvent. A diagram representing the enthalpy of unit mass of the solution and the concentration of the solution for a given temperature is called enthalpy–concentration diagram. On this diagram, various isotherms are plotted. McCabe[45] presented such a diagram for NaOH–H_2O system in 1935 in which reference state for water was that of steam tables (i.e., zero enthalpy of water at 32°F (0°C or 273.15 K) and for sodium hydroxide was zero enthalpy for very dilute (infinitely) solution at 68°F (20°C or 293.15 K). This diagram is presented as Fig. 5.16 in SI units. On this diagram, various isotherms are plotted. Enthalpy–concentration diagrams are useful in the evaluation of (a) the heat required to be added to or removed from the solution when heating or cooling of the solution is carried out, and (b) the temperature of the resultant mixture when two different solutions having different concentrations and temperatures are mixed together by tie-line method.

Such diagrams can be prepared for different systems provided standard heat of formation and heat capacity data are available. Reference 44 gives extensive data on standard heat of formation (at 25°C or 298.15 K) for sodium hydroxide and its aqueous solutions. Heat capacity data for sodium hydroxide solutions are presented in Fig. 5.4.

In Table 5.56, standard heat of formation data are tabulated. These data are used to calcuate excess enthalpy (H^E) or heat of solution.

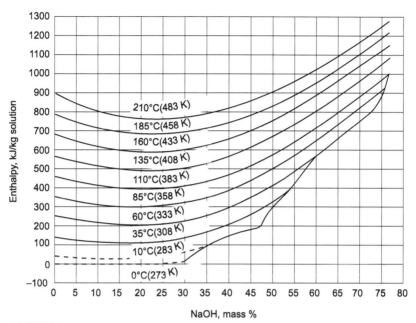

Fig. 5.16 Enthalpy–Concentration Diagram for NaOH–H$_2$O System[47]
(Reproduced with the permission of John Wiley & Sons, Inc., USA.)

Table 5.56 Slandard Enthalpy of Formation of Aqueous Solutions of NaOH[44]

Formula and Description	State	Mole fraction of NaOH, x_1	Mass fraction of NaOH, w_1	Standard enthalphy of formation at 25°C (298.15 K) ΔH_f°, kJ/mol
NaOH, 0 H$_2$O	c	1.0000	1.0000	−425.609
2.5 H$_2$O	aq	0.2857	0.4703	−452.290
3 H$_2$O	aq	0.2500	0.4252	−456.278
4.H$_2$O	aq	0.2000	0.3569	−461.935
4.5 H$_2$O	aq	0.1818	0.3303	−463.784
5 H$_2$O	aq	0.1667	0.3075	−465.185
6 H$_2$O	aq	0.1429	0.2701	−467.072
8 H$_2$O	aq	0.1111	0.2172	−468.905
10 H$_2$O	aq	0.0909	0.1817	−469.646
12 H$_2$O	aq	0.0769	0.1561	−469.972
15 H$_2$O	aq	0.0625	0.1289	−470.156
20 H$_2$O	aq	0.0476	0.0999	−470.198
25 H$_2$O	aq	0.0385	0.0816	−470.131
30 H$_2$O	aq	0.0323	0.0689	−470.060
40 H$_2$O	aq	0.0244	0.0526	−469.930
50 H$_2$O	aq	0.0196	0.0425	−469.834
75 H$_2$O	aq	0.0132	0.0287	−469.700
100 H$_2$O	aq	0.0099	0.0217	−469.646
150 H$_2$O	aq	0.0066	0.0146	−469.621
200 H$_2$O	aq	0.0050	0.0110	−469.608

Note The number in the first column indicates the number of moles of water mixed with one mole caustic soda.

Excess enthalpy data were fitted in empirical equation forms as under.

$$H^E = 1080.055\, x_1^3 x_2^3 - 219.519\, x_1^2 x_2^2 - 37.358 x_1 x_2 - 0.058 \quad (5.70)$$

where H^E = excess enthalpy, kJ/mol solution at 25°C (298.15 K)

x_1 and x_2 are mole fractions of NaOH and H_2O, respectively.

Equation (5.70) is accurate within 0.7% in the concentration range of $x_1 = 0.01$ to 0.286 (mass fraction, $w_1 = 0$ to 0.47). In an alternate form,

$$H^{E'} = 1925.263\, x_1^3 x_2^3 + 166.439\, x_1^2 x_2^2 - 29.813 x_1 x_2 - 43.772 \quad (5.71)$$

where $H^{E'}$ = excess enthalpy, kJ/mol NaOH at 25°C (298.15 K)

Equation (5.71) is accurate within 0.5% in the concentration range of $x_1 = 0.01$ to 0.286 (mass fraction, $w_1 = 0$ to 0.47). Figure 5.17 is the dilution curve for NaOH–H_2O system at 25°C (298.15 K).

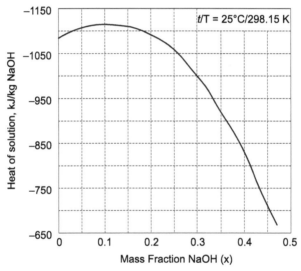

Fig. 5.17 Heat of Solution of Sodium Hydroxide in Water at 25°C (298.15 K)

Enthalpy–concentration diagram can be developed for other pressures with the help of fugacity of the components. The method is explained in detail in Ref. 45.

Example 5.46 Find the temperature of 25% NaOH solution, prepared by diluting 46% NaOH lye at 25°C (298.15 K) with water at 35°C (308 K). All percentages are by mass.

Solution On the chart (Fig. 5.16), place A representing 46% NaOH lye at 25°C (298.15 K). Place the point B representing pure water (0% NaOH) at 35°C (308 K). Join the points A and B. The tie-line AB intersects the vertical axis at 25% concentration to an isotherm of 329.5 K (56.5°C)

Example 5.47 Solve Example 5.46 with standard heat of formation data.

Solution Standard heat of formation data (Table 5.56) along with heat capacity chart (Fig. 5.4) can also be used for finding the temperature of final 25% solution.

Basis 100 (m_1) kg 46% solution.

This will contain 46 kg or 1.1501 kmol of NaOH and 54 kg or 2.9975 kmol of H_2O. Thus, the solution can also be written as NaOH, 2.6063 H_2O.

Final solution, m_2 = 46/0.25 = 184 kg of 25% strength. 100 kg of the final solution will contain 25 kg or 0.625 kmol of NaOH and 75 kg or 4.163 kmol of H_2O. Thus, final solution can be written as NaOH, 6.6608 H_2O.

ΔH_f° of NaOH, 2.6063 H_2O = –453.138 kJ/mol

ΔH_f° of NaOH, 6.6608 H_2O = –468.678 kJ/mol

NaOH, 2.6063 H_2O(sol) + H_2O(l) = NaOH, 6.6608 H_2O(sol)

$$\text{Heat of solution} = -467.678 - (-453.138)$$
$$= -14.54 \text{ kJ/mol (exothermic)}$$
$$\text{Heat generated} = 14.54 \times 1000 \times 1.1501$$
$$= 16\ 722.5 \text{ kJ at } 25^\circ\text{C (298.15K)}$$

84 kg water (m_w) is used at 35°C (308.15 K). Thus, it will add heat of 10°C (10 K) since water was assumed at 25°C (298.15) in the dissolution process.

From steam tables (Appendix IV.1)

Enthalpy of water at 35°C (308.15 K) = 146.65 kJ/kg at 1 atm

Enthalpy of water at 25°C (298.15 K) = 104.9 kJ/kg at 1 atm

Heat added of water = 84 (146.65 – 104.9) = 3507 kJ

Total heat for raising temperature of final solution,

$$H = 16\ 722.5 + 3507 = 20\ 229.5 \text{ kJ}$$

Average heat capcity of 25% solution, C_1 = 3.55 kJ/(kg · K) (Ref. Fig. 5.4)

Final solution temperature, $t_2 = 25 + \dfrac{20\,229.5}{(184 \times 3.55)} = 56.0^\circ\text{C}$

Example 5.48 A 100-kg solution of 32% N (by mass) is prepared by dissolving ammonium nitrate and urea in water at 25°C (298.15 K) in such a manner that mole ratio of NH_4NO_3 to urea is 1.1758. Its endothermic heat of dissolution is given by following emperical equation[47].

$$H^E = 40.3044 - 2.5962\,(m^\ominus) + 0.1582\,(m^\ominus)^2 - 3.4782 \times 10^{-3}\,(m^\ominus)^3 \text{ kJ/mol}$$
of NH_4NO_3. 1.1758 NH_2CONH_2

where ($m^\ominus$) = molality of solution

= moles of NH_4NO_3. 1.1758 NH_2CONH_2/kg water

Calculate heat effect of the solution.

Solution *Basis* 100 kg of solution containing 32% N

Molar mass of NH_4NO_3 = 80.0434

Molar mass of NH_2CONO_2 = 60.0553

Molar mass of nitrogen = 28.0134

Let n_a kmol of NH_4NO_3 be dissolved in water.

Urea dissolved = 1.1758 n_a kmol

Total nitrogen = n_a + 1.1758 n_a = 2.1758 n_a kmol

$$\equiv 60.9516\ n_a \text{ kg} \equiv 32$$
$$n_a = 0.525 \text{ kmol} = 42.02 \text{ kg } NH_4NO_3$$

Urea dissolved = 1.1758 × 0.525 × 60.0553 = 37.07 kg

Water in the soution = $100 - (42.02 + 37.07) = 20.91$ kg

Moles dissolved = 0.525 kmol of NH_4NO_3, 1.1758 NH_2CONH_2
= 525 mol

Molality $m^{\ominus} = \dfrac{525}{20.91} = 25.1076$ mol/kg water

Substituting $m^{\ominus}$ in the equation

$H^E = 40.3044 - 2.5962 \times 25.1076 + 0.1582 (25.1076)^2 - 3.4782 \times 10^{-3} (25.1076)^3$
= 19.7964 kJ/mol NH_4NO_3, 1.1758 NH_2CONH_2

For 100 kg of solution,

H^E (sol) = 19.7964×525 = **10 393 kJ (endothermic)**

5.17 LIQUID–LIQUID MIXTURES

The heat of dissolution of one liquid into another is calculated in a manner similar to that of a solid–liquid system. Enthalpy–concentration diagrams can also be plotted for a liquid–liquid system. Such a diagram representing H_2SO_4–H_2O system is given in Fig. 5.18. Similar diagrams for mixed acids, ammonia–water system, benzene–toluene system and nitrogen–oxygon system are given in Figs 5.21, 5.22 and 6.1 and 6.3, respectively.

Example 5.49 The endothermic heat of mixing n-amyl alcohol [pentanol-1, $C_2H_5(CH_2)_2CH_2OH$] and benzene (C_6H_6) to form a solution containing 47.3 mole % benzene is 816 kJ/mol solution at 20°C (293 K). Calculate the integral heat of solution of n-amyl alcohol and of benzene at this concentration.

Solution Heat of mixing = 896 kJ/kmol (endothermic)

Molar masses of n-amyl alcohol and benzene are 88 and 78, respectively.

Basis 1 kmol of solution containing 47.3 mole % benzene.

Benzene present in the solution = $0.473 \times 78 = 36.894$ kg

n-amyl alcohol present in the solution = $0.527 \times 88 = 46.376$ kg

Integral heat of solution of n-amyl alcohol = $\dfrac{896}{46.376}$ = **19.32 kJ/kg n-amyl alcohol**

Integral heat of solution of benzene = $\dfrac{896}{36.894}$ = **24.29 kJ/kg benzene**

Example 5.50 It is desired to dilute 93% aqueous sulphuric acid at 30°C (303 K) with 15% acid at 0°C (273 K). The final desired concentration of the acid is 77%. Use Fig. 5.18. All percentages are by mass. Calculate (a) the resultant temperature of the 77% solution, (b) the heat to be removed per kg of 77% acid to cool it from the above temperature to 25°C (298.15 K), (c) the answer (b) by taking the mean heat capacity of 77% H_2SO_4 between 20°C (293 K) and its boiling point, (d) by material balance the quantity of 15% acid to be mixed up with 100 kg 93% acid for getting 77% acid product, and (e) the answer (d) by using Fig. 5.18 and applying coordinate geometry principles.

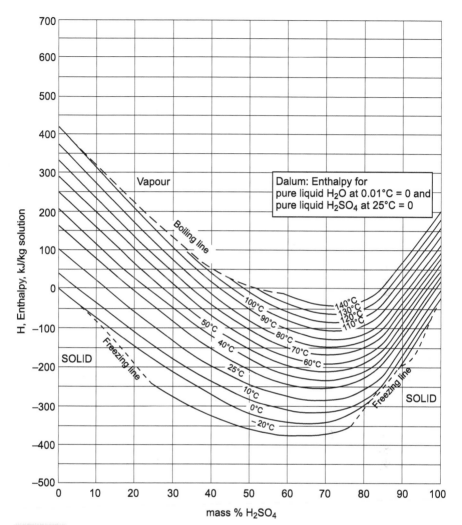

Fig. 5.18 Hx Diagram for H_2SO_4/H_2O (Redrawn from Data Contained in Ref. 44, 48 & 49)

Solution   Refer Fig. 5.18.

Place the point A to represent 93% H_2SO_4 at 30°C (303 K) and the point B to represent 15% H_2SO_4 at 0°C (273 K). Join A and B. The tie-line AB intersects the vertical line representing 77% H_2SO_4 at 106.5°C (379.5 K) (represented by the point C).

Thus, the resultant temperature of 77% solution will be 106.5°C (379.5 K), if no heat is lost to the surrounding during the mixing.

Enthalpy of 77% H_2SO_4 at 379.65 K = – 106.5 kJ/kg solution
From Fig. 5.5,

Heat capacity of 77% acid at 379.5 K = 2.06 kJ/(kg · K)

Heat capacity of 77% acid at 298.15 K = 1.94 kJ/(kg · K)

Enthalpy of 77% H_2SO_4 at 298.15 K = – 274 kJ/kg solution

Change in enthalpy of 77% acid when it is cooled from 379.5 K to 298.15 K = -274
$- (-106.5) = $ **-167.5 kJ/kg solution**
Based on an average heat capacity of 2.05 kJ/(kg · K) for the 77% solution (Ref.
Fig. 5.5), the enthalpy change = 2.05 (379.5 $-$ 298.15) = **166.8 kJ/kg solution**
Basis 100 kg of 93% acid
Let x kg of 15% acid be mixed to produce (100 + x) kg 77% acid.
Acid balance $0.93 \times 100 + x \times 0.15 = (100 + x)0.77$
$$x = 25.8 \text{ kg}$$
Let the intersection point at 77% strength on Fig. 5.18 be C. According to coordinate-
geometry principles (tie-line method),

$$\frac{93\% \text{ acid quantity}}{15\% \text{ acid quantity}} = \frac{CB}{CA} = \frac{9.9 \text{ units}}{2.5 \text{ units}}$$

Quantity of 15% acid required to be mixed = $100 \times \left(\frac{2.5}{9.9}\right)$ = **25.3 kg**

Example 5.51 Data on the heat of formation of aqueous sulphuric acid are given
in Table 5.57.

Table 5.57 Standard Heat of Formation of Aqueous Sulphuric Acid Solution[44]

Formula and Description	State	ΔH_f^o at 25°C (298.15 K) kJ/mol H_2SO_4	mass % H_2SO_4
H_2SO_4, 0 H_2O	1	$- 814.0$	100.0 - pure H_2SO_4
1 H_2O	aq	$- 841.79$	84.5
2 H_2O	aq	$- 855.44$	73.1
3 H_2O	aq	$- 862.91$	64.5
4 H_2O	aq	$- 867.88$	57.6
5 H_2O	aq	$- 871.48$	52.1
6 H_2O	aq	$- 874.22$	47.6
7 H_2O	aq	$- 876.37$	43.8
8 H_2O	aq	$- 878.08$	40.5
9 H_2O	aq	$- 879.43$	37.7
10 H_2O	aq	$- 880.53$	35.3
12 H_2O	aq	$- 882.13$	31.2
15 H_2O	aq	$- 883.62$	26.6
20 H_2O	aq	$- 884.92$	21.4
25 H_2O	aq	$- 885.59$	17.9
30 H_2O	aq	$- 885.98$	15.4
40 H_2O	aq	$- 886.46$	12.0
50 H_2O	aq	$- 886.77$	9.82
75 H_2O	aq	$- 887.29$	6.77
100 H_2O	aq	$- 887.64$	5.16
150 H_2O	aq	$- 888.19$	3.50
200 H_2O	aq	$- 888.63$	2.65

Note The number in the first column indicates the number of moles of water mixed with
one mole of sulphuric acid.

Solve Example 5.50 with the above data assuming that both acids are available at 298.15 K (25°C).

Solution   *Basis* 100 kg 93% acid and 25.8 kg 15% acid

Since the interpolation of heat of formation for intermediate concentration is required, data given in Table 5.57 are plotted in Fig. 5.19.

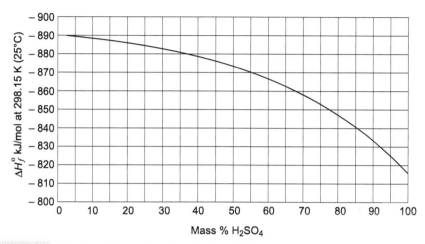

Fig. 5.19   Enthalpy of Formation of Sulphuric Acid Solution

Following values are read from Fig. 5.19.

For 93% H_2SO_4, $\Delta H_f^o = -830$ kJ/mol H_2SO_4

For liquid 100% H_2SO_4, $\Delta H_f^o = -814.0$ kJ/mol H_2SO_4

Heat of solution, $H_1^E = -830 - (-814.0) = -16$ kJ/mol H_2SO_4

For 15% H_2SO_4, $\Delta H_f^o = -886.2$ kJ/mol H_2SO_4

Heat of solution, $H_2^E = -886.2 - (-814.0) = -72.2$ kJ/mol H_2SO_4

For 77% H_2SO_4, $\Delta H_f^o = -851.0$ kJ/mol H_2SO_4

Heat of solution, $H_3^E = -851.0 - (-814.0) = -37$ kJ/mol H_2SO_4

93% solution contains 93 kg or 0.9482 kmol H_2SO_4 per 100 kg solution. 15% solution contains 15 kg or 0.1529 kmol H_2SO_4 per 100 kg solution. Hence 77% final solution will contain 0.9482 + 0.1529 (25.8/100) = 0.9876 kmol H_2SO_4.

0.9482 kmol H_2SO_4 in 100 kg 93% H_2SO_4(sol) + 0.0394 kmol H_2SO_4 in 25.8 kg 15% H_2SO_4 (sol) = 0.9876 kmol H_2SO_4 in 125.8 kg 77% H_2SO_4 (sol)

$$\text{Heat of soltuion} = 0.9876 \times 1000 \times (-37) - [0.9482 \times 1000 \times (-16)$$
$$+ 0.0394 \times 1000 \times (-72.2)]$$
$$= -36\ 541 - [-15\ 171 - 2845]$$
$$= -18\ 525 \text{ kJ at } 25°C \ (298.15 \text{ K}) \qquad \text{(exothermic)}$$

Average heat capacities of 93% H_2SO_4, 77% H_2SO_4 and 15% H_2SO_4 solutions are read as 1.6, 2.05 and 3.7 kJ/(kg · K), respectively. From Fig 5.5.

Heat evolved by cooling 93% H_2SO_4 solution to 25°C (298.15 K) = 100 × (30 − 25) × 1.6 = 800 kJ

Heat consumed by 15% H_2SO_4 solution to heat
up to 25°C (298.15 K) = 25.8(25 − 0) × 3.7 = 2386.5 kJ
Net heat evolved = 18 525 − 2386.5 + 800 = 16 938.5 kJ

Temperature of 77% solution = $25 + \dfrac{16938.5}{(125.8 \times 2.05)}$ = 90.7°C   or   363.85 K

Another important unit process in the organic industry is nitration. This reaction is usually carried out with the help of mixed acids. Figures 5.20 and 5.21 are useful in evaluating the enthalpy changes taking place during the mixing and also during the nitration reaction. The following examples clarify the use of these figures.

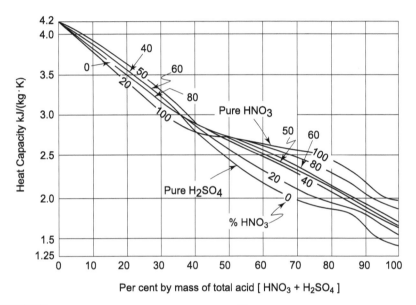

Fig. 5.20   Heat Capacity of Aqueons Mixed Acids[50]
(Reproduced with permission of Pergamon Press Ltd., UK)

Example 5.52   In Example 3.8, a mixed acid is produced by blending the three acids. If all the acids are available at 35°C (308.15 K), calculate the heat to be removed to maintain the temperature of the final mixed acid at 35°C (308.15 K).

Solution   *Basis* 1000 kg of mixed acid
For calculating the heat removal, the enthalpies of each of the acids to be mixed are calculated as follows

(a) *Spent acid at 35°C (308.15 K)*
Total acid content of spent acid = 11.3 + 44.4 = 55.7%

HNO_3 content of anhydrous mixture = $\left(\dfrac{11.3}{55.7}\right) \times 100 = 20.3\%$

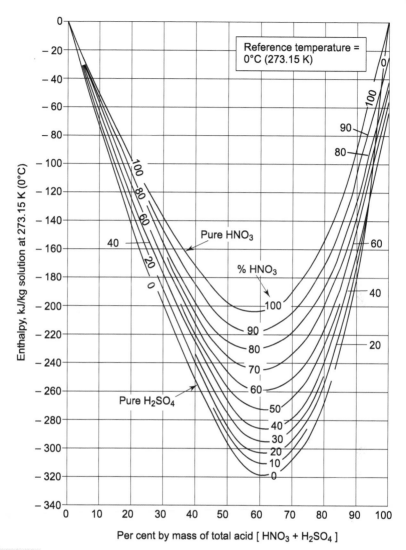

Fig. 5.21 Enthalpy-concentration Diagram for Mixed Acids[50]
(Reproduced with permission of Pergamon Press Ltd., UK

Locate 55.7% on the x-axis on Fig. 5.21 and then draw a vertical line which intersects the curve representing the 20.3% HNO_3 content. Read the enthalpy of the mixture equal to $- 296.7$ kJ/kg at 0°C (273.15 K).

Similarly, the heat capacity (C_{11}) of the mixture is found to be 2.45 kJ/(kg · K) from Fig. 5.20.

$$\text{Enthalpy of spent acid } H_1 = - 296.7 + 2.45 \ (308.15 - 273.15)$$
$$= - 210.95 \text{ kJ/kg}$$

(b) Aqueous 90% HNO₃ at 35°C (308.15 K)

Total acid content = 90%

HNO_3 content of anhydrous acid = 100%

Enthalpy at 0°C (273.15 K) = – 87.8 kJ/kg

$$C_{12} = 2.2 \text{ kJ/(kg} \cdot \text{K)}$$

Enthalpy of 90% HNO_3 H_2 = – 87.8 + 2.2 (308.15 – 273.15)

$$= – 10.8 \text{ kJ/kg}$$

(c) Aqueous 98% H_2SO_4 at 35°C (308.15 K)

Total acid content = 98%

HNO_3 content of anhydrous acid = 0%

Enthalpy at 0°C (273.15 K) = – 35.5 kJ/kg

$$C_{13} = 1.45 \text{ kJ/(kg} \cdot \text{K)}$$

Enthalpy of 98% $H_2\ SO_4$ H_3 = – 35.5 + 1.45 (308.15 – 273.15)

$$= 15.25 \text{ kJ/kg}$$

This value agrees well with the value read from Fig. 5.18.

(d) Final mixed acid at 35°C (308.15 K)

Total acid content = 92%

HNO_3 content of anhydrous acid = $\left(\dfrac{32}{92}\right) \times 100 = 34.8\%$

Enthalpy at 0°C (273.15 K) = –148.9 kJ/kg

$$C_{14} = 1.8 \text{ kJ/(kg} \cdot \text{K)}$$

Enthalpy of final acid, H_4 = –148.9 + 1.8 (308.15 – 273.15) = –85.9 kJ/kg

Heat of mixing = 1000 (–85.9) – [76.3 (–210.95) + 345.9

$$(–10.8) + 577.7 (+15.25)]$$

$$= –85\ 900 – [–16\ 095 – 3736 + 8810]$$

Heat of mixing = – **74 879 kJ** (**exothermic**)

Note   In case the exothermic heat is not removed from the system, the fortified mixed acid will attain a temperature

$$= \left[\frac{74\ 879}{(1000 \times 1.8)} + 308.15\right] = 349.75 \text{ K } (76.6°C)$$

Example 5.53   A typical run data are given by Albright[51] for the nitration of benzene using the mixed acid. The feed to the reactor is 400 kg/h benzene and 1135 kg/h mixed acid [consisting of 56% H_2SO_4, 31.5% HNO_3 and 12.5% H_2O (by mass]. Assume that conversion of benzene to nitrobenzene is 99.3% with 100% yield of mononitrobenzene (MNB). Calculate the heat changes taking place during the above reaction. Also, calculate the excess acid used.

Solution   *Basis* 400 kg/h of benzene feed to the reactor

Feed rate of mixed acid = 1135 kg/h

HNO_3 fed to the reactor = 1135 × 0.315 = 357.53 kg/h

The reaction taking place in the reactor is

$$C_6H_6 \ + \ HNO_3 \ = \ C_6H_5NO_2 \ + \ H_2O$$
$$78 \qquad\quad 63 \qquad\quad\ 123 \qquad\quad 18$$

For 100% conversion of benzene, nitric acid required

$$= \left(\frac{63}{78}\right) \times 400 = 323.08 \text{ kg/h}$$

$$\text{Excess HNO}_3 = 357.53 - 323.08 = 34.45 \text{ kg/h}$$

$$\% \text{ Excess} = \left(\frac{34.45}{323.08}\right) \times 100 = \mathbf{10.66}$$

Actual conversion of benzene to MNB is 99.3%

$$\text{Benzene converted} = 400 \times 0.993 = 397.2 \text{ kg/h}$$

$$\text{HNO}_3 \text{ consumed} = \left(\frac{63}{78}\right) \times 397.2 = 320.82 \text{ kg/h}$$

$$\text{Water formed} = \left(\frac{18}{78}\right) \times 397.2 = 91.66 \text{ kg/h}$$

The composition of spent acid at the end of the reaction is given in Table 5.58.

Table 5.58 Composition of Spent Acid

Component	kg/h	mass %
HNO_3	357.53 − 320.82 = 36.71	4.06
H_2O	141.87 + 91.66 = 233.53	25.84
H_2SO_4	633.60	70.10
Total	903.84	100.00

Feed mixed acid

$$\text{Total acid content} = 56 + 31.5 = 87.5\%$$

$$\text{HNO}_3 \text{ content of anhydrous acid} = \left(\frac{31.5 \times 100}{87.5}\right) = 36\%$$

$$H_1 \text{ at } 0°C \text{ (273.15 K)} = -186.5 \text{ kJ/kg}$$
$$C_{11} = 1.88 \text{ kJ/(kg} \cdot \text{K)}$$
$$H_1' \text{ at } 25°C \text{ (298.15 K)} = -186.5 + 1.88 \text{ (298.15} - 273.15)$$
$$= -139.5 \text{ kJ/kg}$$

Spent acid

$$\text{Total acid content} = 70.10 + 4.06 = 74.16\%$$

$$\text{HNO}_3 \text{ content of anhydrous acid} = \left(\frac{4.06 \times 100}{74.16}\right) = 5.5\%$$

$$H_2 \text{ at } 0°C \text{ (273.15 K)} = -288.9 \text{ kJ/kg}$$
$$C_{12} = 1.96 \text{ kJ/(kg} \cdot \text{K)}$$
$$H_2' \text{ at } 225°C \text{ (298.15 K)} = -288.9 + 1.96 \text{ (298.15} - 273.15)$$
$$= -239.9 \text{ kJ/kg}$$

Pure HNO$_3$

$$H_3 \text{ at } 0°C \text{ (273.15 K)} = 0 \text{ kJ/kg}$$
$$C_{13} = 1.98 \text{ kJ/(kg} \cdot \text{K)}$$
$$H_2' \text{ at } 25°C \text{ (298.15 K)} = 1.98 \text{ (298.15} - 273.15) = 49.5 \text{ kJ/kg}$$

Standard heat of reaction   The heat of formation of mono-nitrobenzene is + 12.50 kJ/mol at 25°C (298.15). For other compounds, refer Appendix IV.

$$\Delta H_r^o = -285.83 + 12.50 - (-174.10 + 49.08)$$
$$= -148.31 \text{ kJ/mol } C_6H_6$$
$$\text{Benzene reacted} = \frac{397.2}{78.1118} = 5.085 \text{ kmol/h}$$

Total heat changes, $\phi = 903.84 \, H_2' + 320.82 \, H_3' - 1135 \, H_1' + 5.085 \, \Delta H_r^o$

$$= 903.84 \, (-239.9) + 320.82 \, (49.5) - 1135$$
$$(-139.5) + 5.085 \, (-148.31) \, 1000$$
$$= -216 \, 831 + 15 \, 881 + 158 \, 333 - 754 \, 156$$
$$= -796 \, 773 \text{ kJ/h at } 25°C \, (298.15 \text{ K})$$
$$\equiv -221.326 \text{ kW} \quad \textbf{(exothermic)}$$

5.18 GAS–LIQUID SYSTEM

Absorption and desorption of gases (such as ammonia, hydrogen chloride, hydrogen bromide, etc.) in water and other liquids are commonly encountered in the process industry. Enthalpy changes are invariably associated with these unit operations.

The enthalpy–concentration diagram[52] for ammonia–water is given in Fig. 5.22. Pátek et al have presented[52] empirical equations for calculating thermodynamic properties of aqueous ammonia solutions. This diagram is useful in determining the equilibrium vapour composition of aqueous ammonia solution. Also, it can be used to determine the final temperature of aqueous solution prepared by mixing liquid or gaseous ammonia in water or by diluting a strong aqueous solution. It is quite useful in establishing material and energy balances of an ammonia absorption refrigeration system (refer Example 8.4) which is becoming increasingly popular for utilization of low-level heat such as low-pressure steam, flue gases from a furnance or diesel engine, etc.

In addition, data on the heat of formation for the ammonia–water system are presented in Table 5.59 which can be also be used for mixing calculations.

Table 5.59   Standard Heat of Formation of Aqueous Ammonia Solution[44]

Formula and Description	State	ΔH_f^o at 25°C (298.15 K) kJ/mol NH_3	mass % NH_3
NH_3, 0 H_2O	g	– 46.11	100.0
1 H_2O	aq	– 75.36	48.6
2 H_2O	aq	– 77.66	32.1
5 H_2O	aq	– 79.27	15.9
10 H_2O	aq	– 79.81	8.63
20 H_2O	aq	– 80.02	4.51
50 H_2O	aq	– 80.15	1.85
100 H_2O	aq	– 80.19	0.94
∞ H_2O	aq	– 79.69	0.0

Note   The number of the first column indicates the number of moles of water mixed with one mole of ammonia.

Example 5.54 Ammonia vapours (100%) from a nitrogenous fertilizer solution plant at the rate of 140 kg/h are taken to a vent scrubber. Vapours enter the scrubber at 101.3 kPa a (760 Torr) and 50°C (323 K). Water is sprayed at the top of the scrubber at 30°C (303 K). Assume (a) complete absorption of ammonia, and (b) 15% NH_3 (mass) strength of the solution. Calculate the temperature of resultant solution (i) with the help of Fig. 5.22, and (ii) with the help of data given in Table 5.59 and assuming average heat capacity of 15% ammonia solution to be 4.145 kJ/(kg · K).

Solution Enthalpy of ammonia gas at 101.3 kPa a (760 Torr) and 50°C (323 K)

= 1600.83 kJ/kg with T_0 = 273.15 K and h = 200 kJ/kg   (Ref. 24)

Correcting vapour enthalpy to h = 0 at T_0 = 273.15 K, place the point A to represent ammonia gas having enthalpy of 1400.83 kJ/kg. Point B represents liquid water at 30°C (303 K). Tie-line AB intersects 15% aqueous ammonia solution axis at **100°C (373 K)**.

For 15% NH_3, ΔH_f^o = – 79.3 kJ/mol NH_3 (Ref. Table 5.59)
For gaseous NH_3, ΔH_f^o = – 46.11 kJ/mol NH_3

Heat of solution = – 79.3 – (– 46.11) = – 33.19 kJ/mol NH_3

$$\text{Total heat generated} = \frac{33\,190 \times 140}{17.0305} = 272\,840 \text{ kJ/h} \equiv 75.789 \text{ kW}$$

$$\text{Aqueous solution rate} = \frac{140}{0.15} = 933.33 \text{ kg/h}$$

$$\text{Rise in temperature} = \frac{272\,840}{(4.145 \times 933.33)} = 70.5 \text{ K or °C}$$

Temperature of aqueous solution = 70.5 + 303 = 373.5 K **(100.35°C)**

Note Rise in temperature is significantly high. At 100.35°C (373.5 K), 15% solution will have very high vapour pressure. Hence, this result is of academic interest and the solution is kept cool by removal of heat.

Example 5.55 Solve Example 5.32 with the help of data given in Table 5.60.

Solution For 2% NH_3 (mass), ΔH_f^o = –80.14 kJ/mol NH_3
For gaseous NH_3, ΔH_f^o = –46.11 kJ/mol NH_3

Heat of solution = –80.14 – (– 46.11) = – 34.03 kJ/mol NH_3

$$\text{Heat generated for making 2\% solution} = 34\,030 \times \frac{2}{17.0305}$$

$$= \textbf{3996.4 kJ/100 kg solution}$$

$$\text{Error introduced in Example 5.32} = \left(\frac{3996.4 - 3456}{3996.4} \right) 100 = 13.5\%$$

Note   It may be seen that an error of the order of 13.5% is introduced by using the heat of reaction instead of data on the actual heat of formation. This is because the latter data are determined experimentally and also take into consideration heat of mixing.

Example 5.56   Refer Example 4.10 and Example 5.37. It is reported in literature[53] that the exothermic heat of solution of formaldehyde gas in water is substantially independent of concentration and has a value of 62.75 kJ/mol HCHO at 25°C (298.15 K) up to a concentration of about 40% (by mass) of HCHO. Considering a small concentration of methanol in the absorber feed gas, its heat of solution may be neglected. Assume heat capacity of 37% HCHO solution to be 3.45 kg/(kg · K). Make heat balance of the absorber and calculate the heat duty of the cooler.

Solution   Enthalpy of gas mixture, entering the absorber

$$\phi_5 = \phi_3 - \phi_4$$
$$= 15\ 505\ 407 - 11\ 395\ 056 = 4110\ 351 \text{ kJ/h} = 1141.76 \text{ kW}$$

Heat evolved by absorption, $\phi_6 = 111.375 \times 62.75 \times 1000$
$$= 6988\ 781 \text{ kJ/h} \equiv 1941.33 \text{ kW}$$

Table 5.60   Heat Capacity Data of Absorber Exit Gas Stream

Component	$\dot{n}_i$ kmol/h	Heat capacity (C^o_{mpab}) equation constants			
		$\dot{n}_i \times a_i$	$\dot{n}_i \times b_i \times 10^3$	$\dot{n}_i \times c_i \times 10^6$	$\dot{n}_i \times d_i \times 10^9$
CO_2	8.786	187.7	564.8	− 360.7	86.1
CO	0.990	28.7	− 2.8	11.5	− 4.7
H_2	1.980	56.6	2.0	− 0.3	1.5
CH_4	0.619	11.9	32.3	7.4	− 7.0
$(CH_3)_2O$	0.990	65.1			
O_2	212.712	5 536.0	2500.5	− 498.3	119.6
N_2	1058.167	31 310.1	− 5439.7	13 948.8	− 5256.6
H_2O	147.167	4 781.8	11.7	1 994.2	− 669.2
Total	1431.344	41 978.0	− 2331.2	15 052.6	− 5730.3

Enthalpy of absorber exit gas stream,

$$\phi_7 = \int_{298.15}^{323.15} C^o_{mpab}\ dT$$
$$= 1063\ 379 \text{ kJ/h} \equiv 295.38 \text{ kW}$$

Enthalpy of fresh water,
$$\phi_8 = 5532.15 \times 4.1868\ (303.15 - 298.15)$$
$$= 115\ 810 \text{ kJ/h} = 32.17 \text{ kW}$$

Enthalpy of formaldehyde solution,
$$\phi_9 = 9030.4 \times 3.45\ (323.15 - 298.15)$$
$$= 778\ 872 \text{ kJ/h} = 216.35 \text{ kW}$$

Heat removal in the cooler
$$= \phi_5 + \phi_6 + \phi_8 - \phi_7 - \phi_9$$
$$= 1141.76 + 1941.33 + 32.17 - 295.38 - 216.35 = \textbf{2603.53 kW}$$

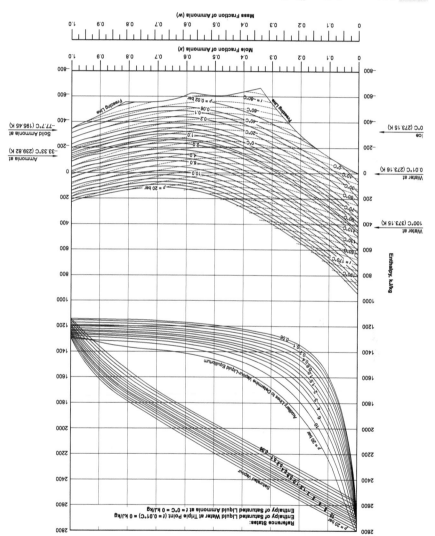

Fig. 5.22 Enthalpy-concentration Diagram[52] for NH_3-H_2O System
(Reproduced with the permission of Elsevier Science Ltd., UK).

5.19 HEAT OF SOLUTION BY PARTIAL MOLAR QUANTITIES

Excess enthalpy (an extensive property) of a solution can be defined as the difference between the actual enthalpy of the solution and the enthalpy value it would have as an ideal solution. Mathematically,

$$H_n^E = H_n - H_n^{id} \tag{5.72}$$

where H_n^E = excess enthalpy of n kmol mixture, kJ,

H_n = enthalpy of n kmol mixture, kJ

$$H_n^{id} = n_1 H_1 + n_2 H_2 \tag{5.73}$$

where, H_n^{id} = enthalpy of a kmol binary ideal solution

$n = n_1 + n_2$

H_1 and H_2 are pure component enthalpies at p and T.

If H_n^E is known, H_n can be calculated.

When expressed in terms of mole fractions of a binary system, Eq. (5.72) and Eq. (5.73) can be written as

$$H^E = H - H^{id} \text{ kJ/kmol mixture} \tag{5.74}$$

$$H^{id} = x_1 H_1 + x_2 H_2 \text{ kJ/kmol mixture} \tag{5.75}$$

For binary solutions (usually liquid mixtures), extensive H_n^E data are reported in literature which are determined experimentally. Experimental data are normally determined at one temperature and are correlated in empirical forms, such as

$$H^E = x_1 x_2 (A + Bx_1 + Cx_1^2) \tag{5.76}$$

or $$H^E = x_1 x_2 [a + b (x_2 - x_1) + c(x_2 + x_1)^2 + d(x_2 - x_1)^3] \tag{5.77}$$

Equation (5.77) is shown as a polynomial of order three but it can be a a polynomial of order two also. In other words, $d = 0$. Since H_1 and H_2 are constant for a given species, actual enthalpy H can now be expressed in terms of mole fractions and can be calculated for any given concentration for a definite temperature and pressure.

Partial molar enthalpy is defined as

$$H = \bar{H}_1 x_1 + \bar{H}_2 x_2 \tag{5.78}$$

where $\bar{H}_1$ and $\bar{H}_2$ are partial molar enthalpies at a given temperature and pressure. Partial derivative of H_m gives

$$\bar{H}_1 = \left(\frac{\partial H}{\partial x_1} \right)_{p,T,x_2} \tag{5.79}$$

and $$\bar{H}_2 = \left(\frac{\partial H}{\partial x_2} \right)_{p,T,x_1} \tag{5.80}$$

Since $x_1 + x_2 = 1$, it can be proved (Ref. 3) with the help of Gibbs–Duhem equation that

$$\bar{H}_1 = H + x_2 \frac{dH}{dx_1} = H - x_2 \frac{dH}{dx_2} \tag{5.81}$$

and
$$\bar{H}_2 = H + x_1 \frac{dH}{dx_2} = H - x_1 \frac{dH}{dx_1} \tag{5.82}$$

With the help of Eq. (5.81) and Eq. (5.82), expressions can be developed for $\bar{H}_1$ and $\bar{H}_2$ in terms of mole fractions. Equation (5.78) can then be used for calculating actual mixture enthalpy at a given temperature and pressure. Equations (5.81) and (5.82) suggest that when a plot of H vs x_1 is drawn, a tangent at a given concentration on the curve will give two abscissa on the y-axis; $x_1 = 0$ gives $\bar{H}_2$ and $x_1 = 1$ gives $\bar{H}_1$ on the y-axis.

Correlating equations for multicomponent systems are complex in nature and the reader is advised to check Ref. 54.

Example 5.57   Excess molar enthalpies for system acetone(1) and ethyl acetate(2) at 1 atm and 35°C (308.15 K) are reported by Shen et al[55] by the following empirical equation :

$$H^E = x_1 x_2 \,(542.4 + 55.4\,(x_2 - x_1) - 132.8(x_2 - x_1)^2$$
$$- 168.9 \,(x_2 - x_1)^3] \quad \text{kJ/kmol mixture}$$

Assume that average molar heat capacities of acetone and ethyl acetate are 124.8 and 134.9 kJ/(kmol · K), respectively.

(a) Calculate H over 0°C (273.15 K) for solutions heaving concentrations, ranging from $x_1 = 0$ to 1 in steps of 0.1.

(b) Develop expressions of $\bar{H}_1$ and $\bar{H}_2$ for concentrations, ranging from $x_1 = 0$ to 1 in steps of 0.1.

(c) Draw a graph of H va x_1. Draw tangents at $x_1 = 0.3$ and 0.6 and read values of $\bar{H}_1$ and $\bar{H}_2$ on the y-axis. Compare values, read from the graph, with those calculated in (b).

Solution

Reference temperature, $T_0 = 273.15$ K

Enthalpy of acetone at 308.15 K,

$$H_1 = 124.8\,(308.15 - 273.15) = 4368 \text{ kJ/kmol}$$

Enthalpy of ethyl acetate at 308.15K,

$$H_2 = 134.9\,(308.15 - 273.15) = 4721.5 \text{ kJ/kmol}$$

H^{id} at 308.15 K for the solution can be calculate by the equation,

$$H^{id} = H_1 x_1 + H_2 x_2 \tag{5.74}$$

For $x_1 = 0.1,$

$$H^E = 0.1 \times 0.9\,[542.4 + 55.4\,(0.9 - 0.1) - 132.8\,(0.9 - 0.1)^2$$
$$- 168.9\,(0.9 - 0.1)^3]$$
$$= 37.4 \text{ kJ/kmol mixture at 308.15 K} \quad \text{(endothermic)}$$

$$H = 37.4 + (4368 \times 0.1 + 4721.5 \times 0.9)$$
$$= 37.4 + 4686.2 = 4723.6 \text{ kJ/kmol mixture at 308.15 K}$$

In a similar manner, the following table is prepared.

Table 5.61 Actual Enthalpies of Acetone–ethyl Acetate Mixtures at 35°C (308.15K)

x_1	Enthalpy, kJ/kmol mixture			
	H^E	H^{id}	H	
0	0	4721.5	4721.5	(pure ethyl acetate)
0.1	37.4	4686.2	4723.6	
0.2	78.6	4650.8	4729.4	
0.3	111.8	4615.5	4727.3	
0.4	131.2	4580.1	4711.3	
0.5	135.6	4544.5	4680.1	
0.6	126.6	4509.4	4636.0	
0.7	107.1	4474.1	4581.2	
0.8	79.7	4438.7	4518.4	
0.9	45.0	4403.4	4448.4	
1.0	0	4368.0	4368.0	(pure acetone)

$$\bar{H}_1 = H + x_2 \frac{dH}{dx_1}$$

$$H = H^E + H^{id}$$
$$= x_1 x_2 [542.4 + 55.4 \, (x_2 - x_1) - 132.8 \, (x_2 - x_1)^2 - 168.9 \, (x_2 - x_1)^3]$$
$$+ 4368.0 x_1 + 4721.5 x_2$$

Substituting $x_2 = 1 - x_1$ and simplifying,

$$H = 4721.5 - 57.4 x_1 + 1137.7 x_1^2 - 3993.6 x_1^3 + 3909.2 x_1^4 - 1351.2 \, x_1^5.$$

$$\frac{dH}{dx_1} = -57.4 + 2275.4 x_1 - 11\,980.8 \, x_1^2 + 15\,636.8 \, x_1^3 - 6756.0 \, x_1^4$$

$$\bar{H}_1 = H + (1 - x_1) \frac{dH}{dx_1} \tag{5.81}$$

$$\bar{H}_1 = 4664.1 + 2275.4 x_1 - 13\,118.5 \, x_1^2 + 23\,624.0 \, x_1^3 - 18\,483.6 \, x_1^4$$
$$+ 5404.8 \, x_1^5 \tag{i}$$

Similarly $\bar{H}_2 = H + x_1 \dfrac{dH}{dx_2} = H - x_1 \dfrac{dH}{dx_1}$ \hfill (5.82)

$$\bar{H}_2 = 4721.5 - 1137.7 \, x_1^2 + 7987.2 \, x_1^3 - 11\,727.6 \, x_1^4 + 5404.8 \, x_1^5 \tag{ii}$$

Equations (i) and (ii) are to be used to calculate $\bar{H}_1$ and $\bar{H}_2$, listed in the following table.

Table 5.62 Partial Molar Enthalpies of Acetone and Ethyl Acetate at 35°C (308.15 K)

x_1	Partial molar enthalpy, kJ/kmol mixture	
	$\bar{H}_1$	$\bar{H}_2$
0	—	4721.5
0.1	4782.3	4717.0
0.2	4755.6	4722.9
0.3	4667.3	4752.9

(Contd.)

Table 5.62 (Contd.)

x_1	Partial molar enthalpy, kJ/kmol mixture	
	$\bar{H}_1$	$\bar{H}_2$
0.4	4569.4	4805.8
0.5	4488.9	4871.4
0.6	4434.3	4937.5
0.7	4402.3	4996.2
0.8	4384.2	5050.2
0.9	4372.3	5119.6
1.0	4368.0	—

H values, listed in Table 5.61, can also be calculated for each concentration using Eq. (5.78)

Figure 5.23 is the plot of H vs x_1.

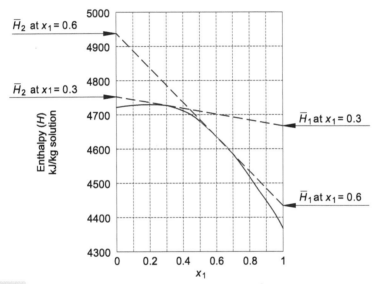

Fig. 5.23 Enthalpy of Acetone-Ethylacetate Solutions at 35°C (308.15 K)

At $x_1 = 0.3$, $\bar{H}_1 = $ 4667.0 and $\bar{H}_2 = 4753.0$ both in kJ/kmol

At $x_1 = 0.6$ $\bar{H}_1 = $ 4434.0 and $\bar{H}_2 = 4938.0$ both in kJ/kmol

Example 5.58 Excess molar enthalpies of methanol (1) and formic acid (2) at 1 atm and 30°C (303.15 K) are given by the following empirical equation.

$$H^E = x_1 x_2 [221.89 (2x_1 - 1)^3 + 231.41 (2x_1 - 1)^2 - 87.49 (2x_1 - 1) - 416.89] \text{ kJ/kmol mixture} \quad \text{(Ref. 56)}$$

Heat capacity equation constants for methanol and formic acid are available in Table 5.3. Repeat parts (a), (b) and (c) of Example 5.57 for this system.

Solution

Reference temperature, $T_0 = 298.15$ K

Enthalpy of methanol at 303.15 K,

$$H_1 = \int_{298.15}^{303.15} (54.7 - 22.0844 \times 10^{-3} T + 147.634 \times 10^{-6} T^2) dT = 926.17 \text{ kJ/kmol}$$

Enthalpy of formic acid at 303.15 K,

$$H_2 = \int_{298.15}^{303.15} (133.43 - 347.5111 \times 10^{-3} T + 785.7561 \times 10^{-6} T^2) dT$$

$$= 1509.52 \text{ kJ/kmol}$$

$$H^{id} = 926.17 \, x_1 + 1509.52 \, x_2$$

$$H^E = x_1 x_2 [(221.89 (2x_1 - 1)^3 + 231.41 (2x_1 - 1)^2 - 87.49 (2x_1 - 1) - 416.89]$$
$$+ 926.17 \, x_1 + 1509.52 \, x_2$$

$$= -1775.12 \, x_1^5 + 3512.16 \, x_1^4 - 1967.76 \, x_1^3 + 550.6 \, x_1^2 - 903.23 \, x_1$$
$$+ 1509.52$$

$$\frac{dH}{dx_1} = -8875.6 \, x_1^4 + 14\,048.64 \, x_1^3 - 5903.28 \, x_1^2 + 1101.2 \, x_1 - 903.23$$

$$\bar{H}_1 = H + x_2 \frac{dH}{dx_1}$$

Substituting for H and (dH/dx_1) and simplifying,

$$\bar{H}_1 = 7100.48 \, x_1^5 - 19412.08 \, x_1^4 + 17984.16 \, x_1^3 - 6453.88 \, x_1^2 + 1101.2 \, x_1$$
$$+ 606.29$$

$$\bar{H}_2 = H - x_1 \frac{dH}{dx_1}$$

$$\bar{H}_2 = 7100.48 \, x_1^5 - 10536.48 \, x_1^4 + 3935.52 \, x_1^3 - 550.6 \, x_1^2 + 1509.52$$

Table 5.63 Enthalpies of Methanol–formic Acid System at 30°C (303.15 K)

x_1	Enthalpy, kJ/kmol			
	H^E	H	$\bar{H}_1$	$\bar{H}_2$
0	0	1509.52	606.3	1509.52
0.1	−28.1	1423.07	668.0	1506.97
0.2	−52.6	1340.21	683.5	1504.39
0.3	−75.4	1259.11	701.4	1498.13
0.4	−94.1	1182.12	740.9	1476.27
0.5	−104.0	1113.62	800.1	1427.17
0.6	−102.0	1057.90	864.5	1347.98
0.7	−84.1	1017.04	915.8	1253.18
0.8	−54.1	988.74	940.2	1183.07
0.9	−20.3	964.24	936.7	1212.31
0.10	0	926.17	926.17	1458.44

Figure 5.24 is the plot of H vs x_1.

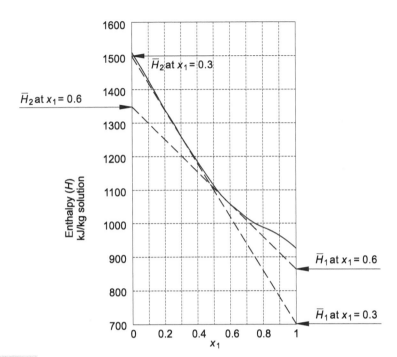

Fig. 5.24 Enthalpy of Methanol-Formic Acid Solutions at 30°C (303.15 K)

The following values are read from the figure.

At $x_1 = 0.3$ $\bar{H}_1 = 701.0$ and $\bar{H}_2 = 1498.0$ both in kJ/kmol

At $x_1 = 0.6$ $\bar{H}_1 = 865.0$ and $\bar{H}_2 = 1348.0$ both in kJ/kmol

Note Figures 5.23 and 5.24 can be considered as enthalpy–concentration diagrams with single (base) isotherm for the respective systems at 1 atm.

Dissolved inorganic salts have significant heat effect when dissolved in a binary mixture of organic liquids. Reference 56 gives such heat effects for various inorganic salts ($NaCl$, $CaCl_2$, $ZnCl_2$ and NH_4Cl) in the mixtures of methanol and formic acid.

Example 5.59 Plot $\bar{H}_m^E$ vs x_1 for acetone (1) - ethylacetate (2) system at 35°C (308.15 K), using data, calculated in Example 5.57. Find $\bar{H}_{m1}^E$ and $\bar{H}_{m2}^E$ at $x_1 = 0.3$ & 0.6.

Solution

Read $\bar{H}_{m1}^E$ and $\bar{H}_{m1}$ at $x_1 = 0.3$ & 0.6 from Fig. 5.25.

Partial molar excess enthalpies for sulphur trioxide (1)–water (2) system is reported[57] in literature. Partial molar enthalpy (H^E) is the heat of solution.

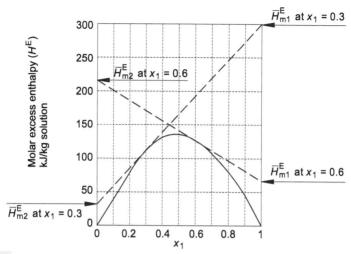

Fig. 5.25 Molar Excess Enthalpy of Aceton–Ethylacetate Solutions at 35°C (308.15 K)

Table 5.64 Partial Molar Heats of Dilution of Sulphur Trioxide (Liquid) in Water (Liquid)[57]

Mole fraction of $SO_3(1)$	Mass per cent			Enthalpy, kJ/mol		
	$SO_3(1)$	H_2SO_4	Free SO_3 (based on H_2SO_4)	H^E solution	$\bar{H}_2^E$ water in solution	$\bar{H}_1^E$ SO_3 in solution
(1)	(2)	(3)	(4)	(5)	(6)	(7)
0.00^a	0.0	0.0	—			− 181.079
0.02	8.33	10.2	—	− 3.266	− 0.042	− 161.192
0.04	15.60	19.1	—	− 6.322	− 0.084	− 157.005
0.05	19.00	23.2	—	− 7.913	− 0.335	− 156.168
0.07	25.1	30.8	—	− 10.969	− 0.879	− 154.074
0.10	33.6	40.5	—	− 15.282	− 2.093	− 134.438
0.15	44.0	53.8	—	− 21.562	− 3.559	− 125.981
0.20	52.6	64.4	—	− 27.758	− 5.066	− 117.691
0.25	59.7	73.1	—	− 32.657	− 10.844	− 98.683
0.30	65.6	80.6	—	− 36.802	− 16.663	− 83.317
0.35	70.5	86.4	—	− 39.649	− 21.604	− 73.269
0.40	74.8	91.6	—	− 41.868	− 26.502	− 64.812
0.45	78.4	96.1	—	− 43.585	− 32.657	− 56.940
0.50^c	81.6	100.0	—	− 44.338	− 44.338	− 44.338
0.52	82.5	—	6.4	− 43.752	− 66.654	− 22.609
0.55	84.5	—	15.4	− 42.287	− 71.887	−18.213
0.60	87.0	—	29.0	− 39.230	− 81.643	− 10.886
0.65	89.2	—	41.2	− 35.672	− 81.643	− 10.886
0.70	91.2	—	52.1	− 32.155	− 84.908	− 9.295
0.75	93.0	—	62.0	− 27.675	− 97.762	− 4.229
0.80	94.7	—	71.0	− 22.944	− 98.641	− 3.977
0.85	96.2	—	79.2	− 17.794	− 100.274	− 3.349
0.90	97.6	—	86.7	− 12.686	− 113.923	− 1.633
0.95	98.8	—	93.6	− 6.699	− 129.791	− 0.042
1.00^b	100.0	—	100.0	—	− 154.912	—

[a]Heat of solution of 1 mol SO_3 in an infinite amount of water.
[b]Heat of solution of 1 mol water in an infinite amount of SO_3.
[c]Heat of formation of pure H_2SO_4 liquid from $SO_3(1)$ and $H_2O(1)$; i.e., 0.5 mol solution = 49 g

H_2SO_4

Basis At reference temperature of 18°C (291.15 K),

$$\bar{H}_1^E = 0.0 \text{ kJ/mol for } SO_3(l), \bar{H}_2^E = 0.0 \text{ kJ/mol for } H_2O(l).$$

(Reproduced with the permission of the American Chemical Society, USA)

Example 5.60 A solution containing 96.1% H_2SO_4 is diluted with pure water to form 23.2% H_2SO_4 solution. Using partial molar quantities given in Table 5.64, calculate heat of dilution at 18°C (291.15 K).

Also, calculate the temperature of 23.2% solution after dilution. All percentages are by mass.

Solution *Basis* 100 kg 96.1% H_2SO

From Table 5.64, it is clear that 100 kg 96.1% H_2SO_4 solution contains 78.4 kg SO_3 and 21.6 kg water.

$$SO_3 \text{ in the solution} = \frac{78.4}{80.063} = 0.98 \text{ kmol}$$

$$H_2O \text{ in the solution} = \frac{21.6}{18.015} = 1.2 \text{ kmol}$$

The resultant solution has 23.2% H_2SO_4, i.e., 100 kg 23.2% H_2SO_4 contains 19 kg SO_3 and 81 kg water.

$$\text{Mass of the resultant solution after dilution} = \frac{78.4}{0.19} = 412.63 \text{ kg}$$

$$\text{Water added for dilution} = 412.63 - 100 = 312.53 \text{ kg}$$

$$\text{In the resultant solution, water} = \frac{(412.63 - 78.4)}{18.015} = 18.55 \text{ kmol}$$

The dilution process can be written as
0.98 kmol SO_3 in 1.2 kmol H_2O

$$+ 17.37 \text{ kmol } H_2O = 0.98 \text{ kmol } SO_3 \text{ in } 18.55 \text{ kmol } H_2O$$

In terms of enthalpies,
H^E of original solution + $\bar{H}_2^E$ of water + H^E of mixing = H^E of final solution

The enthalpies of aqueous acids can be calculated using the partial molal enthalpies given in Table 5.64.

H^E of original solution (96.1% acid) at 291.15 K

$$= 0.98 \times (- 56\ 940) + 1.2\ (-32\ 657)$$
$$= -55\ 801 - 39\ 188 = -94\ 989.6 \text{ kJ}$$

H^E of resultant solution (23.2% acid) at 291.15 K $= 0.98 \times (-156\ 168) + 18.57 (-335)$

$$= -153\ 045 - 6221 = -159\ 266.6 \text{ kJ}$$

H^E of water at 291.15 K = 0 kJ (basis of the table)

$$H^E = -159\ 266.6 - (-94\ 989.6)$$
$$= -64\ 277 \text{ kJ/100 kg original acid}$$
$$\equiv \textbf{-642.77 kJ/kg original acid}$$

From Fig. 5.5,

Average specific heat = 3.43 kJ/kg · K)

$$\text{Rise in temperature} = \frac{64\,277}{(412.63 \times 3.43)} = 45.4\,\text{K}$$

Final temperature of the resultant solution = 45.4 + 291.15 = 336.55 K (63.4°C)

Check: Using Fig. 5.18, it can be found that the resultant temperature of the final solution is 336 K (63°C).

Example 5.61 Refer Example 5.60. Instead of water at 291.15 K (18°C), if ice at 273.15 K (0°C) is added, what will be the heat of dilution?

Solution *Basis* 100 kg of original acid

Latent heat of fusion of ice at 273.15 K = 333.7 kJ/kg   (Refer Table 5.8)

Enthalpy of ice with reference to 291.15 K = − 333.7 − 18 × 4.1868

$$= -\,409.1\,\text{kJ/kg}$$

$H^E = -\,64\,277 + 409.1 \times 312.63 = 63\,620$ kJ/100 kg original solution

This means that energy, equivalent to **636.20 kJ/kg** of original acid need be supplied to maintain the temperature 291.15 K of the original acid.

Example 5.62 Refer Example 5.60. What is the quantity of ice required to be added in 96.2% acid for dilution so that the heat of dilution is zero?

Solution *Basis* 100 kg of original acid

Let x kg be the ice required. The ice should absorb all the exothermic heat of dilution.

$$410.4\,x = 64\,277$$

Therefore, $x = 156.62$ kg

This means that if 156.62 kg ice and (312.63 − 56.62) = 156.01 kg water at 291.15 K are added, the temperature of the resultant solution will rise over 291.15 K.

The elaborate thermodynamic treatment of the excess properties and partial molar properties are outside the scope of the book. However, this subject is dealt in sufficient detail in Refs. 3 and 21. Thermodynamics Research Centre, USA publishes International Data Series[58] for a number of binary systems of non-electrolyte organic substances.

Excess enthalpy data can be easily transformed into partial molar excess enthalpy. Normally, molar excess enthalpy is plotted against mole % concentration of the component for a given temperature. At a desired concentration, a tangent is drawn on the graph and the intercepts on the y-axis give partial molar excess enthalpies. This procedure is identical to the partial molar enthalpies, derived from the plot of actual enthalpy of mixture (H) and mole fraction.

It can noted that if H_1 and H_2 of pure components are assumed zero, $\bar{H}_1^E$ and $\bar{H}_2^E$ are same as $\bar{H}_1$ and $\bar{H}_2$. In other words, if reference states of pure components is selected as zero enthalpy at a temperature of excess enthalpy measurements, partial molar enthalpy of a component will be equal to its partial molar excess enthalpy.

Example 5.63   Derive equations for partial molar excess enthalpies for methanol (1)-formic acid (2) system at 30°C (303.15 K) and tabulate values for $x_1 = 0$ to 1 in steps of 0.1. Also plot H^E vs x_1 and read $\bar{H}_1^E$ and $\bar{H}_2^E$ for $x_1 = 0.3$

Solution

$H^E = x_1 \, x_2 \, [221.89 \, (2x_1 - 1)^3 + 231.41 \, (2x_1 - 1)^2 - 87.49 \, (2x_1 - 1)$
$- 416.89]$ kJ/kmol mixture

Substituting $x_2 = 1 - x_1$ and simplifying,

$$H^E = -1775.12 \, x_1^5 + 3512.16 \, x_1^4 - 1967.76 \, x_1^3 + 550.6 \, x_1^2 - 319.88 \, x_1$$

$$\frac{dH^E}{dx_1} = -8875.6 \, x_1^4 + 14048.64 \, x_1^3 - 5903.28 \, x_1^2 + 1101.2 \, x_1 - 319.88$$

$$\bar{H}_1^E = H^E + x_2 \frac{dH^E}{dx_1}$$

$$= 7100.48 \, x_1^5 - 19412.08 \, x_1^4 + 17984.16 \, x_1^3 - 6453.88 \, x_1^2$$
$$+ 1101.2 \, x_1 - 319.88$$

Similarly,

$$\bar{H}_2^E = H^E - x_1 \frac{dH^E}{dx_1}$$

$$= 7100.48 \, x_1^5 - 10536.48 \, x_1^4 + 3935.52 \, x_1^3 - 550.6 \, x_1^2$$

Using the equations of $\bar{H}_1^E$ and $\bar{H}_2^E$, values are tabulated for x_1 in Table 5.65.

Table 5.65   Partial Excess Molar Enthalpies of Methanol(1) and Formic Acid(2) at 30°C (303.15 K)

x_1	$\bar{H}_1^E$ kJ/kmol	$\bar{H}_2^E$ kJ/kmol
0	−319.88	0
0.1	−258.18	−2.553
0.2	−242.71	−5.126
0.3	−224.78	−11.386
0.4	−185.27	−33.248
0.5	−126.10	−82.350
0.6	−61.65	−161.54
0.7	−10.34	−256.34
0.8	13.98	−326.46
0.9	10.51	−297.21
1.0	0	−51.08

Fig. 5.26 is the plot of H^E vs x_1.

At $x_1 = 0.3$, $\bar{H}_1^E = $ **−225.0 kJ/kmol**   and $\bar{H}_2^E = $ **−11.4 kJ/kmol**

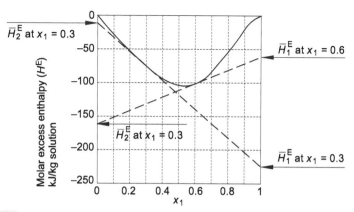

Fig. 5.26 Molar Excess Enthalpy of Methanol-Formic Acid Solutions at 30°C (303.15 K)

5.20   DATA SOURCES

There are a number of institutions in the world which have compiled thermodynamic data for organic and inorganic compounds. Among these, Thermodynamics Research Centre (TRC), USA, is one of the oldest and highly respected data centres in the world. The TRC Thermodynamic Tables (formerly, the API Research Project 44 and the Manufacturing Chemists Association Research Project) are the most favourably cited source of evaluated thermophysical and thermodynamic information (Ref. 59). Founded by Dr F D Rossini in 1942, the Centre is constantly engaged in updating the information.

Design Institute for Physical Property Data (DIPPD), sponsored by the American Institute of Chemical Engineers (AIChE), USA, is also actively engaged in compiling the physical, thermodynamic and transport properties of various compounds. Further supplements are periodically published covering data on additional chemicals.

National Institute of Standards and Technology (NIST), USA, is yet another source which have brought out NIST Chemistry WebBook (Ref. 8), available online.

In addition to the above, there are a large number of other data sources such as DECHEMA databooks, Ullmann's Encyclopedia of Industrial Chemistry, *Perry's Chemical Engineers' Handbook*[21], etc. A series of tables are published by the Commission on Thermodynamics and Thermochemistry of the Physical Chemistry Division of the International Union of Pure and Applied Chemistry (IUPAC)[60], compiling internationally agreed values of the thermodynamic properties of liquids and gases. The reader may refer the relevant references for obtaining the requisite data for process engineering calculations.

EXERCISES

5.1 A thermic fluid (derived from a petroleum stock) is used as a heating medium in a particular process. A pump sucks the thermic fluid at atmospheric pressure and 200°C

(473 K). The circulation rate is 10 000 L/h. The fluid discharged from the pump, passes through a heater (coil type) where it receives the heat from the product gases of combustion. The heat transfer rate is 232.6 kW. The motor of the pump consumes 1.1 kW. The overall mechanical efficiency of the pump and motor is 50%. The pressure of the fluid at the outlet of the heater is 100 kPa g. Assume (i) negligible kinetic energy changes, (ii) negligible potential energy changes, (iii) negligible friction losses and (iv) no heat loss to the surrounding. If the mean specific gravity and mean heat capacity of the fluid are 0.75 and 2.68 kJ/(kg · K), respectively at the operating conditions, calculate the outlet temperature of the fluid. **[241.7°C (514.85 K)]**

5.2 Temperature of pure oxygen is raised from 350 to 1500 K. Calculate the amount of heat to be supplied for raising the temperature of 1 kmol oxygen using the following C_{mp}^0 data given in Table 5.1[5, 7] and the absolute enthalpies given in Table 5.22.

[(i) 39 122.6 kJ; Ref. 5 (ii) 39 066 kJ; Ref. 7
(iii) 39 146 kJ; Table 5.22]

5.3 Heat capacity data for gaseous SO_2 are reported in Table 5.1[7, 9] and also by the following equation[61].

$$C_{mp}^0 = 43.458 + 10.634 \times 10^{-3} T - 5.945 \times \frac{10^5}{T^2}$$

Calculate the heat required to raise the temperature of 1 kmol pure sulphur dioxide from 300 to 1000 K (27 to 727°C), using the above three equations. Also, calculate the same by using absolute enthalpies given in Table 5.22.

[(a) 34 164.6 kJ/kmol (Ref. 7) (b) 34 385.8 kJ/kmol (Ref. 9)
(c) 33 871.9 kJ/kmol (Ref. 61) (d) 33 564 kJ/kmol (Table 5.22)]

5.4 In a fertilizer plant, naphtha (C:H = 6:1) is used as the feedstock. The gas mixture coming out of the absorber has the following composition by volume on dry basis: CH_4: 0.25%, CO: 0.38% CO_2: 0.10%, H_2: 74.62%, N_2: 24.35% and Ar: 0.3%.

The gas mixture contains 0.0126 kmol water vapour per kmol of the dry gas mixture. The mixture comes out at 70°C (343 K) and is passed through a methanator preheater where it is heated to 345°C (618 K). Calculate the heat duty of the preheater per 100 kmol of the dry gas mixture. If the above gas mixture is saturated with water vapour when it comes out of the absorber, find the total pressure of the gas mixture at the inlet of the preheater. **[(a) 818 540 kJ, based on data of Table 5.1**
(b) 817 114 kJ, based on data of Table 5.22 (c) 25.05 bar a]

5.5 A heat exchanger for cooling a hot hydrocarbon liquid uses 10 000 kg/h of cooling water, which enters the exchanger at 21°C (294 K). The hot oil at the rate of 5000 kg/h enters at 150°C (423 K) and leaves at 65°C (338 K) and has an average heat capacity of 2.51 kJ/(kg · K). Calculate the outlet temperature of water.
[46.5°C (319.65 K)]

5.6 A mixture of isomeric diphenyl-diphenyloxides (Diphyl DT*) is used as a thermic fluid in a liquid phase heating system[20]. The thermic fluid enters an indirect fired heater at 180°C (453 K) and leaves it at 260°C (533 K). The heat capacity of the fluid is given by

$$C_l = 1.436 + 0.002 \ 18 \ T \ kJ/(kg · K)$$

where *T* is in K.
 (i) Calculate the supply of heat in the heater per kg of the liquid heated.
 (ii) If the heat capacity of Diphyl DT at 180°C (453 K) and 260°C (533 K) are 2.03 and 2.206 kJ/(kg · K) respectively, how much error will be involved in the computation of heat load using the mean heat capacity value?
[(i) 200.9 kJ/kg (ii) −15.7%]

*Registered trade mark of Bayer, Germany.

5.7 Liquid benzene, C_6H_6, at 30°C (303 K) is mixed and dissolved continuously in liquid toluene, C_7H_8, at 100°C (373 K) in molar proportion 3:2 in an insulated mixing tank. If the heat of mixing is assumed to be zero, what is the temperature of the mixed solution?

Table 5.66 Heat Capacity Data [21] for Benzene and Toluene

Temperature °C (K)	Heat capacity (C_l), kJ/(kg · K)	
	Benzene	Toluene
10 (283)	1.591	1.524
65 (338)	2.018	—
86 (358)	—	2.236

(a) Assume the variation of the heat capacity is linear with temperature, i.e.
$$C_l = a + bT \text{ kJ}(kg \cdot K)$$
where a and b are constants.   [63.45°C (336.6 K)]

(b) Solve the problem by using data given in Table 5.3.   [61.1°C (334.25 K)]

5.8 Using Antoine equation, calculate vapour pressure of
(a) acetic acid at 43°C (316.15 K)
(b) sulphur trioxide at 62°C (335.15 K)   [(a) 5.48 kPa (b) 2.253 bar]

5.9 Using Watson equation, calculate latent heat of vaporization of
(a) acetone at 40°C (313.15 K)
(b) carbon disulphide at 140°C (413.15 K)
[(a) 30.072 kJ/mol (b) 21.98 kJ/mol]

5.10 Using Antoine equation, calculate the normal boiling point (T_B) of chlorobenzene. Also, calculate its latent heat of vaporization at T_B using Riedel equation.
[(a) 129.27°C (402.42 K) (b) 35 450 kJ/kmol]

5.11 Using Riedel equation and NIST equation, calculate latent heat of vaporization at T_B and at 25°C (298.15 K) for the following compounds.
(a) Benzene
(b) Acetone

Table 5.67 Latent Heat of Vaporization

Equation	λ_v at T_B, kJ/kmol		λ_v at 25°C (298.15 K), kJ/kmol	
	Benzene	Acetone	Benzene	Acetone
5.26	30 628	30 091	—	—
5.27	30 712	29 101	33 826	30 984
5.25	—	—	31 811	30 931

5.12 Naphthalene is evaporated in a jacketed closed vessel. Pure naphthalene is fed to the vessel at 30°C (303 K) and is vaporised at atmospheric pressure by condensing the eutectic mixture of diphenyl-diphenyl oxide vapours in the jacket at 171 kPa a. Assume no subcooling of the vapours. Calculate the quantity of eutectic mixture of diphenyl oxide condensed per 100 kg naphthalene evaporated.
Data on Naphthalene[21]:
Formula: $C_{10}H_8$
Molar mass = 128.1735
Melting point = 80.2°C (353.2 K)
Boiling point = 218°C (491 K)

Latent heat of fusion, $\lambda_f = 150.7$ kJ/kg
Latent heat of vaporization, $\lambda_v = 316.1$ kJ/kg
Heat capacity of solid naphthalene,
$$C_s = -0.092 + 0.0046 \, T \text{ kJ}/(\text{kg} \cdot \text{K})$$
where T is the temperature in K

Table 5.68 Heat Capacity of Liquid Naphthalene

Temperature, °C (K)	C_l kJ/(kg · K)
80 (353)	1.738
200 (473)	2.135

Assume linear relationship of C_l with T and use the same for evaluating the heat load. Use data given in Table 5.6. **[277.1 kg eutectic mixture]**

5.13 Superheated steam at a pressure of 4.4 bar a and 270°C (543.15 K) is available from one source at the rate of 10 000 kg/h. Another source supplies saturated 4.4 bar a steam at the rate of 7500 kg/h. Both the streams are mixed. Assuming no heat loss, calculate the conditions of steam after mixing.
[4.4 bar a, 216°C (489.15 K), superheated]

5.14 Superheated steam is available at 5 bar a and 250°C (523.15 K). Calculate the quantity of water needed to be sprayed at 30°C (303.15 K) for saturating 100 kg of superheated steam. **[8.15 kg]**

5.15 A cylinder drying range (in a textile mill) uses saturated steam at 310 kPa a. The low-pressure steam is obtained by pressure reduction from steam source at 780 kPa a and desuperheating with condensate saturated at atmospheric pressure. The letdown system is shown in Fig. 5.27.

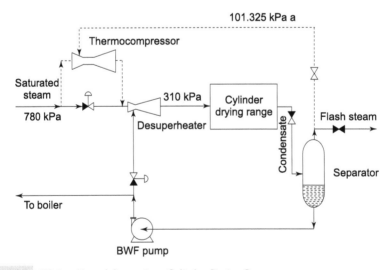

Fig. 5.27 Efficient Use of Steam in a Cylinder Drying Range

As a part of an energy-saving drive, it is proposed to compress the flash steam at atmospheric pressure through a steam jet thermocompressor (an ejector) with the help of motive 780 kPa a saturated steam. This proposed modification is indicated in dotted lines in Fig. 5.27. Calculate the percentage reduction in steam consumption of 780 kPa a with the use of the thermocompressor. **[6.35%]**

5.16 In a fertilizer plant, partial oxidation of naphtha yields the gas mixture having the composition on a dry basis:

H_2: 55.7%, CO: 34.5%, CO_2: 2.8%; CH_4: 0.5% and N_2: 6.5% (by volume)

Steam to dry gas mixture is 1.85 on molar basis.

The temperature of the gas mixture is 1200°C (1473 K). The hot gases are passed through a waste heat boiler (WHB) in which they are cooled to 300°C (573 K) by heat exchange with water. Saturated steam is produced at 40 bar g. Based on 100 kmol of gas mixture, calculate the amount of steam generated. Assume that water is fed at 20°C (20 K) lower than its saturation temperature (why?) and there is no heat loss to surroundings. **[5452 kg]**

5.17 Liquid ammonia is stored at 705 kPa a in a tank. It is discharged to an atmospheric storage. Calculate the percentage flash vapours produced letting down the pressure.

Table 5.69 Properties of Ammonia[26]

Pressure, kPa a	Saturation temperature °C (K)	Enthalpy, kJ/kg		
		Sensible h	Total H	Latent λ_v
705	14 (287.15)	265.56	1475.1	1209.6
101.3	− 33.3 (239.82)	49.1	1418.7	1369.6

[Reference state: $h = 200$ kJ/kg at 0°C (273.15 K)] **[15.8%]**

5.18 In Fig. 5.28, a two-stage compressor is demonstrated to liquefy ammonia vapours. This is a common system for atmospheric ammonia storage facility. Vapours from the storage tank are sucked at 108.4 kPa a (saturated) at the rate of 100 kg/h. Compressed vapour from the first stage are taken to a flash cooler where liquid ammonia obtained from the aftercooler of the second stage is sprayed. The product rate from the flash cooler is 100 kg/h liquid ammonia at 3°C (276 K). The cooled saturated vapours are sucked in the second stage. The vapours discharged by the second stage are cooled in the aftercooler in which the cooling water enters at 32°C (305 K). Calculate (a) the quantity of liquid ammonia obtained from the after cooler, and (b) the flow rate of cooling water in the aftercooler in kg/s assuming a rise of 8°C (8 K). Use data of Table 5.70.

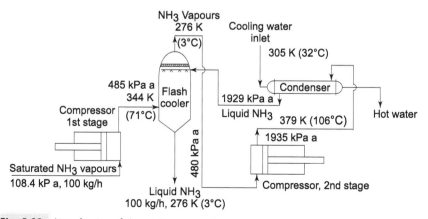

Fig. 5.28 Liquefaction of Ammonia

Table 5.70   Properties of Ammonia[26]

Conditions of ammonia vapours	Pressure kPa a	Saturation temperature °C (K)	Enthalpy, kJ/kg		
			Sensible h	Total H	Latent λ_v
Saturated	108.37	− 32 (241)	54.97	1420.65	1365.68
Superheated	485.0	71 (344)		1632.68	
Saturated	480.0	3 (276)	213.92	1464.93	1251.00
Superheated	1935.0	106 (379)		1663.91	
Saturated	1930.3	48 (321)	431.07	1491.07	1060.00

[(a) 137.13 kg/h (b) 1.402 kg/s]

5.19 A chiller has a refrigeration load of 65 kW at −20°C (253.15 K) in a bulk drug plant. It is met by evaporating refrigerant R-134a at 101.325 kPa a in shell. Saturated liquid R-134a at 40°C (313.15 K) is throttled through an expansion valve to the chiller for the purpose. Neglecting heat gain from atmosphere and assuming that R-134a vapour from the chiller shell leave with 10°C (10 K) superheat, calculate the requirement of liquid R-134a at 40°C (313.15K)

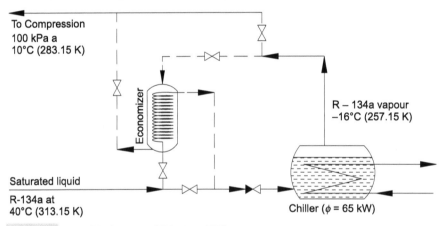

Fig. 5.29   Use of Refrigerant 134a in a Chiller

As an energy-conservation measure, vapours from the chiller are utilized to cool incoming liquid at 40°C (313.15 K) and leave the economizer at 100 kPa and 10°C (283.15 K). Assuming average heat capacity of saturated liquid R-134a to be 1.35 kJ/(kg · K), calculate temperature of liquid R-134a before the expansion valve. Also, calculate the requirement of liquid R-134a in the chiller with economizer in opeation. Read thermodynamic properties of saturated R-134a from Table 5.7. Additional enthalpy date of R-134a are as under.

Table 5.71   Enthalpy of Superheated R-134a[26]

Pressure, kPa a	Temperature	Enthalpy, (kJ/kg)
101.325	−16°C (257.15K)	391.0
100	10°C (283.15K)	412.0

(Requirements of liquid R-134a at 40°C (313.15 K) without and with economizer are 0.4456 and 0.4176 kg/s, respectively.)

5.20 Pure liquid carbon dioxide is available at 0°C (273.15 K). It is required at 1.0 MPa g and 40°C (313 K) for purging purpose. Using the p–H diagram for CO_2 (Fig. 5.11), (a) calculate the per cent of vapour formed by pressure reduction from saturation pressure to 10 bar g, and (b) calculate the heat required to be provided in a vaporiser to achieve final gas at 40°C (313 K). **[(a) 27.7% (b) 311 kJ/kg CO_2]**

5.21 In Example 5.19, pure CO_2 was assumed to be available at 200 bar a for dry ice production. Assume now that the composition of dry gas is as follows:

CO_2: 94.7%, H_2: 1.5%, N_2: 3.0% and O_2: 0.8% (by volume)

Also, consider that CO_2 condenser (shown in Fig. 5.10), employing ammonia as refrigerant, is not used. Calculate (a) the heat load on the water cooler for the production of 100 kg/h of dry ice, (b) the temperature and quantity of CO_2 liquid produced by venting the inerts to maintain pressure in the condenser if cooled gas at 40°C (313 K) is let down from 200 bar to 40 bar a, and (c) the raw-gas requirement for 100 kg of dry ice production.

Table 5.72 Properties of Carbon Dioxide[24]

Temperature,°C/K	Saturation pressure, bar	Latent heat of liquid CO_2, kJ/kg
–4/269.15	31.301	242.44
–3/270.15	32.166	239.65
–2/270.15	33.038	236.79
–1/272.15	33.939	233.86
0/273.15	34.859	231.00

Hint Use pseudo-critical properties of the gas mixture for finding the correction in heat capacity or use Fig. 5.3.

[(a) 17.936 kW (b) (– 3.3°C) 269.85 K, 78.0% liquefaction (c) 307.82 kg or 7.192 kmol]

5.22 Liquid ammonia at – 24°C (244 K) is transported in an uninsulated tank wagon[62]. The average ambient temperature is 25°C (298.15 K). The inside volume of the tank wagon is 60.663 m³. The wagon is loaded with 32 tonnes of ammonia (total). In transit, the wagon receives the heat from the atmosphere as given by the equation

$$\phi = 1.3 \, (T_a - T) + 3.76 \text{ kW}$$

where T_a is the ambient temperature and T is the temperature of ammonia inside the tank wagon in K.

Calculate the time required to attain – 17°C (256.15 K) in the wagon of ammonia by two methods: (a) the numerical integration approach for each 2°C (2 K) rise in temperature, and (b) use average values of temperature and heat exchange rates.

Table 5.73 Properties of Saturated Ammonia[24]

Temperature °C (K)	Saturation pressure kPa a	Density, kg/m³		Enthalpy, kJ/kg	
		h Liquid	H Vapour	ρ_l Liquid	ρ_g Vapour
–29 (244.15)	125.48	676.25	1.0844	68.32	1425.06
–27 (246.15)	138.06	673.50	1.1858	77.25	1427.94
–25 (248.15)	151.63	671.25	1.2947	86.20	1430.77
–23 (250.15)	166.24	668.70	1.4114	95.17	1433.55

(Contd.)

Table 5.73 (Contd.)

Temperature °C (K)	Saturation pressure kPa a	Density, kg/m³		Enthalpy, kJ/kg	
		h Liquid	H Vapour	ρ_l Liquid	ρ_g Vapour
−21 (252.15)	181.97	666.15	1.5364	104.17	1436.30
−19 (254.15)	198.86	663.60	1.6699	113.18	1438.97
−17 (256.15)	216.97	661.05	1.8124	122.22	1441.61

[(a) 7.319 h (b) 7.283 h]

5.23 Dry air is transported in 50 mm NB pipe at the rate of 1650 Nm³/h. Air enters the pipe at 190°C (463 K) and is utilized at another end of the pipe which is 150 m away. The pipe is bare and the ambient temperature is 35°C (308 K). The heat loss from such a pipe is given by Fig. 5.30. Assume that the heat capacity of dry air is 1.006 kJ/(kg · K). Calculate the temperature of air at the utilisation point by adopting the numerical integration approach for each 10°C (10 K) cooling.

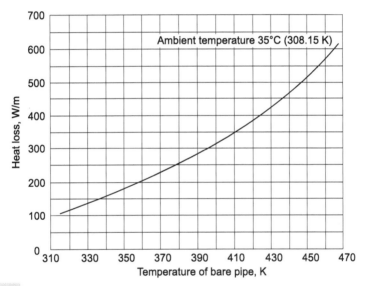

Fig. 5.30 Heat Loss from Bare Pipe of 50 mm NB Size

[98.45°C (371.6 K)]

5.24 Calculate the bubble point (T_{BB}) and dew point (T_{DP}) of a benzene–toluene mixture having 0.6 mole fraction benzene at 101.325 kPa. Also, determine enthalpy of the liquid mixture at T_{BB} and that of the vapour mixture at T_{DP} above 0°C (273.15 K). Compare the enthalpy values with those read from Fig. 6.1. Assume that the mixture is an ideal solution.

[T_{BB} = 89.6°C (362.75 K), Enthalpy at T_{BB} =13 281 kJ/kmol liquid mixture T_{DP} = 95.85°C (369.0 K), Enthalpy at T_{DP} = 45 821 kJ/kmol vapour mixture]

5.25 Natural gas having the following composition[63] is compressed and cooled to 41.4 bar a and − 6.5°C (266.5 K). Calculate the liquid and vapour fractions.

Table 5.74 Natural Gas Liquefaction

Component	mole %	K_i
CH_4	89.57	2.70
C_2H_6	5.26	0.38
C_3H_8	1.97	0.098
$i\text{-}C_4H_{10}$	0.68	0.038
$n\text{-}C_4H_{10}$	0.47	0.024
C_5H_{12}	0.38	0.0075
C_6H_{14}	0.31	0.0019
C_7H_{16}	0.24	0.0007
CO_2	1.12	0.9000

[**L = 0.041, V = 0.959 mole fractions**]

5.26 A partial condensation process, based on cryogenic principle, is selected for upgrading a crude hydrogen stream to the required purity. The feed source for the cold box is a crude stream from a demethanizing unit[38] and contains 75% hydrogen, 20% methane, 4.5% ethane and 0.5% nitrogen (by volume). At first, any moisture present in the feed gas is removed in the absorber. It is available at 27.5 bar a and 27°C (300 K). In the revert gas brazed aluminium exchanger of the cold box, the incoming gas mixture is cooled to − 162°C (111 K) by the exchange of heat with revert gases (Fig. 5.31). The required refrigeration is achieved partly by throttling the condensed liquid to 140 kPa a. Uncondensed gases in the separator are reverted through the exchanger and are recycled to the process. Low pressure gas is used as a fuel.

The equilibrium constant K of the components can be calculated using data given in Table 5.14.

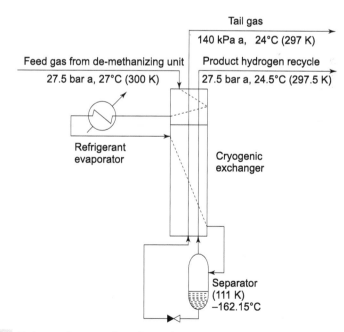

Fig. 5.31 Hydrogen Recovery from Gases from De-Methanizing Unit

The product hydrogen and tail gas leave the cold box at 24.5°C (297.5 K) and 24°C (297 K), respectively. Heat infilteration from the atmosphere amounts to 20.9 kW for the plant, processing the feed gas at the rate of 18 720 Nm^3/h. Supplementary refrigeration is provided in the form of an external refrigeration set. Calculate (a) the recovery of hydrogen defined as kmol hydrogen recycled to that in the feed, and (b) the purity of product hydrogen stream in terms of hydrogen.

Table 5.75 Enthalpy of Gases[26]

Conditions	Enthalpy*, kJ/kg			
	Hydrogen	Methane	Ethane	Nitrogen
27.5 bar a and 27°C(300 K)	3972.1	888.43	607.82	305.67
27.5 bar a and 24.5°C(297.5 K)	3935.7	883.44	604.90	303.17
140 kPa a and 24°C(297 K)	3917.6	907.34	665.26	308.14
NBP, °C/K	−252.78/20.37	−161.48/111.67	−88.58/184.57	−195.8/77.35

*Reference state: Enthalpy of saturated liquid at NBP = 0 kJ/kg

[(a) 99.45% (b) 95.1% (c) 4.69 kW (1.334 TR)]

5.27 Calculate the heat of formation of the following compounds at 25°C (298.15 K) using the data on heats of combustion.
(a) Gaseous n-heptane
(b) Gaseous ethyl alcohol
(c) Liquid 1, 3-butadiene

[(a) − 187.62 (b) − 234.95 (c) + 87.19 all in kJ/mol]

5.28 Calculate the standard heat of formation of the following liquids at 25°C (298.15 K) using the data of standard heat of formation of vapours at 25°C (298.15 K) and the latent heat of vaporization at 25°C (298.15 K).
(a) Water
(b) Methanol
(c) Carbon disulphide
For water, refer steam tables (Appendix V.1). For methanol and carbon disulphide, use NIST equation [Eq. (5.27)].

[(a) − 285.82 (b) − 238.99 (c) 89.72; all in kJ/mol]

5.29 Calculate the energy required to dissociate a kilogram of sodium bicarbonate at 25°C (298.15 K).
$$2 \ NaHCO_3(s) = Na_2CO_3(s) + CO_2(g) + H_2O(g)$$
[807.15 kJ/kg of $NaHCO_3$]

5.30 In the ferrite process for the manufacture of caustic soda, soda ash and gangue from pyrites roaster are mixed and heated. The following reaction takes place and CO_2 evolves. Calculate the standard heat of reaction at 25°C (298.15 K).
$$Na_2CO_3(s) + Fe_2O_3(s) = Na_2O.Fe_2O_3(s) + CO_2(g)$$
ΔH_f^o for $Na_2O.Fe_2O_3$ (s) = −1412.2 kJ/mol
[149.17 kJ/mol Na_2CO_3 or kJ/mol Fe_2O_3]

5.31 Refer Exercise 4.17. Make the heat balance and calculate the heat to be added or removed from the system using the absolute enthalpy data given in Table 5.22.
[81 522 kJ (endothermic)]

5.32 Refer Exercises 3.24 and 4.3. Assume heat of formation of coke ($CH_{0.6}$) to be 101.1 kJ/mol at 25°C (298.15 K). Calculate the heat generated during decoking assuming products of combustion as carbon dioxide and water. **[35 kJ]**

5.33 Refer Example 4.20. Make heat balance of the plant assuming that air is preheated in the heat exchanger up to 250°C (523 K).

[Heat transfer duty of R I = 2612.6 kW

Heat transfer duty of R II = 5559.2 kW

Steam generation in boiler = 12 888.2 kg/h

Steam consumption in evaporator = 4011.7 kg/h]

5.34 Obtain an empirical equation for calculating the heat of reaction of temperature T (in K) for the reactions

(a) $CH_4(g) + C_2H_4(g) = C_3H_8(g)$

[*Ans.* $\Delta H_{rT} = 78\ 154 - 27.598\ T + 49.565 \times 10^{-3}\ T^2 - 29.686 \times 10^{-6}\ T^3 + 6.622 \times 10^{-9}\ T^4$]

(b) $CO(g) + H_2O(g) = CO_2(g) + H_2(g)$

[*Ans.* $\Delta H_{rT} = -40\ 198 - 11.544\ T + 34.02 \times 10^{-3}\ T^2 - 22.018 \times 10^{-6}\ T^3 + 4.956 \times 10^{-9}\ T^4$]

(c) $CO(g) + 2\ H_2(g) = CH_3OH(g)$

[*Ans.* $\Delta H_{rT} = -74\ 748 - 61.38\ T + 25.827 \times 10^{-3}\ T^2 - 15.76 \times 10^{-6}\ T^3 - 10.49 \times 10^{-9}\ T^4$]

Using the same equation, calculate the heat of reaction at 320°C (593 K) for the reaction (c). **[– 100 078 kJ/kmol]**

5.35 Enthalpy of a sour gas mixture from a refinery having composition; H_2S: 0.57%, CO_2: 2.46%, N_2: 0.31%, CH_4: 88.41%, C_2H_6: 5.33%, C_3H_8: 2.07% and $n\text{-}C_4H_{10}$: 0.85% (by volume), can be satisfactorily represented by the following equation[64] in the pressure range of 3000 to 5000 psia (206.4 to 344.7 bar a) and 250 to 350°F (394 K to 482 K).

$$H = -34.38 + 0.7209\ t' + 7.763 \times 10^{-6}\ t'^2 + 1.075 \times 10^5/p$$

where H = Enthalpy, Btu/lb

t' = Temperature, °F

p = Pressure, psia

Convert the above equation in SI units.

5.36 Refer Exercise 4.15. Assume that the gaseous mixture enters the reactor at 315°C (588 K). Using the data of C^0_{mpi} given in Table 5.1, calculate the outlet temperature of the product gas stream leaving the reactor. **[396.45°C (669.6 K)]**

5.37 Typical compositions of feed gas from various hydrogen-production plants to a high-temperature shift converter are given in Table 5.76.

Table 5.76 Typical Compositions of Feed gas to HT Shift Converter

Gas	Partial oxidation of natural gas vol. %	Partial oxidation of fuel oil vol. %	Reforming of natural gas vol. %
CO	37	46	15
H_2	60	48	56
CO_2^*	2	5	7
N_2	–	–	21.7
Ar	1	1*	0.3
Steam to Gas ratio (x)	1.8		1.2

*Includes sulphur compounds also

Prove that in the temperature range of 345°C (618 K) to 510°C (783 K), the rise in temperature (in K) across the converter will be

$$\Delta T = \frac{12.5a}{1 + 1.2x}$$

where   a = moles of CO reacted per 100 moles of dry inlet gas

and   x = steam to dry gas mole ratio at the inlet

Hint   Use the mean heat capacity in the range 345°C (618 K) to 510°C (783 K) and assume that changes in composition due to the reaction does not appreciably affect the mean heat capacity of the gas mixture. Also, take the average heat of reaction between 618 K and 783 K.

5.38   Oxides of nitrogen (NO_x) are the pollutants. The offgases from the dissolution of uranium oxides contain nitrogen, oxygen and nitrogen oxides. In order to eliminate NO_x from the gases, a converter is employed[65] in which zeolite extrudates (of 1.5 mm diameter) are packed. The offgases are mixed with ammonia and passed through a catalyst bed, thereby reducing NO_x concentration to 50 ppm (v/v). The reaction taking place in the converter is

$$8\ NH_3(g) + 6\ NO_2(g) = 7\ N_2(g) + 12\ H_2O(g)$$

The bed temperature increases significantly during the conversion [up to 760°C (1033 K)], depending on the inlet NO_x concentration due to the exothermic heat of reaction. The conversion efficiency is nearly 100% when the bed temperature does not exceed about 480°C (753 K). At higher bed temperatures, the conversion efficiency drops to as low as 85% due to cracking of the excess ammonia gas which is needed to drive the reaction to completion. For temperature control, nitrogen is introduced along with the offgases and ammonia, if necessary. To prevent the formation of ammonium nitrate, the bed temperature is not allowed to drop below 315°C (588 K). Figure 5.32 represents the process schematically. Calculate (a) the excess ammonia, and (b) the exit temperature of gases.

[**(a) 56.6% (b) 430.6°C (703.75 K)**]

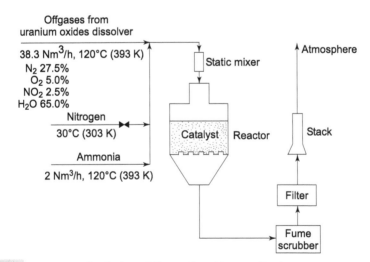

Fig. 5.32   Elimination of NO_x from Offgases from Uranium Oxides

5.39 Refer Exercise 5.38. Assume that offgases from the dissolver have the composition: N_2: 26.5%, O_2: 5.0%, NO_2: 3.5% and H_2O: 65.0% (v/v).

Flow rate of offgases and ammonia are kept constant. Calculate the required flow rate of nitrogen for the control to exit temperature at 480°C (753 K).

[7.31 Nm³/h]

5.40 In the manufacture of benzaldehyde, a mixture of dry air and toluene is fed to the converter at a temperature of 175°C (448 K) and 100 kPa g pressure. The mixture passes through the catalyst bed in the converter. The product gas stream leaves the converter at 195°C (468 K). The reaction proceeds as follows:

$$C_6H_5CH_3(g) + O_2(g) = C_6H_5CHO(g) + H_2O(g)$$

In order to maintain the high yield of benzaldehyde, dry air is supplied in 100% excess. The side reaction taking place is the combustion of toluene to CO_2 and H_2O.

$$C_6H_5CH_3(g) + 9\ O_2(g) = 7\ CO_2(g) + 4\ H_2O(g)$$

Pilot runs indicate that at the above operating conditions, the overall conversion is 13% based on toluene. Approximately, 0.5% of the toluene charged burns to CO_2 and H_2O.

Assume that the mean heat capacity of benzaldehyde between 25°C (298.15 K) and 195°C (468 K) is 130 kJ/(kmol · K). Calculate (a) the composition of the wet gas stream leaving the converter, and (b) the heat to be removed from or added to the system per kmol toluene fed to the converter.

[(a) C_7H_8: 8.36%; C_6H_5CHO: 1.20%; O_2: 17.59%;
N_2: 72.32%; CO_2: 0.34% and H_2O: 0.19 (on mole basis)
(b) 34 843 kJ heat liberated per kmol toluene fed to the converter

5.41 In the process for manufacture of carbon disulphide (CS_2), natural gas is reacted with sulphur vapours over an activated catalyst according to the equation:

$$\overset{\text{Activated catalyst}}{CH_4(g) + 2\ S_2(g)} \underset{704°C\ (977\ K)}{=} CS_2(g) + 2\ H_2S(g)$$

Pilot runs indicate that with natural gas containing 60 mole % CH_4 and 40 mole % N_2 reacting with sulphur vapours, S_2, the conversion of sulphur is 80% when 2 moles of natural gas are fed per mole of S_2(g). Refer Fig. 5.33.

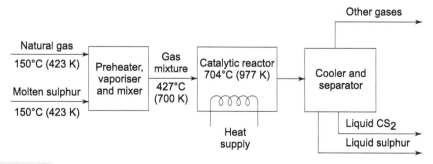

Fig. 5.33 Manufacture of Carbon Disulphide

The temperature in the catalyst reactor is maintained at 704°C (977 K) by supplying heat to the reactor. The gaseous mixture leaving the reactor passes through a cooler and separator where liquid carbon disulphide and liquid sulphur are separated.

Calculate (a) the excess reactant and the percentage excess of the reactant, (b) the kg of CS_2 produced per kmol of $S_2(g)$ (c) the analysis, mole %, of the hot gaseous mixture leaving the catalytic reactor, (d) the heat change, kJ per kmol of $S_2(g)$ entering the reactor to maintain the temperature at 704°C (977 K) using absolute enthalpies, given in Table 5.21 and (e) the vapour pressure of CS_2 at 25°C (298 K), using the Antoine equation. Absolute enthalpies for S_2 at 700 K and 977 K are + 22 951 and 33 118 kJ/kmol respectively.

[(a) CH_4 in 140% excess (b) 30.4 kg CS_2 produced per kmol $S_{2(g)}$ feed (c) CH_4: 26.67%; N_2: 26.67%; S_2: 6.67%; CS_2:13.33%; H_2S: 26.66% (on mole basis) (d) − 2806 kJ/kmol S_2 (exothermic) (e) 48.1 kPa]

Notes (i) From answer (e), it is clear that liquid carbon disulphide had appreciable vapour pressure of about 48.1 kPa even at 298.15 K. This means that the CS_2 should be cooled to a lower temperature than 298.15 K or some other means should be provided for separating out the CS_2, e.g., adsorption on activated carbon, so as to reduce the potentially high losses of CS_2 in waste gas streams.

(ii) Answer (d) indicates that the reaction is slightly exothermic under operating conditions. However, in actual practice, the radiation and convection heat losses will be encountered from the hot shell of the reactor. Hence some heat may have to be supplied to the reactor in actual use.

5.42 The recovery of sulphur from hydrogen sulphide is achieved by the oxidation of H_2S which is available from petroleum refineries when the sour natural gas is purified. The H_2S-rich gaseous stream, also containing some inerts (e.g., N_2) is converted to liquid sulphur by the oxidation process. The two principal equipment in the plant are a furnace boiler where a portion of the H_2S is oxidized to SO_2 to form liquid sulphur. The main reactions are

$$H_2S(g) + 1.5\ O_2(g) = SO_2(g) + H_2O(g)$$
$$[SO_2(g) + 2\ H_2S(g) = 3\ S(1) + 2\ H_2O(g)]$$

The simplified flow diagram of the process is Fig. 5.34.

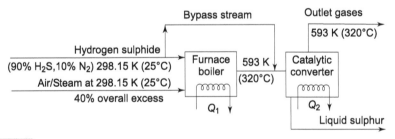

Fig. 5.34 Recovery of Sulphur from Hydrogen Sulphide

Calculate (a) the composition (volume percent) of the hot gases, leaving the converter. Assume 40% overall excess air and complete conversion of H_2S and SO_2 to sulphur. (b) The heat transfer at Q_1 in kJ/kmol of H_2S, entering the furnace boiler, to maintain the temperature 320°C (593 K), assuming no heat losses (c) The heat transfer at Q_1 in kW for a production of 9000 kg/h of sulphur.

[(a) O_2: 6.11%; N_2: 83.73%; H_2O: 10.16% (on mole basis)
(b) – 417 390 kJ/kmol H_2S (exothermic)
(c) Heat evolved at Q_1 is 10 869.5 kW]

5.43 Refer Exercise 4.44. Assume that the gas mixture enters the reactor at 66.2 bar a and 300°C (573 K).

(a) Assuming ideal gas behaviour of ingoing and outcoming gas mixtures, calculate the temperature of outcoming gas mixture.

(b) At the operating pressure and temperature, residual enthalpy for the ingoing gas mixture is 962 kJ/kmol mixture while that for the outgoing gas mixture is 914 kJ/kmol gas mixture. Based on the real gas enthalpies, calculate the temperature of outgoing gas mixture.   [(a) 331.85°C (605.0 K) (b) 333.25°C (606.4 K)]

5.44 A jacketed bubble column reactor is used for continuous production of (mono) chloracetic acid (MCA). Such a reactor behaves like an ideal mixed flow reactor in which composition is uniform and does not change with time. Cooling water is used as a cooling medium in the jacket. Reaction of acetic acid can be written as

$$CH_3COOH(l) + CL_2(g) = CH_2ClCOOH(l) + HCl(g)$$

The reaction is carried out at 1.1 atm a and 100°C (373 K). Feeds to the reactors are introduced at 40°C (313 K). Conversion of acetic acid is restricted to 50% to avoid formation of dichloroacetic acid (DCA). Chlorine is fed in 20% excess over stoichiometric requirement.

Liquid is withdrawn from the side at the top while unconverted chlorine and hydrogen chloride saturated with acetic acid (AA) and MCA leave from top of the column. Gas and vapour are taken to an overhead condenser in which cooling water is used as cooling medium. Most of the AA and and MCA are condensed and recycled back to the reactor. Cooled gas–vapour mixture at 40°C (313 K) escape the condenser from the top. For a production rate of 1000 kg/h MCA, calculate (a) heat of reaction at the reaction temperature , (b) heat duty of the overhead condenser, and (c) heat duty of the jacket.   (a) ΔH_r = –87.842 kJ/mol reactant at 100°C (373.15K)
(b) 43.347 kW (c) 214.713 kW

5.45 Unsteady-state kinetics have assumed importance in the industry to define the safe limits of operating conditions of a reactor. Transient material and energy balance calculations together with reaction rate calculations make it possible to identify the runaway conditions which may lead to explosion.

The rate of thermal decomposition of molten salt in a continuous stirred tank reactor (CSTR) is defined as[66]

$$R = \frac{dm}{d\theta} = m \frac{\{e^{(0.080\,73T - 40.1841)}\}}{183672}$$

where R = Rate of conversion of reactant to gaseous product, kg/s
   m = Mass of the reactant in the reactor, kg
   T = Temperature of mass, K
   θ = Time, s

The decomposition reaction is exothermic in nature and the heat of reaction is 607 kJ/kg of reactant assuming the reactant in molten condition and the products in gaseous condition. It is nearly constant in the temperature range of 262°C (547K) to 307°C (580 K). Average heat capacity of the mass in the reactor may be taken as 1.675 kJ/(kg . K).

Assume that the reactor is charged with 250 kg of reactant and its temperature is 262°C (535 K). If the feed to the reactor is cut off and outside cooling is shut off, the system behaves like a batch reactor. Also assume that the reactor is well insulated.

Thus, the reactor conditions can be considered adiabatic.

Calculate the rate of reaction, mass of reactant and the reaction temperature after 24 s using iterative calculations.   [**0.029 65 kg/s, 249.3 kg and 262.85°C (536 K)**]

5.46   The heat of solution of $NiSO_4.7 H_2O$ at 18°C (291.15 K) is 17.58 kJ/kmol. Calculate the heat of crystallization of $NiSO_4.7 H_2O$ at 18°C (291.15 K) in kJ/kg solute.

[**– 62.63 kJ/kg solute (exothermic)**]

5.47   The heat of solution[21] of $CuSO_4.5 H_2O$ is 11.933 kJ/mol solute at 18°C (291.15 K). Assuming that the heat of solution of $CuSO_4.5 H_2O$ at 25°C (298.15 K) is nearly same as that of 18°C (291.15 K), calculate the heat of formation of $CuSO_4.5 H_2O$ at 25°C(298.15 K).   [**– 2212.46 kJ/mol**]

5.48   The endothermic heat of dilution of one mol $KClO_3$ in 5.56 moles of water at 18°C (291.15 K) is 37.26 kJ/mol $KClO_3$[67]. Calculate the heat absorbed when 1000 kg solution is to be prepared at 18°C (291.15 K) having the above composition.

[**Heat absorbed = 167 290 kJ**]

5.49   In Fig. 5.35, an isotherm of $NaClO_3$–H_2O system at 20°C (293.15 K) is given[66]. (a) How much heat is absorbed in dissolving 200 kg $NaClO_3$ to make a 40% solution at 20°C (293.15 K)? (b) How much heat is absorbed in making 500 kg of 30% of $NaClO_3$ solution at 20°C (293.15 K)? (c) A 40% $NaClO_3$ solution is diluted at 20°C (293.15 K). Calculate the heat to be added to or removed from the solution at 20°C (293.15 K).   [**(a) 32 160 kJ (b) 26 445 kJ**

(c) Heat added to the solution is 27.6 kJ/kg $NaClO_3$]

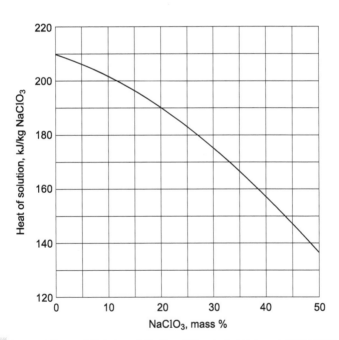

Fig. 5.35   Integral Heat of Solution of Sodium Chlorate in Water at 20°C (293.15 K)

5.50   Standard heat of formation data of potassium hydroxide and its aqueous solutions are given in Table 5.77.

Table 5.77 Heat of Formation of Aqueous Potassium Hydroxide Solutions[44]

Formula and description	State	ΔH_f^o at 25°C (298.15 K) kJ/mol KOH
KOH, 0 H$_2$O	c	−424.764
3 H$_2$O	l	−469.462
3.5 H$_2$O	l	−471.302
4 H$_2$O	l	−472.955
4.5 H$_2$O	l	−474.503
5 H$_2$O	l	−475.712
6 H$_2$O	l	−477.093
8 H$_2$O	l	−478.775
10 H$_2$O	l	−480.725
12 H$_2$O	l	−480.306
15 H$_2$O	l	−480.825
20 H$_2$O	l	−481.189
25 H$_2$O	l	−481.302
30 H$_2$O	l	−481.369
40 H$_2$O	l	−481.461
50 H$_2$O	l	−481.520
75 H$_2$O	l	−481.595
100 H$_2$O	l	−481.637
150 H$_2$O	l	−481.700
200 H$_2$O	l	−481.742

Note The number in the first column indicates the number of moles of water, mixed with one mole of potassium hydroxide.

Fit an empirical equation between excess enthalpy of the aqueous potassium hydroxide solution as a function of mole fraction of KOH [similar to Eq. (5.70) and Eq. (5.71)]. Draw a heat of dilution curve for KOH–H$_2$O system.

Hint Use of a spreadsheet program such as Microsoft Excel© would be handy in these calculations.

5.51 It is desired to dilute 60% NaOH solution at 100°C (373 K) to 10% strength by adding water at 35°C (308 K). (a) Find the resultant temperature of 10% solution, using Fig. 5.16. (b) Calculate the heat to be removed to cool down the above solution to 25°C (298.15 K) using Figs. 5.16 and 5.4.

[**(a) 63°C (335 K) (b) (i) 131.3 kJ/kg; (ii) 141 kJ/kg**]

5.52 A 100 kg of solution of 32% N (by mass) is prepared by dissolving 50 kg of urea and rest ammonium nitrate in water at 25°C (298.15 K). Using emprical equation, given in Example 5.48, calculate heat effect of the solution.

Data ΔH_r^o of NH$_2$CONH$_2$. 3 H$_2$O, = −320.98 kJ/mol urea [**+13 786 kJ**]

5.53 A 100-kg solution of 20% N (by mass) is prepared by dissolving 30 kg of ammonium nitrate and the rest, urea in water at 25°C (298.15 K). Using the empirical equation given in Example 5.48, calculate heat effect of the solution.

Data ΔH_r^o of NH$_4$NO$_3$.30 H$_2$O = −342.105 kJ/mol NH$_4$NO$_3$ [**+ 15 381.2 kJ**]

5.54 Data of endothermic heat of mixing of ethyl alcohol and ethyl acetate at 25°C (298.15 K) are given in Table 5.78. Calculate the integral heat of solution of ethyl acetate in kJ/kg ester for each value given in the table. Plot a graph giving the integral heat of solution on the y-axis and mass fraction of easter on the x-axis.

Table 5.78 Heat of Mixing of Ethanol and Ethyl Acetate[68]

Mole fraction of ethanol	Enthalpy of mixing (H^E) at 25°C (298.15 K), kJ/kmol
0.05	326.6
0.10	596.1
0.20	1032.3
0.30	1319.8
0.40	1467.0
0.50	1486.1
0.60	1385.8
0.70	1176.3
0.80	859.1
0.90	531.3
0.95	245.8

5.55 The molar excess enthalpy of ethanol-*n*-hexane mixture containing 0.18 mole fraction ethanol at 45°C (318 K) and 101.325 kPa is reported to be 561.4 kJ/kmol (endothermic) mixture. Calculate the enthalpy of the mixture based on reference temperature of 0°C (273.15 K). **[7515.2 kJ/kmol]**

5.56 Calculate the heat of mixing for Exercise 3.16 per 100 kg of mixed acid. Assume that both the aqueous acids are available at 30°C(303 K) and the mixed acid temperature should not exceed 40°C (313 K). **[9369 kJ (exothermic)]**

5.57 In an experimental run of 2-methylnaphthalene[69], the spent acid obtained at the end of the run contains 11.3% HNO_3, 44.4% H_2SO_4 and 44.3% H_2O. It is fortified by the addition of 98% H_2SO_4 and 69% HNO_3. The fortified mixed acid has the composition: HNO_3: 25%, H_2SO_4: 40% and H_2O: 35%. Use Fig. 5.21.

Calculate (a) the quantities of 98% H_2SO_4 and 69% HNO_3 required to fortify 100 kg of spent acid, and (b) the heat liberated per kg spent acid at 0°C (273.15 K) fortified. All percentages are by mass.

[(a) 22.84 kg 98% H_2SO_4 and 44.11 kg 69% HNO_3 (b) 168.9 kJ/kg spent acid]

5.58 Calculate the heat evolved by mixing anhydrous liquid ammonia at atmospheric pressure [boiling point ≈ − 33.33°C (239.82 K)] and water at 25°C (298.15 K) to produce 100 L aqueous solution of ammonia having 4.5% (by mass) strength (as NH_3) at 25°C (298.15 K). Use Fig. 5.22 and Table 5.59 for calculations. The specific gravity of 4.5% solution is 0.98 at 25°C (298.15 K).

[(i) 2547 kJ from Fig. 5.22 (ii) 2547.7 kJ from Table 5.60]

5.59 Ammonia liquor having 32.0% (mass) strength is mixed with a dilute solution having 4.5% (mass) strength to produce a solution having final strength of 15.9% (mass). Assume that both the solutions are available at 25°C (298.15 K). Calculate the cooling required to maintain the temperature at 25°C (298.15 K) of 1000 kg of the final 15.9% solution using Table 5.59.

Also, calculate the quantities of 32% and 4.5% solutions, required to be mixed using Fig. 5.22. **[11 546 kJ, 580.6 kg 4.5% solution and 419.4 kg 32% solution]**

5.60 Dry gas mixture from a methane-chlorination reactor having the following molar composition enters an absorber at 45°C (318K)

CH_4: 53.8%, CH_3Cl: 18.3%, CH_2Cl_2: 2.65%, CH_3Cl: 0.65%, CCl_4: 0.15% and HCl: 24.45%

It is scrubbed with water in a falling-film type carbate absorber to remove HCl. Assume that nearly 100% hydrogen chloride gas is removed. Water enters the absorber at 30°C (303 K) and acid-free gases leave the absorber at 6.85 kPa g in saturated conditions at 30°C (303 K). Use Table 5.1 for heat capacity equation constants of the gases.

(a) If the tower is designed for 30% (mass) acid production, calculate the heat to be removed from the system. Assume that 30% acid is to be produced at the bottom at 25°C (298.15 K).

(b) If the tower is designed to produce 5% (mass) acid, calculate the temperature of the 5% acid at the bottom. Assume the heat capacity of aqueous 5% acid to be 4.19 kJ/(kg . K).

Table 5.79   Heat of Formation of Aqueous Hydrochloric Acid Solutions[44]

Formula and description	State	Heat of formation at 25°C (298.15 K), ΔH_f^o, kJ/mol HCl	mass % HCl in aqueous solution
HCl, 0 H_2O	gas	– 92.31	100
1 H_2O	aq	– 121.55	67.0
1.5 H_2O	aq	– 132.67	57.5
2 H_2O	aq	– 140.96	50.3
2.5 H_2O	aq	– 145.48	44.8
3 H_2O	aq	– 148.49	40.3
4 H_2O	aq	– 152.92	33.6
5 H_2O	aq	– 155.77	28.9
6 H_2O	aq	– 157.68	25.3
8 H_2O	aq	– 160.00	20.2
10 H_2O	aq	– 161.32	16.9
15 H_2O	aq	– 163.03	11.9
20 H_2O	aq	– 163.85	9.21
25 H_2O	aq	– 164.34	7.50
30 H_2O	aq	– 164.67	6.33
40 H_2O	aq	– 165.10	4.82
50 H_2O	aq	– 165.36	3.90
75 H_2O	aq	– 165.72	2.63

Note   The number in the first column indicates the number of moles of water mixed with one mole of hydrogen chloride.

[(a) 454.8 kW (b) 54.3°C (327.45 K)]

5.61 Excess molar enthalpies for system cyclohexane(1) and cyclohexanone(2) at 1 atm and 50°C (323 K) are reported by Shen et al[55] by the following empirical equation.

$$H^E = x_1 x_2 [3836.7 - 959.3 (x_2 - x_1) + 815.2 (x_2 - x_1)^2 - 485.6 (x_2 - x_1)^3] \text{ kJ/kmol mixture}$$

Mean heat capacities[21] of cyclohexane (1) and cyclohexanone (2) in the temperature range 0°C to 50°C (27.15 K to 323.15 K) may be taken as 155.78 and 176.84 kJ/ (kmol · K), respectively.

(a) Tabulate H, $\bar{H}_1$, $\bar{H}_2$ over 0°C (273.15 K) for concentrations, ranging from $x_1 = 0$ to 1 in step of 0.1.

(b) Plot a graph of H vs x_1 and read $\bar{H}_1$, and $\bar{H}_2$ at $x_1 = 0.4$ and $x_1 = 0.7$.

5.62 Excess molar enthalpies for the system benzene(1) and cyclohexane(2) at 1 atm and 25°C (298.15 K) are reported by Smith et al by the following empirical equation[70].

$$H^E = x_1 x_2 [3200 + 168.0005 (x_1 - x_2) + 122.666 (x_1 - x_2)^2] \text{ kJ/kmol mixture}$$

Mean heat capacities[3] of benzene (1) and cyclohexane (2) in the temperature range of 0°C to 25°C (273.15 K to 298.15 K) may be taken as 129.8 and 150.83 kJ/ (kmol. K), respectively.

Repeat parts (a) and (b) of Exercise 5.61 for this system

5.63 Excess molar enthalpies for system 1,2- dichloroethane (1) and dimethyl carbonate(2) at 1 atm and 40°C (313.15 K) are given by the following empirical equation (Ref. 3).

$$H^E = x_1 x_2 (1040 x_1^2 - 1121.41x_1 - 523.24] \text{ kJ/kmol mixture}$$

Assume average molar heat capacities of components 1 and 2 as 123.9 and 173.33 kJ/(kmol . K), respectively. Repeat parts (a), (b) and (c) of Example 5.57 for this system.

5.64 A vent stream from a bromine-manufacturing unit is measured to be 100 Nm^3/h having 1.25% by mole bromine and the rest air. It is scrubbed with aqueous NaOH solution in a packed tower containing 5% NaOH (by mass).

$$NaOH \text{ (sol)} + Br_2 \text{ (g)} = NaOBr \text{ (sol)} + NaBr(sol) + H_2O(l)$$

Once thorough scrubbing is carried out with 20% excess NaOH. Assume that 100% bromine is absorbed. Also assume that vent stream enters the tower at 40°C (313.15K) and inerts leave the tower at the same temperature. Neglect moisture carried by inerts.

Calculate (a) heat effect of scrubbing at 25°C (298.15K), and (b) composition of the solution, leaving the packed tower.

[(a) − 0.644 kW, (b) 5.72% NaOBr, 4.95% NaBr, 0.77% NaOH and rest water (by mass)]

5.65 Refer Exercise 4.46. Assume (a) average molar heat capacity of dry flue gas as 30.7 kJ/(kmol dry gas · K) in the temperature range of 50 to 175°C (223 K to 448 K), (b) temperature and heat capacity of purged-out solution to be 50°C (323K) and 4 kJ/(kg · K), respectively. Calculate the heat duty of the cooler to cool the recirculating solution and required cooling water flow in the cooler for a rise of 8°C (8 K).

[1154.67 kW, 129.9 m^3/h.]

Note Heat duty of the cooler is very high. It would be preferred if the major portion of heat of flue gas is fruitfully utilized before introducing into the venturi scrubber. One alternative is to utilize low level heat for achieving refrigeration in absorption refrigeration system (see Example 8.5 and Exercise 8.16).

5.66 Refer Exercise 5.44 . Vent gases containing chlorine, hydrogen chloride and acetic acid (small quantity of MCA is neglected for stoichiometric calculations) is scrubbed in aqueous NaOH solution of 10% strength (by mass) in a falling film-type carbate absorber. In order to ensure effective scrubbing, 10% excess NaOH is used. Reactions taking place in the scrubber are

$$2 NOH(sol) + Cl_2(g) = NaOCl(sol) + NaCl(sol) + H_2O(l)$$
$$NaOH(sol) + HCl(g) = Nacl(sol) + H_2O(l)$$
$$NaOH(sol) + CH_3COOH(g) = CH_3COONa(sol) + H_2O(l)$$

Assume once thorough scrubbing and near 100% scrubbing of all three noxious gases. Calculate heat effect of scrubbing at 25°C (298.15 K). If average heat capacity of the aqueous solution is 3.5 kJ/(kg . K), what will be the outlet temperature of solution from the scrubber?   **[(a) −460.155 kW, (b) 98°C (371.15 K)]**

5.67 It is desired to increase the strength of an acid having 19.1% H_2SO_4 by adding oleum having 29.0 mass % free SO_3 (on the basis of 100% acid) both at 18°C (291.15 K) to 53.8% H_2SO_4 concentration. Calculate the heat evolved per kg of the original weak acid, fortified. Use the data provided in Table 5.46.

[Heat evolved = 556.36 kJ/kg original weak acid]

5.68 Refer Exercise 5.67. What will be the expected rise in temperature? If the above 53.8% H_2SO_4 solution boils at 132°C (405 K), is it possible to achieve the rise in temperature of the solution without cooling? If not, what will happen?

[Rise in temperature works out to 135.3°C (135.3 K) which gives the resultant temperature as 153.3°C (426.3 K). This is not possible as the solution will start boiling at 132°C (405 K).]

Note It should be noted that this answer refers to a case when no heat is removed from the system. However, if the exothermic heat of dilution calculated in Exercise 5.67 is removed by indirect cooling, it is possible to achieve the concentration of 53.8% H_2SO_4.

5.69 It is desired to dilute oleum containing 41.2% free SO_3 with a large volume of water so that the resultant mixture can be considered infinitely dilute. What will be the heat of evolution? **[– 1407.8 kJ/kg oleum]**

5.70 A flask contains M_0 kmol of a binary mixture of composition x_0 (mole fraction) of a component A at its bubble point. Heat is supplied to the flask at the rate of ϕ kW. The average latent heat of vaporization of the binary is λ_v kJ/kmol. The relative volatility of the mixture is α. Assuming that (i) the heat of mixing of the binary is negligible, (ii) the variation of the bubble point with the composition is insignificant, and (iii) the heat loss to the surroundings is negligible, prove that the mole fraction x of the component A in the liquid mixture at the end of θ h is given by following equation,

$$(1 - K\theta)^{(\alpha - 1)} = \frac{x\,(1 - x_o)^\alpha}{[x_o\,(1 - x)^\alpha]} \qquad K\,\theta < 1$$

where $K = \dfrac{\phi}{M_0 \cdot \lambda_v}$

Note When $K\,\theta = 1$, the complete mixture is boiled off and hence the condition $K\,\theta > 1$ is non-existent.

5.71 A flask contains 5 kg of a mixture consisting of 50 mole % n-heptane and 50 mole % n-octane at its bubble point at atmospheric pressure. The flask is supplied heat at the rate of 0.5 kW with the help of an electric mantle. The average relative volatility (α) and average latent heat of vaporization (λ_v) of the mixture can be assumed to be 2.16 and 33 500 kJ/kmol, respectively. Assume negligible heat of mixing of the two components. Also, the bubble point variation with the change in composition may be neglected. Calculate (a) the time required to attain a liquid mixture of 30 mole % n-heptance in the flask, and (b) the composition of the liquid mixture after 15 min from the start to heating. Compute the left-over quantities of the liquid mixture in both the above cases. **[(a) Time: 34.2 min, Quantity: 1.76 kg (b) Composition: 43.66 mole % n-heptane, Quantity: 3.59 kg]**

5.72 Refer Exercise 4.48. Calculate the required temperature of superheated ammonia, if (a) preheated air containing 0.016 kg H_2O/kg dry air is introduced to the reactor at 280°C (553.15 K), (b) the ammonia content of the inlet dry gas mixture is maintained at 10% (v/v), (c) the conversion of ammonia is 100%, and (d) the outlet temperature is required to be controlled at 910°C (1183 K). **[105.3°C (378.45 K)]**

References

1. Kuhn, H and Forster, Hing; *Principles of Physical Chemistry*, John Wiley & Sons, Ltd., UK, 2000, P. 511.
2. Himmelblau, D M; *Basic Principles and Calculations in Chemical Engineering*, 7th Ed., Pearson Education, Inc., USA, 2004.

3. Smith, J M, Abbott M M, Van Ness H C and Bhatt B I; *Introduction to Chemical Engineering Thermodynamics*, 6th Ed., Tata Mc Graw-Hill Education (India), New Delhi. New York, 2010.

4. Spencer, H M; *Ind. Engng. Chem.*, **40**(11), 1948, p. 2152.

5. Thinh, T P, Duran J L, Ramalho R S and Kaliaguine, S; *Hydrocarbon Processing*, **50**(1): 1971, p. 98.

6. Yaws, C L, Ni, H M and Chiang, P Y; *Chem. Engng.*, **95**(7), May 9, 1988, p. 91.

7. Reklaitis, G V and Schneider, D R; *Introduction to Material and Energy Balances*, John Wiley & Sons, USA, 1983.

8. NIST Chemistry WebBook, an Online Database No. 69), by National Institute of Standards and Technology, USA, Sept., 2008.

9. Frechette G, Herbert, J C, Thinh, T P and Trong, T K; Central Laboratory, Transport Ministry Government of Quebec, Quebec, Canada (private communication, unpublished results).

10. Yaws, CL *Chemical Properties Handbook*, McGraw-Hill, USA, 1999.

11. Weiss, A H and Joffee, J; *Ind. Engg. Chem.*, **49**(1): 1957, p. 120.

12. Lee, B I and Kesler, M G; *AIChE J.*, **21**(3): 1975, p. 510.

13. Reid, R C, Prausnitz, J M and Poling, B E; *The Properties of Gases and Liquids*, 4th Ed., McGraw-Hill, USA, 1987.

14. Yaws, C L; *Physical Properties*, McGraw-Hill, USA, 1977.

15. Yaws, C L and X Pan; *Chem. Engg.*, **99**(4): 1992, p. 132.

16. Bertetti, J W and McCabe, W L; *Ind. Engg. Chem.*, **28**(3), 1936, p. 375.

17. Wilson, H R and McCabe, W L; *Ind. Engg. Chem*, **34**(5), 1942, p. 558.

18. Standiford, F C and Badger, W L; *Ind. Engg. Chem.*, **46**(11), 1954, p. 2400.

19. *Lurgi Atlas on Sulphuric Acid*, Lurgi GmbH, Germany, 1986.

20. A technical manual on *Diphyl-Organic Heat Transfer Media*, Bayer AG, Germany, 1971.

21. Green, D W and Perry, R H; *Perry's Chemical Engineers' Handbook*, 8th Ed., McGraw-Hill, USA, 2008.

22. Kelley, K. K; Bulletin 584, Bureau of Mines, USA, 1960.

23. *API Technical Data Book-Petroleum Refining*, Vols. I and II, 2nd Ed., Published by the American Petroleum Institute, USA, 1970.

24. Bhatt, B I; *Design Data Book, Properties of Stream, Selected Refrigerants, n-Hexane and Brines*, CBS Publishers & Distributors, New Dehli, 2007.

25. Abboud, J L M and Notario, R; *Pure Appl. Chem.* **71** (4), 1999, P. 645.

26. NIST Standard Reference Database 23 (REFPROP), Ver.8, NIST, USA, 2007.

27. A Technical Manual on Dowtherm A, The Dow Chemical Company, USA, 1991.

28. *ASHRAE Handbook: Fundamentals*, American Society of Heating, Refrigerating and Air-conditioning Engineers, Inc., USA, 1993.

29. Corpstein, R R, Dove, R A and Dickey, D S; *Chem. Engg. Progress*, **75**(2): 1979, p. 66.

30. Sisson B; *Chem. Engg.*, **84**(4): February 14, 1977, p. 105.

31. Adhia, J D; *Chem. Age of India*, **26**(10): 1975, p. 749.

32. *Pressure-Enthalpy Diagram for Carbon Dioxide*, Published by Büse Anlagenbau GmbH, Germany, 1982.

33. *Tappi*, **47**(10): 1964, p. 197A.

34. Dadyburjor, D B; *Chem. Engg. Progr.*, **74**(4), 1978, p, 85.

35. *Engineering Data Book*, 9th Ed., Gas Processors Suppliers Association, USA, 1972.

36. Gess, M A, Danner, R P and Nagrekar, M; *Thermodynamic Analysis of Vapour-Liquid Equilibria*, American Institute of Chemical Engineers, USA, 1991.

37. Benenati, R F; *Chem. Engg.*, **84**(6): March 14, 1977, p. 129.

38. *AIChE Student Contest Problem*, 1965.

39. Thinh, T P and Trong, T K; *The Canadian J. of Chem. Engg.*, **54**(8): 1976, p. 344.
40. Yaws, C L and Chiang, P Y; *Chem. Engg.*, **95**(17), Sept. 26, 1988, p. 81.
41. *Physical and Thermodynamic Properties of Elements and Compounds*, United Catalysts. Inc., USA.
42. Ganapathy, V; *Hydrocarbon Processing*, **72**(2), 1922, p.93.
43. Wolfgang Gerhartz, *Ullmann's Encyclopedia of Industrial Chemistry*, 5th Ed., Vol. A 10, VCH Verlagsgesellschaft mbH,Germany, 1987 p. 332.
44. Wagman, D D; *et al*, The NBC Tables of Chemical Thermodynamic Properties, *J. Phy. Chem. Ref. Data*, Vol. II, Supplement 2, 1982.
45. McCabe, W L; *Transactions of AIChE*, **31**, 1935, p. 129.
46. Kroschwitz, J I; *Kirk-othmer Encyclopaedia of Chemical Technology*, IVth Ed., Vol. 1, John Wiley & Sons, Inc., 1991. p. 1005.
47. Luff, B B and Reed, R B; *J. Chem. Engg. Data*, **24**(3), 1979, p. 206.
48. Bump, T R and Sibbitt, W L; *Ind. Engg. Chem.*, **47**: 1955, p. 1665-1670.
49. Gable, C M, Betz, H F and Maron, S H; *J. of Am. Chem. Soc.*, **72**: 1950, p. 1445-1448.
50. Urbanski, Chemistry and Technology of Explosives, Vol.1 Pergamon Press Ltd., UK, 1964.
51. Albright, K F; *Chem. Engg.*, **73**: May 9, 1966, p. 161.
52. Pátek, J and Klomfar, J; *Int. J. of Refrig.*, **18**(4), 1995, p. 226.
53. Walker, J F; *Formaldehyde*, 3rd Ed., Reinhold Publishing Corporation, UK, 1964.
54. Van Ness, H C and Abbott, M M; *Classical Thermodynmics of Nonelectroyte Solutions, With Applications to Phase Equilibria*, McGraw-Hill, USA, 1982.
55. Shen, S, Wang, Y, Shi, J, Benson, G C and Lu, B C Y; *J. Chem. Engg. Data*, **37**, 1992, p. 400.
56. Tamilarasan, R, Anand Prabhu, A, Rajenthrien, M, Dharmendira Kumar, M and Yoo, C K; *J. Chem. Engg. Data*, **54**, 2009 p. 4.
57. Morgen, R A; *Ind., Engg. Chem.*, **34** (5): 1942, p. 571.
58. *International Data Series (IDS)*, Series A, Journal Published by the Thermodynamics Research Centre, USA.
59. *TRC Thermodynamic Tables-Hydrocarbons, and TRC Thermodynamic Tables-Non-Hydrocarbons*, Published by Thermodynamics Research Centre (regularly updated), USA.
60. *International Thermodynamic Tables of the Fluid State* by International Union of Pure and Applied Chemistry (IUPAC), UK.
61. Duecker, W W and West, J R; *The Manufacture of Sulphuric Acid*, Reinhold Publishing Corporation, USA, 1959.
62. Joharapurkar, V R and Khemani, M; *Chemical Processing & Engineering*, Annual Issue, 1971, p. 84.
63. Woicik, J F; *Chem. Engg.*, **83**(17): August 16, 1976, p. 89.
64. Carroll, J J; *Chem. Engg.*, **108**(10): 2001, p. 91.
65. Mays, E B and Schwab, M R; *Chem. Engg.*, **84**(4): February 17, 1975, p. 112.
66. Horwitz, B A, *Chem. Engg.*, **90**(18): Sept. 5, 1983, p. 115.
67. *The Chlorate Manual*, Kerr-McGee Chemical Corporation, USA, 1972.
68. Murti, P S and Winkle, M V; *Ind., Engg. Chem.*, **3**: 1911, p. DS 65.
69. Brink, J A and Shreve, R N; *Ind. Engg. Chem.*, **46**(4): 1954, p. 694.
70. Smith, B D, Muthu, O, Dewan, A, and Gierlach, M; *J. Phy. Chem. Ref. Data*, **11**(4), 1982, p. 1127.

Stoichiometry and Unit Operations

The material and energy balances of chemical reactions as well as simple physical processes such as mixing were discussed in Chapters 4 and 5. However, in chemical engineering, unit operations are as much important as the unit processes. It is therefore desirable to study the stoichiometric aspects of the unit operations in detail.

6.1 DISTILLATION

Distillation or fractionation is an operation in which one or more components of the liquid mixtures of two or more components are separated using thermal energy. Basically, the difference in vapour pressures of different components at the same temperature is responsible for such a separation.

Usually, the throughput to the distillation column with the composition of the feed is known. The desired purities of the components dictate the compositions of overhead and bottom products. These data are sufficient to establish the overall material balance of the column.

Knowing the flow rates of the distillate and bottom products, it is easy to evaluate the thermal loads of the overhead condenser and reboiler.

The following examples will demonstrate the material and energy balances of such a column.

Example 6.1 A vapour at 138°C (411 K) and standard atmospheric pressure, containing 0.72 mole fraction benzene and 0.28 mole fraction toluene serves as a feed to a fractionating column in which it is separated into a distillate containing 0.995 mole fraction benzene and bottoms with 0.97 mole fraction toluene. The reflux ratio is desired to be 1.95 kmol/kmol distillate product. For a feed of 100 kmol, compute the overall material and energy balances. Assume that there is no heat loss to the surrounding and the heat of solution is negligible.

Solution   *Basis* 100 kmol of feed

A schematic representation of the distillation column is given in Fig. 6.1.

Benzene in the feed = $100 \times 0.72 = 72$ kmol

Toluene in the feed = $100 - 72 = 28$ kmol

Let D be the distillate and B the bottom product in kmol.

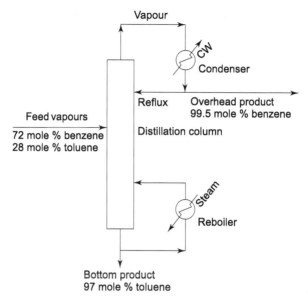

Fig. 6.1 Rectification of Benzene–Toluene Mixture

Overall material balance;

$$\text{Feed} \quad F = B + D \qquad (6.1)$$

Note This equation is entirely general. As long as consistent units are used, the mass units or mole units can be used.

$$B + D = 100 \qquad (i)$$

Balance of benzene,

$$x_D \times D + x_B \times B = x_F \times F \qquad (6.2)$$

where, x_D, the mole fraction of benzene in distillate = 0.995
x_B, the mole fraction of benzene in bottoms = 0.03
x_F, the mole fraction of benzene in feed = 0.72

$$0.995\, D + 0.03\, B = 0.72 \times 100$$
$$= 72 \qquad (ii)$$

Solving Eqs (i) and (ii)

$$D = 71.5 \text{ kmol}$$
$$B = 28.5 \text{ kmol}$$

For the enthalpy data, refer to Fig. 6.2.

Heat load of condenser

$$\text{Reflux ratio, } R = \frac{\text{Moles of distillate refluxed}}{\text{Moles of distillate removed from the column}} = 1.95$$

$$\text{Total overhead vapours} = D\,(1 + R)$$
$$= 71.5 \times 2.95 = 210.925 \text{ kmol}$$

Reference temperature, $T_o = 273.15$ K (0°C)

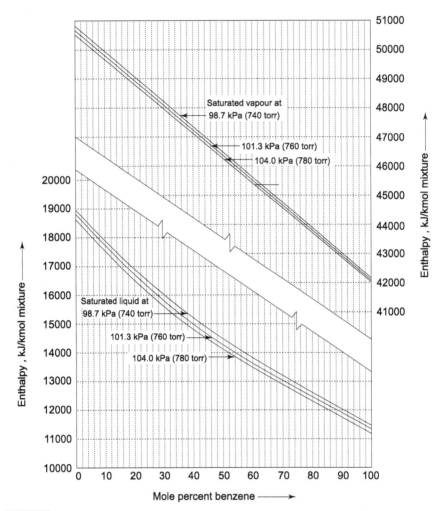

Fig. 6.2 Enthalpies of Benzene–Toluene Mixtures above 0°C (273.15 K)[1]
(Reproduced with pertmission of the American Chemical Society, USA).

From Fig. 6.2,

Enthalpy of vapours (overhead) = 42 170 kJ/kmol mixture

Enthalpy of liquid (overhead) = 11 370 kJ/kmol mixture

Since the condenser is not expected to subcool the liquid, the enthalpy removed in the condenser (latent heat duty)

$$= 42\ 170 - 11\ 370 = 30\ 800 \text{ kJ/kmol mixture}$$

Total heat load of condenser, H_C = 30 800 × 210.925 = **6496 490 kJ**

Heat load of reboiler

Enthalpy of distillate product, H_D = 11 370 × 71.5 = 812 955 kJ

Specific enthalpy of bottom product = 18 780 kJ/kmol mixture

Total enthalpy of bottoms H_B = 18 780 × 28.5 = 535 230 kJ

Enthalpy of feed, H_F = 44 500 × 100 kJ/kmol mixture

Total enthalpy of feed $= 44\ 500 \times 100 = 4450\ 000$ kJ
Heat load of reboiler, $H_n =$ enthalpy of distillate + heat load of condenser
+ enthalpy of bottoms − enthalpy of feed
$= 812\ 955 + 6496\ 490 + 535\ 230 - 4450\ 000$
$= \mathbf{3394\ 675}$ **kJ**

Note If the feed is liquid at its boiling point (enthalpy $= 12\ 945$ kJ/kmol mixture), what will be the heat load of the reboiler? **6550 175 kJ**

Will there be any change in the heat load of the condenser?

Example 6.2 A pressurised distillation colimn is used for separation of nitrogen from air by cryogenic distillation. Satured liquid air at 21.0 bar a is flashed to 5.50 bar a and the vapour–liquid mixture is introduced to the column. Due to flashing, liquid air is converted to 30% vapour (by mole). Vapour from top of the column is taken to an overhead condenser (heat pump II) in which liquid oxygen is used as cooling medium at 1.2 bar a. Vapour are essentially pure (99.9 mole%) N_2. The bottom product from the column contains 58.8 mole% O_2. Reflux ratio is maintained at 3.0 to achieve desired purities. Assume 79% N_2 and 21% O_2 in air and neglect presence of argon in it. Feed rate to the column is 2000 kg/h. Distillation column is schematically shown in Fig. 6.3.

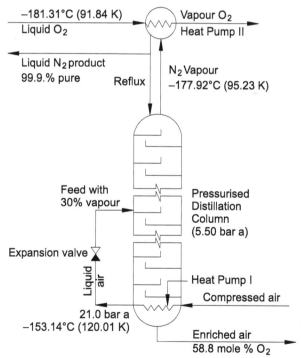

Fig. 6.3 Cryogenic Separation of Nitrogen

Table 6.1 Enthalpy of Nitrogen–Oxygen Mixtures[2] at 5.50 Bar a

Mole %	Liquid Phase			Vapour Phase		
N_2	Bubble Point		Enthalpy	Dew Point		Enthalpy
(x, y)	°C	K	kJ/kmol	°C	K	kJ/kmol
0 (Pure O_2)	−162.97	110.18	1121.4	−162.97	110.18	7183.4
2.5	−163.66	109.49	1125.7	−163.24	109.91	7173.5
5	−164.31	108.84	1128.8	−163.50	109.65	7160.8
10	−165.51	107.64	1132.1	−164.05	109.10	7127.8
20	−167.63	105.52	1131.0	−165.18	107.97	7038.8
30	−169.43	103.72	1124.6	−166.37	106.78	6928.4
40	−170.99	102.16	1115.9	−167.65	105.50	6803.4
50	−172.39	100.76	1106.6	−169.01	104.14	6667.7
60	−173.66	99.49	1097.2	−170.48	102.67	6523.2
70	−174.83	98.32	1088.0	−172.07	101.08	6370.4
80	−175.93	97.22	1079.3	−173.81	99.34	6209.0
90	−176.95	96.20	1071.0	−175.73	97.42	6037.3
100 (Pure N_2)	−177.92	95.23	1063.2	−177.92	95.23	5852.3

Enthalpy of saturated liquid air at 21.0 bar a and −153.74°C (120.01 K) = 2595.2 kJ/kmol.

Reference conditions: Enthalpy at 1.013 25 bar a of saturated liquid nitrogen at −195.8°C (77.35 K) and of saturated liquid oxygen at −182.96°C (90.19 K) = 0 kJ/kmol

(a) Calculate composition of vapour–liquid mixture after flashing of liquid air to 5.50 bar a.

(b) Make matherial and energy balances of the distillation column and calculate the heat duty of the overhead condenser and the reboiler, considering 5% heat gain/loss from atmosphere.

Assume near constant pressure (5.5 bar a) in the column.

Solution *Basis* Liquid air feed rate = 2000 kg/h

Average molar mass of air = $0.79 \times 28 + 0.21 \times 32 = 28.84$ kg/kmol

$$\text{Feed rate, } F = \frac{2000}{28.84} = 69.348 \text{ kmol/h}$$

Let D and W be flow rates of distillated and residue, respectively.

$$D + W = F$$
$$D + W = 69.348 \qquad (i)$$

Nitrogen balance

$$69.348 \times 0.79 = 0.999\ D + 0.422\ W$$
$$54.840 = D + 0.4224\ W \qquad (ii)$$

Solving the equations, **W = 25.118 kmol/h**

D = 44.230 kmol/h

Liquid air at 21.0 bar a (having enthalpy = 2595.2 kJ/kmol) is flashed to 5.55 bar a. Flashing results is 30% vapour formation. Thus, 1 kmol of liquid air will result in 0.3 kmol of vapour and 0.7 kmol of liquid. For finding composition of both phases, energy balance is required. Figure 6.4 is *t-x-y* diagram and Fig. 6.5 is enthalpy–concentration diagram of the N_2–O_2 mixture at 5.5 bar a.

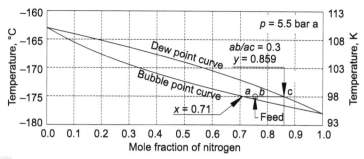

Fig. 6.4   *t-x-y* Diragram of Nitrogen and Oxygen at 5.5 bar

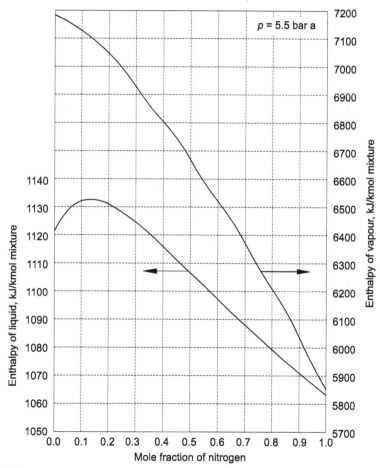

Fig. 6.5   Enthalpy–Concentration Diagram of Nitrogen–Oxygen System at 5.5 bar

A trial-and-error method will have to be adopted for flash caculations.

Trial - I Assume $x = 0.75$ (mole fraction of N_2) in liquid phase. Since flashed vapour will be in equilibrium with the liquid, vapour compsition can be found by drawing a horizontal line at $x = 0.75$ on Fig. 6.4. The line crossing the y–x line, shows the composition of vapour phase as $y = 0.8833$ (mole fraction of nitrogen). From Fig. 6.5,

$$H_L = 1083.65 \text{ kJ/kmol}, \quad H_V = 6050.0 \text{ kJ/kmol}$$
$$\text{Enthalpy of mixture} = 0.3 \times 6071.7 + 1083.65 \times 0.7$$
$$= 2580.06 \text{ kJ/kmol} \neq 2595.2 \text{ kJ/kmol}$$

Trial - II Assume $x = 0.735$. $y = 0.9183$ (Fig. 6.4)
$$H_L = 1085.6 \text{ kJ/kmol}, H_V = 6119.1 \text{ both in kJ/kmol}$$
$$\text{Enthalpy of mixture} = 0.3 \times 6119.1 + 0.7 \times 1085.6$$
$$= 2592.8 \text{ kJ/kmol} \neq 2595.2 \text{ kJ/kmol}$$

Trial - III Assume $x = 0.71$, $y = 0.859$ (Fig. 6.4)
$$H_L = 1085.5 \text{ kJ/kmol}, \quad H_V = 6118.6 \text{ both in kJ/kmol}$$
$$\text{Enthalpy of mixture, } H_F = 0.3 \times 6118.6 + 0.7 \times 1085.5$$
$$= 2595.4 \text{ kJ/kmol} \approx 2595.2 \text{ kJ/kmol}$$

Thus flashing will result in liquid phase with 0.71 mole fraction N_2 and vapour phase with 0.859 mole fraction N_2.

Total enthalpy of feed, $\phi_F = F \cdot H_F$
$$= 2595.2 \times 69.348$$
$$= 179\,972 \text{ kJ/h} \equiv 49.992 \text{ kW}$$
Total overhead vapours $= D\,(R + 1)$
$$= 44.23\,(3 + 1) = 176.92 \text{ kmol/h}$$
Specific enthalpy of overhead vapour = 5852.3 kJ/kmol (i.e., of 100% N_2)
Total enthalpy of overhead vapour,
$$\phi_v = 5852.3 \times 176.92$$
$$= 1035\,389 \text{ kJ/h} \equiv 287.608 \text{ kW}$$
Since the condenser is not expected to subcool the liquid, enthalpy removed in the liquid, enthalpy removed in the overhead condenser
$$\phi_C'' = 5852.3 - 1063.2 = 4789.1 \text{ kJ/kmol}$$
Heat duty of condenser, $\phi_C' = 4789.1 \times 176.92$
$$= 847\,288 \text{ kJ/h} \equiv 235.358 \text{ kW}$$
Consider 5% heat gain from surroundings.

Adual heat duty of condenser, $\phi_C = \dfrac{847\,288}{0.95}$
$$\mathbf{= 891\,882 \text{ kJ/h} \equiv 247.745 \text{ kW}}$$

Note that the overhead condenser (heat pump II) is also working as a rebolier for another atmospheric cryogenic distillation column. Nitrogen vapour at 5.5 bar a is used as a heating medium for vaporizing liquid oxygen at lower pressure.
Bottom product is a liquid mixture, consisting 42.2 mole% N_2.
Specific enthalpy of bottom product = 1113.8 kJ/kmol
Total enthalpy of bottom product,
$$\phi_W = 1113.8 \times 25.118$$
$$= 27\,976 \text{ kJ/h} \equiv 7.771 \text{ kW}$$
Heat load of reboiler (heat pump I),
$$\phi_B' = \phi_D + \phi_C' + \phi_W - \phi_F$$
$$= 1063.2 \times 44.23 + 847\,288 + 27\,976 - 179\,972$$
$$= 742\,317 \text{ kJ/h} \equiv 206.199 \text{ kW}$$

Considering 5% heat gain,

actual heat duty of reboiler, ϕ_B = 742 317 × 0.95

$$= \textbf{705 201 kJ/h} \equiv \textbf{195.889 kW}$$

Example 6.3 Azeotropic distillation of isopropyl alchol (IPA) is carried out in a 3-column system using cyclohexane as an entrainer as shown in Fig. 6.6 . The feed contains 67.5 mole % IPA and balance water. Recycle stream D_3 is also an azeotrope of the same composition.

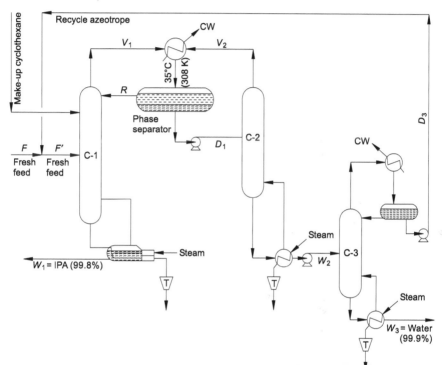

Fig. 6.6 Azeotropic Distillation of IPA–Water

Vapour mixture (V_1) from C-1 is sent to an overhead condenser along with vapour mixture (V_2) from C-2. Vapour mixture at the bubble point is condensed and collected in a separator at 35°C (308 K) wherein the condensate separates in two layers. The top layer contains 74.9% cyclohexane, 19.3% IPA and rest water (mole basis) and is refluxed back to C-1. The bottom layer (D_1) is analyzed to contain 2.4% cyclohexane, 23.0% IPA and rest water (mole basis). Bottom product W_1 from C-1 is 99.8 mole % IPA. A reflux ratio of 1.75 kmol/kmol D_1 is required for this separation. Stream D_1 is fed to column C-2. Top vapour stream V_2 is a ternary azeotrope and contains 48.8% cyclohexane, 20.6% IPA and rest water (mole basis). It contains all the cyclohexane, entering in D_1.

Bottom product W_2 from C-2 is fed to C-3. Top vapour stream D_3 is a binary azeotrope of IPA and water. It is recycled and mixed with fresh feed. Bottom product from C-3 is water with 0.1% IPA by mole.

All columns are operated at near atmospheric pressure. Carry out material balance of all three columns.

Solution V_2 vapour mixture is a ternary azeotrope in which all cyclohexane of D_1 stream will be recycled.

V_2 *Stream*
Cyclohexane balance;

$$0.024 \, D_1 = 0.488 \, V_2$$
$$D_1 = 20.333 \, V_2$$
$$\text{IPA in } V_2 = 0.206 \, V_2$$
$$\text{Water in } V_2 = (1 - 0.488 - 0.206) \, V_2 = 0.306 \, V_2$$

W_2 *Stream*

$$\text{IPA in } W_2 = 0.23 \, D_1 - 0.206 \, V_2$$
$$= 0.23 \times 20.333 \, V_2 - 0.206 \, V_2 = 4.471 \, V_2$$
$$\text{Water in } W_2 = (1 - 0.024 - 0.23) \, D_1 - 0.306 \, V_2$$
$$= 0.746 \times 20.333 \, V_2 - 0.306 \, V_2 = 14.862 \, V_2$$
$$W_2 \text{ stream} = 4.471 \, V_2 + 14.862 \, V_2 = 19.333 \, V_2$$

D_3 stream is an azeotrope containing 67.5 mole % IPA.

$$\text{Water in } W_3 \text{ stream} = (1 - 0.675) \, F = 0.325 \, F$$

Basis 100 kmol/h of fresh feed (F)
Overall material balance

$$W_1 + W_3 = 100 \tag{i}$$
$$0.998 \, W_1 + 0.001 \, W_3 = 67.5 \tag{ii}$$

Solving two equations, $W_1 = \mathbf{67.603 \ kmol/h}$
$$W_3 = \mathbf{32.397 \ kmol/h}$$
$$\text{IPA is } W_3 = 32.397 \times 0.001 = 0.032 \text{ kmol/h}$$
$$\text{IPA in } D_3 = 4.471 \, V_2 - 0.032$$
$$D_3 = (4.471 \, V_2 - 0.032) \, / \, 0.675 = 6.624 \, V_2 - 0.047$$
$$\text{Total feed to C–1} = F + D_3 = F'$$
$$= 100 + 6.624 \, V_2 - 0.047 = 6.624 \, V_2 + 99.953$$
$$\text{Water in } D_3 = 6.624 \, V_2 - 0.047 - (4.471 \, V_2 - 0.032)$$
$$= 2.153 \, V_2 - 0.015$$
$$\text{Water in } W_3 = 14.862 \, V_2 - (2.153 \, V_2 - 0.015)$$
$$= 12.709 \, V_2 + 0.015 = W_3 \times 0.999$$
$$= 33.397 \times 0.999$$
$$V_2 = 2.624 \text{ kmol/h}$$
$$D_3 = 2.153 \times 2.624 - 0.015 = 5.634 \text{ kmol/h}$$
$$D_1 = 20.333 \times 2.624 = 53.354 \text{ kmol/h}$$
$$F' = 6.624 \times 2.624 + 99.953 = 117.334 \text{ kmol/h}$$

$$\text{Reflux ratio} = \frac{R}{D_1} = 1.75 \text{ kmol/kmol}$$
$$R = 1.75 \times 53.354 = 93.37 \text{ kmol/h} = V_1 + V_2 - D_1$$
$$V_1 = 93.37 - 2.624 + 53.354 = 144.1 \text{ kmol/h}$$

Table 6.2 Composition of Streams

Component	R kmol/h	mole %	V_2 kmol/h	mole %	D_1 kmol/h	mole %	V_1 kmol/h	mole %
IPA	18.020	19.3	0.541	20.6	12.271	23.0	29.750	20.65
Water	5.415	5.8	0.803	30.6	39.802	74.6	44.414	30.82
Cyclohexane	69.935	74.9	1.280	48.8	1.281	2.4	69.936	48.53
Total	93.370	100.0	2.624	100.0	53.354	100.0	144.100	100.00

$$\text{Recycle ration,} \quad \frac{D_3}{F} = \frac{5.634}{100} = \textbf{0.056 kmol/kmol fresh feed}$$

6.2   ABSORPTION AND STRIPPING

Absorption is a unit operation in which a mixture of gases is brought in contact with liquid. A definite component of the gas mixture is dissolved in the liquid or solution. The operation is sometimes also termed as *scrubbing*. It may be physical absorption only or it may be accompanied by a chemical reaction.

Stripping or desorption is an operation in which a dissolved gas of a solution is stripped off from the liquid using a stripping medium, e.g., steam, air, etc.

In this operation also, the overall material balance yields the desired information.

Example 6.4   An absorption tower, packed with Tellerette packings, is used to absorb carbon dioxide in an aqueous monoethanol amine (MEA) solution[3]. The volumetric flow rate of the incoming dry gas mixture is 1000 m³/h at 45°C (318 K) and 101.3 kPa a (760 Torr). The CO_2 content of the gas is 10.4 mole %, while the outgoing gas mixture contains 4.5 mole % CO_2. A 3.2 M MEA solution is introduced at the top of the tower at the rate of 0.625 L/s. Dissolved CO_2 concentration of the entering solution is 0.166 kmol/kmol of MEA. Find the concentration of dissolved CO_2 in the solution leaving the tower.

Solution

Basis 0.625 L/s of MEA solution

Concentration of MEA solution = 3.2 M

Chemical formula of MEA

$= HOCH_2CH_2NH_2$

Molar mass of MEA = 61

Concentration of MEA in the solution

$= 61 \times 3.2$

$= 195.2$ g/L solution

Total MEA entering the tower

$= 195.2 \times 0.625 \times 3600/1000$

$= 439.2$ kg/h

Moles of MEA entering the tower

$= 3.2 \times 0.625 \times 3600/1000$

$= 7.2$ kmol/h

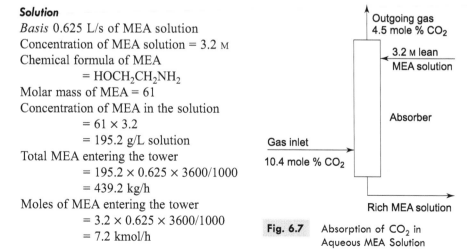

Fig. 6.7   Absorption of CO_2 in Aqueous MEA Solution

Dissolved CO_2 in lean MEA = 0.166 kmol/kmol MEA

CO_2 in lean MEA = 0.166 × 7.2 = 1.1952 kmol/h

Volumetric flow rate of dry gas mixture = 1000 m^3/h

Specific volume of gas at 45°C (318 K) and

101.3 kPa a, V = 26.107 m^3/kmol (Ref. Table 7.8)

$$\text{Molar flow rate of gas } q_v = \frac{1000}{26.107} = 38.3 \text{ kmol/h}$$

Moles of CO_2 in the inlet gas = 38.3 × 0.104 = 3.98 kmol/h

CO_2-free gas = 38.10 – 3.98 = 34.12 kmol/h

Outgoing gas contains 4.5 mole % CO_2.

$$\text{Molar flow rate of outgoing gas mixture} = \frac{34.12}{(1 - 0.0455)} = 35.75 \text{ kmol/h}$$

CO_2 absorbed = 38.10 – 35.75 = 2.35 kmol/h

Total CO_2 in rich MEA solution = 1.1952 + 2.35 = 3.5452 kmol/h

$$\text{Concentration of } CO_2 \text{ in rich MEA solution} = \frac{3.5452}{7.2}$$

$$= \textbf{0.4924 kmol/kmol MEA}$$

Example 6.5 A dry gas mixture containing NO_2, N_2O_4 and N_2 enters the bottom of an absorption tower[4]. Caustic soda solution (containing 23.6% by mass NaOH is introduced at the top of the column at 25°C (298.15 K). 50 000 m^3/h of a gas mixture enters having the composition 5.46% NO_2, 2.14% N_2O_4 and the rest N_2 on dry basis. The outgoing gas is found to contain 3.93% NO_2, 0.82% N_2O_4, 0.25% NO and the rest N_2 on dry basis. The aqueous solution enters at the rate of 500 L/min. The density of the solution can be taken as 1.25 kg/L. The temperature and pressure of the feed gas are 22.5°C (295.5 K) and 100 kPa a (750 Torr) respectively. The outgoing gas mixture leaves the scrubber at 90 kPa a and 29.4°C (302.55 K) with 0.045 kmol moisture per kmol dry gas mixture.

(a) Calculate the composition of the aqueous liquor leaving the column.

(b) Calculate the heat effect of scrubbing at 25°C (298.15 K).

Solution *Basis* 50 000 m^3/h of gas mixture at 295.5 K and 100 kPa a

Specific volume of gas at 295.5 K and 100 kPa = 24.57 m^3/kmol

$$\text{Molar flow rate of incoming gas mixture} = \frac{50\,000}{24.57} = 2035 \text{ kmol/h}$$

NO_2 content of the gas = 2035 × 0.0546 = 111.11 kmol/h

N_2O_4 content of the gas = 2035 × 0.0214 = 43.55 kmol/h

N_2 content of the gas = 2035 – (111.11 + 43.55)

$$= 1880.34 \text{ kmol/h}$$

When the mixture passes through the tower, N_2 remains unaffected, i.e. the outgoing gas mixture contains 1880.34 kmol/h of N_2.

The outgoing gas mixture contains 95% N_2.

$$\text{Molar flow rate of outgoing gas mixture} = \frac{1880.34}{0.95} = 1979.3 \text{ kmol/h (dry)}$$

Table 6.3 Composition of Outgoing Dry Gas Mixture

Component	mole %	kmol/h
NO_2	3.93	77.78
N_2O_4	0.82	16.23
NO	0.25	4.95
N_2	95.00	1880.34
Total	100.00	1979.30

NO_2 removed from the gas mixture = $111.11 - 77.78 = 33.33$ kmol/h
N_2O_4 removed from the gas mixture = $43.55 - 16.23 = 27.32$ kmol/h
The absorption in the tower is accompanied by the chemical reactions listed below.

$$2\,NO_2(g) + 2\,NaOH(s) = NaNO_2(s) + NaNO_3(s) + H_2O(l) \qquad \text{(i)}$$
$$N_2O_4(g) + 2\,NaOH(s) = NaNO_2(s) + NaNO_3(s) + H_2O(l) \qquad \text{(ii)}$$
$$3\,NO_2(g) + 2\,NaOH(s) = 2\,NaNO_3(s) + H_2O(s) + NO(g) \qquad \text{(iii)}$$

The last reaction is actually the result of two consecutive reactions:

$$3\,NO_2(g) + H_2O(l) = 2\,HNO_3(l) + NO(g) \qquad \text{(iiiA)}$$
$$2\,HNO_3(l) + 2\,NaOH(s) = 2\,NaNO_3(s) + 2\,H_2O(l) \qquad \text{(iiiB)}$$

Table 6.4 Molar Masses

Component	Molar mass (rounded values)
NO_2	46
N_2O_4	92
NO	30
$NaOH$	40
$NaNO_2$	69
$NaNO_3$	85
H_2O	18

N_2O_4 absorption [Reaction (ii)]
NaOH consumed = $2 \times 40 \times 27.32 = 2185.6$ kg/h
$NaNO_2$ produced = $69 \times 27.32 = 1885.1$ kg/h
$NaNO_3$ produced = $85 \times 27.32 = 2322.2$ kg/h
H_2O produced = $18 \times 27.32 = 491.8$ kg/h

NO production [Reaction (iii)]
NO_2 consumed = $3 \times 4.95 = 14.85$ kmol/h
NaOH consumed = $2 \times 4.95 \times 40 = 396$ kg/h
$NaNO_3$ produced = $2 \times 4.95 \times 85 = 841.5$ kg/h
H_2O produced = $4.95 \times 18 = 89.1$ kg/h

Thus, out of 32.33 kmol/h of NO_2 absorbed, 14.85 kmol/h are consumed for the production of NO. The rest is absorbed as per Reaction (i).
NO_2 absorbed as per Reaction (ii) = $33.33 - 14.85 = 18.48$ kmol/h

NO_2 absorption (Reaction (i))
NaOH consumed = $18.48 \times 40 = 739.2$ kg/h

$$\text{NaNO}_2 \text{ produced} = \frac{69 \times 18.48}{2} = 637.6 \text{ kg/h}$$

$$\text{NaNO}_3 \text{ produced} = \frac{85 \times 18.48}{2} = 785.4 \text{ kg/h}$$

$$\text{H}_2\text{O produced} = \frac{18 \times 18.48}{2} = 166.3 \text{ kg/h}$$

Total NaNO_2 produced $= 1885.1 + 637.6 = 2522.7$ kg/h
Total NaNO_3 produced $= 2322.2 + 841.5 + 785.4 = 3949.1$ kg/h
Total H_2O produced $= 491.8 + 89.1 + 166.3 = 747.2$ kg/h
Total NaOH consumed $= 2185.6 + 396 + 739.2 = 3320.8$ kg/h

Material balance of liquid

Flow of liquor = 500 L/min = 625 kg/min = 37 500 kg/h
NaOH in the feed = 37 500 × 0.236 = 8850 kg/h
Leftover NaOH in the outgoing liquid = 8850 − 3320.8 = 5529.2 kg/h
Moisture in the exist gas stream = 1979.3 × 0.045
    = 89.1 kmol/h ≡ 1603.2 kg/h
Water in the outgoing solution = 37 500 − 8850 + 747.2 − 1603.2
    = 27 794 kg/h

Table 6.5 Composition of Final Liquor

Component	$\dot{m}_i$ kg/h	mass %	$\dot{n}_i$ kmol/h	mole %
NaOH	5 529.2	**13.90**	138.23	**7.83**
NaNO_2	2522.7	**6.34**	36.56	**2.07**
NaNO_3	3949.1	**9.92**	46.46	**2.63**
H_2O	27 794.0	**69.84**	1544.11	**87.47**
Total	39 795.0	**100.00**	1765.36	**100.00**

Heat effect of scrubbing
Reference temperature $T_0 = 298.15$ K

Table 6.6 Heat Capacity Equation Constants for Incoming Gas Mixture

Component	$\dot{n}_i$ kmol/h	Heat capacity equation constants			
		$\dot{n}_i \cdot a_i$	$\dot{n}_i \cdot b_i \times 10^3$	$\dot{n}_i \cdot c_i \times 10^6$	$\dot{n}_i \cdot d_i \times 10^9$
NO_2	111.11	2 620.0	5954.9	−3 498.9	726.6
N_2O_4	43.55	1 404.7	8257.7	−6 023.1	1563.8
N_2	1880.34	55 641.0	−9666.8	24 788.3	−9341.5
Total	2035.00	59 865.7	4545.8	15 266.3	−7051.1

Enthalpy of incoming gas mixture,

$$\phi_1 = \int_{298.15}^{295.65} (59\ 865.7 + 4545.8 + 10^{-3}\,T + 15\ 266.3 \times 10^{-6}\,T^2 - 7051.1 \times 10^{-9}\,T^3)\,dT$$

$$= -155\ 941.3 \text{ kJ/h} \equiv -43.317 \text{ kW}$$

Table 6.7 Heat Capacity Equation Constants for Outgoing Gas Mixture

Component	$\dot{n}_i$ kmol/h	Heat capacity equation constants			
		$\dot{n}_i \cdot a_i$	$\dot{n}_i \cdot b_i \times 10^3$	$\dot{n}_i \cdot c_i \times 10^6$	$\dot{n}_i \cdot d_i \times 10^9$
NO_2	77.78	1834.1	4168.6	−2449.3	508.6
N_2O_4	16.23	523.5	3077.4	−2244.7	582.8
NO	4.95	146.0	−10.2	56.1	−23.9
N_2	1880.34	55641.0	−9666.8	24 788.3	−9341.5
H_2O	89.10	2895.0	7.1	1177.1	−405.2
Total	2068.40	61039.6	−2423.9	21 327.5	−8679.2

Enthalpy of outgoing gas mixture,

$$\phi_2 = \int_{298.15}^{302.55} 61\,039.6 - 2423.9 \times 10^{-3}\,T + 21\,327.5 \times 10^{-6}\,T^2 - 8679.2 \times 10^{-9}\,T^3)\,dT$$

$$= 272\,801.8 \text{ kJ/h} \equiv 75.778 \text{ kW}$$

From Table 6.5, final aqueous liquor has following molar ratios:

$$H_2O : NaOH = 1544.11 : 138.23 = 11.17 : 1$$
$$H_2O : NaNO_2 = 1544.11 : 36.56 = 42.23 : 1$$
$$H_2O : NaNO_3 = 1544.11 : 46.46 = 33.24 : 1$$

From Ref. 5, following heat of formation data are taken

Table 6.8 Heat of Formation Data[5]

Compound Formula and Description	State	ΔH_f^o, kJ/kmol
NaOH	c	−425.609
NaOH, 7.193 H_2O (23.6% by mass)	aq	−468.257
NaOH 11.17 H_2O	aq	−469.837
$NaNO_2$	c	−358.650
$NaNO_2$, 42.23 H_2O	aq	−346.303
$NaNO_3$	c	−467.850
$NaNO_3$, 33.24 H_2O	aq	−450.100

Since 23.6% NaOH solution enters the scrubber at 25°C (298.15 K), its enthalpy is zero.

Heat of reactions
Reaction (i)

$$\Delta H_{r1}^o, = -346.303 - 450.100 - 285.83 - [2\,(-468.257) + 2\,(+33.18)]$$
$$= -212.079 \text{ kJ/2 mol } NO_2 \equiv -106.04 \text{ kJ/mol } NO_2$$

Reaction (ii)

$$\Delta H_{r2}^o = -346.303 - 450.100 - 285.83 - [2\,(-468.257) + 9.16]$$
$$= -154.879 \text{ kJ/mol } N_2O_4$$

Reaction (iii)

$$\Delta H_{r3}^o = 2\,(-450.100) - 285.83 + 90.25 - [2\,(-468.257) + 3\,(33.18)]$$
$$= -258.806 \text{ kJ/3 mol } NO_2 \equiv -86.269 \text{ kJ/mol } NO_2$$

All three reactions are exothermic.

In addition to above 3 reactions, 138.23 kmol/h (unreacted) NaOH have undergone dilution from 23.6% to 13.90% (by mass).

Heat of dilution $= -469.837 - (-468.257) = -1.58$ kJ/mol NaOH

Total Heat effect due to reactions and dilution,

$$\phi_3 = -106.04 \times 1000 \times 18.48 - 154.879 \times 1000 \times 27.32 - 86.269$$
$$\times 1000 \times 14.85 - 1.58 \times 138.23 \times 1000$$
$$= -1959\ 619 - 4231\ 294 - 1281\ 095 - 218\ 403$$
$$= -7690\ 411\ \text{kJ/h} \equiv -2136.225\ \text{kW} \quad \text{(exothermic)}$$

Heat effect of scrubbing system,

$$\phi_4 = -\phi_1 + \phi_2 + \phi_3$$
$$= 155\ 921.3 - 7690\ 411 + 272\ 801.7$$
$$= -7261\ 688\ \text{kJ/h} \equiv \textbf{-2017.136 kW} \quad \text{(exothemic)}$$

For maintaing circulation temperature to 25°C (298.15 K) 2017.136 kW heat flux must be removed from the system. In the above caculations, sufficiently accurate heat of formation data of aqueous solution were used from Ref. 5, considering exact number of moles of water associated with each compound. However Appendix V.1 lists values only for solutions having 1 molality concentration (designated as ai state in the table). These values can be used for evaluation of the heat effect as under.

$$(\Delta H^o_{r1})' = -344.8 - 447.48 - 285.83 - [2\ (-470.11) + 2\ (33.18)]$$
$$= -204.25\ \text{kJ/2 mol NO}_2 \equiv -102.125\ \text{kJ/mol NO}_2$$
$$(\Delta H^o_{r2})' = -344.8 - 447.48 - 285.83 - [2(-470.11) + (9.16)]$$
$$= -147.05\ \text{kJ/mol N}_2\text{O}_4$$
$$(\Delta H^o_{r3})' = 2\ (-447.48) - 285.83 + 90.25 - [2\ (-470.11) + 3\ (33.18)]$$
$$= -249.86\ \text{kJ/3 mol NO}_2 \equiv -83.287\ \text{kJ/mol NO}_2$$

Heat effect due to dilution of unreacted NaOH solution is neglected.

$$\phi'_3 = -102.125 \times 1000 \times 18.48 - 147.05 \times 1000 \times 27.32 - 83.283$$
$$\times 1000 \times 14.85$$
$$= -1887\ 270 - 4017\ 406 - 1236\ 753$$
$$= -7141\ 429\ \text{kJ/h} \equiv \textbf{-1983.730 kW}$$

Error by approximate method

$$= \frac{[-7690\ 411 - (-7141\ 429)]}{-7690\ 411} \times 100 = 7.14\ \%$$

Note In absence of data on standard heat of formation compounds under actual dilutions, data for aqueous solutions, having 1 molality strength, may be used for approximate calculations of the heat effect.

6.3   EXTRACTION AND LEACHING

When a mixture of liquids is not easily separable by distillation, extraction is employed. In this operation, a 'solvent' is added to the liquid–liquid mixture. As a result, two immiscible layers are formed, both of which contain varying amounts of different components. These isolated layers are removed as *extract phase* and *reffinate phase* using density difference. Invariably, distillation has to follow extraction for the recovery of the solvent for re-use. For example, furfural is a common solvent in the extraction operations in a petroleum refinery.

Normally, the term 'extraction' is used for liquid–liquid separation. Leaching is also basically a solid–liquid extraction operation in which a particular component of the solid is leached out with the help of a solvent. A common example of such an operation is the leaching of oil from an oilcake using *n*-hexane as a solvent.

Example 6.6 A mixture containing 47.5% acetic acid and 52.5% water (by mass) is being separated by the extraction in a counter-current multistage unit[6]. The operating temperature is 24°C (297 K) and the solvent used is pure *iso*-propyl ether. Using the solvent in the ratio of 1.3 kg/kg feed, the final extraction composition on a solvent-free basis is found to be 82% by mass of acetic acid. The raffinate is found to contain 14% by mass of acetic acid on a solvent-free basis. Calculate the percentage of acid of the original feed which remains unextracted.

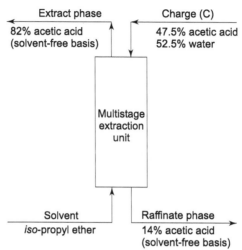

Fig. 6.8 Extraction of Acetic Acid

Solution *Basis* 100 kg of feed mixture
Let E and R be the masses in kg of the extract phase and raffinate phase respectively.
Overall material balance
$$\text{Feed } F = E + R$$
$$E + R = 100 \tag{i}$$
Balance of acetic acid
$$x_F \cdot F = x_E \cdot E + x_R \cdot R \tag{6.3}$$
where x_F mass fraction of acetic acid in feed = 0.475
x_E mass fraction of acetic acid in extract = 0.82
x_R mass fraction of acetic acid in raffinate = 0.14
$$0.82\,E + 0.14\,R = 0.475 \times 100 = 47.5 \tag{ii}$$
Solving Eqs (i) and (ii),
$$E = 49.2 \text{ kg}$$
$$R = 50.8 \text{ kg}$$
Acetic acid leftover in raffinate = $50.8 \times 0.14 = 7.11$ kg
Acetic acid which remained unextracted = $\left(\dfrac{7.11}{47.5}\right)100 = \mathbf{15\%}$

Example 6.7 A multiple-contact counter-current extractor is employed to extract oil from halibut livers with the help of ethyl ether[6]. The fresh livers are charged to the extractor at the rate of 1000 kg/h and contain 25.7% oil (by mass). Pure ether enters the bottom of the extractor. The overflow from the extractor contains 70% oil (by mass). The underflow rate is 0.23 kg solution/kg of oil-free solids and is known to contain 12.8% oil (by mass). Based on these operating conditions, make the material balance and find the flow rate of ether to the extractor. Also, compute the percentage recovery of oil.

Solution Figure 6.9 gives the schematic representation of the multiple-contact counter-current extractor.

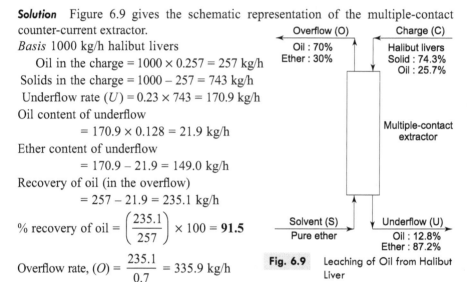

Basis 1000 kg/h halibut livers

Oil in the charge = $1000 \times 0.257 = 257$ kg/h

Solids in the charge = $1000 - 257 = 743$ kg/h

Underflow rate $(U) = 0.23 \times 743 = 170.9$ kg/h

Oil content of underflow

$$= 170.9 \times 0.128 = 21.9 \text{ kg/h}$$

Ether content of underflow

$$= 170.9 - 21.9 = 149.0 \text{ kg/h}$$

Recovery of oil (in the overflow)

$$= 257 - 21.9 = 235.1 \text{ kg/h}$$

% recovery of oil = $\left(\dfrac{235.1}{257}\right) \times 100 =$ **91.5**

Overflow rate, $(O) = \dfrac{235.1}{0.7} = 335.9$ kg/h

Fig. 6.9   Leaching of Oil from Halibut Liver

Ether content of overflow = $335.9 - 235.1 = 100.8$ kg/h

Total ether fed to the system = ether in the underflow + ether in the overflow

$$= 149 + 100.8 = \textbf{249.8 kg/h}$$

Example 6.8   Recovery of acetic acid from aqueous waste mixtures is of economic importance in a variety of industries such as cellulose acetate manufacture, etc. Study of the vapour–liquid equilibrium data of acetic acid–water reveals low relative volatility (average $\alpha = 1.8$) of the constituents and therefore, a tall column (theoretical stages > 30) and substantial energy are required for the separation. Azeotropic distillation or liquid–liquid extraction followed by distillation are therefore preferred routes for the recovery[7].

In an acetic acid plant, weak acid having 30% acid (by mass) is obtained. Since the water content of the weak acid is high (70%), extraction followed by distillation is chosen for the recovery of acid. A flowsheet of the system[7] is shown in Fig. 6.10. The following operating data are collected from a plant[8].

A. Stream	Mass % acetic acid (AA)
Feed to extractor (*F*)	30
Extract phase from extractor (*E*)	21
Raffinate phase from extractor (*R*)	5.5
Bottom layer of decanter (*R′*)	1
Waste water from solvent stripping column (*W*)	4

B. Distribution co-efficient[7] (*M*) in the decanter is 0.89 at 18°C (291.5 K).

C. Overhead product (*D*) from the solvent stripping column (C₃) is to have azeotropic composition; i.e., 76 mole % ethyl acetate and 24 mole % water. Figure 6.11 shows the ternary liquid–liquid equilibrium diagram[7]. Based on the feed rate of 1000 kg/h of weak acid, establish the material balance at each point on the flow sheet.

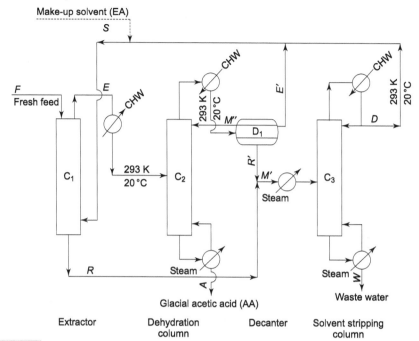

Fig. 6.10   Recovery of Acetic Acid by Ethyl Acetate Extraction

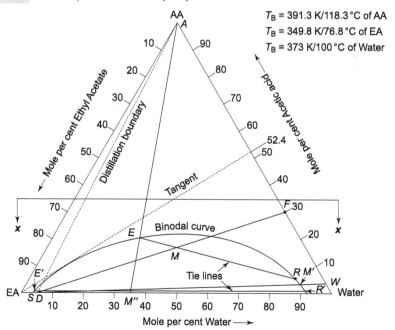

T_B = 391.3 K/118.3 °C of AA
T_B = 349.8 K/76.8 °C of EA
T_B = 373 K/100 °C of Water

Fig. 6.11 (a)   Ternary Liquid-Liquid Diagram[6] at 20°C (293.15 K)

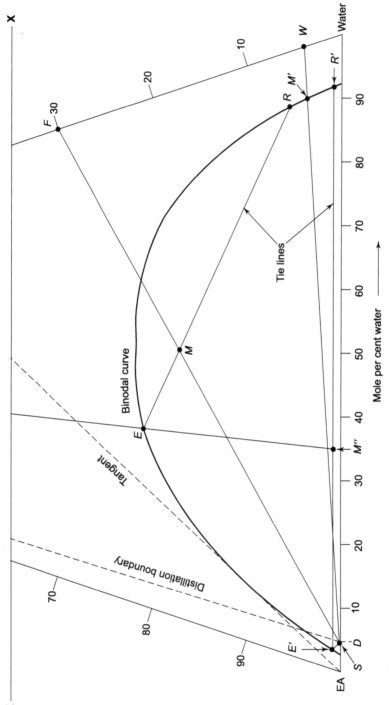

Fig. 6.11 (b) Section xx of Ternary Diagram[6] at 20°C (293.15 K)

Solution *Basis* Feed rate, $F = 1000$ kg/h

In Fig. 6.11, a binodal curve is given. It indicates the change of solubility of ethyl acetate and water-rich phases upon addition of acetic acid. Any point on the curve represents homogeneous liquid mixture saturated with either ethyl acetate or water. Any mixture outside the curve will be a homogeneous phase. Any mixture underneath the curve, such as M, will form two insoluble, saturated liquid phases of equibilirium compositions, indicated by E (rich in ethyl acetate) and R (rich in water). The line ER joining these equilibrium compositions is a *tie-line* which passes through M, representing the mixture as a whole. The other tie-line is $E'R'$ (which passes through M'). Tie-lines are drawn based or actual experimental results.

At times, there are two binodal curves on a ternary diagram (refer Exercise 6.9). In such a case, the liquid mixture between two binodual curves separate in two phases. Mixtures outside the binodal curves on either side are homogeneous.

Overall Material Balance

Composition of stream D is given as 0.76 mole fraction ethylacetate and 0.24 mole fraction water. When converted to mass fractions, they are 0.94 and 0.06, respectively.

Mark points F, A, W, R, R', and D on the ternary diagram [Fig. 6.11 (a) and (b)]. The line joining the points A and D gives the distillation boundary. Any mixture on the right side of the line cannot achieve composition of the left-side region in a single distillation column. The reverse is also true.

Using line ratio principle (Lever rule),

$$\frac{W}{A} = \frac{AF}{FW} = \frac{15.77 \text{ units}}{5.87 \text{ units}}$$

or

$$\frac{W}{A+W} = \frac{AF}{FW} = \frac{15.77}{(15.77+5.87)} = \frac{15.77}{21.64}$$

But

$$A + W = F = 1000$$

$$W = \frac{15.77 \times 1000}{21.64} = 728.7 \text{ kg/h}$$

$$A = 1000 - 728.7 = 271.2 \text{ kg/h}$$

Material balance across C_3

Feed M' to C_3 is a mixture of R and R' and hence M' lies on line RR'. M' is a mixture of D and W. Line DW will intersect RR' at M'.

$$R + R' = D + W$$

$$\frac{W}{D} = \frac{DM'}{M'W} = \frac{19.31 \text{ units}}{1.81 \text{ units}}$$

$$D = \frac{1.81}{19.31} \times 728.7 = 68.3 \text{ kg/h}$$

$$M' = D + W = 728.7 + 68.3 = 797.0 \text{ kg/h}$$

$$\frac{R'}{R} = \frac{RM'}{R'M'} = \frac{4.63 \text{ units}}{6.57 \text{ units}}$$

$$\frac{R'}{M'} = \frac{4.63}{(4.63+6.57)} = \frac{4.63}{11.2}$$

$$R' = \frac{4.63 \times 793.0}{11.2} = 327.8 \text{ kg/h}$$

$$R = 797.0 - 327.8 = 469.2 \text{ kg/h}$$

Material balance across C_2

The distrbution coefficient (M) is given at 291 K(18°C). Assume that it is same as that at 20°C (293 K).

$$M = \frac{\text{Mass fraction of AA in solvent-rich layer } (E')}{\text{Mass fraction of AA in solvent-lean layer } (R')} = 0.89$$

The mass fraction of AA in upper layer $(E') = 0.89 \times 0.01 = 0.0089$

The point E' lies on the binodal curve and has 0.0089 mass fraction AA. Mark E' on the diagram. Join E' and R', forming a tie-line.

$$E = A + E' + R'$$

Let $\qquad\qquad E' + R' = M''$

$$E = A + M''$$

Thus, point M'' can be located on the diagram by intersecting AE and $E'R'$.

$$\frac{M''}{A} = \frac{EA}{M''E} = \frac{15.6 \text{ units}}{3.97 \text{ units}}$$

$$M'' = \frac{15.6 \times 271.2}{3.97} = 1065.7 \text{ kg/h}$$

$$E = M'' + A = 1065.7 + 271.2 = 1336.9 \text{ kg/h}$$

$$E' = M'' - R' = 1065.7 - 327.8 = 737.9 \text{ kg/h}$$

Material balance across C_1

$$F + S = M = E + R$$

$$M = 1336.9 + 469.2 = 1806.1 \text{ kg/h}$$

$$S = 1806.1 - 1000 = 806.1 \text{ kg/h}$$

Also, $\qquad\qquad S = D + E' = 68.3 + 737.9 = 806.2 \text{ kg/h}$

Thus S lies on line DE'. The point S can be located by the Lever rule on the line DE'.

$$\frac{E}{R} = \frac{MR}{EM}$$

$$\frac{MR}{EM} = \frac{1336.9}{467.5}$$

$$\frac{MR}{ER} = \frac{1336.9}{(1336.9 + 467.5)} = 0.741$$

Using this ratio, point M can be located on line ER. Join FM and extend it to intersect $E'D$ at S.

$$\text{Loss of AA in waste water} = \left(\frac{728.7 \times 0.04}{100 \times 0.3} \right) 100 = 9.72\%$$

$$\text{Acetic acid recovery} = 100 - 9.72 = 91.28\%$$

All the streams are tabulated in Table 6.9.

Table 6.9 Summary of Material Balance Calculations

| Stream | Flow rate, kg/h | Composition, % by mass | | |
		Acetic acid (AA)	Ethyl acetate (EA)	Water
Feed ($F = A + W$)	1000.0	30	70	—
Solvent ($S = E' + D$)	806.1	0.82	3.74	95.44
Extract (E)	1336.9	20.9	28.0	51.1
Raffinate (R)	469.2	5.5	86.1	8.4
Acetic acid (A)	271.2	100.0	—	—
Top layer from D_1 (E')	737.9	0.89	3.54	95.57
Bottom layer from D_1 (R')	327.8	1.0	91.4	7.6
Feed to C_3 ($M' = R + R'$)	797.0	3.64	88.3	8.06
Overhead from C_3 (D)	68.3	—	6.0	94.0
Waste water (W)	728.7	4.0	96.0	—
Stream $M = E + R = F + S$	1806.1	16.9	43.0	40.1

Note Ternary diagrams are useful in defining the limits of operation. A tangent drawn from the point representing 100% ethyl acetate to the binodal curve will give the maximum limit of extraction (roughly 52 mass % AA). The weak acid of 30% strength can be separated by azeotropic distillation; i.e., with columns C_2 and C_3 only but the entrainer (ethyl acetate) requirement will be quite high (approx.15.4 kg per kg water). If the waste acid contained less water, probably azeotropic distillation could have been more economical. Also entrainer selection depends on the azeotropic composition. Other entrainers, such as mixture of ethyl acetate and benzene (15 to 20% by vol.), cyclohexanone, methyl cyclohexanone, etc., are also in use, depending on weak acid strength.

6.4 CRYSTALLIZATION

Crystallization is a unit operation in which the dissolved solids of the solution are separated out by solubility differences at different temperatures and/or concentrations of the solution (by evaporation). In this operation, the final mother liquor is always saturated. Solubility data are extensively tabulated in *Perry's Chemical Engineer's Handbook*[9].

Example 6.9 What will be the yield of glauber salt ($Na_2SO_4.10 H_2O$) if a pure 32% solution is cooled to 20°C (293.15 K) without any loss due to evaporation?
Data Solubility of Na_2SO_4 in water[9] at 20°C (293.15 K) is 19.4 kg per 100 kg water.

Solution *Basis* 100 kg of free water
Initial solution is 32% concentrated, i.e., 100 kg of original solution contains 32 kg of Na_2SO_4 and 68 kg of water.
Water associated with Na_2SO_4 = (molar mass of 10 H_2O/molar mass of Na_2SO_4) × 32

$$= \left(\frac{180}{142}\right) \times 32 = 40.56 \text{ kg}$$

Free water = 68 − 40.56 = 27.44 kg

Glauber salt present in 100 kg of free water

$$= \frac{[(32 + 40.56) \times 100]}{27.44} = 264.4 \text{ kg}$$

The final mother liquor (at 293.15 K) contains 19.4 kg Na_2SO_4 per 100 kg water. Water associated with Na_2SO_4 in the solution

$$= \frac{(180 \times 19.4)}{142} = 24.6 \text{ kg}$$

Free water = $100 - 24.6 = 75.4$ kg

Glauber salt present in 100 kg of free water

$$= \left[\frac{(19.4 + 24.6)}{75.4} \right] \times 100 = 58.36 \text{ kg}$$

Yield of Glauber salt per 100 kg of free water

$$= 264.4 - 58.36$$
$$= 206.04 \text{ kg } Na_2SO_4 \times 10 \text{ } H_2O$$

% yield of glauber salt $= \left(\dfrac{206.04}{264.4} \right) \times 100 = 77.93$

Note   The same problem can be solved algebraically by assuming x kg yield of crystals per 100 kg of original solution and making a material balance of Na_2SO_4 in the original solution, mother liquor and crystals.

Example 6.10   A saturated solution of $MgSO_4$ at 80°C (353 K) is cooled to 30°C (303 K) in a crystallizer. During cooling, mass equivalent to 4% solution is lost by evaporation of water. Calculate the quantity of the original saturated solution to be fed to the crystallizer per 1000 kg crystals of $MgSO_4.7$ H_2O. Solubilities of $MgSO_4$ at 30°C (303 K) and 80°C (353 K) are 40.8 and 64.2 kg per 100 kg water respectively[9].

Solution   *Basis* 100 kg of free water in the original solution.

Initial saturated solution is at 353 K.

Associated water in the original solution = (molar mass of 7 H_2O/molar mass of $MgSO_4$) × 64.2

$$= \left(\frac{126}{120.3} \right) \times 64.2 = 67.24 \text{ kg}$$

Free water = $100 - 67.24 = 32.76$ kg

$MgSO_4.7$ H_2O in 100 kg of free water

$$= \frac{[(64.20 + 67.24) \times 100]}{32.76} = 401.2 \text{ kg}$$

It is stated that 4% of the original solution gets evaporated.

Evaporation = $(401.2 + 100) \times 0.04 = 20.05$ kg

In the mother liquor, the free water quantity will be

$$= 100 - 20.05 = 79.95 \text{ kg}$$

At 303.15 K, associated water with $MgSO_4$

in the mother liquor $= \left(\dfrac{126}{120.3} \right) \times 40.8 = 42.73$ kg

Free water in the mother liquor = $100 - 42.73 = 57.27$ kg

Crystals of $MgSO_4 \cdot 7 H_2O$ in the mother liquor for

$$79.95 \text{ kg free water} = \frac{[(42.73 + 40.80) \times 79.95]}{57.27} = 116.6 \text{ kg}$$

Yield of crystals $= 401.2 - 116.6 = 284.6 \text{ kg } MgSO_4 \cdot 7 H_2O$

However, it is desired to get 1000 kg of crystals.
Quantity of original solution to be fed to the crystallizer

$$= \frac{(501.2 \times 1000)}{284.6} = \textbf{1761.1 kg}$$

Alternate Method
A short-cut to the above calculations can be had with the use of the equation[9] given below:

$$C = R \frac{[100W - S(H - E)]}{[100 - S(R - 1)]} \qquad (6.4)$$

where C = mass of crystals in the final magma in kg
R = molar mass of hydrated solute/molar mass of anhydrous solute

$$= \frac{246.3}{120.3} = 2.05$$

S = solubility of solute (kg) at the final temperature in 100 kg of water
= 40.8 kg
W = mass of anhydrous solute in the original solution = 64.2
H = total mass of solvent in the batch at the beginning of the process
= 100 kg (basis for calculations)
E = evaporation during the process = $(64.2 + 100) \times 0.04 = 6.57$ kg
Substituting the above values in Eq. (6.4)

$$C = \frac{2.05 [(100 \times 64.2) - 40.8 (100 - 6.57)]}{[100 - 40.80 (2.05 - 1)]}$$

$$= 93.54 \text{ kg yield of crystals}$$

For yield of 1000 kg of crystals, the charge to the crystallizer

$$= \frac{(164.2 \times 1000)}{93.54} = \textbf{1755.4 kg}$$

Note Example 6.9 can be solved with the help of the above equation, in which case $E = 0$.

In many instances, crystallization is an attractive separation technique than distillation or extraction. Consider separation of a mixture of xylenes. Boiling point data of xylenes (Table 5.5) reveal that they are very close for three isomers. However, melting points of these isomers (Table 5.8) are far apart to consider crystallization as an alternative for their separation. Similarly, consider separation of acetic acid (AA) from its dilute aqueous solution (Example 6.8). Water is a low boiler and has much higher latent heat of vaporization (λ_v) as compared to that of AA. Hence, if distillation is considered for the separation of AA, considerable energy will have to be spent to boil off water, apart from an expensive tall column. Instead, close analysis of eutectic diagram of AA-water system[10] suggests that crystallization is an attractive alternative to distillation for such dilute solutions. It was seen in Example 6.8 that a 3-column system is needed to separate AA by extraction.

Final waste stream (W) contains 4% AA. Also stream A may have some impurity of the solvent. If crystallization is used instead, pure crystals of AA can be obtained with much less energy input. Special equipments (e.g. scrapped surface heat exchangers) will, however, be needed for such a crystallization process.

For eutectic systems, the crystallization process has a key advantage over distillation as the solid phase separated by cooling is pure. The following examples will be useful in understanding phase diagrams.

Example 6.11 A feed to the crystallizer consists of 70% p-dichlorobenzene (p-DCB) and 30% o-DCB (by mass). It is fed to a crystallizer at 52°C (325 K). Using Fig. 6.12, evaluate the following.

(a) The feed is cooled to 17°C (290 K). Calculate the percentage recovery of p-DCB.

(b) The mixture is further cooled to − 18°C (255 K) without separating crystals, formed at 17°C (290 K). Calculate the additional recovery of p-DCB.

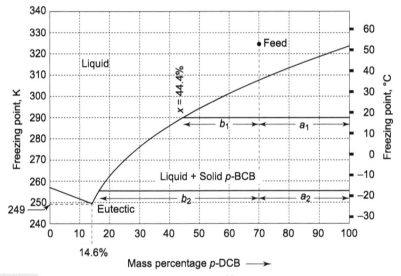

Fig. 6.12 Eutectic Diagram of p-DCB and o-DCB[11]
(Reproduced with the permission of Putman Publishing Co., USA)

Solution (*a*) The feed point, representing 70% p-DCB and 325 K is shown on Fig. 6.12. Cooling of the mixture is represented by a vertical line. A horizontal line at 290 K provides material balance.

$$\text{Solids } (p\text{-DCB}) \text{ separated} = \frac{b_1}{(a_1 + b_1)}\ 100 = \frac{4.91 \times 100}{(4.91 + 5.76)} = 46.0\%$$

Mother liquor at 290 K will contain 44.4% p-DCB.

$$\text{Recovery of } p\text{-DCB} = \frac{(46.0 \times 100)}{70} = \mathbf{65.7\%}$$

(b) At 255 K, solids (p-DCB) separated $= \dfrac{b_2}{(a_2 + b_2)} \times 100 = \dfrac{10.22 \times 100}{(5.76 + 10.22)} = 64.0\%$

Mother liquor at 290 K will contain 16.7% p-DCB.

$$\text{Recovery of } p\text{-DCB} = \frac{(64.0 \times 100)}{70} = \mathbf{91.4\%}$$

$$\text{Additional recovery} = 91.4 - 65.7 = \mathbf{25.7\%}$$

Note It is desirable to separate first crop of crystals in a centrifuge at 290 K and only mother liquor (containing 44.4% p-DCB) should further be cooled to achieve additional recovery of 25.7%. Such an operation will result in saving in refrigeration requirement.

Example 6.12 In a batch reaction, a mixture of o- and p-nitrochlorobenzenes (NCB) is produced which is 98% solvent-free. These isomers are to be fractionated into pure products by crystallization. The crystallization section of the plant is shown in Fig. 6.13. The feed, containing 80% p-isomer and 20% o-isomer (mass %), is fed to a simple crystallizer where it is cooled to 16°C (289 K). At this temperature both the isomers form an eutectic mixture, containing 33.1 mole % p-NCB. The liquid mixture, after the removal of crystals of the p-isomer, is taken to an extractive crystallization unit in which p-nitrotoluene is used as a solvent[12]. The operating temperature of the extractive crystallization unit is 5°C (278 K). Isotherms of the ternary system are given in Fig. 6.14. Bottoms from both the crystallization units are collected as p-isomer product. This product is 98% (mass %) pure on a solvent-free basis from the centrifuges. The top product from the extractive unit contains 5% (by mass) solvent.

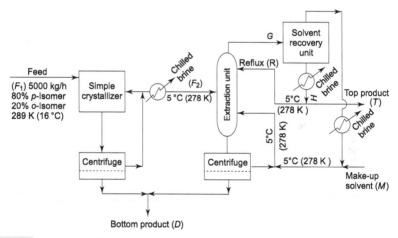

Fig. 6.13 Extractive Crystallization of o- and p-nitrochlorobenzenes

The solid reflux from the evaporator plays a determining role in the cost of the extraction unit and the empirical relationship between the two parameters is given by

$$C_T = a + R + \frac{1}{R^2}$$

where C_T = cost of extractive crystallization unit
  a = constant
  R = reflux ratio

Based on a feed rate of 5000 kg/h solvent-free product from the reactor, calculate (a) flow rates of products and their purities, and (b) flow rate of the make-up solvent.

Isotherms :
T_1 = 278 K (5°C)
T_2 = 293 K (20°C)
T_3 = 313 K (40°C)
T_4 = 333 K (60°C)

A-*o*-Nitrochlorobenzene
B-*p*-Nitrochlorobenzene
C-*p*-Nitrotoluene

Freezing temp.
T_{FA} = 305.4 K/32.3°C
T_{FB} = 355.9 K/82.8°C
T_{FC} = 324.3 K/51.2°C

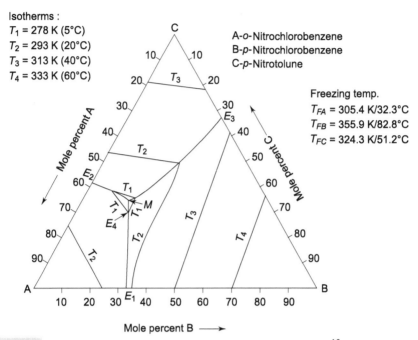

Fig. 6.14   Ternary Isotherms for Nitrochlorobenzenes and Nitrotoluene[12]
(Reproduced with the permission of the Indian Institute of Chemical Engineers)

Solution   *Basis* 5000 kg/h solvent-free mixture (*F*) to simple crystallization unit
Molar mass of NCB = 157.5
p-NCB (B) in the feed = 4000 kg/h = 25.4 kmol/h
o-NCB (A) in the feed = 1000 kg/h = 6.35 kmol/h

In the simple crystallization unit, the eutectic mixture is formed by cooling it to 16°C (289 K). The mother liquor of this unit will contain 33.1 mole % B. The product from the centrifuge will be pure B. Since A does not get crystallized out, it can be used to make the material balance.

Total mother liquor entering extractive crystallization unit

$$= \frac{6.35}{(1-0.331)} = 9.49 \text{ kmol/h}$$

B in the mother liquor = 9.49 – 6.35 = 3.14 kmol/h

For optimizing solid reflux,

$$\frac{dC_T}{dR} = 1 - \frac{2}{R^3} = 0$$

$$R^3 = 2$$

$$R = 1.26$$

The path of extractive crystallization is shown in Fig. 6.13. Point E_1 represents the eutectic mixture (F_2). Points E_2 and E_3 represent eutectic compositions, containing 42.2 mole % and 67.5 mole % *p*-nitrotoluene (C), respectively. *M* is the point representing the ternary eutectic. The molar composition of the ternary eutectic is

48.3% A, 16.5% B and 35.2% C. With the addition of solvent C in F_2, the composition of the ternary mixture follows the path E_1M. Point E_4 lies on the isotherm of 5°C (278 K) and hence it represents the composition of the mother liquor.

Table 6.10 Composition of Mother Liquor from Extractive Crystallization Unit

Component	Composition of E_4 mixture	
	mole %	mass %
o-nitrochlorobenzene (A)	51	53.1
p-nitrochlorobenzene (B)	19	19.8
p-nitrotoluene (C)	30	27.1

Let T and D be the flow rates of the top product from extraction unit and bottom product from both units together respectively and x be the mass fraction of the B in T. Overall material balance:

p-isomer (B)

$$0.98 \, D + xT = 4000 \qquad \text{(i)}$$

o-isomer (A)

$$0.02 \, D + (1 - 0.05 - x) \, T = 1000 \qquad \text{(ii)}$$

Material balance around solvent recovery unit

p-isomer (B)

$$2.26 \, Tx = 0.198 \, G = xH \qquad \text{(iii)}$$

o-isomer (A)

$$2.26 \, T \, (0.95 - x) = 0.531 \, G \qquad \text{(iv)}$$

Solving Eqs (i) to (iv),

$$T = 1337.6 \text{ kg/h} \quad G = 3939.0 \text{ kg/h}$$
$$D = 3729.5 \text{ kg/h} \quad x = 0.258$$

Table 6.11 Composition of Various Streams

Component	T		D		G	H
	kg/h	mass %	kg/h	mass %	kg/h	kg/h
A	925.6	69.2	74.6	2.0	2091.9	2091.9
B	345.1	25.8	3654.9	98.0	779.9	779.9
C	66.9	5.0	Nil	—	1067.2	151.2
Total	1337.6	100.0	3729.5	100.0	3939.0	3023.0

Purity of top product = **69.2% A**, Purity of bottom product = **98.0% B**
Loss of solvent in T = Make-up solvent = **66.9 kg/h**
Compositions of H, T and R are same.

6.5 PSYCHROMETRY

Psychrometry is the subject which deals with the properties of gas–vapour mixtures. In this type of operation, the gas is brought into contact with a pure liquid in which the gas is essentially insoluble. As a consequence, the liquid can evaporate and the gas becomes saturated with respect to the liquid. Alternatively, by cooling the gas, condensation of the liquid can take place. It is not necessary that the gas is saturated with respect to the liquid in each case. Unsaturation of the gas is expressed in different ways.

6.5.1 Humidification Operations

One of the most important psychrometric operations is the air–water contact operation. These operations are also referred to as humidification operations. In fact, humidification operations are so often encountered in day-to-day practice that whenever reference is made to a psychrometric operation, it is understood to be a humidification operation, unless clarified. Humidification operations also involve dehumidification.

6.5.2 Terminology

The common terminologies used for air–water contact operations are listed below.

(i) Dry-bulb temperature (DB)   The temperature of the air-water vapour mixture, recorded by the immersion of a thermometer in the mixture, is termed as dry-bulb temperature (DB).

(ii) Absolute humidity (H)   The mass of water vapour, present in a unit mass of dry air is termed as absolute humidity (H). It follows, therefore, that the units of H are g water vapour/kg dry air, or kg water vapour/kg dry air. Note that commonly used symbol in literature for humidity and enthalpy is same; i.e., H.

In some books, absolute molar humidity (H_m) is referred to. This is expressed as kmol water vapour/kmol dry air.

According to Dalton's law of partial pressure (see Chapter 2), each constituent in a mixture of perfect gases exerts the same pressure as if it alone were present in the space occupied by the mixture at the temperature of the mixture. Total pressure of the gases is the sum of their partial pressures and the volume of the mixture of gases is the same as the volume occupied by each gas at its partial pressure.

$$p = \text{total pressure of the system} = p_w + p_a \qquad (6.5)$$

In humidification operation, usually p is the standard atmospheric pressure (101.325 kPa or 760 Torr).

p_w = partial pressure of water vapour in the mixture, kPa

p_a = partial pressure of air in the mixture, kPa

If n_w are the number of moles water vapour present in n_a moles of dry air,

$$H_\mathrm{m} = \frac{n_w}{n_a} \qquad (6.6)$$

$$n_w = \frac{p_w \cdot V}{RT} \quad \text{and} \quad n_a = \frac{p_a \cdot V}{RT}$$

$$H_\mathrm{m} = \frac{p_w}{p_a} \qquad (6.7a)$$

$$= \frac{p_w}{p - p_w} \qquad (6.7)$$

Thus, molar humidity is the ratio of partial pressure of water vapours to the partial pressure of air.

Absolute humidity can be expressed as

$$H = \frac{H_m \cdot M_w}{M_a} \qquad (6.8)$$

where M_w = molar mass of water = 18.0153 kg/kmol

M_a = molar mass of air = 28.9697 kg/kmol

$$H = \frac{18.0153}{28.9697} H_m = 0.622 \, H_m \qquad (6.9)$$

Combinig Eq. (6.7a) and Eq. (6.9)

$$H_m = 0.622 \frac{p_w}{(p - p_w)} \qquad (6.10)$$

When $p_w = p_s$, the vapour pressure of water at DB, the air is fully saturated. The absolute humidity at 100% saturation is called saturation humidity (H_s).

$$H_s = 0.622 \frac{p_w}{(p - p_s)} \qquad (6.11)$$

(iii) Percentage humidity or percentage absolute humidity or percentage saturation   Percentage humidity is defined as the ratio of the actual absolute humidity to the saturation humidity.

$$\text{Percentage humidity} = \left(\frac{H}{H_s}\right) \times 100 \qquad (6.12a)$$

$$= \frac{p_w \, (p - p_s)}{p_s \, (p - p_w)} \times 100 \qquad (6.12)$$

(iv) Relative humidity **or** *percentage relative humidity* **or** *relative saturation (RH)*   Relative humidity is defined as the ratio of the partial pressure of water vapour in air to the vapour pressure of water at the dry bulb temperature (DB).

$$RH = \left(\frac{p_w}{p_s}\right) \times 100 \qquad (6.13)$$

Use of Eq. (6.5) to (6.13) requires the vapour pressure data. Vapour (sublimation) pressure of ice is given by the equation[13].

$$\ln\left(\frac{p_v}{p_o}\right) = a_1 \, (1 - \vartheta^{-1.5}) + a_2 \, (1 - \vartheta^{-1.25}) \qquad (6.14)$$

where p_v = vapour (sublimation) pressure of ice, Pa

p_o = reference pressure = 611.657 Pa

$a_1 = -13.928\ 169$ $a_2 = 34.707\ 8238$ $\vartheta = T/T_o$

T = desired absolute temperature, K

T_o = reference temperature = 273.16 K

Equation (6.14) is valid for temperature range of –80°C (193.15 K) to 0.01°C (273.16 K) and is accurate within 0.5%. Table 6.12 lists vapour (sublimation) pressure of ice based on Eq. (6.14).

Table 6.13 lists vapour pressure of water between 0°C (273.15 K) to 101.9°C (375.05 K).

(v) Humid heat (C$_H$)   Humid heat is defined as the heat capacity of 1 kg dry air and the moisture contained in it.

$$C_H = 1.006 + 1.84\ H\ \text{kJ/(kg dry air} \cdot \text{K)} \tag{6.15}$$

Insignificant error (less than 0.5%) will be realised by the use of Eq. (6.15) in the temperature range – 40°C to 80°C (233 K to 353 K).

(vi) Humid volume (V$_H$)   Humid volume is the volume of a mixture of air and accompanying water vapour per kg of dry air. This is also known as *psychrometric volume*.

$$V_H = \frac{RT}{p_w \cdot M_w} \tag{6.16}$$

$$V_{H_s} = \frac{RT}{p_s \cdot M_w} \tag{6.17}$$

R = Universal gas constant = 8.314 472 m^3 · kPa/(kmol · K)

(vii) Dew point (DP)   Dew point is the temperature at which the air–water vapour mixture becomes saturated when the mixture is cooled at constant total pressure in the absence of liquid water. During measurement of *DP*, air–water vapour mixture is cooled and temperature corresponding to first dew is measured and hence it is termed as dew point. This means that the partial pressure of water vapour in the mixture equals the vapour pressure of water at *DP*. Dew point is always lower or equal to the dry bulb temperature.

(viii) Wet-bulb temperature (WB)   If a thermometer, having the bulb covered with a wet wick, is kept in air–water vapour mixture, it will read a steady value after a few seconds. This temperature is called the wet-bulb temperature (*WB*). It represents the dynamic equilibrium of the heat transfer by convection to the surface and the mass transfer to the surroundings from the surface.

When wet-bulb temperature is measured, errors due to the effects of radiation, convection, conduction and diffusion are expected. It is therefore recommended that air velocity of the order of 2.5 – 10.0 m/s is achieved over the long wet wick (extending well up the thermometer stem) for true measurement of the wet-bulb temperature. For this purpose, a whirling psychrometer is normally preferred.

Wet-bulb temperature is always lower than or equal to dry bulb temperature.

At 100% saturation, *DB = DP = WB*

This is an important property of psychrometry.

(ix) Adiabatic Saturation Temperature (AST)   Adiabatic process is the one in which no heat flows into or out of the system but during which thermal changes usually

Table 6.12 Vapour (Sublimation) Pressure of Ice[13]

| Temperature* | | Vapour pressure, Pa — Temperature interval, °C (K) | | | | | | | | | |
°C	K	0	1	2	3	4	5	6	7	8	9
-80	193.15	0.0546	—	—	—	—	—	—	—	—	—
-70	203.15	0.2613	0.2250	0.1934	0.1660	0.1423	0.1218	0.1041	0.0888	0.0757	0.0643
-60	213.15	1.080	0.9429	0.8220	0.7156	0.6222	0.5403	0.4685	0.4057	0.3509	0.3030
-50	223.15	3.936	3.477	3.068	2.704	2.380	2.093	1.838	1.612	1.413	1.236
-40	233.15	12.841	11.462	10.220	9.104	8.101	7.202	6.396	5.674	5.028	4.451
-30	243.15	38.012	34.241	30.817	27.711	24.896	22.347	20.040	17.955	16.072	14.373

| Temperature* | | Temperature interval, °C (K) | | | | | | | | | |
°C	K	0.0	0.1	0.2	0.3	0.4	0.5	0.6	0.7	0.8	0.9
-29	244.15	42.163	41.730	41.301	40.876	40.455	40.038	39.625	39.216	38.811	38.410
-28	245.15	46.727	46.251	45.779	45.312	44.849	44.391	43.937	43.487	43.042	42.600
-27	246.15	51.742	51.219	50.701	50.188	49.679	49.176	48.677	48.182	47.693	47.208
-26	247.15	57.247	56.674	56.105	55.542	54.984	54.431	53.883	53.340	52.802	52.270
-25	248.15	63.287	62.658	62.034	61.416	60.804	60.198	59.597	59.001	58.411	57.827
-24	249.15	69.908	69.218	68.535	67.858	67.187	66.522	65.863	65.210	64.563	63.922
-23	250.15	77.159	76.404	75.656	74.914	74.179	73.451	72.730	72.014	71.306	70.604
-22	251.15	85.095	84.269	83.451	82.639	81.835	81.038	80.248	79.465	78.690	77.921
-21	252.15	93.775	92.872	91.977	91.089	90.210	89.338	88.475	87.618	86.770	85.929
-20	253.15	103.26	102.27	101.30	100.33	99.365	98.413	97.469	96.533	95.605	94.686
-19	254.15	113.62	112.54	111.47	110.41	109.37	108.33	107.29	106.27	105.26	104.26
-18	255.15	124.92	123.75	122.58	121.43	120.28	119.15	118.02	116.91	115.80	114.70
-17	256.15	137.25	135.97	134.70	133.44	132.19	130.95	129.72	128.51	127.30	126.11
-16	257.15	150.68	149.28	147.90	146.53	145.17	143.82	142.48	141.16	139.84	138.54
-15	258.15	165.30	163.78	162.28	160.78	159.30	157.83	156.38	154.93	153.50	152.08
-14	259.15	181.22	179.56	177.92	176.30	174.69	173.09	171.51	169.94	168.38	166.83

(Contd.)

Table 6.12 Vapour (Sublimation) Pressure of Ice (Contd.)

Temperature*		Vapour pressure, Pa Temperature interval, °C (K)									
°C	K	0	1	2	3	4	5	6	7	8	9
−13	260.15	198.52	196.72	194.94	193.18	191.42	189.69	187.96	186.26	184.56	182.88
−12	261.15	217.32	215.37	213.44	211.52	209.61	207.73	205.85	204.00	202.16	200.33
−11	262.15	237.74	235.63	233.52	231.44	229.37	227.32	225.29	223.27	221.27	219.29
−10	263.15	259.90	257.61	255.33	253.07	250.82	248.60	246.39	244.20	242.03	239.88
−9	264.15	283.94	281.45	278.97	276.52	274.09	271.68	269.28	266.91	264.56	262.22
−8	265.15	309.98	307.28	304.61	301.95	299.31	296.70	294.11	291.53	288.98	286.45
−7	266.15	338.19	335.27	332.37	329.49	326.64	323.81	321.00	318.21	315.45	312.70
−6	267.15	368.73	365.57	362.43	359.32	356.23	353.16	350.12	347.10	344.11	341.14
−5	268.15	401.76	398.34	394.95	391.58	388.24	384.92	381.63	378.37	375.13	371.92
−4	269.15	437.47	433.78	430.11	426.47	422.86	419.27	415.72	412.19	408.69	405.21
−3	270.15	476.06	472.06	468.10	464.17	460.27	456.39	452.55	448.74	444.95	441.20
−2	271.15	517.72	513.41	509.13	504.88	500.67	496.49	492.34	488.22	484.14	480.08
−1	272.15	562.67	558.02	553.41	548.82	544.28	539.77	535.29	530.85	526.44	522.06
0	273.15	611.154	606.14	601.16	596.22	591.32	586.46	581.63	576.83	572.08	567.36
0.01	273.16	611.657	—	—	—	—	—	—	—	—	—

*Temperature values correspond to ITS-90 temperature scale.

Table 6.13 Vapour Pressure of Water

Vapour Pressure, kPa

| Temperature | | Temperature Interval, °C or K | | | | | | | | | |
t °C	T K	0	0.1	0.2	0.3	0.4	0.5	0.6	0.7	0.8	0.9
0	273.15	0.6108	0.615	0.6195	0.6241	0.6286	0.6333	0.6379	0.6426	0.6473	0.6519
1	274.15	0.6566	0.6615	0.6663	0.6711	0.6759	0.6809	0.6858	0.6907	0.6958	0.7007
2	275.15	0.7055	0.7109	0.7159	0.721	0.7262	0.7314	0.7366	0.7419	0.7473	0.7526
3	276.15	0.7575	0.7633	0.7687	0.7742	0.7797	0.7851	0.7907	0.7963	0.8019	0.8077
4	277.15	0.8129	0.8191	0.8249	0.8306	0.8365	0.8423	0.8483	0.8543	0.8603	0.8663
5	278.15	0.8718	0.8785	0.8846	0.8907	0.8970	0.9033	0.9095	0.9158	0.9222	0.9286
6	279.15	0.9345	0.9415	0.9481	0.9546	0.9611	0.9678	0.9745	0.9813	0.9881	0.9949
7	280.15	1.0012	1.0086	1.0155	1.0224	1.0295	1.0366	1.0436	1.0508	1.0580	1.0652
8	281.15	1.072	1.0799	1.0872	1.0947	1.1022	1.1096	1.1172	1.1248	1.1324	1.14
9	282.15	1.1472	1.1556	1.1635	1.1714	1.1792	1.1872	1.1952	1.2032	1.2114	1.2195
10	283.15	1.227	1.2294	1.2443	1.2526	1.261	1.2694	1.2779	1.2864	1.2951	1.3038
11	284.15	1.3116	1.3212	1.33	1.3388	1.3478	1.3567	1.3658	1.3748	1.3839	1.3931
12	285.15	1.4014	1.4116	1.421	1.4303	1.4397	1.4492	1.4587	1.4683	1.4779	1.4876
13	286.15	1.4965	1.5072	1.5171	1.5269	1.5369	1.5471	1.5572	1.5673	1.5776	1.5879
14	287.15	1.5973	1.6085	1.6191	1.6296	1.6401	1.6508	1.6615	1.6723	1.6831	1.694
15	288.15	1.7039	1.7159	1.7269	1.7381	1.7493	1.7605	1.7719	1.7832	1.7947	1.8061
16	289.15	1.8168	1.8293	1.841	1.8529	1.8648	1.8766	1.8886	1.9006	1.9128	1.9249
17	290.15	1.9362	1.9494	1.9618	1.9744	1.9869	1.9994	2.0121	2.0249	2.0377	2.0505
18	291.15	2.0624	2.0765	2.0896	2.1028	2.116	2.1293	2.1426	2.156	2.1694	2.183
19	292.15	2.1957	2.2106	2.2245	2.2383	2.2523	2.2663	2.2805	2.2947	2.309	2.3234
20	293.15	2.3366	2.3523	2.3668	2.3815	2.3963	2.4111	2.4261	2.441	2.4561	2.4713
21	294.15	2.4853	2.5018	2.5171	2.5326	2.5482	2.5639	2.5797	2.5955	2.6144	2.6274
22	295.15	2.6422	2.6595	2.6758	2.6922	2.7086	2.7251	2.7418	2.7584	2.7751	2.7919
23	296.15	2.8076	2.8259	2.843	2.8602	2.8775	2.895	2.9124	2.93	2.9478	2.9655
24	297.15	2.9821	3.0014	3.0195	3.0378	3.056	3.0744	3.0928	3.1113	3.1299	3.1485

(*Contd.*)

Table 6.13 (Contd.)

Vapour Pressure, kPa

| Temperature | | Temperature Interval, °C or K | | | | | | | | | |
t °C	T K	0	0.1	0.2	0.3	0.4	0.5	0.6	0.7	0.8	0.9
25	298.15	3.166	3.186	3.205	3.224	3.2432	3.2625	3.282	3.3016	3.3213	3.3411
26	299.15	3.3597	3.3809	3.4009	3.4211	3.4413	3.4616	3.482	3.5025	3.5232	3.544
27	300.15	3.5636	3.586	3.607	3.6282	3.6496	3.671	3.6925	3.7141	3.7358	3.7577
28	301.15	3.7782	3.8016	3.8237	3.846	3.8683	3.8909	3.9135	3.9363	3.9593	3.9823
29	302.15	4.004	4.0286	4.0519	4.0754	4.099	4.1227	4.1466	4.1705	4.1945	4.2186
30	303.15	4.2415	4.2673	4.2918	4.3164	4.3411	4.3659	4.3908	4.4159	4.4412	4.4667
31	304.15	4.4911	4.518	4.5439	4.5698	4.5958	4.6219	4.6482	4.6746	4.7011	4.7279
32	305.15	4.7534	4.7816	4.8087	4.8359	4.8632	4.8907	4.9184	4.9461	4.974	5.002
33	306.15	5.0288	5.0585	5.0869	5.1154	5.1441	5.173	5.202	5.2312	5.2605	5.2898
34	307.15	5.318	5.349	5.3788	5.4088	5.439	5.4693	5.4997	5.5302	5.5609	5.5918
35	308.15	5.6216	5.6541	5.6854	5.7168	5.7485	5.7802	5.8122	5.8443	5.8766	5.9088
36	309.15	5.94	5.9739	6.0067	6.0396	6.0727	6.106	6.1395	6.1731	6.207	6.241
37	310.15	6.2739	6.3093	6.3437	6.3783	6.4131	6.448	6.4831	6.5183	6.5537	6.5893
38	311.15	6.624	6.6609	6.6969	6.733	6.7693	6.8058	6.8425	6.8794	6.9166	6.9541
39	312.15	6.9908	7.0294	7.0673	7.1053	7.1434	7.1817	7.2202	7.2589	7.2977	7.3367
40	313.15	7.375	7.414	7.454	7.494	7.534	7.574	7.614	7.654	7.695	7.737
41	314.15	7.777	7.819	7.861	7.902	7.943	7.986	8.029	8.071	8.114	8.157
42	315.15	8.199	8.242	8.285	8.329	8.373	8.417	8.461	8.505	8.549	8.594
43	316.15	8.639	8.685	8.73	8.775	8.821	8.867	8.914	8.961	9.007	9.054
44	317.15	9.101	9.147	9.195	9.243	9.291	9.339	9.387	9.435	9.485	9.534
45	318.15	9.582	9.633	9.682	9.731	9.781	9.831	9.882	9.933	9.983	10.034
46	319.15	10.086	10.138	10.19	10.242	10.294	10.346	10.399	10.452	10.506	10.559
47	320.15	10.612	10.666	10.72	10.775	10.83	10.884	10.939	10.994	11.048	11.104
48	321.15	11.162	11.216	11.274	11.331	11.388	11.446	11.503	11.56	11.618	11.676
49	322.15	11.736	11.794	11.852	11.911	11.971	12.031	12.091	12.151	12.211	12.272

(Contd.)

Table 6.13   (Contd.)

| Temperature | | Vapour Pressure, kPa | | | | | | | | | |
| t °C | T K | 0 | 0.1 | 0.2 | 0.3 | 0.4 | 0.5 | 0.6 | 0.7 | 0.8 | 0.9 |
						Temperature Interval, °C or K					
50	323.15	12.335	12.961	13.613	14.293	15.002	15.741	16.511	17.313	18.147	19.016
60	333.15	19.92	20.861	21.838	22.855	23.921	25.009	26.15	27.334	28.563	29.838
70	343.15	31.162	32.535	33.958	35.434	36.964	38.549	40.191	41.891	43.652	45.474
80	353.15	47.36	49.311	51.329	53.416	55.573	57.803	60.108	62.489	64.948	67.487
90	363.15	70.109	70.362	70.63	70.898	71.167	71.437	71.709	71.981	72.254	72.527
91	364.15	72.815	73.075	73.351	73.629	73.907	74.186	74.465	74.746	75.027	75.31
92	365.15	75.608	75.876	76.162	76.447	76.734	77.022	77.31	77.599	77.89	78.182
93	366.15	78.489	78.767	79.06	79.355	79.651	79.948	80.245	80.544	80.844	81.145
94	367.15	81.461	81.749	82.052	82.356	82.661	82.968	83.275	83.583	83.892	84.202
95	368.15	84.526	84.825	85.138	85.452	85.766	86.082	86.4	86.717	87.036	87.356
96	369.15	87.686	67.997	88.319	88.643	88.967	89.293	89.619	89.947	90.275	90.618
97	370.15	90.944	91.266	91.598	91.931	92.266	92.602	92.939	93.276	93.615	93.954
98	371.15	94.301	94.636	94.979	95.323	95.667	96.012	96.359	96.707	97.056	97.407
99	372.15	97.761	98.109	98.463	98.816	99.171	99.528	99.885	100.244	100.602	100.964
100	**373.15**	**101.325**	101.688	102.052	102.417	101.782	103.15	103.517	103.887	104.258	104.629
101	374.15	105.001	105.374	105.749	106.125	106.501	106.879	107.258	107.638	108.019	108.402

(Reproduced from (1) Perry's Chemical Engineers Handbook, 6th Edition, McGraw.Hill, USA, 1984 and (ii) 1980 JSME Steam Tables in SI, The Japan Society of Mechanical Engineers, Japan with permissions). Temperature values correspond to ITS-68 temperature scale.

occur within the system. When a definite quantity of water is allowed to evaporate in a stream of air adiabatically, the dry-bulb temperature of air drops and the humidity of air increases. The final temperature of the intimately-mixed stream is termed as adiabatic saturation temperature (*AST*).

For air–water systems, *WB* and *AST* are practically same. This is because the latent heat of vaporization of water is quite high in comparison to the sensible heat content of air–water mixture. However, for any other gas vapour system, two temperatures may differ appreciably.

Carrier[14] presented the following equation which is very useful in correlating most psychrometric properties of air–water vapour mixtures, known as *DBT*, *WBT* and the barometric (total) pressure.

$$p_W = p_{WB} - \left(\frac{(p - p_{WB})(T_{DB} - T_{WB})}{1546 - 1.44(T_{WB} - 273.15)} \right) \tag{6.18}$$

where p_W = actual partial pressure of water vapour at *DP*, kPa
  p_{WB} = vapour pressure of water vapour at wet bulb temperature, kPa
  p = total pressure, kPa
  T_{DB} = dry-bulb temperature, K
  T_{WB} = wet-bulb temperature, K

(x) Enthalpy of humid air Enthalpy of air–water vapour mixture is the sum of the enthalpies of each constituent at its partial pressure and common (dry bulb) temperature.

$$i_a = 1.006(T_{DB} - 273.15) + H.i_w \text{ kJ/kg dry air} \tag{6.19}$$

where i_w = total enthalpy of water vapour at T_{DB}, kJ/kg
At saturation,

$$i_{as} = 1.006(T_{DP} - 273.15) + H_s.i_{ws} \text{ kJ/kg dry air} \tag{6.20}$$

Values of i_w and i_{ws} can be had from Steam Tables (Appendix IV).

$$d = i_{as} - i_a \tag{6.21}$$

Thus *d* is the difference in enthalpy of saturated air and enthalpy of air–water vapour mixture at T_{DB} on adiabatic saturation. This is also known as *enthalpy deviation*. Note that for differentiation in nomenclature, enthalpy is denoted by *i*.

6.5.3 Psychrometric Chart for Air–water System

The psychrometric properties of the air–water system, as described in the above section, can be conveniently plotted in a chart form which is known as a psychrometric chart. Such a chart is more convenient for determining the properties of moist air and is useful for delineating the various humidification processes.

Fig. 6.15 is a psychrometric chart for the normal temperature range of – 10°C (263.15 K) to 55°C (328.15 K) at 101.325 kPa. Similarly, Fig. 6.16 is the high-temperature psychrometric chart for the temperature range of 20°C (293.15 K) to 120°C (393.15 K) at 101.325 kPa. Table 6.14 gives the correction factors for different barometric pressures. These factors are to be applied to the values read from Figs. 6.15 and 6.16 when the barometric pressure is other than 101.325 kPa.

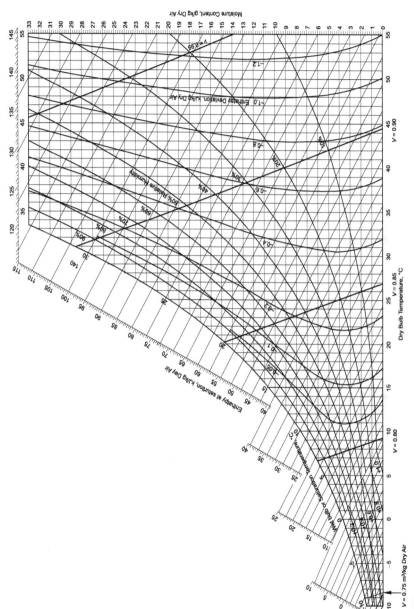

Fig. 6.15 Normal Temperature Psychromtric Chart
(Reproduced with the permission of Carrier Corporation, USA)

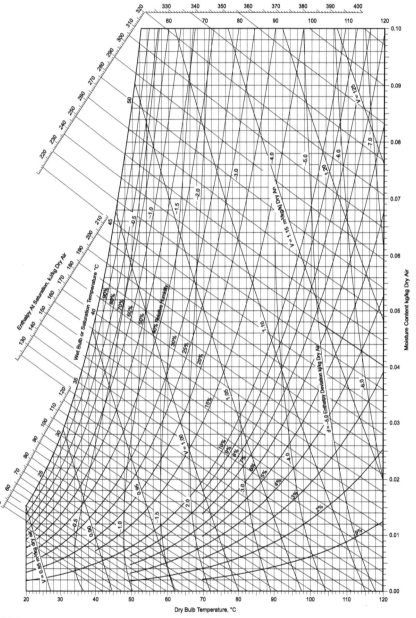

Fig. 6.16 High Temperature Psychromtric Chart
(Reproduced with the permission of Carrier Corporation, USA)

Table 6.14 Corrections in Psychrometric Properties of Air Due to Change in Barometric Pressure[15]

Barometric Pressures, kPa a (Torr)	Correction factor for		
	Humid (Specific) Volume	Humidity	Enthalpy
101.3 (760)	1.000	1.000	1.000
100.0 (750)	1.013	1.016	1.008
98.7 (740)	1.027	1.030	1.018
97.3 (730)	1.041	1.045	1.026
96.0 (720)	1.055	1.062	1.040
94.7 (710)	1.070	1.077	1.054
93.3 (700)	1.085	1.094	1.070
92.0 (690)	1.101	1.110	1.081
90.7 (680)	1.117	1.126	1.093
89.3 (670)	1.134	1.142	1.105
88.0 (660)	1.150	1.160	1.117
86.7 (650)	1.169	1.180	1.130

In both the psychrometric charts, dry-bulb temperatures are plotted on the abscissa (x-axis). Right ordinate (y-axis) represents the absolute humidity in a g moisture per kg dry air for Fig. 6.15 and kg moisture/kg dry air for Fig. 6.16. In addition, constant humid volume lines, wet-bulb lines and enthalpy deviation [d – refer Eq. (6.21)] are plotted on the graph. Enthalpy value at saturation are given on the left. Enthalpy of an unsaturated air–water vapour mixture is obtained by adding enthalpy deviation algebraically to the saturation enthalpy. It may be noted on the charts that DB and WB lines meet at one point on the saturation line which is called dew point (DP).

The use of psychrometric charts eliminates the input of physical properties in heat and mass balance calculations. In absence of this chart, Eq. (6.18) can be used to correlate various properties.

Example 6.13 Air at 7 bar g and 40°C (313 K) is used for pneumatic instruments. If its dew point is measured to be – 40°C (233.15 K) at atmospheric pressure (i.e., 101.325 kPa) with the help of a dew point instrument, calculate the dew point of air under line pressure.

Solution

$$H_m = \left(\frac{p_w}{p_1 - p_w} \right) \qquad \text{Eq. (6.7)}$$

p_{w1} = Vapour pressure of ice at 233.15 K
  = 12.84 Pa   (Table 6.11)
p_1 = 101.325 kPa

$$H_m = \frac{12.84}{(101\,325 - 12.84)} = 0.000\ 1267 \text{ kmol/kmol dry air}$$

At p_2 = 7 bar g = 801.325 kPa a = 801 325 Pa a

$$\left(\frac{p_{w_2}}{p_2 - p_{w_2}} \right) = 0.000\ 1267$$

or p_{w_2} = 101.505 Pa

From Table 6.12, dew point = – **20.18°C (252.97 K)**

Note From the above calculation, it is clear that the dew point of a gas is independent of its molar mass. Further, dew point under pressure is higher than at atmospheric pressure.

Example 6.14 The dry-bulb temperature and dew point of ambient air were found to be 29°C (302 K) and 18°C (291 K) respectively. The barometer reads 100.0 kPa a (750 Torr).

Compute (a) the absolute molar humidity, (b) the absolute humidity, (c) the % RH, (d) the % saturation, (e) the humid heat, and (f) the humid volume. Also, read these values from the psychrometric chart (Fig. 6.15) and evaluate enthalpy of air.

Solution   Partial pressure of water in air

$$= \text{vapour pressure of water at } DP$$

$$p_w = 2.0624 \text{ kPa} \qquad \text{(Table 6.13)}$$

$$p = 100.0 \text{ kPa a}$$

$$H_m = \left(\frac{p_w}{p - p_w}\right) = \frac{2.0624}{(100.0 - 2.0624)}$$

$$= \mathbf{0.021\ 06\ kmol\ water\ vapour/kmol\ dry\ air}$$

$$H = 0.622\ H_m$$

$$= 0.622 \times 0.021\ 06$$

$$= \mathbf{0.0131\ kg\ moisture/kg\ dry\ air}$$

At saturation, $DB = WB = DP$

Vapour pressure at saturation

(i.e., at 302.15 K), $p_s = 4.004$ kPa

$$\% \, RH = \frac{p_w}{p_s} \times 100 = \left(\frac{2.0624}{4.004}\right) \times 100 = \mathbf{51.51}$$

$$H_s = \left[\frac{p_s}{(p - p_s)}\right] 0.622$$

$$= 0.622 \times \frac{4.004}{(100.0 - 4.004)} = 0.025\ 94 \text{ kg/kg dry air}$$

$$\% \text{ saturation} = \left(\frac{H}{H_s}\right) \times 100$$

$$= \left(\frac{0.0131}{0.025\ 94}\right) \times 100 = \mathbf{50.49}$$

$$C_H = 1.006 + 1.84\ H$$

$$= 1.006 + 1.84\ (0.0131) = \mathbf{1.03\ kJ/(kg\ dry\ air \cdot K)}$$

$$\text{Humid volume, } V_H = \left[\left(\frac{H}{M_W}\right) + \left(\frac{1}{M_a}\right)\right] 22.414 \times \left[\frac{DB}{273.15}\right] \times \left(\frac{101.325}{p}\right)$$

$$= (0.000\ 73 + 0.034\ 48)\ (22.414)\ (1.1062)\ (1.0133)$$

$$= \mathbf{0.8846\ m^3/kg\ dry\ air}$$

The above results can be had from the psychrometric chart (Fig. 6.15) and by applying correction factors from Table 6.14.

$$H = 0.0131 \text{ kg moisture/kg dry air at } 101.3 \text{ kPa a}$$
$$= 0.0132 \text{ kg moisture/kg dry air at } 100.0 \text{ kPa a}$$
$$\% \, RH = 52.2$$
$$V_{\mathrm{H}} = 0.8744 \text{ m}^3/\text{kg dry air at } 101.325 \text{ kPa a}$$
$$= 0.8858 \text{ m}^3/\text{kg dry air at } 100.0 \text{ kPa a}$$

From Fig. 6.15, $WB = 21.5°C$ (294.55 K)

$i_{as} = 62.3$ kJ/kg dry air and $d = -0.28$ kJ/kg dry air

Hence enthalpy of ambient air-water mixture

$$i_a = 62.3 - 0.28 = 62.02 \text{ kJ/kg dry air at } 101.325 \text{ kPa a}$$
$$= 62.52 \text{ kJ/kg dry air at } 100.0 \text{ kPa a}$$

Example 6.15 In a textile industry located in Ahmadabad, it is desired to maintain 80% RH in the weaving department. For this reason, fresh air is first saturated and then heated to obtain 80% RH. Fresh air enters the spray chamber (air-washer) at 41°C (314 K) DB and 24°C (297 K) WB. Air comes out from the air-washer at 95% RH which is subsequently heated indirectly to attain 80% RH with the help of saturated steam at 300 kPa a pressure.

Compute (a) the moisture added to the air during the above operation, (b) the DB and WB temperatures of the final air and (c) the heating load of the steam coil per kg dry air. (d) If the fresh air rate is 25 000 m³/h, calculate the steam consumption in kg/h.

Solution *Basis* 1 kg of dry air entering the air-washer

The two operations (i.e., saturation and heating) are shown schematically in Fig. 6.17. Both the paths of operation are indicated on the psychrometric chart in Fig. 6.18.

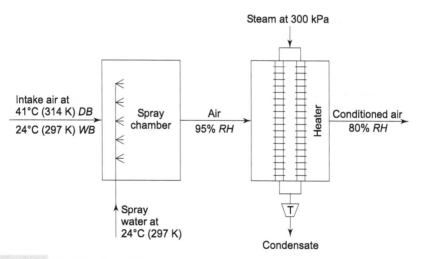

Fig. 6.17 Humidification of Air

Let H_1 and H_2 be the absolute humidities of air before and after saturation, respectively. Further, the heating operation is performed at constant humidity and hence the absolute humidity of air before and after heating remains constant.

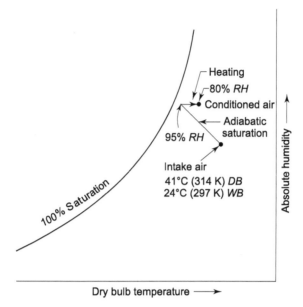

Fig. 6.18 Psychrometric Path for Humidification of Air

From the psychrometric chart (Fig. 6.15), H_1 = 11.8 g/kg dry air. During saturation, the path of operation is the same as the wet bulb temperature line (or adiabatic saturation line). Travel on this line till 95% *RH* is attained. At 297.15 K *WB* and 95% *RH*,

$$H_2 = 17.76 \text{ g/kg dry air}$$

Moisture added to the air during the saturation,

$$H = H_2 - H_1 = 17.76 - 11.8 = \textbf{5.96 g/kg dry air}$$

During heating, the absolute humidity remains constant. Hence follow the horizontal line on the psychrometric chart till 80% *RH* is attained. From the psychrometric chart (Fig. 6.15), parameters of conditions

$$\textbf{\textit{DB} = 27.8°C (300.95 K)}$$
$$\textbf{\textit{WB} = 25°C (298.15 K)}$$
$$DP = 24°C (297.15 \text{ K})$$

Humid heat $C_H = 1.006 + 1.84 (0.017\,76)$
$$= 1.039 \text{ kJ/(kg dry air} \cdot \text{K)}$$

Temperature change during heating,

$$\Delta T = (300.95 - 297.15) = 3.8 \text{ K}$$

Heat supply = $1.039 \times 3.8 = \textbf{3.95 kJ/kg dry air}$

Actual air at 41°C *DB* and 24°C *WB*

$$= 25\,000 \text{ m}^3/\text{h}$$

From Fig. 6.15,

Humid volume, $V_H = 0.9067 \text{ m}^3/\text{kg dry air}$

Mass flow rate of air, $q_m = \dfrac{25\,000}{0.9067} = 27\,572.5 \text{ kg dry air/h}$

Total heat load on heater, $\phi = 27\,572.5 \times 3.95 = 108\,911$ kJ/h $\equiv 30.25$ kW

At steam pressure $p = 300$ kPa a

Latent heat of evaporation, $\lambda_v = 2163.2$ kJ/kg　　　　(See Appendix IV.2)

Steam consumption at the heater $= \dfrac{108\,911}{2163.2} = \textbf{50.35 kg/h}$

Alternative calculations:

From Fig. 6.15, the enthalpy of air after saturation,

$$i_{a2} = 72.4 \text{ kJ/kg dry air}$$

Enthalpy of air after heating $i_{a3} = 76.4 - 0.1 = 76.3$ kJ/kg dry air

Change in enthalpies $= 76.3 - 72.4 = \textbf{3.9 kJ/kg dry air}$

Total heat load of heater $= 3.9 \times 27\,372.5 = 106\,753$ kJ/h $\equiv 29.65$ kW

$$\text{Steam consumption} = \frac{106\,753}{2163.2} = \textbf{49.35 kg/h}$$

Note In the heater, it is assumed that only latent heat of steam is given up and no subcooling takes place. Why?

Example 6.16 An induced draft cooling tower of 530 kW (150.7 TR) is designed to cool cooling water from 45°C (318 K) to 32°C (305 K). Air-flow rate is 48 kg/s and is supplied at 35°C (308 K) DB and 27°C (300 K) WB. Approach of the cooling tower is 5°C (5 K). Make-up water is supplied at 30°C (303 K), having dissolved solids (DS) content of 500 mg/L. From scaling and corrosion considerations, permissible DS content in the circulating cooling water is 2000 mg/L. Assume windage or drift loss of 0.3% of the circulation rate.

Calculate (a) make-up water, required for cooling tower, and (b) temperature, absolute humidity and percentage saturation of the air, leaving the induced draft fan.

Solution

$$M = E + B + W$$

where　$M = $ Make-up water to cooling tower, kg/s

$B = $ Blow down from cooling tower, kg/s

$E = $ Evaporation rate, kg/s

$W = $ Windage or drift loss, kg/s

Average cooling water temperature,

$$t_{av} = \frac{45 + 32}{2} = 38.5°C \text{ or } 311.65 \text{ K}$$

From stream Tables (Appendix A IV.1),

$$\lambda_v = 2410.5 \text{ kJ/kg at } 38.5°C$$

$$E = 530/\lambda_v = 530/2410.5 = 0.2199 \text{ kg/s}$$

Let　$\dot{m}_c = $ Circulation rate of cooling water, kg/s

$C_L = $ Specific heat of cooling water $= 4.1868$ kJ/(kg·K)

$t_i = 45°C, \quad t_o = 32°C$

Heat load of cooling tower,

$$\phi = 530 = \dot{m}_c \times C_L \times (t_i - t_o)$$

$$\dot{m}_c = \frac{530}{4.1868\,(45-32)} = 9.7376 \text{ kg/s}\,(\approx 35.06 \text{ m}^3/\text{h})$$

$$W = 0.3 \times 9.7376 / 100 = 0.0292 \text{ kg/s}$$

Dissolved solids balance

$$M \cdot x_m = (B + W)\,x_c \qquad\qquad\qquad (i)$$

where $\quad x_m$ = Mass fraction of DS in make-up water

x_c = Mass fraction of DS in circulating water

$$500 \times 10^{-6} \times M = (B + 0.0292) \times 2000 \times 10^{-6}$$

$$M = 0.2199 + 0.0292 + B \qquad\qquad\qquad (ii)$$

Solving two equations,

$$B = 0.0441 \text{ kg/s} \quad (\approx 0.159 \text{ m}^3/\text{h})$$

$$M = \mathbf{0.2932 \text{ kg/s}\ (\approx 1.056\ m^3/h)}$$

Energy balance of cooling tower,

$$\phi = \dot{m}_a\,(i_2 - i_1)$$

where, $\quad \dot{m}_a$ = mass-flow rate of dry air, kg/s

i_1 = enthalpy of incoming air, kJ/kg dry air

i_2 = enthalpy of outgoing air, kJ/kg dry air

$$48\,(i_2 - i_1) = 530$$

$$i_2 - i_1 = 11.042 \text{ kJ/kg dry air}$$

Locate the point 1 on the psychrometric chart (Fig. 6.15), representing 35°C *DB* and 27°C *WB*. Absolute humidity of incoming air can be read as 0.0196 kg moisture/kg dry air on the y-axis. Horizontal line, passing from the point 1 intersects 100% saturation curve at the dew point of incoming air which is read as 24.3°C (297.45 K).

Moisture balance,

$$E = \dot{m}_a\,(H_2 - H_1)$$

where, H_1 and H_2 are absolute humidities of incomins and outgoing air, respectively.

$$0.2199 = 48\,(H_2 - 0.0196)$$

$$H_2 = 0.024 \text{ kg moisture/kg dry air}$$

Enthalpy of incoming air,

$$i_1 = 1.006\,(T_{DP} - 273.15) + H_2 \times i_{WS} + C_{H_1}\,(T_{DB} - T_{DP})$$

$$i_{WS} = 2546.2 \text{ kJ/kg at } 24.4°C \text{ (Appendix IV.1)}$$

$$C_{H_1} = 1.006 + 1.84 \times 0.0196 = 1.042 \text{ kJ/(kg dry air} \cdot \text{K)}$$

$$i_1 = 1.006\,(297.45 - 273.15) + 0.0196 \times 2546.2 + 1.042\,(308.15 - 297.45)$$

$$= 85.5 \text{ kJ/kg dry air}$$

Value of i_1 can also be derived from Fig. 6.15.

On psychromatric chart, *DP* corresponding to

$$H_2 = 0.024 \text{ can be read as } 28.1°C \text{ (301.25 K)}.$$

$$C_{H_2} = 1.006 + 0.024 \times 1.84 = 1.05 \text{ kJ/(kg dry air} \cdot \text{K)}$$

$$i_{ws} = 2552.7 \text{ kJ/kg dry air at } 28.1°C \text{ (Appendix IV.1)}$$

$$i_2 = i_1 + 11.04$$

$$= 85.5 + 11.04 = 96.54 \text{ kJ/kg dry air}$$

$96.54 = 1.006 \ (301.25 - 273.15) + 0.024 \times 2552.7 + 1.05 \ (T_{DB} - 301.25)$

$T_{DB} = 307.82$ K or $t_{DB} = 34.67°C$

Thus, air leaves the induced draft fan at 34.67°C. Percentage saturation of the outgoing air can be read as **68.5%** from Fig. 6.15.

Example 6.17 A waste-heat recovery unit is installed on a stentering machine (drying machine) in a textile industry. It is basically a packed tower consisting of Pall rings. In the tower, hot air at 120°C (393 K) DB and 57°C (330 K) WB enters at the bottom and water is sprayed at the rate of 1.167 L/s at 32°C (305 K). Saturated air leaves the top at 40°C (313 K) while the hot water comes out at 50°C (323 K) from the bottom of the tower. The hot-air rate is measured to be 2000 kg/h. Calculate (a) the heat loss rate from the hot air in the bed, and (b) the percentage heat recovery in hot water, based on heat loss from the air.

Solution *Basis* 1 kg of dry air fed to the tower

From Fig. 6.16, the following figures are read.

Absolute humidity of air at 393 K *DB*, 330 K *WB*, $H_1 = 0.0972$ kg/kg dry air

$\qquad\qquad DP$ of the above air = 52°C (325.15 K)

Absolute humidity of saturated air at 313 K, $H_2 = 0.0492$ kg/kg dry air

$\qquad$ Moisture condensed in the tower, $H = H_1 - H_2$

$\qquad\qquad\qquad\qquad\qquad\qquad\qquad = 0.0972 - 0.0492$

$\qquad\qquad\qquad\qquad\qquad\qquad\qquad = 0.048$ kg/kg dry air

Humid heat of air at 393 K *DB* and 330 K *WB*,

$\qquad C_{H_1} = 1.006 + 1.84 \ (0.0972) = 1.185$ kJ/(kg dry air $\cdot$ K)

Humid heat of saturated air at 313 K,

$\qquad C_{H_2} = 1.006 + 1.84 \ (0.0492) = 1.0965$ kJ/(kg dry air $\cdot$ K)

Enthalpy of entering air,

$\qquad i_{a1} = 1.006 \ (325 - 273) + 0.0972 \times 2596 + 1.185 \ (393 - 325)$

$\qquad\qquad = 52.31 + 252.33 + 80.58 = 385.22$ kJ/kg dry air

From Fig. 6.16,

$\qquad i'_{a1} = (393.8 - 7.5) = 386.3$ kJ/kg dry air

Enthalpy of outgoing air,

$\qquad i_{a2} = 1.006 \ (313 - 273) + 0.0492 \times 2574.4 = 166.9$ kJ/kg dry air

From Fig. 6.16,

$\qquad i'_{a2} = 168.0$ kJ/kg dry air

Total heat removed from the air (based on Fig. 6.12),

$\qquad i = (i'_{a1} - i'_{a2})$

$\qquad\quad = 386.3 - 168.0 = 218.3$ kJ/kg dry air

Mass flow rate of dry air, $q_m = \dfrac{2000}{(1 + 0.0972)} = 1822.82$ kg/h

Heat loss rate from air, $\phi_1 = 218.3 \times 1822.82 = 397\,922$ kJ/h $\equiv$ **110.534 kW**

Heat gained by water, $\phi_2 = 1.167 \times 3600 \times 4.1868 \ (323 - 305)$

$\qquad\qquad\qquad\qquad\quad = 316\,613$ kJ/h $\equiv 87.95$ kW

$\qquad$ % Heat recovery $= \dfrac{87.95 \times 100}{110.534} = \mathbf{79.57}$

6.5.4 Psychrometric Operations other than Air–Water Contact Operations

In Sec. 6.5.1, air–water contact operations were studied in detail. The terminology outlined in the section can be extended to any liquid–gas contact operation, such as the water–gas system, nitrogen–acetone system, carbon disulphide-hydrogen system, benzene–nitrogen system, air–*n*-hexane system, etc. Psychrometric charts can also be constructed for these systems. The use of a computer is essential for generating the data necessary to construct these charts. However, in normal practice, these charts are not in day-to-day use and hence the calculations outlined in Sec. 6.5.1 can be used for these systems.

Example 6.18 It is desired to absorb 600 kg/h of carbon disulphide (CS$_2$) vapour on activated carbon from a stream of CS$_2$ in gaseous hydrogen. The CS$_2$-rich hydrogen stream enters the adsorber at a temperature of 20°C (293 K), total pressure of 106.7 kPa a (800 Torr) and dew point of 0°C (273 K). CS$_2$-lean stream leaves with a dew point of − 20°C (253 K). The exhausted activated carbon is regenerated by passing superheated steam through the adsorbent. The entering (regenerated) activated carbon has a CS$_2$ content of 0.04 kg CS$_2$ per kg of bone-dry (BD) activated carbon and that leaving has a CS$_2$ content of 0.32 kg CS$_2$ per kg of BD activated carbon.

The flow diagram is shown in Fig. 6.19.

Calculate (a) the volumetric flow rate of the entering CS$_2$–H$_2$ mixture, (b) the requirement of inlet activated carbon in kg/h and (c) the temperature to which the CS$_2$–H$_2$ mixture entering the system would have to be cooled after compression to 405 kPa a to remove as much CS$_2$ by condensation as done by adsorption. Use Eq. (5.24) and the data contained in Table 5.4.

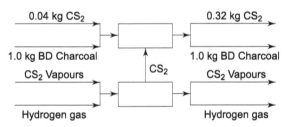

Fig. 6.19 Recovery of Carbon Disulphide by Adsorption

Solution *Basis* 800 kmol of inlet CS$_2$ – H$_2$ mixture

CS$_2$ entering with H$_2$ = $(p_{CS_2}) \times n/p$

where p_{CS2} is the partial pressure

of CS$_2$ in the inlet mixture = vapour pressure of CS$_2$ at dew point
= 16.93 kPa at 273.15 K (0°C) [Eq. (5.24)]

p is the total pressure = 106.7 kPa a

n is the total number of moles of mixture = 800 kmol

$$\text{CS}_2 \text{ entering with H}_2 = \left(\frac{16.93}{106.7}\right) \times 800 = 126.9 \text{ kmol}$$

Hydrogen in the mixture = $800 - 126.9 = 673.1$ kmol

$$CS_2 \text{ leaving the adsorber} = \left[\frac{p_{CS_2}}{(p - p_{CS_2})} \right] \times n_{H_2}$$

where p_{CS_2} is the vapour pressure of CS_2 at dew point in
  outlet mixture = 6.19 kPa at 253.15 K ($-20°$C) [Eq. 5.24)]
  p is the total pressure = 101.325 kPa
  n_{H_2} = no. of moles of H_2 = 673.1 kmol

$$CS_2 \text{ leaving the adsorber} = \left[\frac{6.19}{(101.325 - 6.19)} \right] \times 673.1 = 43.8 \text{ kmol}$$

CS_2 adsorbed on activated carbon = $126.9 - 43.8 = 83.1$ kmol
  mass of CS_2 adsorbed = $83.1 \times 76.1407 = 6327.3$ kg
The design adsorption rate of CS_2 is 600 kg/h.

$$\text{Molar flow rate of inlet gas mixture} = \left(\frac{800}{6327.3} \right) \times 600 = 75.86 \text{ kmol/h}$$

Specific volume of an ideal gas at 106.7 kPa and 293.15 K,

$$V = \frac{RT}{p} = 8.314\ 472 \times \frac{293.15}{106.7} = 22.843 \text{ m}^3/\text{kmol}$$

Volumetric flow rate of incoming gas = $75.86 \times 22.843 = \textbf{1732.87 m}^3\textbf{/h}$
CS_2 absorbed per kg BD activated carbon

$$= 0.32 - 0.04 = 0.28 \text{ kg}$$

$$\text{Mass flow rate of activated carbon, } q_m = \left(\frac{600}{0.28} \right) \times 1.04 = \textbf{2228.57 kg/h}$$

In an alternate proposition, $p = 405$ kPa a
Final desired concentration of the outlet $CS_2 - H_2$ mixture = $\dfrac{43.8}{673.1}$

$$= 0.0651 \text{ kmol } CS_2/\text{kmol } H_2$$

$$= \frac{p_{CS_2}}{(p - p_{CS_2})} = \frac{p_{CS_2}}{(405 - p_{CS_2})}$$

Solving the equation, $p_{CS_2} = 24.763$ kPa

The saturation temperature of CS_2 corresponding to the vapour pressure of 24.754 kPa is calculated to be 8.55°C (281.7 K) with the help of Eq. (5.24). Hence it can be concluded that the original $CS_2 - H_2$ mixture must be cooled to 281.7 K at 405 kPa a for achieving the same concentration of the outlet CS_2–H_2 mixture with adsorption.

Note This example also covers the material balance of another unit operation known as 'adsorption'.

Example 6.19 A plant employing Hooker-type diaphragm cells produces caustic soda at the rate of 4000 kg/h. Chlorine produced in this plant is first scrubbed in water and later cooled in a Trombone cooler with the help of chilled water to remove the water contained in chlorine. It leaves the cooler saturated at 18°C (291.15 K) and enters an adsorption tower to remove the last traces of water. Concentrated sulphuric acid (90% by mass) is sprayed at the top of the tower. The acid leaving the bottom of the tower is made-up in concentration by adding the required quantity of 98% (by mass) sulphuric acid and is then recirculated. The quantity of acid circulated is so large that hardly any change in its temperature or concentration takes place. The heat of dilution of 1 kmol of 100% sulphuric acid with liquid water can be approximated by the formula[16],

$$Q = \frac{74\,780\,n}{(n+1.7983)} \text{ kJ/kmol } H_2SO_4 \text{ (at 101.325 kPa and 291.15 K)}$$

where $n = $ kmol of H_2O/kmol of H_2SO_4
Find the heat liberation rate in the tower.

Solution *Basis* 4000 kg/h of NaOH produced
The reactions taking place in the Hooker cell are as follows:

$$2\,NaCl \rightarrow 2Na{+} + 2\,Cl^-$$
$$2\,Cl^- \rightarrow Cl_2 \qquad \text{(At anode)}$$
$$2\,Na^+ + H_2O \rightarrow 2\,NaOH + 2\,H^+$$
$$2\,H^+ \rightarrow H_2 \qquad \text{(At cathode)}$$

From the above reaction, it can be seen that when two moles of NaOH are produced, one mole of Cl_2 is produced.

$$2 \text{ kmol NaOH} = 1 \text{ kmol } Cl_2$$

$$\text{Chlorine produced} = \left(\frac{71}{80}\right) \times 4000 = 3550 \text{ kg/h}$$

$$\text{Molar flow rate of } Cl_2 = \frac{3550}{71} = 50 \text{ kmol/h}$$

Chlorine leaves the Trombone cooler saturated with water vapour at 291.15 K.
Total pressure of system, $p = 101.325$ kPa
Partial pressure of water, $p_w = 2.0624$ kPa at 291.15 K

$$\text{Moisture in chlorine} = \left[\frac{2.0624}{(101.325 - 2.0624)}\right] \times \left(\frac{18.0154}{70.906}\right)$$

$$= 0.005\,279 \text{ kg water vapour/kg dry } Cl_2$$

Total water vapour in saturated $Cl_2 = 3550 \times 0.005\,279 = 18.74$ kg/h
Now, heat liberated in the absorption tower,

$$Q = \frac{74\,780\,n}{(n+1.7983)} \text{ kJ/kmol } H_2SO_4 \qquad \text{(i)}$$

In order to obtain the heat of dilution per kmol water absorbed, it is necessary to differentiate Eq. (i) with respect to n.

$$\frac{dQ}{dn} = Q'$$

$$= \frac{134\,477}{(n+1.7983)^2} \text{ kJ/kmol } H_2O \qquad \text{(ii)}$$

For 90% concentration of acid,

$$n = \left[\frac{10}{18.0153}\right]\bigg/\left[\frac{90}{98.0776}\right]$$

$$= 0.6049 \text{ kmol } H_2O/\text{kmol acid}$$

$$Q' = \frac{134477}{(0.6049 + 1.7983)^2}$$

$$= 23\ 285 \text{ kJ/kmol } H_2O \equiv 1292.5 \text{ kJ/kg } H_2O$$

In addition to the heat of dilution, latent heat of vaporization is also given up by water vapour when it condenses.

$$\lambda_v = 2459.0 \text{ kJ/kg at } 291.15 \text{ K (Ref. Appendix IV.1)}$$

Total specific heat load $= Q' + \lambda_v$

$$= 1292.5 + 2459.0 = 3751.5 \text{ kJ/kg}$$

Total heat liberated, $\phi = 3751.5 \times 18.74$

$$= 70\ 303 \text{ kJ/h} \equiv \mathbf{19.53 \text{ kW}}$$

Example 6.20   Feed purge gas (dry) from the ammonia synthesis loop contains N_2: 20.6%, H_2: 62.0%, Ar: 4.1%, CH_4: 11.1% and NH_3: 2.2% (mole %). Feed gas is available at 50 bar g and − 10°C (263 K). It is heated to 10°C (283 K) by exchanging heat with demineralised water, available at 34°C (307 K). Pressure drop in the heat exchanger is 50 kPa. Cooled water is sprayed at the top of the absorber and aqueous ammonium hydroxide solution containing 4% NH_3 (mass) is produced. Assume that (i) the gas leaves the absorber at saturated conditions at the feed water temperature, (ii) ammonia slip from the absorber is 50 ppm (v/v), and (iii) pressure drop in the absorber is negligible. Refer Fig. 6.20 for the process flow. Calculate (a) the temperature of feed water to absorber, and (b) the temperature of the aqueous ammonia solution leaving the absorber.

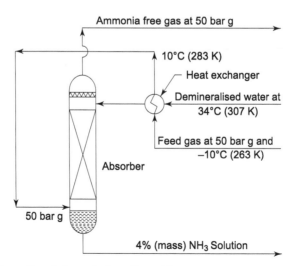

Fig. 6.20   Absorption of Ammonia from Purge Gas

Solution *Basis* 100 kmol of feed gas

Assume that heat capacity constants of Table 5.1 are valid at high pressure.

Heat capacity constants

$\Sigma n_i \cdot a_i = 20.6 \times 29.5909 + 62 \times 28.6105 + 4.1 \times 20.7723 + 11.1 \times 19.2494$
$\qquad + 2.2 \times 25.6503$
$\qquad = 609.573 + 1773.851 + 85.166 + 213.668 + 56.431 = 2738.689$

$(\Sigma n_i \cdot b_i) \times 10^3 = 20.6 \times (-5.141) + 62 \times 1.0194 + 11.1 \times 52.1135 + 2.2 \times 33.4806$
$\qquad = -105.905 + 63.203 + 578.46 + 73.657 = 609.415$

$(\Sigma n_i \cdot c_i) \times 10^6 = 20.6 \times 13.1829 + 62 \times (-0.1476) + 11.1 \times 11.973 + 2.2 \times 0.3518$
$\qquad = 271.568 - 9.151 + 132.9 + 0.774 = 396.091$

$(\Sigma n_i \cdot d_i) \times 10^9 = 20.6 \times (-4.968) + 62 \times 0.769 + 11.1 \times (-11.3173) + 2.2 \times (-3.0832)$
$\qquad = -102.341 + 47.678 - 125.622 - 6.783 = -187.068$

Heat gained by gas mixture

$$= 2738.689 \, (283 - 263) + 609.415 \times 10^{-3} \, \frac{(283^2 - 263^2)}{2}$$

$$+ \, 396.091 \times 10^{-6} \, \frac{(283^3 - 263^3)}{3} - 187.068 \times 10^{-9} \, \frac{(283^4 - 263^4)}{4}$$

$$= 54\,773.8 + 3327.4 + 590.7 - 76.2 = 58\,615.7 \text{ kJ}$$

Heat gained by ammonia alone = 1533.8 kJ (based on temperature difference)

Ammonia in feed gas = 2.2 kmol

Ammonia-free feed gas = 97.8 kmol

Average $\Sigma \, (n_i . C^\circ_{mpi})$ for 97.8 kmol

$$\text{ammonia free gas mixture} = \frac{(58\,615.7 - 1533.8)}{20}$$

$$= 2854.1 \text{ kJ/(K} \cdot 97.8 \text{ kmol gas)}$$

In the outgoing gas mixture from the absorber,

ammonia-free gas = 99.995% (mole basis)

$$\text{Outgoing gas mixture} = \frac{97.8}{0.999\,95} = 97.805 \text{ kmol}$$

Ammonia absorbed = 2.2 − 0.005 = 2.195 kmol ≡ 37.382 kg

$$\text{Flow rate of 4\% ammonia solution} = \frac{37.382}{0.04} = 934.55 \text{ kg}$$

Water content of solution = 934.55 − 37.382 = 897.168 kg

Assume at first that the water outgoing with the gas mixture from the absorber is negligible.

$$\text{Fall in water temperature} = \frac{58\,615.7}{(897.168 \times 4.1868)} = 15.6 \text{ K}$$

Temperature of water leaving the heat exchanger

$$= 307 - 15.6 = \mathbf{291.4 \text{ K } (18.25°C)}$$

Vapour pressure of water at 291.4 K = 2.116 kPa   (Table 6.13)

Total pressure = 50 bar g = 5101.325 kPa a

Assuming ideal gas behaviour, moisture content of the gas mixture

$$= \frac{97.805 \times 2.116}{(5101.325 - 2.116)} = 0.0406 \text{ kmol} \equiv 0.73 \text{ kg}$$

Total demineralised water requirement = 897.17 + 0.73 = 897.9 kg

Actual fall in temperature of water in heat exchanger

$$= \frac{58\,615.7}{(897.9 \times 4.1868)} = 15.59 \text{ K}$$

This figure is quite close to 15.6 K, calculated earlier.

Now from Table 5.59,

$$\Delta H_f^o \text{ of 4\% solution} = -80.093 \text{ kJ/mol } NH_3$$

and $\qquad \Delta H_f^o$ of pure $NH_3 = -46.11$ kJ/mol NH_3

Heat of solution of 4% NH_3 solution = $-80.093 - (-46.11)$

$$= -33.983 \text{ kJ/kmol } NH_3$$

Total heat evolved = $33\,983 \times 2.195 = 74\,593$ kJ

In the absorber, gas is further heated form 283 K to 291.4 K.

Heat picked up by the ammonia-free gas mixture (97.8 kmol)

$$= 2854.1 \,(291.4 - 283.15) = 23\,546 \text{ kJ}$$

Heat picked up by the ammonia solution

$$= 74\,593 - 23\,546 = 51\,047 \text{ kJ}$$

Assuming heat capacity of 4% NH_3 solution to be same as that of water, i.e., 4.1868 kJ/(kg·K),

$$\text{Rise in temperature} = \frac{51\,047}{934.55 \times 4.1868} = 13.05 \text{ K}$$

Temperature of aqueous ammonia solution leaving the absorber

$$= 291.4 + 13.05 = \textbf{304.45 K (31.3°C)}$$

Note It is assumed that the heat of solution calculated at 25°C (298.15 K) remains unchanged for all practical purpose.

6.6 DRYING

Drying is a unit operation in which the solvent is evaporated with the help of heat and the final product is normally in the solid form. In most of the drying operations, the heat is provided by hot air or any other gas in which the solvent evaporates. The balance of bone-dry solids (tie material) helps in calculating the evaporation of the solvent. Similarly, the solvent contents of the incoming and outgoing gas allow the calculations of the volumetric or mass flow rate of gas.

In many of the drying operations, water is the solvent which is evaporated in air. The air–water mixture is exhausted out of the atmosphere via a once-through system. Recently, there has been increasing interest in evaporating organic solvents which must be recovered for both economic and environmental reasons. The required system design is a 'closed loop' with a provision for solvent recovery. The design (material and energy balance) calculations for closed-cycle dryers to evaporate solvents differ from once-through units to evaporate water in three major respects:

(i) The solvent must be recovered rather than discharged to the atmosphere.

(ii) Air cannot be used as the drying medium in most cases due to safety reasons. The drying gas is usually nitrogen. Properties of both are practically the same.

(iii) The properties of solvents are very different from that of water and from each other.

The first of the above differences indicates that the system is a closed loop and the solvent is recovered usually by adsorption/desorption followed by a scrubber/condenser with its recycle stream cooled by water or a refrigerant. The drying gas is returned from the condenser, reheated and recycled. Exercise 8.22 is a typical example in which *n*-hexane is used as a solvent.

The need for reliable and accurate physical properties data was adequately stressed in Chapter 5. In drying calculations, the effect that physical properties have on design factors has been studied extensively[17]. The percentage change in results caused by a +1% change in properties of a simulated solvent at the dryer inlet temperature of 149°C (422 K) and dryer outlet temperature of 60°C (333 K) are given in Table 6.15. For the simulated solvent, properties considered were; the latent heat of vaporization of 465 kJ/kg, molar mass of 100 and heat capacities of liquid and vapour to be 1.884 and 1.465 kJ/(kg·K), respectively.

Table 6.15   Effect of + 1% Change in Physical Properties on the Final Results While Drying a Simulated Solvent[16]

Physical property	% Change in final results of	
	Volumetric flow rate	Heat load
Latent heat of vaporization	0.76	0.77
Boiling point	0.09 to 0.52	0.05
Molar mass	− 0.05 to 0.20	Nil
Heat capacity of liquid	0.19	0.20
Heat capacity of vapour	− 0.06 to − 0.14	− 0.06

The following example relates to the drying of cloth in which water is the solvent.

Example 6.21   A direct–contant counter current rotary drier is to be used for drying a crystalling organic solid. Wet solid enters the drier at 30°C (303 K), containing 25% moisture. Atmospheric air is heated to 120°C (393 K) in a heater by condensing saturated steam at 4 bar a pressure. The solid leaves the driver at 80°C (353 K) with moisture content of 2%. Dried product output is 1000 kg/h. Heat capacity of the dry solid can be taken as 1.43 kJ/(kg · K). As conditions of atmospheric air vary during the year, fully saturated air at 35°C (308 K) can be taken as a worst case for design of the air heater. Air leaves at 50°C (323 K) from the drier.

Calculate (a) flow rate of incoming air, (b) humidity of air, leaving the drier, and (c) steam consumption in the heater.

Solution

Basis Product rate of 1000 kg/h

Let $\dot{m}_a$ = Mass flow rate of dry air through the drier, kg/s

H_1 = Absolute humidity if incoming air, kg/kg dry air

H_2 = Absolute humidity if outgoing air, kg/kg dry air

At inlet of air heater, for 100% saturated air at 35°C,

$$H_1 = 0.036 \text{ kg moisture/kg dry air (Fig. 6.15)}$$

X_1 = Moisture regain of incoming solid

$$= \frac{0.25}{1 - 0.25} = 0.3333 \text{ kg/kg dry solid}$$

X_2 = Moisture regain of outgoing solid, kg/kg dry solid

$$= \frac{0.02}{1 - 0.02} = 0.0204 \text{ kg/kg dry solid}$$

$$\dot{m}_s = \text{mass flowrate of solid} = \frac{1000}{3600}(1 - 0.02)$$

$$= 0.2722 \text{ kg/s}$$

Moisture balance,

$$\dot{m}_s (X_1 - X_2) = \dot{m}_a (H_2 - H_1)$$
$$0.2722 (0.3333 - 0.0204) = \dot{m}_a (H_2 - 0.036)$$
$$\dot{m}_a (H_2 - 0.036) = 0.085 \qquad \text{(i)}$$

Reference temperature

$$t_0 = 0°C \quad \text{or} \quad T_0 = 273.15 \text{ K}$$

Enthalpy of solid at inlet,

$$i_{s1} = C_s (t_i - 0) + X_1 \, C_L (t_i - 0)$$
$$= 1.43 (30 - 0) + 0.3333 \times 4.1868 (30 - 0) = 84.7638 \text{ kJ/kg dry solid}$$

Enthalpy of solid at outlet,

$$i_{s2} = C_s (t_0 - 0) + X_2 \, C_L (t_0 - 0)$$
$$= 1.43 (80 - 0) + 0.0204 \times 4.1868 (80 - 0)$$
$$= 121.2329 \text{ kJ/kg dry solid}$$

Enthalpy of incoming air,

$$i_{a1} = 1.006 (T_{DP_1} - 273.15) + H_1 \, i_{WS1} + C_{H_1} (T_{DB} - T_{DP1})$$

where T_{DB} = Dry–bulb temperature of air = 120 + 273.15 = 393.15 K

T_{DP_1} = Dew point of air = 35 + 273.15 = 308.15 K

From Appendix IV.1,

$$i_{WB_1} = 2565.4 \text{ kJ/kg at 35°C}$$
$$C_{H_1} = 1.006 + 1.84 \times 0.036 = 1.072 \text{ kJ/(kg dry air·K)}$$
$$i_{a1} = 1.006 (308.15 - 273.15) + 0.036 \times 2565.4 + 1.072 (393.15 - 308.15)$$
$$= 218.68 \text{ kJ/kg dry air}$$

Enthalpy of outgoing air,

$$\dot{m}_s \cdot i_{s1} + \dot{m}_a \cdot i_{s1} = \dot{m}_s \cdot i_{s2} + \dot{m}_a \cdot i_{a2} + \phi_L$$

where ϕ_L = Heat loss

Assume ϕ_L to be 10% of heat input.

$$0.9 (0.2722 \times 84.7638 + \dot{m}_a \times 218.68) = 0.2722 \times 121.2329 + \dot{m}_a \times i_{a2}$$

$$\dot{m}_a (196.812 - i_{a2}) = 12.234 \qquad \text{(ii)}$$

i_{a2} is dependent on DP of outgoing air which is unknown. Hence, a trial-and-error method will have to be adopted.

$$i_{a2} = 1.006 \ (T_{DP_2} - 273.15) + H_2 \ i_{WB_2} + (1.006 + 1.84 \ H_2)$$
$$(323.15 - T_{DP_2}) \qquad \text{(iii)}$$

Assume $\qquad t_{DP_2} = 42.4°C$

$\qquad\qquad\qquad T_{DP_2} = 42.4 + 273.15 = 315.55 \text{ K}$

From Fig. 6.15, $H_2 = 0.056$ kg moisture/kg dry air

$\qquad\qquad\qquad i_{WB_2} = 2578.7$ kJ/kg at 42.4°C $\qquad$ (Appendix IV.1)

$\qquad\qquad\qquad i_{a2} = 1.006 \ (315.55 - 273.15) + 0.056 \times 2578.6$
$\qquad\qquad\qquad\qquad + (1.006 + 1.84 \times 0.056) \ (323.15 - 315.55)$
$\qquad\qquad\qquad\qquad = 195.5$ kJ/kg dry air

From Eq. (1),

$$\dot{m}_a \ (0.056 - 0.036) = 0.085$$
$$\dot{m}_a = 4.25 \text{ kg/s}$$

Substituting values of $\dot{m}_a$ and i_{a2} in Eq. (2) 4.25 $(196.812 - i_{a2}) = 12.234$

or $\qquad\qquad\qquad i_{a2} = 193.9$ kJ/kg dry air

Both values of i_{a2} are nearly same. Hence required air flow rate is **4.25 kg/s (15 300 kg/h)** on dry basis.

Humidity of outgoing air,

$$H_2 = \textbf{0.056 kg/kg dry air}$$

Heat duty of air heater,

$$\phi = \dot{m}_a \ (i_{a1} - i_{aa})$$

where, $\quad i_{aa} = $ Enthalpy of atmospheric air at 35°C

$\qquad\qquad\quad = 1.006 \ (308.15 - 273.15) + 0.036 \ (2565.4)$

$\qquad\qquad\quad = 127.56$ kJ/kg dry air

$\qquad\quad \phi = 4.25 \ (218.68 - 127.56) = 387.26 \text{ kW}$

$\qquad\quad \lambda_v = 2133.0$ kJ/kg at 4 bar a $\qquad$ (Appendix IV-1)

$$\text{Steam Consumption} = \frac{387.26}{2133}$$

$$= 0.1816 \text{ kg/s} \equiv \textbf{653.76 kg/h}$$

Example 6.22 In a textile mill, wet cloth passes through a hot-air dryer. The cloth enters with 90% moisture regain and leaves at 6% moisture regain at a speed of 1.15 m/s. The width of the cloth is 120 cm and its specific density on bone-dry basis is 0.095 kg/m². The temperature of the cloth leaving the dryer is 95°C (368 K). The ambient air enters the dryer at 30°C (303 K) *DB* and 25°C (298 K) *WB* while hot air leaves the dryer at 120°C (393 K) *DB* and 55°C (328 K) *WB*. Saturated steam is used at 8 bar a and consumption rate is measured to be 885 kg/h. The heat capacity of cloth is 1.256 kJ/(kg · K).

(i) Calculate (a) the bone-dry production of the dryer, (b) the evaporation taking place in the dryer, and (c) the air circulation rate.

(ii) Make the complete heat balance of the dryer.

Solution   *Basis*   Cloth speed = 1.15 m/s

Production of bone-dry cloth = $1.15 \times 1.20 \times 3600 \times 0.095$

$$= \textbf{471.96 kg/h}$$

Moisture regain of the cloth is defined as the kg moisture per kg bone-dry cloth.

Inlet moisture of the cloth = 0.90 kg moisture/kg bone-dry cloth

Outlet moisture of the cloth = 0.06 kg moisture/kg bone-dry cloth

$$\text{Evaporation} = 471.96 \, (0.9 - 0.06)$$
$$= \textbf{396.45 kg/h}$$

From Fig. 6.15 and Fig. 6.16,

Humidity of inlet air, H_1 = 0.018 05 kg moisture/kg dry air at 303.15 K *DB* and 298.15 K *WB*

Humidity of outlet air, H_2 = 0.0832 kg moisture/kg dry air at 393.15 K *DB* and 328.15 K *WB*

Rise in humidity of circulating air

$$= H_2 - H_1$$
$$= 0.0832 - 0.018 \, 05 = 0.065 \, 15 \text{ kg moisture/kg dry air}$$

Fresh air rate, $q_{m_1} = \dfrac{396.45}{0.065\,15} = 6085.2$ kg dry air/h

This fresh air (or exhaust) rate should not be misunderstood as the recirculation rate of air. Usually, the air recirculation rate is five to ten times the fresh air entry.

Humid volume of air at 303.15 K *DB* and 298.15 K *WB*,

$$V_{\text{H}} = 0.8837 \text{ m}^3/\text{kg dry air}$$

Volumetric flow rate of incoming air,

$$q_v = 6085.2 \times 0.8837 = \textbf{5377.5 m}^3/\textbf{h}$$

Heat balance of the dryer

DP of ambient air = 296.5 K

Latent heat of evaporation of water at 296.5 K, λ_{v_1} = 2446.4 kJ/kg

DP of exhaust air = 322.5 K

Latent heat of evaporationof water at 322.5 K,

$$\lambda_{v_2} = 2384.1 \text{ kJ/kg}$$

Reference temperature, T_0 = 273.15 K

Heat picked up by cloth, $\phi_1 = 471.96 \times 1.256 \, (368 - 303) + 471.96$
$$\times \, 0.06 \, (368 - 303) \times 4.1868$$
$$= 46\,237.2 \text{ kJ/h} \equiv 12.844 \text{ kW}$$

It will be assumed that the evaporation takes place at DP of the exhaust air, i.e., 322.5 K

Heat utilised for evaporation,

$$\phi_2 = 396.45 \, (322.5 - 303.15) + 396.45 \times 2384.1$$
$$= 952\,847.75 \text{ kJ/h} \equiv 264.68 \text{ kW}$$

Enthalpy of ambient air over 273.15 K,

$$i_{\text{al}} = 1.006 \, (303.15 - 273.15) + 2556.4 \times 0.018\,05$$
$$= 76.32 \text{ kJ/kg dry air}$$

From Fig. 6.15, $i'_{\text{al}} = 76.4 - 0.2 = 76.2$ kJ/kg dry air

Enthalpy of exhaust air over 273.15 K, $DP = 322.8$ K (49.8°C)
$$i_{a2} = 1.006\ (322.8 - 273.15) + 2591.5 \times 0.0832 + (1.006$$
$$+\ 1.84 \times 0.0832)\ (393 - 328.8)$$
$$= 49.95 + 215.61 + 81.36 = 347.07 \text{ kJ/kg dry air}$$
From Fig. 6.16,
$$i'_{a2} = 354.8 - 7.0 = 347.8 \text{ kJ/kg dry air}$$
Enthalpy lost in air $= 347.8 - 76.2 = 271.6$ kJ/kg dry air
$$\phi_2 = 1652\ 740 \text{ kJ/h} \equiv 459.094 \text{ kW}$$
This enthalpy also takes into account the heat lost due to evaporation.
Heat lost in exhaust air (sensible heat part) $= 459.094 - 264.68 = 194.414$ kW
At 8 bar a from Appendix IV.2,
$$h = 720.94 \text{ kJ/kg} \qquad \lambda_v = 2046.5 \text{ kJ/kg}$$
Total input by steam $= (720.94 + 2046.5)\ 885 = 2449\ 184$ kJ/h $\equiv 680.329$ kW
It will be assumed that only the latent heat of steam is useful in heating the air and
thus the condensate leaves at saturation temperature, having the sensible heat.
Heat lost in condensate, $\phi_4 = 720.94 \times 885$
$$= 638\ 032 \text{ kJ/h} \equiv 177.231 \text{ kW}$$
Specific steam consumption,
$$q_{m_2} = \frac{885}{396.45} = \textbf{2.232 kg/kg evaporation}$$

Table 6.16   Heat Balance of Dryer

	kW	%
Input Steam	680.329	100.00
Output		
Sensible heat of cloth	12.844	1.89
Heat utilised for evaporation	264.68	38.90
Heat lost in exhaust air	194.414	28.58
Heat lost in condensate	177.231	26.05
Unaccounted heat loss (by difference)	31.16	4.58
Total	680.329	100.00

6.7   EVAPORATION

Evaporation is basically a similar operation to drying except that the final product
is in the liquid form. This operation is usually carried out in a closed equipment (an
exception is the open pan evaporator) and air is not used for the evaporation.

The energy crisis has led to a reconsideration of the evaporation systems.
Multiple-effect evaporation is not the only answer for reducing the energy input.
Mechanical vapour recompression, thermal recompression, use of flash steam,
etc., are also considered as additional economy measures. However, each plant
or operation must be evaluated from various considerations and the final choice
must be made only after that. For example, the steam condensate purity can be
lost in the case of thermal recompression, prohibiting the return of the condensate
for use as the boiler feed make-up water.

Multiple effect evaporators have gained popularity in concentrating effluents in chemical industries. Vapours from the evaporators are partially utilised for evaporation by recompression. Balance vapours are condensed and used as boiler feed make-up or cooling tower make-up water.

Example 6.23   A quadruple-effect evaporator is fed with 1060 kg/h of 4% (by mass) caustic soda solution in a textile mill[18]. It is concentrated to 25% (by mass) lye. The saturated steam at 7 bar g is fed to the first effect. The cold feed also enters the first effect at 30°C (303 K). The final effect operates at 50.60 kPa a (vacuum of 380 Torr). The operating pressure in first, second and third effects are observed to be 3.7, 2.35 and 0.8 bar g, respectively. Neglect the boiling point elevation effects and assume that no heat loss due to radiation takes place from the evaporator bodies.

Table 6.17   Heat Capacity Data

Solution	Heat Capacity, kJ/(kg · K)
Feed (C_{1F})	4.04
Solution leaving first effect (C_{11})	3.977
Solution leaving second effect (C_{12})	3.936
Solution leaving third effect (C_{13})	3.894
Solution leaving fourth effect (C_{14})	3.873

Evaluate the thermal performance of the system.

Solution   *Basis* Weak liquor flow rate = 1060 kg/h
The flow patterns of the liquid and vapours are shown in Fig. 6.21.

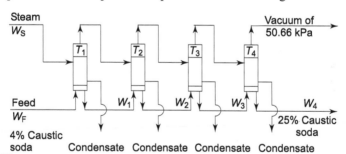

Fig. 6.21   Quadruple Effect Forward Feed Evaporator

Solids in the weak liquor = $1060 \times 0.04 = 42.4$ kg/h

Concentrated liquor, leaving the fourth effect = $\dfrac{42.4}{0.25} = 169.6$ kg/h

Total evaporation in all four effects = $1060 - 169.6 = 890.4$ kg/h

Table 6.18   Operating Conditions in the Evaporator Stages

Effect number	Pressure, kPa g	Saturation temperature, °C (K)	Latent heat of evaporation of steam, λ_v kJ/kg
First	370	149.6 (422.6)	2114.4 (λ_{v1})

(Contd.)

Table 6.18   (Contd.)

Effect number	Pressure, kPa g	Saturation temperature, °C (K)	Latent heat of evaporation of steam, λ_v kJ/kg
Second	235	137.5 (410.5)	2151.5 (λ_{v2})
Third	80	117.2 (390.3)	2210.2 (λ_{v3})
Fourth	−50.66	81.7 (354.7)	2304.6 (λ_{v4})

Latent heat of steam at 700 kPa g, λ_s = 2046.3 kJ/kg

Let W_F be the feed flow rate = 1060 kg/h

W_S be the feed flow of steam to the first effect in kg/h

W_1 be the feed flow of liquor, leaving the first effect in kg/h

W_2 be the feed flow of liquor, leaving the second effect in kg/h

W_3 be the feed flow of liquor, leaving the third effect in kg/h

W_4 be the feed flow of liquor, leaving the last effect = 169.6 kg/h

Enthalpy balance of the first effect

$$W_s \, \lambda_s = W_F \cdot C_{1F} \, (T_1 - T_F) + (W_F - W_1) \, \lambda_{v1}$$
$$W_s \times 2046.3 = 1060 \times 4.04 \, (422.6 - 303) + (1060 - W_1) \, 2114.4$$
$$W_s = 1345.57 - 1.033 \, W_1 \tag{i}$$

Enthalpy balance of the second effect

$$(W_F - W_1) \, \lambda_{v1} = W_1 \cdot C_{11} \, (T_2 - T_1) + (W_1 - W_2) \, \lambda_{v2}$$
$$(1060 - W_1) \, 2114.4 = W_1 \times 3.977 \, (410.5 - 422.6) + (W_1 - W_2) \, 2151.4$$
$$W_1 = 531.38 + 0.510 \, W_2 \tag{ii}$$

Enthalpy balance of the third effect

$$(W_1 - W_2) \, \lambda_{v2} = W_2 \cdot C_{12} \, (T_3 - T_2) + (W_2 - W_3) \, \lambda_{v3}$$
$$(W_1 - W_2) \, 2151.5 = W_2 \times 3.936 \, (390.2 - 410.5) + (W_2 - W_3) \, 2210.2$$
$$W_1 - 1.990 \, W_2 = - 1.027 \, W_3 \tag{iii}$$

Enthalpy balance of the fourth effect

$$(W_2 - W_3) \, \lambda_{v3} = W_3 \cdot C_{13} \, (T_4 - T_3) + (W_3 - W_4) \, \lambda_{v4}$$
$$(W_2 - W_3) \, 2210.2 = W_3 \times 3.894 \, (354.7 - 390.2) + (W_3 - 169.6) \, 2304.6$$
$$W_2 - 1.98 \, W_3 = - 176.84 \tag{iv}$$

Solving the above four equations algebraically,

$$W_3 = 416.7 \text{ kg/h} \qquad W_2 = 648.2 \text{ kg/h} \qquad W_1 = 862 \text{ kg/h}$$

Steam consumption, W_s = 455.2 kg/h

Mathcad solution gives the same values.

$$\text{Steam economy} = \frac{890.4}{455.2} = \textbf{1.956 kg evaporation/kg steam}$$

$$\text{Specific steam consumption} = \frac{1}{1.956} = \textbf{0.511 kg steam/kg evaporation}$$

Note   The above problem is quite simplified for calculation purposes. However, the actual enthalpies of the solutions are different from that of water and the boiling point elevations are quite significant. The reader may try the solution of the above problem with the actual enthalpies in Fig. 5.16.

Example 6.24 Short path distillation (SPD) units in series are commonly used to concentrate heat–sensitive products under high vacuum. β-Carotene is a provitamin and is used as a supplement in many food products. Red palm oil is a known source of β-carotene. First the oil is esterified with methanol. Typical esterified mass contains 45% methyl palmitate, 5% methyl stearate. 40% methyl oleate, 10% methyl linoleate (by mass) and 600 mg/kg β-carotene. Three-stage evaporation system consisting of SPD units in series are used for concentrating β-carotene to 40% as shown in Fig. 6.22.

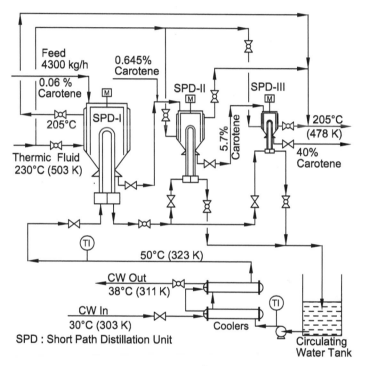

Fig. 6.22 Triple-effect Evaporation System for β-carotene Concentration

Residue from first and second stages are found to contain 0.645% and 5.7% β-carotene by mass. Esterified red palm oil is fed at a rate of 4300 kg/h to first effect at 100°C (373 K). Thermic fluid enters shells of SPDs at 230°C (503 K) and leaves the system at 205°C (478 K). Operating temperatures of three evaporators are 195°C (468 K), 190°C (463 K) and 180°C (453 K), respectively.

SPDs have inbuilt U-tube bundles. Esters condense on outside surface. To avoid chances of internal fouling of U-tubes (which are difficult to descale), circulating water system is used which is charged with demineralized water. Circulating water enters SPD-I at 50°C (323 K) and leaves at 58°C (331 K). 90% of circulating water from SPD-I is used in SPD-II while balance 10% is used in SPD-III. Circulating water in turn is cooled to 50°C (323 K) by exchanging heat with cooling water $\Delta t = 8$°C in external coolers.

Carry out mass and energy balance of the system.

(a) *Data* Average heat capacity of esterified red palm oil and thermic fluid are 2.56 and 2.95 kJ/ (kg · K), respectively.

(b) Average density of esterified red palm oil and thermic fuid are 0.825 and 0.71 kg/L, respectively.

(c) Average latent heat of evaporation of ester can be taken as 450 kJ/kg.

Solution

Basis Feed rate of esterified red palm oil to SPD-I = 4300 kg/h

β-carotene content of oil = $4300 \times 600 \times 10^{-6}$ = 2.58 kg/h

$$\text{Feed to SPD- II} = \frac{2.58}{0.006\,45} = 400 \text{ kg/h}$$

Evaporation of esters in SPD-I = 4300 − 400 = 3900 kg/h

$$\text{Feed to SPD-III} = \frac{2.58}{0.057} = 45.263 \text{ kg/h}$$

Evaporation of esters in SPD-II = 400 − 45.263 = 354.737 kg/h

$$\text{Final concentrated stream from SPD − III} = \frac{2.58}{0.4} = 6.45 \text{ kg/h}$$

Evaporation of esters in SPD-III = 45.263 − 6.45 = 38.813 kg/h

Heat requirement in SPD-I, ϕ_1 = 4300 × 2.56 (468.15 − 373.15) + 3900 × 450
$$= 1045\,760 + 1755\,000 = 2800\,760 \text{ kJ/h}$$
$$\equiv 777.989 \text{ kW}$$

Heat requirement in SPD-II, ϕ_2 = 400 × 2.56 (463.15 − 468.15) + 354.737 × 450
$$= -5120 + 159\,632 = 154\,512 \text{ kJ/h} \equiv 42.92 \text{ kW}$$

Heat requirement in SPD-III, ϕ_3 = 45.263 × 2.56 (453.15 − 463.15) + 38.813 × 450
$$= -1159 + 174\,66 = 16\,307 \text{ kJ/h} \equiv 4.53 \text{ kW}$$

Total heat requirement = $\phi_1 + \phi_2 + \phi_3$
$$= 2800\,760 + 154\,512 + 16\,307 = 2971\,579 \text{ kJ/h}$$
$$\equiv 825.439 \text{ kW}$$

Thermic fluid (hot oil) mass flow rate,

$$\dot{m}_t = \frac{2971\,579}{2.95\,(503.15 - 478.15)} = 40\,292.6 \text{ kg/h}$$

Volumetric flow rate of thermic fluid,

$$q_t = 40\,292.6/0.71$$
$$= 56\,750 \text{ L/h} \approx 56.75 \text{ m}^3/\text{h}$$

Mass flow rate of circulating cooling water in SPD-I,

$$\dot{m}_{CCW1} = \frac{1755\,000}{8 \times 4.1868} = 52\,397 \text{ kg/h} \approx 52.4 \text{ m}^3/\text{h}$$

Mass flow rate of CCW in SPD-II,

$$\dot{m}_{CCW2} = 52\,397 \times 0.9 = 47\,157 \text{ kg/h}$$

Rise in CCW temperature in SPD-II

$$= \frac{159\,632}{47157 \times 4.1868} = 0.809 \text{ K or } {}^{\circ}\text{C}$$

Mass flow rate of CCW in SPD-III,

$$\dot{m}_{CCW3} = 52\,397 - 47\,157 = 5240 \text{ kg/h}$$

Rise in CCW temperative in SPD-III

$$= \frac{17\,466}{5240 \times 4.1868} = 0.796 \text{ K or } {}^{\circ}\text{C}$$

Overall rise in CCW temperature $= \dfrac{(1755\,000 + 159\,632 + 17\,466)}{52\,397 \times 4.1868}$

$$= \frac{1932\,098}{219\,375.8} = 8.807{}^{\circ}\text{C or K}$$

Required cooling water flow in external coolers

$$= \frac{1932\,098}{8 \times 4.1868} = 57\,684 \text{ kg/h} \approx 57.4 \text{ m}^3/\text{h}$$

6.8 LESS CONVENTIONAL OPERATIONS

In the preceding sections, the more commonly encountered operations were discussed. Reverse osmosis, dialysis, thickening, etc., are less conventional operations. A few examples relating to reverse osmosis and pervaporation were dealt in Chapter 3. The following illustration will deal with the thickening operation.

Example 6.25 A four-compartment washing thickener is employed in the recausticizing system of a kraft mill for washing of the white mud to recover soda values[19]. The unit is operated with the top two trays and the bottom two trays in parallel as shown in Fig. 6.23. The top two trays are operated in a counter-current fashion with respect to the bottom two trays. The entering white mud, M_2 is mixed with the overflow from the bottom two trays, O_1 and fed to the feedbox of the top two trays. The underflow from the top two trays, M_1 is mixed with the effluent from the water scrubber from a calcining kiln, W, and fed to the feedbox of the bottom two trays. The overflow from the top two trays, O_2 passes onto the weak wash storage where it is employed for dissolving the smelt from the recovery furnaces. The underflow from the bottom two trays, M_0 is considered washed white mud and is pumped to the white mud storage tank. Later, it is filtered and the cake is calcined in a rotary kiln to CaO. The average of several samples taken over a 24-hour period shows the following results:

Table 6.19 Operating Data of Thickener

Stream	Suspended solids, mass %	Na$_2$O concentration, kg/L of liquor	Specific gravity	Slurry, L/s
M_2	34.90	0.1342	1.167	2.845
O_2	0.03	0.0272	1.037	14.193

(Contd.)

Table 6.19 Operating

Stream	Suspended solids, mass %	Na₂O concentration, kg/L of liquor	Specific gravity	Slurry, L/s
M_1	19.40	0.0252	1.034	—
W	3.70	0.0024	1.000	14.977
O_1	0.02	0.0096	1.014	—
M_o	40.20	0.0162	1.022	3.627

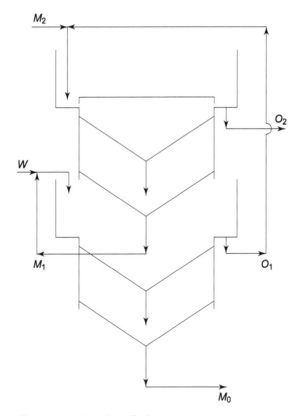

Fig. 6.23 Four-Compartment Washing Thickener

Assuming that the liquor contains only caustic soda and the suspended solids are calcium carbonate (specific gravity = 2.711), make a material balance on all streams of the slurry, suspended solids, liquor and Na₂O.

Solution The material balance of each stream will be considered individually.

Stream M_2

1 kg of M_2 contains 0.349 kg CaCO₃ and 0.651 kg of liquor.

$$\text{Volume of CaCO}_3 = \frac{0.349}{2.711} = 0.1287 \text{ L}$$

$$\text{Volume of liquor} = \frac{0.651}{1.167} = 0.5578 \text{ L}$$

Total volume of 1 kg of M_2 slurry $= 0.1287 + 0.5578 = 0.6865$ L

$$\text{Specific gravity of } M_2 \text{ slurry} = \frac{1}{0.6865} = 1.4567$$

Slurry flow $= 2.845 \times 3600 \times 1.4567 = 14\,919.5$ kg/h

Suspended solids in $M_2 = 14\,919.5 \times 0.349 = 5206.9$ kg/h

Liquor present in $M_2 = 14\,919.5 \times 0.651 = 9712.6$ kg/h

$$\text{Na}_2\text{O in } M_2 = \frac{(9712.6 \times 0.1342)}{1.167} = 1116.9 \text{ kg/h}$$

Stream O_2

Since the suspended solids are very low (only 0.03%), the specific gravity of the slurry will be assumed to be the same as that of the liquor in it.

Slurry flow $= 14.193 \times 3600 \times 1.037 = 52\,985.3$ kg/h

Suspended solids in $O_2 = 52\,985.3 \times 0.0003 = 15.9$ kg/h

Liquor present in $O_2 = 52\,985.3 - 15.9 = 52\,969.4$ kg/h

$$\text{Na}_2\text{O in } O_2 = \frac{(52\,969.4 \times 0.0272)}{1.037} = 1389.4 \text{ kg/h}$$

Stream M_1

$$\text{Total volume of 1 kg of } M_1 \text{ slurry} = \left(\frac{0.194}{2.711}\right) + \left(\frac{0.806}{1.037}\right) = 0.85 \text{ L}$$

$$\text{Specific gravity of slurry} = \frac{1}{0.85} = 1.176$$

Assume that all the suspended solids in M_2 are recovered in M_1.

$$\text{Slurry flow in } M_1 = \frac{5206.9}{0.194} = 26\,839.7 \text{ kg/h}$$

Liquor flow in $M_1 = 26\,839.7 - 5206.9 = 21\,632.8$ kg/h

$$\text{Na}_2\text{O in } M_1 = \frac{(21\,632.8 \times 0.0252)}{1.034} = 527.2 \text{ kg/h}$$

Stream O_1

In this stream also, the specific gravity of the slurry will be assumed to be the same as that of the liquor, since suspended solids are negligible.

Slurry flow in $O_1 =$ slurry flow in $O_2 +$ slurry flow in M_1
$-$ slurry flow in M_2

$= 52\,985.3 + 26\,839.7 - 14\,919.5$

$= 64\,905.5$ kg/h

Solids in $O_1 = 64\,905.5 \times 0.0002 = 13.0$ kg/h

Liquor present in $O_1 = 64\,905.5 - 13.0 = 64\,892.5$ kg/h

$$\text{Na}_2\text{O in } O_1 = \frac{(64\,892.5 \times 0.0096)}{1.014} = 614.4 \text{ kg/h}$$

Stream W

$$\text{Total volume of 1 kg } W \text{ slurry} = \left(\frac{0.037}{2.711}\right)+\left(\frac{0.963}{1}\right) = 0.9766 \text{ L}$$

$$\text{Specific gravity of } W \text{ slurry} = \frac{1}{0.9766} = 1.024$$

Slurry flow in W = 14.977 × 3600 × 1.024 = 55 211.2 kg/h
Solids in W = 55 211.2 × 0.037 = 2042.8 kg/h
Liquor present in W = 55211.2 – 2042.8 = 53 168.4 kg/h

$$\text{Na}_2\text{O in } W = \frac{(53\,168.4 \times 0.0024)}{1.000} = 127.6 \text{ kg/h}$$

Stream M_0

$$\text{Total volume of 1 kg } M_0 \text{ slurry} = \left(\frac{0.402}{2.711}\right)+\left(\frac{0.598}{1.022}\right) = 0.7334 \text{ L}$$

$$\text{Specific gravity of } M_0 \text{ slurry} = \frac{1}{0.7334} = 1.3635$$

Slurry flow in M_0 = 3.627 × 3600 × 1.3635 = 17 803.5 kg/h
Solids in M_0 = 17 803.5 × 0.402 = 7157.0 kg/h
Liquor present in M_0 = 17 803.5 – 7157 = 106 46.5 kg/h

$$\text{Na}_2\text{O in } M_0 = \frac{(10\,646.5 \times 0.0162)}{1.022} = 168.8 \text{ kg/h}$$

The material balance calculations are summarised in Table 6.20.

Table 6.20 Material Balance of Thickener

Item	Stream, kg/h					
	M_2	O_2	M_1	O_1	W	M_0
Slurry	14 919.5	52 985.3	26 839.7	64 905.5	55 211.2	17 803.5
Suspended solids	5 206.9	15.9	5 206.9	13.0	2 042.8	7 157.0
Liquor	9 712.6	52 969.4	21 632.8	64 892.5	53 168.4	10 646.5
Na$_2$O	1 116.9	1 389.4	527.2	614.4	127.6	168.8

Exercises

6.1 An aqueous solution containing 30% ethanol (by mass) is fed to a distillation column at a rate of 4000 kg/h at its bubble point. The top product from the column contains 92% ethanol (by mass) while the bottom product is nearly pure water. Assume a reflux ratio of 2. Based on enthalpy–concentration data given in Table 6.21, calculate theoretical heat duties of overhead condenser and reboiler. The column operates at 101.325 kPa.

Table 6.21 Enthalpy of Ethanol–water Mixtures at Atmospheric Pressure

Mole froction ethanol (x, y)	Liquid Phase			Vapour Phase		
	Bubble point		Enthalpy	Dew point		Enthalpy
	°C	K	kJ/kmol	°C	K	kJ/kmol
0.0-water	100.0	373.15	7550	100.0	373.15	48 150
0.0417	90.0	363.15	7125	98.9	372.05	48 250
0.0891	85.6	358.75	6880	97.6	370.75	48 300
0.1436	83.4	356.55	6915	96.1	369.25	48 328
0.207	82.0	355.35	7097	94.2	367.35	48 436
0.281	81.4	354.55	7397	91.8	364.95	48 450
0.477	79.8	352.95	8105	84.	357.85	48 631
0.61	79.0	352.15	8471	80.4	353.55	48 694
0.779	78.31	351.46	8945	78.42	351.57	48 950
1.0-ethanol	78.25	351.4	9875	78.25	351.4	48 435

Reference conditions: Enthalpy at 101.325 kPa of saturated ethanol at 0°C (273.15 K) and that of water at 0.01°C (273.16 K) equal to 0 kJ/kmol.

[**Heat duty of overhead condenser = 1060.01 kW,**
Heat duty of reboiler = 1104.891 kW]

6.2 A 50:50 mixture (by mass) of diethanolamine (DEA)–triethanolamine (TEA) is distilled in a packed tower to produce a 99.0% (by mass) DEA distillate product and 95.0% (by mass) TEA bottom product. To preclude the thermal degradation of the amine solution, the absolute pressure in the reboiler must be limited to 1.33 kPa (10 Torr). The reflux ratio is 0.8 kmol/kmol distillate product. Compute the overall material and energy balances for 10 000 kg/h feed, assuming (i) no heat loss to the surroundings, and (ii) negligible heat of mixing.

Table 6.22 Data on DEA and TEA

	Phase	mass % DEA	Temperature °C (K)	Enthalpy kJ/kg
Distillate	Liquid	99.0	147 (420)	372.2
Distillate	Vapour	99.0	147 (420)	1572.6
Feed	Liquid	50.0	157 (430)	418.7
Bottoms	Liquid	5.0	194 (467)	558.1

[**Distillate product = 4787.2 kg/h, Bottoms product = 5212.8 kg/h**
Enthalpy removed in the condenser = 2873.29 kW,
Heat load of reboiler = 3013.3 kW]

6.3 A feed consisting of 50 : 50 (by mass) of toluene and methylcyclohexane (MCH) is fed to an extractive distillation column[20] at the rate of 10 000 kg/h. The distillation operation is shown in Fig. 6.24. It is desired to recover 95% of toluene as 99% pure product (free from solvent) from the solvent recovery tower. The ratio of the recycled solvent to the fresh feed is kept at 3.3. The recycled solvent contains 99.1% phenol and 0.9% toluene. The overhead product from the extractive distillation column should not contain more than 0.2% phenol. All the percentages are expressed on mass basis. Compute (a) feed rate F_2 and its composition, (b) overhead product rate from the extractive distillation column and its composition, and (c) make-up phenol rate. [**(a) and (b) see Table 6.23**]

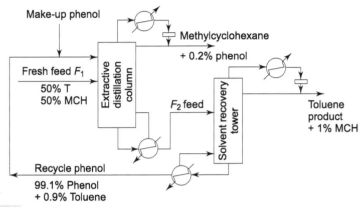

Fig. 6.24   Extractive Distillation of Toluene with Methylcyclohexane

Table 6.23   Material Balance of Extractive Distillation Column

Rate, kg/h	Feed F_2 37 798	Overhead product from extractive distillation column, 5212.4
Composition, mass %		
Toluene	13.35	4.8
MCH	0.13	95.0
Phenol	86.52	0.2

(c) Make-up phenol rate = 10.4 kg/h]

6.4   Azeotropic distillation is a known technique for separation of ethanol from ethanol–water azeotrope. In this process, benzene is added as an entrainer which forms a ternary azeotrope at 101.3 kPa (760 Torr) and 65°C (338 K) having composition of 22.8% C_2H_5OH, 53.9% C_6H_6 and 23.3% H_2O on mole basis. As shown in Fig. 6.25, the fresh feed of ethanol and water containing 96% (mass) ethanol is fed to the azeotropic column.

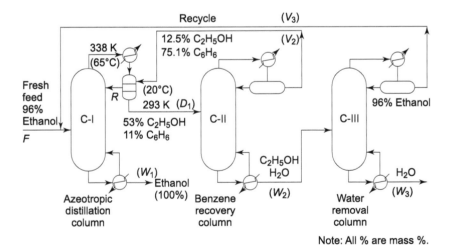

Note: All % are mass %.

Fig. 6.25   Separation of Ethanol and Water using Benzene

A separator separates a phase richer in benzene at 20°C (293 K) which is refluxed back to the distillation column. Benzene is recovered in the second column while water is removed in the third column. Calculate (a) the recycle rate of ethanol–water mixture from the third column per 100 kg of fresh feed, and (b) composition of reflux (R) to the first column C-I.   **[(a) 46.9 kg per 100 kg fresh feed (b) 8.71% C_2H_5OH and 91.29% C_6H_6 (by mass)]**

6.5 Purge distillation columns are often used to purge undesirable components[21] from a reactor recycle stream. Typical systems are shown in Fig. 6.26 and Fig. 6.27.

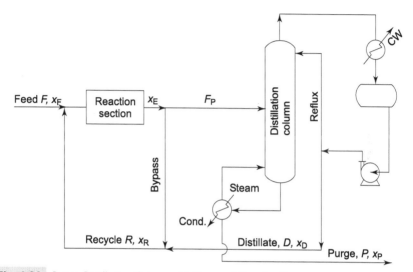

Fig. 6.26   Purge Distillation Column with Purge of Heavier Component

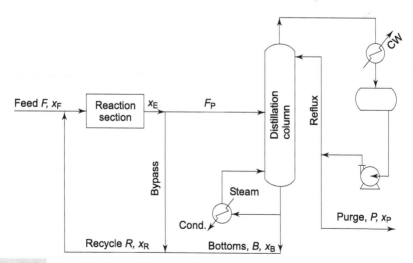

Fig. 6.27   Purge Distillation Column with Purge of Lighter Component

(a) It can seen in Fig. 6.26 that the undesirable component to be purged is the heavier component. The purge stream is the bottom product from the column.

(i) Prove that recycle composition is independent of the feed (F_P) to the purge distillation column.

(ii) Develop an equation for the minimum possible feed rate (F_{pm}) to the purge distillation column.

(b) In Fig. 6.27, the undesirable component to be purged is the lighter component. The purge stream is the overhead distillate product. Prove that the minimum feed rate (F_{pm}) to the purge column is related as

$$F_{pm} = P \times x_p / x_E$$

6.6 Acetonitrle (ACN, formula : C_2H_3N) forms minimum boiling azeotrope with water at 101.325 kPa at 77°C (350.15 K) having 69 mole % ACN. An aqueous stream containing 50% ACN by mass is to be separated by pressure swing distillation technique[22] as shown in Fig. 6.28.

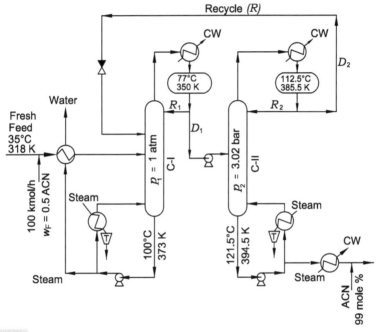

Fig. 6.28   Pressure Swing Disstillation of ACN-water System

In column C-I, fresh feed with recycle stream (R) (i.e., distillate from C-II; D_2) ACN is distilled out at 101.325 kPa in the form of azeotrope from C-I while bottom product is water with negligible impurity of ACN. Azerotrope from C-I top is fed to C-II; D_2 which is operated at 3.02 bar a. Top product from C-II is again an azeotrope containing 60 mole % ACN at 112.5°C (385.65 K). The bottom product from C-II; D_2) is 99.0 mole % ACN at 121.5°C (394.65 K). Calculate recycle ratio as kmol 60 mole % ACN azeotrope recycled per kmol fresh feed.   **R = 1.027 kmol/kmol**

6.7 In the manufacture of aqueous hydrochloric acid, the gas obtained from the burner contains 35% HCl (by volume) and balance N_2. The gas is passed through an absorption tower where 96% of HCl is absorbed in water. The gas enters the absorption tower at 45°C (318 K) and 100 kPa (750 Torr) and leaves it at 30°C (303 K) and 98 kPa (735 Torr).

Water enters at 35°C (308 K) and 3.9% (by mass) HCl solution leaves the tower. If the volumetric flow rate of the feed gas is 100 m^3/h, calculate (a) the volumetric flow rate of the gas mixture leaving the column, (b) the % HCl (by volume) in the outgoing gas mixture, and (c) the temperature of the outgoing solution. Use the data given in Table 5.77 and assume heat capacity of 3.9% solution as 4.19 kJ/(kg·K).

[(a) **69.54 m^3/h** (b) **2.1% HCl (by volume)** (c) **44°C (317.15 K)**]

6.8 Isothermal and isobaric absorption of SO_2 is carried out in a packed tower containing Raschig rings[23]. The gases enter the bottom of the tower containing 14.8% SO_2 by volume. Water is distributed at the top of the column at the rate of 16.5 L/s. The total volume of the gas handled at 101.3 kPa (760 Torr) and 30°C (303 K) is 1425 m^3/h. The gases leaving the tower are found to contain 1% SO_2 by volume. Calculate the % SO_2 by mass in the outlet water. [**0.86% SO_2 by mass**]

6.9 It is desired to purify branched nine carbon atom alkane (C9) from a mixture of C9, acetic acid (AcOH) and acetic anhydride (Ac_2O). A process flow diagram of the recovery system and the ternary diagram[24] at 30°C (303 K) are given in Fig. 6.29 and Fig. 6.30, respectively. Fresh feed at 30°C (303 K) to the system contains 76% C9, 18% AcOH and balance Ac_2O (by mass). Using the ternary diagram, make complete material balance calculations for the entire system for the production rate of 1000 kg/h of C9 (stream N) from Column-1. [**See Table 6.24**]

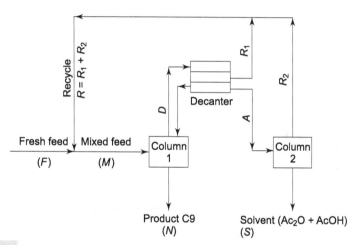

Fig. 6.29 Process Flowsheet for C9 Recovery

Table 6.24 **Material Balance of C9 Purification System**

Stream	Flow rate kg/h	Composition, % by mass		
		AcOH	Ac_2O	C9
N	1000	—	—	100.0
R_1	1023.7	37.2	7.2	55.9
R_2	78.9	64.0	—	36.0
F	1315.8	18.0	6.0	76.0
M	2418.4	27.6	6.3	66.1
A	394.7	72.8	20.0	7.2
D	1418.4	47.0	10.8	42.2
S	315.8	75.0	25.0	—

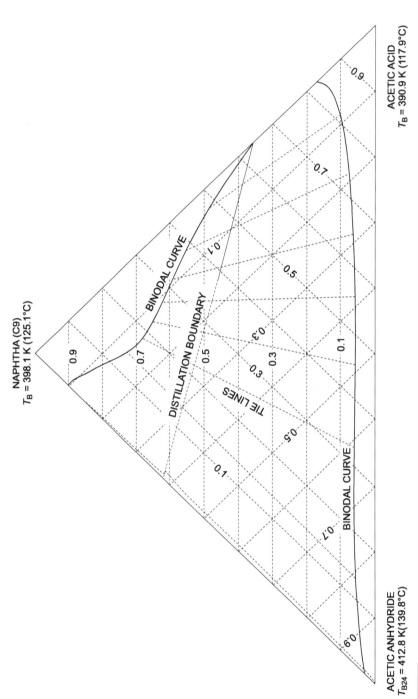

NAPHTHA (C9)
T_B = 398.1 K (125.1°C)

ACETIC ACID
T_B = 390.9 K (117.9°C)

ACETIC ANHYDRIDE
T_{B24} = 412.8 K(139.8°C)

BINODAL CURVE

DISTILLATION BOUNDARY

TIE LINES

BINODAL CURVE

Fig. 6.30 Ternary Diagram[24] of C9-Ac_2O and AcOH System at 30°C (303.15 K)
(Courtesy: Eastman Chemical Company, USA.)

6.10 Raw hydrogen is prepared in a catalytic reformer by reacting naphtha and steam. The analysis of gases from the reformer yields 16.5% CO_2, 78% H_2 and the rest N_2 (by volume). The volumetric flow rate of the gas at 27°C (300 K) and 101.3 kPa is 6500 m^3/h in terms of 100% H_2. In order to remove CO_2, the gas is passed through perforated plate-type scrubber in which triethanolamine $[N(CH_2CH_2OH)_3 - TEA]$ is sprayed at the top of the tower[25]. The gases enter the bottom of the tower at 16 bar g. The outgoing gases from the scrubber contain 0.5% CO_2 (by volume). Aqueous solution of 50% by mass TEA is circulated at the rate of 15 L/s (density = 1.05 kg/L). The solution enters the tower at 63°C (336 K) and has the concentration of CO_2 equivalent to 2420 mL per litre of solution at 101.3 kPa (760 Torr) and 27°C (300 K). It leaves the tower at 77°C (350 K) and goes to another regenerating system in which CO_2 is stripped off at 83°C (356 K) to 110°C (383 K) until the regenerated solution becomes fit for reuse.

Calculate (a) The volumetric flow of the raw gases at 16 bar g and 200°C (473 K) using the ideal gas law, (b) the amount of CO_2 removed from the raw gas, and (c) the concentration of CO_2 in the outcoming TEA solution from the tower.

[(a) 782.3 m^3/h (b) 54.77 kmol/h, (c) 27 237 mL per L]

6.11 A gaseous product containing 18% CO_2, 77% H_2 and the rest N_2 (by mole) enters a packed tower in which DAPOL (diamine-iso-propanol) is used as a scrubbing agent. The tower operates in counter-current fashion at 4 bar g pressure. The volumetric flow rate of the gas mixture is 3000 m^3/h, measured at 27°C (300 K) and 101.3 kPa (760 Torr). The outgoing gas mixture contains 0.2 mole % CO_2. Aqueous DAPOL solution of about 27.5% (by mass) enters the tower[25]. In the entering solution, 2200 mL of CO_2 is present in a litre solution at 101.3 kPa (760 Torr) and 27°C (300 K). The outgoing gas mixture from the tower is found to contain 5800 mL of CO_2 in a litre solution at 101.3 kPa and 27°C (300 K). The DAPOL solution, rich in CO_2, is taken to an actifier kettle where CO_2 is stripped off at 94 to 103°C (367 K to 376 K).

Calculate (a) the volumetric flow rate of raw gas at 4 bar g and 250°C (523 K) using the ideal gas law, (b) the amount of CO_2 absorbed, and (c) the volumetric flow rate of DAPOL solution. [(a) 1056.8 m^3/h (b) 21.87 kmol/h (c) 41.3 L/s]

6.12 Refer Example 6.4. Assume that the gas at the inlet contains N_2: 22.2%, H_2: 66.6%, CO: 0.5%, CO_2: 10.4% and CH_4: 0.3% (by volume) on dry basis. It enters the absorber at 60°C (333 K) at saturated conditions. The aqueous MEA solution enters at 45°C (318 K). The gas leaves the absorber at 45°C (318 K) and 90 kPa (675 Torr). The heat capacity of aqueous MEA solution can be taken as 4.19 kJ/(kg · K). If the exothermic heat of absorption is 1675 kJ/kg CO_2, calculate the outlet temperature of the aqueous MEA solution. [84.75°C (357.9 K)]

6.13 25 000 Nm^3/h of the gas mixture, consisting of 82.6% H_2, 1.1% HCl, 11.6% N_2 and 4.7% CCl_4 (by volume) is introduced to an absorber[26] at 3.4 bar g and 30°C (303 K). Caustic soda solution containing 15% NaOH (by mass) at 38°C (311 K) is introduced at the top at the rate of 3930 kg/h. In the scrubber, 99.9% HCl is removed by reaction with NaOH and the gas mixtures leaves the absorber at 3.38 bar g.

$$NaOH(aq) + HCl(l) = NaCl(aq) + H_2O(l)$$

Calculate (a) the flow rate and composition of the bottom solution, (b) the heat generated at 25°C (298.15 K), and (c) the heat to be removed for preparing 15% NaOH solution by diluting 50% NaOH (by mass) solution with water at 30°C (303 K). Use Fig. 5.16 for calculating the heat of solution.

[(a) 4074.8 kg/h containing 17.65% NaCl, 2.40% NaOH (by mass)
(b) $\Delta H_r^\circ = -446.13$ kW (c) 75 kW]

6.14 Refer Exercise 4.48 and Exercise 5.72. The gas mixture and secondary air enter the absorber at 1.5 bar g and 40°C (313 K). The tail gas leaves the absorber at 10 kPa g and 50°C (323 K). Demineralised water is introduced at 25°C (298.15 K) and final 58% HNO_3 (mass) is withdrawn from the bottom at 40°C (313 K). The cooling water enters the cooling coil located in the absorber at 30°C (303 K) and the rise in its temperature is recorded to be 8°C (8 K).

The data on standard heat of formation of aqueous nitric acid are given in Table 6.25. Calculate the cooling water flow rate in the cooling coil.

Table 6.25 Standard Heat of Formation of Aqueous Nitric Acid Solution[5]

Formula and description	State	Heat of formation at 25°C (298.15 K), ΔH_f^0, kJ/mol HNO_3	mass % HNO_3 in solution
HNO_3, 0 H_2O	1	−174.1	100
1 H_2O	aq	−187.63	77.8
2 H_2O	aq	−194.56	63.6
3 H_2O	aq	−198.57	53.8
4 H_2O	aq	−201.10	46.7
5 H_2O	aq	−202.77	41.2

Note The number in the first column indicates the number of moles of water mixed with one mole of nitric acid.

[**409.6 m³/h**]

6.15 Oil is to be extracted from meal by a continuous counter-current extractor. The unit is charged with 1000 kg/h meal based on oil-free solids. Untreated meal contains 0.4 kg oil and 0.025 kg benzene per kg oil-free meal. Fresh solvent is benzene containing 1.5% oil (mass %). The ratio of the fresh solvent to the oil-free meal is kept at 0.065 kg/kg. The solid meal retains 0.507 kg solution per kg solid. The solution retained by the meal contains 11.83% oil (by mass). Make a complete material balance and find the composition and the amount of overflow from the extractor[6]. The process is shown in Fig. 6.31.

[**Overflow rate = 583 kg/h containing 60% oil**]

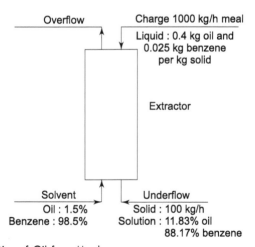

Fig. 6.31 Extraction of Oil from Meal

6.16 A crystallizer is charged with 7500 kg of an aqueous solution at 104°C (377 K), 29.6% (by mass) of which is anhydrous sodium sulphate. The solution is cooled. During the cooling operation, 5% of the initial water is lost by evaporation. As a result, crystals of $Na_2SO_4.10 H_2O$ crystallize out. If the mother liquor is found to contain 18.3% (by mass) anhydrous Na_2SO_4, calculate the yield of crystals and the quantity of mother liquor. **[Yield of crystals = 3472.1 kg, Final mother liquor = 3763.9 kg]**

6.17 Copper as crude ferrous sulphate is purified by dissolving it in water and recrystallizing it in a crystallizer. First, copperas is dissolved in pure water to give a solution containing 28% $FeSO_4$ (by mass). The solution is cooled to 10°C (283 K) to give out the crystals of $FeSO_4.7 H_2O$. The loss of water due to evaporation during the cooling operation is 5% on the basis of total solution, charged to the crystallizer. It is desired to yield 0.5 t of $FeSO_4.7 H_2O$ crystals. The original copperas contains 96% $FeSO_4.7 H_2O$ (by mass). Find the quantity of copperas charged to the crystallizer. The solubility of $FeSO_4$ at 10°C (283 K) is 20.51 g per 100 g water[9]. Assume that the solubility of $FeSO_4$ at 10°C (283 K) is unaffected by the impurities present in copperas. **[719.7 kg copperas]**

6.18 An aqueous solution containing 58% $NaNO_3$ (by mass) from an evaporator is crystallized to yield the crystals containing 4% water (by mass). The crystals are removed from the crystallizer which carry off 4% free water. The mother liquor, containing 0.5 kg $NaNO_3$ per kg water, is recycled to the evaporator with 1000 kg/h feed containing 20% $NaNO_3$ (by mass). Find (a) the yield of crystals, (b) the recycled mass flow rate of the mother liquor, (c) the total feed rate to the evaporator, and (d) the feed composition.

[(a) 208.3 kg/h (wet crystals) (b) 321 kg/h (c) 1321 kg/h (d) 23.2% $NaNO_3$ (by mass)]

6.19 Liquid paraffin wax is crystallized in a continuous crystallizer which is essentially a scrapped-surface heat exchanger. The test results on a particular crystallizer are as follows:

Product rate of liquid paraffin wax = 675 kg/h
Temperature, in = 59°C (332 K)
Temperature, out = 47°C (320 K)
Mean heat capacity, C_l = 2.93 kJ/(kg · K)
Latent heat of crystallization, λ_f = 168.7 kJ/kg
Crystallization temperature = 47°C (320 K)
Power input at shaft = 17 kW
Jacket cooling water flow = 1.92 L/s
Rise in Jacket water temperature = 5.8°C (5.8 K)

Assuming no radiation loss, calculate the mass flow rate of the crystals and the percentage crystallization taking place in the heat exchanger. **[491.5 kg/h, 72.8%]**

Note The scrapped-surface heat exchanger provides a high ratio of heat-transfer surface to a relatively small material volume, coupled with continuous product film removal and vigorous agitation, using a rotor (screw) inside the heat exchanger.

6.20 Feed to a vacuum crystallizer contains 82% urea, 0.5% biuret and 17.5% water by mass. In the crystallizer, 50% water is evaporated at 50°C (323 K) at which temperature the solubility of urea is 205 g per 100 g water. If the mother liquor is found to contain 1.6% biuret, find the yield of urea crystals and its biuret content. **[78.12% yield and 0.11% biuret content (mass)]**

6.21 A 1000 kg mixture of NaCl and NH_4Cl is to be separated by the fractional crystallization. It contains 40% NaCl by mass. It is dissolved in pure water at 50°C (323 K).

(a) If stoichiometric quantity of water is used for dissolution, calculate the quantity of the component remaining undissolved and also the quantity of the saturated solution.

(b) If the saturated solution at 50°C (323 K) mentioned in (a) above is cooled to 10°C (283 K), calculate the additional quantity of the original mixture which can be dissolved and also the total quantity of the component remaining out of the solution.

(c) If the saturated solution at 50°C (323 K) mentioned in (a) above is heated to 100°C (373 K), calculate the additional quantity of the original mixture which can be dissolved and also the total quantity of the component remaining out of the solution.

Table 6.26   Solubility Data of NaCl–NH$_4$Cl System

| Temperature | Solubility, g/100 g water | |
°C (K)	NaCl	NH$_4$Cl
10 (283)	18.25	12.49
50 (323)	14.26	22.50
100 (373)	10.77	33.98

[(a) **3647 kg saturated solution, 19.7 kg NaCl remains undissolved**
(b) **266 kg mixture can be treated, 426.5 kg NH$_4$Cl is separated**
(c) **510.2 kg mixture can be treated, 297.2 kg NaCl is separated**]

6.22 Figure 6.32 is the solubility diagram of ammonium nitrate and urea in water. It gives solubility isotherms and isocons of nirogen concentration. Phase boundaries on the diagram are useful in fixing the paths of dissoultion with addition of water or crystallization with concentration (i.e., removal of water).

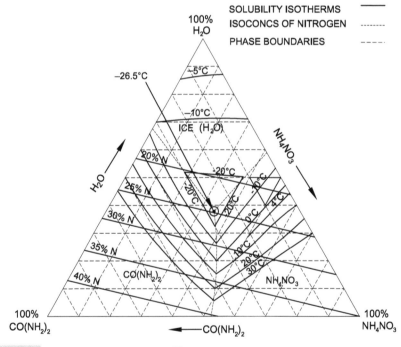

Fig. 6.32   Ternary Solubility Diagram[27] for Ammonium Nitrate-Urea-Water System

(a) An aqueous solution of urea is available having 20% urea by mass. Its nitrogen content is increased to 25% N (by mass) by adding ammonium nitrate to the solution. Using Fig. 6.32 and geometric principles, find the composition of the final solution and calculate the quantity of ammonium nitrate to be added to 100 kg of original solution to achieve 25% N strength. Also, read 'salt out' temperature. **[158.05 kg, 17.9°C (291.05 K)]**

(b) An aqueous solution of ammonium nitater is available having 40% NH_4NO_3 by mass. It is to be fortified to 30% N (by mass) by adding urea to the solution. Using Fig. 6.32 and geometric principles, find the composition of final solution and calculate quantity of urea to be added to 100 kg of original solution to achieve 30% N strength. Also, read 'salt out' temperature. **[100.25 kg, 24.4°C (297.55 K)]**

(c) An aqueous solution of 25% N (by mass) is to be produced by mixing aqueous 50% NH_4NO_3 solution with aqueous 70% urea solution (by mass). Using Fig. 6.32 and geometric principles, calculate the quantity of 50% NH_4NO_3 solution to be mixed with 100 kg 70% urea solution to achieve aqueous solution of 25% N strength. Also read 'salt out' temperature of the final solution. **[95.58 kg, −8.3°C (264.85 K)]**

6.23 Refer Example 5.48. Nitrogen solution has 32% N strength (by mass). Use Fig. 6.32.
(a) Find its 'salt out' temperature. **[−7.9°C (265.25 K)]**
(b) The solution is cooled to −20°C (253.15 K).
   (i) What will be the composition of final solution? **[37% NH₄ NO₃, 30% urea by mass]**
   (ii) Assume that crystals do not have any bound moisture. Calculate the amount of crystals separated and composition thereof. **[Crystals : 38.33 kg, 49.91% urea by mass]**

6.24 Nitrogen gas containing 5 ppm (v/v) of moisture (max.) is required for deriming (i.e. removal of condensed phases from the exchanger) a cold box of a cryogenic plant.
Calculate (a) The dew point of nitrogen when measured with the dew point apparatus at atmospheric pressure and (b) the dew point at 8 bar a when measured with the help of an online instrument. **[(a) −65.5°C (207.65 K) (b) −48.05°C (225.1 K)]**

6.25 Purge gas (dried in adsorder) stream from ammonia synthesis loop contains N_2: 21.5%, H_2: 64.5%, Ar: 4.2% and CH_4: 9.8% on mole basis. It is processed in a cold box to recover hydrogen by cryogenic method. Feed gas mixture enters cold box at 45 bar a and 20°C (293.15 K) with an average pressure dew point of −40°C (233.15 K). The cold box is operated continuously at 8000 Nm^3/h feed rate for 300 days before it is derimed. Assuming that all moisture in the purge stream is condensed and solidified in the cold box heat exchanger, calculate the quantity of water so condensed. **[132.1 kg]**

6.26 On a particular day in Mumbai, a newspaper reported the weather conditions of the previous day as 35°C (308 K) *DB*, 80% *RH* and barometric pressure of 100 kPa (750 Torr). Calculate (a) the absolute humidity, (b) the dew point, (c) the percentage saturation, (d) the humid heat, and (e) the enthalpy over 0°C (273.15 K). **[(a) 0.0292 kg/kg dry air (b) 31°C (304 K). (c) 79%, (d) 1.06 kg/(kg dry air · K) (e) 103.8 kJ/kg dry air]**

6.27 A textile mill situated in Mumbai considers 34°C (307 K) *DB* and 27.5°C (300.5 K) *WB* temperatures as design intake-air temperatures for an air-conditioning system. It is desired to bring down the *RH* to 50% for the supply to the spinning department. Although this is possible by heating the air, the temperature of the final air is considered high for the comfort of the workers. It is, therefore desired to chill the air with chilled water at 15°C (288 K) and make it cold saturated air. Later, the cold air is to be heated so that the final conditions of air are 30°C (303 K) and 50% RH. The air rate for design is 60 000 m³/h. Refer Figs. 6.33 for process flow and 6.34 for the psychrometric path.

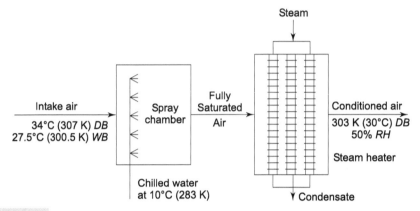

Fig. 6.33   Dehumidification of Air

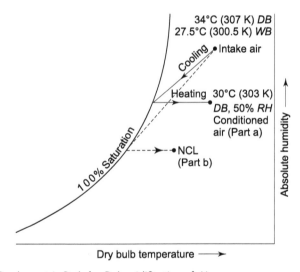

Fig. 6.34   Psychrometric Path for Dehumidification of Air

(a) (i) Find the cooling load, (ii) final humidity, (iii) the heating load, and (iv) steam consumption in the heater, if the saturated steam is fed to it at 400 kPa a.

(b) hysiological studies in USA show the neutral comfort level (NCL) of moist air to correspond to an absolute humidity of 10 g/kg dry air. For this comfort humidity level and 50% RH, recalculate parts (i), (ii), (iii) and (iv) of (a).

[(a) **Cooling load = 676.31 kW (192.43 TR), Final H = 13.2 g/kg dry air,**
Heating load = 225.32 kW and steam consumption = 380.3 kg/h
(b) **Cooling load = 915.34 kW (260.45 TR), Final DB = 25.2°C (298.35 K),**
Heating load = 212.20 kW and steam consumption = 358.2 kg/h]]

6.28 A saturated CO_2-water vapour mixture comes out from a spray cooler at 117.3 kPa a (880 Torr) and 40°C (313 K) before its compression. Find the absolute humidity of the mixture. **[0.0275 kg/kg dry CO_2]**

6.29 In a process for bleaching the jute, chlorine is used as a bleaching agent. The jute is bleached in a chlorine atmosphere containing some moisture. In a particular experiment, the *DP* was measured to be 18°C (291 K) while the total pressure in the system is 101.3 kPa a (760 Torr). Find the moisture content of chlorine in (a) kg/kg dry chlorine and (b) ppm (mass). **[(a) 0.005 279 kg/kg dry Cl2 (b) 5171 ppm]**

6.30 In Example 5.40, oxidation of HCl gas to chlorine is referred to. It is calculated that the gas mixture after oxidation comes out at 326.35°C (599.5 K). This mixture is passed through a Trombone cooler where it is indirectly cooled to 50°C (323 K) with the help of water. As a result, some water is condensed. Condensed water also dissolves some HCl gas. The concentration of aqueous acid is found to be 33% by mass. Calculate the quantity of acid produced per kmol HCl gas fed to the burner and the heat load of the cooler. Use the data contained in Table 5.79. Assume heat capacity of 33% acid to be 2.6 kJ/(kg · K).

[3.39 kg 33% acid per kmol HCl feed gas, 28 172 kJ/kmol HCl]

6.31 Refer Exercise 4.25. Carbon dioxide, saturated with SO_3 at 7 bar a and 80°C (353 K) from the reactors is taken to an overhead condenser in which refrigeration is provided. Mixture is cooled to 30°C (303 K) and condensed SO_3 is refluxed in the first reactor. CO_2 saturated with SO_3 at 6.8 bar a and 30°C (303 K) leaves from the top of the overhead condenser to a water scrubber after pressure reduction to atmospheric pressure. Assume (i) ideal behaviour of gas and liquid, and (ii) negligible dissolution of CO_2 in condensed liquid SO_3. Calculate the amount of SO_3 refluxed to the reactor and heat duty of the overhead condenser for urea feed rate of 350 kg/h.

Data (i) Vapour pressure SO_3 at 30°C (303 K) = 346.1 Torr

   (ii) Latent heat of vaporization of SO_3 (λ_v) = 42.55 kJ/mol at 30°C (303 K)

[SO_3 refluxed = 695.34 kg/h, Heat duty of condenser = 18.647 kW]

6.32 Refer Exercise 6.13. HCl-free (0%) gas mixture leaving the absorber is compressed from 3.3 bar a to 11.5 bar a in a compressor. The mixture is cooled in an aftercooler from which it leaves at 11.3 bar a and 40°C (313 K). Calculate the amount of CCl_4 condensed. **[3887.6 kg/h]**

6.33 Activated charcoal, a regenerative adsorbent, is employed industrially to remove volatile organic compounds (VOC) from inert gases. The absorbed vapour is then recovered by passing superheated steam through the adsorbent till the partial pressure of the organic vapour in the steam falls to a sufficiently low level so that the adsorbent can be recirculated to the process. It is desired to remove 1000 kg/h of benzene from a benzene-rich nitrogen stream. This stream is to be supplied to the adsorber at a temperature of 60°C (333 K), a total pressure of 104 kPa (780 Torr) and a dew point of 40°C (313 K). The sream leaves at 101.3 kPa (760 Torr) and a dew point of 10°C (283 K). The entering (regenerated) activated carbon has a benzene content of 0.05 kg per kg bone-dry (BD) activated carbon and that leaving has a benzene content of 0.35 kg per kg BD activated carbon. The process is schematically represented in Fig. 6.35.

Calculate (a) the mass flow rate of nitrogen on bone-dry basis in kg/h, (b) the requirement of inlet–activated carbon on bone-dry basis in kg/h, and (c) the pressure to which the benzene–nitrogen inlet stream would have to be compressed at a constant temperature of 60°C (333 K) to achieve the same removal of benzene as with the activated carbon under the process conditions outlined above. Use Eq. (5.24) and the data contained in Table 5.4. **[(a) 1476.9 kg/h (b) 3333 kg/h (c) 872.7 kPa a]**

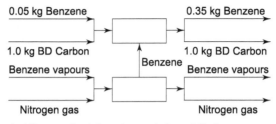

Fig. 6.35 Removal of Benzene by Adsorption on Activated Carbon

6.34 In industrial practice, *n*-hexane is used to extract the oil from soybean flakes. In a process of this type, the soybean flakes leaving the extraction unit are reduced in solvent content by a stream of nitrogen which vaporizes the hexane. The reduction is from 0.61 kg hexane per kg bone-dry (BD) flakes to 0.025 kg hexane per kg BD flakes. The entering nitrogen leaves at 70°C (343 K) with a relative saturation of 65%. The pressure in the desolventizer is 101.325 kPa (760 Torr) and 25 000 kg/h of BD flakes pass through the disolventizer. The processes are shown in Fig. 6.36.

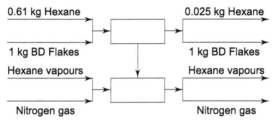

Fig. 6.36 Hexane Recovery

Calculate (a) the kmol of wet gases (i.e., nitrogen plus hexane) leaving the disolventizer per kg of soybean flakes (BD basis) processed, and (b) the volumetric flow rate of wet gases, leaving the desolventizer. (c) The nitrogen leaving the desolventizer is compressed and cooled to 20°C (293 K), thus condensing out the hexane picked up in the desolventizer. What must be the pressure in the condenser if the gas is to have a dew point of 10°C (283 K) at the pressure of desolventizer? Use Eq. (5.24) and the data contained in Table 5.4.

[(a) 0.0106 kmol/kg BD flakes (b) 7461.3 m³/h (c) 162.3 kPa]

6.35 It is desired to dry a solid organic pigment in a continuous counter-current adiabatic dryer. The drying air enters at 100°C (373 K) and 114 kPa (855 Torr) with a saturation temperature (i.e., *DP*) of 21°C (294 K). The wet pigment is fed at the rate of 100 kg/h containing 50% water and is to be dried to 3% water (by mass). Under these conditions, 2.08 kg of water is evaporated per 100 m³ of the entering air. The air leaves at a total pressure of 108 kPa a (810 Torr). Refer to Fig. 6.37 for the process flow diagram.

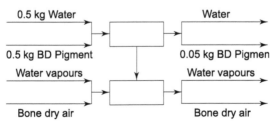

Fig. 6.37 Pigment Drying

Calculate (a) the kmol of bone-dry air per kg of water evaporated from the pigment, (b) the *DP* of outgoing air, and (c) the volumetric flow rate of the entering air.

[(a) **1.729 kmol BD air/kg water, (b) 34.85°C (308 K) and (c) 2329.3 m³/h**]

6.36 In an edible–oil extraction plant, soybean flakes are extracted with *n*-hexane. Miscella, containing 40% oil (average molar mass = 872) and 60% *n*-hexane (by mass), is distilled in a steam jacketted vessel. The plant precesses 200 t/d soybean flakes. The vessel is maintained under vacuum of 197.5 Torr and 60°C (333.15 K) with the help of a steam ejector system. Solvent vapour pass through a condenser in which cooling water condenses hexane vapour. Non-condensibles (essentially air leak) saturated with solvent, leave the condenser at 40°C (313.15 K) and 310 Torr absolute pressure and are ejected to atmosphere through an ejector, having a suction capacity of 25 m³/h under actual suction conditions.

(a) Assuming density of *n*-hexane at 35°C (308.15 K) to be 0.645 kg/L, calculate the loss of hexane per t of soybean flakes processed.

(b) As an economic measure, a chiller is installed after the cooling water condenser. Non-condensibles, saturated with hexane leave the chiller at 10°C (283.15 K) and 310 Torr absolute pressure. Additonal hexane is thus condensensed in the chiller. Calculate the loss of hexane per t of soybean flakes with the chiller.

(c) Calculate the heat loads of condenser and chiller.

[(a) **Hexane loss = 5.723 L/t (b) Hexane loss = 0.45 L/t and (c) cooler duty = 5 kW, chiller duty = 3.158 kW (0.899 TR)**]

6.37 Paper in the form of sheets passes through a set of pressure rolls to remove some water and then through a series of hot surface dryers where additional water is removed. The following data were collected from the machine[28].

Machine speed = 5 m/s
Paper width = 3.8 m
Moisture leaving the dryer = 5% (by mass)
Moisture leaving the presses = 60% (by mass)
Specific density of paper = 0.081 kg/m² (on bone-dry basis)
Filler clay present = 20% of total solids

Assuming that the filler clay and (cellulosic) fibre are the only solids present and that none is lost in the drying section, calculate (a) the bone-dry paper production, (b) the amount of fibre, water and filler leaving the dryers and (c) the water lost in the drying section.

[(a) **133 t/d on bone-dry basis (b) Water in the paper = 277.0 kg/h Filler in the paper = 1052.9 kg/h Fibre in the paper = 4211.7 kg/h (c) Evaporation = 7620 kg/h**]

6.38 Activated carbon pellets are dried from 30% moisture content to 2% (by mass). Hot air can be used for drying but its temperature must be kept below 125°C (398 K) to avoid chances of combustion in the dryer. For this reason, superheated steam is considered a better drying medium than hot air. Superheated steam enters the dryer at 300°C (573 K) and 101.325 kPa and leaves the dryer at 150°C (423 K). Pellets are fed to the dryer at 30°C (303 K) and dried product leaves at 110°C (383 K). For a production rate of 1000 kg/h of dried pellets, carry out the material and energy balances of the dryer. Assume heat capacity of bone dry pellets to be 1.3146 kJ/(kg·K). Also consider 5% heat loss (based on heat input) from the system.

[**Superheat steam flow to the dryer = 8130.15 kg/h**]

6.39 A spray dryer is used for drying 'acid black' dye as shown in Fig. 6.38. Operating data of the spray drier are given below.

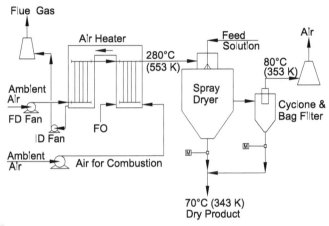

Fig. 6.38 Spray Drying of Dye Solution

Solution feed rate = 970 kg/h at 60°C (333 K)
Solid content of feed = 25% by mass
Solvent to be evaporated = Water
Moisture content of the product = 3% by mass
Residence time in drying zone = 35 s
Feed temperature = 60°C (313 K)
Product temperature = 70°C (343 K)
Inlet fuel gas temperature = 280°C (553 K)
Outlet temperature of gases = 80°C (353 K)
Specific heat of dye powder = 1.4 kJ/(kg·K)

Air is supplied at 35°C (308 K), fully saturated, to the heater in which fuel oil with NCV = 41 300 kJ/kg is burnt as fuel. Overall thermal efficiency of the heater may be taken as 70%. Assume 10% heat loss from the dryer.

Calculate (a) flow rate of air, (b) humidity of air, leaving the dryer, and (c) consumption of fuel oil in the air heater.

[(a) 10 018 kg/h of dry air, (b) 0.1079 kg/kg dry air and (c) 91.0 kg/h]

6.40 A forced circulation evaporator is used to concentrate caustic soda solution from 50% to 75% by mass. Saturated steam at 6 bar a is used for heating on shell side of the heat exchanger. Caustic soda solution is circulated through nickel alloy tubes. A vacuum of 660 Torr is maintained in the vapour–liquid separator. Feed to the evaporator is 50 000 kg/h at 35°C (308 K). Boiling point elevation for 75% solution is 81°C (354 K). Carryout mass and energy balances of the evaporator system and calculate the economy. Use actual enthalpies of caustic soda solutions from Fig. 5.16.

[Evaporation = 16 666.7 kg/h, Steam consumption
= 31 073.9 kg/h, Economy = 0.5364 kg/kg]

6.41 A thin black liquor from the digesters in a kraft pulp mill is concentrated by passing it through a sextuple-effect evaporator system[28]. The flow of the thin liquor is 50 L/s and a solid content of 15% (by mass). The concentrated liquor leaves the system at 55% solids (by mass). The density of the thin liquor can be assumed to be 1.08 kg/L. Saturated steam at 300 kPa a is consumed at the rate of 28 500 kg/h. Calculate (a) the total evaporation taking place in the system, and (b) the steam economy of the system. [(a) 141 382 kg/h (b) 4.961 kg evaporation/kg steam]

6.42 A sulphite paper mill concentrates spent cooking liquor from 10% to 50% (by mass) dissolved solids in a quadruple-effect evaporator system[28]. Saturated steam is available at 103 kPa g and a vaccum of 660 Torr is maintained in the fourth effect. The feed to the evaporator is 8.85 L/s in the forward direction at a specific gravity of 1.05 and 40°C (313 K). The liquor can be assumed to have a negligible elevation in the boiling point and its heat capacity can be assumed to be 4.1868 kJ/(kg·K) at all concentrations. It can also be assumed that no salt or other solids separate on evaporation and that the heat effect of dilution/concentrartion is negligible. The condensate leaves the steam chests at the saturation temperature of steam. Radiation can be neglected. All the evaporator bodies are to be of the same size (75.84 m² per effect). The operating data of the system are given in Table 6.27.

Table 6.27 Operating Conditions of Forward Feed Evaporator

Effect	Temperature, °C (K)	Overall heat transfer coefficient, kW/(m²·K)
First	103.0 (376.0)	4.14
Second	94.0 (367.0)	5.62
Third	80.5 (353.5)	4.08
Fourth	51.6 (324.6)	1.99

Evaluate the thermal performance of the system.

[Total evaporation = 26 712 kg/h, Steam consumption = 10191.6 kg/h, Steam economy = 2.621 kg evaporation/ kg steam]

6.43 The evaporator system described in Exercise 6.42 is operated in the backward feed manner. The operating conditions are described in Table 6.28.

Table 6.28 Operation Conditions of Backward Feed Evaporator

Effect	Temperature, °C (K)	Overall heat transfer coefficient, kW/(m²·K)
First	689.0 (362)	1.99
Second	74.5 (347.5)	4.08
Third	64.5 (337.5)	5.62
Fourth	51.6 (324.6)	4.14

Evaluate the thermal performance of the system.

[Steam consumption = 8294 kg/h Steam economy = 3.221 kg evaporation/kg steam]

6.44 A two-stage washer is employed in a neutral sulphite semichemical pulp mill for washing the cooking liquor from the pump discharged from a continuous digester[29]. This washer is actually a drum-type filter, but for purposes of analysis, it can be considered as two distinct contacting stages in which the pulp mat is washed by a counter-currently moving stream of wash liquor. The pulp slurry fed to this system contains 1.5% suspended pulp solids and 9.25% dissolved salts (by mass) which are to be recovered. The specific gravity of the liquor in which the pulp is suspended is 1.30. Fresh wash water containing no dissolved salts enters the second stage at the rate of 9.85 L/s and the washed pulp leaving this stage has a solids content of 18% (by mass), suspended in a liquor of 1.03 specific gravity. This specific gravity corresponds to 1.63% dissolved salts (by mass). The washing system handles 175 t/d of oven dry pulp. Assuming that the wash liquor leaving a given contacting stage is in equilibrium with the liquor associated with the pulp leaving the same stage, calculate the efficiency for each stage and the overall efficiency.

[**First-stage-efficiency = 97.97%, Second-stage efficiency = 26.51%, Overall efficiency = 98.51%**]

6.45 A fractionating column is designed to separate water from an aqueous solution containing methylene chloride (1.68 mass %) and methanol (2.02 mass %). The fractionation is achieved by blowing live steam (available at 3.5 bar g) in the column as shown in Fig. 6.39. The bottom product (W) from the column is pure water, practically free from any impurity. The overhead vapours are taken to a condenser where the vapours are condensed. The condensed liquid flows to a decanter where it separates into two layers. The compositions[30] of the layers are given in Table 6.29.

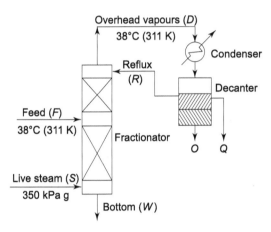

Fig. 6.39 Recovery of Methylene Chloride and Methanol from Aqueous Solution by Fractionation

Table 6.29 Composition of Immiscible Layers in Decanter

Component	mass %	
	Upper Layer (Q or R)	Lower Layer (O)
Methylene chloride	7.63	90.70
Methanol	16.06	9.30
Water	76.31	Nil

A part of the upper layer is withdrawn as a product (Q) while the rest is recycled back to the tower (R). The reflux ratio of 0.5 kmol/kmol of the overhead product drawn can be taken for calculations. Assume that the tower operates at nearly atmospheric pressure and the temperature of the overhead vapours is 38°C (311 K).

Radiation losses can be assumed to be 2%. Based on fresh feed rate of 10 000 kg/h, compute (a) the flow rate of streams Q and O, (b) the steam input rate and (c) the bottom product (W) rate.

Use Eq. (5.24) and the data contained in Table 5.4.

[**(a) Flow rate of Q = 1209.4 kg/h, Flow rate of O = 83.5 kg/h**
(b) Steam input = 2576 kg/h (c) Bottom product rate, W = 11 283 kg/h]

References

1. Griswold, J and Stewart, P B; *Ind. Engg. Chem.*, **39**(6): 1947, p. 758.
2. NIST Standard Refrence Database 23 (REFPROP), Ver. 8, Naitonal Institute of Standards and Technology, USA, 2007.
3. Teller, A J and Ford, H E; *Ind. Engg. Chem.*, **50**(8): 1958, p. 1201.
4. Chambers, F S and Sherwood, T K; *Ind. Engg. Chem.*, **29**(12): 1937, p. 1415.
5. Wagman, D D *et al*, The NBS Tables of Chemical Thermodynamic Properties, *J. Phy. Chem. Ref. Data*, Vol. II, Supplement 2, 1982.
6. Ellis, S R M; *Chem. Engg.* **63**: Sep. 1956, p. 185.
7. Eaglesfield, P, Kelly, B K and Short, J F; *The Industrial Chemist*, June, 1953, p. 147 and p. 243.
8. Brown, W V; *Chem. Engg. Progress,* **59**(10): 1963, p. 65.
9. Green, D W and Perry, R H; *Perry's Chemical Engineers's Handbook*, 8th Ed., McGraw-Hill Education, USA, 2008.
10. Heist, J A, *Chem. Engg.*, **86**(10), 1979, p. 72.
11. Meyer, D W; *Chemical Processing*, **53**(1): Jan. 1990, p. 50.
12. Khare, B M and Chivate, M R; *Indian Chemical Engineer, Transactions* **XVI** (4): 1974, p. 25.
13. Wagner, W, Saul, A and Pruss, A; *J. Phy. Chem. Ref. Data*, **23** (3), 1994, p. 527.
14. Carpenter, J H; *Fundamentals of Psychrometics (SI Units)*, Carrier Corporation, Publication No. T 300 - 20, USA, 1983.
15. Private communication with Anhydro A/S, Denmark.
16. *Tappi*, **47**(7): 1964, p. 171A.
17. Cook, E M; *Chem. Engg. Progress,* **74**(4): 1978, p. 75.
18. Bhatt, B I, Deshpande, S P and Subrahmaniyam, K; *Chemical Age of India*, **20**(12): 1970, p. 1135.
19. *Tappi*, **48**(3): 1965, p. 170A.
20. Smith, B D; *Design of Equilibrium Stage Processes*, McGraw-Hill, USA, 1963, p. 424.
21. Luyben, W L; *Chem Engg. Prog.*, **77**(10): 1981, p. 78.
22. Repke, Jen-Uwe and Klein, A; *Proceedings of the 15th European Symposium on Computer Aided Process Engeering*, (Ed L Puigianer and A Espuna), Elsevier Science B. V., 2005.
23. *Tappi*, **47**(8): 1964, p. 114A.
24. Partin, L R; *Chem Engg Prog.*, **89**(1): 1993, p. 43.
25. Gregory, L B and Scharmann, W G; *Ind. Engg Chem.*, **29**(5): 1937, p. 514.
26. AIChE Student Contest Problem, 1961.
27. *Fertilizer Manual*, Development and Transfer of Technology Series No. 13, published by UNIDO, Austria, 1980, p. 129.
28. *Chemical Engineering. Problems in the Pulp and Paper Industry*, Technical Association of the Pulp and Paper Industry (*Tappi*), USA.
29. *Tappi*, **47**(3): 1964, p. 136A.
30. Drew, J W; *Chem. Engg. Progr.*, **71**(2): 1975, p. 95.

CHAPTER 7

Combustion

Fuels are burnt with oxygen to supply energy to the process industry. Excluding the use of electrical energy for the supply of thermal energy in isolated cases, fuels are extensively used to supply thermal energy. Nuclear energy and solar energy are also used to supply thermal energy in specific cases. Considering the important role of fuels in the process industry, this chapter will be exclusively devoted to combustion.

Combustion is a unit process in which the oxidation reaction takes place. It is the rapid oxidation of combustible substances accompanied by the release of energy while the constituent elements are converted to their respective oxides. However, all oxidation reactions are not termed as combustion, e.g., the oxidation of toluene to benzaldehyde, oxidation of hydrogen chloride to chlorine, etc., are not normally termed as combustion processes. Broadly, the union of carbon, hydrogen and sulphur with oxygen is termed as combustion. If the products of combustion are carbon dioxide, water and sulphur dioxide respectively from the above three elements, the combustion is termed as a complete combustion. If carbon monoxide appears in the product gases, the combustion is termed incomplete or partial combustion because CO can further combine with oxygen to produce CO_2. Although SO_2 can be further oxidized to SO_3, it is customary to regard the union as a complete union for stoichiometric calculations. However, the complete union of S and O_2 yields SO_3 which requires specific conditions for the union.

7.1 FUELS

Fuels can be broadly classified as follows:

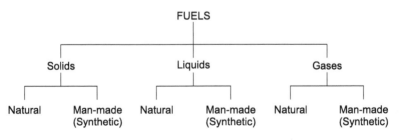

The classical fossil fuel (natural) is coal. Lignite is also found in nature. It is an earthy-brown fuel, generally low in mineral-matter content. Wood is used as a solid fuel in many instances. Coke, bagasse, rice husk, saw dust, Petcoke, etc., are other examples of synthetic solid fuels.

Crude oil obtained from sub-soil drilling is a natural liquid fuel. Gasoline (petrol), diesel oil, alcohols, kerosene, fuel oils and other organic liquids are man-made liquid fuels. Manufacture of biocrude from organic waste using high pressure steam is a reality on a pilot scale. Biodiesel, obtained from catalytic transesterification of vegetable oils, is an alternate to the traditional diesel fuel.

Natural gas (and associated gas) is an important natural gaseous fuel. Coke oven gas, producer gas, blast-furnace gas, liquefied petroleum gas (LPG) and refinery gas are examples of synthetic gaseous fuels. Dimethyl ether (DME) is gaining popularity as a synthetic gaseous fuel.

The combustibles in the fuel should be known for stoichiometric calculations. The analyses of various fuels must be known for this reason. It will now be seen how the analyses of each of the fuels are represented. In particular, the interpretation of coal analysis requires a clear understanding of the subject.

7.2   CALORIFIC VALUES OF FUELS

The *calorific value* of a fuel is nothing but the heat of combustion of the fuel. It is defined as the total heat produced when a unit mass of fuel is completely burnt with pure oxygen. It is also said to be the *heating value* of the fuel.

As discussed earlier, when a fuel is burnt, hydrogen combines with oxygen and gets converted into water. When water vapour is present in the flue gases, the latent heat of vaporization is lost. Hence this quantity of heat is not available for any useful purpose. Therefore, when the calorific value of a fuel is determined, considering that the water is present in the vapour form, it is said to be *net calorific value* (NCV) or *net heating value* (NHV) or *lower heating value* (LHV).

If the above vapours are condensed, the latent heat of water vapour can be made available for useful purposes. Thus, if this part of heat is added to the net calorific value, *gross calorific value* (GCV) or *gross heating value* (GHV) or *higher heating value* (HHV) is obtained.

Usually, NCV and GCV of the fuels are reported at 25°C (298.15 K). Appendix V.2 at the end of the text gives the NCV and GCV of various compounds. Normally, NCV and GCV are reported in kJ/kg or kJ/mol units; kJ/m^3 (for gaseous fuels) units are also used occasionally, depending on the convenience. It is customary to specify the abbreviations NCV or GCV when the calorific values are reported, as the case may be. However, if no mention is made, the reported calorific value is taken as GCV.

The calorific value of a fuel is determined in a calorimeter in which the fuel is burnt with pure oxygen and the heat liberated is absorbed in water. The rise in temperature of water gives the calorific value of the fuel.

$$NCV = GCV - (\text{mass } \% \text{ hydrogen}) \ (9) \ (\lambda_v) \ \text{kJ/kg} \qquad (7.1)$$

In this equation, λ_v is the latent heat of water vapour at the reference temperature. Normally, 25°C (298.15 K) is considered to be the reference temperature at which $\lambda_v = 2442.5$ kJ/kg.

Appendix V.2 includes GCV for many organic compounds containing nitrogen, sulphur and phosphorous. One would therefore imagine that corresponding exothermic heat can be realized by burning these compounds. Although throretically true, several halogenated and nitrogen–containing organic compounds cannot be easily burnt. For example, acrylonitrile (AN) is one of the most difficult compounds to incinerate. An operating temperature of 850°C (1123 K) with a mean residence time of 0.3 s is recommended to incinerate AN. Similarly, combustion of carbon tetrachloride also requires specific operating conditions. For these reasons, supporting fuel, (e.g., hydrocarbon, fuel oil, etc.) is required to burn such compounds, Knowledge of flash point, ignition temperature, activation energy and other parameters is required to know the kinetics of the combustion process.

7·3   COAL

Coal is the most important fossil fuel. In India, although the coal reserves are abundant, most of the collieries are situated in Madhya Pradesh, West Bengal, Bihar and the banks of the river Godavari. As a result, the transportation of coal to other parts of the country is quite expensive. In addition, the best–grade coal is limited in quantity as compared to *steam coal*. Hence, the best–quality coal is reserved for the manufacture of steel.

Two different analyses of coal are reported, namely *proximate analysis* and *ultimate analysis*. Both of them will now be separately studied.

7.3.1 Proximate Analysis

Normally, the proximate analysis of *air-dried coal* is reported as follows. An *air-dried* coal sample is one which is exposed to the atmosphere of a laboratory to bring it in equilibrium with the humidity conditions of the laboratory so that the sample does not gain or lose mass during analysis.

Moisture   Water expelled in its various forms when tested under specified conditions.

Volatile Matter (VM)   Total loss in weight minus the moisture in coal when coal is heated under specified conditions.

Mineral Matter   Inorganic residue left over when coal or coke is incinerated in air to constant mass under specified conditions. It is ordinarily referred to as *ash*.

Fixed Carbon (FC)   Obtained by subtracting from 100, the sum of the percentages by mass of moisture, VM and mineral matter.

Ordinarily, percentage sulphur (by mass) does not form a part of the proximate analysis. However, due to the harmful effects of sulphur dioxide and sulphur trioxide m to the environment, produced by burning sulphur, percentage sulphur (by mass) is also included when only proximate analysis is to be specified. IS: 1350 (Part-I) gives the methods of test for coal/coke/lignite relating to proximate analysis.

IS: 1350 (Part-II) relates to determination of the calorific value of coal/coke/lignite.

IS: 1350 (Part-III) relates to the determination of sulphur in coal/coke/lignite.

7.3.2   Forms and Conditions of Moisture in Coal/Lignite

(i) Total moisture   Coal that is exposed to water in the seam or in a washery, or the coal wetted by rain, can carry free moisture. This moisture plus the moisture within the material is known as the total moisture.

(ii) Moisture at 40°C (313 K) and 60% RH   The moisture present in coal which is equilibrated at 40°C (313 K) at 60% relative humidity *(RH)* is sometimes reported.

(iii) Moisture at 40°C (313 K) and 96% RH   This is also termed as the near saturation moisture or bed moisture. It is the moisture present in coal which is equilibrated at 40°C (313 K) and 96% *RH* and is exclusive of free visible moisture.

(iv) Free moisture   It represents the visible wetness of coal only.

(v) Moisture in air-dried sample   This is the moisture content of coal when it is equilibrated with the ambient conditions of the laboratory.

7.3.3   Tests for Proximate Analysis

The general procedures for the analysis relating to proximate analysis is described below as per IS: 1350 (Part-I). For full details, the original standard may be referred to.

(i) Moisture   The moisture in the sample is determined by drying the known mass of the coal at 108°C ± 2°C (381 K ± 2 K).

(ii) Volatile Matter (VM)   The method for the determination of VM consists of heating a weighed quantity of air-dried sample at a temperature of 900°C ± 10°C (1173 K ± 10 K) for a period of seven minutes. Oxidation has to be avoided as far as possible. VM is the loss in mass other than that due to moisture.

(iii) Mineral Matter (Ash)   In this determination, the sample is heated in air up to 500°C (773 K) for 30 min from 500°C to 815°C (773 K to 1088 K) for a further 30 to 60 min and maintained at this temperature until the sample mass becomes constant.

(iv) FC   As explained earlier, FC is determined by deducting the moisture, VM and mineral matter (as mass %) from 100.

7.3.4   Ultimate Analysis of Coal

The ultimate analysis of coal gives the constituent elements, namely; carbon, hydrogen, nitrogen and sulphur. The percentage carbon given in the ultimate analysis should not be confused with FC, the latter being always lower than the former. The oxygen content of the coal is obtained by finding the difference of 100 and the sum of other constituent elements. IS: 1350 gives the test methods for the ultimate analysis of coal.

For the ultimate analysis, the coal sample is burnt in a current of oxygen. As a result, the hydrogen, carbon and sulphur get oxidized to water, carbon dioxide and sulphur dioxide, respectively. Water and carbon dioxide are absorbed in suitable solvents and the constituents are determined gravimetrically. Sulphur products are retained by lead chromate. Precautions have to be taken to eliminate the oxides of nitrogen which can form during combustion. The nitrogen in the coal is determined by the Kjeldahl method.

The hydrogen determined by the above procedure includes the hydrogen content of organic matter of VM and the hydrogen of the moisture present in the coal. The actual hydrogen burnt during combustion is calculated by subtracting 11.2% of the mass percentage moisture content of the air-dried sample of the coal from the total hydrogen determined by above process.

The classification of coal is done on the basis of proximate analysis. A technologically significant grading system adopted in India is given in Table 7.1.

Table 7.1 Classification of Bituminous Coal[1]

S.No.	Class	Grade	Specifications
1.	Non-coking coal, produced in all states—other than Assam, Meghalaya, Arunachal Pradesh and Nagaland	A	HU* exceeding 25 960 kJ/kg or 6200 kcal/kg
		B	HU exceeding 23 450 kJ/kg or 5600 kcal/kg but not exceeding 25 960 kJ/kg or 6200 kcal/kg
		C	HU exceeding 20 680 kJ/kg or 4940 kcal/kg but not exceeding 23 450 kJ/kg or 5600 kcal/kg
		D	HU exceeding 17 580 kJ/kg or 4200 kcal/kg but not exceeding 20 680 kJ/kg or 4940 kcal/kg
		E	HU exceeding 14 070 kJ/kg or 3360 kcal/kg but not exceeding 17 580 kJ/kg or 4200 kcal/kg
		F	HU exceeding 10 050 kJ/kg or 2400 kcal/kg but not exceeding 14 070 kJ/kg or 3360 kcal/kg
		G	HU exceeding 5440 kJ/kg or 1300 kcal/kg but not exceeding 10 050 kJ/kg or 2400 kcal/kg
2.	Non-coking coal, produced in Assam, Meghalaya, Arunachal Predesh and Nagaland		Not graded

(Contd.)

Table 7.1 (*Contd.*)

S.No.	Class	Grade	Specifications
3.	Coking coal	Steel grade I	Ash content not exceeding 15%
		Steel grade II	Ash content exceeding 15% but not exceeding 18%
		Washery grade I	Ash content exceeding 18% but not exceeding 21%
		Washery grade II	Ash content exceeding 21% but not exceeding 24%
		Washery grade III	Ash content exceeding 24% but not exceeding 28%
		Washery grade IV	Ash content exceeding 28% but not exceeding 35%
4.	Semi-coking and weakly coking coal	Semi-coking I	Ash plus moisture content not exceeding 19%
		Semi-coking II exceeding	Ash plus moisture content exceeding 19% but not 24%
5.	Hard coke	By product premium	Ash content exceeding 25%
		By product ordinary	Ash content exceeding 25% but not exceeding 30%
		Beehive premium	Ash content not exceeding 27%
		Beehive superior	Ash content exceeding 27% but not exceeding 31%
		Beehive ordinary	Ash content exceeding 31% but not exceeding 36%

$$*HU = \text{Useful heat value}$$
$$= 8900 - 138 \,(\text{Ash} + \text{Moisture}) \; \text{kcal/kg}$$
$$= 37\,262.5 - 577.8 \,(\text{Ash} + \text{Moisture}) \; \text{kJ/kg}$$

Notes

1. In the case of coal having moisture less than 2% and VM content less than 19%, the HU shall be the value arrived at as above reduced by 628 kJ/kg (150 kcal/kg) for each 1% reduction in VM content below 15%.

2. Moisture at 40°C (313 K) and 60% *RH* [Sec. 7.4.2 (ii)] shall be used in evaluation of HU.

Another classification of coals and lignites is recommended in IS: 770 which depends on (i) the nature, rank and combustible matter of fuel, (ii) the nature and quantities of the impurities present in the fuel, and (iii) the size of the fuel.

Attempts have been made to correlate the ultimate analysis of a fuel with its calorific value. One of the most commonly used relationships is that given by Dülong.

GCV of coal in kJ/kg of fuel

$$= 33\,950\,C + 144\,200\left[H - \left(\frac{O}{8}\right)\right] + 9400\,S \qquad (7.2)$$

where $\qquad$ C = mass fraction of carbon

$\qquad\qquad$ S = mass fraction of sulphur

$\qquad$ H – (O/8) = mass fraction of net hydrogen

$\qquad\qquad\qquad$ = total hydrogen – 1/8 (oxygen)

The above equation assumes that the calorific value of a fuel is the algebraic sum of heating values of the constituents, which is not entirely correct. Hence, the equation can be taken as a rough estimate only. Calorimetric data are always preferred to empirical equations.

A Calderwood equation[2] is useful in finding the total carbon content of the coal if the proximate analysis and the GCV of it are known.

Mass % carbon = 5.88 + 0.00 512 (B – 40.5 S)

$$\pm\,0.0053\left[80 - 100\left(\frac{VM}{FC}\right)\right]^{1.55} \qquad (7.3)$$

where $\qquad$ B = GCV in Btu/lb

$\qquad\qquad$ S = mass % sulphur

If 100 (VM/FC) > 80, the sign outside the main parentheses is negative and *vice versa*.

Example 7.1 A sample from Godavari colliery has the following proximate and ultimate analyses.

Table 7.2 Analysis of Coal from Godavari Colliery

Air dried coal				As received analysis	
Proximate analysis	mass %	Ultimate analysis	mass %	Ultimate analysis	mass %
Moisture	7.0	Carbon	54.0	Carbon	50.22
Volatile matter	26.0	Hydrogen	3.0	Hydrogen	2.79
Fixed carbon	46.0	Sulphur	0.4	Sulphur	0.37
Ash	21.0	Nitrogen	2.2	Nitrogen	2.05
		Ash	21.0	Ash	19.53
		Oxygen (by diff.)	19.4	Oxygen	18.04
				Moisture	7.00
Total	100.0		100.0		100.00

The gross calorific value (as analysed on dry ash-free basis) = 23 392 kJ/kg at 25°C (298.15 K). Calculate (a) the net hydrogen in the coal, (b) the combined water in the coal, (c) GCV based on the Dülong formula, (d) NCV (actual) of the coal, (e) the carbon content of coal, using Calderwood equation, and (f) the moisture-free and ash-free proximate analyses of coal.

Solution *Basis* 100 kg as received coal

$\qquad$ Oxygen in the coal = 18.04 kg = 0.564 kmol

Equivalent hydrogen (to combine

with oxygen present in the coal) = 2 × 0.564 = 1.128 kmol ≡ 2.255 kg

or $\qquad$ Net hydrogen = 2.79 – $\dfrac{18.04}{8}$ = **0.535 kg or mass %**

Combined water = 1.128 kmol = 20.304 kg
Moisture in coal = 7% or kg
Water produced by burning H_2 = 20.304 − 7.0
= **13.304 kg or mass %**

From Dülong's formula, GCV = 33 950 C + 144 200 $\left[H - \left(\dfrac{O}{8} \right) \right]$ + 9400 S

$$= 33\ 950 \times \left(\frac{50.22}{100} \right) + 144\ 200$$

$$\times \left(\frac{0.535}{100} \right) + 9400 \times \left(\frac{0.37}{100} \right)$$

$$= 17\ 049.7 + 771.5 + 34.8$$

$$= \textbf{17 856 kJ/kg}$$

Total hydrogen in the fuel = 2.79% or kg = 1.395 kmol
Total water vapour in the product gas stream

$$= 1.395 \times 18 + 7 = 32.11\ \text{kg}$$

Total heat of vaporization = $\dfrac{2442.5 \times 32.11}{100}$ = 784.3 kJ/kg fuel

Reported GCV on dry ash-free basis

$$= 23\ 392\ \text{kJ/kg}$$

To convert the GCV to as-received coal basis, correction factor

$$= (1 - \text{Moisture} - \text{Ash}) = 1 - 0.21 - 0.07 = 0.72$$

GCV of as-received coal = 23 392 × 0.72 = 16 842.2 kJ/kg
Thus, Dülong's formula has given about 5.87% higher GCV.

NCV of the fuel = 16 842.2 − 784.3

$$= \textbf{16 057.9 kJ/kg coal on as-received basis}$$

Calderwood Equation

Total carbon = 5.88 + 0.005 12 (B − 40.5 S)

$$\pm\ 0.0053 \left[80 - 100 \left(\frac{VM}{FC} \right) \right]^{1.55}$$

$$100 \left(\frac{VM}{FC} \right) = \frac{100 \times 26}{46} = 56.52;\ \text{i.e.} < 80$$

B = 16 842.2 kJ/kg = 7240.8 Btu/lb
Total carbon = 5.88 + 0.00 512 (7240.8 − 40.5 × 0.37)
+ 0.0053 (80 − 56.52)$^{1.55}$
= 5.88 + 37.00 + 0.71 = **43.59**

Table 7.3 Proximate Analysis of Ash-free and Moisture-free Coal

	kg	mass %
Volatile matter	26	36.11
Fixed carbon	46	63.89
Total	72	100.00

7.4 LIQUID FUELS

All liquid fuels are organic in nature. The ultimate analyses of liquid fuels are reported as indicated in the case of coal. Usually liquid fuels contain negligible water. Mostly carbon, hydrogen, oxygen and sulphur are the constituents of the fuel. The gross calorific value is normally reported with the ultimate analysis.

Table 7.4 reports typical analyses of crude oils of different origins in India. Table 7.5 gives typical characteristics of other liquid fuels marketed in India.

In Chapter 2, it was mentioned that specific gravity of petroleum fractions (expressed in °API) is an important property. Approximate GCV and NCV of the petroleum derivatives are plotted as a function of °API in Fig. 7.1.

Example 7.2 Crude oil is found to contain 87.1% carbon, 12.5% hydrogen and 0.4% sulphur (by mass). Its GCV at 25°C (298.15 K) is measured to be 45 071 kJ/kg oil. Calculate its NCV at 25°C (298.15 K).

Solution *Basis* 1 kg of crude oil

$$\text{Hydrogen burnt} = 0.125 \text{ kg}$$

$$\text{Water formed} = \left(\frac{0.125}{2}\right) \times 18 = 1.125 \text{ kg}$$

Latent heat of water vapour at 25°C (298.15 K)

$$= 1.125 \times 2442.5 = 2747.8 \text{ kJ}$$

$$\text{NCV} = \text{GCV} - \text{latent heat of water vapours}$$

$$= 45\,071 - 2747.8 = \mathbf{42\,323.2 \text{ kJ/kg oil}}$$

All organic liquids (exceptions being carbon tetrachloride, fluorocarbon compounds, etc.) are combustibles. Methanol, ethanol, acetone, etc., can be used as fuels. There is a recent interest in utilizing methanol and ethanol mixed fuels to avoid environmental hazards due to presence of pollutants in flue gases.

7.5 GASEOUS FUELS

Gaseous fuels are ideal from the standpoint of complete combustion. The air to be supplied for complete combustion easily diffuses with the fuel and ensures complete combustion. In comparison to all the three types of fuels, gaseous fuels of petroleum origin offer higher heating values.

Methane, ethane, propane, butanes and other gaseous hydrocarbons can be used as gaseous fuels. Natural gas (and associated gas) essentially consists of methane with small quantities of higher hydrocarbons. Coal gas, sewage (bio -) gas, etc., are also used as fuels which are lean in nature. Liquefied petroleum gas (LPG) contains chiefly propane and butanes. It is a fuel with a high heating value. Dimethyl ether (DME) is also a high heating value fuel for auto vehicles, power generators, boilers, etc.

In addition, various industrial waste gases can also be used as fuels. The major sources of industrial waste gases are from the iron and steel industry, power plants, fertilizer industry, petroleum refinery, and non-ferrous industry. The waste gases of the iron and steel industry are the coke-oven gas and the blast furnace

Table 7.4 Typical Characteristic Data of Some Indian Crude Oils

| Property | Crude from | | | | | | |
	Bassein Ankaleshwar	Bombay High	Cauvery High	Basin	Gandhar	Heera
API gravity	46.9	38.4	39.4	46.4	46.9	36.3
Specific gravity at 15.55°C (288.7 K)	0.793	0.833	0.828	0.795	0.793	0.842
Asphaltenes, mass %	ND	0.14	0.28	0.16	0.06	0.26
Characteristic factor, KUOP	ND	11.85	11.7	11.6	12.15	11.98
Pour point, °C (K)	15+ (288+)	33+ (306+)	30+ (303+)	27+ (303+)	27+ (300+)	33+ (306+)
Reid vapour pressure at 37.8°C (310.95 K), kPa	46.1	22.6	33.3	26.5	40.2	18.6
Salt Content, g/m^3	8.6	42.8	31.4	< 2.8	22.8	17.1
Sulphur, mass %	0.05	0.15	0.17	0.06	0.041	0.24
Kinematic viscosity, mm^2/s	1.90 at 37.8°C (310.95 K)	4.25 at 37.8°C (310.95 K)	3.28 at 40°C (313.15 K)	1.14 at 40°C (313.15 K)	2.21 at 40°C (313.15 K)	5.24 at 37.8°C (310.95 K)
Wax content, mass %	4.0	11.5	10.6	10.6	8.9	14.6

(*Contd.*)

Table 7.4 (Contd.)

Property	Crude from					
	Lakwa	Moran	Nahorkatiya	Narianam	North Gujarat Mix	Ratna
API gravity	26.5	34.9	31.3	47.1	26.8	35.2
Specific gravity at 15.55°C (288.7 K)	0.896	0.850	0.869	0.792	0.893	0.849
Asphaltenes, mass %	ND	ND	ND	0.12	0.45	0.53
Characteristic factor, KUOP	ND	11.35	11.4	11.90	12.0	12.0
Pour point, °C (K)	27+ (300+)	30+ (303+)	30+ (303+)	0+ (273+)	21+ (294+)	36+ (309+)
Reid vapour pressure at 37.8°C (310.95 K), kPa	12.7	50.0	35.3	53.9	4.3	14.7
Salt Content g/m³	ND	ND	ND	82.7	74.2	496.4
Sulphur, Mass %	0.26	0.25	0.25	0.085	0.17	0.26
Kinematic viscosity, mm²/s	8.82 at 37.8°C (310.95 K)	4.2 at 37.8°C (310.95 K)	4.88 at 37.8°C (310.95 K)	1.50 at 40°C (310.95 K)	63.44 at 37.8°C (310.95 K)	9.52 at 37.8°C (310.95 K)
Wax content, mass %	8.5	13.47	10.1	2.8	6.8	20.0

(*Source: Indian Institute of Petroleum, Dehradun, Uttarakhand.*)

Table 7.5 Characteristic Data of Liquid Fuels

Characteristic	Diesel Fuel (IS:1460–1974) - as amended up to Oct. 1985		Motor gasolene (IS:2769 1971) IInd Revision		Fuel oils (IS:1593–1983) IInd Revision	
	HSD	LDO	87 Octane	93 Octane	Grade MV2	Grade HV
Flash point (min.), °C (K)	32 (305)	66 (339)	ND	ND	66 (339)	66 (339)
Pour point (max.) °C (K)	6 (279)	12 (285)- winter 18 (291)- summer	ND	ND	—	—
Kinematic viscosity, mm²/s	2.0-7.5 at 38°C (311 K)	2.5–15.7 at 38°C (311 K)	ND	ND	180 at 50°C (323 K)	370 at 50°C (323 K)
API gravity (typical)	40.7 – 42.8	35-37	63.9	57.9	19	19
Special gravity at 15.55°C (288.7 K)	0.822 – 0.812	0.85 - 0.84	0.724	0.747	0.94	0.94
Distillation	90% (min.) recovery at 306°C 215°C (488 K)	—	FBP (max.) = 215°C (488 K)	FBP (max.) = (639 K)	ND	ND
Reid vapour pressure, at 37.8°C (310.95 K), (max.), kPa	ND	ND	68.6	68.6	Negligible	Negligible

(Contd.)

Table 7.5 (Contd.)

Characteristic	Diesel Fuel (IS:1460–1974) - as amended up to Oct. 1985		Motor gasolene (IS:2769 1971) IInd Revision		Fuel oils (IS:1593–1983) IInd Revision	
	HSD	LDO	87 Octane	93 Octane	Grade MV2	Grade HV
Water content (max.), mass %	0.05	0.10	ND	ND	1.0	1.0
Sulphur content, (max) mass % as S	1.0	1.8	0.25	0.40	4.0	4.0
Lead (max.), g/L	—	—	0.56	0.80	—	—
Sediments, (max.) mass %	1.0	0.10	ND	ND	0.25	4.0
Estimated C/H ratio (by mass)	6.2 - 6.3	6.35 - 6.5	5.6	5.8	7.0 - 7.5	7.0 - 7.5
Gross calorific value, kJ/kg (normal/typical)	46 050/46470	45550/45680	47270	47020	41 870/44 170	41 870/44 170
Additional requirement					Ash max. 01% (by mass)	

(*Contd.*)

Table 7.5 (Contd.)

| Characteristic | Kerosene (IS:1459 -1974) IInd Revision Amendment No. 2, Nov. 1984 | Low Sulphur Heavy Stock (LSHS) or Heavy Petroleum Stock (Hps) | Aviation Turbine Fuel (Kerosene type) (IS:1571-1982) 4th Revision | Naphtha | |
				Low Aromatic (LAN)	High Aromatic (HAN)
Flash point (min.), °C (K)	35 (308)	93 (366)	38 (311)	15 (298)	15 (298)
Pour point (max.), °C (K)	—	72+ (345+)	ND	—	—
Kinematic Viscosity, mm²/s	ND	500 at 50°C (323 K)	8 at – 20°C (253 K) 100 at 100oC (373 K)	ND	ND
API gravity (typical)	45.4	16-20	51-39	76.6-61.8	86-70.6
Specific gravity at 155.55°C (288.7 K)	0.8	0.96-0.93	0.775-0.930	0.68-0.732	0.65-0.7
Distillation	FBP (max.) = 300°C (573 K)	ND	FBP (max.) = 288°C (561 K)	FBP (max.) = 180°C (453 K)	FBP (max.) = 180°C (453 K)
Reid vapour pressure, at 37.8°C (310.95 K), (max.), kPa	ND	Negligible	ND	68.7	68.7
Water content (max.), mass %	ND	1.0	Nil	—	—
Sulphur content (max.), mass % as S	0.25	1.0	0.2	0.25	0.25
Lead (max.), g/L	—	—	—	0.002	0.002

(Contd.)

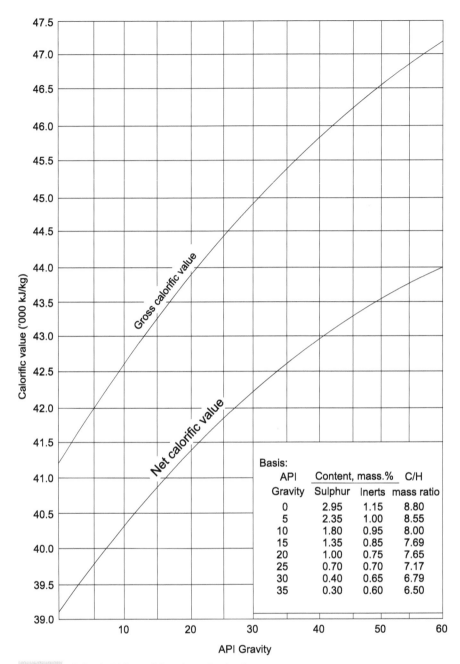

Fig. 7.1   Calorific Values of Petroleum Derivatives

gas. Of late, addition to the list of recoverable byproduct waste gases in the steel industry is the gas produced during the steel production. Waste gases are also collected from other installations, such as carbide furnaces, phosphorous smelting furnaces, aluminium reduction furnaces, off gases in carbon black plant, etc. Hydrogen, carbon monoxide, nitrogen, carbon dioxide, methane, ethylene and other hydrocarbons are the main constituents of industrial waste gases. Purge (tail) gas streams in chemical process industry are normally utilised as fuel in industry. Constituents, such as hydrogen and carbon monoxide have economical significance as base materials for chemical processes. Therefore, the use of these gases as fuel cannot be fully justified considering the potential for their utilization (refer Example 4.18 and Example 4.38). Cryogenics, pressure swing or vacuum swing adsorption, membrane diffusion and other methods are developed for the economic recovery of a constituent (such as hydrogen) from a gas mixture. Tail gas stream from such a separation plant is used as a fuel.

Table 7.6 lists the gaseous fuels of industrial importance.

Table 7.6 Properties of Gaseous Fuels[3] of Indistrial Importance

Fuel	Source	Average composition (by volume)	GCV, kJ/Sm^3	Remarks
Blast furnace gas	Byproduct of iron making	58% N_2, 27% CO, 12% CO_2 2% H_2 and CH_4	3350-3770	Good fuel when clean. Used mainly at source.
Butane	Byproduct of iron making	C_4H_{10} (usually has some butylene: C_4H_8 and propane: C_3H_8)	119 330-79 550	Liquefies under slight pressure, sold as liquid (cylinder gas).
Casing-head gas	Oil wells	Varies, mostly butane, propane	44 800-75 360	Used mostly in oil fields.
Carburetted water gas enriched with oil vapour	Manufactured from coal,	34% H_2, 32% CO, 16% CH_4, 7% N_2, 5% C_2H_4, 4% CO_2, 2% C_6H_6	18 630-22 360	Good fuel but usually costly, part of most city gas.
Coke oven gas	Byproduct from coke-ovens	48% H_2, 32% CH_4, 8% N_2, 6% CO, 3% C_2H_4, 2% CO_2 and 1 % O_2	18 630-22 360	Good fuel when clean, often used at source.
Liquefied petroleum gas (LPG)	Refineries and NG processing plants	26% C_3H_8, 24% i-butane, 50% n-butane	105 000-115 000	Good domestic fuel. Also used in gas engines for power generation. Costly.
Natural gas or associated gas	Gas wells	Varies, mostly CH_4, C_2H_6, C_3H_8	35 380-42 910	Ideal fuel, piped to point of use.
Offgas	Carbon black plant	15% H_2,18% CO, 0.5% CH_4, 4% CO_2, 0.5% C_2H_2 and 62% N_2	4200-4500	Good fuel, requires cleaning.
Oil gas	Manufactured from petroleum	54% H_2,27% CH_4,10% CO, 3% N_2, 3% CO_2, 3% C_2H_4	18 630-20 528	Good fuel, often mixed with coke-oven gas.
Producer gas	Manufactured from coal, coke, wood, etc.	51% N_2, 25% CO, 16% H_2, 6% CO_2, 2% CH_4	5020-6180	Requires cleaning.
Propane	Byproduct of gasoline	C_3H_8	93 160	Similar to butane.
Refinery gas	Byproduct of petroleum processing	Varies; mostly butane and propane	44 800-75 360	Used mainly at refineries, sold as liquefied fuel also (cylinder gas).

(Contd.)

Table 7.6 (Contd.)

Fuel	Source	Average composition (by volume)	GCV, kJ/Sm³	Remarks
Sewage gas	Sewage disposal plants	65% CH_4, 30% CO_2, 2% H_2, 3% N_2, traces of O_2, CO and H_2S	22 400-26 170	Good fuel.
Gas from Fermentor	Distillery spent wash	55 to 65% CH_4, 1 to 2% H_2S and rest CO_2	20 680-24 440	Good fuel.

*1 Sm³ means value occupied by and ideal gas at 101.353 kPa a and 15.55°C (288.7 K) or 60 °F.
*Part of table reproduced with the permission of McGraw-Hill Book Company, New York, USA.
Further updated with industrial information.*)

Example 7.3 The GHV of gaseous propane is 2219.17 kJ/mol at 25°C (298.15 K). Calculate its NHV.

Solution *Basis* 1 mol of gaseous propane (formula: C_3H_8)
The combustion reaction is
$$C_3H_8(g) + 5\ O_2(g) = 3\ CO_2(g) + 4\ H_2O(g\ or\ l)$$
Thus, when 1 mole of propane is burnt, 4 moles of water are produced.

Mass of water produced = $4 \times 18.0153 = 72.06$ g

$$\text{NHV of } C_3H_8(g) = 2219.17 - \frac{(72.06 \times 2442.5)}{1000} = \textbf{2043.16 kJ/mol}$$

Note The NHV reported in Appendix V.2 is 2043.11 kJ/mol.

Example 7.4 Calculate the gross and net calorific values of the natural gas at 25°C (298.15 K) which has the following molar composition:
CH_4: 89.4%, C_2H_6: 5.0%, C_3H_8: 1.9%, iso-C_4H_{10}: 0.4%, n-C_4H_{10}: 0.6%, CO_2: 0.7% and N_2: 2.0%

Solution *Basis* 1 mol of natural gas
In a mixture of gases, the heating value of the mixture is made up of the heating values of individual gases present in it.

Table 7.7 Heating Values of Natural Gas

Component	mol n_i	Molar mass M_i	kg $n_i \cdot M_i$	Heating value* kJ/mol		Total heating value kJ	
				GCV	NCV	$n_i \cdot$ GCV	$n_i \cdot$ NCV
CH_4	0.894	16.0425	14.342	890.65	802.62	796.24	717.54
C_2H_6	0.050	30.069	1.503	1560.69	1428.64	78.03	71.43
C_3H_8	0.019	44.0956	0.838	2219.17	2043.11	42.16	38.82
iso-C_4H_{10}	0.004	58.1222	0.232	2868.20	2648.12	11.47	10.59
n-C_4H_{10}	0.006	58.1222	0.349	2877.40	2657.32	17.26	15.94
CO_2	0.007	44.0095	0.308	—	—	—	—
N_2	0.020	28.0134	0.560	—	—	—	—
Total	1.000		18.132			**945.16**	**854.32**

*See Appendix V.2

Alternate calculations for NCV

Combustion reactions are

$$CH_4 + 2 O_2 = CO_2 + 2 H_2O$$
$$C_2H_6 + 3.5 O_2 = 2 CO_2 + 3 H_2O$$
$$C_3H_8 + 5 O_2 = 3 CO_2 + 4 H_2O$$
$$C_4H_{10} + 6.5 O_2 = 4 CO_2 + 5 H_2O$$

Total of water formed = $2 \times 0.894 + 3 \times 0.05 + 4 \times 0.019 + 5$
$$(0.004 + 0.006) = 2.064 \text{ mol} \equiv 37.184 \text{ g}$$

Heat lost due to vaporization of water

$$= \frac{(37.184 \times 2442.5)}{1000} = 90.82 \text{ kJ/mol fuel}$$

$$NCV = 945.16 - 90.82 = 854.34 \text{ kJ/mol}$$

Average molar mass of the natural gas = 18.132

$$GCV = \frac{(945.16 \times 1000)}{18.132} = \mathbf{52\,126.6 \text{ kJ/kg}}$$

$$NCV = \frac{(854.32 \times 1000)}{18.132} = \mathbf{47\,116.7 \text{ kJ/kg}}$$

Specific volume at 101.3 kPa
and 25°C (298.15 K) = 24.465 m³/kmol   (Table 7.8)

$$GCV = \frac{(945.16 \times 1000)}{24.465} = \mathbf{38\,633.1 \text{ kJ/m}^3}$$

$$NCV = \frac{(854.32 \times 1000)}{24.465} = \mathbf{34\,920 \text{ kJ/m}^3}$$

Note In this example, the heating values are expressed in three different units.

7.6 AIR REQUIREMENT AND FLUE GASES

For any combustion reaction, oxygen is a must which will combine with carbon, hydrogen and sulphur. Pure oxygen is an expensive proposition and is ruled out for burning a fuel in normal practice. Air is the cheapest source of oxygen for combustion which contains about 21 mole % oxygen. However, one drawback of air utilization is the presence of nitrogen during combustion which amounts to about 79 mole % of air. Nitrogen reduces the flame temperature considerably and also accounts for high heat loss to the stack.

The *theoretical* or *stoichiometric* amount of air is the minimum air required to burn the fuel completely so that carbon, hydrogen and sulphur are converted to CO_2, H_2O and SO_2, respectively. Consider the following combustion reactions:

Combustion reaction	*Ignition temperature*[2]
$C + O_2 = CO_2$	407°C (680 K)
$H_2 + \dfrac{1}{2} O_2 = H_2O$	582°C (855 K)
$S + O_2 = SO_2$	243°C (516 K)

This shows that each atom of carbon and sulphur requires one mole of oxygen (each) for complete combustion. One mole of hydrogen requires half a mole of oxygen. From the first two reactions, it follows that methane requires two moles of oxygen for complete combustion. Similarly, it is easy to calculate the theoretical oxygen demand of a fuel.

$$\text{Theoretical air demand in moles} = \frac{\text{Theoretical oxygen demand in moles}}{0.21} \quad (7.4)$$

In actual practice, theoretical air is usually not sufficient to achieve complete combustion. Two obvious phenomena of incomplete or partial combustion are carbon monoxide formation and carbon appearance in the flue gases. *Excess air* supply (or, in other words, excess oxygen supply) is a must for complete combustion. It is defined as follows:

$$\% \text{ Excess air} = \frac{(\text{actural air supply} - \text{theoretical air demand}) \times 100}{\text{theoretical air demand}} \quad (7.5)$$

The actual percentage excess air depends on the fuel used for combustion. Normally, gaseous fuels require very less excess air. Liquid and solid fuels require somewhat more excess air than gaseous fuels depending on their combustion. Current designs of combustion equipment permit gaseous fuels to be burnt with 5 to 15% excess air while liquid and solid fuels require 10 to 50% excess air.

The effect of excess air is to reduce the flame temperature and to increase the heat losses through the flue gases.

Air is usually supplied at ambient conditions. Some moisture (depending on the humidity of air) enters the combustion chamber with the air.

The theoretical as well as actual air requirements are normally expressed in either kg/kg fuel or m^3/kg fuel units, depending on the convenience. For converting moles of air into mass, the average molar mass of air can be taken as 29. For converting moles of air into volume units, the ideal gas law can be used. For ready reference, Table 7.8 gives the specific volume of air at different ambient conditions. Normally, 101.353 kPa a (760.21 Torr or 14.7 lbf/in^2) and 15.55° C (288.7 K) or 60°F are considered standard conditions (STP) in natural gas processing industry. In India, NTP [101.325 kPa a (760 Torr)] and 0°C (273.15 K)] conditions are common for specifying air requirements.

Flue gases are the product gases which are produced by burning a fuel. Normally, flue gases contain CO_2, CO, H_2O, O_2, SO_2, (SO_3) and N_2. SO_3 is usually in very low concentration in the flue gases.

The flue gases are analyzed with the help of an instrument called the *Orsat analyzer*. Since the water of the flue gases interferes with the analysis, it is removed by sampling the gas through a strong sulphuric acid container. The dry gases are collected in a measuring tube. CO_2 and SO_2 are absorbed in aqueous K_2CO_3 solution from the gas. The reduction in the volume of the sample gas gives the volume % (or mole %) of (CO_2 + SO_2), expressed as CO_2. Pyrogalol is used for O_2 measurement while the aqueous solution of Cu_2Cl_2 is used for CO determination. By subtracting the sum of moles of CO_2, O_2 and CO from 100, the mole % of N_2 can be calculated (dry basis). Thus, with an Orsat apparatus, the molar analysis of dry flue gases can be obtained. Excess air can be conveniently read from a nomograph (Fig. 7.2) if the dry flue gas analysis is known. The Orsat

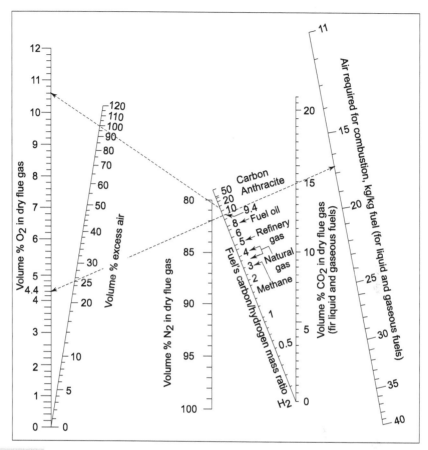

Fig. 7.2 Combustion Air Requirements for Fuels[4]
(*Reproduced with permission of McGraw-Hill, Inc., USA*)

test is a manually performed test and has a number of disadvantages. It is slow, involves tedious labour and has relatively poor accuracy. A Fyrite apparatus is available for quick manual determination of CO_2 and O_2 in dry flue gas which also works on chemical absorption principle. Both these instruments have a serious disadvantage that there is no mechanism to provide an output signal for a recorder or control system.

For measurement of oxygen in flue gas on a continuous basis there are three common methods, the paramagnetic sensor, the wet electrochemical cell and the zirconium oxide ceramic cell. Out of the three methods, the zirconium oxide cell is the most preferred oxygen sensor for continuous monitoring of oxygen in hot dirty gases without sample conditioning. While the Orsat apparatus and Fyrite apparatus give flue gas analysis on a dry basis, the zirconium oxide cell gives oxygen content on a wet basis. In addition to continuous oxygen monitoring across the stack, CO, SO_2 and NO_x analyzers are also available. While CO analysis provides useful data on leftover combustibles in the flue gas, monitoring of SO_2 and NO_x has assumed importance due to their pollution effects in the environment. For continuous monitoring of O_2 and CO, the reader is advised to refer Ref. 5.

The water vapour, present in the superheated form in flue gases, comes from the following three sources:
(i) The water vapour produced by the combustible hydrogen present in the fuel.
(ii) The moisture of the fuel gets evaporated during combustion. Solid fuels have usually considerable moisture but liquid and gaseous fuels contain negligible moisture.
(iii) The water vapour accompanying the air enters the combustion chamber.

The water vapour present in the flue gases reduces the availability of heat from the flue gases. This was discussed in detail in Sec. 7.2 while discussing the concept of NCV.

One of the important determinations in combustion calculations is the (water) *dew point* (*DP*) of the flue gases. The greater the water vapour present in the flue gases, the higher is the dew point. Usually in a boiler house, the excess heat of flue gases from a steam generator is recovered in an economizer (where the incoming water is preheated) or in an air preheater (where the incoming air is preheated). In either case, if the temperature of the incoming water/air is less than *DP* of the flue gases, condensation of water vapour may take place. In these droplets of water, CO_2 and SO_2 are dissolved (forming H_2CO_3 and H_2SO_3, respectively). These acids are corrosive and effect the tubes.Therefore, it is necessary to introduce water/air into the economizer/air preheater at a temperature higher than the *DP* of flue gases and hence the importance of *DP* evaluation.

For calculating the *DP*, the method outlined in Chapter 6 is recommended. First, calculate the partial pressure of the water vapour in flue gases and then obtain the *DP* from a table on the vapour pressure of water (Table 6.13).

The above dew point (*DP*), should not be confused with (*sulphuric*) *acid dew point*. The latter requires special attention when an oil containing sulphur compounds is burnt. Most of the sulphur compounds in the oil are oxidized in the combustion to form SO_2. The conversion of SO_2 to SO_3 depends on the sulphur content of the fuel and flame temperature. This conversion is not very dependent on excess air. Research in combustion engineering has demonstrated that a very small amount of SO_2 is converted to SO_3 in the furnace, slightly more across the high temperature superheater. Most of the SO_3 is catalytically generated in the lower temperature superheater zone of the boiler, where gas temperature is in the range of 602 to 752°C (875 K to 1025 K). This happens to be the ideal temperature for vanadium oxides in oil–ash deposits and iron oxides on metal surfaces to act as catalysts in the presence of sufficient oxygen for conversion of SO_2 to SO_3. Although SO_3 exists at temperatures above the acid dew point, H_2SO_4 is formed by condensation at the cold end of the boiler as the gases encounter cooler metal temperatures. Dry SO_3 is non-corrosive but condensed acid is highly corrosive. Condensation of sulphuric acid creates extensive corrosion in the heater, economizer, gas ducts, induced draft fan and metal chimney. Therefore, while designing an oil-fired boiler, particularly one with high sulphur content, such as furnace oil (IS: 1593), care should be taken to avoid the acid dew point. Figure 7.3 can be used for prediction of the acid dew point of the flue gas. The graph is based on (a) carbon fraction and sulphur content of the fuel, (b) excess air, and (c) chemical equilibrium of the two sulphur oxides. For the assumptions underlying in preparation of the graph, the reader is requested to refer Ref. 6.

Table 7.8 Specific Volume of Ideal Gas at Various Temperatures and Pressures

Specific volume, m^3/kmol

Absolute pressure, kPa (Torr)	Temperature, K (°C)											
	273 (0)	278 (5)	283 (10)	288 (15)	288.7 (15.55)	293 (20)	298 (25)	303 (30)	308 (35)	313 (40)	318 (45)	323 (50)
98.7 (740)	23.020	23.441	23.867	24.284	24.330	24.705	25.127	25.548	25.969	26.391	26.812	27.234
99.3 (745)	22.865	23.284	23.702	24.121	24.167	24.539	24.958	25.377	25.795	26.214	26.632	27.051
100.0 (750)	22.711	23.129	23.595	23.960	24.006	24.376	24.792	25.207	25.623	26.039	26.455	26.870
100.7 (755)	22.562	22.975	23.388	23.801	23.847	24.214	24.627	25.040	25.453	25.866	26.279	26.692
101.3 (760)	22.414	22.824	23.235	23.645	23.690	24.055	24.465	24.876	25.286	25.696	26.1 07	26.517
102.0 (765)	22.268	22.675	23.086	23.490	23.535	23.898	24.306	24.713	25.121	25.528	25.936	26.343
102.7 (770)	22.123	22.528	22.933	23.338	23.382	23.743	24.148	24.553	24.958	25.363	25.768	26.173

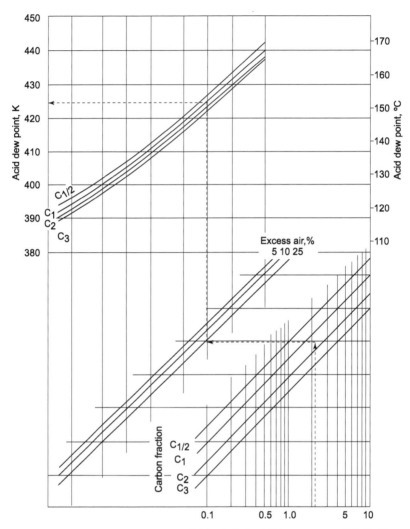

Fig. 7.3 Prediction of Acid Dew Point of Flue Gas[6]
(Reproduced with the permission of Gulf Publishing Co., USA).

Empirical equations are available for predicting acid dew points due to condensation of sulphurous acid (H_2SO_3), sulphuric acid (H_2SO_4), hydrochloric acid (HCl), etc. Reader is advised to refer Ref. 7 for these equations.

Air emission regulations globally have added to design challenges. Low initial investment and low operating costs are no longer the only criteria to select a combustion equipment. Design of such equipment is also required to limit the emissions of CO, NO_x, SO_x and particulates. Of these objectionable pollutants, NO_x has drawn significant attention. NO_x generation is a function of temperature, oxygen and residence time of gases in high–temperature zones. Reduction of flue–gas temperature from 1480°C to 1260°C (1753 K to 1533 K) is claimed to reduce NO_x generation by a factor of 10. Excess air level of 15 to 20% results in lower CO emissions without excess NO_x generation.

A new innovative approach to combustion of gaseous fuels is introduced. Flue gases, leaving the furnace after air preheating section, are partially recycled and mixed with the gaseous fuel being fired. Flue–gas circulation in the range of 30 – 35% has been found to limit the NO_x emission below 10 ppm (v/v). Such a recirculation calls for total review of design of fire-side hardware. Flue–gas recirculation is found to be less effective with oil-firing.

Exercise 7.24 gives a case study of flue–gas recirculation and its effect on flame temperature.

Selection of fuel also plays an important role in emissions. Ethanol mixed gasoline (petrol), DME, methanol, hydrogen, etc., are gaining prominence in light of lower emissions. Catalytic converters (usually having monolith structure) are developed for auto vehicles to reduce pollutants' emissions.

Example 7.5 The coal specified in Example 7.1 is burnt with 100% excess air. Calculate (a) The theoretical oxygen requirement per unit mass of coal, (b) the theoretical dry air requirement per unit mass of coal, and (c) the wet and Orsat analyses of flue gases when the coal is burnt with 100% excess dry air.

Solution *Basis* 100 kg of coal as-received

Table 7.9 Oxygen Requirement of Coal

Constituent	mass kg	kmol	O_2 requirement for complete combustion kmol
Carbon	50.22	4.185	+ 4.185
Hydrogen	2.79	1.395	+ 0.698
Sulphur	0.37	0.012	+ 0.012
Oxygen	18.04	0.564	− 0.564
Total	71.42	6.156	4.331

Stoichiometric O_2 requirement = 4.331 kmol = 138.6 kg

Theoretical O_2 requirement to fuel ratio = $\dfrac{138.6}{100}$

$$= \textbf{1.386 kg } \mathbf{O_2}\textbf{/kg coal}$$

The above O_2 is fed in the form of air. Therefore, N_2 also enters with O_2.

$$N_2 \text{ entering with } O_2 = \left(\frac{79}{21}\right) \times 4.331 = 16.293 \text{ kmol}$$

Total theoretical dry air requirement

for complete combustion = 4.331 × 32 + 16.293 × 28

= 138.6 + 456.2 = 594.8 kg

Average molar mass value of 29 for air yields theoretical dry air requirement of 598.1 kg.

Ratio, $\dfrac{\text{Theoretical air requirement}}{\text{Fuel}} = \dfrac{594.8}{100} = \mathbf{5.948 \; kg/kg \; coal}$

Actual air supply = $5.948 \times 2 = 11.896$ kg/kg coal

Actual O_2 supply = $4.331 \times 2 = 8.662$ kmol

N_2 accompanying $O_2 = \left(\dfrac{79}{21}\right) \times 8.662 = 32.586$ kmol

or $\qquad\qquad\qquad = 2 \times 16.293 = 32.586$ kmol

N_2 in the coal $= \dfrac{2.05}{28} = 0.073$ kmol

Total N_2 in the flue gas = $32.586 + 0.073 = 32.659$ kmol

Total moisture in the flue gas = $1.395 + \left(\dfrac{7.00}{18}\right) = 1.784$ kmol

Table 7.10 Composition of Flue Gases

Component	kmol	Wet analysis, mole %	Dry analysis considering SO_2 as CO_2 (Orsat analysis), mole %
CO_2	4.185	9.74	10.19
SO_2	0.012	0.03	—
O_2	4.331	10.08	10.52
N_2	32.659	76.00	79.29
H_2O	1.784	4.15	—
Total	42.971	100.00	100.00

$$\dfrac{C}{H} = \dfrac{50.22}{2.79} = 18 \quad \text{(mass ratio)}$$

For C/H = 18 and excess air = 100%, volume % O_2 and N_2 in dry flue gas can be read from Fig. 7.2 as 10.6% and 80.3%, respectively.

Example 7.6 The ultimate analysis of a residual fuel oil (RFO) sample is given below:

C: 88.4%, H: 9.4% and S: 2.2% (by mass)

It is used as a fuel in a power-generating boiler with 25% excess air. Air is available at 30°C (303 K) DB and 20°C (293 K) WB temperatures. Find (a) the theoretical dry air requirement, (b) the actual dry air supplied, (c) the Orsat composition of flue gases, (d) the concentration of SO_2 in ppm (mass) and in ppm (v/v) in the flue gas, (e) the concentration of SO_2 in mg/m^3 in the gases if the gases are discharged at 250°C (523 K) and 100.7 kPa a (755 Torr), and (f) acid dew point of the flue gas.

Solution *Basis* 100 kg of RFO

Table 7.11   Oxygen Requirement of RFO

Constituent	mass, kg	kmol	O_2 requirement for complete combustion, kmol
Carbon	88.4	7.367	7.367
Hydrogen	9.4	4.700	2.350
Sulphur	2.2	0.069	0.069
Total	100.0	12.136	9.786

Theoretical O_2 requirement = 9.786 kmol

Theoretical N_2 requirement = $\left(\dfrac{79}{21}\right) \times 9.786 = 36.814$ kmol

Total dry air requirement (theoretical) = $9.786 + 36.814 = 46.6$ kmol $\equiv 1351.4$ kg

$$\frac{\text{Theoretical } O_2 \text{ requirement}}{\text{Fuel}} = \frac{1351.4}{100}$$

$$= \textbf{13.51 kg dry air/kg RFO}$$

Actual air supply = $46.6 \times 1.25 = 58.25$ kmol

mass of actual air supply = $58.25 \times 29 = 1689.25$ kg

Ratio, $\dfrac{\text{Actual air supply}}{\text{Fuel}} = \dfrac{1689.25}{100} = \textbf{16.9 kg dry air/kg RFO}$

Table 7.12   Composition of Dry Flue Gases

Constituent	Molar mass	kmol	Mass, kg	Orsat, analysis
CO_2	44	7.367	324.15	13.30
SO_2	64	0.069	4.42	—
O_2	32	2.447	78.30	4.38
N_2	28	46.018	1288.50	82.32
Total		55.901	1695.37	100.00

$$\frac{C}{H} = \frac{88.4}{9.4} = 9.4 \text{ (mass ratio)}$$

From Fig. 7.2, for C/H = 9.4 and excess air = 25%,

Volume % O_2 in dry flue gas = 4.4

Volume % N_2 in dry flue gas = 82.0

Combustion air requirement = 16.75 kg/kg fuel

Humidity of air

at 30°C *DB* and 20°C *WB* = 0.0106 kg/kg dry air (Fig. 6.15)

Moisture entering with air = $0.0106 \times 1689.25 = 17.906$ kg

$$\equiv 0.995 \text{ kmol}$$

Water formed by combustion = 4.7 kmol

Total water vapour present in the flue gases = $4.7 + 0.995$

$$= 5.695 \text{ kmol} \equiv 102.51 \text{ kg}$$

Mole fraction of $SO_2 = \dfrac{0.07}{(55.925 + 5.695)} = 0.001\ 136$

The mole fraction represents kmol of SO_2 per kmol of wet gases. Volumetric relationship follows the same pattern.

ppm by volume/volume $= 0.001\ 136 \times 10^6 = \mathbf{1136}$

$$\text{Concentration by mass of } SO_2 = \frac{4.48 \times 10^6}{(1696.14 + 102.51)}$$
(ppm by mass)

$$= \mathbf{2490.8\ mg/kg\ (wet\ basis)}$$

Volume of wet flue gases at 250°C (523.15 K) and 100.7 kPa a

$$V = \frac{[(55.925 + 5.695) \times 8.314 \times 523.15]}{100.7}$$

$$= 2660.7\ m^3$$

$$\text{Concentration of } SO_2 = \frac{(4.48 \times 10^6)}{2660.7} = \mathbf{1683.8\ mg/m^3}$$

For the given RFO analysis, C/H mole ratio $= \dfrac{7.37}{4.70} = 1.57$

S content $= 2.2$ mass %

From Fig. 7.3 for 25% excess air, acid dew point $= \mathbf{424.4\ K\ (151.4°C)}$

Note SO_2 is considered as a pollutant in the flue gases. Since its concentration is usually low, it is customary to represent the concentration of it in either ppm (mass or v/v) or in mg/m^3. The case with the CO or NO_x content of the flue gases is similar. Since the flue gas temperature (523 K) is above the acid dew point (424.4 K), corrosion problem is not envisaged. Reader may calculate sulphurous acid (H_2SO_3) dew point using formula, given in Exercise 7.28.

Example 7.7 The Orsat analysis of the flue gases from a boiler house chimney gives $CO_2 : 11.4\%$, $O_2 : 4.2\%$ and $H_2 : 84.4\%$ (mole %). Assuming that complete combustion has taken place, (a) calculate the % excess air, and (b) find the C : H ratio in the fuel.

Solution   Basis: 100 kmol dry flue gases

O_2 accounted $= O_2$ in $CO_2 + O_2$ as such $= 11.4 + 4.2 = 15.6$ kmol

For the calculations of the actual supply of O_2, nitrogen is a tie component which provides the clue as it comes from air.

$$O_2 \text{ available from air} = \left(\frac{21}{79}\right) \times 84.4 = 22.435 \text{ kmol}$$

Excess $O_2 = 4.2$ kmol

O_2 unaccounted $= 22.435 - 15.6 = 6.835$ kmol

This O_2 must have been utilized for the burning of hydrogen

Hydrogen burnt $= 2 \times 6.835 = 13.67$ kmol

Theoretical oxygen requirement $= 11.4 + 6.835 = 18.235$ kmol

or $\hspace{3cm} = 22.435 - 4.2 = 18.235$ kmol

$$\% \text{ excess air} = \left(\frac{4.2 \times 100}{18.235} \right) = \textbf{23.03}$$

Mass of hydrogen burnt $= 13.67 \times 2 = 27.34$ kg

Mass of carbon burnt $= 11.4 \times 12 = 136.8.$ kg

Carbon/hydrogen (mass) ratio in the fuel

$$= \frac{136.8}{27.34} = \textbf{5.00}$$

7.7 COMBUSTION CALCULATIONS

In the above sections, fuels were classified/charactrised and the air requirements of various fuels were studied. In industries, the fuels are fired in boilers, producing steam, hot water or hot oil. In various furnaces, the fuels are burnt to provide the heat for the chemical reaction or for the phase change. For example, in a primary reformer of a fertilizer plant, the combustion of fuel provides the heat for endothermic reforming reactions. In foundries, the metal is melted by burning the fuel.

In all the above cases, the firing rate of the fuel is known. There is no direct measurement of the air input. However, the Orsat analysis of the flue gases, leaving the chimney of a furnace, is made available. The analysis of the fuel can be had from the laboratory. Various temperatures can be measured at different points on the combustion side.

The useful heat gain can be calculated by knowing the total steam generated and its conditions. The feed water temperature is an important parameter.

In furnaces, the heat gain can be calculated easily, based on the methods outlined in Chapter 5.

The thermal efficiency of boiler or a furnace is calculated, using the following equation:

$$\text{Thermal efficiency} = \left(\frac{\text{useful heat gain}}{\text{total heat input}} \right) \times 100 \qquad (7.6)$$

Usually, thermal efficiencies (i.e., total heat inputs) are defined on the GCV basis of the fuels. However, in many cases, NCV is specified for thermal efficiency calculations.

The common heat losses of the combustion side are mentioned below.

(i) The heat is lost in the flue gases which leave the chimney at a high temperature. Usually, the flue gases leave at around 200°C (473 K). Boilers, fired with biofuels, such as rice husk, saw dust, etc., can be designed to have lower fuel gas temperature [below 150°C (423 K)] as they have no sulphur.

(ii) The heat is lost in the refuse which remains at the end of combustion. In the refuse, some combustibles are always left over which account for the heat loss. When coal is fired, the refuse is called *cinder* or *ash*. When liquid fuel is burnt, carbon deposition in the furnace can take place. Gaseous fuels normally do not leave any refuse.

(iii) The solid fuels contain considerable moisture. This and the moisture produced by the burning of net hydrogen have to be evaporated. For this, latent heat is expended which accounts for the heat loss. Liquid and gaseous fuels contain very low moisture.

(iv) The blow-down heat loss in steam boilers.

(v) The radiation loss from the surfaces of the furnace or boiler. Usually, this heat loss is difficult to calculate, if not impossible. Empirical equation are available in liberation to predict radiation loss.

Considering the various heat losses mentioned above, one would like to minimize them in order that the available useful heat is maximized.

The heat loss in the refuse and in the moisture of coal can be minimized by selecting the 'better' coal. Very often, the choice may not exist for a buyer in India and hence there is a limited scope in the reduction of these heat losses.

The radiation heat loss can be kept to a minimum by properly lagging the surfaces while the blow-down losses can be reduced by feeding better quality water in the steam boilers. IS:10 392 gives the requirements of feed water and boiler water for low and medium–pressure boilers. Both these measures have assumed considerable importance in the process industry due to the energy crisis.

There are two aspects to the problem of heat loss through the flue gases:

(i) Reduce the temperature of the outlet flue gas to the chimney to maximum 'possible' level by using the economizer and/or air preheater. Although, in many boiler plants/furnaces a possibility exists, it is not always possible to reduce the temperature below a certain limit such as the one dictated by the acid dew point.

(ii) Minimize the use of excess air. This can be controlled by checking the Orsat analysis of the flue gases. High CO_2 content and low O_2 content of the flue gases are desired, but too low excess air may result in CO and carbon formation, which indicate incomplete combustion. Therefore, excess air is supplied to ensure complete combustion.

When a fuel is burnt, based on enthalpy balance, it is possible to calculate the adiabatic reaction temperature which is termed as *adiabatic flame temperature* or simply, *flame temperature* in combustion. This can be calculated based on the methods outlined in Chapter 5. Usually, adiabatic flame temperatures are not obtained in practice due to radiation losses. Hence actual flame temperatures are lower than adiabatic flame temperatures.

The greater the adiabatic flame temperature (AFT), the higher is the rate of heat transfer because of increased temperature differences. For this reason also, excess air should be limited to the bare minimum. However, higher AFT is found responsible for higher NO_x emission. In many furnaces, e.g., where heat treatment is carried out, the flame temperature in the furnace is a controlling variable in the process. In another case, sulphur is not accepted in the fuel due to possible sulphur pick-up by the product in the furnace. Where such controls are necessary, the selection of the fuel is critical.

Steam generating units are tested in accordance with several codes. Among these, Power Test Code (PTC) 4.1 for stationary steam generating units, published by the Americans Society of Mechanical Engineers (ASME) and British Standard BS: 2885 are popular. These codes also give the computational methods of evaluation of the boiler efficiency. In Table 7.13, simplified boiler heat–balance calculations are enumerated.

Table 7.13 Boiler Heat-balance Calculations

Basis 1 kg of fuel

Heat Input

1. H_1 = Gross calorific value, kJ
2. Heat of input fuel

$$H_2 = C_s (T_f - T_0) \text{ kJ} \tag{7.7}$$

where T_f is the temperature of fuel (K), T_0 is the reference temperature (K) and C_s is the heat capacity of fuel, [kJ/ (kg · K)]

3. Heat of input air,

$$H_3 = W_a C_H (T_a - T_0) \text{ kJ} \tag{7.8}$$

where W_a is the input dry air (kg/kg fuel), T_a is the temperature of incoming air (K) and C_H is the humid heat of air, [kJ/(kg dry air · K)]

$$C_H = 1.006 + 1.84 H \text{ and}$$

H is the humidity of air (kg/kg dry air)

Total heat input,

$$H_I = H_1 + H_2 + H_3 \text{ kJ} \tag{7.9}$$

Heat Output

1. *Heat gain in steam generation*
   (a) Economizer;

$$H_4 = W_f (h_{ew} - h_{fw}) \text{ kJ} \tag{7.10}$$

where W_f is the water fed (kg/kg fuel), h_{ew} is the enthalpy of the outlet water from the economizer (kJ/kg) and h_{fw} the enthalpy of the feed water (kJ/kg).

   (b) Boiler (steam generator);

$$H_5 = W_s (H_{bs} - h_{ew}) \text{ kJ} \tag{7.11}$$

where W_s is the steam generated (kg/kg fuel) and H_{bs} is the enthalpy of saturated steam (kJ/kg).

   (c) Superheater;

$$H_6 = W_s (H_{ss} - H_{bs}) \text{ kJ} \tag{7.12}$$

where H_{ss} is the enthalpy of superheated steam (kJ/kg).

2. *Heat lost in flue gases*
   Approximate calculations;

$$H_7 = w_{fg} . C^o_{mpi} (T_{fg} - T_0) \text{ kJ} \tag{7.13a}$$

where w_{fg} is the mass of the dry flue gas (kg/kg), T_{fg} is the temperature of flue gases, entering the chimney (K) and C^o_{mpi} is the humid heat of flue gases [kJ/(kg dry gas · K)]
   Accurate calculations;

$$H_7 = (\Sigma n_i . C^o_{mpi}) (T_{fg} - 298.15) \text{ kJ} \tag{7.13b}$$

where n_i is the number of kmol of the ith component, present in the flue gas mixture per kg of fuel and C^o_{mpi} is the mean heat capacity at T_{fg}, [kJ/(kmol-K)] (Refer Table 7.14 for C^o_{mpm} values).

3. *Heat loss due to evaporation*
   (a) Heat loss due to evaporation of moisture, formed by burning hydrogen of the fuel;

$$H_8 = W_{mf} . \lambda_v \text{ kJ} \tag{7.14}$$

where W_{mf} is the mass of moisture formed by burning hydrogen (kg/kg coal) and λ_v is the latent heat of vaporization of water at the dew point of flue gases (kJ/kg)
   (b) Heat loss due to evaporation of moisture, present in the fuel;

$$H_9 = W_{mfr} . \lambda_v \text{ kJ} \tag{7.15}$$

where W_{mfr} is the mass of moisture (of fuel) evaporated.

(Contd.)

(Contd.)

4. *Loss due to incomplete combustion of carbon as carbon monoxide*

$$H_{10} = \left[\frac{CO}{(CO + CO_2)} \right] C(23\ 560)\ kJ \tag{7.16}$$

where CO is the % by volume of carbon monoxide in dry flue gases, CO_2 is the % by volume of carbon dioxide in dry flue gases and C is the burnt carbon (kg/kg fuel).

5. *Loss due to unconsumed carbon in refuse*

$$H_{11} = W_c\ (32\ 762)\ kJ \tag{7.17}$$

where W_c is the mass of the unburnt carbon in the refuse (kg/kg fuel).

6. *Loss due to blow-down*

$$H_{12} = W_{bl}\ (h_{bw} - H_{fw})\ kJ \tag{7.18}$$

where W_{bl} is the mass of the water blown down (kg/kg fuel) and h_{bw} is the enthalpy of the boiler water (kJ/kg)

$$W_f = W_s + W_{bl} \tag{7.19}$$

7. *Balance unaccounted loss*

$$H_{13} = H_I - \sum_{i=4}^{i=12} H_i \tag{7.20}$$

Notes

(i) The reference temperature T_o can be taken as 25°C (298.15 K) or the ambient air temperature, depending on the convenience.

(ii) λ_v is the latent heat of vaporization of water at the dew point temperature. However, if dew point calculations are to be avoided, it (λ_v) may be taken as 2490 kJ/kg which is a good approximation.

(iii) The unaccounted heat loss (H_{13}) accounts for radiation, grit, emission, etc.

Calculation of heat loss in flue gas involving polynomial heat capacity equation (Ref. Table 5.1) is quite laborious. Also, the humid heat equation (Eq. 6.15) when applied to the flue gas gives gross error at times in the heat loss value. It is, therefore, suggested to use mean heat capacity (C_{mpm}^o) data given in the Table 7.14 for heat–loss calculations in Eq. (7.13b). Refer Sec. 5.12 for discussion on mean heat capacity.

Table 7.14 Mean Heat Capacity Data for Combustion Gases

Tempera-ture K (°C)	Mean heat capacity over 25°C (298.15 K) C_{mpm}^o, kJ/(kmol · K) at 101.325 kPa a (760 Torr)					
	Gas component					
	CO_2	O_2	N_2	CO	H_2O	H_2
350 (77)	39.24	26.35	28.60	28.60	33.17	28.95
400 (127)	39.92	26.60	28.75	28.77	33.46	28.98
425 (152)	40.26	29.72	28.83	28.86	33.61	29.00
450 (177)	40.60	29.84	28.91	28.95	33.75	29.01
475 (202)	40.94	29.96	28.98	29.03	33.90	29.03
500 (227)	41.28	30.09	29.06	29.12	34.04	29.05
525 (252)	41.62	30.21	29.14	29.21	34.19	29.06
550 (277)	41.96	30.33	29.21	29.30	34.34	29.08
575 (302)	42.30	30.45	29.29	29.38	34.48	29.09

(Contd.)

Table 7.14   (Contd.)

Tempera-ture K (°C)	Mean heat capacity over 25°C (298.15 K) C^o_{mpm}, kJ/(kmol · K) at 101.325 kPa a (760 Torr)					
	Gas component					
	CO_2	O_2	N_2	CO	H_2O	H_2
600 (327)	42.64	30.57	29.36	29.47	34.63	29.11
625 (352)	42.98	30.70	29.44	29.56	34.78	29.13
650 (377)	43.32	30.82	29.52	29.65	34.92	29.15
675 (402)	43.66	30.94	29.59	29.73	35.07	29.16
700 (427)	44.00	31.06	29.67	29.82	35.22	29.18
725 (452)	44.34	31.18	29.75	29.91	35.36	29.19
750 (477)	44.68	31.31	29.82	30.00	35.51	29.21
775 (502)	45.02	31.43	29.90	30.08	35.66	29.23
800 (527)	45.36	31.55	29.97	30.17	35.80	29.24

Different methods for performance evaluation of a furnace are compared by Fehr[8]. A designer may be concerned with maximum extraction of heat from a fuel on its way through the installation. On the other hand, an engineer involved in energy audit may be concerned with the best utilization of available heat. For example, the audit engineer normally divides the heat utilization into sub-sections, tries to find faults by sections and points out the steps for correction. Dr. Fehr had defined a number of efficiencies for performance evaluation. He has also stressed the importance of reference temperature, reliable data on calorific values of fuels and measurement of correct operating parameters for evaluation of the performance.

Example 7.8   A boiler in a sugar factory is burnt with bagasse having the following composition[9].

Proximate analysis (mass %)

Moisture	:	52.0%
Volatile matter	:	40.2%
Fixed carbon	:	6.1%
Ash	:	1.7%

Ultimate analysis (mass %)

Carbon	:	23.4
Hydrogen (net)	:	2.8
Sulphur	:	Traces
Nitrogen	:	Traces
Oxygen	:	20.1
Moisture	:	52.0
Ash	:	1.7

The GCV of bagasse is measured to be 10 300 kJ/kg (moist basis, i.e., as-received basis). In a typical run of the boiler, the following test data were collected.

Orsat analysis of flue gases: 15.65% CO_2 on volume basis

Air supply for combustion: 100.0 kPa a (750 Torr), 35°C (308 K) DB and 23°C (296 K) WB.

Water is fed to the economizer at 70°C (343 K).

Flue gases leave the chimney at 160°C (433 K) and 99.3 kPa a (745 Torr).

Steam is produced at 21.5 bar a and 370°C (643 K).

Rate of steam generation = 2.6 kg/kg fuel

Calculate (a) the theoretical air requirement, (b) the actual air supply as % excess air, (c) the dew point of flue gases, (d) the thermal efficiency of the boiler, (e) the heat balance of the boiler, and (f) the adiabatic flame temperature.

Assume that the refuse does not contain any combustibles and complete combustion of bagasse takes place.

Solution *Basis* 100 kg of bagasse fired in the boiler

Table 7.15 Oxygen Requirement of Bagasse

Constituent	kg	kmol	O_2 requirement, kmol
Carbon	23.4	1.95	+ 1.95
Hydrogen	2.8	1.40	+ 0.70
Oxygen	20.1	0.63	– 0.63
Total	46.3	3.98	2.02

Theoretical oxygen requirement = 2.02 kmol = 64.64 kg

N_2 entering with O_2 through air = $\dfrac{79}{21}$ × 2.02 = 7.6 kmol ≡ 212.8 kg

Total theoretical air = 64.64 + 212.80 = 277.44 kg

Theoretical air/fuel ratio = $\dfrac{277.44}{100}$ = **2.77 kg dry air/kg fuel**

CO_2 produced = 1.95 kmol

Dry flue gases contain 15.65% CO_2.

Total dry flue gases = $\dfrac{1.95}{0.1565}$ = 12.46 kmol

Let x kmol be the excess O_2 in the flue gases.

Excess (O_2 + nitrogen) from air = 12.46 – 1.95 = 10.51 kmol

Total O_2 entering the furnace = (2.02 + x) kmol

Total N_2 entering through air = $\dfrac{79}{21}$ (2.02 + x)

$$= (7.6 + 3.76\,x)\ \text{kmol}$$

$$x + 7.6 + 3.76\,x = 10.51$$

$$x = 0.61\ \text{kmol}$$

% Excess air = $\left(\dfrac{0.61}{2.02}\right)$ × 100 = **30.2**

Moisture in flue gases

Moisture produced by the combustion
of net hydrogen of the fuel = 1.4 kmol

Free moisture in bagasse = 52.0 kg = 2.889 kmol

Moisture of air

Absolute humidity of air at 308 K

DB and 296 K *WB* at 101.325 kPa = 12.8 g/kg dry air   (Fig. 6.15)

= 0.0206 kmol/kmol dry air

Molar humidity at 100.0 kPa = 13.0 g/kg dry air

= 0.020 95 kmol/kmol dry air (Ref. Table 6.14)

Moisture entering with air = $\left[\dfrac{(2.02 + 0.61)}{0.21}\right]$ 0.020 95 = 0.262 kmol

Total moisture in the flue gases = 1.4 + 2.889 + 0.262 = 4.551 kmol

Table 7.16 Composition of Flue Gases

Component	Molar mass	kmol	mole % (wet basis)	kg
CO_2	44	1.95	11.47	85.80
O_2	32	0.61	3.59	19.52
N_2	28	9.89	58.17	276.92
H_2O	18	4.551	26.77	81.92
Total		17.001	100.00	464.16

Average molar mass of moist flue gases = $\dfrac{464.16}{17.001}$ = 27.3*

*__Note__ Average molar mass of lean fuels like bagasse, lignite, rice husk, saw dust, etc., is lower than normal average molar mass of the flue gas, i.e., approximately 29.

Partial pressure of water vapour in flue gases = 100 × 0.2677 = 26.77 kPa

Dew point of flue gases = **66.7°C (339.85 K)**   (Ref. Table 6.13)

Absolute humidity of flue gases = $\dfrac{81.92}{(464.16 - 81.92)}$

= 0.2143 kg/kg dry flue gas

For approximate calculations, the average heat capacity (humid heat) equation [Eq. (6.14)] can be used.

C_{Hf} = 1.006 + 1.84 × 0.2143 = 1.4 kJ/(kg dry gas · K)

Latent heat of water at 339.85 K = 2343.6 kJ/kg

Heat balance

For the heat balance calculations, assume T_0 = 298.15 K

Heat lost in flue gases, $H_7 = W_{fg}, C_{Hf}(T_{fg} - T_0)$

= (464.16 − 81.92) × 1.4 (433.15 − 298.15)

= 72 243 kJ

Table 7.17 Mean Heat Capacity Data

Compounds	n_i kmol	C^o_{mpmi}, kJ/(kmol · K) between 298.15 – 433 K (Refer Table 7.14)	$n_i \cdot C^o_{mpmi}$, kJ/K
CO_2	1.95	40.366	78.714
O_2	0.61	29.759	18.153
N_2	9.89	28.854	285.366
H_2O	4.551	33.652	153.150
Total	17.001		535.383

Heat lost in flue gases, $H_7 = 535.383 (433.15 - 298.15) = 72\,276.7$ kJ

For computing the heat loss in the moisture evaporated during combustion, the latent heat value at the dew point (i.e., 2343.6 kJ/kg at 339.85 K) needs to be considered.

Heat loss due to evaporation of free moisture,

present in bagasse, $H_9 = 52 \times 2343.6 = 121\,867$ kJ

Heat loss due to evaporation moisture, produced by burning of

net hydrogen of the fuel, $H_8 = 1.4 \times 18 \times 2343.6 = 59\,059$ kJ

Heat gain

Water enters the economizer at 70°C (343.15 K) (which is above the *DP* of flue gases).

From Appendix IV,

Enthalpy of feed water at 343.15 K, $h_{fw} = 292.97$ kJ/kg

Enthalpy of superheated steam at

21.5 bar a and 643.15 K, $H_{ss} = 3180.15$ kJ/kg

Net heat gained by water

in steam raising $= 3180.15 - 292.97 = 2887.18$ kJ/kg

Total heat gained by water, $H_6 = 2.6 \times 2887.18 \times 100 = 750\,667$ kJ

Heat input

Heat supplied by fuel, $H_1 = 100 \times 10\,300 = 1030\,000$ kJ

Overall thermal efficiency of the

$$\text{boiler (on GCV basis)} = \left(\frac{750\,667}{1030\,000} \right) \times 100 = \mathbf{72.88}$$

Heat input by air

$$C_{Ha} = 1.006 + 1.84 (0.013) = 1.03 \text{ kJ/(kg dry air} \cdot \text{K)}$$

Heat input by air, $H_3 = (9.89 \times 28 + 2.63 \times 32) \times 1.03 \times (308.15 - 298.15)$

$= 3719$ kJ

In Table 7.18, the sensible heat of bagasse is neglected.

Table 7.18   Heat Balance of Bagasse Fired Boiler

	Heat in kJ	%
Input		
Burning of fuel	1030 000	99.64
Air	3 719	0.36
Total	1033 719	100.00
Output		
Steam raising	750 667	72.62
Heat lost in flue gases	72 277	6.99
Heat loss due to evaporation:		
(i) Free moisture of fuel	121 867	11.79
(ii) Moisture produced by burning net	59 059	5.71
hydrogen of fuel		
Unaccounted heat loss by difference (due	29 849	2.89
to radiation, blow-down, etc.)		
Total	1033 719	100.00

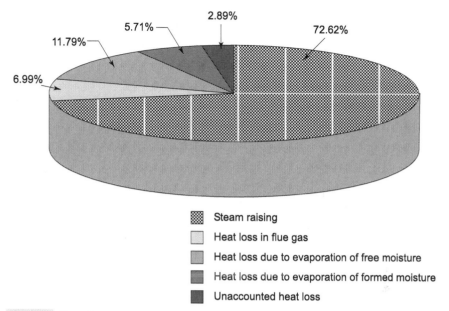

        ☷ Steam raising
        ▫ Heat loss in flue gas
        ▨ Heat loss due to evaporation of free moisture
        ▦ Heat loss due to evaporation of formed moisture
        ◼ Unaccounted heat loss

Fig. 7.4   Heat Flow Diagram of a Boiler Fired with Bagasse

Figure 7.4 gives the split-up of the heat supply. It is known as a *heat-flow diagram*.

The boiler capacity is usually rated **from and at (F&A)** 100°C (373.15 K) and 101.325 kPa.

At these conditions, water needs to be supplied with the latent heat of vaporization (2256.9 kJ/kg) only to generate saturated steam.

Equivalent boiler capacity

$$\text{from and at (F\&A) } 100°C \text{ (373.15 K)} = \frac{750\,667}{(2256.9 \times 100)} = 3.326 \text{ kg/kg fuel}$$

Boiler rating at F&A 100°C (373.15 K) gets reduced by 21.85% for actual steam generation at 21.5 bar a and 370°C (643 K).

Now in combustion calculations, adiabatic flame temperatures are likely to exceed 1200°C (1473 K) in furnaces. Particularly, when a fuel is fired with air close to stoichiometric requirements, these temperatures are quite high and therefore equations valid in the high–temperature range (> 1500 K) should be utilised. In furnaces fired with bagasse, lignite and other poor quality coals, adiabatic flame temperatures could be around 1227°C (1500 K) or less.

Keeping the above facts in mind, empirical constants of the heat capacity equation for the correct temperature range should be utilised. In Table 5.1 data for CO_2, H_2O, N_2 and O_2 are available for temperature up to 4000 K. SO_2 content of flue gas is normally low and hence the SO_2 content can be combined with the CO_2 content (as is the case with Orsat analysis) and data for CO_2 can be used for the combined concentration.

Actual flame temperatures will be lower than adiabatic flame temperatures and the difference depends on the design of the furnace.

Adiabatic flame temperature (AFT)
For the evaluation of AFT, NCV of the fuel must be considered. This is because moisture is present in the vapour form in the flue gases.

$$\text{NCV of fuel (at 298.15 K)} = 10300 - \left[\frac{(52 + 1.4 \times 18)}{100}\right] \times 2442.5$$

$$= 8414.4 \text{ kJ/kg}$$

Heat input based on NCV, $H_1' = 8414.4 \times 100 = 841\ 440$ kJ

$T_0 = 298.15$ K and $T =$ adiabatic flame temperature

Table 7.19   Heat Capacity Equation Constants for Flue Gas of Bagasse Fired Boiler

Heat capacity equation constants	Component				
	CO_2	O_2	N_2	H_2O	Total
n_i kmol	1.95	0.61	9.89	4.551	17.001
$(n_i \cdot a_i)_1^*$	41.662	15.875	292.751	154.338	504.626
$(n_i \cdot a_i)_2^*$	72.489	11.224	307.759	114.496	505.988
$(n_i \cdot b_i)_1 \times 10^3$	125.354	7.171	− 54.657	− 13.719	64.149
$(n_i \cdot b_i)_2 \times 10^3$	45.312	13.248	31.617	98.853	187.03
$(n_i \cdot c_i)_1 \times 10^6$	− 80.051	− 1.430	137.059	69.166	124.744
$(n_i \cdot c_i)_2 \times 10^6$	− 14.389	− 5.066	− 4.007	− 24.302	− 47.764
$(n_i \cdot d_i)_1 \times 10^9$	19.113	0.342	− 52.173	− 22.103	− 54.821
$(n_i \cdot d_i)_2 \times 10^9$	1.602	0.705	0.023	2.196	4.526

*1 and 2 refer to heat capacity data for temperature ranges 298.15 − 1500 K and 1500 − 4000 K, respectively.

Enthalpy of flue gas up to 1500 K,

$$H_2' = 504.626\ (1500 - 298.15) + 64.149 \times 10^{-3}\ \frac{(1500^2 - 298.15^2)}{2} + 124.744$$

$$\times 10^{-6}\ \frac{(1500^3 - 298.15^3)}{3} - 54.821 \times 10^{-9}\ \frac{(1500^4 - 298.15^4)}{4}$$

$$= 606\ 485 + 69\ 313 + 139\ 235 - 69\ 275 = 745\ 761 \text{ kJ}$$

Enthalpy of flue gas above 1500 K,

$$H_7'' = H_1' - H_2'$$
$$= 841\ 440 - 745\ 761 = 95\ 679 \text{ kJ}$$

Solving by Mathcad,

$$F(T) := \int_{1500}^{T} \left(505.988 + 187.03\,10^{-3}\cdot T - 47.764\,10^{-6}\cdot T^2 + 4.526\,10^{-9}\cdot T^3\right) dT - 95679$$

$T := 1600$

$\text{soln} := \text{root}(F(T), T)$

$\text{soln} = 1636.83$ K

Adiabatic flame temperature, $t/T = \mathbf{1359.68°C}$ **(1636.83 K)**

Example 7.9 A stoker-fired water-tube boiler is fired with coal at the rate of 3.9 t/h[10]. The proximate analysis of the fuel indicates 12.68% ash and 7.91% moisture (by mass). The GCV of the coal is measured to be 26 170 kJ/kg. The boiler produces steam at 30 bar a and 430°C (703 K) at the rate of 29 t/h. The Orsat analysis of the flue gases indicated CO_2: 12.8%, O_2: 6.5% and the rest N_2 (volume basis). The combustibles (essentially carbon) present in cinder as a percentage of the coal supplied were found to be 2.7% (by mass). The feed–water temperature was measured to be 90°C (363 K). Flue gases leave the economizer at 150°C (423 K) and 100.7 kPa a (755 Torr). Air enters the burner at 30°C (303 K) *DB* and 22°C (295 K) *WB* temperatures. Assume that negligible oxygen and sulphur were present in the coal. Evaluate the boiler performance.

Solution *Basis* 100 kmol of dry flue gases

$$N_2 \text{ in the flue gases} = 100 - 12.8 - 6.5 = 80.7 \text{ kmol}$$

$$O_2 \text{ supply from air} = \left(\frac{21}{79}\right) 80.7 = 21.45 \text{ kmol}$$

Oxygen accounted for $= 12.8 + 6.5 = 19.3$ kmol in flue gas

O_2 utilized for hydrogen burning

$$\text{(i.e., unaccounted } O_2) = 21.45 - 19.3 = 2.15 \text{ kmol}$$

$$\text{Hydrogen burnt} = 2.15 \times 2 = 4.3 \text{ kmol}$$

$$\text{Water produced} = 4.3 \text{ kmol}$$

New basis Coal firing rate = 3.9 t/h

$$\text{Carbon retained in the cinder} = \frac{(2.7 \times 3.9 \times 1000)}{100} = 105.3 \text{ kg/h}$$

$$\equiv 8.775 \text{ kmol/h}$$

(FC + VM) in coal $=100 - 12.68 - 7.91 = 79.41\%$

$$\frac{\text{Carbon unburnt}}{\text{(FC + VM } - \text{ unburnt C)}} \text{ratio} = \frac{2.7}{(79.41 - 2.7)} = \frac{2.7}{76.41} = 0.0352$$

$$\text{Carbon in the flue gasses} = 12.8 \text{ kmol} = 153.6 \text{ kg}$$

$$\text{Hydrogen in the flue gases} = 4.3 \times 2 = 8.6 \text{ kg}$$

$$\text{Total burnt combustibles} = 153.6 + 8.6 = 162.2 \text{ kg}$$

Total unburnt for 100 kmol

$$\text{dry flue gas} = 0.0352 \times 162.2$$

$$= 5.71 \text{ kg as C} \equiv 0.48 \text{ kmol}$$

O_2 required to burn the unburnt carbon = 0.48 kmol

$$\text{Excess } O_2 = 6.5 - 0.48 = 6.02 \text{ kmol}$$

Total theoretical O_2 required

$$\text{for complete combustion} = 12.8 + 0.48 + 2.15 = 15.43 \text{ kmol}$$

$$\text{Excess air} = \left(\frac{6.02}{15.43}\right) \times 100 = \mathbf{39.0\%}$$

Free moisture entering with coal = 7.91%

Now for 76.71 kg combustibles of coal, free moisture entering the boiler is 7.91 kg.

For 162.2 kg combustibles of coal, free moisture

appearing in the flue gases $= \left(\dfrac{7.91}{76.71}\right) \times 162.2 = 16.73$ kg $\equiv 0.929$ kmol

Humidity of air at 303 K *DB*

and 295 K *WB* at 101.3 kPa a $= 0.0134$ kg/kg dry air   (Fig. 6.15)

$= 0.0216$ kmol/kmol dry air

Humidity at 100.7 kPa a $= 1.008 \times 0.0134 = 0.0135$ kg/kg dry air

$\equiv 0.0218$ kmol/kmol dry air (Ref. Table 6.14)

Total moisture of air entering

the combustion zone $= 0.0218 \, (21.45 + 80.7) = 2.227$ kmol

Total moisture in flue gases $= 4.30 + 0.929 + 2.227 = 7.456$ kmol

Table 7.20 Composition of Flue Gases

Component	kmol	kg (dry gas)	mole % (wet basis)	Orsat analysis, %
CO_2	12.8	563.2	11.91	12.8
O_2	6.5	208.0	6.05	6.5
N_2	80.7	2259.6	75.10	80.7
H_2O	7.456	—	6.94	—
Total	107.456	3030.8	100.00	100.00

Average molar mass of dry flue gas $= 30.31$

$$\text{Moisture in flue gas} = \frac{7.456 \times 18}{3030.8} = 0.0443 \text{ kg/kg dry gas}$$

Partial pressure of water vapour in the flue gases $= 100.7 \times 0.0694 = 6.99$ kPa

DP of the flue gases $= 39°C \, (312.15$ K$)$

Latent heat of water at 312.15 K $= 2409.3$ kJ/kg

Heat balance

Reference temperature, $T_0 = 25°C \, (298.15)$

Enthalphy of water at 90°C (363.15 K), $h_{fw} = 376.94$ kJ/kg

Enthalpy of steam at 30 bar a and 703.15 K, $h_{ss} = 3299.9$ kJ/kg

Heat gained by water in the boiler (i.e., in the economizer,

boiler and superheater) $= 3299.9 - 376.94 = 2922.96$ kJ/kg

Total hear gained, $\phi_6 = 2922.96 \times 29\,000$

$= 84\,765\,840$ kJ/h $\equiv 23\,546.07$ kW

Equivalent steam generation from and at 100°C (373.15 K)

$$= \frac{84\,765\,840}{(2256.9 \times 1000)} = 37.559 \text{ t/h}$$

Calorific value of carbon

GCV (= NCV) $= 393\,510$ kJ/kmol

For 162.2 kg combustibles of coal, unburnt carbon is 0.48 kmol. For 3900 kg/h coal firing rate.

$$\text{unburnt C} = \left(\frac{0.48}{162.2}\right) \times 3900 \times 0.7671 = 8.853 \text{ kmol}$$

Heat lost in the combustibles, $\phi_{11} = 8.853 \times 393\,510$

$= 3\,483\,744$ kJ/h $\equiv 967.71$ kW

Total free moisture evaporated from coal = $\left(\dfrac{16.73}{162.2}\right) \times 3900 \times 0.7671 = 308.6$ kg/h

Heat loss due to evaporation of free moisture, $\phi_9 = 308.6 \times 2409.3$
$$= 743\ 510 \text{ kJ/h} \equiv 206.53 \text{ kW}$$

Moisture formed due to combustion

of the net hydrogen of the coal = $\left(\dfrac{4.3}{162.2}\right) \times 3900 \times 0.7671 = 79.311$ kmol/h

Heat loss due to evaporation of the moisture due to combustion,
$$\phi_8 = 79.311 \times 18 \times 2409.3$$
$$= 3439\ 512 \text{ kJ/h} \equiv 955.42 \text{ kW}$$

Heat capacity of flue gas, $C_{Hf} = 1.006 + 1.84 \times 0.0443$
$$= 1.0875 \text{ kJ/(kg dry gas} \cdot \text{K)}$$

Heat lost in flue gases $H_7 = 1.0875 \times 100 \times 30.31\ (423.15 - 298.15)$
$$= 412\ 027 \text{ kJ for 100 kmol dry flue gas}$$

Alternate calculations

Table 7.21 Mean Heat Capacity Data

Component	n_i kmol	C^o_{mpmi} between 298 K and 423 K, kJ/(kmol · K)	$n_i \cdot C^o_{mpmi}$ kJ/K
CO_2	12.8	40.23	514.944
O_2	6.5	29.71	193.115
H_2O	80.7	33.59	2710.713
N_2	7.456	28.82	214.882
Total	107.456	—	3633.654

For 100 kmol of dry flue gas, heat
    lost in the flue gases $H'_7 = 3633.654\ (423.15 - 298.15)$
$$= 454\ 207 \text{ kJ for 100 kmol dry flue gas}$$

H_7 and H'_7 differ by 9.29%.

Total heat loss in flue gases
    for 3.9 t/h fuel firing rate, $\phi_7 = 454\ 207 \times (3900/162.2) \times 0.7671$
$$= 8377\ 599 \text{ kJ/h} \equiv 2327.11 \text{ kW}$$

Heat of fuel burning, $\phi_1 = 3.9 \times 1000 \times 26\ 170$
$$= 102\ 063\ 000 \text{ kJ/h} \equiv 28\ 350.83 \text{ kW}$$

Neglect the heat input of air which is at 30°C (303 K).

Table 7.22 Heat Balance of a Coal Fired Water-Tube Boiler

	Heat flow, kW	%
Input		
Fuel firing	28 350.83	100.00
Output		
(a) Steam generation	23 546.07	83.05
(b) Heat loss in flue gases	2327.11	8.21

(Contd.)

Table 7.14 (Contd.)

	Heat flow, kW	%
(c) Heat loss in the combustibles, left in the cinder	967.71	3.41
(d) Heal loss due to evaporation:	206.53	0.73
(i) Of free moisture of coal		
(ii) Of moisture produced by burning of net H_2	955.42	3.37
of coal		
(e) Unaccounted heat loss (by difference)	347.99	1.23
Total	28 350.83	100.00

Overall thermal efficiency of the boiler = 83.05%

Figure 7.5 gives the split-up of the heat losses.

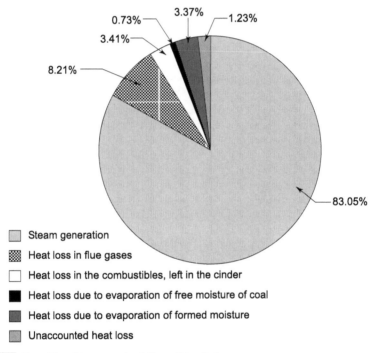

Fig. 7.5 Heat Flow Diagram of a Water Tube Boiler

Example 7.10 Fuel oil having the following ultimate analysis is fired in a boiler: 85% carbon, 9% hydrogen, 3% sulphur, 2% oxygen and 1% nitrogen (by mass). Assume insignificant amount of steam requirement for atomization of fuel oil. GCV of the fuel oil is measured to be 43 540 kJ/kg at 25°C (298.15 K).
(a) Calculate NCV of the fuel.
(b) Calculate the theoretical air requirement in kg/kg fuel oil.
(c) If the above fuel oil is burnt with theoretical oxygen, calculate the adiabatic temperature.

(d) If the above fuel oil is burnt with 30% excess air, calculate the adiabatic flame temperature.

(e) Acid dew point of the flue gas for the case (d).

(f) If the above fuel oil is burnt with inadequate air and if 10% of the carbon burns to CO (and rest to CO_2), calculate the adiabatic flame temperature. Assume that dry air and fuel oil are available at 25°C (298.15 K). Use C°_{mpi} data of Table 5.1.

Solution   *Basis* 100 kg of fuel oil

Table 7.23   Theoretical Air Requirement of Fuel Oil

Constituent	kg	Molar mass	kmol	Theoretical O_2 requirement, kmol
Carbon	85	12	7.083	7.083
Hydrogen	9	2	4.500	2.250
Sulphur	3	32	0.094	0.094
Oxygen	2	32	0.063	– 0.063
Nitrogen	1	28	0.036	—
Total	100		11.776	9.364

Theoretical O_2 requirement for complete combustion = 9.364 kmol

$$N_2 \text{ entering with } O_2 \text{ through air} = \left(\frac{79}{21}\right) \times 9.364 = 35.226 \text{ kmol}$$

$$\text{Total } N_2 \text{ in the flue gases} = 35.226 + 0.036 = 35.262 \text{ kmol}$$
$$\text{Total air} = 9.364 \times 32 + 35.226 \times 28 = 1286 \text{ kg}$$

$$\text{Dry air required (stoichiometric)/fuel oil ratio} = \frac{1286}{100} = \textbf{12.86 kg/kg}$$

$$\text{Water vapour formed} = 4.5 \text{ kmol} = 81 \text{ kg}$$
$$\text{Latent heat loss in water vapour} = 2442.8 \times 81 = 197\,867 \text{ kJ/100 kg fuel}$$
$$NCV = 43\,540 - 1978.67$$
$$= 41\,561.33 \text{ kJ/kg at 298.15 K}$$

Total heat liberated by complete combustion (assuming that formed moisture is in vapour form),

$$H_1 = 100 \times 41\,561.33 = 4156\,133 \text{ kJ}$$

Table 7.24   Composition of Flue Gases without Excess Air

Component	kmol	mole % (wet basis)	Orsat analysis, mole %
CO_2	7.083	15.09	16.91
H_2O	4.500	9.59	—
SO_2	0.094	0.20	—
N_2	35.262	75.12	83.09
Total	46.939	100.00	100.00

Note   It may be noted that maximum CO_2 content of dry flue gas can be 17% (v/v) for fuel oil conforming to IS:1593. Also theoretical air requirement is approximately 13 kg/kg fuel oil.

Use C^o_{mpi} data from Table 5.1.

$T_0 = 298.15$ K   and $T =$ adiabatic flame temperature (AFT)

Table 7.25   Heat Capacity Equation Constants for Flue Gas

Heat capacity equation constant	Component			
	CO_2	N_2	H_2O	Total
n_i, kmol	7.177	35.262	4.500	46.939
$(n_i \cdot a_i)^*_1$	153.338	1043.779	152.609	1349.726
$(n_i \cdot a_i)^*_2$	266.798	1097.29	113.213	1477.301
$(n_i \cdot b_i)_1 \times 10^3$	461.367	− 194.878	− 13.565	252.924
$(n_i \cdot b_i)_2 \times 10^3$	166.773	112.729	95.768	375.270
$(n_i \cdot c_i)_1 \times 10^6$	− 294.627	488.672	63.391	257.436
$(n_i \cdot c_i)_2 \times 10^6$	− 52.958	− 14.288	− 24.03	− 91.276
$(n_i \cdot d_i)_1 \times 10^9$	70.343	− 186.02	− 21.855	− 137.532
$(n_i \cdot d_i)_2 \times 10^9$	5.894	0.081	2.171	8.146

*1 and 2 refer to heat capacity data for temperature ranges 298.15 – 1500 K and 1500 – 4000 K, respectively.

In calculations of heat capacity constants, moles of SO_2 are added in moles of CO_2.

Enthalpy of flue gas up to 1500 K,

$$H'_7 = 1349.726\,(1500 - 298.15) + 252.924 \times 10^{-3}\,\frac{(1500^2 - 298.15^2)}{2}$$

$$+ 257.436 \times 10^{-6}\,\frac{(1500^3 - 298.15^3)}{3} - 137.532 \times 10^{-9}\,\frac{(1500^4 - 298.15^4)}{4}$$

$$= 1622\,168 + 273\,298 + 287\,341 - 173\,792 = 2009\,015 \text{ kJ}$$

Enthalpy of flue gas above 1500 K,

$$H''_7 = H_1 - H'_7$$
$$= 4156\,133 - 2009\,015 = 2147\,118 \text{ kJ}$$

Solving by Mathcad,

$$F(T) := \int_{1500}^{T} \left(1477.301 + 375.2710^{-3} \cdot T - 91.27610^{-6} \cdot T^2 + 8.14610^{-9} \cdot T^3\right) dT - 2147118$$

$$T := 2000$$

$$\text{soln} := \text{root}(F(T), T)$$

$$\text{soln} = 2612.71 \quad K$$

Adiabatic flame temperature, $t/T = 2339.56°C$ (2612.71 K).

Note   Maximum flame temperature can thus be 2339.7°C (2612.7 K) for fuel oil, conforming to IS:1593.

Combustion with 30% excess air

Actual O_2 supply = $9.364 \times 1.30 = 12.173$ kmol

Excess O_2 = $12.173 - 9.364 = 2.809$ kmol

$$N_2 \text{ entering with } O_2 \text{ through air} = \left(\frac{79}{21}\right) \times 12.173 = 45.794 \text{ kmol}$$

Total N_2 in the flue gases $= 45.794 + 0.036 = 45.83$ kmol

Table 7.26 Composition of Flue Gases with 30% Excess Air

Component	kmol	mole % (wet basis)	Orsat analysis, (mole %)
CO_2	7.083	11.74	12.86
H_2O	4.500	7.46	—
O_2	2.809	4.66	5.03
N_2	45.830	75.98	82.11
SO_2	0.094	0.16	—
Total	60.316	100.00	100.00

Table 7.27 Heat Capacity Constants for Flue Gases with 30% Excess Air

Heat capacity equation constant	Component				
	CO_2	O_2	N_2	H_2O	Total
n_i, kmol	7.177	2.809	45.830	4.500	60.316
$(n_i \cdot a_i)_1^*$	153.338	73.105	1356.599	152.609	1735.651
$(n_i \cdot a_i)_2^*$	266.798	51.779	1426.147	113.213	1857.937
$(n_i \cdot b_i)_1 \times 10^3$	461.367	33.024	− 253.283	− 13.565	227.543
$(n_i \cdot b_i)_2 \times 10^3$	166.773	61.004	146.514	95.768	470.059
$(n_i \cdot c_i)_1 \times 10^6$	− 294.627	− 6.586	635.126	68.391	402.304
$(n_i \cdot c_i)_2 \times 10^6$	− 52.958	− 23.328	− 18.570	− 24.03	− 118.886
$(n_i \cdot d_i)_1 \times 10^9$	70.343	− 1.576	− 241.77	− 21.855	− 194.858
$(n_i \cdot d_i)_2 \times 10^9$	5.894	3.247	0.105	2.171	11.417

*1 and 2 refer to heat capacity data for temperature ranges 298.15 – 1500 K and 1500 – 4000 K, respectively.

$$T_0 = 298.15 \text{ K} \quad \text{and} \quad T = \text{AFT}$$

Enthalpy of flue gas up to 1500 K,

$$H_7' = 1735.651 (1500 - 298.15) + 227.543 \times 10^{-3} \frac{(1500^2 - 298.15^2)}{2}$$

$$+ 402.304 \times 10^{-6} \frac{(1500^3 - 298.15^3)}{3} - 194.858 \times 10^{-9} \frac{(1500^4 - 298.15^4)}{4}$$

$$= 2085\,992 + 245\,872 + 449\,038 - 246\,232 = 2534\,670 \text{ kJ}$$

Enthalpy of flue gas above 1500 K,

$$H_7'' = H_1 - H_7'$$
$$= 4156\,133 - 2534\,670 = 1621\,463 \text{ kJ}$$

Solving by Mathcad,

$$F(T) := \int_{1500}^{T} \left(1857.937 + 470.059 10^{-3} \cdot T - 118.886 10^{-6} \cdot T^2 + 11.417 10^{-9} \cdot T^3\right) dT - 1621463$$

$T := 1600$

$\text{soln} := \text{root}(F(T), T)$

$\text{soln} = 2178.66 \qquad K$

Adiabatic flame temperature, $t/T = 1905.51°C/2178.66$ K

For $\dfrac{C}{H} = 1.574$ (mole ratio) and excess air = 30%,

From Fig. 7.3, acid dew point = **156°C (429 K)**

Incomplete combustion

At times, carbon monoxide appears in the flue gas if inadequate air is supplied.

Total carbon burnt = 7.083 kmol

Carbon burnt to CO = 0.708 kmol

Carbon burnt to CO_2 = 6.375 kmol

$$O_2 \text{ for combustion of carbon} = 6.375 + \left(\dfrac{0.708}{2}\right) = 6.729 \text{ kmol}$$

$$O_2 \text{ supplied} = 6.729 + 2.250 + 0.094 - 0.063 = 9.01 \text{ kmol}$$

$$N_2 \text{ entering with } O_2 \text{ through air} = \left(\dfrac{79}{21}\right) \times 9.01 = 33.895 \text{ kmol}$$

$$\text{Total } N_2 \text{ in the flue gases} = 33.895 + 0.036 = 33.931 \text{ kmol}$$

Table 7.28 Composition of Flue Gases with Inadequate Air

Component	kmol	mole % (wet basis)	Orsat analysis (mole %)
CO_2	6.375	13.98	15.74
CO	0.708	1.55	1.72
H_2O	4.500	9.87	—
N_2	33.931	74.40	82.54
SO_2	0.094	0.20	—
Total	45.608	100.00	100.00

Heat of combustion of CO to CO_2 = 282 980 kJ/kmol

Unavailable heat due to CO formation = 282 980 × 0.708 = 200 350 kJ

Actual heat liberated (based on NCV), $H_1' = 4156\ 133 - 200\ 350 = 3955\ 783$ kJ

Table 7.29 Heat Capacity Equation Constants for Flue Gas with Inadequate Air

Heat capacity equation constant	Component				
	CO_2	CO	N_2	H_2O	Total
n_i, kmol	6.469	0.708	33.931	4.500	45.608
$(n_i \cdot a_i)^*_1$	138.212	20.551	1004.381	152.609	1315.753
$(n_i \cdot a_i)^*_2$	270.479	19.411	1055.872	113.213	1458.975
$(n_i \cdot b_i)_1 \times 10^3$	415.854	− 1.995	− 187.522	− 13.565	212.772
$(n_i \cdot b_i)_2 \times 10^3$	150.321	6.102	108.474	95.768	360.665
$(n_i \cdot c_i)_1 \times 10^6$	− 265.563	8.258	470.226	68.391	281.312
$(n_i \cdot c_i)_2 \times 10^6$	− 47.733	− 1.915	− 13.749	− 24.03	− 87.427

(Contd.)

Table 7.29   (Contd.)

Heat capacity equation constant	Component				
	CO_2	CO	N_2	H_2O	Total
$(n_i \cdot d_i)_1 \times 10^9$	63.405	-3.335	-178.999	-21.855	-140.784
$(n_i \cdot d_i)_2 \times 10^9$	5.313	0.215	0.078	2.171	7.777

*1 and 2 refer to heat capacity data for temperature ranges 298.15 – 1500 K and 1500 – 4000 K, respectively.

$$T_0 = 298.15 \text{ K} \quad \text{and} \quad T = \text{AFT}$$

Enthalpy of flue gas up to 1500 K,

$$H_7' = 1315.753\,(1500 - 298.15) + 212.772 \times 10^{-3}\,\frac{(1500^2 - 298.15^2)}{2}$$

$$+ 281.312 \times 10^{-6}\,\frac{(1500^3 - 298.15^3)}{3} - 140.784 \times 10^{-9}\,\frac{(1500^4 - 298.15^4)}{4}$$

$$= 1581\,338 + 229\,911 + 313\,991 - 177\,902 = 1947\,338 \text{ kJ}$$

Enthalpy of flue gas above 1500 K,

$$H_7'' = H_1' - H_7'$$
$$= 3955\,783 - 1947\,338 = 2008\,445 \text{ kJ}$$

Solving by Mathcad,

$$F(T) := \int_{1500}^{T} \left(1458.975 + 360.665 10^{-3} \cdot T - 87.427 10^{-6} \cdot T^2 + 7.777 10^{-9} \cdot T^3\right) dT - 2008445$$

$$T := 1600$$

$$\text{soln} := \text{root}\,(F(T), T)$$

$$\text{soln} = 2561.42 \quad \text{K}$$

Adiabatic flame temperature, t/T = 2288.27°C/2561.42 K

Note   This example is cited to illustrate the influence of excess/inadequate air on (i) the theoretical flame temperature and (ii) the total moles of flue gases. The flame temperature has a strong effect on (i) furnace design, and (ii) furnace performance.

Example 7.11   A water-tube boiler is fired with heavy fuel oil having the ultimate analysis, C: 85.1%, H: 10.9%, S: 1.5%, O: 2.5% (by mass). The ash content and free moisture content of the fuel oil can be assumed to be negligible. Also, assume insignificant quantity of steam requirement for atomization. The test run data of the boiler are given below.

Steam generated at 16 bar a (saturated) = 4365 kg/h
Fuel oil-firing rate = 400 kg/h
GCV of the fuel = 42 260 kJ/kg at 25°C (298.15 K)
Orsat analysis of the flue gases: CO_2: 7.01%, O_2: 11.94% and N_2: 81.05% (volume basis)

Air supply: *DB* 35°C (308 K), *WB* 27.5°C (300.5 K), 100.7 kPa a (755 Torr)
Average temperature of the flue gases = 290°C (563 K)
Pressure at the bottom of the stack = 99.3 kPa a (745 Torr)
Temperature of the water fed to the boiler = 43°C (316 K)
Assume that fuel oil is fired at 80°C (353 K) and the heat capacity of the fuel
oil is 1.758 kJ/(kg·K)
Evaluate the thermal performance of the boiler.

Solution *Basis* 100 kg of fuel oil

Table 7.30 Oxygen Requirement of Fuel Oil

Constituent	mass, kg	kmol	Theoretical O_2 requirement, kmol
Carbon	85.1	7.092	7.092
Hydrogen	10.9	5.450	2.725
Sulphur	1.5	0.047	0.047
Oxygen	2.5	0.078	– 0.078
Total	100.0	12.667	9.786

Material balance of carbon
Moles of CO_2 appearing in the flue
  gases (including the moles of SO_2) = 7.092 + 0.047 = 7.139 kmol
Since the flue gases contain 7.01 mole % CO_2,

$$N_2 \text{ in dry flue gas} = \frac{(7.139 \times 81.05)}{7.01} = 82.541 \text{ kmol}$$

$$O_2 \text{ in dry flue gas} = \frac{(11.94 \times 7.139)}{7.01} = 12.16 \text{ kmol}$$

Total dry flue gas = 7.139 + 82.541 + 12.16 = 101.84 kmol

Material balance of oxygen

$$\text{Moles of } O_2 \text{ from air} = \left(\frac{21}{79}\right) \times 82.541 = 21.941 \text{ kmol}$$

Moles of dry air entering the boiler = 82.541 + 21.941 = 104.482 kmol
Total O_2 entering the burner = 21.941 + 0.078 = 22.019 kmol
Excess O_2 = 22.019 – 9.864 = 12.155 kmol
This excess O_2 tallies with O_2 present in the flue gas.

$$\text{\% Excess air} = \left(\frac{12.155}{9.786}\right) \times 100 = 124.21$$

Per cent excess air indicates poor combustion control.
Material balance of water vapour
Moisture formed due to combustion of (net) hydrogen of the fuel
                = 5.45 kmol
Absolute humidity of at 101.3 kPa a = 0.0204 kg/kg dry air   (Fig. 6.15)
                = 0.0329 kmol/kmol dry air
Corrected humidity at 100.7 kPa a = 0.0205 kg/kg dry air   (Ref. Table 6.14)
                = 0.0331 kmol/kmol dry air

$$\text{Moisture from air} = 0.0331 \times 104.482 = 3.458 \text{ kmol}$$
$$\text{Total moisture is the flue gases} = 5.45 + 3.458 = 8.908 \text{ kmol}$$

Table 7.31 Composition of Flue Gases

Component	kmol	kg (dry gas)	mole % (wet basis)	Orsat analysis, %
CO_2	7.092	312.0	6.40	7.01
SO_2	0.047	3.0	0.04	—
O_2	12.155	389.0	10.98	11.94
N_2	82.541	2311.1	74.53	81.05
H_2O	8.908	—	8.04	—
Total	110.743	3015.1	100.00	100.00

$$\text{Average molar mass of dry flue gas} = \frac{3015.1}{(110.743 - 8.908)} = 29.61$$

Partial pressure at water vapour

in the flue gases, $p_w = 99.3 \times 0.0804 = 7.984$ kPa

Dew point $= 41.4°C$ (314.4 K)   (Ref. Table 6.13)

Heat loss in flue gases

$$\text{Humid heat of flue gas, } C_{Hf} = 1.006 + 1.84 \times \left[\frac{8.908 \times 18.0153}{(110.743 - 8.908)\, 29.61} \right]$$
$$= 1.1039 \text{ kJ/(kg dry gas} \cdot \text{K)}$$

$$\text{Total heat lost in flue gas } H_7 = (110.743 - 8.908) \times 29.61 \times 1.1039$$
$$(563.15 - 298.15) = 882\,086 \text{ kJ}$$

Alternate calculations

Table 7.32 Sensible Heat Calculations of Flue Gases

Component	n_i, kmol	C^o_{mpmi}, kJ/(kmol $\cdot$ K) 298.15 – 563.15 K	$n_i \cdot C^o_{mpmi}$, kJ/K
CO_2	7.092	42.134	298.814
SO_2	0.047	42.628	2.004
O_2	12.155	30.393	369.427
N_2	82.541	29.251	2414.407
H_2O	8.908	34.413	306.551
Total	110.743		3391.203

Total heat lost in flue gases, $H_7' = 3391.203\,(563.15 - 298.15) = 898\,669$ kJ
H_7 and H_7' differ by 1.85%.

However, the fuel firing rate is 400 kg/h.

$$\text{Total heat lost in the flue gases } \phi_7 = 898\,669 \times \left(\frac{400}{100} \right)$$
$$= 3\,594\,676 \text{ kJ/h} \equiv 998.52 \text{ kW}$$

Heat gain in boiler

Inlet temperature of water $= 316$ K

Enthalpy of water $= 179.99$ kJ/kg

Steam pressure $= 16$ bar a

From steam tables (Appendix IV.2), T_s = 474.52 K (201.37°C)

h = 858.56 kJ/kg $\qquad \lambda_v$ = 1933.2 kJ/kg $\qquad H$ = 2791.7 kJ/kg

Total heat supplied in the boiler = 2791.7 − 179.99 = 2611.71 kJ/kg

Total heat utilized for steam generation, ϕ_5 = 2611.71 × 4365

$$= 11\,400\,114 \text{ kJ/h} \equiv 3166.70 \text{ kW}$$

Heat loss due to evaporation of moisture

Latent heat of vaporization of water at 314.15 K = 2403.5 kJ/kg

Heat loss due to evaporation of moisture, ϕ_8 = 5.45 × 18 × $\left(\dfrac{400}{100}\right)$ × 2403.5

$$= 943\,133 \text{ kJ/h} \equiv 261.98 \text{ kW}$$

Heat input by fuel combustion

GCV of the fuel oil = 42 260 kJ/kg

Heat input, ϕ_1 = 400 × 42260

$$= 16904\,000 \text{ kJ/h} \equiv 4695.56 \text{ kW}$$

Heat input by air

Average humid heat of air, C_{Ha} = 1.006 + 1.84 × 0.0205

$$= 1.0437 \text{ kJ/(kg dry air·K)}$$

$$\text{Total dry air rate} = \frac{(104.482 \times 29 \times 400)}{100} = 12\,112 \text{ kg/h}$$

Sensible heat of incoming air, ϕ_3 = 12 112 × 1.0437 (308.15 − 298.15)

$$= 126\,413 \text{ kJ/h} \equiv 35.11 \text{ kW}$$

Sensible heat of fuel oil

Sensible heat input of fuel oil, ϕ_2 = 400 × 1.758 (353.15 − 298.15)

$$= 38\,676 \text{ kJ/h} \equiv 10.74 \text{ kW}$$

Table 7.33 Heat Balance of Boiler

	Heat flow, kW	%
Input		
Heat of combustion	4695.56	99.03
Heat of moist air	35.11	0.74
Heat of fuel oil	10.74	0.23
Total	4741.41	100.00
Output		
Heat utilised for steam generation	3166.70	66.79
Heat lost in flue gases	998.52	21.06
Heat lost due to evaporation of formed moisture	261.98	5.52
Unaccounted heat loss (by difference)	314.21	6.63
Total	4741.41	100.00

Figure 7.6 is the heat flow diagram of the boiler fired with heavy fuel oil. Overall thermal efficiency of the

$$\text{boiler based on GCV of the fuel} = \frac{(3166.70 \times 100)}{4695.56} = \mathbf{67.44\%}$$

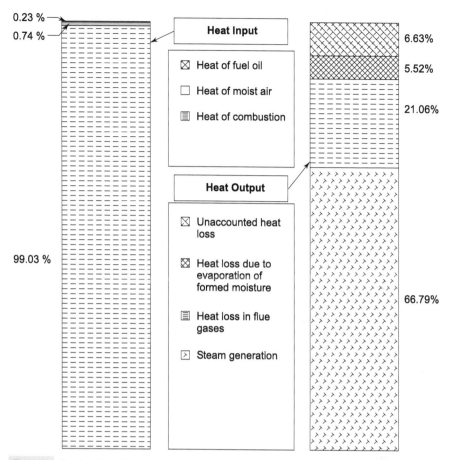

Fig. 7.6 Stacked Bar Diagram for a Boiler Fired with Heavy Fuel Oil

$$\text{NCV of the fuel} = 42260 - \left(\frac{18.0153}{2.016}\right) \times 0.109 \times 2442.8$$

$$= 39880 \text{ kJ/kg}$$

Overall thermal efficiency of the

$$\text{boiler, based on NCV of the fuel} = \frac{(11400114 \times 100)}{(400 \times 39880)} = \mathbf{71.47\%}$$

Both thermal efficiencies indicate poor performance of the boiler on account of very high excess air and relatively high flue gas temperature.

$$\text{Steam to fuel ratio} = \frac{4365}{400} = 10.91 \text{ at 16 bar a}$$

$$\text{Equivalent boiler capacity from and at 373.15 K} = \frac{11400114}{2256.9} = 5051.2 \text{ kg/h}$$

Air flow rate at 100.7 kPa a and at 308.15 K

$$= (104.48 + 3.34) \times \left(\frac{400}{100}\right) \times 25.453$$

$$= 10\ 977.4\ \text{m}^3/\text{h}$$

Volumetric flow rate of flue gases, $q_v = \dfrac{nRT}{p}$

$$= 110.743 \times \left(\frac{400}{100}\right) \times 8.3145 \times \left(\frac{563.15}{99.3}\right)$$

$$= \mathbf{20\ 887.5\ m^3/h}$$

Example 7.12 A coal having the ultimate analysis, C: 67.2%, H: 5.5%, S: 0.4%, O: 6.1% and ash 20.8% (by mass) is used for gassifying. Free moisture in the coal is found to be 2.6% (by mass). The producer gas obtained from the coal has the molar composition N_2: 51.0%, CO: 25% H_2: 16%, CO_2: 6% and CH_4: 2% (on dry basis; SO_2 neglected). The dew point of the producer gas is measured to be 22°C (295 K) at 100.7 kPa a (755 Torr).

Compute (a) Nm^3 of the producer gas obtained per kg coal used, (b) Nm^3 of air supplied per kg coal gassified, and (c) quantity of steam supplied per kg coal used.

Solution Producer gas is made for use in industrial furnaces by passing air plus a small quantity of steam through a thick fuel (coal) bed in which the fuel is burnt partially.

Basis 100 kmol of dry producer gas

Table 7.34 Material Balance of Producer Gas Generator

Component	kmol	Molar mass	kmol C	kmol O_2	kmol H_2
N_2	51	28	—	—	—
CO	25	28	25	12.5	—
H_2	16	2	—	—	16
CO_2	6	44	6	6	—
CH_4	2	16	2	—	4
Total	100		33	18.5	20

$$\text{Mass of carbon} = 33 \times 12 = 396\ \text{kg}$$
$$\text{Mass of oxygen} = 18.5 \times 32 = 592\ \text{kg}$$
$$\text{Mass of hydrogen} = 20 \times 2 = 40\ \text{kg}$$

All the nitrogen comes from air.

$$O_2 \text{ supplied through air} = \left(\frac{21}{79}\right) \times 51 = 13.56\ \text{kmol}$$

Coal contains 67.2% carbon. Assuming that all the carbon appears in the producer gas,

$$\text{Total coal gassified} = \frac{396}{0.672} = 589.3\ \text{kg}$$

O_2 coming from coal = 589.3 × 0.061 = 36 kg ≡ 1.13 kmol

Total O_2 accounted = 13.56 + 1.13 = 14.69 kmol

O_2 from decomposition of water (steam) = 18.5 − 14.69 = 3.81 kmol

H_2 from decomposition of steam = 2 × 3.81 = 7.62 kmol

Mass of H_2 = 7.62 × 2 = 15.24 kg

Moles of steam decomposed = 7.62 kmol

H_2 from fuel = 20.0 − 7.62 = 12.38 kmol

$$\frac{\text{Dry producer gas}}{\text{Coal}} = \frac{100}{589.3} = 0.1697 \text{ kmol/kg coal}$$

$$\equiv \textbf{3.803 Nm}^3\textbf{/kg coal}$$

The vapour pressure of water at 295.15 K,

$$p_w = 2.642 \text{ kPa} \qquad \text{(Refer Table 6.13)}$$

$$\text{Absolute humidity} = \frac{2.642}{(100.7 - 2.642)}$$

$$= 0.027 \text{ kmol/kmol dry gas}$$

Water vapour in the producer gas = 0.027 × 100 = 2.7 kmol

$$\frac{\text{Moist producer gas}}{\text{Coal}} = \frac{102.7}{589.3} = 0.1743 \text{ kmol/kg coal}$$

$$\equiv \textbf{3.906 Nm}^3\textbf{/kg coal}$$

Dry air supplied = 51 + 13.56 = 64.56 kmol

Mass of dry air = 51.0 × 28 + 13.56 × 32 = 1862 kg

$$\frac{\text{Dry air}}{\text{Coal}} = \frac{1862}{589.3} = 3.16 \text{ kg/kg coal}$$

$$\frac{\text{Volume of dry air}}{\text{Coal}} = \left(\frac{3.16}{29}\right) \times 22.414 = \textbf{2.442 Nm}^3\textbf{/kg coal}$$

$$\text{Total steam supplied} = 7.62 + 2.7 - \left(\frac{589.3 \times 0.026}{18}\right)$$

$$= 9.47 \text{ kmol}$$

$$\frac{\text{Steam}}{\text{Coal}} = \frac{(9.47 \times 18)}{589.3} = \textbf{0.289 kg/kg coal}$$

Example 7.13 A gas producer generates the gas having the following molar composition on dry basis:

CO: 25%, H_2: 8%, CO_2: 5% and N_2: 62.0%

Based on the dew point measurements, the gas is found to contain 0.056 kg water vapour per kg dry producer gas. It is available at 800°C (1073 K).

The above gas is used as a fuel in an open–hearth steel furnace at the rate of 27650 kg/h (on dry basis) with air at 35°C (308 K) *DB* and 22°C (295 K) *WB*. The furnace is capable of taking a 75 t charge. On an average, the total heat gained by the charge is calculated to be 9400 kW. The flue gases leave the furnace at 560°C (833 K) and enter the waste heat boiler. The temperature of the outgoing flue gases from the boiler plant is 205°C (478 K). In the waste heat boiler, the steam is generated at 12.5 bar a and 300°C (573 K) at the rate of 7.1 t/h. The Orsat analysis of the flue gases indicate 16.9% CO_2, 2.8% O_2 and 80.3% N_2 (by volume). The inlet and oulet temperatures of water to and from the economizer are 65°C (338 K) and 160°C (433 K), respectively. Flue gases leave the chimney at 100.0 kPa a (750 Torr).

Evaluate the thermal performance of the furnace and the waste heat boiler.

Solution The flow diagram of the above operations is given in Fig. 7.7.
Basis 100 kmol of dry producer gas

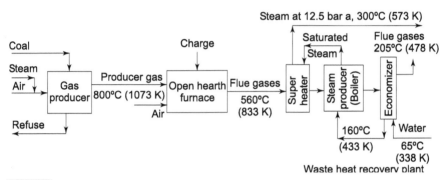

Fig. 7.7 Producer Gas Utilization and Waste Heat Recovery

Table 7.35 Oxygen Requirement of Producer Gas

Constituent	kmol	Molar mass	kg	Theoretical O_2 requirement for complete combustion, kmol
CO	25	28	700	12.5
H_2	8	2	16	4.0
CO_2	5	44	220	—
N_2	62	28	1736	—
Total	100	100	2672	16.5

Water vapour in the producer gas = 2672 × 0.056 = 149.63 kg
$$\equiv 8.31 \text{ kmol}$$
Total wet producer gas = 100 + 8.31 = 108.31 kmol
Total CO_2 produced after combustion = 25 + 5 = 30 kmol
The flue gas contain 16.9% CO_2 by volume.

$$\text{Moles of flue gases} = \frac{30}{0.169} = 177.51 \text{ kmol}$$

Excess O_2 in the flue gases = 177.51 × 0.028 = 4.97 kmol
N_2 in the flue gases = 177.51 × 0.803 = 142.54 kmol
N_2 entering in the form of air = 142.54 − 62 = 80.54 kmol

$$O_2 \text{ supplied through air} = \frac{21 \times 80.54}{79} = 21.41 \text{ kmol}$$

$$\text{Excess } O_2 = 21.41 - 16.5 = 4.91 \text{ kmol}$$

$$\text{Excess air} = \left(\frac{4.91}{16.5}\right) \times 100 = 29.76\%$$

Total dry air entering $= 21.41 \times 32 + 80.64 \times 28 = 2943$ kg

Absolute humidity of ambient air at

$$308 \text{ K } DB \text{ and } 295 \text{ K } WB = 11.4 \text{ g/kg dry air} \qquad (\text{Ref. Fig. 6.15})$$
$$= 0.0184 \text{ kmol/kmol dry air}$$

Moisture of air entering the furnace $= 2943 \times 0.0114 = 33.55$ kg
$$\equiv 1.864 \text{ kmol}$$

Moisture produced by combustion of H_2 = 8 kmol

Total moisture in the flue gases $= 8.31 + 1.864 + 8 = 18.174$ kmol

Heat balance of furnace

Reference temperature: $T_0 = 298.15$ K

Heat input:

$$T_1/t_1 = 1073.15 \text{ K}/800^\circ\text{C}$$

Table 7.36 Composition of Flue Gases

Constituent	kmol	mole % (wet basis)	Orsat analysis, %
CO_2	30.00	15.34	16.91
O_2	4.91	2.51	2.77
N_2	142.54	72.86	80.33
H_2O	18.174	9.29	—
Total	195.624	100.00	100.00

Table 7.37 Heat Capacity Equation Constants for Producer Gas

Component	n_i, kmol	Heat capacity (C_{mpi}^{o}) equation constants			
		$n_i \cdot a_i$	$n_i \cdot b_i \times 10^3$	$n_i \cdot c_i \times 10^6$	$n_i \cdot d_i \times 10^9$
CO	25	725.6925	-70.4125	291.0925	-117.6575
H_2	8	228.884	8.1552	-1.1808	6.152
CO_2	5	106.8275	312.4205	-205.253	48.9995
N_2	62	1834.6358	-318.742	817.3398	-308.016
H_2O	8.31	270.0094	0.6615	109.7809	-37.7889
Total	108.31	3166.0492	-58.9173	1011.7794	-408.3109

$$H_2' = \int_{T_0}^{T} (\Sigma n_i \cdot C_{mpi}^{o}) \, dT$$

$$= 3166.0492 \, (T_1 - T_0) - (58.9173 \times 10^{-3}) \frac{(T_1^2 - T_0^2)}{2}$$

$$+ (1011.7794 \times 10^{-6}) \frac{(T_1^3 - T_0^3)}{3} - (408.3109 \times 10^{-9}) \frac{(T_1^4 - T_0^4)}{4}$$

$$= 2453\,688 - 31\,307 + 407\,878.8 - 134\,579$$

$$= 2695\,680.8 \text{ kJ}$$

For 2672 kg dry producer gas, H'_2 equals 2695 680.8 kJ.
Actual rate of dry producer gas is 27 650 kg/h.

$$\phi_2 = \left(\frac{27\,650}{2672}\right) \times 2695\,680.8$$

$$= 27\,895\,050 \text{ kJ/h} \equiv 7748.63 \text{ kW}$$

Sensible heat of air

Humid heat $C_H = 1.006 + 1.84 \times 0.0114$

$$= 1.027 \text{ kJ/(kg dry air} \cdot \text{K)}$$

$$H_3 = 1.027 \times 2943 \times (308.15 - 298.15) = 30\,225 \text{ kJ}$$

$$\phi_3 = \left(\frac{27\,650}{2672}\right) \times 30\,225$$

$$= 312\,770 \text{ kJ/h} \equiv 86.88 \text{ kW}$$

Heat of combustion

GCV of $H_2 = 285\,830$ kJ/kmol

CV of CO $= 282\,980$ kJ/kmol

Total heat liberated by the combustion of H_2 and CO

$$H'_1 = 25 \times 282\,980 + 8 \times 285\,830 = 9366\,140 \text{ kJ}$$

$$\phi_1 = \left(\frac{27\,650}{2672}\right) \times 9366\,140$$

$$= 96\,921\,321 \text{ kJ/h} = 26\,922.59 \text{ kW}$$

Heat output

Useful heat gain by the charge

in the furnace, $\phi_4 = 9400$ kW

Partial pressure of water

vapour in the flue gases, $p_w = 0.0929 \times 100 = 9.29$ kPa

DP of the flue gas mixture $= 44.6°C$ (317.55 K)

Latent heat of water at *DP* $= 2396.3$ kJ/kg

Heat loss due to evaporation of moisture, produced by burning

the hydrogen of the fuel, $\phi_8 = 8 \times 18 \times 2396.3 \times \left(\frac{27\,650}{2672}\right)$

$$= 3570\,774 \text{ kJ/h} \equiv 991.88 \text{ kW}$$

Heat loss in the outgoing flue gases

Moisture in the flue gas $= \dfrac{18.174 \times 18}{[(195.684 - 18.174)\,29]}$

$$= 0.0635 \text{ kg/kg dry gas}$$

Humid heat of flue gas $= 1.006 + 1.84 \times 0.0635$

$$= 1.123 \text{ kJ/(kg dry gas} \cdot \text{K)}$$

Heat loss, $\phi'_7 = (195.624 - 18.174) \times 1.123$

$$\times 29 \,(833.15 - 298.15) \times \left(\frac{27\,650}{2672}\right)$$

$$= 31\,993\,829 \text{ kJ/h} \equiv 8887.17 \text{ kW (approximate)}$$

Alternate calculations

Table 7.38 Mean Heat Capacity of Flue Gas

Component	n_i, kmol	C^o_{mpm1} 298.15 – 833 K	$n_i \cdot C^o_{mpm1}$ kJ/K	C^o_{mpm2} 298.15 – 478 K	$n_i \cdot C^o_{mpm2}$ kJ/K
CO_2	30.00	45.81	1374.30	40.94	1228.20
O_2	4.91	31.72	155.75	29.97	147.15
N_2	142.54	30.07	4286.18	29.00	4133.66
H_2O	18.174	35.85	651.54	33.92	616.46
Total	195.624		6467.77		6125.47

$$\text{Heat loss in flue gas, } \phi_7 = 6469.67\ (833.15 - 298.15) \times \left(\frac{27\ 650}{2672}\right)$$
$$= 35\ 817\ 444 \text{ kJ/h} \equiv 9949.29 \text{ kW}$$

Note Approximate heat loss (ϕ_7') differs significantly (by 10.65%) as compared to ϕ_7 as the flue gas temperature (833.15 K) is quite high and high CO_2 content.

Table 7.39 Heat Balance of Open Hearth Furnace

	kW	%
Heat input		
Heat of combustion	26 922.59	77.46
Sensible heat of fuel	7 748.62	22.29
Sensible heat of air	86.88	0.25
Total	34 758.09	100.00
Heat output		
Useful heat gain in furnace	9 400.00	27.04
Heat loss due to evaporation of moisture formed by the combustion of H_2	991.88	2.85
Sensible heat loss in flue gases	9 949.29	28.63
Unaccounted heat loss	14 416.92	41.48
Total	34 758.09	100.00

Heat balance of boiler

Total heat entering the waste heat boiler, $\phi_7 = 9949.29$ kW

Heat output Basis 1 kg of steam

Refer Appendix IV.

Economizer Heat load, $H_4 = 675.47 - 272.03 = 403.44$ kJ/kg

Boiler At 12.5 bar a

$T_s = 463$ K (181.8°C) $h = 806.69$ kJ/kg

$\lambda_v = 1977.4$ kJ/kg $H_{ss} = 2784.1$ kJ/kg at T_s

Heat load, $H_5 = 2784.1 - 675.47 = 2108.63$ kJ/kg

At 12.5 bar a and 573.15 K,

total heat of superheated steam, $i = 3045.6$ kJ/kg

Heat load of the superheater, $H_6 = 3045.6 - 2784.1 = 261.5$ kJ/kg

Total heat load of economizer,

$$\phi_4' = 403.44 \times 7100$$
$$= 2864\ 424 \text{ kJ/h} \equiv 795.67 \text{ kW}$$

Total heat load of boiler, $\phi_5' = (2784.1 - 675.47)\ 7100$
$$= 14\ 971\ 273\ \text{kJ/h} \equiv 4158.69\ \text{kW}$$
Total heat load of superheater,
$$\phi_6' = 261.5 \times 7100$$
$$= 1856\ 650\ \text{kJ/h} \equiv 515.74\ \text{kW}$$
Total useful heat recovery, $\phi_4' + \phi_5' + \phi_6' = 5470.1\ \text{kW}$
Equivalent boiler capacity from and at 373.15 K
$$= \frac{5470.1 \times 3600}{2256.9} = 8725.4\ \text{kg/h}$$
Heat loss in flue gas; $\phi_8' = 177.57 \times 29 \times 1.123$
$$(478.15 - 298.15)\ (27650/2672)$$
$$= 10\ 771\ 558\ \text{kJ/h} = 2992.1\ \text{kW}$$
$$\text{(approximate)}$$
Alternate calculations   (Refer Table 7.38)
Heat loss in flue gases, $\phi_8 = 6125.47\ (478.15 - 298.15)\ (27650/2672)$
$$= 11\ 409\ 605\ \text{kJ/h} \equiv 3169.33\ \text{kW}$$

Table 7.40   Heat Balance of Waste Heat Boiler

	kW	%
Heat output		
Steam raising		
Economizer	795.67	8.00
Steam generator	4158.69	41.80
Superheater	515.74	5.18
Heat lost in flue gases	3169.33	31.85
Unaccounted heat loss	1309.86	13.17
Total	9949.29	100.00

The heat flow diagrams for the furnace as well as the waste heat boiler are combined in Fig. 7.8.

Example 7.14   In Example 7.5, coal firing, in Example 7.6, RFO (GCV = 41 030 kJ/kg) firing and in Example 7.10, fuel oil firing have been specified.

Also, consider firing of lignite and petcoke (a by product of petroleum refinery). Ultimate analyses and GCV of both the fuels are as follows.

Table 7.41   Ultimate Analyses of Lignite and Petcoke (mass %)

Element	Lignite	Petcoke
Carbon	37.0	86.70
Hydrogen	3.0	3.18
Sulphur	3.0	5.92
Nitrogen	1.5	1.22
Oxygen	18.5	1.16
Moisture	25.0	0.80
Ash (mineral matter)	12.0	1.00
GCV, kJ/kg	14 860	34 460

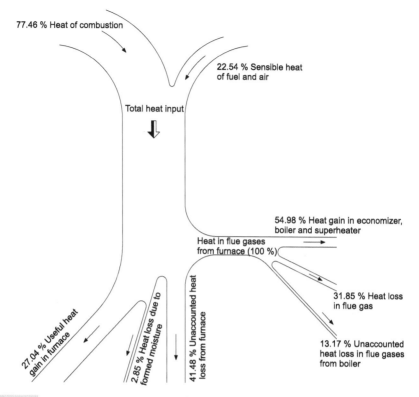

Fig. 7.8   Heat Flow Diagram of a Furnace Accompanied by a Steam Generator

Consider excess air reuirement of 30% for fuel oil, 60% for lignite and 40% for petcoke for complete combustion. Assume ambient air at 35°C (308 K) DB and 27.5°C (300.5 K) WB for firing.

Calculate SO_2 concentration of moist flue gas and total SO_2 emission for 1 GJ heat liberation on GCV basis for each fuel firing,

Solution

Moisture content of ambient air at 35°C *DB* and

$$27.5°C \ WB = 0.0204 \text{ kg/kg dry air} \quad \text{(Ref. Fig. 6.15)}$$
$$= 0.0329 \text{ kmol/kmol dry air}$$

Case A: Coal firing of Example 7.5

$$\text{Dry air supply} = 8.662 + 32.586$$
$$= 41.248 \text{ kmol/100 kg coal}$$

Moisture entering with air $= 41.248 \times 0.0329 = 1.357$ kmol

Total wet flue gas $= 42.971 + 1.357 = 44.328$ kmol

$$SO_2 \text{ concentration} = \frac{0.012 \times 10^6}{44.328} = \textbf{270.7 ppm (v/v)}$$

Total SO_2 emission for 1 GJ heat liberation,

$$n_{SO_2} = \frac{(0.012 \times 10^9)}{(100 \times 16\,842.2 \times 10^3)}$$

$$= 7.125 \times 10^{-3} \text{ kmol}$$

$$m_{SO_2} = 0.456 \text{ kg}$$

Case B: RFO firing of Example 7.6

Dry air supply = 58.25 kmol/100 kg RFO

Moisture entering with air = 58.25 × 0.0329

= 1.916 kmol

Total wet flue gas = 55.901 + 4.7 + 1.916 = 62.517 kmol

$$SO_2 \text{ concentration} = \frac{0.069 \times 10^6}{62.517} = 1103.7 \text{ ppm (v/v)}$$

Total SO_2 emission for 1 GJ heat liberation,

$$n_{SO_2} = \frac{(0.069 \times 10^9)}{(100 \times 41\,030 \times 10^3)}$$

$$= 16.82 \times 10^{-3} \text{ kmol}$$

$$m_{SO_2} = 1.076 \text{ kg}$$

Case C: Fuel oil firing of Example 7.10

Dry air supply with **30% excess air** = (9.786 × 1.3)/0.21 = 60.58 kmol

Moisture entering with air = 60.58 × 0.0329 = 1.993 kmol

Total wet flue gas = (9.786 × 0.3) + (60.58 × 0.79) + 7.092

+ 0.047 + 2.725 + 1.993

= 62.651 kmol

$$SO_2 \text{ concentration} = \frac{0.047 \times 10^6}{62.651} = 750.2 \text{ ppm (v/v)}$$

Total SO_2 emission for 1 GJ heat liberation,

$$n_{SO_2} = \frac{(0.047 \times 10^9)}{(100 \times 42\,260 \times 10^3)}$$

$$= 11.12 \times 10^{-3} \text{ kmol}$$

$$m_{SO_2} = 0.712 \text{ kg}$$

Case D: Lignite firing

Basis 100 kg of lignite

Table 7.42   Oxygen Requirement for Lignite Firing

Element	kg	kmol	O_2 required, kmol
Carbon	37.0	3.083	3.083
Hydrogen	3.0	1.5	0.750
Sulphur	3.0	0.094	0.094
Oxygen	18.5	0.578	(–)0.578
Total	61.5	5.255	3.349

Theoretical O_2 requirment = 3.349 kmol

Actual O_2 supply = 3.349 × 1.6 = 5.358 kmol

$$N_2 \text{ entering with } O_2 = \frac{79 \times 5.358}{21} = 20.156 \text{ kmol}$$

Total dry air = 5.358 + 20.156 = 25.514 kmol

Moisture entering with air = 25.514 × 0.0329 = 0.839 kmol

Total moisture in flue gas = 1.5 + (25/18) + 0.839

= 3.728 kmol

Table 7.43 Flue Gas Composition

Compnent	kmol	Wet flue gas analysis. mole %	Orsat analysis, mole %
CO_2	3.083	10.59	12.51
SO_2	0.094	0.32	—
O_2	2.009	6.90	7.91
N_2	20.210	69.39	79.58
H_2O	3.728	12.80	—
Total	29.124	100.00	100.00

$$SO_2 \text{ concentration} = \frac{0.094 \times 10^6}{29.124} = \textbf{3227.6 ppm (v/v)}$$

Total SO_2 emission for 1 GJ heat liberation,

$$n_{SO_2} = \frac{0.094 \times 10^9}{100 \times 14\,860 \times 10^3} = \textbf{63.26} \times \textbf{10}^{-3} \textbf{ kmol}$$

$$m_{SO_2} = \textbf{4.048 kg}$$

Case E: Petcoke firing

Basis 100 kg of petcoke

Table 7.44 Oxygen Requirement for Petcoke Firing

Element	kg	kmol	O_2 required, kmol
Carbon	86.70	7.225	7.225
Hydrogen	3.18	1.590	0.795
Sulphur	5.94	0.186	0.186
Oxygen	1.16	0.036	−0.036
Total	96.98	9.037	8.170

Theoretical oxygen requirment = 8.17 kmol

Actual O_2 supply = 8.17 × 1.4 = 11.438 kmol

$$\text{Nitrogen entering with } O_2 = \frac{79 \times 11.438}{21}$$

= 43.029 kmol

Total dry air = 11.438 + 43.029 = 54.467 kmol

Moisture entering with air = 54.467 × 0.0329 = 1.792 kmol

Total moisture in flue gas = 1.59 + (0.8/18) + 1.792

= 3.426 kmol

Table 7.45   Flue Gas Composition

Compnent	kmol	Wet flue gas analysis, mole %	Orsat analysis, mole %
CO_2	7.225	12.65	13.79
SO_2	0.186	0.33	—
O_2	3.268	5.72	6.08
N_2	43.029	75.31	80.13
H_2O	3.426	5.99	—
Total	57.134	100.00	100.00

$$SO_2 \text{ concentration} = \frac{0.186 \times 10^6}{57.134} = \textbf{3255.5 ppm (v/v)}$$

Total SO_2 emission for 1 GJ heat liberation,

$$n_{SO_2} = \frac{0.186 \times 10^9}{100 \times 34\,460 \times 10^3}$$

$$= \textbf{53.976} \times \textbf{10}^{-3} \textbf{ kmol}$$

$$m_{SO_2} = \textbf{3.454 kg}$$

Table 7.46   Comparison of SO_2 Emissions

Firing	Excess air	SO_2 concentration in flue gas, ppm (v/v)	SO_2 emission for 1 GJ heat liberation, kg
Coal	100	270.7	0.456
RFO	25	1103.7	1.076
Fuel oil	30	750.2	0.712
Lignite	60	3227.6	4.048
Petcoke	40	3255.5	3.454

Fig. 7.9 is schematic representation of SO_2 emissions for different fuels.

Note   Firing with lignite and petcoke result in high SO_2 emissions, causing higher air pollution.

Exercises

7.1   The proximate analysis of a Chirimiri coal sample shows 5.3% moisture, 24.6% VM, 49.8% FC and 20.3% ash. The sulphur content of the coal is found to be 0.7%. Calorimetric tests give the gross-calorific value of the coal on dry ash-free basis as 24 070 kJ/kg. Using the Calderwood equation, find the carbon per cent of the coal.   **[46.21% carbon]**

7.2   A coal sample from Chirimiri colliery has following proximate and ultimate analyses.

Gross calorific value = 27 235 kJ/kg on dry ash-free basis

Calculate (a) the net hydrogen available for combustion, (b) the combined water, (c) the gross calorific value, using the Dulong's formula, (d) the carbon content, using

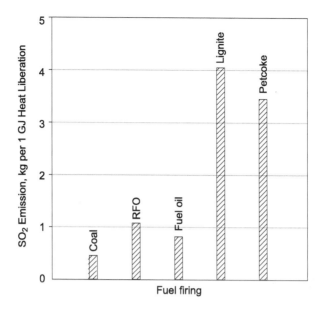

Fig. 7.9 SO₂ Emissions for Different Fuels

the Calderwood equation, (e) the analysis of coal on ash-free and moisture-free basis, (f) theoretical air requirement in kg per kg dry coal, and (g) the analysis of flue gases, if the coal is burnt with 60% excess air.

Table 7.47 Analysis of Coal

Proximate analysis		Ultimate analysis	
	mass %		mass %
Moisture	4.0	Carbon	61.5
VM	26.7	Hydrogen	3.5
FC	55.1	Sulphur	0.4
Ash	14.2	Ash	14.2
Oxygen (by diff.)	18.6	Nitrogen	1.8
Total	100.0	Total	100.0

[(a) Net H_2 = 1.18% (b) Combined water = 16.92% (c) GCV from Dulong's formula = 21 778 kJ/kg (d) Calderwood equation, carbon = 55.96% (e) VM = 32.64%, FC = 67.36% (f) Theoretical air required = 7.2 kg/kg coal (g) Refer Table 7.48]

Table 7.48 Composition of Flue Gases

Component	Actual analysis (wet basis) mole %	Orsat analysis, mole %
CO_2	11.88	12.48
SO_2	0.03	—
O_2	7.55	7.92
N_2	75.92	79.60
H_2O	4.62	—
Total	100.00	100.00

7.3 A sample of fuel oil has C/H ratio 9.33 (by mass) and contains sulphur to the extent of 1.3% (mass). The GCV of the fuel is measured to be 41 785 kJ/kg at 25°C (298.15 K). Calculate its NCV at 25°C (298.15 K). **[39 685.4 kJ/kg fuel oil]**

7.4 Read the gross calorific values of gaseous *n*-propanol and liquid acetone at 25°C (298.15 K) from Appendix V.2. Find the net calorific value of each using latent heat of water at 25°C (298.15 K). **[NHV of *n*-propanol (g) = – 1892.72 kJ/mol, NHV of acetone (l) = – 1658.0 kJ/mol]**

7.5 Refer Exercise 4.1. Calculate theoretical specific energy requirement per tonne ammonia for case (a) and case (b).

Hint Use NCV of methane to calculate specific energy consumption.

(a) 17.673 GJ/t NH₃, (b) 20.845 GJ/t NH₃

7.6 Refer Exercise 4.2. Calculate theoretical specific energy requirement per tonne methanol. **25.049 GJ/t CH₃OH**

Note Specific energy requirements, calculated, in Exercises 7.5 and 7.6 for ammonia and methanol, respectively, are considered minimum energy requirements. Specific energy consumptions for these products using different feed stocks and processes (including fuels) are compared with these bench marks for evaluation of the efficiency of the technology/process.

7.7 Refer Example 5.29. It is decided to mix 10% ethanol (by mass) in the motor spirit for improving its octane number. Calculate average NCV of the blend and prove that it will emit nearly same greenhouse gas (i.e. CO_2) into the atmosphere as that with motor spirit when compared on heat values. **[NCV of blend = 42 325.7 kJ/kg]**

7.8 Calculate the GHV and NHV at 25°C (298.15 K) of the associated gas having the composition, CH_4: 74.4%, C_2H_6: 8.4%, C_3H_8: 7.4%, *i*-C_4H_{10}: 1.7%, *n*-C_4H_{10}: 2.0%, *i*-C_5H_{12}: 0.5%, *n*-C_5H_{12}: 0.4%, N_2: 4.3% and CO_2: 0.9% (on volume basis). **[GHV: 49 537 kJ/kg or 44 801 kJ/m³, NHV: 45 012 kJ/kg or 40 708 kJ/m³ (at 298.15 K and 101.3 kPa)]**

7.9 A sample of refinery gas is found to contain, H_2: 74.0%, CH_4: 13.5%, C_2H_6: 7.4%, C_3H_8: 3.6%, *n*-C_4H_{10}: 1.2% and *n*-C_5H_{12}: 0.3% (mole basis). Calculate the GCV and NCV at 25°C (298.15 K) of refinery gas.

Table 7.49 GCV and NCV of refinery gas

GCV	NCV
572.269 kJ/mol	508.275 kJ/mol
23 391 kJ/m³	20 776 kJ/m³
68 486 kJ/kg	60 828 kJ/kg

7.10 The purge gas obtained from ammonia synthesis loop has the composition[11], H_2: 69.0%, N_2: 23.0%, Ar: 2.7% and CH_4: 5.3% (mole basis). It is burnt with 20% excess air. Calculate (a) the GCV and NCV at 25°C (298.15 K) of the purge gas, (b) theoretical air required, and (c) the molar composition of the dry flue gases. **[(a) GCV = 25 075 kJ/kg, NCV = 21 493 kJ/kg, (b) Theoretical air required = 6.39 kg/kg purge gas (c) Flue gas composition: CO_2: 2.18%, Ar: 1.11%, N_2: 93.01%, O_2: 3.7% (on dry volume basis)]**

7.11 Synthetic natural gas (SNG from a US-based plant) has the molar composition, CH_4: 96.59%, H_2: 1.29%, CO: 0.22% and CO_2: 1.90%. Calculate the GCV and NCV at NTP.

Table 7.50   Heating Values of SNG

GCV	NCV
864 589 kJ/kmol	778 993 kJ/kmol
52 649 kJ/kg	47 437 kJ/kg
38 574 kJ/Nm^3	34 755 kJ/Nm^3

7.12 Refer Example 4.20. Calculate GCV and NCV at 25°C (298.15 K) of wet tail gas (Table 4.21), leaving abosorber of the formaldehyde plant in kJ/Nm^3.

[GCV = 203.6 kJ/Nm^3, NCV = 185.1 kJ/Nm^3]

7.13 A sample of coal is found to contain 65% carbon and 12.7% ash (by mass). The refuse obtained after burning the fuel is found to have 8.6% carbon. Assume that negligible oxygen is present in the coal. Flue gas analysis showed CO_2: 10.6%, O_2: 8.7% and N_2: 80.7% (by volume). Calculate (a) the actual mass of (dry) air used to burn the coal, (b) the actual mass of flue gases produced by burning the coal, and (c) the amount of combustible hydrogen present in the fuel.

[(a) 14.86 kg/kg fuel (b) 15.46 kg (wet)/kg fuel (c) 4.32% (by mass)]

7.14 A furnace is fired with fuel oil. The Orsat analysis of the flue gases indicates 10.6% CO_2, 6.0% O_2 and rest N_2 (by volume). Find (a) the percentage excess air, and (b) the C : H ratio in the fuel oil, assuming that fuel oil does not contain nitrogen.

[(a) 37.10% (b) C : H ratio = 5.71 : 1 (mass)]

7.15 A fuel gas constitutes of CO_2: 3.4%, C_2H_4: 3.7%, C_6H_6: 1.5%, O_2: 0.3%, CO: 17.4%, H_2: 36.8%, CH_4: 24.9% and N_2 : 12.0% (on mole basis). It is burnt with air in a furnace. The Fyrite analyzer indicated 10.0 mole % CO_2 (on dry basis) in the flue gases. Find (a) the percent excess air used, and (b) the complete Orsat analysis.

[(a) 37.07%, (b) O_2: 5.9%, N_2: 84.1%]

7.16 The Orsat analysis of the flue gases shows CO_2: 12.4%, CO: 3.1%, O_2: 5.4% and N_2: 79.1% (by volume). All the hydrogen but only 85% of the carbon in the (solid) fuel appears in the flue gases. Calculate the per cent excess air used. Assume that negligible oxygen and nitrogen are present in the fuel. **[5.6%]**

7.17 Bottled gas [Liquefied Petroleum Gas (LPG)], conforming to IS: 4576, is found to contain 1.2% ethane, 25.2% propane, 23.9% *i*-butane and 49.7% *n*-butane (on mole basis). It is available at Rs. 30 per kg. Associated gas, having the molar composition CH_4: 86.6%, C_2H_6: 8.6%, C_3H_8: 3.9%, *n*-C_4H_{10}: 0.7%, *i*-C_4H_{10}: 0.2%, is available at Rs. 15/Nm^3.

A fuel is to be selected from the above two for curing a refractory lined furnace. Which is cheaper?   **[Cost of energy: Bottled gas: Rs 653.40 per GJ (LCV basis),**
Associated gas: Rs 364.85 per GJ (LCV basis)]

7.18 Blast furnace gas is used as a fuel for steel manufacture. A sample of blast furnace gas is found to contain H_2: 3.2%, CO: 26.2%, CO_2: 13.0%, N_2: 57.6% (mole %). The gas is made available at 60°C (333 K). The air for combustion is available at 25°C (298.15 K) *DB*, 18°C (291 K) *WB* and 100.0 kPa (750 Torr). The gas is desired to be burnt with 20% excess air. Compute (a) the theoretical requirement of air per kg fuel, (b) the molar composition of flue gases (wet basis), and (c) the adiabatic flame temperature.   **[(a) 0.7 kg/kg fuel, (b) CO_2: 22.96%, O_2 1.73%, H_2O: 2.68%,**
rest N_2 (by volume), (c) 2509.55°C (2782.7 K)]

7.19 The coal mentioned in Exercise 7.1 is fired in a battery of three water tube Babcock and Wilcox make boilers. The operating data on a particular date are given below.

Fuel–firing rate = 2500 kg/h

Excess moisture sprinkled on coal over the moisture in the coal as fired = 5%

Air is supplied at 34°C (307 K) *DB*, 24°C (297 K) *WB* and 100.0 kPa (750 Torr). Orsat analysis of flue gases indicates CO_2: 8.8%, O_2: 9.2% and rest N_2 (volume basis).

Flue gas temperature entering the economizer = 270°C (543 K)
Flue gas temperature leaving the economizer = 190°C (463 K)
Draft at the base of chimney = 0.2 kPa g
Temperature of water entering the economizer = 38°C (311 K)
Temperature of water leaving the economizer = 95°C (368 K)

Steam

Pressure = 9 bar g
Temperature = 200°C (473 K)
Steam generation = 12 150 kg/h under pressure

The cinder (refuse) contains 5.9% combustibles. Assume that coal contains negligible nitrogen and the combustibles in the refuse are carbon. Use the mean heat capacity data provided in Table 7.14.
Evaluate the boiler performance.

[**Excess air = 32%, Dew point of flue gases = 46.2°C (319.35 K) (comments?)**]
Volumetric flow rate of moist air = 29 849 m^3/h, Volumetric flow rate of flue gases = 47 165 m^3/h
Overall thermal efficiency of the boiler = 72.4%]

Table 7.51 Heat Balance of Water-tube Boilers

Heat input by burning the coal*	12 436.11 kW	100%
Heat output	kW	%
1. Useful heat gain		
Economizer	805.44	6.48
Boiler	8 026.80	64.54
Superheater	169.76	1.37
2. Heat lost in flue gases	1 724.688	13.87
3. Heat lost in refuse	289.58	2.33
4. Heat lost due to evaporation of moisture of coal and water produced by burning H_2	1 168.318	9.39
5. Unaccounted heat loss	251.524	2.02

*Enthalpy of combustion air is neglected.

7.20 A vertical cross-tube boiler is fitted with a low air–pressure burner, firing furnace oil[12]. The boiler pressure was 7 bar g. Carbon dioxide content in the dry flue gases was 6.5% (by volume) and the temperature of the flue gases was 370°C (643 K) on an average. The pressure of the flue gases at the base of chimney was 100.7 kPa (755 Torr). Air enters at 25°C (298.15 K) *DB* and 22°C (295 K) *WB*.

The ultimate analysis of the furnace oil indicates:
C: 84.0%, H: 12.7%, O: 1.2%, S: 0.4% and N: 1.7% (by mass).
GCV of the oil at 25°C (298.15 K) = 43 730 kJ/kg

Determine (a) the mass of air theoretically required to burn one kg of fuel oil, (b) the volume of dry and wet flue gases per kg of furnace oil at NTP when burnt with theoretical air, (c) theoretical percentage of CO_2 in the dry flue gases, (d) actual volume of the flue gases per kg of fuel oil burnt and per cent excess air, (e) the dew point of flue gases, (f) heat loss due to hot flue gases leaving the chimney per kg of oil, and (g) heat loss due to evaporation of moisture produced due to the burning of the furnace oil.

[**(a) 14.02 kg, (b) Dry flue gases = 10.14 N m^3/kg oil, Wet flue gases = 11.84 N m^3/kg oil (c) 15.5% CO_2, (d) Volume of flue gases = 62.05 m^3/kg oil, Excess air = 129.24% (e) 41.2°C (314.35 K) (f) 12 531.4 kJ/kg oil over 298.15 K, (g) 2747.2 kJ/kg oil over 298.15 K**]

7.21 In an oil mill, there are two water–tube boilers, each with an evaporation capacity of 20 000 kg/h at a rated pressure of 16 bar g. Each boiler is fitted with an economizer and a superheater. At a time, only one boiler is on load and the other is standby. The boilers are fired with furnace oil. A trial was conducted to assess the performance of the boiler. Observation were taken every 15 min and average readings obtained during the trial are given as follows.

Duration of trials	= 6 h 15 min
No. of boilers on load	= One
Oil consumption during the trial	= 6630 kg
Ambient air: DB 35°C (308 K), WB 29.5°C (302.5 K)	
Steam sent to the factory as recorded by the meter	= 76.2 t
Average steam temperature	= 280°C (553 K)
Average steam pressure	= 14 bar g
Average oil inlet temperature	= 77°C (350 K)
Average draft at the base of the chimney	= 0.12 kPa g
Average temperature of the water, entering the economizer	= 82°C (355 K)
Average temperature of the water, leaving the economizer	= 115°C (388 K)
Average CO_2 in the flue gases before the economizer	= 11.5% (v/v)
Average temperature of gases before the economizer	= 361°C (634 K)
Average temperature of gases, leaving the economizer	= 277°C (550 K)
There is a continuous blowdown of 1000 kg/h from the boiler.	
Barometer reading	= 100 kPa (750 Torr)
Ultimate analysis of furnace oil: C: 85.65%, H: 11.35%, S: 3.0% (by mass)	
GCV of furnace oil at 25°C (298.15 K)	= 43 040 kJ
Specific gravity of furnace oil	= 0.95
Mean heat capacity of furnace oil	= 1.675 kJ/(kg · K)

Evaluate the thermal performance of the boiler.

[**Excess air = 37.06%, Dew point of the flue gases = 48.7°C (321.85 K), Thermal efficiency of boiler (based on GCV) = 70.77%, Air supply to the burner = 18 561.3 m³/h, Volumetric flow rate of flue gases = 34 572 m³/h**]

Table 7.52 Heat Balance of Boiler

Reference temperature = 25°C (298.15 K)		
	kW	%
Input		
Total gross heat input by burning the fuel	12 682.45	99.34
Enthalpy of air	59.00	0.46
Enthalpy of fuel oil	25.67	0.20
Total	**12 767.12**	**100.00**
Output		
Heat gain		
in economizer (useful)	471.39	3.69
in steam generator	7 814.73	61.21
in superheater	689.86	5.40
Heat loss due to blowdown	139.27	1.09
Sensible heat loss in flue gases	1 609.08	12.60
Heat loss due to evaporation of moisture formed by burning of H_2 of fuel	719.29	5.64
Unaccounted heat loss	1 323.50	10.37
Total	**12 767.12**	**100.00**

7.22 Methanol is burnt as a fuel in a high-powered racing engine. (a) Calculate the theoretical dry air requirement per kg of methanol burnt. (b) If the fuel is burnt with 40% excess air and if it is assumed that the combustion is complete, calculate the adiabatic flame temperature, using the data on C_{mp}^o provided in Table 5.1.

Assume the availability of methanol and dry air at 25°C (298.15 K).

[(a) 6.47 kg dry air/kg fuel (b) 1560.12°C (1833.27 K)]

7.23 SNG, described in Exercise 7.9, is to be burnt with 10% excess air in a boiler; both at 25°C (298.15 K). Steam is to be generated at 65 bar a and 400°C (673 K) in the boiler using water at 100°C (373 K). Assume 83% thermal efficiency of the boiler, based on GCV. Calculate

(a) the steam generation per hour if the fuel firing rate can be allowed to be 3000 Nm^3/h,

(b) combustion air requirement, and

(c) adiabatic flame temperature.

Data Moisture content of combustion air = 0.018 kmol/kmol dry air

[(a) 34.905 t/h, (b) 10.342 kmol wet air/kmol fuel, (c) 1882.1°C (2155.25 K)]

7.24 At high adiabatic temperatures, NOx content of flue gas is measured to be high which is an objectionable pollutant. Special treatment of flue gas such as selective catalytic reaction is thus necessary which is a costly proposition. In an innovative COOLFuel[R] technology[13] for gas fired furnaces a part of flue gas is recycled and mixed with the fuel gas, upstream of the burner as shown in Fig. 7.10.

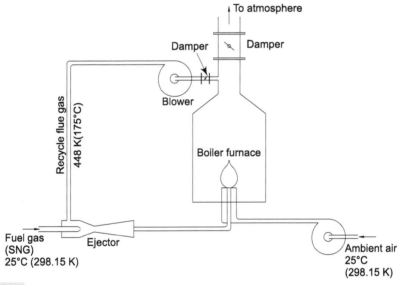

Fig. 7.10 COOLFuel Technology for Gas Firing

For this purpose, an ejector is used in which fuel gas is used as a motive fuel to draw partially recycled flue gas. For the SNG firing, described in Exercise 7.23, recycled flue gas [at 175°C (448 K)] flow rate is fixed in such a way that GCV of mixed gas is 288 200 kJ/kmol mixture at 25°C (298.15 K). Such firing results in lower adiabatic flame temperature, thereby achieving low NO_x emission (~ 30 ppm by v/v) and no costly treatment of flue gas becomes necessary. Calculate

(a) recycle ratio of flue gas, defined as kmol recycled/kmol total flue gases from furnace, (b) combustion air requirement, and (c) adiabatic flame temperature for the revised conditions.

[(a) 0.1517 (b) 10.193 kmol wet air/kmol SNG (c) 1662.15°C (1935.3 K)]

Note As a result of recycle of a part of flue gas, combution air requirement is marginally reduced by 1.43% while adiabatic flame temperature is lowered by 200°C (200 K) for the same heat liberation.

7.25 Water gas is produced by blowing steam and air alternatively over a red-hot bed of coal. A coal with proximate analysis; moisture: 2.7%, VM: 26.9%, FC: 52.9% and ash: 17.5% (by mass) is used for the purpose. The refuse collected after gassification contained 19% combustibles (as carbon). The dry water gas (blue gas) contained H_2: 48.5%, CO: 44.2%, CO_2: 2.3%, N_2: 2.4%, O_2: 1.0% and CH_4: 1.6% (by volume). Assume that coal contains negligible quantities of sulphur, oxygen and nitrogen. Compute (a) kmol of dry blue gas produced per 100 kg coal used,
(b) mass of steam decomposed per kg coal used and
(c) mass % carbon and net hydrogen in coal.
[**(a) 13.02 (b) 1.16 kg (c) C: 79.23%, H (net): 0.57%**]

7.26 In a carburetted water gas plant, blue water gas and the finished carburetted water gas have the compositions shown in Table 7.53.

Table 7.53 Composition of Gases

Component	Composition, % by volume (on dry basis)	
	Blue water gas	Carburetted water gas
H_2	49.0	37.0
CH_4	0.8	14.0
CO	41.0	30.5
C_3H_6	—	7.0
CO_2	4.7	5.6
O_2	—	0.4
N_2	4.5	5.5
Total	100.0	100.0

For carburetting the water gas, furnace oil having the composition 87% carbon and 13% hydrogen (by mass) is used. After carburetion, the tar (uncarburized material) removed from the gas contained 20% of all the carbon and 10% of all the hydrogen present in the oil.
Calculate (a) the mass of fuel oil in kg used for carburetion of one kmol blue gas,
(b) the total kmol of the dry carburetted water gas produced per kmol dry blue water gas, and
(c) the amount of steam decomposed (in kg) during the carburetion process per kmol dry carburetted water gas. [**(a) 13.48 (b) 1.754 (c) 2.196**]

7.27 A sample of coal is found to contain the following:
C: 62.0%, H: 3.6%, S: 0.6%, N: 6.0%, O: 9.3% and ash: 18.5% (by mass). GCV of the fuel = 27 800 kJ/kg at 25°C (298.15 K) on dry ash-free basis. It is used to generate the producer gas having the molar composition, H_2: 10.5%, CH_4: 2.1%, C_2H_4: 0.4%, CO:22.0%, CO_2: 7.7%, N2: 57.3% (on dry basis; SO_2 neglected). The dew point of the gas is measured to be 25°C (298.15 K) at 106.7 kPa (800 Torr). The gas is obtained at 927°C (1200 K).

The refuse from the gassifying oven contained 6.2% combustibles (reported as carbon). Air is available at 38°C (311 K) *DB* and 26°C (299 K) *WB*. Steam is introduced at 4 bar a and 350°C (623 K).
Compute (a) the mass of the producer gas generated per kg coal used,
(b) the mass of moist air used per kg coal used,
(c) the amount of steam decomposed in gassifying oven per kg coal, and

(d) the complete heat balance of the generator for 100 kmol dry producer gas.
[(a) **4.16 kg moist producer gas per kg coal**
(b) **3.223 kg moist air per kg coal**
(c) **0.144 kg steam decomposed per kg coal, (d) Refer Table 7.54]**

Table 7.54   Heat Balance of Producer Gas Generator

Reference temperature: 25°C (298.15 K)	Heat, in kJ	%
Input		
GCV of coal	14 582 951	97.91
Steam	283 592	1.91
Air	27 492	0.18
Total	14 894 035	100.00
Output		
GCV of producer gas	11 661 620	78.30
Sensible heat of gas at 1200 K	784 472	5.27
Heat lost in evaporation of formed mois-ture	508 298	3.41
of coal		
Unaccounted heat loss	1 939 645	13.02
Total	14 894 035	100.00

7.28 Waste liquor from a cellulose industry has the following ultimate analysis. C: 7.5%, H: 0.5%, S: 5.7%, H_2O: 58.8% , O : 12.5% and balance inorganics (majority sodium compounds) on mass basis. NCV at 25°C (298.15 K) = 3520 kJ/kg of waste liquor
The above waste liquor is incinerated in a steam generator along with natural gas as the stabilizing fuel. Composition of natural gas may be assumed of Example 7.4. Design of the boiler is based on 15% excess air. The adiabatic flame temperature in the boiler is not permitted to exceed 927°C (1200 K) due to various reasons such as high temperature corrosion due to high sulphur content of the waste liquor, possible thermal decomposition of the organic substances at high temperatures, adhesion of inorganic salts at high temperature on heat transfer surfaces, etc.

Saturated steam is generated at 15 bar g from the boiler. Assume (i) flue gas temperature to be 202°C (475 K), (ii) boiler feed water availability at 77°C (350 K), (iii) availability of both fuels at 25°C (298.15 K), (iv) furnace pressure of 103.5 kPa (776 Torr) and (v) overall boiler efficiency to be 85% on NCV basis.

Calculate (a) the natural gas requirement and waste liquor firing rates, and (b) the water dew point, sulphurous acid (H_2SO_3) dew point and (sulphuric) acid dew point. For evaluation of H_2SO_3 dew point, use the following formula[7].

$$\frac{1000}{T_{DP}} = 3.5752 - 0.1845\ A - 9.333 \times 10^{-4}\ B - 9.13 \times 10^{-4}\ (A \cdot B)$$

where T_{DP} = dew point of H_2SO_3, K
$A = \ln (p_{H_2O})$
$B = \ln (p_{SO_2})$
p_i = partial pressure, kPa

[*Hint*: Use absolute enthalpies, listed in Table 5.22.]
[(a) **4969.5 kg/h waste liquor, 373.8 Nm³/h natural gas, (b) Water dew point = 75.7°C (348.85 K) H_2SO_3 dew point = 72.4°C (345.55 K), H_2SO_4 dew point = 153°C (426 K) from Fig. 7.3]**

7.29 A fuel having composition C_nH_m and no inerts is fired in a furnace. If the mole fraction of oxygen in flue gas is α on dry basis (measured with the help of Fyrite apparatus), prove[14] that

$$\% \text{ Excess air} = \left[\frac{100\,\alpha}{1 - 4.762\,\alpha}\right]\left[\frac{19.048 + 3.762\,r}{4 + r}\right]$$

where $r = \dfrac{m}{n} = \dfrac{\text{atoms of hydrogen}}{\text{atoms of carbon}}$

In a furnace, fired with pure methane, the oxygen content of flue gas is found to be 5% O_2 (by volume) on dry basis. Calculate the % excess air.   **[27.97%]**

7.30 Assume that the mole fraction of inerts (N_2, Ar, etc.) of the fuel, considered in Exercise 7.29, is 'a'. Prove that

$$\% \text{ Excess air} = \left[\frac{100\,\alpha}{1 - 4.762\,\alpha}\right]\left[\frac{19.048 + 3.762\,r}{4 + r} + c_f\right]$$

where $c_f = \dfrac{4\alpha}{[n(1 - a)(4 + r)]}$

In Exercise 7.29, consider that the fuel (methane) contains 5% inerts. Calculate the % excess air.   **[28.14%]**

7.31 Consider a combination-type firing in which (i) fuels are mixed having compositions $C_{n1}H_{m1}$, $C_{n2}H_{m2}$, ... $C_{ni}H_{mi}$ (without having inerts). If the mole fraction of oxygen in flue gases is a on dry basis, prove that

$$\% \text{ excess air} = \left[\frac{100\,\alpha}{1 - 4.762\,\alpha}\right]\left[\frac{19.048 + 3.762\,r_m}{4 + r_m}\right]$$

where $r_m = \left[\dfrac{\displaystyle\sum_{j=1}^{i} x_j\,n_j\,r_j}{\displaystyle\sum_{j=1}^{i} x_j\,n_j}\right]$

$$r_j = \frac{m_j}{n_j}$$

x_j = mole fraction of the fuel having $C_{nj}\,H_{mj}$ composition

7.32 Assume that mole fraction of inerts (N_2, Ar, etc.) of the fuels considered in Exercise 7.31 are $a_1, a_2, ..., a_i$. Prove that:

$$\% \text{ excess air} = \left[\frac{100\,\alpha}{1 - 4.762\,\alpha}\right]\left[\frac{19.048 + 3.762\,r_m}{4 + r_m} + c_{fm}\right]$$

where $c_{fm} = \left[\dfrac{\displaystyle\sum_{j=1}^{i} 4\,x_j\,a_j}{\displaystyle\sum_{j=1}^{i} \{x_j\,n_j(1 - a_j)(4 + r_j)\}}\right]$

a_j = mole fraction of the fuel having $C_{nj}\,H_{mj}$ composition

and $r_m = \left[\dfrac{\displaystyle\sum_{j=1}^{i}(1 - a_j)x_j\,n_j\,r_j}{\displaystyle\sum_{j=1}^{i}(1 - a_j)x_j n_j}\right]$

7.33 A reformer furnace of an ammonia plant is fired with three fules.

Table 7.55 Fuels Fried in Primary Reformer

Fuel	Average Composition	Firing rate, kmol/h	Incombustibles, mole %
Natural Gas	$CH_{2.75}$	375	2.8
Tail Gas	$CH_{5.55}$	158	82.0
Naphtha	$CH_{1.75}$	102.3	0.5

Flue gas analysis shows 3.5% O_2 on dry basis. Calculate excess air in the furnace.

Hint Use equations, derived in Exercise 7.32.

[*Ans.* **Excess air = 19.02%**]

References

1. The *Gazette of India* (*Extraordinary*) No. 688, December 30., 1988.
2. Culp, A W Jr; *Principles of Energy Conversion*, 2nd Ed., McGraw-Hill, Inc., USA, 1991, p. 56 and 59.
3. Elonka, S M and Kohan A L; *Standard Boiler Operator's Questions and Answers*, Tata McGraw-Hill Publishing Co. Ltd., New Delhi, 1969, p. 177.
4. Tan, S H; *Chem. Engng.*, **86**(18), Aug. 27, 1979, p. 117.
5. *Flue Gas Measurement*, AMETEK Inc., USA. 1988
6. Badger, B V; *Hydrocarbon Processing*, **67**(7), 1987, p. 53.
7. Ganapathy, V; *Hydrocarbon Processing*, **72**(2), 1993, p. 93.
8. Fehr, M; *Hydrocarbon Processing*, **67**(11), 1988, p. 93.
9. Gupta, S C; Saxena S L, Ghosh S K, and Rao P N R; *Steam and Fuel Users Journal*, **17**(1); 1967, p. 25.
10. Kumaran, N C; *Steam and Fuel Users Journal*, **17**(1); 1967, p. 41.
11. Charlesworth, P L; *The Chemical Engineer*, April 1965, p. CE 87.
12. *Liquid Fuels and Steam Utilization*, National Productivity Council, New Delhi, 1969, p. 41.
13. *Chem. Engg.*, **108**(6): 2001, p. 19.
14. Michael Antony, S; *Chem. Engg.*, **88**(25): Dec. 14. 1981, p. 107.

CHAPTER 8

Stoichiometry and Industrial Problems

In the previous seven chapters, an attempt was made to put forward the principles of process calculations in a graded manner. Although many industrial problems have been included in the earlier chapters, this chapter is exclusively devoted to process design problems of industrial nature. Most of them are drawn from industrial practice and hence one should find them interesting.

Example 8.1 Purasiv S® process utilizes molecular sieve unit for removal of sulphur dioxide gas from a sulphuric acid plant's tail gas[1]. Two adsorbers, packed with molecular sieve, are normally installed. While one bed is in service the other one is being regenerated. The normal cycle time is 4 hours. Regeneration of the bed is carried out with dry air and SO_2-rich air is recycled back to the sulphur burner exit gas mixture, thereby increasing the productivity of the sulphur acid plant. Figure 8.1 is the process flow diagram of the adsorption system.

In a sulphuric acid plant of 180 t/d capacity, adsorption system, based on Purasiv S process, is installed. On a particular day, the plant was being operated at 145 t/d capacity. Tail gas is passed through an adsorber. Data on SO_2 concentration at the inlet and outlet of the adsorber during the service cycle period are presented in Table 8.1.

Table 8.1 Adsorption Data for SO_2

Time min.	SO_2 concentration at inlet to adsorber, ppm (v/v)	SO_2 concentration at outlet from adsorber, ppm (v/v)
0	4680	0
10	4660	3
20	4640	5
30	4640	8
40	4660	14
50	4680	19
60	4780	28
70	5010	48
80	5200	59
90	5100	68
100	5200	72

(Contd.)

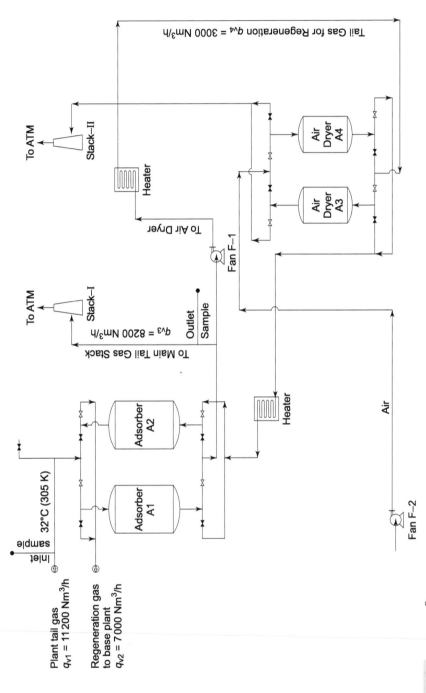

Fig. 8.1 PuraSiv S® Process for Sulphur Dioxide Emission Control

Table 8.1 (Contd.)

Time min.	SO$_2$ concentration at inlet to adsorber, ppm (v/v)	SO$_2$ concentration at outlet from adsorber, ppm (v/v)
110	5140	78
120	4960	84
130	5000	91
140	5020	100
150	4680	106
160	4480	115
170	4440	120
180	4320	124
190	4320	129
200	4300	134
210	4160	142
220	4160	145
230	4120	150
240	4110	155

Plot the graphs of inlet and outlet SO$_2$ concentrations with respect to time and calculate the following.

(a) Average inlet concentration of SO$_2$ during the service cycle.

(b) Average emission rate from the adsorption unit.

(c) Percentage recovery of SO$_2$ by adsorption.

(d) Assume (i) constant flow rate of incoming tail gas at 11 200 Nm^3/h, (ii) 100% recycle of the adsorbed SO$_2$ and (iii) 100% utilization of recovered SO$_2$ to produce sulphuric acid. Calculate the increased production per day.

(e) Emission from PuraSiv S$^{®}$ plant in kg SO$_2$/t H$_2$SO$_4$ produced.

Solution   In Fig. 8.2, inlet and outlet SO$_2$ concentrations are plotted against time.
Area under the SO$_2$ inlet curve, A_1 = 56 007.8 square units

Scale: 100 square units = 10 min × 200 ppm = 2000 ppm · min

Total time of adsorption = 4 h = 240 min

Average concentration of SO$_2$ at inlet = $\dfrac{56\,007.8 \times 2000}{100 \times 240}$

= 4667.3 ppm (v/v)

Area under the SO$_2$ outlet curve, A_2 = 19 106 square units

Scale 100 square units = 10 min × 10 ppm = 100 ppm · min

Average emission rate = $\dfrac{19\,106 \times 100}{100 \times 240}$

= 79.6 ppm (v/v)

Flow rate of tail gas mixture, ingoing to adsorber, q_{V1} = 11 200 Nm^3/h

Inflow of SO$_2$, $\dot{m}_{SO_2,1}$ = 11 200 $\dfrac{Nm^3}{h}$ × 4667.3 × 10^{-6} $\dfrac{Nm^3\ SO_2}{Nm^3\ tail\ gas}$

$\times \dfrac{1}{22.414}\dfrac{kmol}{Nm^3}$ × 64.0638 $\dfrac{kg\ SO_2}{kmol}$

= 149.409 kg/h

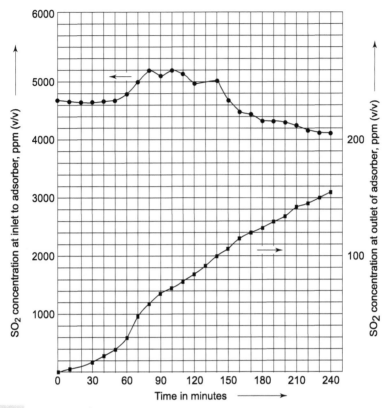

Fig. 8.2 Adsorption/Desorption Data for SO_2

Outflow of SO_2, $\dot{m}_{SO_2,2}$ = 11 200 × 79.6 × 10^{-6} × 64.0638/22.414
$$= 2.548 \text{ kg/h}$$
SO_2 adsorbed (or recycled during regeneration) = 149.409 − 2.548
$$= 146.861 \text{ kg/h}$$

$$\% \ SO_2 \text{ recovery} = \frac{146.861 \times 100}{149.409} = \mathbf{98.29}$$

Reactions: $SO_2 + \dfrac{1}{2} O_2 = SO_3$ \hfill (A)

$$SO_3 + H_2O = H_2SO_4 \hspace{2cm} \text{(B)}$$

1 mole SO_2 will result in 1 mole H_2SO_4.

$$\text{Additional } H_2SO_4 \text{ produced} = \frac{98.0785}{64.0638} \times 146.856$$

$$= 224.829 \text{ kg/h} \equiv \mathbf{5.396 \ t/d}$$

$$\text{Increase in production} = \frac{5.3961 \times 100}{145}$$

$$= \mathbf{3.72\%}$$

$$\text{Emission from the plant} = \frac{2.548 \times 24}{(145 + 5.396)}$$

$$= \textbf{0.407 kg SO}_2\textbf{/t H}_2\textbf{SO}_4$$

Example 8.2   A fertilizer complex uses naphtha (C/H = 6.0) as a raw material to manufacture ammonia. Naphtha is partially reformed with steam in the primary reformer. The off-gases from the primary reformer are fed into the secondary reformer along with the calculated quantity of air. The composition of off-gases and the air fed to the secondary reformer are given in Table 8.2.

Table 8.2   Compositions of Gases

Component	mole % (dry basis)	
	Off-gases from primary reformer	Air
Methane	8.1	—
Ethane	1.4	—
Carbon monoxide	10.3	—
Carbon dioxide	16.4	—
Hydrogen	62.9	—
Nitrogen	0.9	78.08
Oxygen	—	20.98
Argon –	—	0.94

$$\frac{\text{Steam}}{\text{dry offgases}} = 1.035 \text{ kmol/kmol}$$

Moisture in air = 0.0109 kg/kg dry air
$$= 0.0176 \text{ kmol/kmol dry air}$$

The off-gases enter the secondary reformer at 30 bar a and 816° C (1089 K) while the preheated air enters the reformer at 482°C (755 K). The outgoing gases from the secondary reformer have the temperature 899°C (1172 K).

The chief chemical reactions taking place in the reformer are as follows.

Combustion reaction: exothermic

$$H_2 + (1/2\ O_2) = H_2O \tag{A}$$

Reforming reactions: endothermic

$$CH_4 + H_2O = CO + 3\ H_2 \tag{B}$$
$$CH_4 + 2\ H_2O = CO_2 + 4\ H_2 \tag{C}$$
$$C_2H_6 + 2\ H_2O = 2\ CO + 5\ H_2 \tag{D}$$
$$C_2H_6 + 4\ H_2O = 2\ CO_2 + 7\ H_2 \tag{E}$$

The exact extent of each reaction taking place in the secondary reformer is not known but the chemical equilibrium of the shift reaction at 899°C (1172 K) dictates that

$$\frac{(n_{CO_2})\,(n_{H_2})}{(n_{CO})\,(n_{H_2O})} = 0.642$$

where n_i is the number of moles of the ith component in the outgoing gases.

Assume that 96% methane is consumed. The aim of feeding air to the reformer is to provide sufficient nitrogen so that after shift converters, the ratio of $N_2 : H_2$

(on mole basis) becomes 1 : 3 (stoichiometric ratio for ammonia synthesis). Consider all oxygen entering with air is completely consumed in the secondary reformer. Based on 1000 kmol/h dry feed gas mixture, find the composition of the outgoing gases from the secondary reformer. Also, establish the heat balance over the reformer.

Solution   *Basis* 1000 kmol/h of dry incoming gases

The gas mixture contains 14 kmol C_2H_6, 81 kmol CH_4, 103 kmol CO, 164 kmol CO_2, 629 kmol H_2 and 9 kmol N_2 on hourly basis. Steam entering with the mixture is 1035 kmol/h.

Let a be the kmol/h of dry air fed

b be the kmol/h of CO in the product gas

c be the kmol/h of CO_2 in the product gas

d be the kmol/h of H_2 in the product gas

e be the kmol/h of steam in the product gas

Ethane is completely reformed, but methane is reformed to the extent of 96%.

Leftover methane in the product gas $= 81 \times 0.04 = 3.24$ kmol/h

Balance of carbon

Carbon in the incoming gas mixture $= 14 \times 2 + 81 + 103 + 164 = 376$ kmol/h

Carbon in the outgoing gas mixture $= b + c + 3.24$ kmol/h

$$b + c + 3.24 = 376$$
$$b + c = 372.76 \tag{i}$$

Balance of hydrogen

Hydrogen in the incoming gas mixture $= 3 \times 14 + 2 \times 81 + 629 + 1035$
$$= 1868 \text{ kmol/h}$$

Hydrogen in the moisture, entering with air $= 0.0176a$ kmol/h

Total hydrogen, entering the reformer $= (1868 + 0.0176a)$ kmol/h

Hydrogen in the outgoing gas mixture $= (d + e + 3.24 \times 2)$ kmol/h

$$d + e + 6.48 = 1868 + 0.0176a$$
$$d + e - 0.0176a = 1861.52 \tag{ii}$$

Balance of oxygen

$$\text{Oxygen in the incoming gas mixture} = \left(\frac{103}{2}\right) + 164 + \left(\frac{1035}{2}\right)$$

$$= 733 \text{ kmol/h}$$

$$\text{Oxygen entering through air} = 0.2098a + \left(\frac{0.0176}{2}\right)a$$

$$= 0.2186a \text{ kmol/h}$$

Oxygen in the outgoing gas mixture $= (b/2) + c + (e/2)$

$$(b/2) + c + (e/2) = 733 + 0.2186a$$
$$b + 2c + e - 0.4372a = 1466 \tag{iii}$$

Ratio of N_2: H_2

In shift reactors, the reaction taking place is

$$CO + H_2O = CO_2 + H_2 \tag{F}$$

Thus, in shift reactors, all CO will be consumed. At the outlet of the shift reactor, b kmol/h of H_2 will be added to the gaseous mixture.

Total H_2 in the gas mixture

at the outlet of shift reactor $= (b + d)$ kmol/h

Total N_2 in the reformer $= (0.7808a + 9)$ kmol/h

$$\frac{\text{No. of moles of } H_2}{\text{No. of moles of } N_2} = 3.0 \text{ (requirement)}$$

$$\frac{b + d}{(0.7808\,a + 9)} = 3$$

$$b + d = 2.3424a + 27 \qquad \text{(iv)}$$

At the outlet of the secondary reformer, shift conversion will be in accordance with

$$\frac{(n_{CO_2})\,(n_{H_2})}{(n_{CO})\,(n_{H_2O})} = 0.642$$

$$\frac{cd}{be} = 0.642 \qquad \text{(v)}$$

Mathcad solution

Guess values

a := 400   b := 190   c := 175   d := 700   e := 10000

Given

b + c = 372.76

d + e − 0.0176· a = 1861.52

b + 2 · c + e − 0.4372· a = 1466

b + d = 2.3424· a + 27

$$c \cdot \frac{d}{(b \cdot e)} = 0.642$$

vec := Find(a, b, c, d, e)

$$\text{vec} = \begin{pmatrix} 403.345 \\ 195.785 \\ 176.975 \\ 776.011 \\ 1.093 \times 10^3 \end{pmatrix} \frac{\text{kmol}}{\text{h}}$$

Argon in the outlet mixture $= 403.345 \times 0.0094 = 3.79$ kmol/h

Heat balance

Table 8.3 Enthalpy of Incoming Gas Mixture

Temperature of gas mixture = 816° C (1089 K)			
Component	$\dot{n}_i$ kmol/h,	$(H^o - H_0^o + \Delta H_f^o)_i^*$ kJ/kmol	$\dot{n}_i \cdot (H^o - H_0^o + \Delta H_f^o)_i$ kW
CH_4	81	– 12 066	– 271.474
C_2H_6	14	+ 18 221	+ 70.861
CO	103	– 80 632	– 2 306.973
CO_2	164	– 345 840	– 15 754.947
H_2	629	+ 31 785	+ 5 553.536
N_2	9	+ 32 993	+ 82.483
H_2O	1035	– 199 564	– 57 374.506
Total	2035		– 70 142.742

*From Table 5.22

Table 8.4 Enthalpy of Supply Air

Temperature of air = 482°C (755 K)			
Component	$\dot{n}_i$ kmol/h	$(H^o - H_2^o + \Delta H_f^o)_i$ kJ/kmol	$\dot{n}_i \cdot (H^o - H_0^o + \Delta H_f^o)_i$ kW
N2	314.94	+22 253	+ 1 946.733
O2	84.62	+22 921	+ 538.780
Ar	3.79	—	
H_2O	7.10	–213 001	– 420.086
Total	410.45	+2065.427	

Table 8.5 Enthalpy of Product Stream

Temperature of product stream = 899°C (1172 K)				
Component	$\dot{n}_i$ kmol/h	mole % (dry)	$(H^o - H_0^o + \Delta H_f^o)_i$ kJ/kmol	$\dot{n}_i \cdot (H^o - H_0^o + \Delta H_f^o)_i$ kW
CH_4	3.24	0.22	– 5 682	– 5.114
CO	195.79	13.23	– 77 823	– 4 232.296
CO_2	176.98	11.96	– 341 171	– 16 722.367
H_2	776.01	52.44	+ 34 335	+ 7 401.123
N_2	323.94	21.89	+ 35 762	+ 3 218.028
Ar	3.79	0.26	—	—
H_2O	1092.60	—	– 196 002	– 59 486.610
Total	2572.30	100.00		– 69827.236

Heat added to argon = $3.79 \times 20.7723 \,(1172.15 – 755.15)$

$\qquad\qquad\qquad\quad = 32\,829$ kJ/h $\equiv 9.119$ kW

Heat of reaction, ΔH_r = $-69\,827.236 + 9.119 – (-70\,142.742 + 2065.427)$

$\qquad\qquad\qquad\quad = \mathbf{-1740.802}$ **kW (exothermic)**

Note

(i) In this example, it is said that 96% of CH_4 entering the reformer is reformed. During actual design calculations, the approach to the equilibrium of methane–steam reforming is also to be considered. This will complicate the problem further.

(ii) For heat balance calculation, absolute enthalpies at 1 bar a are used. However, actual reactions take place at 30 bar a which means ΔH_r will slightly vary at high pressure. In actual practice, ΔH_r is marginally exothermic which indicates heat loss from the system.

Example 8.3 Portland cement (33 grade) is manufactured by the dry process conforming to the following specifications.

(i) Lime saturation ratio: $\dfrac{(CaO - 0.7\ SO_3)}{(2.8\ SiO_2 + 1.2\ Al_2O_3 + 0.65\ Fe_2O_3)} = 0.9$

(ii) Iron ratio, $\dfrac{Al_2O_3}{Fe_2O_3} = 2.4$ (0.66 min.)

(iii) Magnesia content and sulphur (as SO_3) should not exceed 1.0% and 2.4% (by mass), respectively.

(iv) Silica content of 23% (by mass) is normally acceptable.

The above cement is manufactured in a rotary kiln by using milliolite limestone and clay as raw materials. The analysis of the raw materials is given in Table 8.6. Both the raw materials are to be mixed in 72 : 28 proportion by mass.

Table 8.6 Analysis of Raw Materials

Compound	Milliolite limestone (Porbandar, Gujarat), mass %	Clay, mass %
CaO	54.50	7.13
Fe_2O_3	0.42	7.68
Al_2O_3	0.83	17.15
SiO_2	1.72	55.14
MgO	0.85	2.16
Loss on ignition	41.68	10.74

In the kiln, Andrew Yule's coal (West Bengal's colliery) is also added to supply the heat of combustion. Coal contains C: 67.2%, H: 4.0%, S: 1.7%, O: 2.2%, H_2O: 2.6% and ash: 22.3% (by mass). The gross calorific value of the coal is 25 620 kJ/kg on dry ash-free basis. It is burnt with 10% excess air.

The details of fresh air entering the kiln and the Orsat analysis of stack gases are given in Table 8.7.

Table 8.7 Conditions of Fresh Air and Stack Gases

Inlet fresh air	27°C (300 K) Dry-bulb temperature
	20°C (293 K) Wet-bulb temperature
	100 kPa (750 Torr) Barometric pressure
Stack gases	800°C (1073 K) Dry-bulb temperature
	101.3 kPa (760 Torr) Barometric pressure

The CO_2 content of the stack gas mixture needs to be limited to 23.5% by volume. The clinker obtained from the end of the kiln is cooled and gypsum (essentially pure $CaSO_4$), amounting to 3% (by mass), is added to it. The final mixture is the required product which is crushed to the desired fineness. On the basis of 20 t/h production of Portland cement, calculate

(a) The composition of the final Portland cement
(b) The hydraulic modulus of the cement, i.e., evaluate the ratio $CaO/(SiO_2 + Al_2O_3 + Fe_2O_3)$
(c) The lime–silica ratio CaO/SiO_2
(d) The silica modulus $SiO_2/(Al_2O_3 + Fe_2O_3)$
(e) The analysis of the clinker, obtained from the kiln
(f) It is known that the iron in the clinker is present in the form of tetracalcium aluminoferrite (4 $CaO.Al_2O_3$. Fe_2O_3). The remaining alumina combines with burnt lime to form tricalcium aluminate (3 CaO. Al_2O_3). Remaining silica and burnt lime form dicalcium (2 CaO. SiO_2) and tricalcium (3 $CaO.SiO_2$) silicates. Based on this information, find the chemical constitution of the clinker.
(g) The analysis of raw mix
(h) The Orsat analysis of stack gases
(i) The percentage of total sulphur of the coal going into the stack gases
(j) The amount of limestone, clay and coal required to be fed to the kiln per hour
(k) The volumetric flow rate of the fresh air
(l) The volumetric flow rate of dry stack gas and the dew point of stack gases
The following assumptions can be made in the calculations.
(i) Complete combustion of the coal takes place.
(ii) Negligible SO_2 or SO_3 is present in the stack gases. It may be deleted while calculating the analysis of stack gases.
(iii) No significant calcined products of raw materials are lost in the stack gases (in the form of dust).
(iv) Sulphur present in the clinker is absorbed in it in the form of SO_3 and forms sulphate.

Solution   *Basis* 100 kg of Portland cement
$$SO_3 \text{ content of the cement} = 2.4 \text{ kg}$$
Now let a, b and c be the mass (in kg) of CaO, Al_2O_3 and Fe_2O_3, respectively in the cement.
$$a + b + c = 100 - (23.0 + 1.0 + 2.4) = 73.6 \text{ kg} \quad \text{(i)}$$
$$\frac{(CaO - 0.7 SO_3)}{(2.8 SiO_2 + 1.2 Al_2O_3 + 0.65 Fe_2O_3)} = 0.9$$
$$\frac{(a - 0.7 \times 2.4)}{(2.8 \times 23 + 1.2b + 0.65c)} = 0.9$$
$$a - 1.08\,b - 0.585\,c = 59.68 \quad \text{(ii)}$$
Also,
$$\frac{Al_2O_3}{Fe_2O_3} = 2.4$$
$$\frac{b}{c} = 2.4$$
or,
$$b = 2.4\,c \quad \text{(iii)}$$
Solving the three equations,
$$a = 66.4 \text{ kg CaO}$$
$$b = 5.08 \text{ kg Al}_2O_3$$
$$c = 2.12 \text{ kg Fe}_2O_3$$

Hydraulic modules

$$\frac{CaO}{(SiO_2 + Al_2O_3 + Fe_2O_3)} = \frac{66.4}{(23.0 + 5.08 + 2.12)} = 2.2$$

Lime–silica ratio

$$\frac{CaO}{SiO_2} = \frac{66.4}{23.0} = 2.887$$

Silica modules

$$\frac{SiO_2}{(Al_2O_3 + Fe_2O_3)} = \frac{23.0}{(5.08 + 2.12)} = 3.19$$

Let d be the mass of the clinker.

$CaSO_4$ added to the clinker = 0.03 d kg

Total cement = 1.03 × d kg = 100 kg

d = 97.1 kg

$CaSO_4$ in the clinker = 100 – 97.1 = 2.9 kg

1 kmol of $CaSO_4$ ≡ 1 kmol of CaO ≡ 1 kmol of SO_3

$$2.9 \text{ kg } CaSO_4 \equiv 2.9 \left(\frac{56}{136}\right) \equiv 1.2 \text{ kg } CaO$$

$$2.9 \text{ kg } CaSO_4 \equiv \left(\frac{80}{136}\right) \times 2.9 \equiv 1.7 \text{ kg } SO_3$$

Using the above figures, Table 8.8 is prepared.

Table 8.8 Composition of Clinker and Cement

Compound	Molar mass	Clinker		Cement	
		kg	mass %	kg	mass %
CaO	56	65.20	67.15	66.40	**66.40**
Al_2O_3	102	5.08	5.23	5.08	**5.08**
Fe_2O_3	160	2.12	2.18	2.12	**2.12**
SiO_2	60	23.00	23.69	23.00	**23.00**
MgO	40.3	1.00	1.03	1.00	**1.00**
SO_3	80	0.70	0.72	2.40	**2.40**
Total		97.10	100.00	100.00	**100.00**

Chemical constitution of the clinker

Table 8.9 Molar Mass of Clinker-forming Compounds

Compound	Molar Mass
4 $CaO.Al_2O_3.Fe_2O_3$	486
3 $CaO.Al_2O_3$	270
2 $CaO.SiO_2$	172
3 $CaO.SiO_2$	228

Basis 97.10 kg of clinker

All iron is present in the form of 4 $CaO.Al_2O_3.Fe_2O_3$.

Clinker contains 2.12 kg Fe_2O_3.

$$4\ CaO.Al_2O_3.Fe_2O_3 = \left(\frac{486}{160}\right) \times 2.12 = 6.44\ kg$$

$$Al_2O_3 \text{ in the above complex} = \left(\frac{102}{160}\right) \times 2.12 = 1.35\ kg$$

$$CaO \text{ in the above complex} = \frac{(56 \times 4 \times 2.12)}{160} = 2.97\ kg$$

$$\text{Remainder } Al_2O_3 = 5.08 - 1.35 = 3.73\ kg$$

This remainder Al_2O_3 forms 3 $CaO.Al_2O_3$.

$$\text{Amount of 3 } CaO.Al_2O_3 = \left(\frac{270}{102}\right) 3.73 = 9.87\ kg$$

As per IS: 269-1989, tricalcium aluminate is also calculated by

Amount of $3\,CaO.Al_2O_3$ = 2.65 (Amt. of Al_2O_3) – 1.69 (Amt. of Fe_2O_3)
$$= 9.88\ kg$$

This tallies closely with 9.87 kg calculated above. For tricalcium aluminate content of more than 5%, SO_3 content up to 3% is permitted.

CaO in this complex = 9.87 – 3.73 = 6.14 kg

CaO remained unaccounted = 65.20 – (2.97 + 6.14) = 56.09 kg

The remainder CaO forms dicalcium and tricalcium silicates.

Let e be the weight of 2 $CaO.SiO_2$ and f be the mass of 3 $CaO.SiO_2$.

$$e + f = 56.09 + 23 = 79.09 \tag{iv}$$

Balance of SiO_2

$$\left(\frac{60}{172}\right)e + \left(\frac{60}{228}\right)f = 23.0$$

$$e + 0.754\,f = 65.90 \tag{v}$$

Solving Eqs. (4) and (5),

$$e = 25.47\ kg$$
$$f = 53.62\ kg$$

Table 8.10   Chemical Construction of Clinker

Compound	Mass, kg	mass %
4 $CaO.Al_2O_3.Fe_2O_3$	6.44	**6.63**
3 $CaO.Al_2O_3$	9.87	**10.17**
2 $CaO.SiO_2$	25.47	**26.23**
3 $CaO.SiO_2$	53.62	**55.22**
SO_3	0.70	**0.72**
MgO	1.00	**1.03**
Total	97.10	**100.00**

The raw mix is a mixture of milliolite limestone and clay in 72 : 28 proportion.

Basis 100 kg of raw mix

CaO in the raw mix = 0.545 × 72 + 0.0713 × 28 = 41.24 kg

SiO_2 in the raw mix = 0.0172 × 72 + 0.5514 × 28 = 16.68 kg

Fe_2O_3 in the raw mix $= 0.0042 \times 72 + 0.0768 \times 28 = 2.45$ kg
Al_2O_3 in the raw mix $= 0.0083 \times 72 + 0.1715 \times 28 = 5.40$ kg
MgO in the raw mix $= 0.0085 \times 72 + 0.0216 \times 28 = 1.22$ kg
Loss on ignition $= 100 - (41.24 + 16.68 + 2.45 + 5.40 + 1.22)$
$$= 33.01 \text{ kg (assumed to be } CO_2)$$

The above calculations give mass percentage analysis of raw-mix directly as the basis of calculations in 100 kg. Also, it can be regarded that loss on ignition is due to CO_2 alone. All other volatile matters like moisture will be very little and can be neglected.

Basis 100 kg of coal
The oxygen requirement is shown in Table 8.11.

Table 8.11 Oxygen Requirement of Coal

Element	Mass, kg	kmol	O_2 requirement, kmol
Carbon	67.2	5.600	5.6
Hydrogen	4.0	2.000	1.0
Sulphur	1.7	0.053	0.053
Total	72.9	7.653	6.653

Oxygen present in coal $= 2.2$ kg $= 0.069$ kmol
Theoretical oxygen requirement $= 6.653 - 0.069 = 6.584$ kmol
Excess O_2 supply $= 10\%$
Actual O_2 supply $= 1.1 \times 6.584 = 7.242$ kmol

$$N_2 \text{ entering with } O_2 \text{ in air} = \left(\frac{79}{21}\right) \times 7.242 = 27.244 \text{ kmol}$$

Fresh dry air supply $= 27.244 + 7.242 = 34.486$ kmol

Assuming complete combustion, O_2 consumption can be calculated. For CO_2 and H_2O formation, O_2 consumption will be the same as listed above in Table 8.11. However, S gets oxidised to SO_3 and not to SO_2.

$$O_2 \text{ consumption for } SO_3 = \left(\frac{3}{2}\right) \times 0.053 = 0.08 \text{ kmol}$$

Total O_2 consumed $= 5.6 + 1.0 + 0.08 = 6.68$ kmol
Oxygen unreacted $= 7.242 + 0.069 - 6.68 = 0.631$ kmol
This unreacted O_2 will appear in stack gases.

$$\text{Ratio } O_2/N_2 \text{ in stack gases} = \frac{0.631}{27.244} = \frac{1}{43.176}$$

Composition of stack gases
Basis 100 kmol of stack gases
CO_2 in the stack gases $= 23.5$ kmol
$(O_2 + N_2)$ in the stack gases $= 100 - 23.5 = 76.5$ kmol
Let g be the kmoles of O_2 in stack gases.
$$g + 43.176\,g = 76.5 \qquad\qquad \text{(vi)}$$
$$\boldsymbol{g = 1.732 \text{ kmol } O_2}$$

Table 8.12 Analysis of Stack Gases

Component	mole % (dry basis)
CO_2	23.50
O_2	1.732
N_2	74.768
Total	100.00

In order to evaluate the actual consumptions of limestone, clay and coal, refer to the basis of the 100 kg clinker.

Let h be the mass of the raw mix, i be the mass of coal and j be the kmol of stack gases.

For finding the three unknowns, three simultaneous equations are required.

Now considering the analysis of the raw mix, coal and clinker, it will superficially appear that the S balance is the easiest balance. However, this balance should not be tried as it will lead to a wrong answer because it is assumed that all the S will be absorbed in the clinker in the form of SO_3 to form sulphate. This is not cent per cent true. The distribution of S in the clinker and stack gases is usually unknown.

Balance of non-volatile oxides
From the analysis of the clinker [*Ans.* (e)] it is clear that $(100 - 0.72 =)$ 99.28 kg is the total amount of non-volatile oxides.

$$\text{Amount of non-volatile oxides from raw mix} = \frac{(100 - 33.01)\,h}{100} = 0.6699\,h$$

Ash present in the coal comprises non-volatile oxides.

$$\text{Amount of ash in coal} = 0.223\,i \text{ kg}$$
$$0.6699\,h + 0.223\,i = 99.28 \tag{vii}$$

Balance of carbon

$$\text{Carbon present in the coal} = \left(\frac{67.2}{100}\right) \times i \times \left(\frac{1}{12}\right) = 0.056\,i \text{ kmol}$$

CO_2 (ignition loss) in the raw mix is the source of carbon in the mix.

$$\text{Carbon from the raw mix} = \left(\frac{33.07}{44}\right)\left(\frac{1}{100}\right)h = 0.0075\,h \text{ kmol}$$

The stack gases have 23.5 mole % CO_2.
$$0.056\,i + 0.0075\,h = 0.235\,j \tag{viii}$$

Balance of oxygen
(O_2 from air) + (O_2 from raw mix) + (O_2 from coal) = (O_2 in stack gas) + (O_2 for H in coal) + (O_2 for S in coal)

$$\left[\left(\frac{21}{79}\right) \times (0.7477)\right]j + \left[\frac{33.07}{(44 \times 100)}\right]h + \left[\frac{2.2}{(32 \times 100)}\right]i$$
$$= \left(\frac{23.5}{100}\right)j + \left(\frac{1.732}{100}\right)j + \left(\frac{4}{(2 \times 2 \times 100)}\right)i + \left[\frac{3 \times 1.7}{2 \times 100 \times 32}\right]i$$
$$0.75\,h - 1.01\,i = 5.36\,j \tag{ix}$$

Solving Eqs. (vii), (viii) and (ix),

$$h = 136.69 \text{ kg raw-mix}$$
$$i = 34.57 \text{ kg coal}$$
$$j = 12.61 \text{ kmol stack gases}$$

(Note that in above calculations, the moisture entering with the air is neglected. However, it does not affect the final results of h, i and j).

Now, the balance of S can be made.

$$\text{S present in coal} = 34.57 \times 0.017 = 0.59 \text{ kg}$$

$$\text{S in the clinker} = \left(\frac{32}{80}\right) \times 0.72 = 0.29 \text{ kg}$$

$$\text{Unaccounted S} = 0.59 - 0.29 = 0.3 \text{ kg}$$

This S goes into stack gases.

$$\% \text{ S going into the stack gases} = \left(\frac{0.3}{0.59}\right) 100 = \mathbf{50.85\%}$$

All the above results can be converted into a basis of 20 000 kg/h of Portland cement.

Basis 20 000 kg/h of Portland cement

Clinker output of the kiln = 20 000 × 0.971 = 19 420 kg/h

$$\text{Raw mix required} = \left(\frac{136.69}{100}\right) \times 19\,420 = 26\,545 \text{ kg/h}$$

Limestone required = 0.72 × 26 545 = **19 112.4 kg/h**

Clay required = 26 545 − 19 112.4 = **7432.6 kg/h**

$$\text{Coal required} = \left(\frac{46.39}{100}\right) \times 19\,420 = \mathbf{9009 \text{ kg/h}}$$

$$\frac{\text{Coal}}{\text{Raw mix ratio}} = \frac{9009}{26\,545} = \mathbf{0.3394 \text{ kg/kg}}$$

$$\text{Dry-air required, } \dot{n}_i = 34.486 \times \left(\frac{9009}{100}\right) = 3106.8 \text{ kmol/h}$$

From Fig. 6.15, specific volume of air, vh = 25.523 m³/kg dry air

Volumetric flow rate of dry air = 3106.8 × 25.523

$$= \mathbf{79\,295 \text{ m3/ h}}$$

$$\text{Stack gases, } \dot{n}_2 = 12.61 \times \left(\frac{19\,420}{100}\right) = 2448.9 \text{ kmol/h}$$

Volumetric flow rate of stack gases = $\dot{n}_2 RT_2/p_2$

$$= \frac{(2448.9 \times 8.3145 \times 1073)}{101.325}$$

$$= \mathbf{215\,620.6 \text{ m}^3/\text{h}}$$

From the psychrometric chart (Fig. 6.15), at 27°C (300 K) *DB* and 20°C (293 K) *WB*,

$$\text{Absolute humidity} = 0.0118 \text{ kg moisture/kg dry air}$$
$$= 0.019 \text{ kmol moisture/kmol dry air}$$

Basis 100 kg of coal

Moisture entering the system through air = 0.019 × 34.486 = 0.655 kmol

Free moisture of coal = 2.8 kg = 0.156 kmol

Moisture produced by burning net hydrogen of coal = $\dfrac{4}{2}$ = 2 kmol

Total moisture in stack gases = 0.655 + 0.155 + 2 = 2.81 kmol

$$\text{Stack gas} = \frac{(12.61 \times 100)}{34.57} = 36.48 \text{ kmol}$$

Mole fraction of moisture in stack gases = $\dfrac{2.81}{(36.48 + 2.81)}$ = 0.0715

Partial pressure of water in stack gases, p_w = 101.325 × 0.0715
= 7.245 kPa

Dew point = **39.65°C (312.8 K)** (Ref. Table 6.13)

Notes

(i) Various ratios, such as hydraulic modules, silica modules, etc., are calculated as these ratios are very well known in the cement industry. The quality of the cement can be judged if these ratios are known.

(ii) Chemical constitution of the clinker gives an idea about the complexes forming in the cement and the crystallinity of the clinker.

(iii) In the example cited, raw mix is composed of limestone and clay. However, the use of blast furnace slag is also common. Separate specifications are available for the cement manufactured by using blast furnace slag (IS: 455).

(iv) It was assumed that stack gases do not contain carbon monoxide. However, this is rarely true. A small amount of CO is always present in the stack gases.

(v) Before utilizing the waste heat of stack gases, the particulate matter is usually removed by using a cyclone separator and/or an electrostatic precipitator or a multi-bag filter. Later, they are passed through a heat exchanger where the water is heated and steam is generated (in waste heat boiler).

(vi) It is interesting to study the heat balance of the cement manufacture. Lewis *et al*[3] have worked out the heat balance to which the reference is made.

Example 8.4 A chloromethanes production facility is to be designed on the basis of technology[4], developed by the Tokuyama Corporation, Japan. In this technology, methanol, chlorine and hydrogen chloride gas are used as raw materials. The simplified process is shown in Fig. 8.3.

The first reaction is known as hydrochlorination reaction in which methanol vapour and hydrogen chloride gas (fresh + recycle) react to form methyl chloride.

$$CH_3OH(g) + HCl(g) = CH_3Cl(g) + H_2O(g)$$

In the reactor, side reaction also takes place to produce dimethylether (DME).

$$2\ CH_3OH(g) = (CH_3)_2O(g) + H_2O(g)$$

Byproduct (DME) formation can be controlled by selecting proper operating conditions and a reaction-specific catalyst. The reactor is a shell-and-tube heat exchanger and a proprietary γ-Al_2O_3 catalyst is packed in the tubes. In the shell, exothermic heat of reaction is picked up by water and produces saturated steam at 6 bar a in the associated steam drum. Boiler feed water is supplied at 25°C (298.15 K) to the drum.

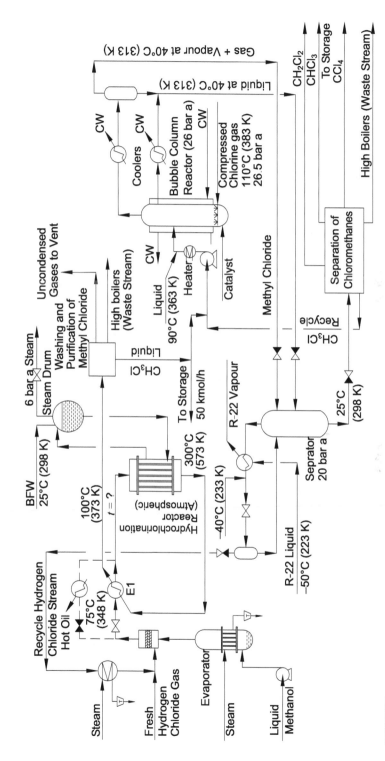

Fig. 8.3 Manufacture of Chloromethanes (Tokuyama Process)

The feed mixture consists of methanol vapour and dry hydrogen chloride gas (neglect recycled impurities for stoichiometric calculations) at 75°C (348 K) in the molar ratio of 1.14, exchange heat with outcoming gas mixture from the reactor. Space velocity of 910 h^{-1} is kept in the reactor. Reaction outlet temperature is controlled at 300°C (573 K).

Conversion of methanol is 93.8% while the selectivity of the reaction of methyl chloride formation is 125. Outcoming gas mixture first exchanges heat with incoming gas mixture and is cooled to 100°C (373 K). Further, it is washed with water to remove unreacted methanol and hydrogen chloride. Recovered aqueous methanol is sent to the distillation column for concentration. It is further washed with concentrated sulphuric acid to remove DME and water. Purified methyl chloride is liquefied. A part of the liquid product is stored while another part is sent to the chlorination reactor. This reactor is basically a bubble column reactor, operating at 26 bar a in cocurrent mode. Chlorine is bubbled at the bottom at 26.6 bar a and 110°C (383 K) in the molar ratio of 0.88 kmol/kmol methy chloride. Liquid methyl chloride is fed at 90°C (363 K) at the bottom. A propietary soluble catalyst is used in very low concentration (say a few mg/L) which also gets chlorinated in the reactor, forming high boiling compound. It can be easily separated from the product mixture during distillation. For stoichiometric calculations, neglect presence of the catalyst and its chlorination. Liquid and gaseous product mixtures come out from top under pressure. Both are separately taken to heat exchagers in which they are cooled to 40°C (313 K). A part of the reaction heat is also removed in the jacket. Cooling water is used in the jacket and the coolers and its temperature increase from 32°C (305 K) to 38°C (311 K). Both the streams are then flashed to 20 bar a in a separator. A chiller is provided at the top of the separator which cools the flashed gas–vapour mixture to −40°C (233 K) by evaporating refrigerant (R-22) in the shell at −50°C (223 K) and 0.64 bar a. Bottom liquid product mixture at 25°C (298 K) is processed in a series of distillation towers to separate all chloromethanes in pure form. Consider recycle quantity of methyl chloride as 98% of that in the bottom mixture of the separator. Rest chloromethanes are taken to storage.

Methyl chloride is fed at the rate of 100 kmol/h to the bubble column reactor. Also, it is desired to produce 50 kmol/h of methyl chloride for sale. Reactions taking place in the chlorination reactor are

$$CH_3Cl(l) + Cl_2(g) = CH_2Cl_2(l) + HCl(g)$$
$$CH_3Cl(l) + 2\ Cl_2(g) = CHCl_3(l) + 2\ HCl(g)$$
$$CH_3Cl(l) + 3\ Cl_2(g) = CCl_4(l) + 3\ HCl(g)$$

Reactor outgoing mixture is analysed to contain 41% CH_3Cl, 33% CH_2Cl_2, 23% $CHCl_3$ and 3% CCl_4 by mole on HCl-free basis.

Establish material and energy balances of both reactors. Also calculate (a) temperature of reactants' mixture entering hydrochlorination reactor, (b) steam generation rate, and (c) cooling load of the jacket of the bubble column reactor and coolers.

Data   Average heat capacity of DME = 28.6 kJ/(kmol · K)

Solution

Basis 100 kmol/h of product mixture on HCl-free basis from bubble column reactor.

Table 8.13 Products from Bubble Column Reactor

Component	$\dot{n}_2$ kmol/h	Equivalent CH_3Cl requirement, kmol/h	Equivalent Cl_2 requirement, kmol/h
CH_3Cl	41	41	—
CH_2Cl_2	33	33	33
$CHCl_3$	23	23	46
CCl_4	3	3	9
Total	100	100	88

Thus required feed rate of CH_3Cl = 100 kmol/h

Molar feed ratio, $\dfrac{\text{Chlorine}}{\text{Methyl Chloride}} = \dfrac{88}{100} = 0.88$

Energy input

Reference temperature T_o = 298.15 K

Methyl Chloride is fed at 90°C (363.15 K)

Enthalpy of methyl chloride liquid at 363.15 K over 298.15 K,

ϕ_1 = 100 [72.77(363.15 − 298.15) − 44.0239 × 10^{-3} (363.15^2 − 298.15^2)/2 + 229.4864 × 10^{-6} (363.15^3 − 298.15^3)/3]

= 100 (4730.0 − 946.2 + 1636.1)

= 541 990 kJ/h ≡ 150.553 kW

Chlorine gas is fed at 110°C (383.15 K).

Enthalpy of cholrine gas at 383.15 K over 298.15 K,

ϕ_2 = 88[28.5463 (383.15 − 298.15) + 23.8795 × 10^{-3} (383.15^2 − 298.15^2)/2 − 21.3631 × 10^{-6} (383.15^3 − 298.15^3)/3 + 6.4726 × 10^{-9} (383.15^4 − 298.15^4)/4]

= 88 (2426.4 + 691.4 − 211.8 + 22.0)

= 257 664 kJ/h ≡ 71.573 kW

Standard heats of reactions

Reaction 1 $CH_3Cl(l) + Cl_2(g) = CH_2Cl_2(l) + HCl(g)$

ΔH_{r1}^o = −124.1 − 92.31 − (−102.4)

= −114.01 kJ/mol CH_3Cl

Reaction 2 $CH_3Cl(l) + 2Cl_2(g) = CHCl_3(l) + 2\,HCl(g)$

ΔH_{r2}^o = −134.6 + 2 (−92.31) − (−102.4)

= −216.82 kJ/mol CH_3Cl

Reaction 3 $CH_3Cl(l) + 3\,Cl_2(g) = CCl_4(l) + 3\,HCl(g)$

ΔH_{r3}^o = −135.5 + 3 (−92.31) − (−102.4)

= −310.03 kJ/mol CH_3Cl

All are exothermic reactions.

Total heat of reaction, ϕ_3 = 114.01 × 1000 × 33 + 216.82 × 1000 × 23 + 310.03 × 1000 × 3

= 3762 330 + 4986 860 + 930 090 = 9679 280 kJ/h

≡ 2688.689 kW (exothermic)

Vapour–HCl mixture is cooled to 40°C (313.15 K).

Vapour pressures Use Antoine equation.

$$CH_3Cl : \log p_{v1} = 4.918\ 58 - \frac{1427.529}{(313.15 + 45.137)} = 0.934\ 26$$

$$p_{v1} = 8.595 \text{ bar at } 313.15 \text{ K}$$

$$CH_2Cl_2 : \log p_{v2} = 3.973\ 23 - \frac{1016.865}{(313.15 - 56.623)} = 0.009\ 26$$

$$p_{v2} = 1.022 \text{ bar at } 313.15 \text{ K}$$

$$CHCl_3 : \log p_{v3} = 4.207\ 72 - \frac{1233.129}{(313.15 - 40.953)} = -0.32\ 256$$

$$p_{v3} = 0.476 \text{ bar at } 313.15 \text{ K}$$

$$CCl_4 : \log p_{v4} = 4.022\ 91 - \frac{1221.781}{(313.15 - 45.739)} = -0.546\ 02$$

$$p_{v4} = 0.284 \text{ bar at } 313.15 \text{ K}$$

At high pressure, *modified* Raoult's law (incorporating activity coefficient) is more appropriate. However, considering similar nature of the chemicals, apply Raoult's law for calculation of partical pressures.

$$p_1 = 8.593 \times 0.41 = 3.5231 \text{ bar}$$
$$p_2 = 1.022 \times 0.33 = 0.3373 \text{ bar}$$
$$p_3 = 0.476 \times 0.23 = 0.1095 \text{ bar}$$
$$p_4 = 0.284 \times 0.03 = 0.0085 \text{ bar}$$

Total pressure, $\quad p = 26 \text{ bar a}$

Partial pressure of HCl,

$$p_{HCl} = 26 - 3.5231 - 0.3373 - 0.1095 - 0.0085$$
$$= 22.0216 \text{ bar}$$

CH_3Cl content of gas phase at 40°C (313.15 K)

$$\dot{n}_{CH_2Cl} = \frac{3.5231 \times 88}{22.0216} = 14.0786 \text{ kmol/h}$$

Similarly, $\quad \dot{n}_{CH_2Cl_2} = \frac{0.3373 \times 88}{22.0216} = 1.3479 \text{ kmol/h}$

$$\dot{n}_{CHCl_3} = \frac{0.1095 \times 88}{22.0216} = 0.4376 \text{ kmol/h}$$

$$\dot{n}_{CCl_4} = \frac{0.0085 \times 88}{22.0216} = 0.034 \text{ kmol/h}$$

Table 8.14 Gas–vapour Mixture at 40°C (313.15 K)

Component	$\dot{n}_i$ kmol/h	mole %	Heat Capacity Equation Constants			
			$\dot{n}_i \cdot a_i$	$\dot{n}_i \cdot b_i \times 10^3$	$\dot{n}_i \cdot c_i \times 10^6$	$\dot{n}_i \cdot d_i \times 10^9$
CH_3Cl	14.0786	13.55	193.3	1440.2	−571.6	48.5
CH_2Cl_2	1.3479	1.30	16.0	232.2	−201.2	70.5
$CHCl_3$	0.4376	0.42	10.5	82.8	−80.5	29.1
CCl_4	0.0340	0.03	1.4	7.0	−7.7	3.0
HCl	88.0000	84.70	2667.2	−66.96	1167.0	−381.4
Total	103.8981	100.00	2888.4	1092.6	306.0	−230.3

Enthalpy of gas–vapour mixture at 313.15 K over 298.15 K,

$\phi_4 = 2888.4 \ (313.15 - 298.15) + 1092.6 \times 10^{-3} \ (313.15^2 - 298.15^2)/2$
$+ \ 306.0 \times 10^{-6} \ (313.15^3 - 298.15^3)/3 - 230.3 \times 10^{-9} \ (313.15^4 - 298.15^4)/4$
$= 43 \ 326 + 5009.3 + 428.9 - 98.7$
$= 48 \ 665.5 \ \text{kJ/h} \equiv 13.518 \ \text{kW}$

Table 8.15 Liquid Mixture at 40°C (313.15 K)

Compo-nent	$\dot{n}_i$ kmol/h	mole %	Heat Capacity Equation Constants		
			$\dot{n}_i \cdot a_i$	$\dot{n}_i \cdot b_i \times 10^3$	$\dot{n}_i \cdot c_i \times 10^6$
CH_3Cl	$41 - 14.0786 = 26.9214$	32.01	1959.1	−1185.2	6178.1
CH_2Cl_2	$33 - 1.3479 = 31.6521$	37.63	3706.8	−4736.2	19 506.4
$CHCl_3$	$23 - 0.4376 = 22.5624$	26.83	2494.0	−2742.8	9951.7
CCl_4	$3 - 0.0340 = 2.9660$	3.53	414.4	−606.5	1740.7
Total		84.1019	100.00	8574.3	−9270.7	37 376.6

Enthalpy if liquid mixture at 313.15 K over 298.15 K,

$\phi_5 = 8574.3 \ (313.15 - 298.15) - 9270.7 \times 10^{-3} \ (313.15^2 - 298.15^2)/2 + 37 \ 376.6$
$\times \ 10^{-6} \ (313.15^3 - 298.15^3)/3$
$= 128 \ 614.5 - 42 \ 503.8 + 52 \ 387.4$
$= 138 \ 498.1 \ \text{kJ/h} \equiv 38.472 \ \text{kW}$

Chloromethanes are present in the vapours. It will be considered that the evaporation of all liquids takes place at 25°C (298.15 K) and subsequently the mixture is heated from 298.15 K to 313.15 K.

Latent heat of evaporation at 25°C (298.15 K).

Use of Watson equation is made (Ref. Table 5.5).

For CH_3Cl : $\dfrac{\lambda_{v1}}{21.535} = \left[\dfrac{416.25 - 298.15}{416.25 - 248.94} \right]^{0.38}$ $\quad \lambda_{v1} = 18.865 \ \text{kJ/mol}$

For CH_2Cl_2 : $\dfrac{\lambda_{v2}}{28.06} = \left[\dfrac{508 - 298.15}{508 - 313} \right]^{0.38}$ $\quad \lambda_{v2} = 28.854 \ \text{kJ/mol}$

For $CHCl_3$: $\dfrac{\lambda_{v3}}{29.24} = \left[\dfrac{536.2 - 298.15}{536.2 - 334.3} \right]^{0.38}$ $\quad \lambda_{v3} = 31.129 \ \text{kJ/mol}$

For CCl_4 : $\dfrac{\lambda_{v4}}{29.82} = \left[\dfrac{556.3 - 298.15}{556.3 - 349.9} \right]^{0.38}$ $\quad \lambda_{v4} = 32.466 \ \text{kJ/mol}$

Evaporation energy

$\phi_6 = 14.0786 \times 1000 \times 18.865 + 1.3479 \times 1000 \times 28.854 + 0.4376 \times 1000 \times 31.129$
$+ \ 0.034 \times 1000 \times 32.466$
$= 265 \ 592.8 + 38 \ 892.3 + 13 \ 622 + 1103.8$
$= 319 \ 210.9 \ \text{kJ/h} \equiv 88.670 \ \text{kW}$

Cooling load of jacket and coolers,

$\phi_7 = \phi_1 + \phi_2 + \phi_3 - \phi_4 - \phi_5 - \phi_6$
$= 541 \ 990 + 9679 \ 280 + 257 \ 664 - 48 \ 665.5 - 138 \ 498.1 - 319 \ 210.9$
$= 9972 \ 558.5 \ \text{kJ/h} \equiv 2770.155 \ \text{kW}$

For a rise of 6 K in CW temperature,

$$\dot{m}_{CW} = \frac{9972\,559.5}{6 \times 4.1868}$$

$$= 396\,984 \text{ kg/h} \equiv 397 \text{ m}^3/\text{h}$$

After flashing in the separtor at 20 bar a, gas–vapour mixture is cooled to -40°C (233.15 K) in the chiller. Using Antoine equations, vapour pressures are calculated as under at 233.15 K.

$p'_{v1} = 0.4864$ bar of CH_3Cl $\qquad p'_{v3} = 0.0062$ bar of $CHCl_3$
$p'_{v2} = 0.0198$ bar of CH_2Cl_2 $\qquad p'_{v4} = 0.0032$ bar a of CCl_4

To find partial pressure of each component, trial-and-error method is required. However, vapour pressures are quite low in comparison to total pressure (20 bar a). Hence, vapour pressures will be assumed to be the partial pressures.

Partial pressure of HCl,

$$\dot{n}'_{HCl} = 20 - 0.4864 - 0.0198 - 0.0062 - 0.0032 = 19.4844 \text{ bar}$$

$$\dot{n}'_{CH_3Cl} = \frac{0.4864 \times 88}{19.4844} = 2.1968 \text{ kmol/h}$$

$$\dot{n}'_{CH_2Cl_2} = \frac{0.0198 \times 88}{19.4844} = 0.0894 \text{ kmol/h}$$

$$\dot{n}'_{CHCl_3} = \frac{0.0062 \times 88}{19.4844} = 0.028 \text{ kmol/h}$$

$$\dot{n}'_{CCl_4} = \frac{0.0032 \times 88}{19.4844} = 0.0145 \text{ kmol/h}$$

Table 8.16 Gas–vapour Mixture Exit of Chiller at 233.15 K

Component	$\dot{n}_i$ kmol/h	mole %	Heat Capacity Equation Constants			
			$\dot{n}_i \cdot a_i$	$\dot{n}_i \cdot b_i \times 10^3$	$\dot{n}_i \cdot c_i \times 10^6$	$\dot{n}_i \cdot d_i \times 10^9$
CH_3Cl	2.1968	2.43	30.2	224.7	−89.2	7.6
CH_2Cl_2	0.0894	0.10	1.1	15.4	−13.3	4.7
$CHCl_3$	0.0280	0.03	0.9	4.1	−3.1	0.9
CCl_4	0.0145	0.02	0.6	3.0	−3.3	1.3
HCl	88.000	97.42	2667.2	−669.6	1167.0	−381.4
Total	90.3307	100.00	2700.0	−422.4	1058.1	−366.9

Enthalpy of gas-vapour miture at 233.15 K over 298.15 K.

$$\phi_8 = 2700\,(233.15 - 298.15) - 422.4 \times 10^{-3}\,(233.15^2 - 298.15^2)/2$$
$$+ 1058.1 \times 10^{-6}\,(233.15^3 - 298.15^3)/3 - 366.9 \times 10^{-9}\,(233.15^4 - 298.15^4)/4$$
$$= -175\,500 + 7293.7 - 4877.8 + 453.8$$
$$= -172\,630.3 \text{ kJ/h} \equiv -47.953 \text{ kW}$$

Since liquid mixture leaves the separator at 25°C (298.15 K), its enthalpy is zero. Additional condensation and latent heat of evaporation at 233.15 K are tabulated below.

Table 8.17 Condensation in Chiller

Component	$\dot{n}_i$ kmol/h	λ_v^* at 233.15 K, kJ/mol
CH_3Cl	$14.0786 - 2.1968 = 11.8818$	22.286
CH_2Cl_2	$1.3479 - 0.0894 = 1.2585$	31.969
$CHCl_3$	$0.4376 - 0.028 = 0.4096$	34.119
CCl_4	$0.034 - 0.0145 = 0.0195$	35.358

*Wastson equation
Condensation heat duty,

$$\phi_9 = 11.8818 \times 1000 \times 22.286 + 1.2585 \times 1000 \times 31.969 + 0.4096 \times 1000$$
$$\times 34.119 + 0.0195 \times 1000 \times 35.358$$
$$= 264\ 798 + 40\ 233 + 13\ 975 + 689$$
$$= 319\ 695 \text{ kJ/h} \equiv 88.804 \text{ kW}$$

Refrigeration duty of chiller.

$$\phi_{10} = \phi_8 + \phi_9 + \phi_4 + \phi_5$$
$$= 172\ 630 + 319\ 695 + 48\ 665.5 + 138\ 498.1$$
$$= 679\ 488.6 \text{ kJ/h} \equiv 188.747 \text{ kW} \equiv 53.667 \text{ TR}$$

Methyl chloride recycled to the bubble column reactor.

$$= (26.9214 + 11.8818)\ 0.98$$
$$= 38.8032 \times 0.98 = 38.027 \text{ kmol/h}$$

Fresh methyl chloride required to be fed to
bubble column reactor $= 100 - 38.027 = 61.973$ kmol/h

Hydrochlorination Reactor
Methyl chloride for sale = 50 kmol/h
Total methyl chloride production from hydrochlorination
reactor $= 61.973 + 50 = 111.973$ kmol/h

New basis: Methanol feed rate = 100 kmol/h
HCl feed rate $= 100 \times 1.14 = 114$ kmol/h

Table 8.18 Feed to Hydrochlorinator

Compo-nent	$\dot{n}_i$ kmol/h	mole %	Heat capacity equation constants			
			$\dot{n}_i \cdot a_i$	$\dot{n}_i \cdot b_i \times 10^3$	$\dot{n}_i \cdot c_i \times 10^6$	$\dot{n}_i \cdot d_i \times 10^9$
CH_3OH	100.0	46.73	2486.9	5087.5	5862.7	−4512.6
HCl	114.0	53.27	3455.2	−867.4	1511.7	−494.0
Total	214.0	100.00	5942.1	4220.1	7374.4	−5006.6

Conversion = 93.8%

CH_3OH converted $= 100 \times 0.938 = 93.8$ kmol/h

$$\text{HCl converted to } CH_3Cl = \frac{125 \times 93.8}{126} = 93.06 \text{ kmol/h}$$

$$\text{DME produced} = \frac{(93.8 - 93.06)}{2} = 0.37 \text{ kmol/h}$$

HCl consumed = 93.06 kmol/h
HCl in exit gas mixture $= 114 - 93.06 = 20.94$ kmol/h
Recycled components in HCl are neglected.

Table 8.19 Gas Mixture Exit of Reactor

Compo-nent	$\dot{n}_i$ kmol/h	mole %	Heat Capacity Equation Constants			
			$\dot{n}_i \cdot a_i$	$\dot{n}_i \cdot b_i \times 10^3$	$\dot{n}_i \cdot c_i \times 10^6$	$\dot{n}_i \cdot d_i \times 10^9$
CH_3OH	6.20	2.90	154.19	315.43	363.49	−279.79
HCl	20.94	9.79	634.67	−159.33	277.68	−90.75
CH_3Cl	93.06	43.49	1260.28	9776.40	−4411.13	731.56
$(CH_3)_2O$	0.37	0.17	10.58	—	—	—
H_2O	93.43	43.66	3035.74	7.44	1234.28	−424.87
Total	214.00	100.00	5095.46	9939.94	−2535.68	−63.83

For refernce temperature of $T_0 = 298.15$ K, enthalpy of gas stream, leaving the reactor at 573.15 K.

$\phi'_{11} = 5095.46 \,(573.15 - 298.15) + 9939.94 \times 10^{-3} \,(573.15^2 - 298.15^2)/2$
$\qquad -2535.68 \times 10^{-6} \,(573.15^3 - 298.15^3)/3 - 63.83 \times 10^{-9} \,(573.15^4 - 298.15^4)/4$
$\qquad = 1401\,251 + 1190\,842 - 136\,738 - 1596$
$\qquad = 2453\,759$ kJ/h $\equiv 681.599$ kW for 100 kmol/h CH_3OH feed rate

Exit gas stream exchanges heat with incoming stream and cools down to 100°C (373.15 K).

Enthalpy reactor exit gas at 373.15 K over 298.15 K,

$\phi'_{12} = 5095.46 \,(373.15 - 298.15) + 9939.94 \times 10^{-3} \,(373.15^2 - 298.15^2)/2$
$\qquad = -2535.68 \times 10^{-6} \,(373.15^3 - 298.15^3)/3 - 63.83 \times 10^{-9} \,(373.15^4 - 298.15^4)/4$
$\qquad = 382\,160 + 250\,226 - 21\,515 - 183$
$\qquad = 610\,688$ kJ/h $\equiv 169.635$ kW for 100 kmol/h CH_3OH feed rate

Heat exchagend in the heat exchanger,

$\phi'_{13} = 2453\,759 - 610\,688$
$\qquad = 1843\,071$ kJ/h $\equiv 511.964$ kW for 100 kmol/h CH_3OH feed rate

If T is the temperature of methanol–HCl mixture at the exit of heat exchange and inlet

$$\int_{348.15}^{T} (5942.1 + 4220.1 \times 10^{-3}\, T + 7374.4 \times 10^{-6}\, T^2 - 5006.6 \times 10^{-9}\, T^3) \, dT$$
$$= 1843\,071$$

Solving by Mathcad,

$$F(T) := \int_{348.15}^{T} \left(5942.1 + 4220.1 \cdot 10^{-3} \cdot T + 7374.4 \cdot 10^{-6} \cdot T^2 - 5006.6 \cdot 10^{-9} \cdot T^3\right) dT - 1843071$$

$T := 500$

$soln := root(F(T), T)$

$soln = 555.37 \qquad$ K

$$T = 555.37 \text{ K } (282.22°C)$$

Production rate of $CH_3Cl = 93.06$ kmol/h
Required production rate = 119.973 kmol/h

Desired methanol feed rate $= \dfrac{100 \times 119.973}{93.06}$

$\qquad = 128.92$ kmol/h $\equiv 4125.4$ kg/h

Reaction 4 $CH_3OH(g) + HCl(g) = CH_3Cl(g) + H_2O(g)$

$$\Delta H_{r4}^0 = -81.96 - 241.82 - (-200.94 - 92.31)$$
$$= -30.53 \text{ kJ/mol } CH_3OH$$

Reaction 5 $2CH_3OH(g) = (CH_3)_2O(g) + H_2O(g)$

$$\Delta H_{r5}^0 = -184 - 241.82 - [2 \, (-200.94)]$$
$$= -23.94 \text{ kJ/2 mol } CH_3OH$$
$$= -11.97 \text{ kJ/mol } CH_3OH$$

Heat generated, $\phi_{14}' = 30.53 \times 1000 \times 93.06 + 11.97 \times 0.74 \times 1000$
$$= 2841 \, 122 + 8858$$
$$= 2849 \, 980 \text{ kJ/h} \equiv 791.661 \text{ kW for 100 kmol/h}$$
$$\text{methanol feed rate}$$

Enthalpy of feed mixture at 555.35 K over 298.15 K,

$$\phi_{15}' = 5942.1 \, (555.35 - 298.15) + 4220.1 \times 10^{-3} \, (555.35^2$$
$$- 298.15^2)/2 + 7374.4 \times 10^{-6} \, (555.35^3 - 298.15^3)/3$$
$$- 500.6 \times 10^{-9} \, (555.35^4 - 298.15^4)/4$$
$$= 2238 \, 216 \text{ kJ/h} \equiv 621.727 \text{ kW for 100 kmol/h}$$
$$\text{methanol feed rate}$$

For 100 kmol/h CH_3OH feed rate, cooling load,

$$\phi_{16}' = 2453 \, 758 + 2849 \, 980 - 2238 \, 216 = 3065 \, 522 \text{ kJ/h}$$
$$= 851.534 \text{ kW}$$

For 128.92 kmol/h CH_3OH feed rate,

$$\text{Cooling load, } \phi_{16} = \frac{128.92}{100} \times 3065 \, 522$$
$$= 3952 \, 071 \text{ kJ/h} \equiv \mathbf{1097.797 \text{ kW}}$$

Enthalpy of saturated steam at 6 bar a = 2755.5 kJ/kg
Enthalpy of water at 25°C (298.15 K) = 104.8 kJ/kg

$$\text{Steam generation, } \dot{m}_s = \frac{3952 \, 071}{(2755.5 - 104.8)} = \mathbf{1491 \text{ kg/h}}$$

Heat exchange duty of E1 for methanol feed rate of 128.92 kmol/h,

$$\phi_{13} = 1843 \, 071 \times 1.2892 = 2376 \, 087 \text{ kJ/h}$$
$$\equiv \mathbf{660.024 \text{ kW}}$$

Example 8.5   A single-stage ammonia–water absorption refrigeration plant is employed as shown in Fig. 8.4 for production of aqueous monoethylene glycol (MEG) brine at – 5°C (268 K).

Liquid ammonia is evaporated in the chiller at –10°C (263 K). Heat load of the chiller is 200 kW (56.9 TR). Assume 2.5% increase in the heat load due to heat gain through insulation of the chiller and heat loss from hot surfaces of the system. Saturated ammonia vapour from the chiller enters the absorber in which they are absorbed at ~ 10 kPa less pressure than that in the chiller in weak aqueous (WA) ammonia solution. Heat of absorption is removed by cooling water.

Strong aqueous (SA) ammonia solution leaves the absorber at saturated conditions exchanges heat with incoming WA solution in the heat exchanger (HE) and enters a packed distillation column at 2.5°C (2.5 K) lower temperature than the saturation temperature of SA solution at the column pressure. Generator (essentially a reboiler) is fed with saturated steam at 3 bar a. From the bottom of the generator, WA solution, having 6.5% (by mass) lower concentration than that of SA solution (also called *split*), is drawn at 0.55 bar lower pressure than that of

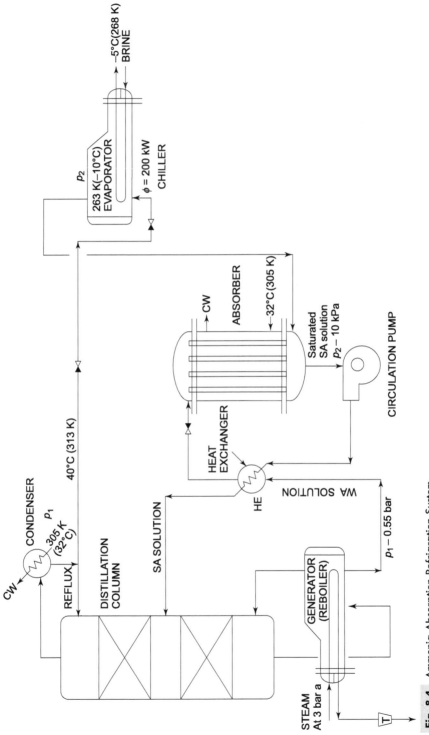

Fig. 8.4 Ammonia Absorption Refrigration System

overhead condenser. Saturated WA solution enters the heat exchanger, exchanges heat with SA solution and enters the absorber.

From the distillation column, top ammonia vapours are taken to a condenser in which they are condensed with the help of cooling water. Liquid ammonia at saturated conditions at 40°C (313 K) from the condenser is divided into two portions. One portion is sent to the chiller for the refrigeration duty while another portion is recycled to the column as reflux at the rate of 0.08 kg/kg ammonia fed to the column. Purity of ammonia (~ 100%) in the chiller is maintained by periodic bleed of a liquid mass from the bottom of the absorber. Thus the refrigeration cycle is completed.

Cooling water is supplied at 2 bar g and 32°C (305 K) in the absorber and the condenser. A rise of 5°C (5 K) is permitted of the cooling water.

Table 8.20 Properties of Ammonia[5]

Temperature °C (K)	Saturation pressure, kPa a	Enthalpy, kJ/kg	
		Liquid	Vapour
−10 (263.15)	290.75	154.05	1450.41
40 (313.15)	1555.0	391.06	1489.82

Basis Specific enthalpy of liquid ammonia at 0°C (273.15 K) = 200 kJ/kg
Make complete material and energy balances of the refrigeration system.

Solution   *Basis* Refrigeration load of 200 kW in evaporator. An increase of 2.5% is to be considered in refrigeration for heat gain/loss.

Actual refrigeration load = 200 × 1.025
$$= 205 \text{ kW} = 205 \text{ kJ/s}$$

Ammonia evaporates at −10°C (263.15 K) in the chiller. Corresponding saturation pressure in the chiller is 290.75 kPa a. Hence operating pressure of the absorber will be 280 kPa a.

Liquid ammonia at 40° (313.15 K) is flashed and sent to chiller.
Enthalpy of ammonia (vapour-liquid mixture) entering the chiller
$$h_1 = 391.06 \text{ kJ/kg}$$
Enthalpy of vapour ammonia leaving the chiller
$$H_2 = 1450.41 \text{ kJ/kg}$$
Enthalpy, available for evaporation in the chiller
$$= H_2 - h_1$$
$$= 1450.41 - 391.06 = 1059.35 \text{ kJ/kg}$$
Ammonia flow through the chiller, $\dot{m}_1 = 205/1059.35 = 0.1935$ kg/s

Strong aqueous (SA) ammonia solution leaves the absorber under saturated conditions. Empirical equations are presented by Pátek et al[6] for calculations of thermophysical properties of aqueous ammonia solutions. Using these equations, strength of SA solution is found to be under saturation at 280 kPa a and 46.5°C (319.65 K). This is calculated as 36.3% by mass (w_2) or 37.61% by mole (x_2). Since split in the distillation is 6.5%, weak aqueous (WA) solution enters absorber at 29.8% by mass (w_1) or 30.99% by mole (x_1). Enthalpy values are calculated using empirical equations and adjusted to the reference state of Table 8.20.

Enthalpy of SA solution leaving absorber
$$h_2 = 169.36 \text{ kJ/kg}$$

The condenser above the distillation tower condenses liquid ammonia (pure) at 40°C (313.15 K). Hence it operates at 1555.0 kPa a. Pressure drop in the distillation system 0.55 bar. SA solution enters the distillation tower at 2.5 K lower than its saturation temperate.

Saturation temperature of 36.3% SA solution at 1555.0 kPa a = 105.15°C (378.30 K)
Temperature of SA solution entering the column
$$= 378.30 - 2.5 = 375.8 \text{ K or } 102.65°C$$
Enthalpy of SA solution at 375.8 K, h_3 = 432.8 kJ/kg

Material balance across absorber
Let $\dot{m}_2$ be the WA solution flow to the absorber.
$$0.298 \, \dot{m}_2 + 0.1935 = (\dot{m}_2 + 0.1935) \, 0.363$$
or $\qquad \dot{m}_2 = 1.8963$ kg/s
Flow of SA solution to the distillation column
$$\dot{m}_3 = 1.8963 + 0.1935 = 2.0898 \text{ kg/s}$$
Reflux to the column at top, $\dot{m}_4$ = 0.08 kg/kg ammonia fed
$$= 0.08 \times 2.0898 \times 0.363 = 0.0607 \text{ kg/s}$$

Heat balance across heat exchanger
Heat gained by SA solution $\quad \phi_1 = (h_3 - h_2) \, 2.0898$
$$= (438.8 - 169.38) \, 2.0898 = 550.537 \text{ kJ/s or kW}$$
$\qquad$ Heat gain by SA solution = Heat loss by WA solution
WA solution leaves the generator under saturated conditions at 1500.0 kPa a. Its temperature and enthalpy are calculated to be 121.7°C (394.85 K) and 543.75 kJ/kg (h_4), respectively. Assume heat capacity of WA and SA solutions to be same.
$$1.8963 \, (432.8 - h_5) = 550.537$$
or $\qquad h_5 = 253.43$ kJ/kg
For WA solution (of 29.8% strength), this enthalpy corresponds to a temperature of 59.45°C (332.6 K).

Heat balance across absorber
Enthalpy of vapours entering the absorber,
$$\phi_2 = 1450.41 \times 0.1935 = 280.654 \text{ kJ/s or kW}$$
Enthalpy of WA solution entering the absorber,
$$\phi_3 = 253.43 \times 1.8963 = 480.579 \text{ kJ/s or kW}$$
Enthalpy of SA solution leaving the absorber
$$\phi_4 = 2.0898 \times 169.36 = 353.929 \text{ kJ/s or kW}$$
$\qquad$ Cooling load of absorber, $\phi_1 = \phi_2 + \phi_3 - \phi_4$
$$= 280.654 + 480.579 - 353.929$$
$$= 407.304 \text{ kJ/s or kW}$$

Heat balance across the distillation column
Ammonia condensed in the condenser
$$\dot{m}_5 = 0.1935 + 0.0607 = 0.2542 \text{ kg/s}$$
Heat removal in condenser, $\quad \phi_5 = 0.2542 \, (1489.82 - 391.06) = 279.29$ kJ/s or kW
Enthalpy of vapours at the top,
$$\phi_6 = 1489.82 \times 0.2542 = 378.712 \text{ kJ/s or kW}$$
Enthalpy of reflux fed back to column,
$$\phi_7 = 0.0607 \times 391.06 = 23.737 \text{ kJ/s or kW}$$
Enthalpy of SA solution fed to the column,
$$\phi_8 = 432.8 \times 2.0898 = 904.465 \text{ kJ/s or kW}$$

Enthalpy of WA solution, leaving the generator,
$$\phi_9 = 1.8963 \times 543.75 = 1031.113 \text{ kJ/s or kW}$$
Heat to be supplied in the generator,
$$\phi_{10} = \phi_6 + \phi_9 - \phi_7 - \phi_8$$
$$= 378.712 + 1031.113 - 23.737 - 904.465$$
$$= 481.623 \text{ kJ/s or kW}$$
A check can be made of overall heat balance.

Heat input		**Heat Output**	
Evaporator	205.000 kW	Condenser	279.305 kW
Generator	481.623 kW	Absorber	407.304 kW
Total	686.623 kW	Total	686.609 kW

Efficiency of refrigeration system or

$$\text{Coefficient of Performance} = \frac{\text{Net refrigeration achieved}}{\text{Heat input to generator}}$$

$$= \frac{200}{481.623} = 0.4153 \text{ kW/kW}$$

At 3 bar a, saturated steam temperature, $T_s = 406.69$ K ($t_s = 133.54°C$), latent heat of evaporation, $\lambda_v = 2163.2$ kJ/kg (Appendix IV.2).

$$\text{Steam consumption in generator} = \frac{481.623}{2163.2}$$

$$= 0.2226 \text{ kg/s} \equiv 801.5 \text{ kg/h}$$

$$\text{Total cooling load} = 686.609 \text{ kW}$$

$$\text{Total cooling water flow} = \frac{686.609}{5}$$

$$= 137.32 \text{ kg/s} \equiv \textbf{494.36 m}^3\textbf{/h}$$

On Fig. 5.22, take a point on the y-axis at $x = 1.0$ and read enthalpy = 1282.82 kJ/kg which represents the incoming ammonia vapours. Take another point, representing WA solution at $w_1 = 0.298$ and temperature of 59.45°C (332.6 K). The line joining both the points crosses SA solution strength abscissa; $w_2 = 0.363$ at 90.3°C (363.45 K) and has enthalpy $h_6 = 367.73$ kJ/kg solution. However, it shows higher saturation pressure (> 1000 kPa a) which does not allow flow of ammonia vapours from the chiller to the absorber. Hence the solution must be cooled to its saturature temperature of 46.5°C (319.65 K) at 280 kPa a.

Heat removal rate in absorber = $\dot{m}_i (h_6 - h_2)$
$$= 2.0898 (367.73 - 169.36) = 414.554 \text{ kJ/s or kW}$$

This agrees well with the earlier calculated value of 407.304 kJ/s. Flow $\dot{m}_1$ can also be calculated from this line using geometric principles.

Note Ammonia-water absorption system can also be used with low grade heat for power generation using Kalina cycle (Ref. 7).

Example 8.6 A pilot plant employs aqueous methyl diethanolamine (MDEA) solution for the removal of acid gases from a gas mixture in a coal liquefaction plant. The composition of the saturated gas mixture entering the absorber is as follows (dry volume %):

H_2: 28.4%, CO: 9.1%, CO_2: 38.4%, CH_4: 22.3%, C_2H_6: 0.7%, N_2: 0.4% and H_2S: 0.7%.

The process[8] is depicted in Fig. 3.5. The absorber has 20 trays and operates at 45 bar g while the stripper has 17 trays and operates at 125 kPa a. The feed gas and aqueous solution enter at 41°C (314 K) and 38°C (311 K), respectively. Based on the following data, make a complete material and energy balance of the acid gas removal system.

(i) The flow rate of the incoming dry gas mixture is 8500 Nm^3/h from a coal gasification unit employing the Synthane process[9].

(ii) Rich MEDA solution contains 0.6 kmol acid gas per kmol MDEA. With 35% (by mass) concentration of MDEA, 65% CO_2 is absorbed from the gas mixture while H_2S absorption can be assumed complete. In actual practice, H_2S slip could be around 50 ppm (v/v).

(iii) Lean MDEA solution should not contain more than 0.15 kmol acid gas per kmol MDEA of which the H_2S concentration should not exceed 0.002 kmol/kmol MDEA. For achieving this concentration in the lean solution, one kmol of water reflux is required per kmol of MDEA is the stripper.

(iv) Physical properties of MDEA

Molar mass of MDEA = 119.2

Specific gravity 1.04 at 20°C (293 K) of 100% solution

1.03 at 30°C (303 K) of 35% solution

1.00 at 100°C (373 K) of 35% solution

Heat capacity 3.77 kJ/(kg · K) over the temperature range of calculations

Normal boiling point (T_B) at 101.3 kPa = 230.6°C (503.75 K)

Vapour pressure at 20°C (293.15 K) = 1.33 Pa (0.01 Torr)

Latent heat of vaporization, λ_v = 518.7 kJ/kg at T_B

(v) Exothermic heat of absorption cum reaction at 25°C (298.15 K):

For H_2S absorption = 1047 kJ/kg

For CO_2 absorption = 1342 kJ/kg

(vi) Assume negligible energy consumption in the vaporizer.

Solution *Basis*   Feed gas rate = 8500 Nm^3/h = 379.23 kmol/h

Ingoing CO_2 = 379.23 × 0.384 = 145.62 kmol/h

Ingoing H_2S = 379.23 × 0.007

= 2.65 kmol/h ≡ 90.31 kg/h

CO_2 absorbed = 145.62 × 0.65

= 94.65 kmol/h ≡ 4165.55 kg/h

Unabsorbed CO_2 in the outgoing

gas mixture = 145.62 – 94.65 = 50.97 kmol/h

Total acid gas removed = 94.65 + 2.65 = 97.30 kmol/h

Absorption of acid gas in the

circulating solution = 0.60 – 0.15 = 0.45 kmol/kmol MDEA

Circulation rate requirement = $\dfrac{97.30}{0.45}$ (100% MDEA basis)

= 216.22 kmol/h ≡ 25 767.3 kg/h

Ciculation rate of 35% (mass)

$$\text{strength solution} = \frac{25\ 767.3}{0.35} = 73\ 621 \text{ kg/h}$$

H_2S in lean MDEA = $216.22 \times 0.002 = 0.43$ kmol/h
CO_2 in lean MDEA = $216.22 \times 0.148 = 32.00$ kmol/h
MDEA soln. with acid gases = $73\ 621 + 0.43 \times 34 + 32 \times 44 = 75\ 044$ kg/h

$$\text{Circulation rate of MDEA solution} = \frac{75\ 044}{(1.03 \times 1000)} = 72.86 \text{ m}^3/\text{h}$$

Vapour pressure of water

at 41°C (314 K), $p_{w1} = 7.777$ kPa   (Refer Table 6.13)
at 38°C (311 K), $p_{w2} = 6.624$ kPa   (Refer Table 6.13)

Mole fraction of water in 35% MDEA solution = 0.9144
Applying Raoult's law,

Partial pressure of water at the absorber top = $6.624 \times 0.9144 = 6.056$ kPa
Total pressure in the absorber, $p_{T_1} = 45$ bar g = 4601.3 kPa a

Pressure drop in the absorber is neglected.

$$H_2O \text{ in the outgoing gas mixture} = \left[\frac{6.056}{(4601.3 - 6.056)}\right](379.23 - 97.30)$$

$$= 0.372 \text{ kmol/h}$$

$$H_2O \text{ in the ingoing gas mixture} = \left[\frac{7.777}{(4601.3 - 7.777)}\right]379.23$$

$$= 0.642 \text{ kmol/h}$$

H_2O condensed = $0.642 - 0.372 = 0.27$ kmol/h $\equiv 4.86$ kg/h
H_2S in rich MDEA solution = $0.43 + 2.65 = 3.08$ kmol/h
CO_2 in rich MDEA solution = $32.0 + 94.65 = 126.65$ kmol/h

Heat balance in the absorber

Base temperature $T_0 = 25°C$ (298.15 K)
Heat generated due to absorption = $90.31 \times 1047 + 4165.5 \times 1342$
$$= 5684\ 723 \text{ kJ/h} \equiv 1579.09 \text{ kW}$$

Table 8.21 Sour-gas Enthalpy Calculations

Compo-nent	$\dot{n}_i$ kmol/h	$\dot{m}_i$ kg/h	Heat capacity equation constants			
			$\dot{n}_i \cdot a_i$	$\dot{n}_i \cdot b_i \times 10^3$	$\dot{n}_i \cdot c_i \times 10^6$	$\dot{n}_i \cdot d_i \times 10^9$
H_2	107.70	215.40	3081.35	109.79	−15.90	82.82
CO	34.51	966.28	1001.76	−97·20	401.82	−162.41
CO_2	145.62	6407.28	3111.24	9361.05	−5977.79	1427.06
CH_4	84.57	1353.12	1627.92	4 407.24	1012.56	−957.10
C_2H_6	2.66	79.80	14.40	473.71	−184.54	23.18
N_2	1.52	42.56	44.98	−7.81	20.04	−7.55
H_2S	2.65	90.10	90.65	—	—	—
H_2O	0.642	11.56	20.86	0.05	8.48	−2.92
Total	379.872	9166.10	8993.16	14 246.83	−4735.33	403.08

$$\text{Average molar mass of dry sour gas} = \frac{(9166.10 - 11.56)}{(379.872 - 0.642)} = 24.14$$

Table 8.22 Treated-gas Enthalpy Calculations

Compo-nent	$\dot{n}_i$ kmol/h	$\dot{m}_i$ kg/h	Heat capacity equation constants			
			$\dot{n}_i \cdot a_i$	$\dot{n}_i \cdot b_i \times 10^3$	$\dot{n}_i \cdot c_i \times 10^6$	$\dot{n}_i \cdot d_i \times 10^9$
H_2	107.70	215.40	3081.35	109.79	-15.90	82.82
CO	34.51	966.28	1001.76	-97.20	401.82	-162.41
CO_2	50.97	2242.68	1089.00	3276.56	-2092.35	499.50
CH_4	84.57	1353.12	1627.92	4407.24	1012.56	-957.10
C_2H_6	2.66	79.80	14.40	473.71	-184.54	23.18
N_2	1.52	42.56	44.98	-7.81	20.04	-7.55
H_2S	Nil	—	—	—	—	—
H_2O	0.372	6.70	12.09	0.03	4.91	-1.69
Total	282.302	4906.54	6871.50	8162.32	-853.46	-523.25

Average molar mass of dry treated gas $= \dfrac{(4906.54 - 6.70)}{(282.302 - 0.372)} = 17.38$

Enthalpy of sour gas at 314 K over 298.15 K

$$= \int_{298.15}^{314} (8993.16 + 14\ 246.83 \times 10^{-3}\ T - 4735.33 \times 10^{-6}\ T^2 + 403.08 \times 10^{-9}\ T^3)\ dT$$

$= 206\ 732$ kJ/h $\equiv 57.42$ kW

Enthalpy of treated gas at 311 K over 298.15 K

$$= \int_{298.15}^{311} (6871.50 + 8162.32 \times 10^{-3}\ T - 853.46 \times 10^{-6}\ T^2 - 523.25 \times 10^{-9}\ T^3)\ dT$$

$= 120\ 420$ kJ/h $\equiv 33.45$ kW

Heat given up in the absorber by the gas mixture $= 57.42 - 33.45 = 23.97$ kW

Moisture condensed in the absorber $= 0.642 - 0.372$

$= 0.27$ kmol $\equiv 4.86$ kg

Heat given up by condensation of water $= 4.86 \times 2411.7$

$= 11\ 721$ kJ/h $\equiv 3.26$ kW

Heat in the lean MDEA solution $= 75\ 044 \times 3.77\ (311.15 - 298.15)$

$= 3677\ 906$ kJ/h $\equiv 1021.64$ kW

Total heat in the rich MDEA solution $= 1021.64 + 23.97 + 3.26 + 1579.09$

$= 2627.96$ kW

$79\ 302.8 \times 3.77 \times (T_1 - 298.15) = 2627.96 \times 3600$

Temperature of the rich MDEA

solution leaving absorber, $T_1 = 329.8$ K (56.5°C)

Material and energy balance across the stripper

Total acid gas leaving the stripper $= 97.30$ kmol/h

Reflux water $= 97.30$ kmol/h

(i.e., 1 kmol water/kmol acid gas)

Acid gas mixture leave the accumulator at 60°C (333 K) in saturated condition.

p_{w3} at 60°C (333 K) $= 19.92$ kPa   (Refer Table 6.13)

$p_{T_2} = 125$ kPa a

Moisture leaving with acid gas mixture from

condensate accumulator $= \dfrac{(19.92 \times 97.30)}{(125 - 19.92)} = 18.45$ kmol/h

Total water in the acid gas from stripper $= 97.30 + 18.45 = 115.75$ kmol/h

Specific moisture content $= \dfrac{115.75}{97.30} = 1.19$ kmol/kmol dry gas

$$p_3 = 40 \text{ kPa g at stripper top} = 141.3 \text{ kPa a}$$
$$p_4/(p_3 - p_4) = 1.19$$
$$p_4 = \text{partial pressure of water at the stripper top}$$
$$= 76.79 \text{ kPa a}$$

Applying Raoult's law,

Vapour pressure of water at the stripper top, $p_{w4} = \dfrac{76.79}{0.9144} = 83.98$ kPa

Temperature of the gas stream

leaving the stripper $= 94.8°C$ (367.8 K)   (Refer Table 6.13)

Solution interchanger

In this heat exchanger, lean MDEA solution cools down from $116°C$ (389.15 K) to $80°C$ (353.15 K).

Heat transfer $= 75\,044 \times 3.77$ (389.15 − 353.15)

$= 10\,184\,972$ kJ/h $\equiv 2829.16$ kW

Assume 2% radiation loss.

Heat picked up by rich MDEA solution $= 2829.16 \times 0.98 = 2772.58$ kW

Let temperature of rich MDEA solution leaving the heat exchanger be T_2.

$79\,302.8 \times 3.77$ $(T_2 - 329.6) = 2772.58 \times 3600$

$$T_2 = 363.15 \text{ K } (90°C)$$

Cooler

In this heat exchanger, lean MDEA solution is cooled to 311.15 K ($38°C$) with the help of cooling water.

Heat transfer duty $= 75\,044 \times 3.77$ (353.15 − 311.15)

$= 11\,882\,467$ kJ/h $\equiv 3300.69$ kW

Rise in cooling water temperature $= 10$ K or $10°C$

Cooling water flow rate $= \dfrac{3300.69 \times 3600}{10 \times 4.1868 \times 1000} \equiv 283.7$ m³/h

Steam requirement in reboiler

Base temperature, $T_0 = 298.15$ K

Enthalpy of rich solution $= 79\,302.8 \times 3.77$ (363.15 − 298.15)

$= 19\,433\,151$ kJ/h $\equiv 5398.10$ kW

Enthalpy of lean solution $= 75\,044 \times 3.77$ (389.15 − 298.15)

$= 25\,745\,345$ kJ/h $\equiv 7151.48$ kW

Mean heat capacities of CO_2 and H_2S at 367.8 K are 38.67 and 34.42 kJ/(kmol · K), respectively at $94.8°C$ (367.95 K).

Enthalpy of acid gases leaving the stripper

$= [94.65 \times 38.67 + 2.65 \times 34.42]$ (367.95 − 298.15)

$= 261\,843$ kJ/h $\equiv 72.73$ kW

Enthalpy of steam at 367.15 K = 2667.6 kJ/kg (Ref. Appendix IV.2)
Enthalpy of water at 298.15 K = 104.77 kJ/kg (Ref. Appendix IV.1)
Enthalpy of water vapour leaving
  stripper with acid gases = 115.59 × 18.0153 (2667.6 − 104.77)
                          = 5336 808 kJ/h ≡ 1482.45 kW
To find the make-up condensate flow rate, material balance across the stripper is required.

  Rich MDEA solution + make-up water ($\dot{m}_w$) + Reflux water = lean MDEA solution + moist gas at the stripper overhead

79 302.8 + $\dot{m}_w$ + 97.3 × 18.0153 = 75 044 + 90.3 + 4165.6 + 115.59 × 18.0153

$\dot{m}_w$ = 326.6 kg/h

Total condensate entering the stripper = 97.3 × 18.0153 + 326.6
                                      = 2079.5 kg/h
      Enthalpy of condensate = (251.09 − 104.77) 2079.5
                             = 304 287 kJ/h ≡ 84.52 kW

Assuming 2% radiation loss,
[Enthalpy of rich solution + enthalpy of condensate
+ enthalpy of supplied by steam (ϕ)] 0.98 = enthalpy of moist acid gas at stripper
top + enthalpy of lean solution + enthalpies of desorption

  (5398.10 + 84.52 + ϕ) 0.98 = 72.73 + 1482.01 + 7151.48 + 1579.09

                     ϕ = 5012.594 kW

Latent heat of steam at 4 bar a = 2133.0 kJ/kg

Steam consumption in reboiler = 5012.59 × $\dfrac{3600}{2133}$ = **8460 kg/h**

Acid gas cooler
Acid gas is cooled to 333.15 K (60°C) in the cooler.
Enthalpy of water vapour at 333.15 K = 2609.7 kJ/kg (Ref. Appendix IV.2)
  Mean heat capacities of CO_2 and H_2S are 38 and 34.3 kJ/(kmol · K), respectively at 60°C (333.15 K).
Enthalpy of acid gases
    leaving the cooler = [94.65 × 38 + 2.65 × 34.3] (333.15 − 298.15)
                       = 129 066 kJ/h = 35.85 kW
Enthalpy removed in the cooler = 1482.01 + 72.73 − 35.85 − [18.29 × 18.0153
(2609.7 − 104.77) + 97.3 × 18.0153 × 4.1868 (333.15 − 298.15)]/3600
                       = 1218.36 kW

    Cooling water flow = $\dfrac{1218.36 \times 3600}{(10 \times 4.1868 \times 1000)}$ ≡ **104.8 m³/h**

Note For the heat exchanger in which heat is exchanged between lean and rich MDEA solutions, radiation loss (2%) was assumed but in coolers, radiation loss was not assumed. This is deliberately done to have conservative designs. By assuming radiation loss in the interchanger, the steam requirement in the reboiler will be high. By not assuming radiation loss in coolers, cooling water flows are high. Thus, both result in conservative utilities' consumptions.

The complete material and energy balance of the system is given in Table 8.23.

Table 8.23 Material and Energy Balance of Acid Gas Removal System

A. Gas Streams

	Gas component								Total	Pressure	Temperature °C (K)
	H_2	CO	CO_2	CH_4	C_2H_6	N_2	H_2S	H_2O			
Molar mass	2.02	28.01	44.01	16.04	30.07	28.01	34.08	18.01			
1. Sour gas flow, entering absorber,											
kmol/h	107.70	34.51	145.62	84.57	2.66	1.52	2.65	0.642	379.872	45 bar g	41 (314)
kg/h	215.40	966.28	6407.28	1353.12	79.80	42.56	90.10	11.56	9166.10		
mole % (dry)	28.4	9.1	38.4	22.3	0.7	0.4	0.7	—	100.00		
2. Treated gas flow, leaving absorber,											
kmol/h	107.7	34.51	50.97	84.57	2.66	1.52	Nil	0.372	282.302	45 bar g	38 (311)
kg/h	215.40	966.28	2242.68	1353.12	79.80	47.56	Nil	6.70	4906.54		
mole % (dry)	38.2	12.2	18.1	30.0	0.9	0.6	Nil (< 50 ppm)	—	100.00		
3. Acid gas flow, leaving condensate accumulator											
kmol/h	—	—	94.65	—	—	—	2.65	18.45	115.75	125 kPa a	60 (333)
kg/h	—	—	4165.55	—	—	—	90.31	332.28	4588.14		
mole % (dry)	—	—	97.3	—	—	—	2.7	—	100.00		

(*Contd.*)

Table 8.23 (Contd.)

B. Liquid Streams

		Component					
		MDEA	H$_2$O	H$_2$S	CO$_2$	Total	Pressure	Temperature, °C (K)
Molar mass		119.12	18.01	34.08	44.01	—	—	—
1. Lean MDEA solution flow to absorber,	kmol/h	216.22	2656	0.43	32.01	2905.00	165 kPa a	116 (389) (at the bottom of the stripper)
	kg/h	25 767	47 854	14.7	1408.3	75 044.0	47 bar g	38 (311) (at the inlet of the absorber)
	mass %	34.34	63.76	0.02	1.88	100		
2. Rich MDEA solution flow from absorber,	kmol/h	216.22	2656.48	3.08	126.66	3.002.44	45 bar g	56.6 (329.6) (at the bottom of the absorber)
	kg/h	25 767	47 854	105.0	5574.3	79 300.3	150 kPa a	90 (363) (at the inlet of the stripper)
	mass %	32.49	60.35	0.13	7.03	100.00		
3. Reflux flow to stripper,	kmol/h	—	97.30	—	—	97.30	125 kPa a	60 (333) (at the bottom of the reflux drum)
	kg/h	—	1752.30	—	—	1752.30		
	mass %	—	100.0	—	—	100.00		
4. Make-up consensate flow,	kmol/h	—	18.17	—	—	18.17	140 kPa a	333 (60)
	kg/h	—	326.6	—	—	326.6		
	mass %	—	100.0	—	—	100.0		

Example 8.7   A caustic soda plant is power intensive. Due to the frequent power interruptions experienced in one plant from grid, it is decided to change the critical drives in the plant by steam-driven turbines and also generate the required power with the help of a steam turbine-alternator set for electrolysis and driving the rest of the rotating machinery with motors.

For a 50 t/d caustic soda plant, the power requirement is nearly 3200 kW for electrolysis. In addition, power is also required for refrigerant and chlorine compressors, cooling water pump and other rotating machinery. The total power requirement at the power turbine shaft is estimated at 6832 kW, thus making available 6500 kW at the alternator shaft, i.e., ~ 95% efficiency.

A four-level cascade steam system is proposed. High pressure (HP) steam is generated at 115 bar a and 440°C (713 K) in the boiler. It is proposed to pass nearly the entire quantity of the HP steam through the power turbine. From this turbine, a definite quantity of medium pressure (MP) steam at 39 bar a and 320°C (593 K) is extracted. The balance of HP and MP steam are further utilised in the power turbine and the final exhaust at 50°C (323 K) and 12 kPa a (95% dry) is taken to a surface condenser (SC). The cascade steam system is shown in Fig. 8.5

MP steam is utilised in four equipments. Saturated steam @ 3 t/h at 15 bar a is required in the second-stage evaporator. This is obtained by letting down MP steam and desuperheating it.

The boiler has a balanced draft furnace. Based on start-up considerations, it is decided to have a forced-draft (FD) fan with a steam turbine drive and the induced-draft fan with a motor. Normal running boiler feed water (BFW) pump is a steam turbine driven while a motor driven BFW pump is a standby and is useful for start-up purpose. This arrangement also satisfies Indian Boiler Regulations requirements. Both, FD fan and BFW pump turbines, are back-pressure type. MP steam is introduced in these turbines while the exhaust steam at 4.4 bar a and 170°C (443 K) join the low-pressure (LP) steam header.

Large cooling water (CW) circulation will be required in the plant. One motor-driven CW pump will be used during the start-up and not in normal run. The circulation rate will be stepped up to full requirements when a turbine-driven CW pump is also put in operation. This turbine is proposed to be a condensing type and it utilises MP steam.

LP superheated steam is desuperheated and is used in the first stage evaporator (@ 9 t/h), ejectors for SC (@ 0.5 t/h), vacuum ejectors for evaporators (@ 2 t/h) and coil-type brine heater (@ 2 t/h).

Ejector steam from SC is condensed in inter/after condensers and the condensate is recycled with the condensate from the SC, evaporators and brine heater. The make-up boiler feed water @ 2 t/h is fed to the deaerator, the function of which is to remove oxygen from the water. This is done by boiling and stripping with saturated LP steam. BFW at 105°C (378 K) is pumped at 123.5 bar g and is fed to the boiler. A small amount of BFW is used for desuperheating. Based on these details, establish a steam balance in which HP steam generation is minimum.

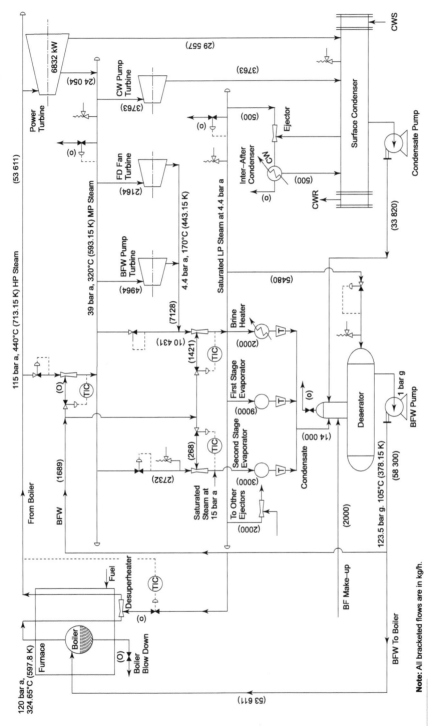

Note: All bracketed flows are in kg/h.

Fig. 8.5 Steam Balance in a Caustic Soda Plant

Data

Deaerator steam requirement = 0.11 kg/kg condensate

FD fan power requirement = 2.47 kW/t steam generated per hour

Energy conversion in turbine = 97% (including gland losses)

Specific volume of compressed water at

123.5 bar g and 105°C (378 K) = 0.955 m³/kg

Efficiency of BFW pump = 65%

Miscellaneous CW requirement, excluding that in SC = 600 m³/h

Permitted rise in CW temperature in SC = 10°C (10 K)

Discharge pressure of CW pump = 5 bar g

Efficiency of CW pump = 60%

Neglect losses between the machine and the driver, excluding that specified for the power turbine.

Solution

Let a = Saturated LP steam input to deaerator, t/h

b = MP steam input to CW pump turbine, t/h

c = MP steam input to BFW pump turbine, t/h

d = MP steam input to FD fan turbine, t/h

e = Exhaust (under vacuum) from power turbine, t/h

g = Letdown from MP steam to LP steam, t/h

h = Letdown from HP steam to MP steam, t/h

Before making the balance of steam at each pressure level, it is necessary to find the specific steam consumptions in different turbines and also, BFW requirement in different desuperheaters.

Table 8.24 Specific Steam Requirements of Turbines

Initial steam conditions	Final steam conditions	Enthalpy available for energy conversion, kJ/kg	Actual energy conversion, (97%), kJ/kg	Specific steam consumption in turbine, kg/kWh
115 bar a 440°C (713.15 K) 3190.7 kJ/kg	39 bar a 320°C (593.15 K) 3020.4 kJ/kg	170.3	165.2	21.79
39 bar a 320°C (593.15 K) 3020.4 kJ/kg	4.4 bar a 170°C (443.15 K) 2793.3 kJ/kg	227.1	220.3	16.34
115 bar a 440°C (713.15 K) 3190.7 kJ/kg	12 kPa a 50°C (323.15 K) 2472.0 kJ/kg 95% dry	718.7	697.1	5.16
39 bar a 320°C (593.15 K) 3020.4 kJ/kg	12 kPa a 50°C (323.15 K) 2472.0 kJ/kg 95% dry	548.4	532.0	6.77

Table 8.25 BFW Requirements for Desuperheating Enthalpy of BFW at 105°C (378 K) = 440.17 kJ/kg

Initial steam conditions			Final steam conditions			BFW Requirement kg/kg initial steam
Pressure bar a	Temp., °C (K)	Enthalpy, kJ/kg	Pressure bar a	Temp., °C (K)	Enthalpy, kJ/kg	
115	440 (713)	3190.7	39	320 (593)	3020.4	0.066 00
39	320 (593)	3020.4	15	Satd.	2789.9	0.098 10
39	320 (593)	3020.4	4.4	Satd.	2741.9	0.121 00
4.4	170 (443)	2793.3	4.4	Satd.	2741.9	0.022 33

Saturated 15 bar a steam

requirement in the second-stage evaporator = 3 t/h

$$\text{Equivalent MP steam} = \frac{3}{(1 + 0.0981)} = 2.732 \text{ t/h}$$

Saturated LP steam header

Requirement = $9 + 2 + 0.5 + 2 + a = 13.5 + a$

Production of superheated LP steam = $c + d$

Equivalent saturated LP steam production = $(1 + 0.022)(c + d) + 1.121 g$

$$1.022\ 33\ (c + d) + 1.121\ g = 13.5 + a \tag{i}$$

Deaerator

Condensate from LP steam consumers = $9 + 2 = 11$ t/h

Condensate from the second-stage evaporator = 3 t/h

Boiler feed make-up water = 2 t/h

Condensate from SC = $b + e + 0.5$ t/h

$$a = 0.11\ (b + e + 16.5)$$

$$a - 0.11\ b - 0.11\ e = 1.815 \tag{ii}$$

Power turbine

This turbine is a special turbine in which steam is partly extracted at a back pressure and also a part is exhausted under vacuum with 5% wetness.

If this turbine is totally a back pressure one,

HP steam requirement = $6832 \times 21.79 = 148\ 869.3$ kg/h

$$\equiv 148.87 \text{ t/h}$$

If this turbine is totally a condensing type,

HP steam requirement = $6832 \times 5.16 = 35\ 253.1$ kg/h

$$\equiv 35.25 \text{ t/h}$$

Both the above cases are extreme cases and the optimum consumption of HP steam will be between 35.25 and 148.87 t/h.

MP steam consumption = $b + c + d + g + 2.74$

MP steam produced by direct letdown = $1.066\ h$

HP steam through power turbine,

produced as MP steam = $b + c + d + g + 2.74 - 1.066\ h$

$$\frac{(b + c + d + g + 2.732 - 1.066h)\ 1000}{21.79} + \frac{1000e}{5.16} = 6832$$

$$5.16\ b + 5.16\ c + 5.16\ d + 21.79\ e + 5.16\ g - 5.50\ h = 754.07 \tag{iii}$$

FD fan

$$\text{Total HP steam produced} = b + c + d + g + 2.732 - 1.066\,h + h + e$$
$$= b + c + d + g + 2.732 - 0.066\,h + e \text{ t/h}$$

$$\text{FD fan power requirement} = 2.732\,(b + c + d + e + g - 0.066\,h + 2.74)\,\text{kW}$$

FD fan turbine steam consumption $= d$

$$= \frac{2.732\,(b + c + d + g - 0.066h + 2.74)\,16.34}{1000}$$

or, $b + c - 23.78\,d + e + g - 0.066h = -2.732$ \hfill (iv)

BFW pump

$$\text{Total BFW} = a + b + e + 16.5 \text{ t/h}$$
$$\text{Head developed} = 123.5 \text{ bar}$$
$$\equiv 1310.7 \text{ m } H_2O \text{ at } 105°C \text{ (378 K)}$$

$$\text{Power requirement of the pump} = \frac{(a + b + e + 16.5)\,1310.7 \times 0.7355 \times 1000}{3600 \times 75 \times 0.65}$$

$$= 5.493\,(a + b + e + 16.5)\,\text{kW}$$

BFW pump turbine steam requirement $= c$

$$= 5.493\,(a + b + e + 16.5)\,\frac{16.34}{1000}$$

$$a + b + e - 11.14\,c = -16.5 \hspace{2cm} \text{(v)}$$

CW pumps

Enthalpy is given up in SC $= 2472.0 - 209.2 = 2262.8 \text{ kJ/kg}$

$$\text{CW requirement in SC} = (b + e)\,\frac{2262.8}{(10 \times 4.1868)}$$

$$= 54.05\,b + 54.05\,e \text{ m}^3\text{/h}$$

$$\text{Total CW requirement} = 54.05\,b + 54.05\,e + 600 \text{ m}^3\text{/h}$$

$$\text{Head developed} = 5 \text{ bar g} = 51 \text{ m } H_2O \text{ at } 323 \text{ K}$$

Power requirement

$$\text{of CW pump} = \frac{(54.05\,b + 54.05\,e + 600)\,51 \times 0.7355 \times 1000}{3600 \times 75 \times 0.60}$$

$$= 0.2315\,(54.05\,b + 54.05\,e + 600)\,\text{kW}$$

Steam consumption

in CW pump turbine $= b$

$$= \frac{0.2315\,(54.05\,b + 54.05\,e + 600)\,6.77}{1000}$$

$$584.01\,b - 54.05\,e = 600 \hspace{2cm} \text{(vi)}$$

Thus, six equations are available with seven unknowns. This is an optimization problem in which the aim is to minimize the production of HP steam, i.e., the boiler capacity. Since all the unknowns are positive (value ≥ 0), and all the equations are linear in nature, linear programming can be applied.

The objective function to be minimised is

$$Z = b + c + d + e + g - 0.066 \, h + 2.732$$

subject to constraint equations developed earlier.

The simplex method in linear algebra states that whenever there exists an optimum-feasible solution, it coincides with one of the basic feasible solutions. To determine the basis solution, the Gauss–Jordan reduction method can be adopted. The coefficient matrix of the constraint equation is as follows:

Table 8.26 Coefficients of Simultaneous Equations

Eq. No.	a	b	c	d	g	h	e	Constant
2	1	−0.11	0	0	0	0	−0.11	1.815
6	0	9.109	0	0	0	0	−0.843	9.358
5	8.977	8.977	−100	0	0	0	8.977	−148.115
4	0	−4.037	−4.037	96	−4.037	0.266	−4.037	11.061
3	0	5.16	5.16	5.16	5.16	−5.50	21.79	754.03
1	−1	0	1.022 33	1.022 33	1.121	0	0	13.5

The rows of the matrix are arranged to preserve the zeros.

From the above matrix, the solutions are

$$a = 1.927\ 44 + 0.1202\ e$$
$$b = 1.022\ 96 + 0.0927\ e$$
$$c = 1.745\ 33 + 0.1089\ e$$
$$d = 0.7152 + 0.049\ e$$
$$g = 11.516\ 04 - 0.0367\ e$$
$$h = -117.693\ 33 + 3.9821\ e$$

Substituting the above value in the objective function,

$$Z = 25.5163 + 0.9511\ e$$

If e is taken as zero, h is negative which is not feasible. Further, h cannot assume a negative value and e should have a minimum value. Therefore, h should be zero.

When $h = 0$,

$$e = 29.5571 \ \text{t/h}$$
$$a = 5.4802 \ \text{t/h}$$
$$b = 3.7629 \ \text{t/h}$$
$$c = 4.9641 \ \text{t/h}$$
$$d = 4.9641 \ \text{t/h}$$
$$g = 2.1635 \ \text{t/h}$$

and
$$Z_{\min} = 53.6109 \ \text{t/h}$$

Mathcad solution

Using 6 equations, the following two matrices are defined.

$$M := \begin{pmatrix} 1 & 0 & -1.02233 & -1.02233 & 0 & -1.121 \\ 1 & -0.11 & 0 & 0 & -0.11 & 0 \\ 0 & 5.16 & 5.16 & 5.16 & 21.79 & 5.16 \\ 0 & 1 & 1 & -23.78 & 1 & 1 \\ 1 & 1 & -11.14 & 0 & 1 & 0 \\ 0 & 584.01 & 0 & 0 & -54.05 & 0 \end{pmatrix} \qquad v := \begin{pmatrix} -13.5 \\ 1.815 \\ 754.07 \\ -2.732 \\ -16.5 \\ 600 \end{pmatrix}$$

soln := lsolve(M, v)

$$\text{soln} = \begin{pmatrix} 5.4802 \\ 3.7629 \\ 4.9641 \\ 2.1635 \\ 29.5571 \\ 10.4313 \end{pmatrix} \quad \frac{t}{h}$$

All these steam consumptions are given in Fig. 8.5.

Example 8.8 In an effort to conserve energy, it is decided to incorporate two boiler feed water (BFW) heaters in the cascade steam system of Example 8.7. BFW from the discharge of the pump enters BFW Heater I where it will be heated from 105°C (378 K) to 137°C (410 K) with the help of saturated LP steam. Further, BFW will be heated to 238°C (511 K) with the help of superheated MP steam in BFW Heater II. Both the BFW heaters are operated at header pressures with negligible pressure drops. Deaerator steam requirement will be reduced to 0.10 kg/kg condensate as a result of receipt of hot condensates from BFW heaters. Revised steam system is shown in Fig. 8.6.

Considering all other parameters unchanged, establish the steam balance.

Solution *Basis* 100 kg BFW, entering BFW Heaters I and II
Heat balance across BFW Heater II
Enthalpy of superheated steam at 39 bar a and 320°C (593.15 K) = 3020.4 kJ/kg
From Appendix IV.2, at 39 bar a, t_s / T_s = 248.84°C/521.99 K,
$$h = 1080.13 \text{ kJ/kg} \quad \text{and} \quad \lambda_v = 1720.6 \text{ kJ/kg}$$
Heat transferred to BFW = 3020.4 − 1080.1 = 1940.3 kJ/kg steam
Enthalpy of condensate at 137°C (410.15 K) and 238°C (511.15 K) are read as 576.2 and 1028.1 kJ/kg, respectively.
Heat picked up by BFW in Heater II = 1028.1 − 576.2 = 451.9 kJ/kg

$$\text{Superheated MP steam input} = \frac{451.9 \times 100}{1940.3} = 23.29 \text{ kg}$$

Further, steam condensate at 248.84°C (521.99 K) will enter BFW Heater I.
Heat balance across BFW Heater I
Steam condensate at 521.84 K (248.84°C) enters BFW Heater I and flashes at 4.4 bar a.

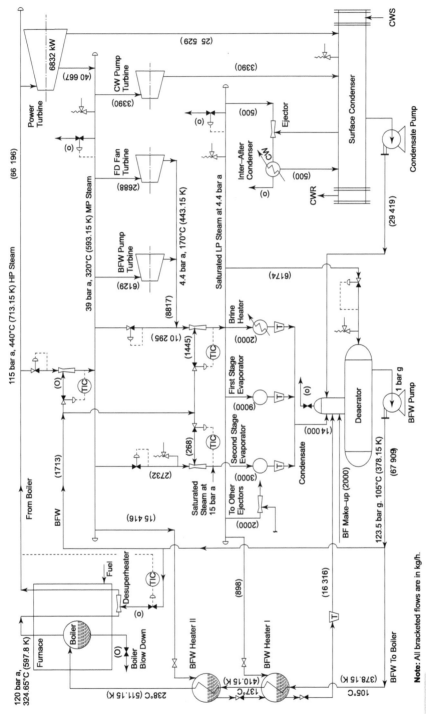

Note: All bracketed flows are in kg/h.

Fig. 8.6 Steam Balance in a Caustic Soda Plant with BFW Heaters

From A IV.2, at 4.4 bar a, $t_s/T_s = 147.09°C$ (420.24 K),
$$h = 619.6 \text{ kJ/kg} \quad \text{and} \quad \lambda_v = 2122.3 \text{ kJ/kg}$$
Heat available from MP steam condensate
$$= 1080.1 - 619.6 = 460.5 \text{ kJ/kg condensate}$$
Total heat available $= 460.5 \times 23.29 = 10\ 725 \text{ kJ}$
Now BFW is heated from 105°C (378.15 K) to 137°C (410.15 K), increasing its enthalpy from 440.2 to 576.2 kJ/kg.

Heat picked up by BFW in Heater I $= 100\ (576.2 - 440.2) = 13\ 600 \text{ kJ}$
Heat required from saturated LP steam $= 13\ 600 - 10\ 725 = 2875 \text{ kJ}$
LP steam condensed $= 2875/2122.3 = 1.325 \text{ kg}$
Total condensate from BFW Heaters, entering deaerator
$$= 23.29 + 1.325 = 24.615 \text{ kg}$$

Thus MP steam and LP steam consumptions are 0.2329 kg and 0.013 25 kg per kg condensate passed through the BFW Heater II and BFW Heater I, respectively.

The condensate enters the deaerator at 147.09°C (420.24 K) and flashes at 1 bar g. Availability of flash steam will result in less LP saturated steam requirement in the deaerator which is estimated at 0.01 kg/kg total condensate, entering the deaerator.

New basis 6832 kW at power turbine shaft
Let j = Total BFW pumped by BFW pump, t/h and
m = BFW used for quenching in desuperheaters, t/h
Assume $h = 0$.
Total BFW, $j = a + b + e + 16.5 + 0.246\ 45\ (j - m)$
and $m = 0.121\ g + 0.260 + 0.022\ 33\ (c + d)$

Saturated LP Steam Header
Requirement $= 9 + 2 + 0.5 + 2 + a + 0.013\ 25\ (j - m)$
Production of saturated LP steam $= 1.022\ (c + d) + 1.121\ g$

Equating the requirement and production, substituting values of j and m and simplifying,
$$1.022\ (c + d) + 1.121\ g - 13.5 + a + 0.013\ 55\ (j - m) \qquad \text{(i)}$$

Deaerator
Total condensate = condensate from SC + 16.0 t/h from ejectors and BF make-up + condensate from BFW Heaters
$$= b + e + 0.5 + 16.0 + 0.246\ 45\ (j - m)$$
$$a = 0.1\ [b + e + 0.5 + 16.0 + 0.246\ 45\ (j - m)] \qquad \text{(ii)}$$

Power turbine
Total MP superheated steam consumption,
$$x = b + c + d + g + 2.732 + 0.2329\ j$$
$$\frac{x \times 100}{21.79} + \frac{1000\ e}{5.16} = 6832 \qquad \text{(iii)}$$

FD fan Total HP steam produced $= x + e$
$$d = \frac{2.47 \times 16.34\ (x + e)}{1000} \qquad \text{(iv)}$$

BFW pump
$$c = \frac{5.493 \times 16.34\ j}{1000} \qquad \text{(v)}$$

CW pump Balance remains unchanged.

$$584.01 \; b - 54.05 \; e = 600 \tag{vi}$$

Mathcad solution

Guess values

a := 5.5	b := 3.8	c := 5	d := 2.2	e := 3.3	m := 1.5
g := 10.5	j := 16	n := 1.5	x := 40	Z := 66	

Given

$$j = a + b + e + 16.5 + 0.24645(j - m)$$

$$m = 0.121 \cdot g + 0.26 + 0.02233(c + d)$$

$$1.02233(c + d) + 1.121 \cdot g = 13.5 + a + 0.01355(j - m)$$

$$a = 0.1[b + e + 16.5 + 0.24645(j - m)]$$

$$x = b + c + d + g + 2.732 + 0.2329 \cdot j$$

$$x \cdot \frac{1000}{21.79} + e \cdot \frac{1000}{5.16} = 6832$$

$$d = 2.47 \cdot 16.34 \frac{(x + e)}{1000}$$

$$c = 5.493 \cdot 16.43 \cdot \frac{j}{1000}$$

$$584.01 \cdot b - 54.05 \cdot e = 600$$

$$Z = b + c + d + e + g + 2.732 + 0.2329(j - m)$$

$$vec := Find(a, b, c, d, e, g, j, m, x, Z)$$

vec =

	0
0	6.1735
1	3.3901
2	6.1287
3	2.6877
4	25.5289
5	10.3098
6	67.9085
7	1.7044
8	41.0642
9	66.1961

$\frac{t}{h}$

All the steam flows are given in Fig. 8.6.

It may be noted that boiler will generate 66.196 t/h HP superheated steam as compared to 53.624 t/h, calculated in Example 8.7. Apparently it looks like spending more energy than the original case. A closer look reveals actual energy savings.

For the original case (Example 8.7),

Heat pick-up in the boiler = 3190.7 − 440.2 = 2750.2 kJ/kg steam

Total heat absorption, ϕ_1 = 53 611 × 2750.2

= 147 440 972 kJ/h ≡ 40 955.83 kW

In the steam system with BFW heaters (Example 8.8),

Heat pick-up in the boiler = 3190.7 − 1028.1 = 2162.6 kJ/kg steam

Total heat absorption, ϕ_2 = 66 196 × 2162.6

= 143 155 470 kJ/h ≡ 39 765.4 kW

Assume boiler efficiency of 75% with NCV of fuel as 40 000 kJ/kg.

$$\text{Energy saving} = \frac{(147\,440\,972 - 143\,155\,470)\,100}{147\,440\,972} = 2.91\%$$

$$\text{Fuel saving} = \frac{(147\,440\,972 - 143\,155\,470)}{0.75 \times 40\,000} = 142.85 \text{ kg/h}$$

There is also a substantial reduction in cooling load of the surface condenser. Steam condensation requirement in the surface condenser will reduce from 33 820 to 29 419 kg/h, representing a reduction of 13.0%.

It is now clear that there are all-around benefits by introduction of BFW Heaters. Howevers, cost of BFW heaters, bigger boilers and bigger turbines will be higher than those for the original case. Additional cost of equipment will have to be weighed against savings in fuel consumption and reduction in cooling tower load. Return of investment will determine the selection of system. Usually, energy saving outweighs the investment in such a case.

Example 8.9 In another energy conservation exercise to the steam system described in Example 8.8, it is decided to draw steam at 7.5 bar a (back pressure) from the turbine as shown in Fig. 8.8. Its temperature is expected to be 200°C (473 K). It is compressed in a thermocompressor with the help of MP steam to achieve 15 bar a steam which will then be desuperheated to its saturation temperature for utilization in second-stage evaporator. The thermocompressor is designed to compress 0.45 kg steam at 7.5 bar a and 200°C (473 K) with 1 kg of MP steam. Establish steam balance with the thermocompressor and BFW Heaters.

Solution

Basis 45 kg of steam at 7.5 bar a and 200°C (473.15 K)

Enthalpy of steam at 7.5 bar a and 473.15 K = 2841.4 kJ/kg (Ref. A IV.3)

Total enthalpy of compressed steam at 15 bar a

= 45 × 2841.4 + 100 × 3020.4

= 429 903 kJ/145 kg steam ≡ 2964.85 kJ/kg steam

From steam tables (A IV.3), this enthalpy corresponds to superheated steam temperature of 267.6°C (540.75 K) at 15 bar a.

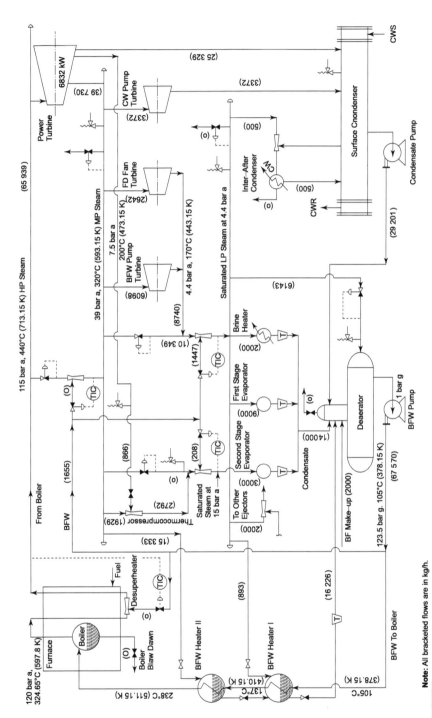

Note: All bracketed flows are in kg/h.

Fig. 8.7 Steam Balance in a Caustic Soda Plant with BFW Heaters and Thermocompressor

At 15 bar a, t_s/T_s = 198.29°C /471.44 K, h = 844.66 and H = 2789.9 kJ/kg

Let y be kg of condensate at 105°C (378 K) to be sprayed in 145 kg compressed steam in the desuperheater.

$$2964.85 \times 145 + y \times 440.2 = (145 + y)\ 2789.9$$

or
$$y = 10.8 \text{ kg}$$

Total saturated steam required in second-stage evaporator = 3000 kg/h

$$\text{Superheated steam to be desuperheated} = \frac{145 \times 3000}{(10.8 + 145)}$$

$$= 2792 \text{ kg/h at 15 bar a and}$$
$$540.75 \text{ K } (267.6°C)$$

Condensate for desuperheating = 3000 − 2792 = 208 kg/h

Superheated steam at 7.5 bar a and 200°C (473 K)

$$= \frac{2797 \times 45}{145} = 868 \text{ kg/h from turbine}$$

Motivating (MP) steam requirement = 2797 − 868
$$= 1929 \text{ kg/h}$$

Heat utilized in power turbine for the extraction of 868 kg/h steam at 7.5 bar a
$$= 3190.7 - 2841.4$$
$$= 349.3 \text{ kJ/kg at 100\% efficiency}$$
$$\equiv 338.82 \text{ kJ/kg at 97\% efficiency}$$

Corresponding power generation = 868 × 338.82 = 294 096 kJ/h
$$\equiv 81.69 \text{ kW}$$

New basis 6832 kW at power turbine shaft
$$m = 0.121\ g + 0.203 + 0.022\ 33\ (c + d)$$

Equation for j remains unchanged.

LP Steam header

Production of saturated LP steam = 1.022 $(c + d)$ + 1.121 g

Requirement of saturated LP steam = 13.5 + a + 0.013 55 $(j - m)$

$$1.022\,(c + d) + 1.121\ g = 13.5 + a + 0.013\ 55\ (j - m) \qquad \text{(i)}$$

Deaerator

$$a = 0.1\ [b + e + 16.5 + 0.246\ 15\,(j - m) \qquad \text{(ii)}$$
$$x = b + c + d + g + 1.929 + 0.2329\ j$$

Power turbine

$$\frac{x \times 100}{21.79} \times \frac{1000\ e}{5.16} = 6832 - 81.69 = 6750.31 \qquad \text{(iii)}$$

Equations for FD fan, BFW pump and CW Pump turbines remain uncharged

Mathcad solution

Guess values

a := 5.5	b := 3.8	c := 5	d := 2.2	e := 3.3	m := 1.5
g := 10.5	j := 16	n := 1.5	x := 40	Z := 66	

Given

$j = a + b + e + 16.5 + 0.24615(j - m)$

$m = 0.121 \cdot g + 0.203 + 0.02233(c + d)$

$1.02233(c + d) + 1.121 \cdot g = 13.5 + a + 0.01355(j - m)$

$a = 0.1[b + e + 16.5 + 0.24615(j - m)]$

$x = b + c + d + g + 1.929 + 0.2329 \cdot j$

$$x \cdot \frac{1000}{21.79} + e \cdot \frac{1000}{5.16} = 6750.3$$

$$d = 2.47 \cdot 16.34 \frac{(x + e)}{1000}$$

$$c = 5.493 \cdot 16.43 \cdot \frac{j}{1000}$$

$584.01 \cdot b - 54.05 \cdot e = 600$

$Z = b + c + d + e + g + 2.797 + 0.2329(j - m)$

$\text{vec} := \text{Find}(a, b, c, d, e, g, j, m, x, Z)$

$\text{vec} =$

	0
0	6.1427
1	3.3716
2	6.0982
3	2.6418
4	25.3294
5	10.3486
6	67.5698
7	1.6503
8	40.1262
9	65.9393

$\dfrac{t}{h}$

All the steam flows are given in Fig. 8.7.

Note This indicates a marginal reduction in HP steam production (257 kg/h) and may not prove economically attractive as the cost of the power turbine may offset the savings. However, the example indicates yet another possibility of energy saving.

Multistage efficient turbines with multiple extraction facilities have resulted in economizing the steam consumptions. The trend is to select an efficient turbine. When all these conditions are taken into account, the most optimal steam balance is obtained.

Steam balance has assumed considerable importance in the process industry. Apart from the increased reliability, it has been proved to be an excellent working tool and an energy-saving measure. Frequent checks of the actual steam balance in the plant enables visualization of the plant's overall steam, condensate and BFW demands, as well as quick identification of upset conditions and their effects[10].

Steam balance making is an art. Brinsko[11] and Matas-Valiente[12] have given a step-by-step procedure for making a steam balance. Useful guidelines can be derived from these articles for making a steam balance for any plant. Using these guidelines, various steam balances are developed in this book. To start with, a steam balance is made with theoretical considerations as is the case with Example 8.7. A number of overriding parameters, based on process conditions, are to be kept in mind before selecting a type of turbine for a particular application. Start-up requirements, power failure, boiler trip, etc., are some of these process conditions. Subsequently, exact consumptions, specified by selected turbine vendors (inclusive of gland losses), are inserted in the balance and thereby the actual working steam balance is obtained.

Example 8.10 Methyl tertialy butyl ether (MTBE) is produced by reaction between methanol and *i*-butene. This is a well-known oxygenating product for improvement of octane number of gasolines. This is a catalytic reaction and in a typical process, sulphuric acid is used as a catalyst[13].

The process flow diagram is given in Fig. 8.8.

The feed to the plant is a C_4-cut stream of a steam cracker which contains 45% *i*-butene and 55% other C_4-hydrocarbons by mass (having average molar mass = 56). It is mixed with methanol such that mole ratio of methanol to *i*-butene at the reactor inlet (mixed feed) is 1.1. Sulphuric acid in the mixed feed is 5% (by mass). Two reactors are used in series. In the first reactor, 90% conversion of *i*-butene is achieved while total conversion of 98% of *i*-butene is achieved at the outlet of the second reactor. While fresh methanol is of 100% strength, recycle methanol stream contains 2% water, 2% MTBE and 6% C_4-hydrocarbons (on mole basis). Water, recycled with methanol, reacts with *i*-butene to form tertiary butyl alcohol (TBA). Also, nearly 0.35% *i*-butene is converted to Di-*iso*-butene (DIB). Reactions taking place in the reactors are given as follows.

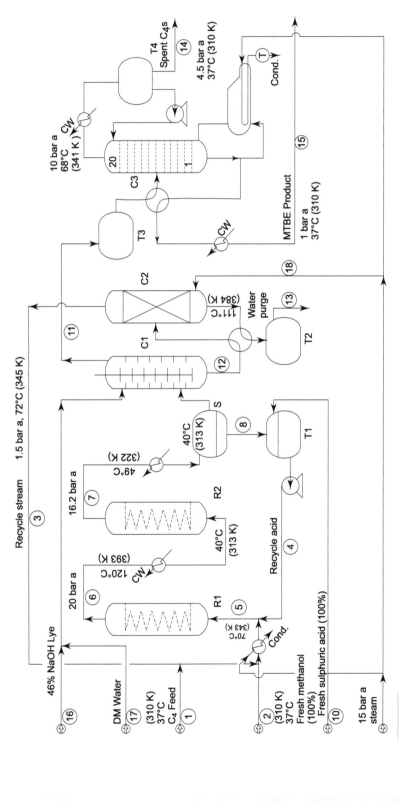

Fig. 8.8 Manufacture of MTBE using Sulphuric Acid as Catalyst

$$CH_3-CH_2-CH=CH_2 + CH_3OH = H_3C-\underset{\underset{CH_3}{|}}{\overset{\overset{CH_3}{|}}{C}}-O-CH_3 \qquad (A)$$

$$\underset{i\text{-Butene}}{} \qquad \underset{\text{MeOH}}{} \qquad \underset{\text{MTBE}}{}$$

$$CH_3-CH_2-CH=CH_2 + H_2O = H_3C-\underset{\underset{CH_3}{|}}{\overset{\overset{CH_3}{|}}{C}}-OH \qquad (B)$$

$$\underset{i\text{-Butene}}{} \qquad \underset{\text{Water}}{} \qquad \underset{\text{TBA}}{}$$

$$\underset{i\text{-Butene}}{2\ C_4H_8} = \underset{\text{DIB}}{(C_4H_8)_2} \qquad (C)$$

In the first reactor (R1), reaction mixture enters at 20 bar a and 70°C (343 K). Reaction temperature is controlled below 120°C (393 K) in the reactor. The product mixture is cooled to 40°C (313 K) and sent to second reactor (R2), operating at 16.2 bar a. Exit temperature from R2 is controlled to 49°C (322 K) by cooling within the reactor.

The product mixture from R2 is cooled to 40°C (313 K) and allowed to separate into two phases; an organic phase and an acid phase in the settler (S). 90% acid is recovered from the settler in T1 with negligible organic impurities. Recovered acid along with fresh acid (of 100% strength) is fed to the mixed feed.

Organic phase from S is sent to Water Washing Column (C1) which is a rotating disc contactor. It operates at 10 bar a. Caustic soda solution of 46% (by mass) strength is used as make-up. Diluted solution is introduced to C1 in stoichiometric quantity.

The extract phase is fed to a packed column (C2) which operates at 1.5 bar a. Live steam at 15 bar a is used for stripping off methanol along with organic impurities at the rate of 4.2 kmol steam per kmol methanol. Overhead vapours are recycled to the reactor at 72°C (345 K). Bottom product from C2 leaves at 111°C (384 K) and is sent to the water purge tank (T2) in which Na_2SO_4 concentration is maintained at 10% (by mass). Methanol in the bottom product from C2 is approximately 0.5% (by mass).

In column C3, the overhead product is C_4-hydrocarbons which contains unconverted i-butene and a small amount of MTBE. Loss of MTBE in the overhead is 1.3% of the total production. The bottom product from C3 contains 99 mole % MTBE, balance being TBA and DIB. C_4-hydrocarbons in the bottom product is approximately 0.5 mole %. This column operates at nearly 10 bar a. Steam 15 at bar a is supplied to the reboiler. Both the products from the column are cooled and sent to storage.

For a production rate of 15 t/h of MTBE (100%), establish the material balance of each process stream.

Solution   *Basis* 15 000 kg/h MTBE (100%)
Overall material balance

$$\text{Desired MTBE production rate} = \frac{15000}{88} = 170.45 \text{ kmol/h}$$

$$\text{Bottom product from C3} = \frac{170.45}{0.99} = 172.18 \text{ kmol/h}$$

Loss of MTBE in the overhead

$$\text{stream from C3} = 170.45 \times \frac{1.3}{98.7} = 2.25 \text{ kmol/h}$$

$$\text{Total MTBE production} = 170.45 + 2.25 = 172.70 \text{ kmol/h}$$

Let fresh feed be F_1 kmol/h (of i-butene + C_4s).

$$i\text{-butene feed rate} = 0.55\ F_1 \text{ kmol/h}$$

Note that i-butene and C_4s have the same molar mass and hence mass % equals mole %.

$$\text{Conversion of } i\text{-butene} = 0.98 \times 0.55\ F_1 \quad \text{(overall)}$$
$$= 0.539\ F_1 \text{ kmol/h}$$
$$i\text{-butene converted to DIB} = 0.0035 \times 0.55\ F_1 = 0.002\ F_1 \text{ kmol/h}$$

Let fresh methanol feed be F_2 kmol/h and recycle stream be R kmol/h of methanol recycle.

$$\text{Methanol content of recycle stream} = 0.9\ R \text{ kmol/h}$$
$$\text{Total methanol charged} = (F_2 + 0.9\ R) \text{ kmol/h}$$
$$\frac{\text{Methanol}}{i - \text{butane}} = 1.1$$
$$\frac{F_2 + 0.9}{0.55\ F_1} = 1.1 \text{ or}$$
$$F_2 + 0.9\ R = 0.605\ F_1 \quad\quad\quad\quad (i)$$
$$\text{Water content of recycle stream} = 0.02\ R \text{ kmol/h}$$
$$i\text{-butene consumed for TBA production} = 0.02\ R \text{ kmol/h}$$
$$i\text{-butene consumed to MTBE} = 0.539\ F_1 - 0.02\ R - 0.002\ F_1$$
$$= 0.537\ F_1 - 0.02\ R \text{ kmol/h}$$
$$\text{Methanol consumed} = 0.537\ F_1 - 0.02\ R \text{ kmol/h}$$
$$\text{Unconverted methanol} = F_2 + 0.9\ R - 0.537\ F_1 + 0.02\ R$$
$$= F_2 - 0.537\ F_1 + 0.92\ R \text{ kmol/h}$$
$$\text{Acid content of mixture} = 5\% \text{ by mass}$$

Table 8.27   Composition of Mixed Feed (without acid)

Component	kmol/h	Molar mass	kg/h
i-butene	$0.55\ F_1$	56	$30.8\ F_1$
C_4s	$0.45\ F_1 + 0.06\ R$	56	$25.2\ F_1 + 3.36\ R$
Water	$0.02\ R$	18	$0.36\ R$
MTBE	$0.02\ R$	88	$1.76\ R$
CH_3OH	$F_2 + 0.9\ R$	32	$32\ F_2 + 28.8\ R$
Total	$F_1 + F_2 + R$		$56\ F_1 + 32\ F_2 + 34.28\ R$

$$\text{Acid content of mixed feed} = \frac{(56\ F_1 + 32\ F_2 + 34.28R)\ 0.05}{0.95}$$
$$= 2.947\ F_1 + 1.684\ F_2 + 1.804\ R \text{ kg/h}$$

Organic phase from S contains 10% acid.

$$\text{Acid in the feed to C1} = 0.1\ (2.947\ F_1 + 1.684\ F_2 + 1.804\ R)$$
$$= 0.2947\ F_1 + 0.1684\ F_2 + 0.1804\ R \text{ kg/h}$$

$$2NaOH + H_2SO_4 = Na_2SO_4 + 2H_2O \qquad (D)$$
$$2 \times 40 \qquad 98 \qquad 142 \qquad 2 \times 18$$
$$Na_2SO_4 \text{ produced} = (0.2947 \ F_1 + 0.1684 \ F_2 + 0.1804 \ R)\frac{142}{98}$$
$$= 0.427 \ F_1 + 0.244 \ F_2 + 0.2613 \ R \text{ kg/h}$$

Water purge contains 10% Na_2SO_4.

$$\text{Water purge flow rate (stream 13)} = \frac{0.427 \ F_1 + 0.244 \ F_2 + 0.2613 \ R}{0.1}$$
$$= 4.27 \ F_1 + 2.44 \ F_2 + 2.613 \ R \text{ kg/h}$$

Methanol in water purge (i.e., loss in stream 13)
$$= \text{Water purge flow} \times 0.005$$
$$= 0.021 \ 35 \ F_1 + 0.0122 \ F_2 + 0.0131 \ R \text{ kg/h}$$
$$\equiv 0.000 \ 67 \ F_1 + 0.000 \ 38 \ F_2 + 0.000 \ 41 \ R \text{ kmol/h}$$

Methanol recycled = methanol unconverted − methanol lost in water purge
$$= F_2 - 0.537 \ F_1 + 0.92 \ R - 0.000 \ 67 \ F_1 - 0.000 \ 38 \ F_2$$
$$- \ 0.000 \ 41 \ R$$
$$= 0.999 \ 62 \ F_2 - 0.537 \ 67 \ F_1 + 0.919 \ 59 \ R \text{ kmol/h}$$
$$= 0.9 \ R \quad \text{(given)}$$

$$0.999 \ 62 \ F_2 - 0.537 \ 67 \ F_1 = -0.01959 \ R$$
or $\qquad F_2 - 0.53787 \ F_1 = -0.0196 \ R \qquad \qquad$ (ii)
$$\text{MTBE produced} = 0.537 \ F_1 - 0.02 \ R = 172.7 \qquad \text{(iii)}$$

Solving the three equations,
$$F_1 = 322.511 \text{ kmol/h} \qquad \text{(Stream 1)}$$
$$F_2 = 172.987 \text{ kmol/h} \qquad \text{(Stream 2)}$$
$$R = 24.592 \text{ kmol/h} \qquad \text{(Stream 3)}$$

Total methanol fed = $172.987 + 22.133 = 195.120$ kmol/h

$$\text{Mole ratio of } \frac{\text{Methanol}}{i - \text{butane}} = \frac{195.120}{177.381} = 1.1 \text{ (Check !)}$$

Acid content of mixed feed (Stream 5) = $2.947 \times 322.511 + 1.684 \times 172.987$
$$+ \ 1.804 \times 24.592$$
$$= 950.44 + 291.31 + 44.36$$
$$= 1286.11 \text{ kg/h} \equiv 13.123 \text{ kmol/h}$$

Recycle acid = 1286.11 kg/h $\qquad \qquad$ (Stream 4)
Make-up acid = $1286.11 \times 0.1 = 128.61$ kg/h $\qquad$ (Stream 10)

Material balance across Reactor R1

Conversion of *i*-butene in R1 = 90% (given)
Assume conversion of water to TBA = 100% in R1
$$\text{Conversion of } i\text{-butene} = 177.381 \times 0.9 = 159.643 \text{ kmol/h}$$
$$\text{TBA formed} = \text{water consumed}$$
$$= 0.492 \text{ kmol/h} = i\text{-butene consumed}$$
$$i\text{-butene consumed to MTBE} = 159.643 - 0.492 = 159.151 \text{ kmol/h}$$
$$= CH_3OH \text{ consumed} = \text{MTBE produced}$$

Material balance across reactor R2

Total *i*-butene conversion = 98%
Additional *i*-butene conversion in R2 = 98 − 90 = 8%

i-butene consumed = $177.381 \times 0.08 = 14.191$ kmol/h

i-butene converted to DIB = $177.381 \times 0.0035 = 0.621$ kmol/h

$$\text{DIB formed} = \frac{0.621}{2} = 0.3105 \text{ kmol/h}$$

i-butene converted to MTBE = $14.191 - 0.621 = 13.57$ kmol/h

$$= CH_3OH \text{ consumed} = MTBE \text{ produced}$$

Material balance across Column C2:

Steam input = $4.2 \times$ moles of CH_3OH in extract phase

$$= 4.2 \times 22.399 = 94.076 \text{ kmol/h}$$

$$\equiv 1693.37 \text{ kg/h} \qquad \text{(Stream-18)}$$

Na_2SO_4 produced = $0.427 \, F_1 + 0.244 \, F_2 + 0.2613 \, R$

$$= 137.71 + 42.21 + 6.43 = 186.35 \text{ kg/h}$$

Acid neutralized = 128.61 kg/h

Na_2SO_4 production, based on

$$\text{acid consumption} = \frac{142 \times 128.61}{98} = 186.35 \text{ kg/h} \qquad \text{(Check !)}$$

$$H_2O \text{ produced} = \frac{36 \times 128.61}{98} = 47.24 \text{ kg/h}$$

NaOH required for neturalization = $186.35 + 47.24 - 128.61$

$$= 104.98 \text{ kg/h}$$

$$\text{Bottom product from C2} = \frac{186.35}{0.09} = 2070.55 \text{ kg/h} \qquad \text{(Stream 13)}$$

Recycle stream R = 24.592 kmol/h = 843.02 kg/h (Stream 3)

Extract phase from C1 = $843.02 + 2070.55 - 1710.37$

$$= 1203.20 \text{ kg/h} \qquad \text{(Stream 12)}$$

Methanol loss in bottom

product from C2 = $0.021 \, 35 \, F_1 + 0.0122 \, F_2 + 0.0131 \, R$

$$= 6.89 + 2.11 + 0.32 = 9.32 \text{ kg/h}$$

Total methanol consumption = $159.151 + 13.57 = 172.721$ kmol/h

This figure matches well with Stream 2.

Water entering in extract phase of C1 = 174.28 kg/h

$$\text{NaOH strength required} = \frac{104.98 \times 100}{(104.98 + 174.28)} = 37.6\%$$

NaOH strength of lye = 46.0%

$$\text{Lye supply} = \frac{104.98}{0.46} = 228.22 \text{ kg/h} \qquad \text{(Stream 16)}$$

Fresh water added = $279.26 - 228.22 = 51.04$ kg/h   (Stream 17)

$$\text{Loss of MTBE} = \frac{199.44 \times 100}{15 \, 199.44} = \mathbf{1.31\%}$$

Material balance results are summarised in Table 8.28.

Table 8.28 Material Balance of MTBE Production Plant

Component	Stream 1				Stream 2				Stream 3			
	kg/h	mass %	kmol/h	mole %	kg/h	mass %	kmol/h	mole %	kg/h	mass %	kmol/h	mole %
i-butene	9 939.34	55.0	177.391	55.0								
C_4s	8 127.28	45.0	145.130	45.0					82.60	9.80	1.475	6.0
MeOH					5535.58	100.0	172.987	100.0	708.26	84.01	22.133	90.0
MTBE									43.30	5.14	0.492	2.0
H_2O									8.86	1.05	0.492	2.0
Total	18 066.62	100.0	322.521	100.0	5535.58	100.0	172.987	100.0	843.02	100.0	24.592	100.0

Component	Stream 5				Stream 6				Stream 7			
	kg/h	mass %	kmol/h	mole %	kg/h	mass %	kmol/h	mole %	kg/h	mass %	kmol/h	mole %
i-butene	9 933.34	38.61	177.381	33.27	993.33	3.86	17.738	4.75	196.63	0.77	3.547	0.99
C_4s	8 209.88	31.91	146.605	27.50	8 209.88	31.91	146.605	39.24	8 209.88	31.91	146.605	40.76
MeOH	6 243.84	24.27	195.12	36.59	1 151.01	4.45	35.969	9.63	716.77	2.79	22.399	6.21
MTBE	43.30	0.17	0.492	0.09	14 048.58	54.61	159.643	42.74	15 242.74	59.25	173.213	48.16
H_2O	8.86	0.04	0.492	0.09	Nil	Nil	Nil	Nil	Nil	Nil	Nil	Nil
H_2SO_4												
TBA	1 286.11	5.00	13.123	2.46	1 286.11	5.00	13.123	3.51	1 286.11	5.00	13.123	3.65
DIB					36.41	0.14	0.492	0.13	36.41	0.14	0.492	0.14
									34.76	0.14	0.310	0.09
Total	25 725.33	100.00	533.213	100.00	25 725.32	100.00	373.570	100.00	25 725.32	100.00	359.689	100.00

(Contd.)

Table 8.28 (Contd.)

Component	Stream 11				Stream 12				Stream 13			
	kg/h	mass %	kmol/h	mole %	kg/h	mass%	kmol/h	mole %	kg/h	mass%	kmol/h	mole %
i-butene	198.63	0.84	3.547	1.10	—	—	—	—	—	—	—	—
C₄s	8 127.28	34.44	145.130	45.04	82.60	6.87	1.475	4.24	—	—	—	—
MeOH	—	—	—	—	716.77	59.57	22.399	64.35	8.51	0.41	0.266	0.25
MTBE	15 197.44	64.41	172.721	53.61	43.30	3.6	0.492	1.41	—	—	—	—
H₂O	—	—	—	—	174.28	14.48	9.682	27.81	1875.69	90.59	104.205	99.02
TBA	36.41	0.16	0.492	0.15	—	—	—	—	—	—	—	—
DIB	34.76	0.15	0.310	0.10	—	—	—	—	186.35	9.00	0.762	0.73
Na₂SO₄	—	—	—	—	186.35	15.48	0.762	2.19	—	—	—	—
Total	23 596.52	100.00	322.200	100.00	1203.20	100.00	34.810	100.00	2070.55	100.00	105.233	100.00

Component	Stream 14				Stream 15			
	kg/h	mass %	kmol/h	mole %	kg/h	mass %	kmol/h	mole %
i-butene	198.63	2.35	3.547	2.36	—	—	—	—
C₄s	8075.31	95.30	144.202	96.13	51.97	**0.34**	0.928	**0.54**
MTBE	199.44	2.35	2.266	1.51	15 000.00	**99.19**	170.455	**99.00**
TBA	—	—	—	—	36.41	**0.24**	0.492	**0.28**
DIB	—	—	—	—	34.76	**0.23**	0.310	**0.18**
Total	8473.38	100.00	150.015	100.00	15123.14	**100.0**	172.185	**100.00**

Example 8.11 Methyl formate is manufactured by carbonylation of methanol in presence of homogeneous phase catalyst as per the following reaction.

$$CH_3OH(l) + CO(g) = HCOOCH_3(l)$$

Continuous reaction is carried out at 45 bar a and 80°C (353.15 K) in presence of a catalyst (of negligible concentration). Conversion of methanol is 30%. Molar ratio of carbon monoxide to methanol in the fresh feed is 1.1. In the carbonylation reactor, composition of liquid remains uniform throughout and does not change with time. Steady-state composition of the liquid in the reactor is assumed to be 70% methanol and 30% methyl formate (by mole). Feed gas composition is 95% CO and 5% H_2 (by mole)[14]. Unconverted CO and H_2 of feed gas stream leaves the reactor from top at 80°C (353.15 K) and passes through an overhead condenser in which chilled water condenses vapours of mthanol and methyl fromate. The gas mixture from the condenser leaves at 44.5 bar a and 20°C (293.15 K) with chilled water. For a production capacity of 30 t/d methyl formate, (a) calculate the condensation load of the overhead condenser, (b) partial pressures and pure component pressures of the gas mixtures entering and leaving the overhead condenser, and (c) heat load of the condenser considering real gas mixtures.

Data (i) Vapour pressures of methyl formate at 20°C (293.15 K) and 80°C (353.15 K) are 0.6374 bar and 4.45 bar, respectively. (ii) Heat capacity of methyl formate is 71.5 and 63.85 kJ/(kmol · K) at 353.15 K and 293.15 K, respectively.

Soultion

Basis 30 t/d methyl formate production rate

Since it is a continuous production facility,

$$\dot{m}_{MF} = \frac{30\,000}{24} = 1250 \text{ kg/h}$$

$$\text{Methanol consumption} = \frac{1250 \times 32}{60}$$

$$= 666.67 \text{ kg/h} \equiv 20.833 \text{ kmol/h}$$

Methanol feed rate will be higher by the amount lost along with the gas mixture, leaving the overhead condenser at 20°C (293.15 K). However, considering it to be a very small amount, it is neglected for reaction chemistry.

$$\text{CO in feed} = 20.833 \times 1.1 = 22.9163 \text{ kmol/h}$$

$$H_2 \text{ in feed gas mixture} = \frac{22.9163 \times 0.05}{0.95} = 1.2061 \text{ kmol/h}$$

CO in gas-mixture at top (entering overhead condenser),

$$\dot{n}_{H_2} = 22.9163 - 20.833 = 2.0833 \text{ kmol/h}$$

H_2 leaving with CO, $\dot{n}_{H_2} = 1.2061$ kmol/h

Reactor pressure is reasonably high and hence the gas mixture, leaving the reactor or overhead condenser cannot be considered to follow ideal gas law nor the liquid mixture be considerd as an ideal soultion (i.e. Raoult's law is not applicable). For non-ideal behavious of the solution and of the gas mixture, at vapour–liquid equilibrium[15],

$$y_i \cdot \phi_i \cdot p = p_{vi} \cdot x_i \cdot \gamma_i \cdot \phi_i^{sat} \tag{8.1}$$

where y_i = mole fraction of ith component in gas mixture

        ϕ_i = fugacity coefficient of ith component at system pressure

        p = system pressure = 40 bar a

        p_{vi} = vapour pressure of ith component, bar

        x_i = mole fractin of ith component in the liquid mixture in equilibrium

        γ_i = activity coefficient of ith component ≈ 1.0 far chemically similar components

        ϕ_i^{sat} = fugacity coefficient of ith component at vapour pressure

Equation (8.1) is required to be applied to vapours which are at well below their critical temperatues. CO and H_2 will escape without any phase change.

For evaluation of ϕ_i and ϕ_i^{sat}, generlized correlation[15] in the form of virial equation

$$\phi = \exp\left[\frac{p_r}{T_r}(B^0 + \omega B^1)\right] = \exp\left[\frac{p_r}{T_r} \cdot \hat{B}\right] \tag{8.2}$$

where p_r = reduced pressure = $\dfrac{\text{pressure in question}}{\text{critical pressure}}$

        T_r = reduced temperature = $\dfrac{\text{temperature in question}}{\text{critical temperature}}$

        ω = acentric factor (Pitzer correlation)   (5.66)

B^0 and B^1 are functions of generalized reduced second virial coefficient ($\hat{B}$) correlation and are dependent on temperature only.

$$B^0 = 0.083 - \frac{0.422}{T_r^{1.6}} \tag{8.3}$$

$$B^1 = 0.139 - \frac{0.172}{T_r^{4.2}} \tag{8.4}$$

Using Antoine constants (Table 5.4), $p_{vMe} = 1.807$ bar at $T = 353.15$ K.

Table 8.29 Evalution of B^0 and B^1 Functions at $T = 353.15$ K

Component	T_{ci}, K	ω_i	T_{ri}	B^0	B^1
Methanol	512.5	0.564	0.6891	−0.6827	−0.6828
Methyl formate	487.2	0.632	0.7249	−0.6231	−0.5253

Table 8.30 Evalution of ϕ and ϕ_i^{sat} at $p = 45$ bar a

Component	p_{ci}, bar	p_{vi}, bar	p_{ri}, at p = 45 bar	p_{ri}^{sat}	ϕ_i	ϕ_i^{sat}
Methanol	80.84	1.807	0.5567	0.224	0.422	0.9659
Methyl formate	60	4.45	0.75	0.0742	0.3723	0.9069

From Eq. (8.1)

$$y_{Me} = \frac{1.807 \times 0.7 \times 0.9659}{0.422 \times 45} = 0.0643$$

$$y_{MF} = \frac{4.45 \times 0.3 \times 0.9069}{0.3723 \times 45} = 0.0723$$

For the gas mixture, entering overhead condenser,

$$y_{CO} + y_{H_2} + y_{Me} + y_{MF} = 1$$

$$y_{CO} + y_{H_2} = 1 - 0.0643 - 0.0723 = 0.8634$$

$$= \frac{\dot{n}_{CO} + \dot{n}_{H_2}}{\dot{n}_t}$$

$$\dot{n}_t = \frac{(2.0833 + 1.2061)}{0.8634} = 3.8098 \text{ kmol/h}$$

$\dot{n}_{Me} = 3.8098 \times 0.0643 = 0.2450$ kmol/h

$\dot{n}_{MF} = 3.8098 \times 0.0723 = 0.2754$ kmol/h

If ideal gas law and ideal solution (i.e. applicability of Raoult's law) behaviour would have been considered,

$$\phi_i = \phi_i^{sat} = 1$$

$$y_{Me}^1 = \frac{1.807 \times 0.7}{45} = 0.0281$$

$$y_{MF}^1 = \frac{4.45 \times 0.3}{45} = 0.0297$$

$$\dot{n}_t^1 = \frac{3.2894}{(1 - 0.0281 - 0.0297)} = 3.4912 \text{ kmol/h}$$

$\dot{n}_{Me}^1 = 3.4912 \times 0.0281 = 0.0981$ kmol/h

$\dot{n}_{MF}^1 = 3.4912 \times 0.0297 = 0.1037$ kmol/h

Presence of organinc vapour (i.e., molar flow rates of methanol and MF) under real conditions are higher by $(0.245 + 0.2754) - (0.0981 + 0.1037) = 0.3186$ kmol/h which is 2.58 times that of ideal conditions.

At the outlet of overhead condenser, temperature and pressure are 20°C (293.15 K) and 44.5 bar a. Pressure drop in the condenser is assumed to be 0.5 bar.

At $\qquad T = 293.15$ K, $\quad p_{vMe} = 0.13$ bar

Table 8.31 Evolution of B^0 and B^1 Functions at $T = 293.15$ K

Component	T_{ci}, K	ω_i	T_{ri}	B^0	B^1
Methanol	512.5	0.564	0.572	−0.9485	−1.6577
Methyl formate	487.2	0.632	0.6017	−0.8683	−1.3136

Table 8.32   Evaluation of ϕ and ϕ_i^{sat} at $p = 44.5$ bar.

Component	p_{ci}, bar	p_{vi}, bar	p_{ri}^{sat}	p_{ri} at $p =$ 44.5 bar	ϕ_i	ϕ_i^{sat}
Methanol	80.84	0.13	0.0016	0.5505	0.1632	0.9947
Methyl formate	60	0.6374	0.0106	0.7417	0.1232	0.9705

Gas-vapour mixture, leaving the overhead condenser will be in equilibrium with the liquid mixture in the condenser. Since liquid mixture in the condenser will depend on actual condensation, it is not known exactly.

Iteration 1 Assume total condensation for the frist iteration.
Liquid phase

$$\dot{n}_{Me}^2 + \dot{n}_{MF}^2 = 0.245 + 0.2754 = 0.5204 \text{ kmol/h}$$

$$x_{Me}^2 = \frac{0.245}{0.5204} = 0.4708$$

$$x_{MF}^2 = 1 - 0.4708 = 0.5292$$

Vapour phase

$$y_{Me}^2 = \frac{0.13 \times 0.4708 \times 0.9947}{0.1632 \times 44.5} = 0.0084$$

$$y_{MF}^2 = \frac{0.6374 \times 0.5292 \times 0.9705}{0.1232 \times 44.5} = 0.0597$$

$$\dot{n}_t^2 = \frac{3.2894}{(1 - 0.0084 - 0.0597)} = 3.5298 \text{ kmol/h}$$

$$\dot{n}_{Me}'^3 = 3.5298 \times 0.0084 = 0.0297 \text{ kmol/h}$$

$$\dot{n}_{MF}'^3 = 3.5298 \times 0.0597 = 0.2107 \text{ kmol/h}$$

Iteration 2 Revised condensate load

$$\dot{n}_{Me}^3 = 0.245 - 0.0297 = 0.2153 \text{ kmol/h}$$

$$\dot{n}_{MF}^3 = 0.2754 - 0.2107 = 0.0647 \text{ kmol/h}$$

$$x_{Me}^3 = \frac{0.2153}{(0.2153 + 0.0647)} = 0.7689$$

$$x_{MF}^3 = 1 - 0.7689 = 0.2311$$

Revised organic vapour loads

$$y_{Me}^3 = \frac{0.13 \times 0.7689 \times 0.9947}{0.1632 \times 44.5} = 0.0137$$

$$y_{Me}^3 = \frac{0.6374 \times 0.2311 \times 0.9705}{0.1232 \times 44.5} = 0.0261$$

$$\dot{n}_t^3 = \frac{3.2894}{(1 - 0.0137 - 0.0261)} = 3.4257 \text{ kmol/h}$$

$$\dot{n}_{Me}'^4 = 3.4257 \times 0.0137 = 0.0469 \text{ kmol/h}$$

$$\dot{n}_{MF}'^4 = 3.4257 \times 0.0261 = 0.0894 \text{ kmol/h}$$

After nine iterations, mole fractions of methanol and MF in liquid mixture closely match with those of previous (8th) iteration.

Methanol methyl formate in outgoing gas mixture.

$$\dot{n}'^{10}_{Me} = 0.0366 \text{ kmol/h}$$

$$\dot{n}'^{10}_{MF} = 0.1626 \text{ kmol/h}$$

Table 8.33 Composition of Gas Mixtures

Component	Ingoing to Overhead Condenser		Outcoming from Condenser	
	kmol/h	mole %	kmol/h	mole %
CO	2.0833	54.68	2.0833	59.72
H_2	1.2061	31.66	1.2061	34.57
CH_3OH	0.2450	6.43	0.0366	1.05
$C_2H_4O_2$	0.2754	7.23	0.1626	4.66
Total	3.8098	100.00	3.4886	100.00
Pressure, bar	45		44.5	
Temperature °C/K	80/353.15		20/293.15	

Methanol condensed = 0.245 − 0.0366 = 0.2084 kmol/h

Methyl formate condensed = 0.2754 − 0.1626 = 0.1128 kmol/h

Methanol loss of 0.0366 kmol/h amounts to 0.18% of feed rate (= 20.833 kmol/h) which is quite small and hence original assumption stands true.

For evalution of pure component pressure (P_i) of the gas mixture, compressibility factor of each component at pure component pressure and system temperature is required. For H_2 and CO, Z values are read from *Perry's Chemical Engineers' Handbook*[14].

$$Z = 1 + \frac{p_r}{T_r}(B^0 + \omega B^1) = 1 + \frac{p_r}{T_r} \cdot \hat{B} \qquad (8.5)$$

Since P_i unknown, an iterative procedure is to be adopted as was done in Example 5.39.

For 1st iteration, assume,

$$P_i(1) = \text{partial pressure, } p_i$$
$$= y_i \cdot p$$
$$t_1/T_1 = 80°C/353.15 \text{ K}, \quad p_1 = 45 \text{ bar}$$

Table 8.34 Calculation of Compressibility Factor for Gas Mixture Entering Overhead Condenser

Component	y_i	$P_i(1) = p_i$ bar $= y_i \times 45$	p_{ci} bar	$p_r = P_i(1)/p_{ci}$	T_{ci}, K	$T_r = T_1/T_{ci}$	p_r/T_r
Methyl formate	0.0723	3.2535	60.0	0.0542	487.2	0.7246	0.0748
Methanol	0.0643	2.8935	80.84	0.0358	512.5	0.6891	0.0519
Carbon Monoxide	0.5468	24.6060	—	—	—	—	—
Hydrogen	0.3166	14.2470	—	—	—	—	—
Total	1.0000	45.0000	—	—	—	—	—

Table 8.35   Calculation of Compressibility Factor (Continuation of Table 8.34)

Component	$\hat{B} = (B^0 + \omega B^1)$	$\left(\dfrac{p_r}{T_r}\right)\hat{B}$	Z_i [Eq. (8.5)]	$Z_i \cdot y_i$
Methyl formate	−0.9551	−0.0715	0.9286	0.0671
Methanol	−1.0678	−0.0555	0.9445	0.0607
Carbon monoxide	—	—	1.0024*	0.5482
Hydrogen	—	—	1.0076*	0.3190
Total	—	—	—	0.9950 (Z_1)

*From *Perry's Chemical Engineers Handbook*[16]

Iteration 2

$$\text{Revised } P_i(2) = \frac{P_i(1) \times Z_i}{Z} \tag{8.6}$$

Table 8.36   Calculation of Compressibility Factor for Gas Mixture Entering Overhead Condenser

Component	y_i	$P_i(2)$ bar [Eq. (8.6)]	p_{ci} bar	$p_r = P_i(2)/p_{ci}$	T_{ci}, K	$T_r = T_1/T_{ci}$	p_r/T_r
Methyl formate	0.0723	3.0363	60.0	0.0506	487.2	0.7246	0.0698
Methanol	0.0643	2.7468	80.84	0.0339	512.5	0.6891	0.493
Carbon Monoxide	0.5468	24.7893	—	—	—	—	—
Hydrogen	0.3166	14.4276	—	—	—	—	—
Total	1.000	45.0000	—	—			

Table 8.37   Calculation of Compressibility Factor (Continuation of Table 8.36)

Component	$\hat{B} = (B^0 + \omega B^1)$	$\left(\dfrac{p_r}{T_r}\right)\hat{B}$	Z_i [Eq. (8.5)]	$Z_i \cdot y_i$	$\dfrac{V_i}{RT} = \dfrac{Z_i \cdot y_i}{P_i(2)}$
Methyl formate	−0.9554	−0.0667	0.9333	0.0675	0.022 22
Methanol	−1.0686	−0.0527	0.9473	0.0609	0.022 18
Carbon monoxide	—	—	1.0024*	0.5481	0.022 11
Hydrogen	—	—	1.0076*	0.3190	0.022 11
Total	—	—	—	0.9950 (Z_1)	0.022 12 (V_1/RT)

Compressibility factor (Z_1), calculated in Iteration 2, is in close agreement (within 0.05%) of that calculated in Iteration 1. Also, $V_i = V_1$ which satisfies Dalton's law. Hence $P_i(2)$ values can be considered as pure component pressures of the components in the gas mixture, entering the overhead condenents.

$$V_1 = 0.022\ 12 \times 0.083\ 14 \times 353.15 = 0.6495 \text{ m}^3/\text{kmol}$$

For the gas mixture, leaving the overhead condenser, similar calculations are summarized below.

$$t_2/T_2 = 20°C/293.15 \text{ K}, \quad p_2 = 44.5 \text{ bar}$$

Iteration 1

Table 8.38 Calculation of Compressibilty Factor for Gas Mixture Leaving Overhead Condenser

Component	y_i	$P_i(1) = p_i$ $= y_i \times 44.5$	p_{ci} bar	$p_r =$ $P_i(1)/p_{ci}$	T_{ci}, K	$T_r =$ T_1/T_{ci}	p_r/T_r
Methyl formate	0.0466	2.0737	60.0	0.0346	487.2	0.6017	0.0574
Methanol	0.0105	0.4673	80.84	0.0058	512.5	0.5720	0.0101
Carbon Monoxide	0.5972	26.5754	—	—	—	—	—
Hydrogen	0.3457	15.3836	—	—	—	—	—
Total	1.0000	44.5000	—	—	—	—	—

Table 8.39 Calculation of Compressibility Factor (Continuation of Table 8.38)

Component	$\hat{B} =$ $(B^0 + \omega B^1)$	$\left(\dfrac{p_r}{T_r}\right)\hat{B}$	Z_i [Eq. (8.5)]	$Z_i \cdot y_i$
Methyl formate	−1.6985	−0.0976	0.9024	0.0421
Methanol	−1.8834	−0.0190	0.9810	0.0103
Carbon monoxide	—	—	0.9909	0.5918
Hydrogen	—	—	1.0093	0.3489
Total	—	—	—	0.9943 (Z_2)

Iteration 2

Table 8.40 Calculation of Compressibilty Factor for Gas Mixture Leaving Overhead Condensers

Component	y_i	$P_i(2)$ bar [Eq. (8.6)]	p_{ci} bar	$p_r =$ $P_i(2)/p_{ci}$	T_{ci}, K	$T_r =$ T_1/T_{ci}	p_r/T_r
Methyl formate	0.0466	1.8845	60.0	0.0314	487.2	0.6017	0.0433
Methanol	0.0105	0.4616	80.84	0.0057	512.5	0.5720	0.0083
Carbon monoxide	0.5972	26.5183	—	—	—	—	—
Hydrogen	0.3457	15.3836	—	—	—	—	—
Total	1.0000	44.5000	—	—	—	—	—

Table 8.41 Calculation of Compressibility Factor (Continuation of Table 8.40)

Component	$\hat{B} =$ $(B^0 + \omega B^1)$	$\left(\dfrac{p_r}{T_r}\right)\hat{B}$	Z_i [Eq. (8.5)]	$Z_i \cdot y_i$	$\dfrac{V_i}{RT} = \dfrac{Z_i \cdot y_i}{P_i(2)}$
Methyl formate	−1.6985	−0.0736	0.9264	0.0432	0.022 908
Methanol	−1.8834	−0.0156	0.9844	0.0103	0.022 394
Carbon monoxide	—	—	0.9909*	0.5918	0.022 315
Hydrogen	—	—	1.0094*	0.3490	0.022 318
Total	—	—	—	0.9943 (Z_2)	0.022 342 (V_2/RT)

Here again compressibility factor (Z_2), calculated in Iteration 2 is in close agreement (within 0.12%) of that calculated in Iteration 1. Also, $V_i = V_2$ which satisfies Dalton's law. Hence P_i (2) values can be considered as pure component pressures of the components in the gas mixture, leaving overhead condenser.

$$V_2 = 0.022\ 342 \times 0.083\ 14 \times 293.15 = 0.5445 \text{ m}^3/\text{kmol}$$

For calculation of real gas enthalpies, the procedure described in Example 5.39 is recommended.

$$H = H^{\text{id}} + H^{\text{R}} \qquad (5.64)$$

At first, pseudo critical properties for ingoing and outcoming gas mixtures from the condenser are to be calculated. For this purpose, effective critical pressure and temperature for hydrogen are required.

Ingoing gas mixture $p_1 = 45$ bar and $T_1 = 353.15$ K
For hydrogen,

$$T_{ec} = \frac{43.6}{\left[1 + \dfrac{21.8}{(2.016 \times 353.15)}\right]} = 42.305 \text{ K}$$

$$p_{ec} = \frac{20.5}{\left[1 + \dfrac{44.2}{(2.016 \times 353.15)}\right]} = 19.302 \text{ bar}$$

and $\omega = 0$ (refer Example 5.39)

Table 8.42 Pseudo Critical Properties of Ingoing Gas Mixture

Component	y_i	ω_i	$y_i \cdot \omega_i$	p_{ci} bar	$y_i \cdot p_{ci}$	T_{ci} K	$T_{ci} \cdot y_i$
CO	0.5468	0.048	0.0262	34.99	19.133	132.91	72.670
H$_2$	0.3166	0	0	19.302	6.111	42.305	13.394
CH$_3$OH	0.0643	0.564	0.0363	80.92	5.203	512.64	32.963
C$_2$H$_4$O$_2$	0.0723	0.632	0.0457	60.00	4.338	487.20	35.225
Total	1.0000	—	0.1082	—	34.785	—	154.252

$$p_{r1} = \frac{45}{34.785} = 1.294 \qquad T_{r1} = \frac{353.15}{154.252} = 2.289$$

From Ref. 13,

$$\left(\frac{H^R}{R\,T_{pc}}\right)^0 = -0.2668 \quad \text{and} \quad \left(\frac{H^R}{R\,T_{pc}}\right)^1 = 0.1464$$

$$\left(\frac{H_1^R}{R\,T_{pc}}\right) = -0.2668 + 0.1082\,(0.1464) = -0.2509$$

$$H_1^R = -0.2509 \times 8.314\,472 \times 154.252 = -321.79 \text{ kJ/kmol mixture}$$

Outcoming gas mixture $p_2 = 44.5$ bar and $T_2 = 293.15$ K
For hydrogen

$$T_{ec} = \frac{43.6}{\left[1 + \dfrac{21.8}{(2.016 \times 293.15)}\right]} = 42.049 \text{ K}$$

$$p_{ec} = \frac{20.5}{\left[1 + \dfrac{44.2}{(2.016 \times 293.15)}\right]} = 19.073 \text{ bar}$$

Table 8.43 Pseudo Critical Properties of Outcoming Gas Mixture

Component	y_i	ω_i	$\omega_i \cdot y_i$	p_{ci} bar	$p_{ci} \cdot y_i$	T_{ci} K	$T_{ci} \cdot y_i$
CO	0.5972	0.048	0.0287	34.99	20.896	132.91	79.368
H$_2$	0.3457	0	0	19.302	6.594	42.049	14.536
CH$_3$OH	0.0105	0.564	0.0059	80.92	0.850	512.64	5.383
C$_2$H$_4$O$_2$	0.0466	0.632	0.0295	60.00	2.796	487.20	22.704
Total	1.0000	—	0.0641	—	31.136	—	121.991

$$p_{r2} = \frac{44.5}{31.136} = 1.4292 \quad \text{and} \quad T_{r2} = \frac{293.15}{121.991} = 2.403$$

From Ref. 13,

$$\left(\frac{H^R}{R\,T_{pc}}\right)^0 = -0.263 \quad \text{and} \quad \left(\frac{H^R}{R\,T_{pc}}\right)^1 = 0.172$$

$$\left(\frac{H_2^R}{R\,T_{pc}}\right) = -0.263 + 0.0641\,(0.172) = -0.252$$

$$H_2^R = -0.252 \times 8.314\,472 \times 121.991 = -255.6 \text{ kJ/kmol mixture}$$

In second step, ideal gas enthalpies will be calculated.

Table 8.44 Heat Capacity Equation Constants for Ingoing Gas Mixture

Component	mole fraction	Heat capacity equation constants			
	y_i	$a_i \cdot y_i$	$y_i \cdot b_i \times 10^3$	$y_i \cdot c_i \times 10^6$	$y_i \cdot d_i \times 10^9$
CO	0.5468	15.872	−1.540	6.367	−2.573
H_2	0.3166	9.058	0.323	−0.047	0.243
CH_3OH	0.0643	1.599	3.271	3.770	−2.902
$C_2H_4O_2$	0.0723	5.169	—	—	—
Total	1.0000	31.698	2.054	10.090	−5.232

Reference temperature $T_0 = 273.15$ K
Enthalpy of ingoing gas mixture,

$$H_1^{id} = 31.698\,(353.15 - 273.15) + \frac{(2.054 \times 10^{-3})}{2}(353.15^2 - 273.15^2)$$

$$+ \frac{(10.090 \times 10^{-6})}{3}(353.15^3 - 273.15^3) - \frac{(5.232 \times 10^{-9})}{4}(353.15^4 - 273.15^4)$$

$$= 2535.84 + 51.46 + 79.59 - 13.06 = 2653.83 \text{ kJ/kmol mixture}$$

$$H_1 = H_1^{id} + H_1^{R}$$

$$= 2653.83 - 321.79$$

$$= 2332.04 \text{ kJ/kmol mixture}$$

Table 8.45 Heat Capacity Equation Constants for Outcoming Gas Mixture

Component	mole fraction	Heat capacity equation constants			
	y_i	$a_i \cdot y_i$	$y_i \cdot b_i \times 10^3$	$y_i \cdot c_i \times 10^6$	$y_i \cdot d_i \times 10^9$
CO	0.5922	17.190	−1.668	6.895	−2.787
H_2	0.3457	9.891	0.352	−0.051	0.266
CH_3OH	0.0105	0.261	0.534	0.616	−0.474
$C_2H_4O_2$	0.0466	2.973	—	—	—
Total	1.0000	30.315	−0.782	7.460	−2.995

Enthalpy pf outcoming gas mixture,

$$H_1^{id} = 30.315\,(293.15 - 273.15) - \frac{0.782 \times 10^{-3}}{2}(293.15^2 - 273.15^2)$$

$$+ \frac{7.460 \times 10^{-6}}{3}(293.15^3 - 273.15^3) - \frac{2.995 \times 10^{-9}}{4}(293.15^4 - 273.15^4)$$

$$= 606.3 - 4.43 + 11.97 - 1.36 = 612.48 \text{ kJ/kmol mixture}$$

$$H_2 = H_2^{id} + H_2^{R}$$

$$= 612.48 - 255.6 = 356.88 \text{ kJ/kmol mixture}$$

Sensible heat transfer in the condenser,

$$\phi_1 = 3.8098\,H_1 - 3.4886\,H_2$$

$$= 8884.6 - 1245.0$$

$$= 7639.6 \text{ kJ/h} \equiv 2.12 \text{ kW}$$

Latent heat removal duty

Assume condensation of methanol and methyl formate at average temperature. Average temperature,

$$t_{avg} = \frac{80 + 20}{2} = 50°C$$

$$T_{avg} = 323.15 \text{ K}$$

$$\lambda_{v1} = 35.21 \left[\frac{512.5 - 323.15}{512.5 - 337.7}\right]^{0.38} = 36.293 \text{ kJ/kmol for } CH_3OH$$

$$\lambda_{v2} = 27.92 \left[\frac{487.2 - 323.15}{487.2 - 304.7}\right]^{0.38} = 26.812 \text{ kJ/kmol for } C_2H_4O_2$$

Heat load of condensation,

$$\phi_2 = 0.2084 \times 36.293 \times 1000 + 0.1128 \times 26.812 \times 1000$$
$$= 10\ 587.9 \text{ kJ/h} \equiv 2.941 \text{ kW}$$

Total heat (refrigeration) duty of condenser

$$\phi = \phi_1 + \phi_2$$
$$= 7639.6 + 10\ 587.9 = 18\ 227.5 \text{ kJ/h}$$
$$\equiv \mathbf{5.063 \text{ kW}} \equiv \mathbf{1.44 \text{ TR}}$$

Example 8.12 Tetrahydrofuran [THF, formula : C_4H_8O, NBP = 66°C (339.15 K)] forms a minimum boiling azeotrope with water at 101.325 kPa and 63.5°C (336.65 K), containing 5.3% by mass of water. Pressure swing distillation[17] method is recommended for separation of THF from the aqueous solution. Process flow is schematically shown in Fig. 8.9.

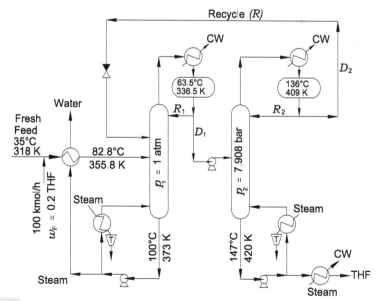

Fig. 8.9 Pressure Swing Distillation of THF(2) -Water(1) Solution

Fresh feed, containing 20% by mass THF, is treated at a flow rate of 100 kmol/h at 35°C (308.15 K). First, it exchanges heat with bottom product (i.e., water) from column CI. Heated feed at 82.8°C (355.95 K) is fed to CI which operates at atmospheric pressure. THF is distilled out in the form of azeotrope while the bottom product is water with negligible impurity of THF. Azeotrope from CI is fed to column CII which operates at 7.908 bar a. Distillate from CII is again an azeotrope containing 12.0% by mass water at 136°C (409.15 K). The bottom product is pure THF with negligible water content. In order to achieve desired purities, reflux ratios of 0.26 kmol/kmol distillate in CI and 0.65 kmol/kmol distillate in CII are required.

Carry out mass and energy balances of the system and calculate utility requirements in the condensers and reboilers.

Data

(i) Excess molar enthalpy of THF-water system is given by the empirical relation

$$H^E = x_1 x_2 \, (-160\ 324.71\ x_1^5 + 322\ 034.46\ x_1^4 - 255\ 536.29\ x_1^3$$
$$+ 104\ 002.98\ x_1^2 - 31166.9\ x_1 + 5468.9) \quad \text{(A)}$$

Where H^E = Excess enthalpy, kJ/kmol mixture at 25°C (298.15 K)

x_1 = mole fraction of water

(ii) Molar heat capacities of aqueous solutions

Feed	85 kJ/(kmol·K)
Distillate	115 kJ/(kmol·K)
(From CI and CII)	

Solution

Basis Molar feed rate of fresh feed, F = 100 kmol/h

mass fraction of THF, w_F = 0.2

$$\text{mole fraction of THF, } x_F = \frac{(0.2/72 \cdot 1057)}{(0.2/72 \cdot 1057) + (0.8/18.0153)}$$

$$= 0.058\ 79$$

Let W_1 and W_2 be bottom products (in pure form) from CI and CII, respectively.

$$W_1 + W_2 = F = 100 \quad \text{(i)}$$
$$W_1 = F\,(1 - x_F) = 100\,(1 - 0.058\ 79)$$
$$= 94.121\ \text{kmol/h}$$
$$W_2 = 100 - 94.121 = 5.879\ \text{kmol/h}$$

Overall material balance of CII

$$D_1 = D_2 + W_2$$
$$D_1 = D_2 + 5.879 \quad \text{(ii)}$$

mass fraction of water in D_2, w_{D_2} = 0.053

mole fraction of water in D_2,

$$x_{D_2} = \frac{(0.053/18.0153)}{(0.053/18.0153) + (0.947/72.1057)} = 0.183$$

Similarly,

mass fraction of water in D_1, $w_{D_1} = 0.12$

mole fraciton of water in D_1,

$$x_{D_1} = \frac{(0.12/18.0153)}{(0.12/18.0153) + (0.88/72.1057)}$$

$$= 0.3531$$

Balance of THF

$$D_1 (1 - 0.183) = (1 - 0.3531) D_2 + 5.879 \qquad \text{(iii)}$$

Solving Eq. (ii) and Eq. (iii),

$$D_1 = 12.203\ 85 \text{ kmol/h and } D_2 = 6.324\ 85 \text{ kmol/h}$$

Reflux in CI, $R_1 = 0.26\ D_1 = 3.173$ kmol/h

Reflux in CII, $R_2 = 0.65\ D_2 = 4.1112$ kmol/h

Table 8.46 Material Balance Across CI

Component	F		D_1		W_1		R_1	
	kmol/h	kg/h	kmol/h	kg/h	kmol/h	kg/h	kmol/h	kg/h
THF(2)	5.879	423.91	9.970 55	718.93	—	—	2.592 34	44.344
Water (1)	94.121	1695.62	2.233 3	40.23	94.121	16 95.62	0.580 66	10.461
Total	100.00	2119.53	12.203 85	759.16	94.121	1695.62	3.173	54.825

Table 8.47 Material Balance Across CII

Component	D_2		W_2		R_2	
	kmol/h	kg/h	kmol/h	kg/h	kmol/h	kg/h
THF(2)	4.091 55	295.02	5.879	423.91	2.6595	191.77
Water (1)	2.233 3	40.23	—	—	1.4517	26.15
Total	6.324 85	335.25	5.879	423.91	4.1112	217.92

Energy balance

Mixing of THF with water is associated with heat effects and therefore aqueous solutions of THF are not ideal solutions. Glew and Watts[18] pressented excess enthalpies for the aqueous solutions which are pressented in a graph of H^E vs x_1 as Fig 8.10.

It can be seen in Fig. 8.10 that parabolic curves appear on both sides of x-axis at $y = 0$. This type of behaviour is rather uncommon as most mixing processes are either exothermic or endothermic for full range. Experimental data were fitted (within $\pm 2\%$ error) in an empirical equation which is given as Eq. (A) in the beginning. With the help of these excess enthalpy data, enthalpies of aqueous soultions can be calculated and a heat balance can be made.

Reference temperature, $t_0 = 0°C$, $T_0 = 273.15$ K

Enthalpy of distillate D_1 at 336.65 K (H_{D_1}) = Enthalpy of distillate D_1 at 298.15 K (H'_{D_1}) + 115 (336.65 − 298.15)

$$= H'_{D_1} + 4427.5$$

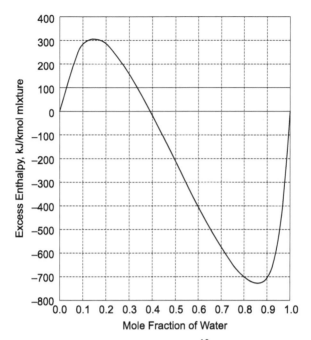

Fig. 8.10 Excess Enthalpies of Aqueous THF Solutions[18] at 25°C (298.15 K).

For $x_1 = 0.183$ using Eq. (A),

$H^E_{D_1} = 300.6$ kJ/kmol mixture at 298.15 K

$H^{id}_{D_1} = x_1 H_1 + x_2 H_2$

$H_1 = $ Enthalpy of water at 298.15 K

$= 1887.41$ kJ/kmol   (Ref. Appendix IV.1)

$$H_2 = \int_{273.15}^{298.15} (58.0956 + 201.896 \times 10^{-3}\, T + 432.6342 \ 10^{-7}\, T)\, dT$$
                                                        (Ref. Table 5.1)

$= 2982.5$ kJ/kmol

$H^{id}_{D_1} = 0.183 \times 1887.41 + (1 - 0.183)\, 2982.5 = 2782.1$ kJ/kmol mixture

$H'_{D_1} = 2782.1 + 300.6 = 3082.7$ kJ/kmol mixture at 298.15 K

$H_{D_1} = 3082.7 + 4427.5 = 7510.2$ kJ/kmol mixture at 336.85 K

Total enthalpy of distillate D_1,

    $\phi_1 = 7510.2\ (12.203\ 85 + 3.173)$

        $= 115\ 483$ kJ/h $\equiv 32.079$ kW

From Table 5.4 and with use of Watson equaiton,

$$\lambda_{THFl} = 29.81 \times 10^3 \left(\frac{540.5 - 336.65}{540.5 - 339.15}\right)^{0.38}$$

       $= 29\ 950.1$ kJ/kmol at 336.65 K

λ_{w1} = 42 331.5 kJ/kmol at 336.65 K

Heat load of condenser of CI

ϕ_2 = (12.203 85 + 3.173) [0.183 × 42 331.5 + (1 − 0.183) 29 950.1]

= 15.376 85 (7746.66 + 24 466.94)

= 495 379 kJ/h ≡ 137.605 kW

Enthalpy of saturated water at 100°C (373.15 K):

H_{w2} = 7549.56 kJ/kmol (Ref. Appendix IV.1)

Enthalpy of feed $H'_F = (H_F^E + H_F^{id})$ at 298.15 K + 85 (308.15 − 298.15)

At x_1 = 0.941 21 using empirical equation (A)

H_F^E = −580.7 kJ/kmol mixture at 298.15 K

H_F^{id} = 0.941 21 × 1887.41 + 0.058 79 × 2982.5

= 1951.8 kJ/kmol mixture at 298.15 K

H'_F = (1951.8 − 580.7) + 850 = 1371.1 + 850

= 2221.1 kJ/kmol at 808.15 K

ϕ_3 of feed = 100 × 2221.1

= 222 110 kJ/h ≡ 61.697 kW

Fesh feed is heated to 355.95 K by exchanging heat with bottom product (water) from CI.

H'_F = 1371.1 + 85 (355.95 − 298.15)

= 6284.1 kJ/kmol at 355.95 K

ϕ_4 of feed = 6284.1 × 100

= 628 410 kJ/h ≡ 174.558 kW

Heat exchange duty = $\phi_4 − \phi_3$

= 628 410 − 222 110

= 406 300 kJ/h ≡ 112.861 kW

Enthalpy of W_1 before heat exchange = 7549.56 × 94.121

= 710 572 kJ/h ≡ 197.381 kW

ϕ_2 = 7549.56 × 94.121 − 406 300

= 710 572 − 406 300

= 304 272 kJ/h ≡ 3232.8 kJ/kmol water

From steam tables (Appendix IV.1), it corresponds to temperature of 42.9°C (316.05 K).

Enthalpy of distillate D_2 at 409.15 K (H'_{D_2}) = Enthalpy of distillate D_2 at 298.15 K (H_{D_2}) + 115 (409.15 − 298.15)

For x_1 = 0.3531 using Eq. (A)

$H_{D_2}^E$ = 70.15 kJ/kmol mixture at 298.15 K

$H_{D_2}^{id}$ = 0.3531 × 1887.41 + (1 − 0.35311) 2982.5

= 2595.8 kJ/kmol mixture at 298.15 K

H'_{D_2} = 2595.8 + 70.15 = 2665.95 kJ/kmol mixture at 298.15 K

H_{D_2} = 2665.95 + 12 765 = 15 430.95 kJ/kmol mixture at 409.15 K

Total enthalpy of distillate D_2 at 409.15 K,

$\phi_6 = 15\ 430.95 \times 6.324\ 85$

$\quad = 97\ 598$ kJ/h $\equiv 27.111$ kW

Boiling point of THF at 7.908 bar a

$$\log(7.908) = 4.121\ 18 - \frac{1202.942}{(T - 46.818)}$$

or $\quad T = 420.04$ K $\quad$ or $\quad t = 146.89°$C

Enthlapy of bottom product (W_2) from CII,

$$H_{w2} = \int_{273.15}^{420.04} (58.0956 + 201.896 \times 10^{-3}T + 432.6342 \times 10^{-7}T^2)\,dT$$

$\quad = 19\ 587.3$ kJ/kmol THF

$\phi_7 = 19\ 587.3 \times 5.879$

$\quad = 115\ 154$ kJ/h $\equiv 31.987$ kW

λ_{w_2} at 409.15 K = 38 841 kJ/kmol $\hfill$ (Ref. Appendix IV.2)

$$\lambda_{THF2} = 29.81 \times 10^3 \left[\frac{540.5 - 409.15}{540.5 - 339.15}\right]^{0.38}$$

$\quad = 25\ 343.3$ kJ/kmol

λ_{vap} of vapour from CII,

$\lambda_{vap} = 38\ 841 \times 0.3531 + 25\ 343.3\ (1 - 0.3531)$

$\quad = 30\ 109.3$ kJ/kmol mixture at 409.15 K

Heat load of condenser of CII,

$\phi_8 = 30\ 109.3\ (4.112 + 6.324\ 85)$

$\quad = 314\ 246$ kJ/h $\equiv 87.290$ kW

Heat duty of reboiler of CII,

$\phi_9 = \phi_8 + \phi_6 + \phi_7 - \phi_1$

$\quad = 314\ 246 + 97\ 598 + 115\ 154 - 115\ 483$

$\quad = 411\ 515$ kJ/h $\equiv 114.31$ kW

Heat duty of reboiler of CI,

$\phi_{10} = \phi_5 + \phi_1 + \phi_2 - \phi_4 - \phi_6$

$\quad = 710\ 572 + 115\ 483 + 495\ 379 - 628\ 410 - 97\ 598$

$\quad = 595\ 426$ kJ/h $\equiv 165.396$ kW

Utility Requirements

In the reboiler of CI, water is boiled at 100°C (373.15 K). Select saturated steam at 2.4 bar a having saturating temperatture of 126.09°C (399.24 K) as a heating medium.

$\lambda_{s1} = 2184.9$ kJ/kg $\hfill$ (Ref. Appendix (IV.2)

Steam consumption in the reboiler of CI,

$$\dot{m}_{s1} = \frac{165.396}{2184.9} = 0.0757 \text{ kg/s} \equiv \textbf{272.52 kg/h}$$

In the reboiler of CII, THF boils at 420.04 K. Select saturated steam at 8.8 bar a having saturation temperature of 174.41°C (447.56 K) as a heating medium.

$\lambda_{s2} = 2032.8$ kJ/kg (Ref. Appendix IV.2)

Steam consumption in the reboiler of CII,

$$\dot{m}_{s2} = \frac{114.31}{2032.8} = 0.0562 \text{ kg/s} \equiv \textbf{202.44 kg/h}$$

Cooling water requirement in condenser of CI,

$$\dot{m}_{cw1} = \frac{495\,379}{8 \times 4.1868}$$

$$= 14\,789.9 \text{ kg/h with } \Delta t = 8°C$$

Cooling water requirement in condenser of CII,

$$\dot{m}_{cw2} = \frac{314\,246}{8 \times 4.1868} = 9382 \text{ kg/h with } \Delta t = 8°C$$

In the final cooler THF is cooled from 420.04 K to 318.15 K (45°C).
Heat duty of cooler,

$$\phi_{11} = 5.879 \int_{318.15}^{420.04} (58.0956 + 201.896 \times 10^{-3}\,T + 432.634 \times 10^{-7}\,T)\,dT$$

$$= 5.879 \times 14\,116.4$$

$$= 82\,990.4 \text{ kJ/h} \equiv 23.05 \text{ kW}$$

Cooling water requirment in cooler,

$$\dot{m}_{cw3} = \frac{82\,990.4}{8 \times 4.1868}$$

$$= 2478 \text{ kg/h with } \Delta t = 8°C$$

Total cooling water requirement,

$$\dot{m}_{cw} = 14\,789 + 9381 + 2478 = 26\,650 \text{ kg/h} \equiv \textbf{26.65 m}^3\textbf{/h}$$

Note Excess enthalpy of feed (H_F^E) is −580.7 kJ/kmol mixture while that of distillate D_1 ($H_{D_1}^E$) is +300.6 kJ/kmol mixture. Because both values of excess enthalpies have opposite signs, heat duty of the rebolier of column CI would have been calculated with ≈ 4% error if ideal solution properties would have been considered. Heat duties of overhead condensers are unaffected due to excess enthalpy values as no subcooling is considered. Heat duty of the reboiler of column CII would have been hardly (~0.1%) erroneous as both excess enthalpy values have positive signs.

Exercises

8.1 A packed column is packed with carbon Raschig rings[19]. It is used to absorb CO_2 in the solution containing $KHCO_3$. The solution is 3 N, based on potassium content. At the inlet, 30% of K in the solution is found to be in the form of bicarbonates. In the exit solution, bicarbonate amounts to 68% of the total K. The entering gas contains 18% CO_2 while the CO_2 content of the leaving gas is 6.9%, both on dry volume % basis. The solution flow rate is 1.65 L/s. Calculate
(a) the analysis of entering and leaving solution in g/L,
(b) the absorption rate of CO_2 in kg/h,
(c) the % recovery of CO_2 from the incoming gas, and
(d) the molar flow rate of inlet gas.

[(a) K_2CO_3: 66.24 g/L, $KHCO_3$: 204 g/L in outgoing solution, K_2CO_3:
144.9 g/L and $KHCO_3$: 90 g/L in incoming solution,
(b) CO_2 absorption rate = 149 kg/h, (c) Per cent recovery = 66.2
(d) Molar flow rate of inlet gas = 28.4 kmol/h]

8.2 Regenerative (Ljungstrom) type combustion air preheater (RAH) has heat transfer
elements, packed in a cylindrical housing in compartments as shown in Fig. 8.11. This
rotor is rotated at a constant slow speed (~ 5 rpm) by an electric motor, and thereby
elements come in contact alternately with flue gas and combustion air streams. In this
process, some air (being at a higher pressure) mixes with the flue gas, necessitating
higher capacities of combustion air fan and induced draft (ID) fan. Variety of elements are available in different materials of construction. Effective cleaning of the
heat transfer elements by soot blowing is provided. While low pressure drop and
less space requirement for RAH are claimed to have been major advantages over a
recuperative tubular type air heater, mixing of air in flue gas is a major disadvantage. RAH is particularly economical for high capacity boilers. In an oil-fired boiler
of 100 t/h steam generation at 62 bar g and 400°C (673 K), flue gas is found to
contain 14.0% CO_2, 3% O_2 and 83.0% N_2 (by volume) on dry basis at the outlet
of boiler furnace. Its dew point is measured to be 46.3°C (319.3 K) at 100 kPa a.
Based on combustion stoichiometry, 1.045 kmol wet flue gas are produced per kmol
wet combustion air, entering the furnace. Flue gas, passed through RAH, is cooled
from 250°C (523 K) to 160°C (433 K). Flue gas at outlet of the RAH is analyzed to
contain 12.5% CO_2 (by volume) on dry basis due to air mixing with flue gas. Combustion air enters RAH at 40°C (313 K) *DB* and 22°C (295 K) *WB*.
Calculate
(a) kmol of dry air mixed with kmol of dry flue gas,
(b) heat transferred in RAH in kJ/kmol,
(c) temperature of combustion air, leaving RAH, and
(d) increase in volumetric capacity of combustion air fan.

[(a) 0.12 kmol/kmol dry flue gas, entering RAH,
(b) 2773.5 kJ/kmol dry flue gas, entering RAH,
(c) 123.8°C (396.95 K) and (d) 12.82%]

Note If a tubular heater is used in place of RAH, heat transfer duty and air temperature at the outlet of the heater are calculated to be 3206.7 kJ/kmol and 139.1°C
(412.25 K), respectively.

8.3 1,3-Butadiene (CH_2: CH–CH: CH_2) of rubber grade purity is manufactured by several
methods, including the dehydrogenation of normal butane or of butylenes, available
from refinery light-end fractions[20]. The process is shown in Fig. 8.12.
Fresh *n*-butane feed and recycled butene-1 ($C_2H_5CHCH_2$) at the indicated flow rates
(Fig. 8.12) are mixed together and passed through a 'charge heater', 'catalytic
reactor train' and a 'separation system'. The reactions taking place in the reactor
are as follows:

$C_4H_{10}(g)$	=	$C_4H_8(g)$	+	$H_2(g)$		(i)
n-Butane		Butene-1		Hydrogen		
$C_4H_8(g)$	=	$C_4H_6(g)$	+	$H_2(g)$		(ii)
Butene-1		1,3-Butadiene		Hydrogen		
$C_4H_8(g)$	=	$2C_2H_4(g)$				(iii)
Butene-1		Ethylene				

Reaction (i) is assumed to go to completion, i.e., all the *n*-butane entering the reactor
is dehydrogenated to butene-1 and hydrogen. A part of butene-1 reacts according
to Eq. (ii), part according to Eq. (iii) and the remainder is recycled. The separation
and cooling system condenses out the product butadiene, sends the gaseous ethylene-
hydrogen mixture for use as a fuel gas and recycles the butene-1. Calculate

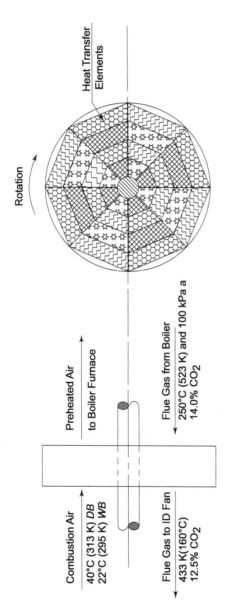

Fig. 8.11 Regenerative Air Preheater

Heat Transfer Elements

Rotation

Preheated Air to Boiler Furnace

Flue Gas from Boiler
250°C (523 K) and 100 kPa a
14.0% CO_2

Combustion Air
40°C (313 K) *DB*
22°C (295 K) *WB*

Flue Gas to ID Fan
433 K(160°C)
12.5% CO_2

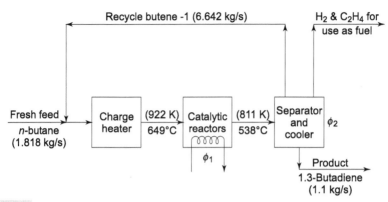

Fig. 8.12 Manufacture of 1,3-butadiene

(a) the composition (mole %) of the hot gaseous mixture leaving the catalytic reactor.

(b) The heat exchange in catalytic reactors to maintain the desired exit temperature of 538°C (811 K) for the product rate of 4000 kg/h of 1,3-butadiene. Indicate whether this represents heat added to or heat removed from the reactor. Use absolute enthalpies given in Table 5.22.

(c) The vapour pressure to which the butadiene will have to be flashed to cool down to 0°C (273.15 K) for condensation. Use may be made of the Antoine equation (Table 5.4).

(d) The butadiene is to be cooled from the gaseous state at 538°C (811 K) to the liquid state of 0°C (273.15 K). Calculate the heat that will have to be removed from the product butadiene to accomplish this cooling and condensation. Assume condensation of all butadiene.

[(a) **Butene-1: 55.77%, 1, 3-butadiene: 9.68%, hydrogen: 24.42% and ethylene: 10.13% (on mole basis) (b)** ϕ_1 = 4528.84 kW **(endothermic)**, **(c)** p = 120.5 kPa, **(d)** ϕ_2 = 1797 kW]

8.4   A demineralizing plant, using ion-exchange technology, produces boiler feed quality water. It employs a strong cation exchanger, a weak anion exchanger and mixed bed units.

The cation exchanger is regenerated with hydrochloric acid solution of about 4% (by mass) strength. At first, acidic solution is introduced in a countercurrent manner. At the end of acid introduction, slow rinse is carried out with the help of pure water. Samples were taken periodically of the effluents during both the regeneration steps and were analysed for total chlorides (as Cl) and free mineral acidity (FMA) as HCl. The analytical data are presented as shown[21] in Table 8.48.

Table 8.48 Analyses of Effluent Samples Collected During Regeneration

Regeneration step	Time from start, min.	Flow rate of effluent, m³/h	Total chlorides as Cl, mg/L	FMA as HCl, mg/L
Acid introduction	0 (start)	—	—	—
	10	63	1 500	—
	15	63	9 000	—
	27	63	50 000	65.8
	44	63	56 000	28 636
	52	63	55 000	46 447
Slow rinse	0 (start)	—	—	—
	15	54	42 000	39 133
	30	54	6 000	2 560
	45	54	2 000	1 097

The chloride content of the effluents above 600 ppm is objectionable as per IS: 2490 (Part - I) which prescribes limits for effluents to be discharged on land for irrigation purpose. For this reason, it was considered to segregate the effluents into two streams, concentrated and dilute, such that nearly 85% of total chlorides eluated are to be segregated in the concentrated stream.

(a) Suggest the duration in which the effluents are to be segregated as concentrated effluents.

(b) Calculate the quantities of concentrated and weak effluents.

(c) Calculate the average concentrations of chlorides and FMA of the concentrated stream.

(d) Calculate the consumption of 31.5% (by mass) HCl for regeneration.

(e) Calculate the excess acid fed over stoichiometric requirement, assuming that the resins are completely regenerated.

[(a) **Period: 50 min, starting from 20 min from start of acid introduction step.,**
(b) **Volume of concentrated effluents = 49.8 m^3 Volume of dilute effluents = 45.3 m^3, (c) Chlorides in concentrated effluents = 49 203 mg/L, FMA in concentrated effluent = 24 982 mg/L, (d) 9.27 t, (e) 43.5% excess acid]**

8.5 In a chemical plant, a bullet (high pressure storage tank) is used for storing liquefied petroleum gas (LPG). Over a period of its utilization, it required repairs, involving hotwork (cutting/welding). Its geometric volume is 22 m^3. For issuance of safety work permit, preparations are to be made.

At first, the bullet is emptied out of LPG such that its pressure is reduced to 0.25 bar g (in gaseous form) and 35°C (308 K). Composition of LPG may be taken as C_2H_6: 1.2%, C_3H_8: 25.2%, i-C_4H_{10}: 23.9% and n-C_4H_{10}: 49.7% (by volume). It is pressure purged with pure dry nitrogen (having less than 0.1% O_2 by volume). Pressure purging is carried out [isothermally at 25°C (298.15 K)] by pressurising the bullet with nitrogen up to 2.5 bar g and depressurzing it to 0.25 bar g during each cycle. Bullet is considered safe for hotwork if the concentration of each hydrocarbon is brought down below its lower flammability limit. Finally, bullet is depressurized to atmospheric pressure for hotwork.

Table 8.49 Data on Flammability Limits[22]

Gas	Flammability limits in air at 101.325 kPa a and 25°C (298.15 K)	
	Higher limit	Lower limit
Ethane	12.5	3.0
Propane	9.5	2.3
Butane (any isomer)	8.5	1.9

(a) Calculate the number of cycles of pressure purging for safe hotwork permit issuance.

(b) Calculate final concentration of each hydrocarbon.

(c) Calculate nitrogen requirement for all cycles of purging.

[(a) **4 cycles (b) ethane: 0.02%, propane: 0.42% and butane: 1.23% (by vol.) (c) 173.2 Nm^3 nitrogen]**

8.6 The LPG bullet, described in Exercise 8.5, is to be prepared for man-entry for thorough inspection. This requires that oxygen content of LPG tank environment should be 18% by volume (min.). For this purpose, compressed dry air at 6 bar g and 35°C (308 K) is used for pressurization after nitrogen purging. Bullet at near atmospheric pressure is pressurization with air to 4 bar g and depressurized to atmospheric pressure during each cycle. Calculate the number of cycles of pressurisation required to attain oxygen level of 18% by volume and also compressed air requirement. Assume ideal gas law. **[2 cycles, Air requirement = 154 Nm³]**

8.7 A three-stage calcination process is used for the solidification of Purex waste[23]. First, an aqueous solution containing 31.55% solids (by mass) is fed to a bent-tube evaporator where it is concentrated to a 60% solution by condensing saturated steam at 185 kPa g pressure. Partially concentrated solution (60%) is sent to a wiped-film evaporator where it is further concentrated to 90% solids by condensing saturated steam at 12 bar g pressure. A slurry containing 90% is fed to an Auger-agitated calciner where the leftover water is removed by electric heating. The system is shown in Fig. 8.13. The operating details of the plant have been given in Table 8.50.

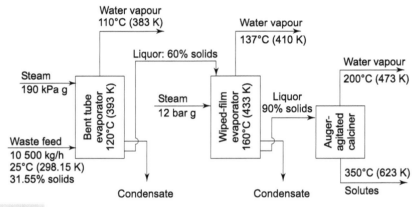

Fig. 8.13 Three-Stage Calcination Process

At 60% solids concentration, the solids remain dissolved in the solution. At 90% concentration, 50% of Na_2CO_3 and Na_2SO_4 (each) precipitate out and a slurry is thus obtained. In the calciner, Na_2NO_3 and NaOH are in liquid state at 350°C (623 K) while the rest are in solid state. In the Auger-agitated calciner, the vapours are at 200°C (473 K) although the product solid mixture is at 350°C (623 K). The boiling point elevations in the bent-tube evaporator and wiped-film evaporator are 10°C (10 K) and 23°C (23 K), respectively.

Table 8.50 Operating Details of the Calcination Plant

	Temperature, °C (K)	Enthalpy, kJ/kg solution
Feed	25 (298.15)	0 (Basis)
Bent-tube evaporator	120 (393)	225.7
Wiped-film evaporator	160 (433)	202.2
Auger-agitated calciner	350 (623)	581.5
		(of final solid mixture)

Table 8.51 Composition of Feed

Component	mass %
$NaNO_3$	23.12
Na_2CO_3	2.96
Na_2SO_4	0.91
$NaAlO_2$	3.60
$NaOH$	0.96
H_2O	68.45
Total	100.00

Establish the material and energy balances of the plant.

Table 8.52 Summary of Results

Stage	Type of concentrator	Feed, kg/h	Water evaporated		Heat load	
			kg/h	mass %	kW	%
1st	Bent-tube evaporator	10 500	4979	69.28	3923.24	68.46
2nd	Wiped-film evaporator	5 522	1840	25.60	1196.06	20.87
3rd	Auger-agitated calciner	3 681	368	5.12	611.64	10.67
Total		—	7187	100.00	5730.94	100.00

[**Steam consumptions: First evaporator: 6518.8 kg/h at 1.9 bar g, Second evaporator: 2196.2 kg/h at 12 bar g**]

8.8 The cell liquor obtained from the Hooker-type S-1 electrolytic diaphragm-type chloral-kali cell contains 10.9% NaOH and 15.26% NaCl (by mass). Without separating the salt from the cell liquor, it is sulphited by passing SO_2 in the solution[24]. The reaction proceeds as follows.

$$2\ NaOH + SO_2 = Na_2SO_3 + H_2O$$

One tonne of cell liquor at 93°C (366 K) is treated with SO_2 in the above manner. The reaction is allowed to take place till no NaOH is left over in the solution. The reaction is quite exothermic and hence the evaporation amounting to 71 kg water takes place. The final temperature of the sulphited liquor is kept at 100°C (373 K).

Use Fig. 8.14 and make the following calculations. (a) Find the yield of Na_2SO_3 at 100°C (373 K). (b) The above mass is concentrated by evaporating the water at 100°C (373 K). The evaporation is carried out till the invariant composition is reached. Find the yield of Na_2SO_3 at the end of evaporation process and also the amount of evaporation taken place. (c) Instead of evaporation as suggested in (b), salt is added to the solution to the extent that the composition of the solution reaches that of invariant point at 100°C (373 K). Find the quantity of salt to be added to the solution and also the yield of Na_2SO_3. (d) As an alternative to (b), the cooling of sulphited liquor is carried out to 0°C (273.15 K). It is known that below 32.5°C (305.5 K), the crystals are hepta-hydrated. Find the yield of crystals.

[(a) 118.1 kg or 68.8% yield (b) 159.7 kg or 93.0% yield
(c) 110.3 kg salt added 150.9 kg or 87.9% yield
(d) 148.5 kg as Na_2SO_3 or 297 kg $Na_2SO_3.7\ H_2O$; 86.5% yield]

8.9 A spray drier is used to produce crystals of magnesium chloride from its aqueous solution. The objective of the operation is to dry $MgCl_2$ to the lowest possible level.

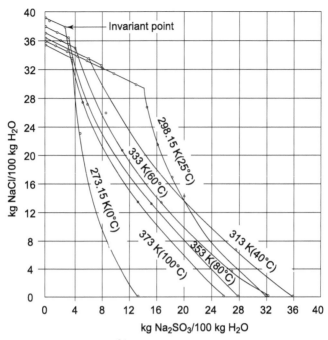

Fig. 8.14 NaCl-Na$_2$SO$_3$-H$_2$O System[24] from 0°C (273.15 K) to 100°C (373.15 K)
(Reproduced with the permission of the American Chemical Society, USA)

However, during the operation, MgCl$_2$ is also subjected to hydrolysis, leading to oxide formation. The reaction is

$$MgCl_2 + H_2O = MgO + 2\ HCl$$

Typical operating conditions of the dryer are given below.

Feed Aqueous solution containing 48% MgCl$_2$ by mass
Feed temperature 120°C (393 K) (boiling point of the solution at 101.325 kPa)
Product rate 5000 kg/h MgCl$_2$
Analysis of the final product 90% MgCl$_2$, 5% MgO and balance water (by mass)
Hot flue gas inlet temperature 525°C (798 K)
Hot flue gas outlet temperature 300°C (573 K)
Inlet hot flue gases contain 0.03 kg moisture per kg dry flue gas and has an average molar mass equal to 29.
Calculate (a) the evaporation of water taking place in the dryer in kg/h,
  (b) the total heat load due to process requirements of the dryer, and
  (c) the volumetric flow rates of incoming and outgoing gas mixtures at 101.325 kPa pressure, assuming 7% miscellaneous heat loss.
Data
  (i) Average heat capacity of the compounds are given below between 120°C (393 K) and 300°C (573 K):

Table 8.53 Heat Capacity Data

Compound	Phase	Heat capacity, kJ/(kg·K)
MgCl$_2$	Solid	0.873
MgO	Solid	1.277
HCl	Gas	0.816

(ii) Average heat capacity of water vapour (superheated) between 120°C (393 K) and 300°C (573 K) = 1.985 kJ/(kg·K)

(iii) Assume that the product discharge temperature is equal to the outlet flue gas temperature.

[(a) 5726.4 kg/h (b) 7380.79 kW (c) (i) Incoming flue gases = 261 587 m³/h (ii) Outgoing flue gases (plus evaporated moisture and HCl gas) = 203 128 m³/h]

8.10 In the steel industry, semifinished steel is treated with dilute sulphuric acid to remove iron oxide scale from the surface. Waste pickle liquor is obtained after the treatment. This liquor will pose an effluent problem and will also result in the loss of valuable acid. Electrolysis can be of use in recovering the acid.

A batch-type electrolytic cell is used to treat the waste sulphate pickle liquor as shown in Fig. 8.15[25]. It consists of an anion exchange membrane, a stainless steel cathode and an antimonial lead anode. The membrane is prepared by embedding anion exchange resin in the normalosmotic membrane matrix such as that of cellulose acetate or polyamide. Such a membrane allows only anions to migrate through it.

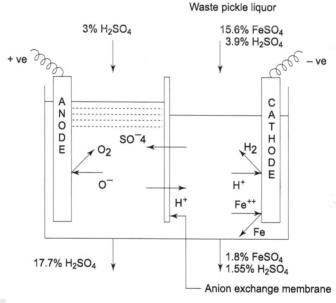

Fig. 8.15 Treatment of Waste Sulphate Pickle Liquor in an Electrolytic Cell

In the cathode compartment, $FeSO_4$ and H_2SO_4 of the waste liquor get electrolysed. Sulphate ions migrate to the anode compartment. Hydrogen ions and iron ions lose the charge to the cathode. As a result, hydrogen gas is evolved and iron is deposited at the cathode. In the anode compartment, water is electrolysed into H^+ and O^- ions. Sulphate ions combine with protons to form H_2SO_4, thereby increasing the strength of the electrolyte. Some protons migrate to the cathode compartment due to high mobility although such migration is deliberately slowed down by anion exchange membrane. The reactions are summarised as follows.

Cathode reactions

$$FeSO_4 = Fe^{++} + SO4^-$$
$$H_2SO_4 = 2 H^+ + SO4^-$$

$$Fe^{++} + 2\,e = Fe$$
$$2\,H^+ + 2\,e = H_2$$

Anode reactions

$$2\,H_2O = 4\,H^+ + 2\,O^{--}$$
$$4\,H^+ + 2\,SO_4^{--} - = 2\,H_2SO_4$$
$$2\,O^{--} = O2 + 2\,e$$

A trial run of the cell was taken. The catholyte charge amounted to 100 kg, yielding an analysis of 15.6% $FeSO_4$ and 3.9% H_2SO_4 (by mass). The anode compartment was filled with 59 kg of 3% H_2SO_4 (by mass) solution so as to make the solution conductive. As electrolysis progresses, the concentration of H_2SO_4 in the catholyte reduces thereby requiring higher voltage. Beyond 1.8% $FeSO_4$ (by mass) concentration in the catholyte, the voltage rise is steep and therefore the operation had to be stopped after 186 min. The average voltage and current during the operation were 4.17 and 4000 A, respectively. In the process, a definite quantity of water got evaporated.

The following observations were made at the end of the trial run.

Concentration of $FeSO_4$ in catholyte = 1.8% (by mass)

Concentration of H_2SO_4 in catholyte = 1.55% (by mass)

Concentration of H_2SO_4 in anolyte = 17.7% (by mass)

Amount of iron deposited at cathode = 5.313 kg

Oxygen evolved at anode = 3.331 Nm^3

Calculate

(a) the amount of catholyte and anolyte produced,

(b) the amount of hydrogen evolved at cathode,

(c) total amount of water evaporated from the cell, and

(d) the overall efficiency of the cell.

[(a) 65.5 kg catholyte, 78.83 kg anolyte (b) 4.54 Nm^3,

(c) 4.196 kg, (d) 41.05%]

8.11 Synthesis gas for ammonia production can be obtained in a number of ways. One such method is partial oxidation of hydrocarbons. In a typical plant, natural gas is used with the following composition[26].

CH_4: 93.25%, N_2: 1.95%, Ar: 0.4%, C_2H_6: 3.32%, C_3H_8: 0.88% and n-C_4H_{10}: 0.2% (by volume)

Oxygen with 98% purity (rest argon) is fed to the unit. The chemistry of partial oxidation of methane can be represented by the following equations:

$$CH_4 + 2O_2 = CO_2 + 2\,H_2O$$
$$CH_4 + CO_2 = 2CO + 2\,H_2$$
$$CH_4 + H_2O = CO + 3\,H_2$$
$$CO + H_2O = CO_2 + H_2 \quad \text{(shift reaction)}$$

Similar reactions can be written for other hydrocarbons also.

Natural gas and oxygen enter the reactor at 149°C (422 K) and 127°C (400 K), respectively. The reactor is to be designed in such a way that the gas mixture leaves the reactor at 1122°C (1395 K) and the methane slip (on wet basis) is 0.35% (v/v). The reactor is designed to operate at 20 bar a. The design approach to equilibrium of steam-methane reforming reaction is 30 and that of shift reaction is 0. Equilibrium constants[27] for the reforming and shift reactions are given below:

$$K_{p1} = \frac{p_{CH_4} \times p_{O_2}}{p_{CO} \times p_{H_2}^3} = 2.5207 \times 10^{-5} \text{ at } 1092°C\ (1365.15\ K)$$

$$K_{p2} = \frac{p_{H_2} \times p_{CO}}{p_{CO} \times p_{H_2O}} = 0.4465 \text{ at } 1122°C \text{ (1395.15 K)}$$

where p_i = partial pressure of ith component, atm

Calculate

(a) the oxygen stream supply in kmol/kmol natural gas,

(b) dry analysis of exit gas mixture,

(c) steam to dry exit gas mole ratio,

(d) oxygen supply per kmol NG, and

(e) net heat transfer in the reactor per kmol feed gas using absolute enthalpies, listed in Table 5.23.

> [(a) 0.7644 kmol O_2/kmol feed gas (b) Composition of dry gas mixture, leaving the reactor:, H_2: 60.03%, CO: 34.50%, CO_2: 3.62%, CH_4: 0.40%, N_2: 0.73%, and Ar: 0.72%, (c) Steam/dry gas ratio = 0.141 kmol/kmol, (d) O_2/NG = 0.7644 kmol/kmol (e) Net heat transfer = 5856 kJ/kmol feed gas (exothermic)]

8.12 Sulphuric acid is one of the most widely used basic chemicals. The major part of sulphuric acid consumption, however, is not bound in a marketable end product but generally ends up as spent acid, creating a waste disposal problem. In the organic chemical industry such as plastics, synthetic fibres including caprolactum, methylacrylate and others, the spent acid with organic impurities, metal sulphates and ammonium hydrogen sulphate is found to be the waste. In the phosphoric acid plant and nitrogenous fertilizer plant, the waste consists of spent acid, containing metal sulphates and ammonium sulphate. In some textile mills, acid waste contains fibrous organic impurities.

To solve the waste problem, recycling the sulphur within the process can be an useful proposition. Dilute spent acids can be reconcentrated, but in most cases, the remaining impurities in the reconcentrated acid do not permit the reuse of reconcentrated acid in the original process.

Regeneration of sulphuric acid can be attained by thermal degradation to SO_2 at high temperatures[28] where all organic compounds are completely burnt. SO_2 thus obtained is reprocessed by the standard catalytic process to produce concentrated acid or oleum.

An acid regeneration plant, equipped with two parallel spent-acid decomposition units, is designed for processing 860 t/d spent acid that has ammonia content. The average chemical composition of spent acid is H_2SO_4: 20%, NH_4HSO_4: 45%, H_2O: 30% and organics: 5% (by mass). For calculation purposes, C:H ratio (mass) and NCV of the organic compounds can be taken as 5.1 and 41 870 kJ/kg, respectively. This spent acid is decomposed by firing with fuel oil [C : H ratio = 6.2 : 1 (by mass) and NCV = 43 000 kJ/kg]. In the decomposition furnace, hot air at 450°C (723 K) is introduced. Gas mixture leaves the furnace at 106.7 kPa (800 Torr) and at about 1002°C (1275 K), the SO_2 content of the exit gas mixture should be less than 6% (v/v). Oxygen requirement in the exit gas mixture is 1.2 kmol per kmol SO_2 for further conversion to SO_3.

In the heat recovery section, the exit gas mixture from the furnace exchanges heat with air and cools down to 350°C (623 K). Subsequently, the gas mixture is cooled and used for acid production. Ambient air at 35°C (308 K) DB and 23°C (296 K) WB is first heated in a steam heater above the dew point of the gas mixture from the furnace and then further heated to 450°C (723 K) in the gas/air heat exchanger. Hot air from the exchanger is divided into two parts. One part is used as combustion air in the furnace, while the rest of the quantity is taken to a waste heat boiler, generating saturated steam at 11 bar a. Figure 8.16 schematically represents the process.

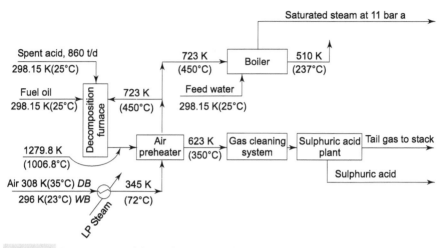

Fig. 8.16   Regeneration of Spent Sulphuric Acid

Make complete material and energy balances of the plant up to the heat recovery system. Assume 2% heat loss during all heat transfers. Usa data given in Appendix V.1 for heat of dilution of NH_4HSO_4.

[(i) **Composition and temperature of exit gas mixture, SO_2: 5.51%, CO_2: 9.13%, O_2: 6.61% and balance N_2 (v/v), 1001.15°C (1274.3 K), (ii) Water dew point of exit gas mixture = 68.6°C (341.6 K), (iii) Fuel oil required = 8.9 kg/100 kg spent acid = 76.54 t/d, (iv) Saturated steam generation at 11 bar a = 14.59 t/h]**

8.13   Benzene can be produced from toluene economically. Thermal dealkylation[27] with hydrogen results in benzene and methane at 34.5 bar a and 650°C (923 K).

Side reaction results in the undesired product diphenyl which is controlled by excess hydrogen.

Reactions can be written as under:

$$C_6H_5CH_3 + H_2 = C_6H_6 + CH_4 \qquad (i)$$
$$2\,C_6H_6 = C_{12}H_{10} + H_2 \qquad (ii)$$

Based on experience, it was decided to use excess hydrogen in such a way that the moles of H_2 in the gross feed should be five times that of 'oil' in the gross feed. Here 'oil' denotes the mixture of benzene, toluene and diphenyl. The process is shown in Fig. 3.6. The gross feed enters the plug flow reactor and the product stream goes to the phase separator. Based on thermodynamic considerations in the separator, the mole ratio of each component in the gas phase and liquid phase is given as, H_2: ∞, CH_4: ∞, C_6H_6: 0.005, C_7H_8: 0.001 and diphenyl: 0. A part of the flash gas mixture is recycled after compression and joins the make-up hydrogen stream, containing 95% H_2 and 5% CH_4 (v/v). Recycle gas stream contains 50% H_2 (v/v).

To avoid accumulation of inerts (CH_4) in the loop, a fixed amount of the flash gas mixture is purged from the separator. The liquid stream leaving the phase separator is treated in successive distillation columns to separate benzene, toluene and diphenyl. The recovered toluene with small amounts of benzene and diphenyl is recycled to feed the toluene header. The benzene column is designed to separate 95% of the benzene and the toluene column can separate 75% of the diphenyl. Based on an experimental study, following data were found.

Table 8.56 Dealkylation of Toluene[29]

Conversion, %	50	66	70	75	85
Yield, %	99	98.5	97.7	97	93

As the conversion increases, the recycle stream will reduce and the compression cost as well as equipment cost will reduce. But as the conversion increases, formation of undesirable products will also increase which in turn will increase the operational cost as well as call for larger separation towers. To find the optimum conversion, a cost study was performed. Such a study revealed that the profit increases directly with the square root of the conversion and with the cube of the yield. Make the material balance of the plant for producing 1000 kg/h of benzene.   [**See Table 8.55**]

8.14 Hydrogen cyanide can be manufactured by reacting ammonia, air and methane (natural gas) as shown in Fig. 8.17. At first ammonia (in gaseous form) and air are mixed and passed over a catalyst bed, packed with Pt-Rh catlyst (90:10 mass ratio), at 900°C (1173.15 K) and at 3 bar a. In this reactor, following reaction takes place.

$$4\ NH_3 + 5\ O_2 = 4\ NO + 6\ H_2O \qquad (i)$$

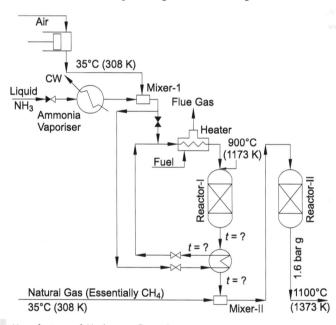

Fig. 8.17 Manufacture of Hydrogen Cyanide

The gas mixture leaving the first reactor, is cooled and mixed with methane essentially. The mixture is then introduced to second reactor, packed with Pt catalyst. Following reactions are known to take place in the reactor.

$$2\ NO + 2\ CH_4 = 2\ HCN + 2\ H_2O + H_2 \qquad (ii)$$
$$CH_4 + 2\ O_2 = CO_2 + 2\ H_2O \qquad (iii)$$
$$CH_4 + 2\ H_2O = CO_2 + 4\ H_2 \qquad (iv)$$
$$CH_4 + H_2O = CO + 3\ H_2 \qquad (v)$$
$$4\ NH_3 + 3\ O_2 = 2\ N_2 + 6\ H_2O \qquad (vi)$$

Table 8.55 Material Balance for Dealkylation of Toluene to Benzene

Basis Benzene product rate = 1000 kg/h

Component/Conditions	Toluene	Hydrogen	Methane	Diphenyl	Benzene	Total	Pressure, bar a	Temperature, °C (K)
Molar mass	92	2	16	154	78			
Fresh toluene feed								
kmol/h	13.24	—	—	—	—	13.24	41.6	35 (308)
kg/h	1218.2	—	—	—	—	1218.2		
Fresh hydrogen feed								
kmol/h	—	27.74	1.46	—	—	29.2	33	15 (288)
kg/h	—	55.48	23.38	—	—	78.86		
mole %	—	95.0	5.0	—	—	—		
Recycle gas stream								
kmol/h	0.009	63.41	63.35	—	0.055	126.824	32	38 (311)
kg/h	0.9	126.82	1013.6	—	4.29	1145.61		
mole %	0.007	50.0	49.95	—	0.043	—		
Toluene recycled								
kmol/h	4.17	—	—	0.07	0.66	4.9	41.7	121 (394)
kg/h	383.64	—	—	10.78	52.22	446.64		
mass %	85.90	—	—	2.41	11.69	100.0		
Reactor inlet								
kmol/h	17.419	91.15	64.81	0.07	0.715	174.164	36.5	650 (923)
kg/h	1602.74	182.3	1036.98	10.78	56.51	2889.31		

(*Contd.*)

Table 8.55 (Contd.)

Basis Benzene product rate = 1000 kg/h

Component/Conditions	Toluene	Hydrogen	Methane	Diphenyl	Benzene	Total	Pressure, bar a	Temperature, °C (K)
Reactor Outlet X								
kmol/h	4.18	78.12	78.05	0.28	13.56	174.19	34.5	704 (977)
kg/h	384.63	156.24	1248.76	42.78	1057.89	2890.3		
Vapour stream from phase separator								
kmol/h	0.01	78.54	78.46	—	0.069	157.079	32	38 (311)
kg/h	1.01	157.08	1255.36	—	5.38	1418.83		
mole %	0.007	50.0	49.95	—	0.043	100.00		
Purge stream (total)								
kmol/h	0.002	14.71	14.70	—	0.013	29.425	3.4	20 (293)
kg/h	0.2	29.42	235.2	—	1.0	265.82		
mole %	0.007	50.00	49.95	—	0.043	100.00		
Liquid stream from phase separator								
kmol/h	4.17	—	—	0.28	13.49	17.94	11.8	38 (311)
kg/h	383.64	—	—	42.12	1052.22	1477.98		
mass %	25.96	—	—	2.85	71.19	100.00		
Benzene product from benzene column								
kmol/h					12.83	12.83	1.7	98 (371)
kg/h					1000.0	1000.0		
Diphenyl from toluene column								
kmol/h				0.22	—	0.22	1.4	204 (477)
kg/h				32.34	—	32.34		

Product gas mixture from the second reactor leaves at 1100°C (1373.15 K) and 1.6 bar g. Its analysis shows the presence of 5.9% HCN, 7.5% H_2, 25.1% H_2O, 1.6% NH_3, 56.7% N_2, 1.2% CO and 2.0% CO_2 (on mole basis). Assume that air (mixture of O_2 and N_2), fed to the first reactor, has moisture content of 0.024 kmol/kmol dry air.

Make material and energy balances of both the reactors for 100 kmol/h exit gas stream from the second reactor.

(a) Calculate (moist) air to ammonia ratio in the feed to Reactor I.
(b) Calculate methane feed rate (in kmol/h) to Reactor II.
(c) Calculate the temperature of the gas stream, leaving Reactor I.
(d) Calculate the required temperature of the gas stream from the first reactor before it is mixed with methane [available at 35°C (308.15 K)].
(e) Calculate the mixed feed temperature by exchanging heat with exit stream from reactor I.
(f) Calculate the heat input to the fired heater to heat mixed feed of ammonia and air from temperature calculated in (e) to 900°C (1173 K)

    (a) 6.519 kmol moist air/ kmol NH_3 (b) 9.1 kmol/h, (c) 1100°C (1373.15 K)
    (d) 451.07°C (724.15 K), (e) 524.76°C (797.91 K), (f) 68.789 kW

8.15 A methanol plant produces methanol by reforming natural gas with steam. Synthesis gas (mixed feed) containing CO, CO_2, H_2 and inerts is passed through a multibed converter.

The following reactions are known to take place in the reactor.

$$CO + 2 H_2 = CH_3OH$$
$$CO_2 + 3 H_2 = CH_3OH + H_2O$$

According to the Le Châtelier principle, molar ratio of $n_{H_2}/(2 \cdot n_{CO} + 3 \cdot n_{CO_2})$ equal to 1 is ideal for methanol synthesis. However, in practice it is preferred to have the ratio marginally greater than 1 due to a possibility of carbon formation and its deposition on the catalyst. Synthesis loop is shown schematically in Fig. 8.18

Make-up gas to the loop contains carbon oxides 70% H_2, 0.33% Ar and 0.67% CH_4 (i.e. 1% inerts). Mixed feed to the converter is fed with a gas mixture in which the following molar ratio is maintained[30].

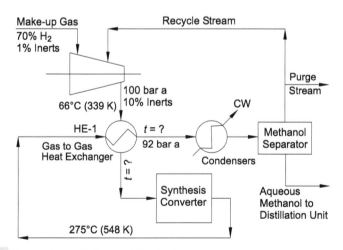

Fig. 8.18 Recycle Loop of Methanol Synthesis

$$\frac{n_{H_2}}{(2n_{CO} + 3n_{CO_2})} = 1.05$$

Mixed feed contains 0.45 mole % CH_3OH and inerts are to be restricted to 10 mole % (33:67 molar ratio of Ar: CH_4). Converter exit gas stream is analysed to contain 3.0 mole % CH_3OH. Reaction equilibrium dictates that equilibrium constant (K) of of water gas shift reaction in the conveter exit gas mixture should be 69 at 275°C (548.15 K).

$$(n_{CO_2} \times n_{H_2})/(n_{CO} \times n_{H_2O}) = 69$$

The converter exit gas stream first exchanges heat with ingoing gas stream and then passes through condensers where methanol is condensed. Major portion of the gas mixture leaving the condensers is recyecled. In order to limit the concentration of inerts, a purge stream is bled from the recycle stream.

(A) Based on a freash feed rate of 100 kmol/h, establish the material balance of the synthesis loop. Calculate (a) desired make-up gas cornposition, (b) recycle ratio, (c) purge rate, (d) product aqueous methanol solution rate and its composition, and (e) composition of various streams.

(B) Mixed gas stream is discharged from the compressor at 100 bar a and 66°C (339 K). Also, reactor exit gas stream temperature is required to be maintained at 275°C (548.15 K). Assuming ideal gas law, calculate (a) the temperature of gas stream entering the converter, and (b) the temperature of reactor exit gas stream (going to condensers) after exchanging heat with incoming gas mixture in HE-1.

(A) Make-up gas : 17.31% CO, 11.69% CO_2, 70% H_2 and 1% inerts,. Recycle ratio = 10.13 kmol/kmol fresh feed, Aqueous solution flow rate = 1046.2 kg/h having 81.87% CH_3OH., (B) (a) 213.32°C (486.47 K), (b) 126.71°C (399.86 K)

8.16 A water chilling package uses water as a refrigerant and lithium bromide (LiBr) solution as an absorbent. It is to be designed to achieve 1500 kW (426.5 TR) by way of producing chilled water at 9°C (282 K). Chilled water from the plant enters the chiller at 12°C (285 K). Chilling is achieved by evaporating water at 7 Torr a pressure and 6°C (279 K) in the evaporator. Water vapours from the evaporator are absorbed in strong aqneous (SA) LiBr solution having 63.3% concentration by mass. Weak aqueous LiBr solution (WA) of 59.5% strength from absorber at 40°C (313 K) is pumped to the regenerator via a heat exchanger in which it exchanges heat with SA solution. In the heat exchanger, WA is heated to 75°C (348 K) while SA is cooled from 101.6°C (374.75 K) to 48.9 C (321.9 K). In the generator, heating coils are provided in which saturated steam at 185 kPa a is used as heating medium. Water vapour at 101.6°C (374.75 K) from the generator travels to the condenser, operating at 10 kPa a, where it is condensed and fed again to the evaporator. Cooling water at 32°C (305 K) enters the absorber. Partially heated cooling water leaves the absorber and enters the condenser coils and leaves the coils at 40°C (313 K). Refrigeration cycle is shown in Fig. 8.19 schematically.

Data

(i) Heat of dilution of LiBr solution (in 3.8% split range) = 498 kJ/kg water at 25°C (298.15 K) (exothermic)

(ii) At 10 kPa a, saturation temperature of water, t_s/T_s = 45.83°C (318.98 K)
Enthalpy of water (h) = 191.83 kJ/kg
Enthalpy of vapour (H) = 2584.8 kJ/kg
Enthalpy of superheated vapour at 10 kPa a 101.6°C (374.75 K),
$$i = 2690.6 \text{ kJ/kg}$$

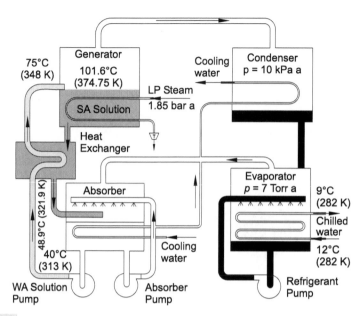

Fig. 8.19   Absorption Refrigeration with Aqueous LiBr Solution

(iii) Average specific heat of LiBr solution (in 3.8% split range) C_l = 1.842 kJ/(kg·K)
(iv) Latent heat of steam at 185 kPa a = 2208.5 kJkg
Assume that generator and condenser as well as evaporator and absorber are under same pressure; 10 kPa a and 7 Torr a, respectively.
Carryout the material and energy balances of the refrigeration cycle and find:
(a) chilled water flow rate,
(b) evaporation rate of water in evaporator,
(c) heat duty of absorber, generator and condenser,
(d) required cooling water flow rate,
(e) steam consumption, and
(f) COP of the refrigeration cycle.
[(a) 119.423 kg/s or 430 m³/h, (b) 0.603 kg/s, (c) ϕ_a = 2100.638 kW,
ϕ_g = 2388.522 kW, ϕ_c = 1614.865 kW, (d) $\dot{m}_C$ = 399.3 m3/h,
(e) $\dot{m}_S$ = 3893^{kg}/h, (f) COP = 0.628 kW/kW

Note   Caustic soda can also be used instead of lithium bromide for absorption of water (i.e., refrigerant). Considering freezing point limitation, an aqueous soution of 46% NaOH strength (by mass) is recommended as the strong solution. A split of 3.5% is normally recommended. Heat of dilution in this concentration range is 886 kJ.kg NaOH (exothermic) at 25°C (298.15 K). This is higher by nearly 78% as compared to LiBr solution which means heat requirement in the generator and cooling water requirement in the absorber will be higher than that of the LiBr system. However, boilng point of 46% N solution at 10 kPa a is 82.5°C (355.5 K) as compared to LiBr solution which means low level heat (i.e., heat source at lower temperature) will be required in the generator. COP of the refrigeration system with NaOH as absorbent will be lower than that with the LiBr system. Aqueous causitc potash solution is yet another alkali which can be considered as an abosrbent.

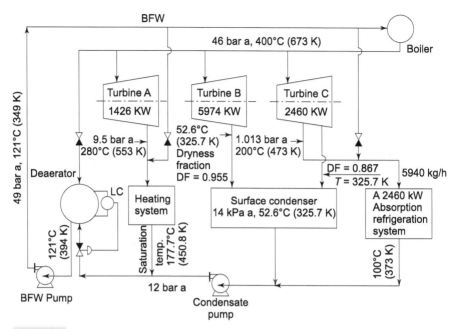

Fig. 8.20 Steam Balance in a Chemical Plant

8.17 Refer Fig. 8.20. Calculate the requirement of the HP steam and boiler feed water (BFW) based on the following assumptions:

(a) Consider 95% energy conversion in each turbine.

(b) Consider 5% loss of energy in the condensate from the condensate system to the deaerator.

[**HP steam flow = 75 254 kg/h, BFW flow = 78 645 kg/h**]

8.18 Refer Example 8.7. Considering high cost of the bolier for steam generation at 115 bar a, it is proposed to instal a bolier to generate steam at 64 bar a and 440°C (713 K). As a consequence, the power turbine will be designed to introduce steam at 64 bar a and 440°C (713 K). Back pressure steam from the power turbine will be at 39 bar a and 385°C (658 K). Exhausts from power turbine and CW pump turbine will be at 12 kPa a and 50°C (323 K) with 99% dryness of steam. Back pressure steam from BFW pump and FD fan turbines will be at 4.4 bar a and 205°C (478 K). Rest requirements are unchanged.

For the revised design conditions, establish the steam balance.   [**Refer Fig. 8.21**]

Note It can be seen that HP steam generation will be higher by 2721 kg/h, representing nearly 5% increase. The cooling tower load will also increase by 12.6%. Enthalpy of steam at 64 bar a and 440°C is 3273.3 kJ/kg which means energy requirement of the boiler will be higher by 8.22%, calling for additional fuel consumption of 404 kg/h with GCV of fuel = 40 000 kJ/kg and at 75% boiler refficiency.

Exercise 8.21 siginifies the importance of steam pressure in cascade steam balance.

8.19 Refer Example 8.7. LP steam header pressure is proposed to be reduced to 4 bar a. As a result,

(i) Temperature of LP steam from BFW pump and FD fan turbines will be reduced to 165°C (438 K),

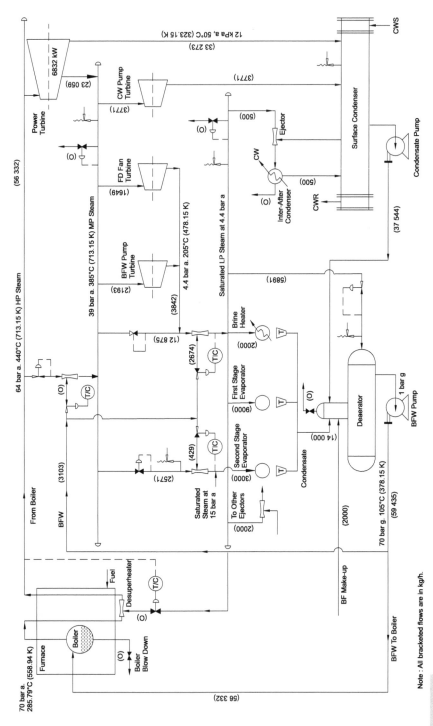

Fig. 8.21 Steam Balance in a Caustic Soda Plant with 64 Bar Stream

Note : All bracketed flows are in kg/h.

(ii) Consumption in ejectors operating with LP steam as motivating fluid will increase by 10%, and

(iii) Consumption of LP steam in heaters will reduce by 1.75% due to increase in latent heat of LP steam. Establish the steam balance. **[Refer Fig. 8.22]**

Note It can be seen that HP steam generation will be lower by 516 kg/h, representing nearly 1% reduction. Thus, operation of a given cascade steam balance can be optimized by selecting right operation parameters (without any modifications). Cooling tower load will increase marginally (~ 0.6%).

8.20 In Example 8.7, letdown of MP steam is substantial which can be reduced gainfully by converting the CW pump turbine from a condensing one to the back-pressure type. Establish the revised steam balance in which the HP steam generation is again minimum. **[Refer Fig. 8.23]**

Note It may be noted that HP steam generation is lower (by 4.8%) as there is a reduction in letdown from MP steam to LP steam. There is also a reduction of heat load (by 8.8%) on the surface condenser.

8.21 In Example 8.7, MP steam is available at 39 bar a and 320°C (593 K). A part of MP steam is reheated in the boiler furnace to 400°C (673 K) as shown in Fig. 8.24. Reheated MP steam is fed to FD fan, BFW pump and CW pump turbines. Total pressure drop in the reheating coils and desuperheater is calculated to be 3 bar. LP steam from these turbines is obtained at 4.4 bar a and 185°C (458 K). Establish steam balance with revised conditions. **[Refer Fig. 8.24]**

Note Conversion of condensing turbine to a back pressure one (Exercise 8.20), incorporation of BFW Heaters (Example 8.8), reheating of intermediate pressure steam (Exercise 8.21), adoption of thermocompressor (Example 8.9), lowering header pressure (Exercise 8.19), etc., could prove useful in minimizing HP steam generation (thereby reduction in fuel consumption) and in heat load of cooling tower. Careful design of a cascade steam system at the project stage can pay rich dividends.

8.22 Polypropylene (PP) drying (i.e., *n*-hexane removal) can be performed in different types of dryers. One such dryer is a flash dryer (convective drying) in which the feed cake is dispersed in a venturi throat with hot recycle gas (nitrogen). Such a dryer requires gas circulation rate of about 1 kg dry nitrogen per kg PP which acts as a heat carrier for drying. In another spiral dryer [31], indirect heating and convective drying are performed thereby nitrogen circulation is significantly reduced. In this type of dryer, heat is transmitted to the thin fast moving product film rising in a spiral path along the inner wall surface. Conveying medium is nitrogen. For PP, the nitrogen circulation requirement is only 0.18 kg dry nitrogen per kg PP. Spiral dryer is also claimed to prevent corrosion due to the avoidance of hexane condensation.

In both the cases, nitrogen at 130°C (403 K) enters the dryer having an *n*-hexane dew point of 34°C (307 K). Nitrogen leaves the dryer at 90°C (363 K) in either case. PP enters the dryer with 35% *n*-hexane on a wet basis at 65°C (338 K). Product PP leaves flash dryter at 55°C (328 K) with *n*-hexane content of 0.05 kg per kg dry PP while the product leaves spiral dryer at 80°C (353 K) with *n*-hexane content of 0.02 kg per kg dry PP. Steam is used in the jacket of the spiral dryer at 4 bar a to maintain the heat transfer surface temperature of 110°C (383 K). The process of spiral drying is shown in Fig. 8.25.

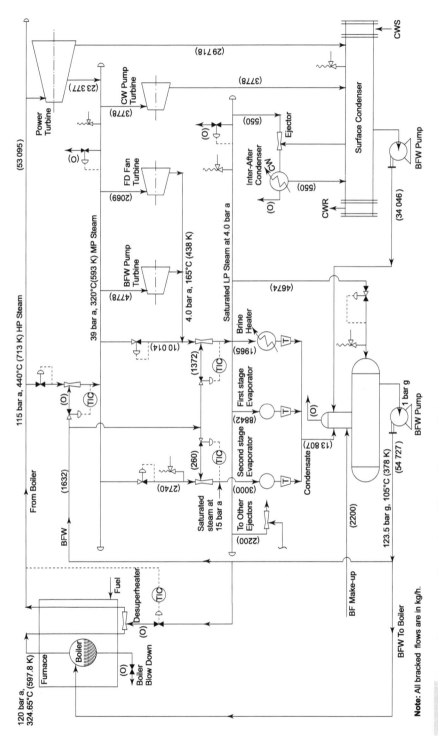

Fig. 8.22 Steam Balance in a Caustic Soda Plant with Lower LP Steam Header Pressure

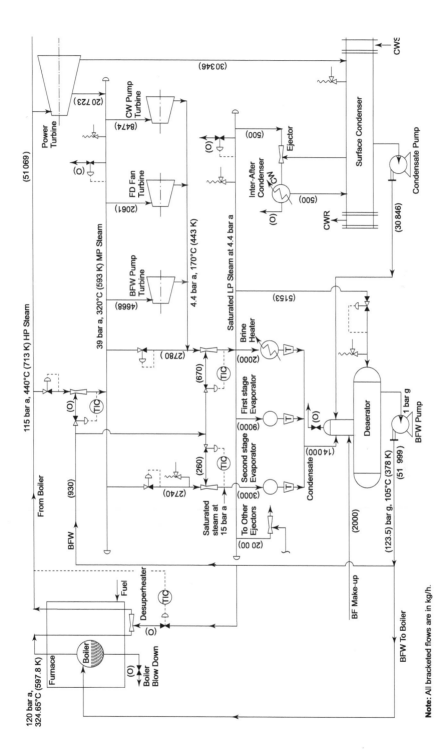

Fig. 8.23 Steam Balance in a Caustic Soda Plant with Backpressure CW Pump Turnbine

Note: All bracketed flows are in kg/h.

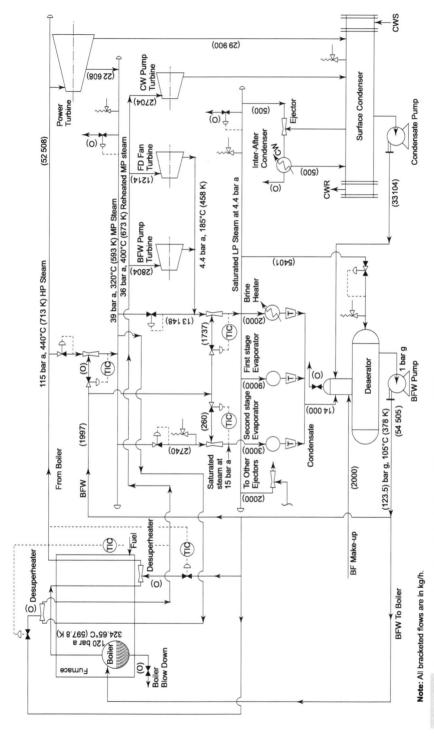

Fig. 8.24 Steam Balance in a Caustic Soda Plant with Reheat of MP Steam

Note: All bracketed flows are in kg/h.

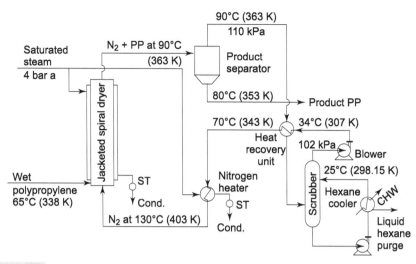

Fig. 8.25   Drying of Polypropylene

Nitrogen rich in *n*-hexane leaves the dryer at 90°C (363 K) and is sent to a direct contact scrubber to separate *n*-hexane from nitrogen. An external water cooler cools recycled *n*-hexane used for scrubbing. Cooled liquid *n*-hexane, equivalent to the amount evaporated in the dryer, is bled out from the circulating solution. Nitrogen at 34°C (307 K), saturated with *n*-hexane, is recycled back to the dryer via a blower through an indirect steam-gas heater. Suction pressure of blower is 102 kPa (765 Torr). Average heat capacity of solid PP and liquid *n*-hexane may be taken as 1.926 and 2.512 kJ/(kg · K), respectively.

For a drying plant having a capacity of 10 000 kg/h dry PP rate, calculate the following.
 (a) Steam requirement in nitrogen heater for spiral dryer,
 (b) Steam requirement in the jacket of the spiral dryer, and
 (c) Temperature of gas mixture, leaving the interchanger.

[**(a) 182.1 kg/h (b) 951.8 kg/h (c) 76.2°C (349.35 K)**]

8.23 In a pharmaceutical plant, a product containing methylene chloride (CH_2Cl_2) as solvent is filtered in an agitated bed filter cum dryer (AFD). After the filtration cycle, dry solvent-free nitrogen is passed at the rate of 100 Nm^3/h through it at 120°C (393 K) for evaportion of solvent at 106 kPa a. Solvent-laden nitrogen leaves the equipement from top at 105 kPa a and 90°C (363 K) with solvent dew point of 10°C (283 K). The gas mixture is first cooled in a cooler to 40°C (313 K) with cooling water at 32°C (305 K). The mixture is then sent to a cryo-condenser to condensate out the solvent.
 (a) In a conventional cryo-condenser, nitrogen gas at −170°C (103 K) and 5 bar a is introduced in the coil as shown in Fig. 8.26 (a). Solvent-laden nitrogen exchanges heat in a countercurrent manner. Solvent is condensed at −31°C (242 K) while nitrogen saturated with solvent leaves the separator at 102 kPa.

   Liquid nitrogen (LN) is normally stored at 6 bar a. It is vaporized to −170°C (103 K) in a serpentine heater with ambient air. It is supplied as a refrigerant to the cryo-condenser and leaves it at 4.8 bar a and 4°C (277 K). Calculate the theoretical nitrogen consumption of LN.
 (b) In a modified system[32], two coils are provided in the cryo-condenser as shown in Fig. 8.26 (b). In one coil, nitrogen vapour at 5 bar a and −170°C (103 K) is introduced and leaves the coil at 4.8 bar a and 4°C (277 K). LN from storage

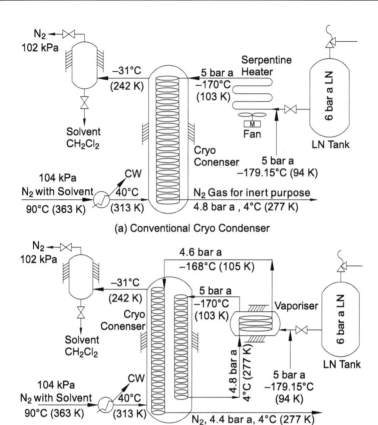

(a) Conventional Cryo Condenser

(b) Modified Cryo Condenser

Fig. 8.26 (a) and (b) Cryo-Condensers

is vaporized in a vaporizer (coil in tank type) at 4°C (277 K). In the vaporizer, nitrogen is cooled to − 168°C (105 K) and leaves it at 4.6 bar a. Cooled nitrogen gas is reintroduced in the second coil and leaves the cryo-condenser at 4.4 bar a and 4°C (277 K).

Calculate

(a) theoretical consumption of LN for the conventional and modified cryo systems, and

(b) heat duty of cooler, prior to the cryo-condenser.

Data

Table 8.57 Enthalpy of Nitrogen[33]

Pressure, bar a	Condition	Enthalpy, kJ/kg
5	Saturated liquid at −179.15°C (94 K)	35.21
5	Saturated vapour	208.54
5	Superheated vapour at −170°C (103.15 K)	220.23
4.8	Gas at 4°C (277.15 K)	408.41
4.6	Gas at − 168°C (105.15 K)	223.40
4.4	Gas at 4°C (277.15 K)	408.53

Reference state Enthalpy of saturated liquid nitrogen at NBP [−195.8°C (77.35 K)] = 0 kJ/kg

[(a) 276.1 kg/h LN in conventional cryo-condenser and
136.9 kg/h LN in modified cryo-condenser
(b) 3.195 kW for cooler

8.24 A chlorine ton container is utilized for chlorinating cooling water. The outside diameter and effective length of the container are 760 mm and 1800 mm, respectively. It is a known fact that when the halogen is consumed from the container, the temperature of the liquid halogen (and so of the container) will drop due to flashing of the halogen from the liquid surface.

(a) When the container is full, it contains 900 kg of liquid chlorine. Chlorination of cooling water is desired at 5.56 g/s ($\approx$ 20 kg/h) at a uniform rate for a long period. For steady-state conditions, the rate at which heat is transmitted by ambient air into the container must equal the rate at which chlorine is vaporized, thereby no change in temperature of liquid chlorine will take place. For a fresh full container, calculate the steady-state temperature of liquid chlorine assuming the ambient temperature to be 30°C (303 K).

(b) Assume that the container has 100 kg liquid chlorine at ambient temperature after certain use. Calculate the temperature of liquid chlorine with the same drawl rate after 2160 s (0.6 h) taking five iterations of 720 s (0.2 h) each.

For the above calculations, assume an overall heat transfer coefficient[34] of 11.4 W/(m$^2 \cdot$ K) based on the effective area of the container which is defined as the area in contact with liquid chlorine.

Properties of chlorine can be calculated using following empirical equations[35] for the temperature range of interest.

Liquid chlorine density, $\rho_1 = -6.5 \times 10^{-3} T^2 + 0.706 T + 1762.16$ kg/m^3

Latent heat of vaporization of chlorine,

$\lambda_v = -2.352 \times 10^{-3} T^2 + 0.6186 T + 274.3$ kJ/kg

Where, T = temperature, K

Assume isobaric heat capacity (C_1) of liquid chlorine to be 0.985 kJ/(kg $\cdot$ K)

Hint (i) For a circle, central angle in radian (α) = cross sectional area of liquid filled surface (A) $\times$ 2/[radius (r)]^2

Arc length (S) = central angle (α) $\times$ radius (r)

Surface area in contact with liquid (A′) = arc length (S) $\times$ length of container (l)

(ii) Neglect sensible heat in the metal and mass of gaseous chlorine in the empty space of the container.

[(a) – 12.67°C (260.48 K), (b) – 34.75°C (238.4 K)]

8.25 A distillation tower is designed for aromatics separation. Design conditions of the column are as follows[36]:

Table 8.58 Composition of Distillation Column Streams

	Composition, mole %		
Component	Feed	Distillate	Bottoms
Benzene	2.2	22.8	0
Toluene	7.4	72.2	0.5
Ethyl benzene	43.4	5.0	47.5
Styrene	47.0	0	52.0

Based on various considerations, a reflux ratio of 6.0 is selected for design. Design pressure of the column is fixed at 21.3 kPa a (160 Torr) and it operates at near constant pressure. All the streams may be taken as saturated liquids. Also, assume that mixtures are ideal mixtures.

For a design feed rate of 100 kmol/h, calculate,
(a) the flow rates of distillate and bottom products,
(b) bubble point and dew point of distillate products,
(c) the heat removal in the overhead condenser assuming that condensation takes place at an average temperature of the dew point and bubble point of the distillate product, and
(d) the heat duty and saturated steam consumption at 2 bar a of the reboiler.

[(a) D = 9.63 kmol/h, B = 90.37 kmol/h (b) T_{DP} = 334.7 K (61.55°C)
and T_{BB} = 328.3 K (55.15°C)
(c) Heat load of condenser = 662.28 kW (d) Heat load of reboiler
= 593.9 kW, Steam consumption = 971 kg/h]

8.26 A carbon black plant generates 40 000 Nm³/h offgas mixture having following composition by volume on dry basis.

H_2 15.3%, N_2: 61.9%, Ar: 0.9%, CH_4: 0.4%, CO: 17.2%, CO_2: 3.9% and C_2H_2: 0.4%

Moisture content 0.15 kmol/kmol dry gas mixture.

Offgas mixture (free from any solid) is available at 0.25 bar g and 250°C (523 K). The following alternatives are considered for its utilization.

(a) *Case-I* The offgas mixture is fired in a boiler to generate steam at 43 bar a and 425°C (698.15 K). Calculate steam generation rate of the boiler.

(b) *Case-II* The offgas mixture is treated in a CO_2-removal plant in which 1% loss of gas mixture is envisaged. CO_2 recovery is considered 97% from the mixture of which 95% product can be made available either in liquid or solid (dry ice) form for sale. The gas mixture from the CO_2-absorber is available at 0.10 bar g and 328 K(55°C), saturated with water vapours. This gas mixture is then utilized for steam generation at 43 bar a and 698.15 K(425°C). Calculate CO_2 production and steam generation rates.

(c) *Case-III* Gas mixture from CO_2-absorber (of Case-II) is passed through a second absorber from where the gas mixture leaves with < 1000 ppm (v/v) of CO_2. It is then compressed, dried and passed through a cold box for cryogenic recovery of H_2 and CO for methanol production by the reaction: CO + 2H_2 = CH_3OH. Hydrogen availability being limiting, equivalent CO is utilized and balance is mixed with reject stream of the cold box. Assume 1% loss of gas-mixture from second CO_2 absorber before cryogenic processing. Neglect CO_2 so recovered from second absorber. Reject stream from cold box at 1 bar g and 25°C (298.15 K) (including remixed excess CO), having practically no moisture, is utilized in boiler to generate steam at 43 bar a and 425°C (698 K). In the cold box, hydrogen recovery is 90% and overall methanol conversion (inducing recovery) from the recovered hydrogen is 90%.

Calculate methanol production and steam generation rate.

The following general assumptions can be made for stoichiometric calculations.

(i) Boiler is supplied feed water at 30°C (303 K).
(ii) Gas mixture is fired with 10% excess air in the boiler. Ambient air at 40°C (313 K) with humidity of 0.017 kmol/kmol dry air.
(iii) Flue gases leave boiler furnace at 745 Torr and 175°C (448 K).
(iv) Unaccounted heat loss in the boiler is 1.5% of total heat input to it.

[**Case-I: Steam generation = 45.255 t/h, Case-II: Steam generation = 41.528 t/h,
CO_2 production = 51.3 t/d, Case-III: Steam generation = 17.218 t/h,
CO_2 production = 51.3 t/d, Methanol production = 72.5 t/d**]

Note   It can be seen in this example that offgas mixture is a valuable input for various products. Cost of the plant and revenue generation from the products will have to be techno-commercially evaluated for deciding over the best alternative to be adopted.

8.27   Offgases from an adipic acid plant have the following composition:
N_2O: 30%, CO_2: 3%, O_2: 8% and balance nitrogen (on dry volume basis)
It is saturated with water at 2 bar g and 313 K(40°C).

Nitrous oxide (N_2O), being a greenhouse gas having many-fold potential than that of CO_2 is required to be dissociated to nitrogen and oxygen before the gases are letout to atmosphere.

Reaction
$$N_2O = N_2 + 1/2\ O_2$$

In an innovative process,[37, 38] nitrous oxide is dissociated over mixed transition metal oxides (as catalyst) in a series of beds. The process is shown in Fig. 8.27.

In this process, a portion of offgas mixture is diluted with a definite quantity of treated gas mixture, being let out to atmosphere such that the temperature of the treated gas mixture from the first bed is limited to 700°C (973 K). Reaction initiation temperature is 450°C (723 K) and hence the mixed gas is heated in E2 to 450°C (723 K) before being introduced to the first bed.

Gas mixture, leaving the first bed, is quenched with a definite (bypass) quantity of offgas mixture such that the gas mixture, entering the second bed, is at 450°C (723 K). In a similar manner, the gas mixture from the second bed is quenched with a definite quantity of offgas mixture. Treated gas mixture from the third bed is found to contain 200 ppm (v/v) N_2O (max.) which is acceptable for venting to atmosphere. The process is claimed to offer many advantages over conventional treatment.

Assume that N_2O dissociation in each catalyst bed is 100%. Calculate the flow rates of offgas mixture, bypassed to the second and third beds for a dry feed rate of 50 kmol/h offgas rate to the first bed. Also calculate the dilution gas rate (i.e., recycle) requirement for the 1st bed.

Make heat balance calculations for the entire system. Calculate (a) the temperatures of gas mixtures, leaving the second and third beds, (b) heat duty of each heat exchanger and (c) saturated steam production rate (in E3) at 4.5 bar a assuming that feed water is supplied at 30°C (303 K).

> [**Flow of offgas to second bed: 96.31 kmol/h, third bed: 185.50 kmol/h, Flow of recycled treated gas mixture: 88.86 kmol/h, Temperature of gas, leaving second bed: 723.4°C(996.55 K), and leaving third bed: 737.37°C (1010.52 K), Heat duty: E2: 464.91 kW, E3: 1803.7 kW, Steam generation: 2481.6 kg/h, E1: 186.69 kW, E4: 85.66 kW and E5: 8.98, Stack gas temparature : 161.05°C (434.2 K)]**

8.28   In a modified Claus process[39], acid gas stream, rich is H_2S is processed to recover elemental sulphur as shown in Fig. 8.28.

A gas stream, derived from acid gas removal section of a plant, is analysed to contain 30% H_2S, 69% CO_2 and 1% H_2 (by mole) on dry basis. Saturated gas is available at 0.2 bar g and 50°C (323 K). Because of corrosive nature of the gas, 40% of the feed is introduced to the burner along with combustion air at 40°C (313 K). Natural gas is introduced as a supporting fuel in the burner which is also introduced at 35°C (308 K).Composition of natural gas may be assumed that of Example 7.4. H_2S is oxidized with combustible air to SO_2.

$$H_2S(g) + (3/2)\ O_2\ (g) = SO_2(g) + H_2O(g) \qquad (i)$$

H_2S and H_2 of feed gas and natural gas are burnt in the burner, forming CO_2 and H_2O. Oxidation stoichiometry may be considered 100% complete with 5% excess air.

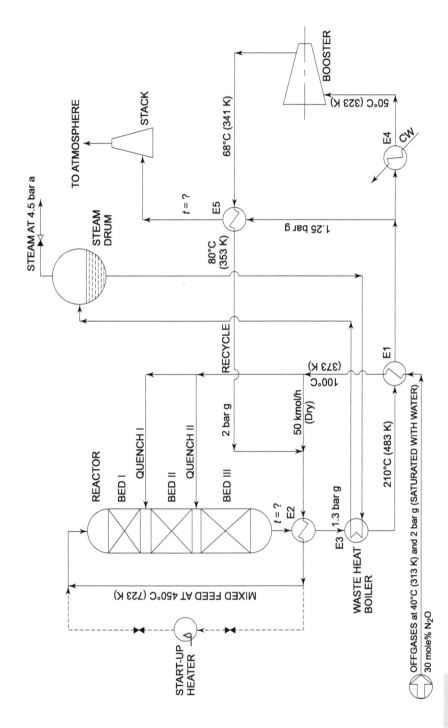

Fig. 8.27 Nitrous Oxide Removal from Offgases in Adipic Acid Plant

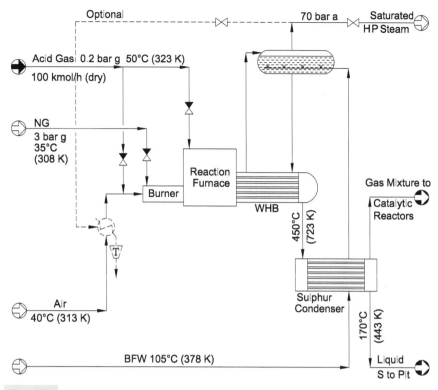

Fig. 8.28   Sulphur Recovery by Modified Clause Process

The gas mixture from the burner is mixed with balance 60% feed gas in the reaction furnace where following reaction takes place.

$$2H_2S(g) + SO_2(g) = 3S(g) + 2H_2O(g) \qquad (ii)$$

Based on residence time and kinetic considerations, 60% of H_2S in the feed to the reaction furnace is converted to elemental sulphur. The gas mixture leaves the reaction furnace at 1100°C (1373 K) and exchanges heat in the waste heat boiler (WHB) to generate saturated (HP) steam at 70 bar a. The cooled gas mixture at 450°C (723 K) leaves WHB and enters sulphur condenser (SC) where it cools down to 170°C (443 K) by exchanging heat with bolier feed water (BFW). At 170°C (443 K), vapour pressure of sulphur is quite low and hence assume nearly complete condensation of sulphur which is drained as liquid elemental sulphur from SC. The gas mixture leaves SC at 0.1 bar g.

The gas mixture, free of sulphur, is further reacted in a battery of 3 catalytic converters to complete conversion (100%) of H_2S of the feed gas to the reaction furnace.

(a) Based on a total flow rate of 100 kmol/h of dry acid gas, make material and energy balances of the modified Claus plant. Calculate the flow rate of natural gas, required to be fired in the burner.

(b) In order to reduce the consumption of supporting (natural gas) fuel, it is considered to heat incoming combustion air to 250°C (523 K) with the help of HP steam. With this option, calculate the flow rate of natural gas requirement in the burner.

Data

(i) Boiling point of sulphur at atmospheric pressure, $t_B/T_B = 444.7°C /717.85$ K

(ii) Latent heat of vaporization of sulphur $\lambda_v = 45.35$ kJ/mol S

(iii) Heat capacity of liquid sulphur, $C_l = 34$ kJ/(kmol · K)

(v) Humidity of combustion air, $H_a = 0.02$ kmol/kmol dry air

NG requirement for (a) 163.95 kmol/h (b) 141.06 kmol/h

8.29 Contaminated process water from a desalter in a petroleum refinery contains various hydrocarbons such as benzene, ethylbenzene, toluene, xylenes, (BETX), etc., as pollutants. Such an effluent, containing volatile organic compounds (VOCs) is not permitted to be discharged without proper treatment.

From a typical refinery[40], flow rate of waster water is 120 m³/h containing 200 mg/L VOCs (consider as benzene). Figure 8.29 is the process flow diagram of the treatment facility.

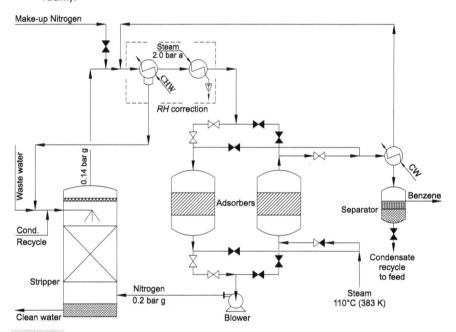

Fig. 8.29 Treatment Facility for Waste Water from a Refinery

Waster water is stripped with nitrogen which is introduced at 0.2 bar g and 50°C (323 K) at the rate of 3400 m³/h. Stripped waste water contains negligible benzene (< 0.5 mg/L). Saturated nitrogen stream, containing benzene vapour, leaves the stripper at 0.14 bar g and 50°C (323 K). This stream cannot be introduced to an adsorber as high moisture will not allow adsorption of benzene. Therefore, the stream is first chilled with chilled water at 5°C (278 K) and then reheated to 45°C (318 K) such that its RH is 40%. Water condensed in the chiller is recycled to the feed waste water stream. Nitrogen stream leaves the chiller and heater at 0.13 and 0.12 bar g, respectively.

Two adsorbers are provided for adsorption of benzene from the nitrogen stream. One adsorber is in service for 8 hours while another is being regenerated. Due to exothermic heat of adsorption, nitrogen leaves the adosorber at 50°C (323 K) containing 20 ppm (v/v) benzene. Purified nitrogen stream is recycled to the stripper via a blower.

After the service period of 8 hours, the bed is isolated for regeneration. Slightly superheated steam [at about ≈ 110°C (383 K)] is introduced in countercurrent direction at the rate of 700 kg/h. Desorption is completed in 4 hours at a uniform rate. The mixture of steam and benzene is taken to a condenser where both are condensed and cooled to 45°C (318 K) with the help of cooling water. Non-condensables (essentially nitrogen) are recycled and introduced with nitrogen stream from the stripper. Liquid mixture from the condenser is taken to a phase separator in which benzene and water separate in two layers. While benzene is recovered from the top, contaminated water layer is recycled for reprocessing along with waste water.

Make material and energy balance of the complete treatment facility and calculate the heat transfer duties of the chiller, heater and condenser.

Heat transfer duties of Chiller: 188.1 kW (53.52 TR), Heater: 21.6 kW and Condenser: 490.3 kW

8.30 Acetic acid is manufactured by carbonylation of methanol by following reaction.

$$CH_3OH(l) + CO(g) = CH_3COOH(l)$$

Continous reaction is carried out at 180°C (453.15 K) and 50 atm in pressence of methyl iodide as a catalyst. Composition of liquid within the reactor remains uniform throughout and does not change with time. The liquid within the reactor contains 85% methanol and 15% acetic acid (by mole). The gas mixture leaves from the top of the reactor which contains 65 kmol/h of carbon monoxide and 35 kmol/h of hydrogen and are accompanied by vapours of acetic acid and methanol. Calculate the flow rate of organic vapours in the real gas mixture (i.e., non-ideal behaviour of gas mixture) and in ideal gas mixture..

Data: Vapour pressures of acetic acid and methanol at 180°C (453.15 K) are 5 bar and 27 bar, respectively.

Acentric factor (ω_i) for acetic acid and methanol are 0.467 and 0564, respectively.

Hint Equations (8.1) and (8.2) can be used to calculate molar flow rates of real gas-vapour mixtures.

[**Non-ideal gas mixture: acetic acid: 7.43 kmol/h and methanol: 124.7 kmol/h Ideal gas mixture: acetic acid: 2.78 kmol/h and methanol: 85.12 kmol/h**]

References

1. Project Report No. EPA-600/2-76-047 (March 1996) by U. S. Environmental Protection Agency (EPA), Washington D.C., USA.

2. IS: 269-1989, *Specifications for Ordinary Portland Cement, 33 Grade,* Bureau of Indian Standards, New Delhi.

3. Lewis, W K, Radasch, A H and Lewis, H C; *Industrial Stoichiometry,* 2nd Ed., McGraw-Hill, USA, 1954, p. 258.

4. Akiyama, S, Hisamoto, T, Takada and Nochizuki, S; *Catalytic Conversions of Methanol to Chloromethanes in catalytic Conversions of Synthesis Gas and Alcholos to Chemicals,* Ed. by R. G. Herman, Plenum Press, USA, 1983, p. 419.

5. Bhatt, B I, *Design Data Book: Properties of Stream, Selected Refrigerants, n-Hexane and Brines,* CBS Publishers & Distributors, New Delhi, 2007.

6. Pátek, J and Klomfar J, *Int. J. Refrig.,* **18**(4), 1995, p. 226.

7. Madhawa Hettiarachchi, H D, Golubovic, M., Worek, W W and Ikegami, Y, *J. Energy Resources Tech.,* **129**, Sept. 2007, p. 243.

8. *The Oil and Gas J.,* **76**(30): July 24, 1978. p. 46.

9. Frith, J F S; *Energy Technology Handbook*, Edited by D.M. Considine, McGraw-Hill, USA, 1977, p. 1–232.

10. Vogt, G A and Wolters, M J; *Chem. Engg. Progr.*, **72** (5): 1976, p. 62.

11. Brinsko, J A; *Hydrocarbon Processing*, **57**(11): 1978, p. 227.

12. Matas-Valiente, P *Chem. Engg.*, **107**(12), 2000, p. 70.

13. Al-Jarallah, A M and Lee, A K K; *Hydrocarbon Processing*, **67**(7): 1988, p. 51

14. Pelzman, A; *Synthesis Gas to Formic Acid via Methanol Carbonylation in Catalytic Converison of Synthesis Gas and Alcohols to Chemicals*, Ed. bny R. G. Heman, Plenum Press, USA, 1983, p. 258.

15. Smith, J M; Van Ness, H C; Abbott, M M; and Bhatt, B I; *Introduction to Chemical Enginerring Thermodynamics*, 7th Edition, Mc Graw-Hill Education (India), 2010, p. 545.

16. Green, D W and Perry, R H; *Perry's Chemical Engineers' Handbook*, 8th edition, McGraw-Hill Education, USA, 2008.

17. Abu-Elshah, S. I. and Luyben, W L; *Ind. Engg. Chem. Process Des. Dev.*, **24**, 1985, p. 132.

18. Glew, D N and Watts, H; *Can. J. Chem.*, **51**, 1971, p. 1933.

19. Comstock, C S and Didge, B F; *Ind. Engg. Chem.*, **29**(5): 1937, p. 520.

20. Austin, G T; *Shreve's Chemical Process Industries*, 5th Edition, McGraw-Hill, USA, 1984, p. 696.

21. Sabadra, P N and Therat, K K *Treatment and Optimization of Process Waters - A paper presented at the Seminar on Water Management in Process Industries, organized by the Indian Institute of Chemical Engineers, New Delhi, 1977.*

22. Dean, J A; *Lange's Handbook of Chemistry*, 14th Ed., McGraw-Hill, USA, 1992, p. 5.135 – 5.141.

23. Cordiner, J B and Bull, H L; *Low Temperature Waste Solidification in Environmental Engineering*, Edited by G. Lindner and K Nyberg, D Reidel Publishing Co., Holland, 1973, p. 413.

24. Kobe, K A and Hellwig, K C; *Ind. Engg. Chem.*, **47**(6): 1955, p. 1120.

25. Horner, C, Winger, A G, Bodamer, G W, and Kunin, R K; *Ind. Engg. Chem.*, **46**(6): 1955, p. 1121.

26. Strelzoff, S, and Pan, L C; *Synthetic Ammonia*, Chemical Construction Corporation, USA, p. 9.

27. *Catalyst Handbook*, Springer-Verlag, New York, USA, 1970.

28. Sander, U and Daradimos, G; *Chem. Engg. Progress*, **74**(9): 1978. p. 57.

29. *AIChE Student Contest Problem 1967.*

30. Mehta, D W; *Hydrocarbon Processing*, **51**(6), 1972, p. 121.

31. Hess, D. and Rossi, R A; *Chem. Engg. Progress*, **79**(14), 1983 p. 43.

32. *Chem. Engg.* **113**(9), 2006, p. 13.

33. *NIST Standard Reference Database 23*, (RFFPROP), Ver. 8, National Instistute of Standards and Technology (NIST), USA, 2007.

34. Horwitz, B A; *Chem. Engg.*, **90**(13), June 27. 1983, p. 68.

35. Angus, S., B. Armstrong and K. M. de reuck, *Chlorine, International Thermodynamic Tables of the Fluid State – 8*, IUPAC Chemical Data Series No. 31, Pergamon Press, UK, 1988.

36. Venkateswara, K and Raviprasad, A; *Chem, Engg.*, **94**(14), Oct. 12. 1987, p. 137.

37. *Chem. Engg.*, 110 (2), p. 15.

38. Private communication with Radici Chimica S. P. A., Italy.

39. Chen, J K and Wong, V W; *Chem. Engg.*, **109**(9), Sept., 2002, p. 66.

40. Worall, M and Zuber, I; *Control of VOCS in Refinery Wastewater*, a paper presented at the Process Optimization Conference at Houston, USA, March 1998.

CHAPTER 9

Stoichiometry and Digital Computation

In the rapidly-growing technology of this modern world, computers play a key role in analyzing complex problems using sophisticated mathematics. The use of a variety of computers for research and problem-solving, both in industry and education, has increased dramatically in the last three decades. In addition, the accelerating growth of personal computers (PCs) has further increased the role of digital computation in routine process engineering work. This chapter briefly introduces the applications of computers in stoichiometry. This is illustrated by using some selected examples from previous chapters.

9.1 APPLICATION/JUSTIFICATION

Process engineers use computers in routine and special jobs for a variety of reasons:

(a) To minimize time for performing repetitive calculations and time-consuming data analyses, e.g., (i) performing battery limit material and energy balances to determine yields and to identify losses, and (ii) computing detailed balances for equipment characterization and to identify instrument malfunction by comparing the computer results with plant measurements and laboratory analysis

(b) To increase the accuracy and reliability of engineering calculations with improved handling of the complex process flow system, e.g., (i) solving atmospheric dispersion models to analyze the effect of particulate stack emission(s) on the plant surroundings, (ii) establishing a control philosophy for multi-feed/product distillation columns, reactors, etc.

(c) To provide a valuable predictive tool (model) for process evaluation, e.g., (i) optimizing the process design by simulation or defining optimum operating conditions to attain maximum benefit of multi-process variable systems, (ii) computing vapour–liquid equilibria for mixtures to predict and simulate separation/distillation column behaviour, (iii) evaluating process equipment, such as reboilers, condensers, etc., and (iv) modeling and designing CSTR, batch, and other reactors

In using computers, a deep understanding of the theories and principles are needed to solve the (complex) problems. One also must be able to state the problem correctly and estimate the expected answers to confirm the validity of the algorithm. Although the knowledge of programming languages is valuable, a number of software packages are available which are user-friendly and require little skill to use them for various tasks of process engineering.

9.2 ANALOG COMPUTATION *VS* DIGITAL COMPUTATION

This chapter mainly deals with digital computation of stoichiometric problems. However, a comparison between analog and digital computers seems very appropriate. An analog computer uses a continuous variable of electricity, namely, a *dc voltage* to represent continuous variables, such as fluid flow, temperatures, compositions, velocities, volumes, pressures, etc. The main advantages of analog system include the following: (a) it is a continuous system and it simulates parameters by actual measurement, (b) it can perform integration and differentiation in addition to the four basic arithmetic functions of addition, subtraction, multiplication and division, and (c) it can handle parallel modes of operation and can therefore be operated on a real-time basis. The use of analog machine requires lengthy set-up time due to voltage and time scaling and patching of wires. The probability of errors in patching and component malfunctions is significant. Also, the accuracy of results is limited.

All these problems are practically eliminated in a digital computer which is a discrete machine, simulating continuous parameters with frequent sampling/counting. All integrations and differentiations must be done numerically which involve approximating continuous differential equations with a discrete finite-difference equation. The selection of the algorithm is a key in solving/simulating the problem. Despite these minor problems, the digital computer is more powerful because of its capability in logical functionality and memory. The digital computers are also superior with regard to flexibility of operation and precision of calculations. Some of the functions cannot conveniently be accomplished with analog computers but they can be performed using digital machines. Particularly in process control, these unique functions include feed forward and cascade controls, non-interacting multi-variables, compensation of process variables, online and automatic tuning, automatic start-up and shutdown, and optimal control.

When a digital computer is used, it is unusual to obtain the correct solution to an engineering problem in the first trial. At the same time, a variety of *canned* (library) computer programs are widely available for solving specific problems and they simplify the use of computers.

9.3 USE OF PROGRAMMABLE CALCULATORS

Since 1859, the slide rule has been a handy calculating tool for scientists and engineers. But it had been replaced by an electronic marvel—the calculator which incorporates a solid circuit. The emergence of hand-held programmable calculators permitted the engineer to solve effortlessly all his complex problems elegantly at his desk that were formerly relegated to full-scale computer solution.

In a keystroke programmable calculator, the program is introduced with the help of keystrokes. Having programmed, data can be fed in with the help of keys and the calculator runs the entire computations at a single keystroke. In a fully programmable calculator, complex problems are permanently stored on small magnetic cards or magnetic tapes and used in the calculator over and over again.

Rapier[1] has given an excellent introduction to calculators. Benenati[2,3] has given examples to demonstrate the capabilities of programmable calculators in solving complex chemical engineering problems.

Certain limitations of the programmable calculators may be worth mentioning here. The memory storage is usually limited in such a calculator. However, such a limitation can be overcome to a certain extent by connecting an additional memory pack to the calculator. Also, the calculator gives only the final answer. If this answer is incorrect, it is difficult to find the step where calculations went wrong. If a printer is attached with the calculator and if certain intermediate answers are also printed on it, it may become possible to check the wrong step. Properties of chemical compounds can be fed in the form of an empirical equation in the calculator. Data in the tabular form occupy a large memory storage and hence when tabular data are to be used for substitution, a computer may be needed. Nevertheless, the emergence of programmable calculators increased the ability of an engineer to a great extent.

9.4 PROGRAMMING LANGUAGES

A program is the set of instructions and logic used by a computer to perform a specific task correctly. Therefore, a programming language is the method of communication between man and machine. There are many languages in use and each of them has its own operational limitations. Among engineers, originally developed in the 1950s for technical applications, FORTRAN (FORmula TRANslator) was the universal language being used for problem-solving and process simulation. Of its versions, the FORTRAN IV was the most versatile language through the mid-70s.

American National Standards Institution (ANSI) had published an improved set of standards in 1977, the FORTRAN X 3.9-1978 or FORTRAN 77. Etter[4] has summarized a variety of real-world applications using these revised standards, which include new features and structures to write more versatile and powerful programs. Another improved version, FORTRAN 90, (ANSI X3.198-1991, identical to International FORTRAN Standards, (ISO/IEC 1539:1991) has been established making the language ever stronger for its use in technical applications.

FORTRAN 90 includes several significant additions to its special character sets that can be used for special purposes and also includes symbols for mathematics, chemistry, etc.

9.5 GENERAL PROCEDURE

A proper approach must be followed for an effective and efficient use of computers. A general procedure described below may be used as a guideline.

1. Define the problem clearly with the input (available) and output (desired to be calculated) data.
2. Develop the algorithm (logic) considering all principles and details.
3. Draw a flow chart, a pictorial step-by-step description of the input data, algorithm, and the output data.
4. Write the computer program or select an appropriate canned program (software).
5. Debug and confirm the validity of the program.
6. Use the program for solving the defined problem.

In the following presentation, some of the important and useful numerical methods[5-10] are introduced in order of increasing complexity. For simulating more complicated and highly complex systems, the reader should refer to advanced books and literature references in related fields.

A combination of FORTRAN 77 and IV standards, spreadsheet software (Microsoft Excel©) and Mathcad software are used throughout this text.

9.6 APPLICATIONS OF FORTRAN

9.6.1 Roots of Equations

One common problem in digital computation is the solution of algebraic and transcendental equations. When these equations are complex or nonlinear, analytical solutions are not practical and then an iterative trial-and-error method is used. An initial value is assumed and used as a trial solution. If the first trial is not sufficiently accurate, a second is generated and the whole process is repeated until the iteration converges within some desired tolerance limit.

A variety of techniques can be used for the initial guess and subsequent new guesses to rapidly arrive at the correct answer. The selection of the technique depends upon the nature of the equations. Sometimes, numerical instability is experienced such that the solution diverges or oscillates around the correct solution.

The computer solution to an algebraic equation can best be illustrated by using some stoichiometric examples. As discussed in Chapter 2, the van der Waals equation accounts for non-ideal behaviour of gases. This equation [Eq. (2.25)], which is of third order cannot be easily solved. Two different computation techniques for solving this equation are introduced in the following illustration.

Example 9.1 Generate a computer solution to Example 2.24(b) by (a) trial-and-error and (b) Newton–Raphson methods.

Solution In this example it is proposed to calculate the specific volume of superheated steam at 10 MPa a (100 bar a) and 350°C (623 K) using the van der Waals equations of state.

$$(p + a/V^2) (V - b) = RT \tag{2.25}$$

where, $\quad a = 27R^2T_c^2/64p_c \ (\text{m}^3)^2 \cdot \text{MPa} /(\text{kmol})^2 \tag{2.26}$

$\quad b = RT_c /8p_c \ \text{m}^3/\text{kmol} \tag{2.27}$

(a) Trial-and-Error Method

Rearranging Eq. (2.25),

$$F(V) = V - \frac{RT}{\left(p + \dfrac{a}{V^2}\right)} - b = 0 \tag{9.1}$$

Calculate V such that $F(V) = 0$. The constants and conditions are known. At random, the initial value of V is selected as 0.1; it is also the initial increment to be added or subtracted from V for successive guesses. The increment ΔV is reduced depending upon the value of the function $F(V)$. The iterations are continued until $F(V)$ is within some desired tolerance. Also, calculations are discontinued if they exceed some pre-set number of iterations; this is done to check for and avoid diverging or oscillating instability. In such a case, this successive guess technique will be unsuccessful and must be changed.

The flow chart for this example is shown in Fig. 9.1 and the FORTRAN names of the variables are given in Table 9.1.

Table 9.1 FORTRAN Names of Variables

FORTRAN Names	Variables	Values
R	R	0.008 314
TC	T_c	674.11
PC	p_c	22.076
T	T	623.0
P	p	10.0
V	V	—
WM	M	18.015
TOL	e	0.000 01
DV	ΔV	0.1 (initially)
A	a	—
B	b	—
FV	$F(V)$	—
SV	v	—

A digital computer program and the solution are shown in Figs. 9.2 and 9.3, respectively.

(b) Newton–Raphson Method

Rearranging the equation in polynomial form,

$$F(V) = pV^3 - (bp + RT)V^2 + aV - ab$$

As discussed earlier in Chapter 2, this method requires the evaluation of the first derivative.

$$F'(V) = 3pV^2 - 2(bp + RT)V + a$$

Subsequent guesses are based on the slope of this function which can be illustrated as

$$V_{n+1} = V_n - F(V_n)/F'(V_n) \tag{2.45}$$

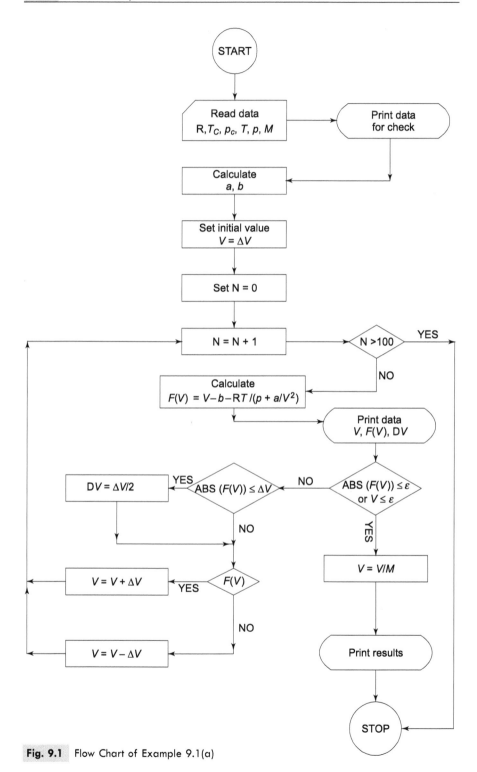

Fig. 9.1 Flow Chart of Example 9.1(a)

```
C    EXAMPLE 9.1 (A)
C
C    THIS PROGRAMME SOLVES VAN DER WAAL'S EQUATION
C
C    READ CONSTANTS

     READ(5,*)R,TC,PC,T,P,WM,TOL,DV
     WRITE(6,12)R,TC,PC,T,P,WM,TOL,DV
  12 FORMAT(9X,'DATA INPUT'/9X,'R=',F10.4,5X,'TC=',F10.4,5X,'PC='
  1  10.4/9X,'T=',F10.4,5X,'P=',F10.4,5X'WM=',F10.4/9X,'TOL=',
  2  F10.5,5X,'DV=',F10.4////14X,'SOLUTION BY TRIAL AND ERROR......'/
  3  17X,'V',13X,'FV',13X,'DV')
     WRITE(*,*) "PRESS ANY KEY TO CONTINUE"
     A=(27. * (R*TC)**2.)/(64. * PC)
     B=R*TC/(8. * PC)
     V=DV
     N=O
  5  N=N+1
     IF (N .GT. 100) STOP
     FV=V-R*T/(P+A/(V**2.))-B
     WRITE(6,13) V,FV,DV
  13 FORMAT(5X,3(5X,F10.5))
     IF(ABS(FV) .LE. TOL .OR. DV .LE. TOL) GOTO 6
     IF(ABS(FV) .LE. DV) DV=DV/2
     IF(FV .LT. 0.) V= V+DV
     IF(FV .GT. 0.) V= V-DV
     GOTO 5
  6  SV=V/WM
C
C    PRINT RESULTS
C
     WRITE(6,14)SV
  14 FORMAT(//10X, 'SPECIFIC VOLUME = ',F10.5,2X,'M3/KG')
     END
```

Fig. 9.2 Computer Program for Trial and Error Solution of van der Waals Equation

To minimize the number of iterations, an initial guess is made using the ideal gas law,

$$V_0 = RT/p \qquad (2.22)$$

The flow for this method is given in Fig. 9.4 and the corresponding program and solution are listed in Figs. 9.5 and 9.6, respectively. The computations are discontinued when the value of $Y = -F(V_n)/F'(V_n)$ is within some desired tolerance. Values for each iterative calculation are printed for illustration only. Normally, either the final answer or an error message, such as 'too many iterations,' etc., is printed. The FORTRAN names for variables are self-explanatory and, therefore, are not listed separately.

Several other methods used to find roots of the equation are listed below. More details about these methods can be found in the appropriate literature.

(a) Half-interval or bisection method This converges slowly but will result in a definite solution. It is a reliable method.

(b) Regular false method This is also a sure method and has a better convergence than the bisection method.

```
DATA INPUT
R  =  .0083  TC  =  647.1100  PC  =  22.0760
T  =  623.0000  P  =  10.0000  WM  =  18.0150
TOL=  .00001  DV  =  .1000


          SOLUTION  BY  TRIAL  AND  ERROR......
             V              FV             DV
          .10000         -.00977         .10000
          .17500         -.04004         .02500
          .20000         -.04783         .02500
          .22500         -.05298         .02500
          .25000         -.05524         .02500
          .27500         -.05462         .02500
          .30000         -.05126         .02500
          .32500         -.04540         .02500
          .35000         -.03730         .02500
          .37500         -.02720         .02500
          .40000         -.01536         .02500
          .41250         -.00885         .01250
          .41875         -.00547         .00625
          .42188         -.00374         .00313
          .42500         -.00199         .00313
          .42656         -.00111         .00156
          .42734         -.00067         .00078
          .42773         -.00045         .00039
          .42813         -.00022         .00039
          .42832         -.00011         .00020
          .42842         -.00006         .00010
          .42847         -.00003         .00005
          .42849         -.00002         .00002
          .42850         -.00001         .00001


      SPECIFIC  VOLUME  =  .02379  M3/KG
```

Fig. 9.3 Computer Output for Example 9.1(a)

(c) *Secant method* This method will converge fast, if at all the solution converges. However, in some highly non-linar functions, it can diverge.

(d) *Newton's second-order method* It includes the second-order derivative of the function which makes it different from the Newton–Raphson method. It is not a sure method but has a faster convergence.

(e) *Graeffe's root squaring method* It is for both real and complex roots of higher degree polynominals. It is a sure method and the rate of convergence depends on the coefficients.

9.6.2 Simultaneous Linear Equations

In real life, process/production engineers frequently deal with multi-component processes, and in turn routine process equations require the solving of simultaneous linear algebraic equations. Such evaluations include (a) determining the performance of distillation column, (b) calculating the battery limit material and energy balances, (c) rating heat exchangers, etc.

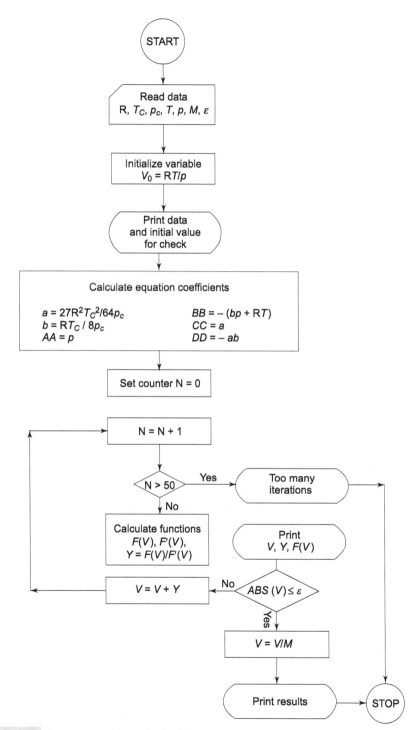

Fig. 9.4 Flow Chart of Example 9.1(b)

```
C        EXAMPLE 9.1 (B)
C
C        THIS PROGRAMME SOLVES VAN DER WAAL'S EQUATION
C        FOR V-VOLUME USING NEWTON-RAPHSON METHOD
C
C        READ DATA INPUT AND CALCULATE VO BY IDEAL GAS LAW

         READ(5,*)R,TC,PC,T,P,WM,TOL
         VO=R*T/P
C
C        CHECK DATA INPUT
C
         WRITE(6,51)R,TC,PC,T,P,VO,TOL,WM
      51 FORMAT(9X,'DATA INPUT FOR VAN DER WAALS EQUATION'/9X,'R =',
      1  F10.4/9X, 'TC =',F10.4/9X, 'PC='10.4/9X,'T=',F10.4/,
      2  9X,'P=',F10.4/9X,'VO=',F10.4/9X,'TO=',F10.6/9X,
      3  'WM=',F10.4///// 2X, 'SOLUTION BY NEWTON-RAPHSON.... ')
C
C        CALCULATE CONSTANTS
C
         A =(27. * (R*TC)**2.)/(64. * PC)
         B =R*TC/(8. * PC)
         AA =P
         BB=-(B*P+R*T)
         CC=A
         DD=-A*B
         Y=0.
         VN=VO
         WRITE(6,52) VN,Y
      52 FORMAT(//16X,'VN',14X,'Y',14X,'FN'//10X,F10.5,5X,F10.5)
         N=O
      12 N=N+1
         IF (N.GE.50) STOP
C
C        CALCULATE FUNCTION AND FIRST DERIVATIVE
C
         FN=AA*VN**3.+BB*VN**2.+CC*VN+DD
         FDN=3.*AA*VN**2.+2.*BB*VN+CC
         Y=-FN/FDN
         WRITE(6,53) VN,Y,FN
         IF(ABS(Y) .LE.TOL) GOTO50
         VN=VN+Y
         GOTO12
      50 SVN=VN/WM
C
C        PRINT RESULTS
C
         WRITE (6,54) SVN,Y
      53 FORMAT(5X,3(5X,F10.5))
      54 FORMAT(//10X, 'SPECIFIC VOLUME =',F10.5,2X, 'M3/KG',5X,
      1  'TOLERANCE=',E12.5)
         END
```

Fig. 9.5   Computer Program for Newton–Raphson Solution of van der Waals Equation

```
DATA INPUT FOR VAN DER WAALS EQUATION

R        =         .0083
TC       =      647.1100
PC       =       22.0760
T        =      623.0000
P        =       10.0000
VO       =         .5180
TO       =         .000010
WM       =       18.0150

SOLUTION BY NEWTON-RAPHSON....

VN              Y              FN
.51796        .00000
.51796       -.06435         .18793
.45361       -.02226         .03897
.43135       -.00279         .00392
.42856       -.00004         .00006
.42852        .00000         .00000

SPECIFIC VOLUME = .02379 M3/KG TOLERANCE = -.12037E-06
```

Fig. 9.6   Computer Output of Example 9.1 (b)

The number of equations must be equal to the number of unknowns. All of these equations need to be independent for obtaining unique solutions. In general,

$$a_{11} X_1 + a_{12} X_2 + \ldots + a_{1n} X_n = C_1$$

$$a_{21} X_1 + a_{22} X_2 + \ldots + a_{2n} X_n = C_2$$

$$\vdots \quad \vdots \quad \vdots \quad \vdots \quad \vdots$$

$$a_{n1} X_1 + a_{n2} X_2 + \ldots + a_{nn} X_n = C_n \qquad (9.2)$$

There are six simultaneous equations and six unknowns. These equations can be solved by using the flow chart given in Fig. 9.7, and program, given in Fig. 9.8. Computer output is given in Fig. 9.9.

If all Cs are zero, the set is considered homogeneous; otherwise, the set is non-homogeneous.

Example 9.2   Solve Example 8.7 with the help of FORTRAN using the Gauss–Jordan elimination method.

Solution

$$a = 5.480 \text{ t/h} \qquad b = 3.762 \text{ t/h}$$
$$c = 4.964 \text{ t/h} \qquad d = 2.164 \text{ t/h}$$
$$e = 29.55 \text{ t/h} \qquad g = 10.43 \text{ t/h}$$

Other methods used to solve simultaneous linear algebraic equations are listed below and related literature should be referred for detailed explanation and applications [5, 6, 7,11].

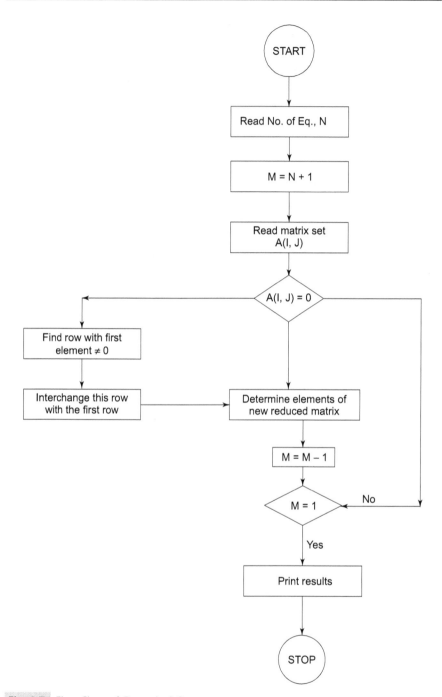

Fig. 9.7 Flow Chart of Example 9.2

```
C      EXAMPLE 9.2
C
C      THIS PROGRAMME SOLVES SIMULTANEOUS EQUATIONS
C      BY GAUSS-JORDAN ELIMINATION METHOS
C      ALLOCATE MATRIX
C
       DIMENSION A(10,11) B(10,10)
C
C      READ NO. OF EQUATIONS AND THEN MATRIX ELEMENTS BY ROW. .
C
       READ(5,*) N
       M=N+1
       DO 10 I=1,N
   10  READ(5,*)(A(I,J),J=1,M)
C      DATA CHECK
C
       WRITE(6,103)N,M
  103  FORMAT(////5X,'INPUT DATA.....'//11X,'NO. OF EQUATIONS
      =',I3,5X,1'M =' I3///)
       DO 20 I=1,N
   20  WRITE(6,104) (A(I,J),J=1,M)
  104  FORMAT(5X,8E12.4)
C      CHECK FOR FIRST ZERO ELEMENT
C
       EPS=.0000001
    9  AA=ABS(A(1,1)
       IF(AA .GT. EPS)GOTO 51
       MM=M-1
       DO 30 I=2,MM
       AB=ABS(A(I,1))
       IF(AB .LE. EPS)GOTO 30
       DO 40 J=1,M
       TEMP=A(I,J)
       A(I,J)=A(1,J)
   40  A(1,J)=TEMP
       GOTO51
   30  CONTINUE
       WRITE(6,105)
  105  FORMAT(//'.....ERROR..... -NO UNIQUE SOLUTION')
       STOP
C
   51  DO 50 J=2,M
       DO 50 I=2,N
   50  B(I-1,J-1)=A(I,J)-A(1,J)*A(I,1)/A(1,1)
       DO 60 J=2,M
   60  B(N,J-1)=A(I,J)/A(1,1)
       M=M-1
       DO 70 J=1,M
       DO 70 I=1,N
       IF (ABS(B(I,J)) .LE. 0.0001) B(I,J)=0
   70  A(I,J)=B(I,J)
       IF((M-1) .NE. 0) GOTO 9
       WRITE(6,106)
  106  FORMAT(///15X,'SOLUTION FOR SIMULTANEOUS EQUATIONS.....'/)
       DO 80 I=1,N
   80  WRITE(6,107)I,(A(I,1))
  107  FORMAT(15X,'X(',I2,') =',E12.4/)
       END
```

Fig. 9.8 Computer Program for Solving Simultaneous Equations using Gauss–Jordan Elimination Method

```
INPUT DATA......

NO. OF EQUATIONS = 6M = 7

-.1000E+01   .0000E+00   .1022E+01   .1022E+01   .1211E+01   .0000E+00   .1350E+02
 .1000E+01  -.1100E+00   .0000E+00   .0000E+00   .0000E+00   .1100E+00  -.1815E+01
 .0000E+00   .5160E+01   .5160E+01   .5160E+01   .5160E+01   .2179E+02   .7540E+03
 .0000E+00  -.4037E+01  -.4037E+01   .9600E+02  -.4037E+01  -.4037E+01   .1106E+02
 .8977E+01   .8977E+01  -.1000E+03   .0000E+00   .0000E+00   .8977E+01  -.1481E+03
 .0000E+00   .9109E+01   .0000E+00   .0000E+00   .0000E+00  -.8403E+00   .9358E+01

SOLUTION FOR SIMULTANEOUS EQUATIONS ....

    X( 1)  =  .5480E+01
    X( 2)  =  .3762E+01
    X( 3)  =  .4964E+01
    X( 4)  =  .2164E+01
    X( 5)  =  .1043E+02
    X( 6)  =  .2955E+02
```

Fig. 9.9   Computer Output for Example 9.2

1. Matrix-inversion method
2. Gaussian elimination method
3. Jacobi-iteration method
4. Gauss-Seidel iteration method

9.6.3   Numerical Integration and Differentiation

Process engineers are often required to solve problems which are best described with integration or differentiating functions. Various numerical methods can be used to obtain a higher degree of accuracy. One of these is introduced in Example 9.3 with stoichiometric application.

Example 9.3   Pure ethylene is heated from 30°C to 250°C (303 K to 523 K) at a constant pressure. Generate a computer solution to calculate the heat added per kmol of ethylene using the following two equations.

(a) $C_{mp}^\circ = 11.8486 + 119.7 \times 10^{-3} T - 365 \times 10^{-7} T^2$

(b) $C_{mp}^\circ = 51.012 + 16.24 \times 10^{-3} T - (10.806 \times 10^5)/T^2$

where C_{mp}° is in kJ /(kmol · K) and T is in K.

Solution

$$Q = \int_{T_1}^{T_2} C_{mp}^\circ \, dT$$

$$= \frac{\Delta T}{3} \left(C_{mp1}^\circ + C_{mpn+1}^\circ \, 4 \sum_{j=2,4,6}^{n} C_{mpj}^\circ + 2 \sum_{j=3,5,7}^{n-1} C_{mpj}^\circ \right)$$

where $C_{mp1}^{\circ} = C_{mp}^{\circ}$ at T_1

$C_{mpn+1}^{\circ} = C_{mp}^{\circ}$ at T_2

$\Delta T = (T_2 - T_1)/n$

n = even number of intervals

$C_{mpj}^{\circ} = C_{mp}^{\circ}$ at T_j

$T_j = T_1 + (j - 1)\Delta T$

A flow chart to solve this equation is given in Fig. 9.10. The program and the results are shown in Figs. 9.11 and 9.12 (a) and (b), respectively.

(a) **Q = 12 083 kJ/kmol ethylene**

(b) **Q = 11 299 kJ/kmol ethylene**

The above problem can be conveniently solved by analytical integration but one may often face the situation in which tabulated data (such as steam tables) are to be utilized for integration. In such a situation, numerical integration with the help of a computer is valuable.

Other methods of numerical integration include

1. Trapezoid rule
2. Romberg method (extension of trapezoid rule)
3. Gauss quadrature (uses unequally spaced intervals)

For details of these methods, the reference is made to related literature in this field.[7–9].

9.6.4   Ordinary Differential Equations

A number of chemical engineering problems are described by a set of differential equations of order one or higher. Normally, equations describing a dynamic or transient process become highly non-linear when combined with chemical reaction(s). To solve such equations, a suitable numerical integration technique must be used for which an approximate solution of predetermined accuracy can be obtained. In the following example, initial value ordinary differential equations are solved by using the Runge–Kutta numerical technique. This method is one of the most popular methods and its derivation can be easily found in the literature.

Example 9.4   Consider a single continuous stirred tank reactor with a second-order irreversible exothermic reaction

$$2\,A \rightarrow B + C$$

The heat generated by the reaction is removed with cooling water being circulated in a jacket (ref. Fig. 9.13).

All related process conditions and parameter values are given below. Generate a computer solution for transient concentration of the reactant A when the feed is entering at the steady-state reaction temperature 87°C (360 K).

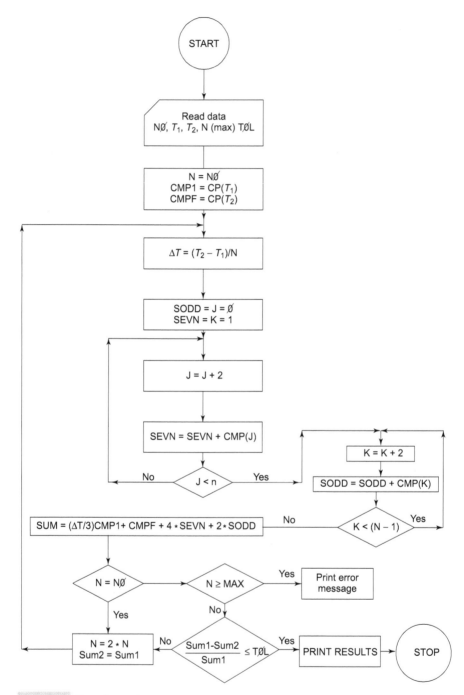

Fig. 9.10 Flow Chart of Example 9.3

```
C
C      EXAMPLE 9.5
C
C      PROGRAM SIMPSON'S RULE FOR INTEGRATION.....
C
C      READ CONSTANTS AND LIMITS
C
       READ (5,*)NO,NMAX,T1,T2,TOL,A,B,C,M
       WRITE(6,12) NO,NMAX,T1,T2,TOL,A,B,C,M
   12  FORMAT(///15X,'DATA INPUT:'//15X,'NO=I4,11X,'NMAX =',I5/15X,'T1
    1  =',E12.5,3X,'T2 =',E12.5,3X,'TOL =',E12.5///15X,'EQUATION...'/
       15X,
    2  'COP=',E12.5, ' + ',E12.5,'* T + ',E12.5,'* T **',I4//15X,
    3  'SOLUTION.....'//20X,'NN'M  7X,'N',9X,'ÉRROR',10X,'SUM1
       ',11X,'SUM2')
       CPI=A+B*T1+C*T1**M
       CPF=A+B*T2+C*T2**M
       N=NO
    5  DT=(T2-T1)/N
       NN=NN+1
       SODD=0
       SEVN=0
       J=0
       K=1
       KF=N-1
    6  J=J+2
       TJ=T1+J*DT
       CPJ=A+B*TJ+C*TJ**M
       SEVN=SEVN+CPJ
       IF(J.LT.N) GOTO6
    7  K=K+2
       TK=T1+K*DT
       CPK=A+B*TK+C*TK**M
       SODD=SODD+CPK
       IF(K.LT.KF)GOTO7
       SUM1=(DT/3.)*(CPI+CPF+4.*SEVN+2.*SODD)
       IF(N.W.NO)GOTO8
       IF(NNN.GE.20) GOTO9
       EROR=ABS((SUM1-SUM2)/SUM1)
       IF(EROR.LE.TOL) GOTO99
    8  WRITE(6,15) NN,N,EROR,SUM1,SUM2
   15  FORMAT(15X,I7,3X,I7,3X,E12.5,3X,E12.5,3X,E12.5)
       N=2*N
       SUM2=SUM1
       GOTO5
    9  WRITE(6,13)
   13  FORMAT(15X,'...TOO MANY INTERVALS....'/5X,'..CHECK DATA..'///)
   99  WRITE(6,15)NN,N,EROR,SUM1,SUM2
       WRITE(6,14)N,DT,CPI,CPF,EROR,SUM2
   14  FORMAT(///15X,'INTERVALS',5X,'=',I5,10X,'DT',10X, '=',E12.5/
       11.5X,'INITIAL VALUE =',E12.5,3X,'FINAL VALUE='E12.5/15X,
       2'ERROR= ',E12.5//15X, 'Q =',E12.5,2X, 'KCAL/KG MOL')
       END
```

Fig. 9.11 Computer Program for Integration of Polynomial Equation with the Help of Simpson's Rule

```
DATA INPUT
  NO = 4                  NAMX = 10000
  T₁ = .30300E+03    T₂ = .52300E+03    TOL = .10000E-03
```

EQUATION...
CPO = .11849E+02 + .114970E+00 * T + -.36500E-04 * T ** 2

SOLUTION.....

NN	N	ERROR	SUM1	SUM₂
1	4	.00000E+00	.12963E+05	.00000E+00
2	8	.31154E-01	.12572E+05	.12963E+05
3	16	.18877E-01	.12339E+05	.12572E+05
4	32	.10309E-01	.12213E+05	.12339E+05
5	64	.53780E-02	.12148E+05	.12213E+05
6	128	.27457E-02	.12114E+05	.12148E+05
7	256	.13871E-02	.12097E+05	.12114E+05
8	512	.69746E-03	.12089E+05	.12097E+05
9	1024	.34901E-03	.12085E+05	.12089E+05
10	2048	.17498E-03	.12083E+05	.12085E+05
11	4096	.87863E-04	.12082E+05	.12083E+05

```
       INTERVALS = 4096                          DT = .53711E-01
  INITIAL VALUE = .4476E+02         FINAL VALUE = .64468E+02
          ERROR = .87863E-04
              Q = .12083E+05 KJ/KMOL
```

Fig. 9.12(a)   Computer Output for Example 9.3(a)


```
DATA INPUT
  NO = 4                  NAMX = 10000
  T₁ = .30300E+03    T₂ = .52300E+03    TOL = .10000E-03
```

EQUATION...
CPO = .51012E+02 + .162400E-01 * T + -.10086E+07 * T ** -2

SOLUTION.....

NN	N	ERROR	SUM₁	SUM₂
1	4	.00000E+00	.11720E+05	.00000E+00
2	8	.14785E-01	.11549E+05	.11720E+05
3	16	.99945E-02	.11435E+05	.11549E+05
4	32	.57595E-02	.11370E+05	.11435E+05
5	64	.30873E-02	.11335E+05	.11370E+05
6	128	.15979E-02	.11316E+05	.12148E+05
7	256	.81296E-03	.11307E+05	.11335E+05
8	512	.40971E-03	.11303E+05	.11316E+05
9	1024	.20620E-03	.11300E+05	.11303E+05
10	2048	.10268E-03	.11299E+05	.11300E+05
11	4096	.51600E-04	.11299E+05	.11299E+05

```
       INTERVALS = 4096                          DT = .53711E-01
  INITIAL VALUE = .44947E+02        FINAL VALUE = .55818E+02
          ERROR = .51600E-04                      KJ/KMOL
              Q = .11299E+05
```

Fig. 9.12(b)   Computer Output for Example 9.3(b)

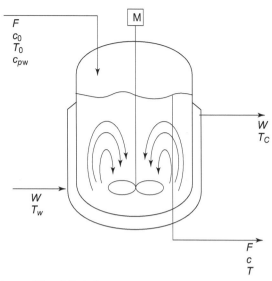

Fig. 9.13 Continuous Stirred Tank Reactor

V = reactor volume, 700 L
c_0 = concentration of reactant A in feed, 140 g/L
c = concentration of reactant A in product stream, g/L
r = reaction rate
$\quad = -k\,c^2$, g/(L · s)
k = reaction rate constant, 1.488×10^{-3} exp $(-1421/T)$, L/(g · s)
T = product stream temperature, K
T_∞ = steady–state reaction temperature, 360 K(87°C)
T_0 = feed temperature, 360 K(87°C)
T_w = cooling water supply temperature, 300 K(27°C)
T_c = cooling water return temperature, K
T_c' = average cooling water temperature $(T_w + T_c)/2$, K
θ = time, s
F = feed rate = 7.5 L/s
W = cooling water rate, g/s
ΔH = heat of reaction = 2100 J/g
ρ = reactant/product density at reaction temperature = 960 g/L
Cps = heat capacity of solution = 3.77 kJ(kg · K)
Cpw = heat capacity of cooling water = 4.1868 kJ/ (kg · K)
UA = heat transfer rate = 18 850 W/K

$$\begin{pmatrix} \text{Flow of} \\ \text{reactant in} \end{pmatrix} = \begin{pmatrix} \text{Flow of} \\ \text{reactant out} \end{pmatrix} - \begin{pmatrix} \text{Reactant} \\ \text{disappearance} \\ \text{by reaction} \end{pmatrix} - \begin{pmatrix} \text{Material} \\ \text{accumulation} \end{pmatrix}$$

$$Fc_0 = Fc - (kc^2)\,V = d(Vc)d\theta \tag{9.3}$$

where $\quad k = 1.488 \times 10^{-3}$ exp $(-1421/T)$
Rearranging the above equation,

$$dc/d\theta = (F/V)(c_0 - c) - kc^2$$

Assuming $T = 360$ K the above equation is solved for concentration c as function of time θ using the fourth-order Runge–Kutta method. The flow chart is given in Fig. 9.14. The computer program and the solution are given in Figs. 9.15 and 9.16 respectively. The transient behaviour is plotted in Fig. 9.17.

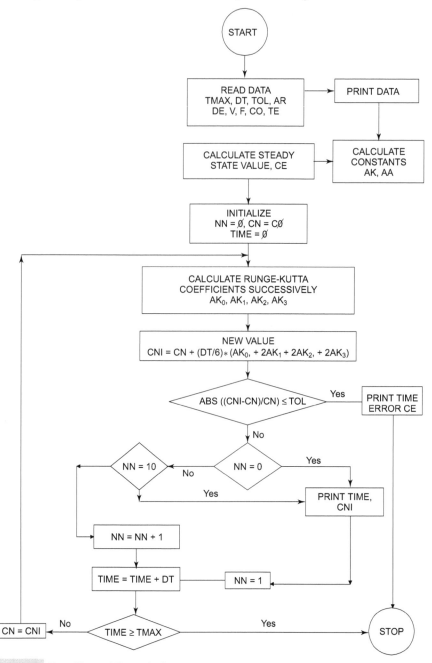

Fig. 9.14 Flow Chart of Example 9.4

```
C
C      EXAMPLE 9.4
C
C      PROGRAM RUNGE-KUTTA : 4TH- ORDER
C
C      READ DATA
C
       READ (5,*)TMAX,DT,TOL,AR,DE,V,F,CO,TE
       WRITE(6,12)TMAX,DT,TOL,AR,DE,V,F,CO,TE
    12 FORMAT(///15X,'DATA INPUT:'//15X,'TMAX =',E12.5,3X,'DT
       =',F10.2,
     1 5X,'TOL =',E12.5,/15X,'AR =',E12.5,3X,'DE =',E12.5/15X,
       'VOL =',
     2 E12.5,3X,'FEED =',E12.5/15X, 'CO =',E12.5,3X,'TE =',E12.5)
    14 FORMAT(///15X,'SOLUTION BY RUNGE-KUTTA.......'//16X,
       'T,SEC',9X,'CON 1CN'/)
       RK=AR*EXP(DE/TE)
       AA=F/V
       CE=(AA/(2. *RK)) * (-1. * (1. *4. *RK*CO/AA) ** 0.5)
       NN=0
       TIME=0
       CN=CO
       WRITE(6,101) TIME,CN
    10 CONTINUE
       AKO=AA * (CO-CN) -RK *CN**2
       AK1=AA * (CO-(CN+AKO/2.)) -RK*(CN+AKO/2.)**2.
       AK2=AA * (CO-(CN+AK1/2.)) -RK*(CN+AK1/2.)**2.
       AK3=AA * (CO-(CN+AK2)) -RK*(CN+AK2/2.)**2.
       CN1=CN+(DT/6.)*(AKO+2.*AK1+2.*AK2+AK3)
       EROR=ABS((CN1-CN)/CN)
       IF(EROR .LE. TOL) GOTO 99
       IF(NN .EQ. 10) GOTO 51
       NN=NN+1
       GOTO 52
    51 WRITE(6,101)TIME,CN1
   101 FORMAT(15X,F8.1,5X,E12.5)
       NN=1
    52 TIME=TIME+DT
       IF(TIME .GE. TMAX) STOP
       CN=CN1
       GOTO 10
    99 WRITE(6,101) TIME,CN1
       WRITE(6,102)EROR,CE,CN1
   102 FORMAT(//15X,'ERROR =',E12.5,5X,' EQUI. CONC.=',E12.5/39X, 'CONV.
       1CONCN. =',E12.5)
       END
```

Fig. 9.15 Computer Program for Evaluation of Transient Behaviour of CSTR

DATA INPUT :

TMAX = .10000E+06	DT = 10.00	TOL = .10000E-04
AR = .14880E-02	DE = -.14210E+04	
VOL = .70000E+04	FEED = .75000E+01	
CO = .14000E+03	TE = .36000E+03	

SOLTUION BY RUNGE-KUTTA.....

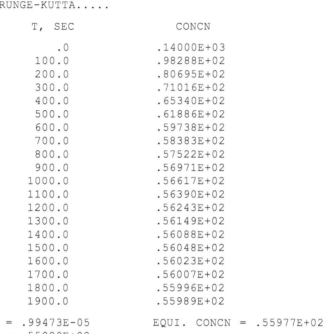

T, SEC	CONCN
.0	.14000E+03
100.0	.98288E+02
200.0	.80695E+02
300.0	.71016E+02
400.0	.65340E+02
500.0	.61886E+02
600.0	.59738E+02
700.0	.58383E+02
800.0	.57522E+02
900.0	.56971E+02
1000.0	.56617E+02
1100.0	.56390E+02
1200.0	.56243E+02
1300.0	.56149E+02
1400.0	.56088E+02
1500.0	.56048E+02
1600.0	.56023E+02
1700.0	.56007E+02
1800.0	.55996E+02
1900.0	.55989E+02

ERROR = .99473E-05	EQUI. CONCN = .55977E+02
CONV. CONCN = .55989E+02	

Fig. 9.16 Computer Output of Example 9.4

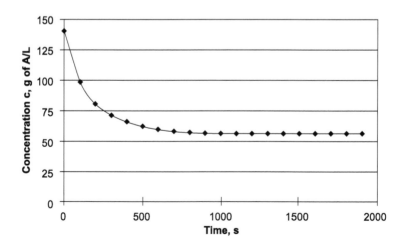

Fig. 9.17 Transient Solution of Example 9.4

Other methods used for solving initial value differential equations are listed below. Derivations and details of using these methods can be found in the literature.

1. Euler's method
2. Predictor-corrector method (Euler's modified, self-starting)
3. Runge–Kutta methods of different orders (first, second, third, sixth...) for solving single and simultaneous equations.
4. Milne's method
5. Hamming's method

The numerical solution of boundary-value problems is somewhat difficult. Mainly, shooting method[9], instead of the previously used trial-and-error method, is used to solve such problems. No further details are given in this book and the reader is advised to refer to the appropriate literature. Similarly, quite a few chemical engineering problems are described by partial differential equations[10]. These problems include calculation of partial molar enthalpies, and so on. Details about various numerical methods used for solving partial differential equations is beyond the scope of this book.

In Example 9.4, a simple case of CSTR is described. However, a complex problem will result when kinetics and thermodynamics are coupled with stoichiometry. Kunzru *et al*[12] have demonstrated the capability of a computer in simulating a catalytic reformer unit. In this application, calculations are made for a plant in which naphtha is reformed in the presence of hydrogen-rich gas to yield high octane gasoline. Such a program can be used in a wide variety of applications such as selection of (a) operating conditions, (b) number of reactors, (c) catalyst bed depth, etc.

9.7 APPLICATIONS OF SPREADSHEET SOFTWARE IN STOICHIOMETRY

Spreadsheet softwares for personal computers were initially introduced as accounting tools. However, these softwares also find applications in chemical engineering and other disciplines. Most widely used spreadsheet software is Microsoft Excel©. Several spreadsheet applications involving process flowsheeting and mass balances have appeared in literature. These softwares are well known for simplicity in use and also for sensitivity analysis that can be performed with case.

In the preceding sections, use of FORTRAN-77 was made to write specific programs. While developing these programs, knowledge of numerical methods and development of a flow chart were necessary. Programming based on the flow chart is a task by itself and usually debugging of the program is necessary before the final program can be put into use.

Real advantage of a spreadsheet software over conventional computer methods, for instance the use of FORTRAN, lies in the simplicity of the numerical formulation. Shorter programming and less debugging time are other benefits. Spreadsheet programs suit the occasional user who does not have the time and resources of a programming facility to help formulate and debug the source code. A few hours of learning a spreadsheet package will enable one to start, using software immediately and produce valuable results. Formulas can be entered easily.

Spreadsheets can be easily manipulated for process calculations and optimization. Input variables and parameters can be varied both manually and automatically. A macro can be built in the spreadsheet to optimize a process design automatically. Thereby, one can appreciate the ability of the spreadsheet to iterate to converge. Spreadsheets also contain readymade programs that will allow one to conduct standard calculations, such as regration analysis for solving simultaneous equations, once data are entered in an appropriate format. In the following examples, the use of a spreadsheet software (Excel© of Microsoft Corporation, USA) is demonstrated in a variety of stoichiometric problems.

Example 9.5   Solve Example 9.1 using a spreadsheet program.

Solution   (Refer Fig. 9.18)

Note   Advantage of using of numerical method (i.e., Newton–Raphson method) is evident as less number of trials are required for getting the solution.

Example 9.6   In Example 8.7 steam balance of a caustic soda plant is given. Its flow chart and solution using FORTRAN are given in Example 9.2. Solve the example using a spreadsheet.

Solution   Refer Fig. 9.19 for the computer output using spreadsheet program.

Example 9.7   In Example 4.17, material balance of a typical ammonia synthesis loop is given in which the inerts content of the mixed feed stream is restricted to 10 mole %. It is desired to carry out the sensitivity analysis of the synloop by changing the inerts content in the mixed feed stream from 10 mole % to 15 mole % in the steps of 0.5 mole %. Using a spreadsheet program, calculate the flow rates of mixed feed, recycle stream and product ammonia stream for a fresh feed rate of 100 kmol/s.

Solution   *Simulation of Ammonia Synthesis Loop*
(Refer Fig. 9.20)

Example 9.6 is a steam balance which can be performed for a variety of conditions as discussed in Chapter 8. In Example 9.7, simulation is carried out for different inerts in the mixed feed. Such iterative calculations enable a designer to select optimum design based on cost of equipment, type of equipment safety and other considerations. Simulation can also be used for plant troubleshooting, controllability and maintenance[13]. A detailed plant simulation enables one to understand interdependency of performance of one equipment on another and helps in their quantitative evaluation. Plant simulation can also help in achieving better quality in terms of product specifications. Sowa[14] has demonstrated the use of process plant simulation in minimizing the waste generation and also in increasing the plant safety.

a. by Trial and Error method

Rearranging the equation, $F(V) = V - R*T / (p + a/V^2) - b$

Input Data:

Pressure, p	10	MPa
Temperature, T	623.00	K
Critical Presure, p_c	22.1	MPa
Critical Temperature, T_c		647.11K
Gas Constant, R		$0.008314 m^3 \times MPa/(kmol \times K)$
Molar Mass, M_m		18.015
Tolerance, e		0.00001
Initial delta V, dV		0.10

Calculation:
$a = 27*R^2*T_c^2/(64*p_c)$　　　$a = 552545.2\ (m^3)^2 \times MPa/(kmol)^2$
$b = R*T_c/(8*p_c)$　　　　　　　$b = 0.030430\ m^3/kmol$

Trial	V	F(V)	dV	New dV	test	Sp.Vol
0	0.1	-0.00981	0.10000	0.05000	FALSE	#N/A
1	0.15000	-0.03031	0.05000	0.02500	FALSE	#N/A
2	0.17500	-0.04014	0.02500	0.02500	FALSE	#N/A
3	0.20000	-0.04794	0.02500	0.02500	FALSE	#N/A
4	0.22500	-0.05309	0.02500	0.02500	FALSE	#N/A
5	0.25000	-0.05535	0.02500	0.02500	FALSE	#N/A
6	0.27500	-0.05472	0.02500	0.02500	FALSE	#N/A
7	0.30000	-0.05136	0.02500	0.02500	FALSE	#N/A
8	0.32500	-0.04550	0.02500	0.02500	FALSE	#N/A
9	0.35000	-0.03739	0.02500	0.02500	FALSE	#N/A
10	0.37500	-0.02728	0.02500	0.02500	FALSE	#N/A
11	0.40000	-0.01543	0.02500	0.01250	FALSE	#N/A
12	0.41250	-0.00893	0.01250	0.00625	FALSE	#N/A
13	0.41875	-0.00554	0.00625	0.00313	FALSE	#N/A
14	0.42188	-0.00381	0.00313	0.00313	FALSE	#N/A
15	0.42500	-0.00206	0.00313	0.00156	FALSE	#N/A
16	0.42656	-0.00118	0.00156	0.00078	FALSE	#N/A
17	0.42734	-0.00074	0.00078	0.00039	FALSE	#N/A
18	0.42773	-0.00051	0.00039	0.00039	FALSE	#N/A
19	0.42813	-0.00029	0.00039	0.00020	FALSE	#N/A
20	0.42832	-0.00018	0.00020	0.00010	FALSE	#N/A
21	0.42842	-0.00012	0.00010	0.00010	FALSE	#N/A
22	0.42852	-0.00007	0.00010	0.00005	FALSE	#N/A
23	0.42856	-0.00004	0.00005	0.00002	FALSE	#N/A
24	0.42859	-0.00003	0.00002	0.00002	FALSE	#N/A
25	0.42861	-0.00001	0.00002	0.00001	FALSE	#N/A
26	0.42863	-0.00001	0.00001	0.00001	TRUE	$0.023792\ m^3/kg$

b. by Newton – Raphson method:
Rearranging the equation: $F(V) = p*V^3 - (b*p + R*T)*V^2 + a*V - a*b$
Derivative w.r.t V　　　$F'(V) = 3*p*V^2 - 2*(b*p + R*T)*V + a$
　　　　　　　　　　　　$V_{n+1} = V_n - F(V)/F'(V)$

Trial	V_n	$F(V_n)$	$F'(V_n)$	$F(V_n)/F'(V_n)$	test	Sp.Vol.
0	0.517962	187743.5	2920158.9	0.064292252	FALSE	#N/A
1	0.453669	38904.51	1751254.1	0.022215234	FALSE	#N/A
2	0.431454	3900.765	1405009.9	0.002776326	FALSE	#N/A
3	0.428678	57.28540	1363819.9	4.20036E-05	FALSE	#N/A
4	0.428636	0.013013	1363200.3	9.54631E-09	FALSE	#N/A
5	0.428636	7.38510E	1363200.1	5.41747E-16	TRUE	$0.023793 m^3/kg$

Fig. 9.18 Spreadsheet Outputs of Example 9.1

Optimization of Steam Balance

```
Notations:
a = Saturated Low Pressure Steam Input to Deaerator, t/h
b = Medium Pressure Steam Input to CW Pump Turbine, t/h
c = Medium Pressure Steam Input to BFW Pump Turbine, t/h
d = Medium Pressure Steam Input to FD Fan Turbine, t/h
e = Exhaust (under vacuum) from Power Turbine, t/h
g = Letdown from Medium Pressure to Low Pressure Header, t/h
h = Letdown from High Pressure to Medium Pressure Header, t/h
Z = Total high Pressure Steam Produced, t/h
```

a	b	c	d	E	g	H	k
-1	0	1.022	1.022	0	1.121	0	13.5
1	-0.11	0	0	-0.11	0	0	1.815
0	5.16	5.16	5.16	21.79	5.16	-5.5	754.03
0	-4.037	-4.037	96	-4.037	-4.037	0.266	11.061
8.977	8.977	-100	0	8.977	0	0	-148.115
0	9.109	0	0	-0.843	0	0	9.358

Z_{min} = b + c + d + e + g + 2.745, for h=0

Solution

Regression   Statistics

Multiple R	1
R Square	1
Adjusted R Square	0
Standard Error	0
Observations	6

Analysis of variance

	df	Sum of Squares	Mean Square	F	Significance F
Regression	6	522275.8497	87045.97495	0	#N/A
Residual	0	5.42036E-24	0		
total	6	522275.8497			

	Coefficients	Standard error	Statis-tics	P - value	Lower 95%	Upper 95%
Inter-cept	0	#N/A	#N/A	#N/A	#N/A	#N/A
a	5.47992043	0	0	0	#N/A	#N/A
b	3.76252185	0	0	0	#N/A	#N/A
c	4.9639907	0	0	0	#N/A	#N/A
d	2.1637615	0	0	0	#N/A	#N/A
e	29.5549366	0	0	0	#N/A	#N/A
g	10.4329685	0	0	0	#N/A	#N/A

Z_{min} = 53.6231791, for h = 0

Fig. 9.19 Spreadsheet Output for Example 9.6

9.8   **APPLICATIONS OF MATHEMATICAL SOFTWARE IN STOICHIOMETRY**

In Sec. 9.7, use of spreadsheet programs was demonstrated in solving stoichiometric problems. However, use of a spreadsheet required the knowledge of algorithm to perform iterations and to specify the condition(s) to terminate the iteration.

Limitation of a spreadsheet can be overcome by use of a mathematical software, which is a versatile, highly functional tool that can solve symbolic and numerical mathematical problems on a personal computer. Phillips[15] *et al* reviewed five

```
Notations: a = Nitrogen in mixed feed, kmol/s
           I = Inerts in mixed feed, mole fraction
           M = Mixed feed, kmol/s
           P = Purge rate, kmol/s
           R = Recycle flow, kmol/s
           N = Ammonia production rate, kg/s
Equations: a = 24.75*I*M/(0.75+0.25*I*M)
           (M-100)/(I*M-1) = (0.35*M+065*I*M+1.775*a)/(I*M)
           P = (M-100)/(I*M-1)
           R = M-100, R >= 100
           N = 0.65*(M*(I-1)-3.5*A)*17.031
Solution:  M^2+B*M+C = 0, where
           B = (3.5385 - 426.1926*I)/(I*(1-I)) and
           C = (1.6154 - 188.192*I)/(I^2 - I^3)
```

I	B	C	M	a	P	R	N
0.100	-434.2307	-1911.5333	438.5890	92.6618	7.9001	338.5890	779.4908
0.105	-438.5392	-1838.8639	442.6930	92.9979	7.5346	342.6930	782.8542
0.110	-442.7241	-1772.2834	446.6916	93.3034	7.2023	346.6916	785.9117
0.115	-446.8057	-1711.0788	450.6030	93.5822	6.8990	350.6030	788.7032
0.120	-450.8013	-1654.6433	454.4423	93.8378	6.6210	354.4423	791.2620
0.125	-454.7253	-1602.4576	458.2224	94.0728	6.3653	358.2224	793.6161
0.130	-458.5901	-1554.0747	461.9542	94.2898	6.1292	361.9542	795.7890
0.135	-462.4063	-1509.1079	465.6472	94.4906	5.9107	365.6472	797.8009
0.140	-466.1833	-1467.2212	469.3096	94.6771	5.7077	369.3096	799.6691
0.145	-469.9288	-1428.1211	472.9484	94.8507	5.5188	372.9484	801.4084
0.150	-473.6501	-1391.5503	476.5700	95.0126	5.3425	376.5700	803.0317

Fig. 9.20 Spreadsheet Output for Example 9.7

well-known software packages; Mathcad, Maple, Matlab, Mathematica and TK Solver. All these packages run on the Windows operating system.

In this book, Mathcad is selected for solving a variety of stoichiometric problems. It was developed by PCT, Inc., USA. It is easy and ideal for repetitive engineering calculations where the objective is to determine the effects of change of a variable on calculated parameters, thereby finding an optimum value. Data can be entered in vectors or matrices or can be imported from a spreadsheet. The software has also the ability to do unit conversions.

User interface with Mathcad is done by selecting an icon from a toolbar that represents the desired calculation. For example, choosing the icon for an integral from the calculus toolbar generates an integral sign with place holders for the integrand and limits of integration. By filling the placeholders, numerical subroutine is performed by Mathcad which calculates the value of the integral. Similar toolbars exist for arithmetic, calculus, matrix, symbolic keywords, graph, etc.

Iteration is an integral part of the software. Algorithms are built-in for solving the equations. A starting value (called 'Guess') is required and it must be appropriate to the particular root of the equation.

In chapters 2 to 8, use of Mathcad was demonstrated as a tool in solving polynomial and simultaneous equations. These are relatively simple applications of Mathcad. In this chapter, small programs are developed to perform repetitive calculations by varying a parameter. Some are general (e.g., equations of state) while some are specific (e.g., ammonia synthesis loop).

The user-friendly Mathcad can boost efficiency of an engineer and save considerable time. The reader is advised to refer to the website for knowing more capabilities of Mathcad.

Example 9.8 Write a generalized program in Mathcad to solve the van der Waals equation [Eq. (2.25)] of state. Solve Example 2.24(b) using the program.

Solution

$$a\left(R, T_c, p_c\right) := 27 \cdot R^2 \cdot \frac{T_c^{\,2}}{64 \cdot p_c}$$

$$b\left(R, T_c, p_c\right) := R \cdot \frac{T_c}{8 \cdot p_c}$$

$$F\left(V, p, T, R, T_c, p_c\right) := \left(p + \frac{a\left(R, T_c, p_c\right)}{V^2}\right) \cdot \left(V - b\left(R, T_c, p_c\right)\right) - (R \cdot T)$$

$V := 0.51\text{\textsterling}$

$V := \text{root}\,(F(V, 100, 623.15, 0.083145, 647.3, 221.2), V)$

Guess value of V may be taken from the Ideal Gas Law.

$V = 0.4288 \quad \dfrac{\text{m}^3}{\text{kmol}}$

$v := \dfrac{V}{18.015\text{\textonehalf}}$

$v = 0.0238 \quad \dfrac{\text{m}^3}{\text{kg}}$

Fig. 9.21 Mathcad Program for van der Waals Equation

In Chapter 2, use of Mathcad was demonstrated to solve the equation with a single unknown (i.e., V). However, before solving the equation with a built-in root function, the basic equation was simplified. By writing a specific program for the basic equation in Mathcad, it can be seen in Fig. 9.21 that substitution of parameters is the only requirement.

Example 9.9 Solve Example 2.25(b) using the program developed in Example 9.8, and calculate pseudo-critical properties by inserting a table.

Solution

Table A lists critical properties of gas mixture.

$A :=$

	0	1	2
0	0.352	32.2	12.97
1	0.148	190.56	45.99
2	0.128	282.34	50.41
3	0.339	132.91	34.99
4	0.015	304.1	73.75
5	0.018	126.09	33.94

$$T_c := \sum_{i=0}^{5} \left(A_{i,0} \cdot A_{i,1} \right) \qquad\qquad p_c := \sum_{i=0}^{5} \left(A_{i,0} \cdot A_{i,2} \right)$$

$$T_c = 127.5644 \ \text{K} \qquad\qquad p_c = 31.4032 \quad \text{bar}$$

$$a\left(R, T_c, p_c\right) := 27 \cdot R^2 \cdot \frac{T_c^2}{64 \, p_c}$$

$$b\left(R, T_c, p_c\right) := R \cdot \frac{T_c}{8 \, p_c}$$

$$F\left(V, p, T, R, T_c, p_c\right) := \left(p + \frac{a\left(R, T_c, p_c\right)}{V^2} \right) \cdot \left(V - b\left(R, T_c, p_c\right)\right) - (R \cdot T)$$

Guess value of V may be taken from the Ideal Gas Law.

$$V := 0.51\ell$$

$$V := \text{root}\left(F(V, 4, 773.15, 0.083145, 127.564, 31.403), V\right)$$

$$V = 16.0897 \quad \frac{L}{\text{mol}}$$

Fig. 9.22 Mathcad Solution for Example 2.21

Example 9.10 Write a generalized program in Mathcad to solve the Beattie–Bridgeman equation of state. Solve Exercise 2.37 using the program.

Solution

$$A\left(A_0, a, V\right) := A_0 \cdot \left(1 - \frac{a}{V} \right) \qquad B\left(B_0, b, V\right) := B_0 \cdot \left(1 - \frac{b}{V} \right) \qquad \varepsilon\left(c, T, V\right) := \frac{c}{V \cdot T^3}$$

$$F\left(A_0, B_0, a, b, c, T, p, R, V\right) := p - \left[R \cdot T \cdot \frac{(1 - \varepsilon(c, T, V))}{V^2} \right] \cdot \left(V + B\left(B_0, b, V\right)\right) + \frac{A\left(A_0, a, V\right)}{V^2}$$

Guess value of V may be taken from the Ideal Gas Law.

$$V := 0.48\ell$$

$$V := \text{root}\left(F\left(5.88, 0.094, 0.05861, 0.01915, 90 \cdot 10^4, 423.15, 73, 0.083145, V\right), V\right)$$

$$V = 0.4005 \quad \frac{m^3}{\text{kmol}}$$

Fig. 9.23 Mathcad Program for Solving Beattie–Bridgeman Equation of State

Example 9.11 Write a generalized program in Mathcad for recycle loop of ammonia synthesis. Solve Example 4.17 using the program.

Solution

$$N_{2m}(a) := a \qquad\qquad\qquad N_2 \text{ in mixed feed}$$

$$H_{2m}(a) := 3 \cdot a \qquad\qquad\qquad H_2 \text{ in mixed fedd}$$

Let y = fraction of inerts in the mixed feed

$$I_m(M, y) := M \cdot y \qquad\qquad\qquad \text{Inerts in mixed feed}$$

$$NH_{3m}(M, a, y) := M - a - H_{2m}(a) - I_m(M, y) \qquad\qquad NH_3 \text{ in mixed fedd}$$

Let x = fractional conversion per pass

N_2 reacted $\qquad N_{2r}(a,x) := x \cdot a$

H_2 reacted $\qquad H_{2r}(a,x) := 3 \cdot x \cdot a$

NH_3 produced $\qquad NH_{3p}(a,x) := 2 \cdot x \cdot a$

N_2 unreacted $\qquad N_{2ur}(a,x) := (1 - x) \cdot a$

H_2 unreacted $\qquad H_{2ur}(a,x) := (1 - x) \cdot 3 \cdot a$

Total NH_3 in outgoing gas from converter

$$NH_{3c}(M,a,x,y) := NH_{3m}(M,a,y) + NH_{3p}(a,x)$$

Let z = fractional separation of ammonia in the condensers

NH_3 separated in the separator

$$NH_{3s}(M,a,x,y,z) := NH_{3c}(M,a,x,y) \cdot z$$

NH_3 uncondensed

$$NH_{3un}(M,a,x,y,z) := (1 - z) \cdot NH_{3c}(M,a,x,y)$$

Total gas mixture after the separator

$$G_s(M,a,x,y,z) := N_{2ur}(a,x) + H_{2ur}(a,x) + NH_{3un}(M,a,x,y,z) + I_m(M,y)$$

Recycle stream

$$R(M,a,x,y,z,P) := G_s(M,a,x,y,z) - P$$

Nitrogen lost in purge

$$N_{2p}(M,a,x,y,z,P) := N_{2ur}(a,x) \cdot \frac{P}{G_s(M,a,x,y,z)}$$

N_2 in recycle

$$N_{2rec}(M,a,x,y,z,P) := N_{2ur}(a,x) - N_{2p}(M,a,x,y,z,P)$$

Guess values for M, P, a.　　M > P

$M := 400 \qquad P := 5 \qquad a := 80$

Given

Let y_f = fractional inerts content in the fresh feed

$$I_m(M,y) \cdot \frac{P}{G_s(M,a,x,y,z)} = y_f \cdot F$$

$F + R(M,a,x,y,z,P) = M$

$N_{2rec}(M,a,x,y,z,P) + a_f = a$

$vec(F, a_f, y_f, x, y, z) := Find(M,P,a)$

Solution of Example 4.17

$$vec(100, 24.75, 0.01, 0.25, 0.1, 0.65) = \begin{pmatrix} 438.5891 \\ 7.9001 \\ 92.6618 \end{pmatrix} \quad \frac{kmol}{s}$$

$M := vec(100, 24.75, 0.01, 0.25, 0.1, 0.65)_0$

$P := vec(100, 24.75, 0.01, 0.25, 0.1, 0.65)_1$

$a := vec(100, 24.75, 0.01, 0.25, 0.1, 0.65)_2$

$M = 438.5891 \quad P = 7.9001 \quad a = 92.6618 \quad$ all in kmol/s

$R(M,F) := M - F$

$$R(M, 100) = 338.5891 \quad \frac{kmol}{s}$$

Recycle ratio $\quad R_r(M, F) := \dfrac{R(M, F)}{F}$

$$R_r(M, 100) = 3.3859 \quad \frac{kmol}{kmol}$$

Ammonia production $\quad NH_{3s}(M, a, 0.25, 0.1, 0.65) = 45.7690 \quad \dfrac{kmol}{s}$

Fig. 9.24 Mathcad Program for Ammonia Synthesis Loop

Note It can be seen in Fig. 9.24 that all parameters can be varied at will. Exercise 4.36 (ref. Exercise 9.3) can be easily solved by the above program.

Example 9.12 In Example 4.17, fresh feed composition shows that N_2: H_2 ratio is 1:3 on volume basis. Vary this ratio from 1:2.8 to 1:3.2 in increments of 0.05, keeping inerts in feed and purge at 1% and 10% mole%, respectively. Assume 25% conversion per pass and 65% separation of ammonia in the separator. It is desired that N_2:H_2 ratio be 1:3 on molar basis in the mixed feed. Evaluate the material balance of the synthesis loop.

Solution With feed gas containing 99% N_2 + H_2 and a molar ratio of 1:2.8 of N_2 : H_2, nitrogen content of feed gas works out to 26.053 mole%. Substitution of these parameters in the program does not yield the results and computer shows an error in calculations. This is because dynamic conditions of the loop do not permit achievement of exact 1:3 molar ratio in the mixed feed. In such cases, Mathcad provides a solution with minimum error which is difficult to achieve by manual calculations.

Approximate results are tabulated in Table 9.2 which are derived using Mathcad program, given in Fig. 9.24 with minimum errors, except for N_2:H_2 ratio of 1:3 in mixed feed.

Generalized program of Example 9.11 is used for evaluation. Instead of fixed a_f, variable a_f substituted in the vector.

Define a_f **as under.**

$$a_f\left(y_f, F, M_r\right) := \frac{\left(100 - y_f \cdot F\right)}{\left(1 + M_r\right)}$$

$$a_f(0.01, 100, 2.80) = 26.0526$$

$$vec(100, 26.0526, 0.01, 0.25, 0.1, 0.65) = \begin{pmatrix} 453.9031 \\ 7.9725 \\ 97.7498 \end{pmatrix} \quad \frac{kmol}{s}$$

$$M := vec(100, 26.0526, 0.01, 0.25, 0.1, 0.65)_0$$

$$P := vec(100, 23.5714, 0.01, 0.25, 0.1, 0.65)_1$$

$$a := vec(100, 23.5714, 0.01, 0.25, 0.1, 0.65)_2$$

M = 453.9031   P = 7.83009   a = 88.0657   all in kmol/s

$R(M, F) := M - F$

$R(M, 100) = 353.9031 \quad \dfrac{kmol}{s}$

Recycle ratio $R_r(M, F) := \dfrac{R(M, F)}{F}$

$R_r(M, 100) = 3.5390 \quad \dfrac{kmol}{kmol}$

Ammonia production $NH_{3s}(M, a, 0.25, 0.1, 0.65) = 65.1838 \quad \dfrac{kmol}{s}$

In a similar manner output for different a_f can be calculated. Outputs at different a_f are tabulated in Table 9.2..

Table 9.2 Effect of Varying Feed Composition of Ammonia Synthesis Loop

Basis 100 kmol/s of fresh feed

Molar ratio of H_2/N_2 in fresh feed	N_2 content in Fresh Feed, mole %	Mixed Feed, M kmol/s	Purge Rate, P kmol/s	Ammonia Production Rate, kmol/s
2.80	26.053	453.9078	7.9726	43.1518
2.85	25.714	449.9192	7.9542	43.8326
2.90	25.385	446.0503	7.9360	44.4934
2.95	25.063	442.2658	7.9179	45.1402
3.00	24.750	438.5891	7.9001	45.7690 (Exact)
3.05	24.444	434.9967	7.8823	46.3838
3.10	24.146	431.5000	7.8648	46.9825
3.15	23.855	428.0874	7.8473	47.5672
3.20	23.571	424.7587	7.8301	48.1378

Note It is interesting to analyse the data of Table 9.2. It can be seen that purge rate P does not vary so significantly as seen in the table. This leads to valuable information concerning control philosophy of the loop. When inerts in the fresh feed do not vary significantly, minor variations in purge rate is able to control the H_2:N_2 in the mixed feed effectively. Thus in this case, purge gas flow needs to be controlled in a very narrow range. However, when there is a significant variation in inerts in fresh feed, purge gas flow needs to be varied significantly which is obvious because inerts, entering the system, must be purged out in the concentrated form.

Example 9.13 Write a generalized program in Mathcad for solving steam balance (Example 8.7).

It is decided to carryout simulation of the steam balance by varying temperature of superheated HP steam from 440°C (713.15 K) to 520°C (793.15 K). Anticipated operating conditions of the cascade steam system are given in Table 9.3.

Solution

Define :

HP superheated steam enthalpy = H_1 kJ/kg
MP superheated steam enthalpy = H_2 kJ/kg
LP superheated steam enthalpy = H_3 kJ/kg
LP saturated steam enthalpy = H_4 kJ/kg
15 bar saturated steam enthalpy = H_5 kJ/kg
Surface condenser steam enthalpy = H_6 kJ/kg
BFW enthalpy = H_7 kJ/kg
Surface condenser condensate enthalpy = H_8 kJ/kg

Let x_1 kg BFW required to quench 1 kg MP superheated steam to 15 bar saturated steam.

$$x_1\left(H_2, H_5, H_7\right) := \frac{\left(H_2 - H_5\right)}{\left(H_5 - H_7\right)} \quad \frac{kg}{kg}$$

$$Q_1\left(H_2, H_5, H_7\right) := \frac{3}{\left(1 + x_1\left(H_2, H_5, H_7\right)\right)} \quad \text{t MP superheated steam required/h}$$

Let x_2 kg BFW required to quench 1 kg MP superheated steam to 4.4 bar saturated steam.

$$x_2\left(H_2, H_4, H_7\right) := \frac{\left(H_2 - H_4\right)}{\left(H_4 - H_7\right)} \quad \frac{kg}{kg}$$

Let x_3 kg BFW required to quench 1 kg LP (4.4) bar superheated steam to saturated LP steam.

$$x_3\left(H_3, H_4, H_7\right) := \frac{\left(H_3 - H_4\right)}{\left(H_4 - H_7\right)} \quad \frac{kg}{kg}$$

Power turbine :

Specific steam consumption in Power Turbine (let down from HP to MP)

$$S_1\left(H_1, H_2\right) := \frac{3600}{\left(H_1 - H_2\right) \cdot 0.97} \quad \frac{kg}{kWh}$$

Specific steam consumption in turbines with letdown from MP to LP steam

$$S_2\left(H_2, H_3\right) := \frac{3600}{\left(H_2 - H_3\right) \cdot 0.97} \quad \frac{kg}{kWh}$$

Specific steam consumption in Power Turbine (letdown from HP to SC)

$$S_3\left(H_1, H_6\right) := \frac{3600}{\left(H_1 - H_6\right) \cdot 0.97} \quad \frac{kg}{kWh}$$

Specific steam consumptions in turbine with letdown from MP to SC

$$S_4\left(H_2, H_6\right) := \frac{3600}{\left(H_2 - H_6\right) \cdot 0.97} \quad \frac{kg}{kWh}$$

Cooling water requirement in SC per t steam

$$Q_{cw}\left(H_6, H_8\right) := \frac{\left(H_6 - H_8\right)}{10 \cdot 4.1868} \quad \frac{m^3}{t}$$

Table 9.3 Anticipated Operating Conditions of a Cascade Steam System (Base Case: Example 8.6)

Units	Case – I Initial	Case – I Final	Case – II Initial	Case – II Final	Case – III Initial	Case – III Final	Case – IV Initial	Case – IV Final	Case – V Initial	Case – V Final
(a) Power turbine – (i) Extraction										
MPa a	11.5	3.9	11.5	3.9	11.5	3.9	11.5	3.9	11.5	3.9
°C (K)	440 (713.15)	320 (593.15)	460 (733)	339 (612)	489 (753)	358 (631)	500 (773)	377 (650)	520 (793)	396 (669)
kJ/kg	3190.7	3020.4	3247.8	3069.7	3320.7	3117.1	3356.0	3163.0	3408.1	3207.9
(a) Power turbine – (ii) Condensing										
MPa a	11.5	0.012	11.5	0.012	11.5	0.012	11.5	0.012	11.5	0.012
°C (K)	440 (713.15)	50 (323) 95% dryness	460 (733)	50 (323) 96.5% dryness	480 (753)	50 (323) 98% dryness	500 (773)	50 (323) 99.5% dryness	520 (793)	58 (332)
kJ/kg	3190.7	2472.0	3247.8	2507.7	3320.7	2543.5	3356.0	2578.7	3408.1	2607.4
(b) Medium pressure turbine – (ii) Extraction										
MPa a	3.9	0.44	3.9	0.44	3.9	0.44	3.9	0.44	3.9	0.44
°C (K)	320 (593.15)	170 (443)	339 (612)	189 (462)	358 (631)	207.6 (480.6)	337 (650)	226 (499)	396 (669)	243 (516)
kJ/kg	3020.4	2793.3	3069.7	2834.9	3117.1	2874.4	3163.0	2913.1	3207.9	2948.6
(b) Medium pressure turbine – (ii) Condensing										
MPa a	3.9	0.012	3.9	0.012	3.9	0.012	3.9	0.012	3.9	0.012
°C (K)	320 (593.15)	50 (323) 95% dryness	339 (612)	50 (323) 96.5% dryness	358 (961)	50 (323) 98% dryness	377 (650)	50 (323) 99.5% dryness	396 (669)	58 (332)
kJ/kg	3020.4	2472.0	3069.7	2507.7	3117.1	2543.5	3163.0	2578.7	3207.9	2607.4
(c) Cooling water requirement										
m³/h		600		635		670		710		740

Note Anticipated operating conditions are calculated by assuming constant thermodynamic efficiency of different turbines.

Guess values :

$a := 1 \quad b := 1 \quad c := 1 \quad d := 1 \quad e := 1 \quad g := 1 \quad Z := 5(\!$

$H_1 := 3190.^{\cdot} \quad H_2 := 3020.^{\prime} \quad H_3 := 2793.^{\cdot} \quad H_4 := 2741.^{\varsigma}$

$H_5 := 2789.^{\varsigma} \quad H_6 := 2472.(\!\quad H_7 := 440.1^{\cdot} \quad H_8 := 209.^{\cdot} \quad$ all in kJ/kg

Given

$$\left(x_3\left(H_3, H_4, H_7\right) + 1\right)\cdot(c + d) + \left(x_2\left(H_2, H_4, H_7\right) + 1\right)\cdot g = 13.5 + a$$

$$a - 0.11\cdot b - 0.11\cdot e = 1.81\varsigma$$

$$\frac{\left(b + c + d + g + Q_1\left(H_2, H_5, H_7\right)\right)}{S_1\left(H_1, H_2\right)} + \frac{e}{S_3\left(H_1, H_6\right)} = 6.83\varsigma$$

$$5.493(a + b + e + 16.5)\cdot S_2\left(H_2, H_3\right) = 1000\,c$$

$$2.47\cdot\left(b + c + d + e + g + Q_1\left(H_2, H_5, H_7\right)\right)\cdot S_2\left(H_2, H_3\right) = 1000\,d$$

$$0.2315\left[Q_{cw}\left(H_6, H_8\right)\cdot(b + e) + 600\right]\cdot S_4\left(H_2, H_6\right) = 1000\,b$$

$$Z = b + c + d + e + g + Q_1\left(H_2, H_5, H_7\right)$$

$$vec\left(H_1, H_2, H_3, H_4, H_5, H_6, H_7, H_8\right) := Find(a, b, c, d, e, g, Z)$$

$$vec(3190.7, 3020.4, 2793.3, 2741.9, 2789.9, 2472.0, 440.17, 209.2) =$$

	0
0	5.4827
1	3.7633
2	4.9665
3	2.1651
4	29.5798
5	10.4299
6	53.6366

$\dfrac{t}{h}$

Fig. 9.25 Mathcad Solution for Cascade Steam Balance

Using the above program, steam flows for all five cases are calculated and tabulated in Table 9.4. It may be noted that only appropriate specific enthalpy values are required to be changed.

Table 9.4 Evaluation of Cascade Steam Balance for Different Operating Conditions

Case	Steam flow, t/h						
	a	b	c	d	e	g	Z
I	5.482	3.763	4.966	2.165	29.577	10.430	53.646
II	5.367	3.681	4.702	2.034	28.607	10.380	52.097
III	5.136	3.525	4.353	1.867	26.663	10.368	49.421
IV	5.183	3.592	4.266	1.818	27.023	10.267	49.567
V	5.076	3.448	4.027	1.704	26.158	10.255	48.191

Note From the above table, it can be seen that steam balance with 480°C (753 K) (Case-III) is probably the best. It is important to note that downstream conditions of various turbines matter significantly in optimization.

Example 9.14   Refer Exercise 8.11. Write a Mathcad Program to solve the problem. Using the program, calculate (a) oxygen requirement in kmol/kmol NG, and (b) steam to dry exit gas mole ratio for operating pressures 1.8, 1.9, 2.0, 2.1 and 2.2 MPa a for each of the temperatures; 1340, 1395 and 1450 K (1067, 1122 and 1177 °C). Assume design approach to equilibrium of steam-reforming reaction as 30 K (30 °C). Equilibrium constants for the steam reforming and shift reaction are given in Table 9.5.

Table 9.5   Values of Equilibrium Constants[16]

Temperature of reforming reaction K(°C)	K_{P1}	Temperature of shift reaction K(°C)	K_{P2}
1310 (1037)	5.8789×10^{-5}	1340 (1067)	0.4993
1365 (1092)	2.5207×10^{-5}	1395 (1122)	0.4465
1420 (1147)	1.1542×10^{-5}	1450 (1177)	0.4038

Solution   *Reforming reactions*

$$CH_4 + H_2O = CO + 3 H_2 \tag{A}$$
$$C_2H_6 + 2 H_2O = 2 CO + 5 H_2 \tag{B}$$
$$C_3H_8 + 3 H_2O = 3 CO + 7 H_2 \tag{C}$$
$$C_4H_{10} + 4 H_2O = 4 CO + 9 H_2 \tag{D}$$

Shift reaction

$$CO + H_2O = CO_2 + H_2O \tag{E}$$

Reactions (B), (C) and (D) go to 100% completion while reactions (A) and (E) go to completion as per the equilibrium.

Reaction (A) is endothermic and hence the methane slip will be determined by the chemical equilibrium at $1395 - 30 = 1365$ K.

Reaction (E) is exothermic and the operating temperature is quite high. Hence its chemical equilibrium at 1395 K will have to be taken for calculations.

Based on above understandings, Mathcad program and computer output for $p = 2.0$ MPa a and $T = 1395$ K (1122 °C) are given in Fig. 9.26.

Solution

Let f_i = mole percent inerts in feed gas

$$n_i(F, f_i) := F \cdot \frac{f_i}{100}$$

Let p be the pressure in MPa and p_1 be the pressure in atmosphere .

$$p_1(p) := p \cdot 9.8692\colon$$

Let F = natural gas feed rate, kmol/h
$\quad f_m$ = mole percent of methane in natural gas
$\quad f_e$ = mole percent of ethane in natural gas
$\quad f_p$ = mole percent of propane in natural gas
$\quad f_{.nb}$ = mole percent of n-butane in natural gas
$\quad f_{ib}$ = mole percent of i-butane in natural gas
$\quad f_i$ = mole percent of inerts in natural gas

$\quad n_{O2}$ = feed rate of oxygen stream, kmol/h
$\quad y$ = mole fraction of oxygen in oxygen stream

n_{CH4} = methane content of reactor exit gas from reactor, kmol/h
s_{CH4} = methane slip in exit gas stream as mole percent on wet basis

r_1 = oxygen requirement in kmol/kmol natural gas
r_2 = steam to dry exit gas ratio, kmol/kmol

Total moles leaving the reactor

$$n\left(n_{H2}, n_{CO}, n_{CO2}, n_{H2O}, n_{CH4}, n_{O2}, y, f_i, F\right) := n_{H2} + n_{CO} + n_{CO2} + n_{H2O} + n_i\left(F, f_i\right) + n_{CH4} + (1 - y)\cdot n_{O2}$$

Guess values :

$n_{H2} := 150$ $\quad$ $n_{CO} := 200$ $\quad$ $n_{CO2} := 10$ $\quad$ $r_2 := 0.15$

$n_{H2O} := 40$ $\quad$ $n_{CH4} := 1$ $\quad$ $n_{O2} := 10$ $\quad$ $r_1 := 0.15$

Given

Overall material balance :

$$n\left(n_{H2}, n_{CO}, n_{CO2}, n_{H2O}, n_{CH4}, n_{O2}, y, f_i, F\right) = n_{CH4}\cdot\frac{100}{s_{CH4}}$$

Hydrogen balance :

$$n_{H2} + n_{H2O} + 2\cdot\left(n_{CH4}\right) = F\cdot\frac{\left(2\cdot f_m + 3\cdot f_e + 4\cdot f_p + 5\cdot f_{nb} + 5\cdot f_{ib}\right)}{100}$$

Oxygen balance :

$$n_{CO}\cdot 0.5 + n_{CO2} + 0.5\cdot n_{H2O} = y\cdot n_{O2}$$

Carbon balance :

$$n_{CO} + n_{CO2} + n_{CH4} = F\cdot\frac{\left(f_m + 2\cdot f_e + 3\cdot f_p + 4\cdot f_{nb} + 4\cdot f_{ib}\right)}{100}$$

Reaction equilibrium :

Equilibrium constant for reforming reaction :

$$K_{p1} = \left(n_{CH4}\cdot n_{H2O}\right)\cdot\frac{n\left(n_{H2}, n_{CO}, n_{CO2}, n_{H2O}, n_{CH4}, n_{O2}, y, f_i, F\right)^2}{\left(n_{H2}^3\right)\cdot n_{CO}\cdot\left(p_1(p)^2\right)}$$

Equilibrium constant for shift reaction :

$$K_{p2} = \frac{\left(n_{H2}\cdot n_{CO2}\right)}{\left(n_{CO}\cdot n_{H2O}\right)}$$

Specific oxygen requirement in kmol oxygen per kmol NG :

$$r_1 = \frac{n_{O2}}{F} \quad \frac{kmol}{kmol}$$

Steam to dry exit gas ration in kmol steam per kmol gas :

$$r_2 = \frac{n_{H2O}}{\left(n\left(n_{H2}, n_{CO}, n_{CO2}, n_{H2O}, n_{CH4}, n_{O2}, y, f_i, F\right) - n_{H2O}\right)}$$

$$\underset{\sim\sim\sim}{vec}\left(F, f_m, f_e, f_p, f_{nb}, f_{ib}, f_i, y, p, K_{p1}, K_{p2}, s_{CH4}\right) := Find\left(n_{H2}, n_{CO}, n_{CO2}, n_{H2O}, n_{CH4}, n_{O2}, r_1, r_2\right)$$

	0
0	161.0174
1	92.5524
2	9.7065
3	37.8203
4	1.0712
5	76.4212
6	0.7642
7	0.1410

$$vec\left(100, 93.25, 3.32, 0.88, 0.2, 0, 2.35, 0.98, 2.0, 2.5207\,10^{-5}, 0.4465, 0.35\right) =$$

All values in matrix are in kmol/h except last two values which are in kmol/kmol..

By varying the parameters, oxygen requirement and steam to dry gas ratio can be calculated at different pressures and temperatures. The calculated values are tabulated in Table 9.6.

Fig. 9.26 Mathcad Program for Solving Example 9.14

Substitution of values of p, T, K_{p1} and K_{p2} in the program permit calculations of material balances for different operating conditions. Table 9.6 is the summary of results.

Table 9.6 Oxygen Requirement and Steam in Exit Gas Stream

Exist gas temperature K(°C)	Operating pressure MPa a	Oxygen requirement, kmol/kmol NG	Steam/dry exit gas mole ratio
1340 (1067)	1.8	0.8617	0.2019
	1.9	0.8787	0.2137
	2.0	0.8950	0.2252
	2.1	0.9107	0.2365
	2.2	0.9272	0.2484
1395 (1122)	1.8	0.7364	0.1232
	1.9	0.7505	0.1322
	2.0	0.7642	0.1410
	2.1	0.7775	0.1497
	2.2	0.7921	0.1592
1450 (1177)	1.8	0.6480	0.0710
	1.9	0.6582	0.0771
	2.0	0.6683	0.0832
	2.1	0.6785	0.0894
	2.2	0.6885	0.0955

9.9 OPTIMIZATION

Optimization is a very important tool in every aspect of chemical engineering. Starting from project scheduling, equipment design, construction, operational analysis of existing processes and improving them, all of these are ultimately required to minimize cost and maximize profit. The capability of the digital computer for performing complex computations can be best used in determining the optimal criteria of all activities. Various optimization techniques are available and their applicability depends upon the nature of the problem to be optimized. If the process can be described by a set of linear equations, linear programming can be used as the most powerful technique for optimization. Typically, this has been widely used to maximize the profit of a petroleum refinery operation by adjusting product cuts based on their demands, prices, and production costs. Optimization of a steam balance is another classical example of linear programming. If the activity or a process is described in stages with branches and loops, dynamic programming is a more suitable technique. Determining the optimum number of effects in case of a multiple effect evaporator system[17] is a typical application of dynamic programming. In general, any decision analysis can use this technique to determine the optimum criteria. The EVolutionary OPeration (EVOP) technique can also be used for optimization. The design of a multiple-effect evaporator system can also be optimized with the help of EVOP[18]. Geometric programming can conveniently be used in the case of linear problems.

For a highly complex system, numerical search techniques are used. In one-dimensional search techniques, Sequential, Golden-search, Lattice, Fibonacci, and Dichotomous are a few of the widely used methods. Some of the multi-dimensional search techniques include Successive Quadratic Programming (SQP), steep ascent, steep ascent pattern and gradient search methods. No one method can be said as being better than another because there is no criterion for defining the effectiveness of a particular numerical optimization technique. The effectiveness depends upon the problem model to be optimized. Optimization can be of the entire system or of a subsystem. A detailed discussion of optimization techniques is beyond the scope of this book.

9.10 CONTROL OF PLANT OPERATION WITH THE HELP OF A COMPUTER

With growing energy crisis and emphasis on quality control, trimming of plant operation has assumed great importance for maximum productivity and efficiency. Computers are increasingly used in the heavy chemical industry for this purpose. A classical example is ammonia synthesis. A computer-controlled quench bed reactor can result in the optimum ammonia production with the minimum energy input in the compression equipment. Similarly, a computer check on the cascade steam balance can result in a significant fuel saving. The computer analyses the plant operating data using stoichiometric principles and prints out the important parameters for a quick check by a production manager. Operators can then be advised suitably for adjusting the operating parameters.

Exercises

9.1 A process vent gas the following composition by volume :
H_2 : 81%, C_2H_6 : 2%, C_2H_4 : 4%, C_3H_8 : 1%, C_3H_6 : 2%, N_2 : 8 % and NH_3 : 2%
Calculate the molar volume of the gas mixture at 2.0 MPa a and 60°C (333 K) using van der Waals equation by (a) spreadsheet (by trial and error method), and (b) Mathcad program. **[0.19 345 m³/kg]**

9.2 Calculate the temperature at which ethane gas will have a density of 50 kg/m³ at a pressure of 4.2 MPa a. Assume Beatti–Bridgeman equation of state (ref. Exercise 2.37). Use the Mathcad program for calculations. **[835.18 K(562°C)]**

9.3 Refer Exercise 4.36. Calculate recycle ratio and purge rate for both the cases using Mathcad program. **[(a) Recycle ratio = 3.553, P = 7.971 kmol/s]**
(b) Recycle ratio = 3.328, P = 7.871 kmol/s]

9.4 Refer Exercise 8.20. Establish the steam balance in Mathcad and calculate the high pressure steam generation for all the five cases, tabulated in Table 9.3. **[Table 9.7]**

Table 9.7   Evaluation of Cascade Steam Balance for Different Operation Conditions

Case	Steam flow, t/h						
	a	b	c	d	e	g	Z
I	5.156	8.480	4.670	2.063	30.369	2.769	51.095
II	5.048	8.228	4.423	1.937	29.392	2.950	49.675
III	4.837	7.795	4.100	1.780	24.476	3.332	47.228
IV	4.874	7.852	4.012	1.731	27.808	3.185	47.333
V	4.777	7.562	3.079	1.623	26.923	3.441	46.083

9.5 Refer Exercise 4.43. Write a Mathcad program for establishing material balance of the synloop. Using the program, calculate various parameters for mixed-feed containing inerts from 0.09 to 0.13 (mole fraction) in increments of 0.05 for the ethylene oxide production rate of 3500 kg/h. Assume other parameters to be constant. **[Table 9.8]**

Table 9.8   Effects of Inerts in Mixed Feed on Ethylene Oxide Manufacture

Inerts in mixed feed mole fraction	Fresh feed F kmol/h	Recycle R_2 kmol/h	Purge P kmol/h	Recycle ratio $= R_2/F$	Ethylene feed rate kg/h
0.090	262.20	2007.8	44.07	7.6575	3252.5
0.095	262.07	2007.9	41.70	7.6617	3248.9
0.100	261.95	2008.0	39.58	7.6656	3245.6
0.105	261.85	2008.1	37.66	7.6690	3242.7
0.110	261.76	2008.2	35.92	7.6722	3240.0
0.115	261.67	2008.3	34.33	7.6750	3237.6
0.120	261.60	2008.4	32.88	7.6777	3235.4
0.125	261.52	2008.5	31.55	7.6801	3233.3
0.130	261.45	2008.5	30.32	7.6823	3231.4

9.6 Refer Example 4.18. Develop a Mathcad program for the double recycle system shown in Fig. 4.4.

Using the above program, calculate mixed-feed flow rate (M), purge flow rate (P), recycle ratio and total ammonia production by varying inerts in the mixed feed from 9% to 12.5% by mole in steps of 0.5 mole %. Also calculate increase in ammonia production with double recycles over single recycle (Example 4.17) for the same inserts level in mixed feed. **[Table 9.9]**

Table 9.9 Effect of Varying Inerts in Mixed Feed with Double Recycle in Ammonia Synthesis Loop

Basis: Fresh feed rate $(F) = 100$ kmol/s, N_2 content of feed $= 24.75$ mole %, Inerts in feed $= 1$ mole %

Inerts in mixed feed mole fraction	Mixed feed flow rate kmol/s	Purge stream kmol/s	Recycle streams		Recycle ratio $(R_1+R_2)/F$ kmol/kmol	Ammonia production rate			Ammonia production rate with single recycle kmol/s	Increase in production, %
			R_1 kmol/s	R_2 kmol/s		From separator kmol/s	From PGR plant kmol/s	Total kg/s		
0.090	449.883	11.951	345.511	7.237	3.527	44.320	0.798	768.375	42.514	6.12
0.095	453.504	11.102	348.248	6.702	3.550	45.944	0.764	795.472	44.140	5.82
0.100	457.011	10.368	350.771	6.240	3.570	47.568	0.735	822.634	45.769	5.54
0.105	460.431	9.727	353.122	5.837	3.590	49.196	0.710	849.923	47.405	5.28
0.110	463.786	9.162	355.335	5.481	3.608	50.831	0.688	877.393	49.050	5.03
0.115	467.093	8.660	357.437	5.165	3.626	52.474	0.668	905.046	50.704	4.81
0.120	470.363	8.212	359.446	4.883	3.643	54.126	0.651	932.873	52.367	4.60
0.125	473.608	7.810	361.377	4.629	3.660	55.790	0.635	960.948	54.044	4.41

9.7 Refer Exercise 8.15. Develop a Mathcad program for the methanol synthesis loop so that various parameters can be calculated by varying (i) mole % H_2 in fresh feed, (ii) mole % of methanol in mixed feed entering the converter, (iii) mole % inerts in mixed feed, entering the converter, (iv) mole ratio of hydrogen to carbon oxides (in stoichiometric proportions), (v) mole % methanol in converter exit gas mixture, and (vi) equilibrium constant (K). For shift gas reaction, following empirical equation is valid in the temperature range 275°C to 840° C (548.15 K to 1113.15 K).

$$\ln K = -4.1227 + (0.4581/T) \, 10^4 \quad T \text{ in K}$$

Using the above program, calculate mixed-feed flow rate (M), purge flow rate (P), recycle ratio, aqueous methanol rate and its concentration (by mass) and molar ratio of CO to CO_2 in the mixed feed for (a) varying inets in the mixed feed form 9% to 12.5% by mole in steps of 0.5%, (b) variying molar hydrogen to carbon oxides ratio from 1.040 to 1.075 in steps of 0.005, and (c) varying temperature of converter exit gas mixture from 275°C to 375°C (548.15 K to 648.15 K) in steps of 25°C (25 K).

Table 9.10 **Effect of Varying Inerts in Mixed Feed in Methanol Sysnthsis Loop**

Basis: Fresh feed rate (F) = 100 kmol/s, H_2 content of feed = 70 mole %, Inerts in feed = 1 mole %
Temperature of conveter exit gas mixture = 275°C (548.15 K)

Inerts in mixed feed	Mixed feed flow rate	Purge stream flow rate	Recycle streams R	Recycle ratio R/F	Aqueous methanol production	Concn. of solution, % CH_3OH	Mole ratio in mixed feed
mole fraction	kmol/s	kmol/s	kmol/s	kmol/kmol	kg/s	(by mass)	CO/CO_2
0.090	1101.477	10.205	1001.477	10.015	1033.91	81.96	0.9706
0.095	1107.620	9.668	1007.620	10.076	1040.38	81.92	0.9625
0.100	1113.145	9.184	1013.145	10.131	1046.21	81.87	0.9547
0.105	1118.141	8.747	1018.141	10.181	1051.47	81.84	0.9473
0.110	1122.680	8.349	1022.680	10.227	1056.28	81.80	0.9402
0.115	1126.823	7.986	1026.823	10.268	1060.63	81.77	0.9333
0.120	1130.620	7.653	1030.620	10.306	1064.64	81.75	0.9266
0.125	1134.111	7.346	1034.111	10.341	1068.35	81.72	0.9201

Table 9.11 **Effect of Varying Ratio of Hydrogen to Carbon Oxides in Mixed Feed in Methanol Sysnthsis Loop**

Basis: Fresh feed rate (F) = 100 kmol/s, H_2 content of feed = 70 mole %, Inerts in feed = 1 mole %
Inerts in mixed feed = 10 mole %
Temperature of conveter exit gas mixture = 275°C (548.15 K)

H_2/ (2 CO+ 3 CO_2)	Mixed feed flow rate	Purge stream flow rate	Recycle streams R	Recycle ratio R/F	Aqueous methanol production	Concn. of solution, % CH_3OH	Mole ratio in mixed feed
Ratio	kmol/s	kmol/s	kmol/s	kmol/kmol	kg/s	(by mass)	CO/ CO_2
1.040	1112.429	9.184	1012.429	10.124	1046.60	81.79	0.9552
1.045	1112.788	9.184	1012.788	10.128	1046.42	81.83	0.9482
1.050	1113.145	9.184	1013.145	10.131	1046.21	81.87	0.9547
1.055	1113.499	9.184	1013.499	10.135	1045.99	81.92	0.9545
1.060	1113.85	9.185	1013.85	10.139	1045.81	81.96	0.9543
1.065	1114.199	9.185	1014.199	10.142	1045.62	82.00	0.9540
1.070	1114.546	9.185	1014.546	10.145	1045.46	82.04	0.9538
1.075	1114.891	9.185	1014.891	10.149	1045.26	82.08	0.9535

Table 9.12 Effect of Varying Temperature of Converter Exit Gas Mixture in Methanol Sysnthsis Loop

Basis: Fresh feed rate (F) = 100 kmol/s, H_2 content of feed = 70 mole %, Inerts in feed = 1 mole %
Inerts in mixed feed = 10 mole %

Temperature of gas leaving converter °C/K	Equilibrium Constant K	Mixed feed flow rate kmol/s	Purge stream flow rate kmol/s	Recycle streams R kmol/s	Recycle ratio R/F kmol/kmol	Aqueous methanol production kg/s	Concn. of solution, % CH_3OH (by mass)	Mole ratio in mixed feed CO/CO_2
275/548.15	69.000	1113.145	9.184	1013.145	10.131	1046.21	81.87	0.9547
300/573.15	47.941	1110.880	9.182	1010.880	10.109	1047.45	81.61	1.2904
325/598.15	34.326	1108.784	9.181	1008.784	10.088	1048.57	81.37	1.7025
350/623.15	25.246	1106.920	9.180	1006.920	10.069	1049.58	81.15	2.1950
375/648.15	19.013	1105.311	9.178	1005.311	10.053	1050.47	80.97	2.7694

Note A few intersting observations can be made from Tables 9.10 , 9.11 and 9.12.

(i) For a given fresh feed rate and hydrogen content of the fresh feed, production rate and concentration of aqueous methanol do not vary significantly. Thus hydrogen is the limiting reactant.

(ii) In Table 9.10, purge flow rate reduces with incersed inerts concentration of the mixed feed.

(iii) In Table 9.10 and 9.11, it can be seen that mole ratio of CO to CO_2 in the mixed feed vary in the narrow range with varations in (a) inerts content of the mixed feed, and also (b) the ratio of hydrogen to carbon oxides. However, this ratio varies (Table 9.12) over a wide range for the variation in the temperature of converter exit gas stream. This is because equilibrium constant of the shift reaction varies substantially with the temperature. **Variation in this ratio means corresponding variation in fresh feed which calls for significant changes in operation for production of synthesis (make-up) gas.** In actual design of methanol synthesis loop, equilibrium constants of reforming reactions for the species in a converter exit gas stream at a given temperature are also calculated. Approach to equilibrium is checked in terms of temperature and catalyst activity for reforming reactions also.

A few side reactions do take place in the converter to produce dimethyl ether, butanol, etc., in small quantities. These chemicals appear in aqueous methanol stream as impurities. Temperature of gas stream, exit of converter, plays a significant role in formation of these byproducts.

References

1. Rapier, P M; *Chem. Engg.* **80**(19), Aug. 20, 1973, p.114.
2. Benenati, R F; *Chem. Engg.* **84**(5), Feb. 28, 1977, p. 201.
3. _____, **84** (6), March 14, 1977, p.129.
4. Etter, D M; *Structured FORTRAN 77 for Engineers and Scientists,* 4th Ed., The Benjamin/ Cummings Publishing Co. Inc., Redwood City, USA, 1993.
5. Niyogi, P; *Numerical Analysis and Algorithms,* Tata McGraw-Hill Publishing Co. Ltd., New Delhi, 2003.
6. Rajaraman, V; *Computer Oriented Numerical Methods,* Prentice-Hall of India, New Delhi, 1971.
7. Forsythe, G E, Malcolm, M A and Moler, C B, *Computer Methods for Mathematical Computations,* Prentice-Hall, Englewood Cliff, NJ, USA, 1977.
8. Johnston, R L; *Numerical Methods — A Software Approach,* John Wiley & Sons, New York, NY, USA, 1982.
9. Davis, M E; *Numerical Methods and Modeling for Chemical Engineers,* John Wiley & Sons, New York, NY, USA, 1984.
10. Finlayson, B A; *Nonlinear Analysis in Chemical Engineering,* McGraw-Hill, New York, NY, 1980.
11. Lapidus, L; *Digital Computation for Chemical Engineers,* McGraw-Hill, New York, USA, 1972.
12. Kunzru, D and Kumar, V; *Indian Chem. Engg., Transactions,* Vol. XXII, No. 1, p. 35.
13. Dimian, A; *Chem. Engg. Progress,* **90**(9), 1994, p. 58.
14. Sowa, C J; *Chem. Engg. Progress,* **90**(11), 1994, p. 40.
15. Phillips, J E and DeCicco, J D; *Chem. Engg. Progress,* **95**(7), 1999, p. 69.
16. *Catalyst Handbook,* Springer-Verlag, New York, USA, 1970.
17. Itahara, S and Stiel, L L; *Ind. Engng. Chem. Proc. Des. and Develop.,* **5**; 1966, p. 309.
18. Bhatt, B I Deshpande, S P and Subrahmanyam, K; *Chemical Age of India,* **20**(12): 1970, p. 1135.

Conversion Tables

Table I.1 Length Units

	Metres (m)	Centimetres (cm)	Inches (inch)	Feet (ft)	Yards (yd)
m	1	100	39.370 08	3.280 84	1.093 613
cm	0.01	1	0.393 701	$3.280\ 84 \times 10^{-2}$	$1.093\ 613 \times 10^{-2}$
inch	0.0254	2.54	1	$8.333\ 333 \times 10^{-2}$	$2.777\ 778 \times 10^{-2}$
ft	0.3048	30.48	12	1	0.333 333
yd	0.9144	91.44	36	3	1

Table I.2 Area Units

	Square Metres (m^2)	Square Centimetres (cm^2)	Square Inches $(inch^2)$	Square Feet (ft^2)	Square Yards (yd^2)
m^2	1	10^4	1550.003	10.763 910	1.195 990
cm^2	10^{-4}	1	0.155	$1.076\ 391 \times 10^{-3}$	$1.195\ 99 \times 10^{-4}$
in^2	6.4516×10^{-4}	6.4516	1	$6.944\ 444 \times 10^{-3}$	$7.716\ 049 \times 10^{-4}$
ft^2	0.092 903	929.0304	144	1	0.111 111
yd^2	0.836 127	8361.274	1296	9	1

Table 1.3 Volume and Capacity Units

	Cubic Metres (m^3)	Cubic Centimetres (cm^3)	Cubic Inches $(inch^3)$	Cubic Feet (ft^3)	UK (Imperial) gallons (UK gal)	US gallons (US gal)
m^3	1	10^6	$6.102\ 376 \times 10^4$	35.314 66	219.969 25	264.172 037
cm^3	10^{-6}	1	$6.102\ 376 \times 10^{-2}$	$3.531\ 466 \times 10^{-5}$	$2.199\ 69 \times 10^{-4}$	$2.641\ 722 \times 10^{-4}$
in^3	$1.638\ 706 \times 10^{-5}$	16.387 06	1	$5.787\ 037 \times 10^{-4}$	$3.604\ 651 \times 10^{-3}$	$4.329\ 006 \times 10^{-3}$
ft^3	$2.831\ 685 \times 10^{-2}$	$2.831\ 685 \times 10^4$	1.728×10^3	1	6.228 88	7.480 52
UK gal	$4.546\ 09 \times 10^{-3}$	$4.546\ 09 \times 10^3$	$2.774\ 194 \times 10^2$	0.160 544	1	1.200 95
US gal	$3.785\ 412 \times 10^{-3}$	$3.7854\ 12 \times 10^3$	2.31×10^2	0.133 681	0.832 673	1

Table 1.4 Mass Units

	Kilograms (kg)	Grams (g)	Tonnes (t)	Pounds (av*) (lb)	Tons (T)	Tons (short) (Ts)
kg	1	1000	10^{-3}	2.204 622	9.8421×10^{-4}	$1.102\ 311 \times 10^{-3}$
g	10^{-3}	1	10^{-6}	$2.204\ 622 \times 10^{-3}$	9.8421×10^{-7}	$1.102\ 311 \times 10^{-6}$
t	1000	10^6	1	2204.622	0.984 21	1.102 311
lb	$453.592\ 37 \times 10^{-3}$	453.592 37	$4.535\ 924 \times 10^{-4}$	1	$4.464\ 286 \times 10^{-4}$	5×10^{-4}
T	1016.027	$1.016\ 271 \times 10^6$	1.016 271	2240	1	1.12
Ts	907.1847	$9.071\ 847 \times 10^5$	0.907 185	2000	0.892 857	1

*av refers to avoirdupois

Table I.5   Density and Concentration Units

	Kilograms per cubic metre (kg/m³)	Grams per cubic centimetre (g/cm³)†	Pounds per cubic foot (lb/ft³)	Pounds per UK gallon (lb/UK gal)	Pounds per US gallon (lb/US gal)
kg/m³	1	10^{-3}	$6.242\ 795 \times 10^{-2}$	$1.002\ 24 \times 10^{-2}$	$8.345\ 406 \times 10^{-3}$
g/cm³	1000	1	62.427 95	10.0224	8.345 406
lb/ft³	16.018 462	$1.601\ 846 \times 10^{-2}$	1	0.160 544	0.133 681
lb/UK gal	99.776 37	9.978×10^{-2}	6.228 837	1	0.832 674
lb/US gal	119.8264	0.119 826	7.480 517	1.200 95	1

† 1 g/cm³ = 1 t/m³ = 1.000 028 g/mL = 1.000 028 kg/L

Table I.6   Force Units

	Newtons (N)	Kilograms force (kgf)	Dynes (dyn)	Pounds-force (lbf)	Poundals (pdl)
N	1	0.101 972	10^5	0.224 809	7.233
kgf	9.806 65	1	$9.806\ 65 \times 10^5$	2.204 62	70.931 35
dyn	10^{-5}	$1.019\ 72 \times 10^{-6}$	1	$2.248\ 087 \times 10^{-6}$	7.233×10^{-5}
lbf	4.448 222	0.453 594	$4.448\ 222 \times 10^5$	1	32.174 03
pdl	0.138 255	$1.409\ 814 \times 10^{-2}$	$1.382\ 255 \times 10^4$	3.1081×10^{-2}	1

Table I.7 Pressure Units

	Newtons per square Metre (N/m² (Pa))	Bars (bar)	Standard Atmospheres (atm)	Kilograms-force per Square Centimetre (kgf/cm²)	Dynes per Square Centimetre (dyn/cm²)
N/m² (Pa)	1	10^{-5}	$9.869\ 232 \times 10^{-6}$	$1.019\ 716 \times 10^{-5}$	10
bar	10^{5}	1	0.986 923	1.019 716	10^{6}
atm	$1.013\ 25 \times 10^{5}$	1.013 25	1	1.033 23	$1.013\ 25 \times 10^{6}$
kgf/cm²	$9.806\ 65 \times 10^{4}$	0.980 665	0.967 841	1	$9.806\ 65 \times 10^{5}$
dyn/cm²	0.1	10^{-6}	$9.869\ 232 \times 10^{-7}$	$1.019\ 716 \times 10^{-6}$	1
Torr	133.3224	$1.333\ 224 \times 10^{-3}$	$1.315\ 79 \times 10^{-3}$	$1.359\ 51 \times 10^{-3}$	1333.224
inHg [0°C (273.15 K)]	3386.38	$3.386\ 385 \times 10^{-2}$	$3.342\ 1 \times 10^{-2}$	$3.453\ 15 \times 10^{-2}$	$3.386\ 38 \times 10^{4}$
mH₂O [0°C (273.15 K)]	2806.65	9.8067×10^{-2}	9.6784×10^{-2}	0.1	$9.806\ 65 \times 10^{4}$
ftH₂O [0°C (273.15 K)]	2989.067	2.989×10^{-2}	2.9499×10^{-2}	3.048×10^{-2}	$2.989\ 067 \times 10^{4}$
lbf/in²	6894.757	$6.894\ 731 \times 10^{-2}$	$6.804\ 596 \times 10^{-2}$	$7.030\ 694 \times 10^{-2}$	$6.894\ 757 \times 10^{4}$

	Torr or Barometric millimetres of mercury [0°C (273.15 K)] (Torr)	Barometric inches of mercury [0°C (273.15 K)] (inHg)	Head of water [0°C (273.15 K)] mH₂O	Head of water [0°C (273.15 K)] ftH₂O	Pounds-force per square inch (lbf/in²)
N/m² (Pa)	$7.500\ 615 \times 10^{-3}$	$2.953\ 005 \times 10^{-4}$	$1.019\ 72 \times 10^{-4}$	$3.345\ 53 \times 10^{-4}$	$1.450\ 377 \times 10^{-4}$
bar	750.0615	29.530 05	10.1972	33.4554	14.503 77
atm	760	29.921 26	10.332 313	33.898 58	14.695 95
kgf/cm²	735.559 16	28.959 03	10	32.808 44	14.223 34
dyn/cm²	$7.500\ 615 \times 10^{-4}$	$2.953\ 005 \times 10^{-5}$	$1.019\ 72 \times 10^{-5}$	$3.345\ 53 \times 10^{-5}$	$1.450\ 377 \times 10^{-5}$
Torr	1	$3.937\ 008 \times 10^{-2}$	$1.359\ 515 \times 10^{-2}$	$4.460\ 34 \times 10^{-2}$	$1.933\ 678 \times 10^{-2}$
inHg [0°C (273.15 K)]	25.4	1	0.345 316	1.132 92	0.491 154
mH₂O [0°C (273.15 K)]	73.5556	2.8959	1	3.280 82	1.422 332
ftH₂O [0°C (273.15 K)]	22.4198	0.882 676	0.3048	1	0.433 526
lbf/in²	51.714 918	2.036 020	$7.030\ 719 \times 10^{-1}$	2.306 667	1

Table I.8 Energy and Heat Units

	Joules (J)	Kilowatt hours (kWh)	Kilocalories ($kcal_{IT}$)	Kilogram-force metres (kgf·m)
J	1	$2.777\ 778 \times 10^{-7}$	$2.388\ 459 \times 10^{-4}$	0.101 972
kWh	3.6×10^6	1	859.8452	$3.670\ 98 \times 10^5$
$kcal_{IT}$	4186.8	1.163×10^{-3}	1	426.935
kgf.m	9.806 65	$2.724\ 06 \times 10^{-6}$	$2.342\ 27 \times 10^{-3}$	1
L.atm	101.325	$2.814\ 583 \times 10^{-5}$	$2.420\ 107 \times 10^{-2}$	10.332 275
Btu_{IT}	1055.056	$2.930\ 711 \times 10^{-4}$	0.251 996	107.586
lbf.ft	1.355 818	$3.766\ 161 \times 10^{-7}$	$3.238\ 315 \times 10^{-4}$	0.138 255

Table I.8 *(Contd).*

	Litre atmospheres (L·atm)	British thermal units (Btu_{IT})	Pound-force feet (lbf·ft)
J	$9.869\ 233 \times 10^{-3}$	$9.478\ 170 \times 10^{-4}$	0.737 562
kWh	$3.552\ 924 \times 10^4$	$3.412\ 142 \times 10^3$	$2.655\ 224 \times 10^6$
$kcal_{IT}$	41.3205	3.968 320	3088.025
kgf·m	$9.678\ 41 \times 10^{-2}$	$9.294\ 909 \times 10^{-3}$	7.233 014
L·atm	1	$9.603\ 756 \times 10^{-2}$	74.733 349
Btu_{IT}	10.412 598	1	778.1694
lbf·ft	$1.338\ 089 \times 10^{-2}$	$1.285\ 067 \times 10^{-3}$	1

Table I.9 Specific Energy Uinits

	Joules per kilogram (J/kg)	Kilocalories per kilogram ($kcal_{IT}$/kg)	Brithsh thermal unit per pound (Btu_{IT}/lb)
J/kg	1	$2.388\ 459 \times 10^{-4}$	$4.299\ 226 \times 10^{-4}$
$kcal_{IT}$/kg	4186.8	1	1.8
Btu_{IT}/lb	2326	0.555 556	1

Table I.10 Power Units

	Kilowatts (kW = kJ/s)	Kilogram force metre per second (kgf·m/s)	Metric horse powers (mhp)	Pound force feet per second (lbf·ft/s)	Horsepowers (hp)
kW	1	101.971 67	1.359 62	737.562	1.341 022
kgf·m/s	$9.806\ 65 \times 10^{-3}$	1	1.3333×10^{-2}	7.233	1.3151×10^{-2}
mhp	0.735 499	75	1	542.4766	0.986 32
lbf·ft/s	$1.355\ 82 \times 10^{-3}$	0.138 255	1.8434×10^{-3}	1	$1.818\ 184 \times 10^{-3}$
hp	0.7457	76.0402	1.013 87	550	1

Table I.11 Temperature Units

	Degrees Kelvin (K)	Degrees Celcius (°C)	Degrees Fahrenheit (°F)	Degrees Rankine (°R)
K	T	$t + 273.15$	$5/9\ (t' + 459.67)$	$5/9\ T'$
°C	$T - 273.15$	t	$5/9\ (t' - 32)$	$5/9\ (T' - 459.67)$
°F	$9/5\ T - 459.67$	$9/5\ t + 32$	t'	$T' - 459.67$
°R	$9/5\ T$	$9/5\ t + 459.67$	$t' + 459.67$	T'

Reference
Thompson, A and Taylor, B N, *Guide for the Use of the International System of Units (SI)*, NIST Special Publication 811, 2008 Edition, National Institute of Standards and Technology, Gaithersburg, MD, USA, March, 2008.

List of Elements

Table II   List of Elements in Alphabetical Order with Atomic Mass (2005) Based on $^{12}C = 12$

Element	Symbol	Atomic Number	Atomic Mass (Atomic Weight)
Actinium	Ac	89	227.027 8*
Aluminium (Aluminum)	Al	13	26.981 538 6
Americium	Am	95	243.061 4*
Antimony (Stibium)	Sb	51	121.760
Argon	Ar	18	39.948
Arsenic	As	33	74.921 60
Astatine	At	85	209.987 1*
Barium	Ba	56	137.327
Berkelium	Bk	97	247.070 3*
Beryllium	Be	4	9.012 182
Bismuth	Bi	83	208.980 40
Bohrium	Bh	107	272.138 0*
Boron	B	5	10.811
Bromine	Br	35	79.904
Cadmium	Cd	48	112.411
Caesium (Cesium)	Cs	55	132.905 451 9
Calcium	Ca	20	40.078
Californium	Cf	98	251.079 6
Carbon	C	6	12.010 7
Cerium	Ce	58	140.116
Chlorine	Cl	17	35.453
Chromium	Cr	24	51.996 1
Cobalt	Co	27	58.933 195
Copper (Cuprum)	Cu	29	63.546
Curium	Cm	96	247.070 4
Darmstadtium	Ds	110	281.162*
Dubnium	Db	105	268.125 5*
Dysprosium	Dy	66	162.500
Einsteinium	Es	99	252.083 0*

(Contd.)

Table II (*Contd.*)

Element	Symbol	Atomic Number	Atomic Mass (Atomic Weight)
Erbium	Er	68	167.259
Europium	Eu	63	151.964
Fermium	Fm	100	257.095 1*
Fluorine	F	9	18.998 403 2
Francium	Fr	87	223.019 7*
Gadolinium	Gd	64	157.25
Gallium	Ga	31	69.723
Germanium	Ge	32	72.64
Gold (Aurum)	Au	79	196.966 569
Hafnium	Hf	72	178.49
Hassium	Hs	108	277.150*
Helium	He	2	4.002 602
Holmium	Ho	67	164.930 32
Hydrogen (Protium)	^{1}H	1	1.007 94
Hydrogen (Deuterium)	^{2}H (also D)	1	2.014 102
Hydrogen (Tritium)	^{3}H (also T)	1	3.016 029*
Indium	In	49	114.818
Iodine	I	53	126.904 47
Iridium	Ir	77	192.217
Iron (Ferrum)	Fe	26	55.845
Krypton	Kr	36	83.798
Lanthanum	La	57	138.905 47
Lawrencium	Lr	103	262.109 6*
Lead (Plumbum)	Pb	82	207.2
Lithium	Li	3	6.941
Lutetium	Lu	71	174.967
Magnesium	Mg	12	24.305 0
Manganese	Mn	25	54.938 045
Meitnerium	Mt	109	276.151 2*
Mendelevium	Md	101	258.098 4*
Mercury (Hydrargyrum)	Hg	80	200.59
Molybdenum	Mo	42	95.94
Neodymium	Nd	60	144.242
Neon	Ne	10	20.179 7
Neptunium	Np	93	237.048 2*
Nickel	Ni	28	58.693 4
Niobium	Nb	41	92.906 38
Nitrogen	N	7	14.006 7
Nobelium	No	102	259.101 0*
Osmium	Os	76	190.23
Oxygen	O	8	15.999 4
Palladium	Pd	46	106.42
Phosphorus	P	15	30.973 762
Platinum	Pt	78	195.084
Plutonium	Pu	94	244.064 2
Polonium	Po	84	209.982 9
Potassium (Kalium)	K	19	39.098 3
Praseodymium	Pr	59	140.907 65

(*Contd.*)

Table II (*Contd.*)

Element	Symbol	Atomic Number	Atomic Mass (Atomic Weight)
Promethium	Pm	61	144.912 7*
Protactinium	Pa	91	231.035 88
Radium	Ra	88	226.025 4
Radon	Rn	86	220.011 4
Roentgenium	Rg	111	280.164 5*
Rhenium	Re	75	186.207
Rhodium	Rh	45	102.905 50
Rubidium	Rb	37	85.467 8
Ruthenium	Ru	44	101.07
Rutherfordium	Rf	104	267.121 5*
Samarium	Sm	62	150.36
Scandium	Sc	21	44.955 912
Seaborgium	Sg	106	271.133 5*
Selenium	Se	34	78.96
Silicon	Si	14	28.085 5
Silver (Argentum)	Ag	47	107.868 2
Sodium (Natrium)	Na	11	22.989 769 28
Strontium	Sr	38	87.62
Sulphur	S	16	32.065
Tantalum	Ta	73	180.947 88
Technetium	Tc	43	97.907 2*
Tellurium	Te	52	127.60
Terbium	Tb	65	158.925 35
Thallium	Tl	81	204.383 3
Thorium	Th	90	232.038 1
Thulium	Tm	69	168.934 21
Tin (Stannum)	Sn	50	118.710
Titanium	Ti	22	47.867
Tungsten (Wolfram)	W	74	183.84
Ununbium	Uub	112	285.174*
Ununhexium	Uuh	116	
Ununoctium	Uuo	118	
Ununpentium	Uup	115	288.192*
Ununquadium	Uuq	114	289.189*
Ununtrium	Uut	113	284.178*
Uranium	U	92	238.050 8
Vanadium	V	23	50.941 5
Xenon	Xe	54	131.293
Ytterbium	Yb	70	173.04
Yttrium	Y	39	88.905 85
Zinc	Zn	30	65.409
Zirconium	Zr	40	91.224

*The value represents atomic mass (weight) of the isotope having the longest half-life.
Reprinted with permission of **International Union of Pure and Applied Chemistry** from Wieser, M E; *Pure Appl. Chem.*, Vol. 78, No. 11, (2006), p. 2051-2066, ©2006 **IUPAC**, USA.

Note IUPAC *does not recommend change of the term 'atomic weight' to 'atomic mass' because the former is clearly understood and widely accepted by chemists without ambiguity. However, the International Bureau of Weights and Measures (BIPM), France recommends use of the term 'atomic mass'.*

Critical Constants of Compounds

Appendix III.1 Critical Constants of Inorganic Compounds

Compound	CAS Reg. No.*	Chemical formula	Molar mass M kg/kmol	Critical temperature T_c K	Critical pressure p_c bar	Critical vol. V_c dm^3/kmol
Air (Pseudo properties) (R^{**}-729)	—	—	28.9697	132.45	37.72	88.3
Ammonia (R-717)	7664-41-7	NH_3	17.0305	405.5	113.5	72.0
Argon (R-740)	7440-37-1	Ar	39.948	150.69	48.63	75.2
Bromine	7726-95-6	Br_2	159.808	588.00	103.00	127.0
Carbon dioxide (R-744)	124-38-9	CO_2	44.0095	304.10	73.75	94.0
Carbon disulphide	75-15-0	CS_2	76.1407	552.00	73.00	173.0
Carbon monoxide	630-08-0	CO	28.0101	132.91	34.99	93.0
Chlorine	7782-50-5	Cl_2	70.906	416.90	79.77	124.0
Cyanogen	460-19-5	C_2N_2	52.0348	400.00	59.80	199.5
Deuterium	7782-39-0	D_2	4.0282	38.40	16.60	60.0
Fluorine	7782-41-4	F_2	37.9968	144.30	52.15	66.0
Helium-4 (R-704)	7440-59-7	He	4.0026	5.30	2.29	57.8
Hydrazine	302-01-2	N_2H_4	32.0452	653.00	147.00	103.8

(Contd.)

---

*Represents Chemical Abstracts Service registry number.
**R stands for refrigerent designation, based on ASHRAE Standard 34-1992.

Appendix III.1 *(Contd.)*

Compound	CAS Reg. No.	Chemical formula	Molar mass M kg/kmol	Critical temperature T_c K	Critical pressure p_c bar	Critical vol. V_c dm³/kmol
Hydrogen (normal) (R-702)	1333-74-0	H_2	2.0159	33.20	12.97	65.0
Hydrogen (normal) (R-702)	1333-74-0	H_2	2.0159	33.20	12.97	65.0
Hydrogen bromide	10035-10-6	HBr	80.9119	363.20	85.50	103.2
Hydrogen chloride	7647-01-0	HCl	36.4609	324.70	83.10	81.0
Hydrogen cyanide	74-90-8	NCN	27.0253	456.79	53.90	139.0
Hydrogen fluoride	7664-39-3	HF	20.0063	461.00	64.80	69.0
Hydrogen iodide	10034-85-2	HI	127.9124	424.00	53.10	129.1
Hydrogen sulphide	7783-06-4	H_2S	34.0809	373.54	90.08	98.0
Iodine	7553-56-02	I_2	253.8089	819.00	53.52	218.2
Neon (R-720)	7440-01-9	Ne	20.1797	44.50	27.25	41.7
Nitric oxide	10102-43-9	NO	30.0061	180.00	64.80	58.0
Nitrogen (R-728)	7727-37-9	N_2	28.0134	126.09	33.94	139.0
Nitrogen tetroxide (Nitrogen dioxide)	10102-44-0	NO_2	46.0055	431.00	101.00	167.0
Nitrous Oxide (R-744A)	10024-97-2	N_2O	44.0128	309.60	72.40	97.0
Oxygen (R-732)	7782-44-7	O_2	31.9988	154.58	50.42	73.0
Ozone	10028-15-6	O_3	47.9982	268.00	67.88	89.4
Sulphur Dioxide (R-764)	7446-09-5	SO_2	64.0638	430.80	78.84	122.0
Sulphur Trioxide	7446-11-9	SO_3	80.0632	491.00	82.10	127.0
Water (R-718)	7732-18-5	H_2O	18.0153	647.3	221.2	55.9

Reference: Somayajulu, G R, *J. Chem. Engg. Data*, Vol. 34, 1989, p. 106-120.

Appendix III.2 Critical Constants of Organic Compounds

Compound	Systematic Name	CAS Reg. No.	Chemical Formula	Molar Mass M kg/kmol	Critical Temperature T_c K	Critical Pressure p_c MPa	Critical Volume V_c cm^3/mol	Ref.
A. Normal Alkanes								
Methane	Methane	74-82-8	CH_4	16.0425	190.564	4.599	98.60	1
Ethane	Ethane	74-84-0	C_2H_6	30.0690	305.32	4.872	145.5	1
Propane	Propane	74-98-6	C_3H_8	44.0956	369.83	4.248	200	1
n-Butane	1-Butane	106-97-8	C_4H_{10}	58.1222	425.12	3.796	255	1
n-Pentane	1-Pentane	109-66-0	C_5H_{12}	72.1488	469.7	3.370	311	1
n-Hexane	1-Hexane	110-54-3	C_6H_{14}	86.1754	507.6	3.025	368	1
n-heptane	1-Heptane	142-82-5	C_7H_{16}	100.2019	540.2	2.74	428	1
n-Octane	1-Octane	111-65-9	C_8H_{18}	114.2285	568.7	2.49	492	1
n-Nonane	1-Nonane	111-84-2	C_9H_{20}	128.2551	594.6	2.29	555	1
n-Decane	1-Decane	124-18-5	$C_{10}H_{22}$	142.2817	617.7	2.11	624	1
B. Branched Alkanes and Cycloalkanes								
Isobuatane	2-Methylpropane	75-28-5	C_4H_{10}	58.1222	407.8	3.640	259	2
Isopentane	2-Methylbutane	78-78-4	C_5H_{12}	72.1488	460.4	3.38	306	2
Neopentane	2,2-Dimethylpropane	463-82-1	C_5H_{12}	72.1488	433.8	3.196	307	2
Isohexane	2-Methylpentane	107-83-5	C_6H_{14}	86.1754	497.7	3.04	368	2
3-Methylpentane	3-Methylpentane	96-14-0	C_6H_{14}	86.1754	504.6	3.12	368	2
Neohexane	2,2-Dimethylbutane	75-83-2	C_6H_{14}	86.1754	489.0	3.10	358	2
Diisopropyl	2,3-Dimethylbutane	79-29-8	C_6H_{14}	86.1754	500.0	3.15	361	2
Cyclohexane (Benzene Hydride)	Hexahydrobenzene	110-82-7	C_6H_{12}	84.1595	553.8	4.08	308	2
Styrene	Vinylbenzene	100-42-5	C_8H_8	104.1491	635.2	3.87	—	2

(Contd.)

Appendix III.2   (Contd.)

Compound	Systematic Name	CAS Reg. No.	Chemical Formula	Molar Mass M kg/kmol	Critical Temperature T_c K	Critical Pressure p_c MPa	Critical Volume V_c cm³/mol	Ref.
C. Unsaturated Aliphatic Hydrocarbons								
Ethylene	Ethene	74-85-1	C_2H_4	28.0532	282.34	5.041	131.1	3
Propylene	Propene	115-07-1	C_3H_6	42.0797	364.9	4.60	184.6	3
1-Butene (But-1-ene)	1-Butylene	106-98-9	C_4H_8	56.1063	419.5	4.02	240.8	3
cis-But-2-ene	(Z)-But-2-ene	590-18-1	C_4H_8	56.1063	435.5	4.21	233.8	3
trans-But-2-ene	(E)-But-2-ene	624-64-6	C_4H_8	56.1063	428.6	4.10	237.7	3
Isobutene (Isobutylene)	2-Methyl-1-propene	115-11-7	C_4H_8	56.1063	417.9	4.00	238.8	3
Allene	1,2-Propadiene	463-49-0	C_3H_4	40.0639	394	5.25	—	3
1,3-Butadiene (trans-Bu-tadiene)	Divinyl (Vinylethylene)	106-99-0	C_4H_6	54.0904	425	4.32	221	3
n-Pentene (Pent-1-ene)	α-Amylene	109-67-1	C_5H_{10}	70.1329	464.8	3.56	298.4	3
Acetylene	Ethyne	74-86-2	C_2H_2	26.0373	308.3	6.138	112.2	3
Methylacetylene (Allylene)	Propyne	74-99-7	C_3H_4	40.0639	402.4	5.63	163.5	3
Ethylacetylene (Ethyl-ethyne)	But-1-yne	107-00-6	C_4H_6	54.0904	440	4.60	208	3
D. Aromatic Hydrocarbons								
Benzene	(6)Annulene	71-43-2	C_6H_6	78.1118	562.05	4.895	256	4
Toluene	Methylbenzene (Phenylmethane)	108-88-3	C_7H_8	92.1384	591.75	4.108	316	4
Ethylbenzene	Phenylethane	100-41-4	C_8H_{10}	106.1650	617.15	3.609	374	4
o-Xylene	1,2-Dimethylbenzene	95-47-6	C_8H_{10}	106.1650	630.3	3.732	370	4
m-Xylene	1,3-Dimethylbenzene	108-38-3	C_8H_{10}	106.1650	**617.0**	3.541	375	4
p-Xylene	1,4-Dimethylbenzene	106-42-3	C_8H_{10}	106.1650	616.2	3.511	378	4

(Contd.)

Appendix III.2 *(Contd.)*

Compound	Systematic Name	CAS Reg. No.	Chemical Formula	Molar Mass M kg/kmol	Critical Temperature T_c K	Critical Pressure p_c MPa	Critical Volume V_c cm^3/mol	Ref.
Biphenyl	Diphenyl (Phenylbenzene)	92-52-4	$C_{12}H_{10}$	154.2078	773	3.38	497	4
Naphthalene	Naphthalene	91-20-3	$C_{10}H_8$	128.1705	748.4	4.05	407	4
E. Aliphatic Alkanols								
Methanol	Methyl alcohol	67-56-1	CH_4O	32.0419	512.5	8.084	117	5
Ethanol	Ethyl alcohol	64-17-5	C_2H_6O	46.0684	514.0	6.137	168	5
n-Propanol (n-Propyl alcohol)	1-Propanol	71-23-8	C_3H_8O	60.0950	536.8	5.169	218	5
Isopropanol (Isopropyl alcohol)	2-Propanol	67-63-0	C_3H_8O	60.0950	508.3	4.764	222	5
n-Butanol (n-Butyl alcohol)	1-Butanol	71-36-3	$C_4H_{10}O$	74.1216	563.0	4.414	274	5
Isobutanol (Isobutyl alcohol)	2-Methyl-1-Propanol	78-83-1	$C_4H_{10}O$	74.1216	547.8	4.295	274	5
sec-Butanol (sec-butyl alcohol)	2-Butanol	78-92-2	$C_4H_{10}O$	74.1216	536.2	4.202	269	5
tert-Butanol (tert-Butyl alcohol)	2-Methyl-2-Propanol	75-65-0	$C_4H_{10}O$	74.1216	506.2	3.972	275	5
F. Oxygen Compounds other than Alkanols								
Ethylene Glycol (Mono)	1,2-Ethanediol	107-21-1	$C_2H_6O_2$	62.0678	720	8	—	6
1,2-Propylene Glycol	1,2-Propanediol	57-55-6	$C_3H_8O_2$	76.0944	676	5.9	—	6
Glycerine (Glycerol)	1,2,3-Propanetriol	56-81-5	$C_3H_8O_3$	92.0938	850	7.5	—	6

(Contd.)

Appendix III.2   (*Contd.*)

Compound	Systematic Name	CAS Reg. No.	Chemical Formula	Molar Mass M kg/kmol	Critical Temperature T_c K	Critical Pressure p_c MPa	Critical Volume V_c cm^3/mol	Ref.
Acetaldehyde	Ethanal	75-07-0	C_2H_4O	44.0526	466	—	154	6
Propionaldehyde	Propanal	123-38-6	C_3H_6O	58.0791	505	5.26	204	6
Acetone	2-Propanone	67-64-1	C_3H_6O	58.0791	508.1	4.700	213	6
Methyl Ethyl Ketone	2-Butanone	78-93-3	C_4H_8O	72.1057	536.7	4.207	267	6
Acetic Anhydride	Ethanoic Anhydride	108-24-7	$C_4H_6O_3$	102.0886	606	4.0	—	6
Formic Acid	Methanoic Acid	64-18-6	CH_2O_2	46.0254	588	—	—	6
Acetic Acid	Ethanoic Acid	64-19-7	$C_2H_4O_2$	60.0520	590.7	5.78	171	6
Propionic Acid	Propanoic Acid	79-09-4	$C_3H_6O_2$	74.0785	598.5	4.67	233	6
n-Butyric Acid	n-Butanoic Acid	107-92-6	$C_4H_8O_2$	88.1051	615.2	4.06	292	6
Methyl Formate	Methyl Methanoate	107-31-3	$C_2H_4O_2$	60.0520	487.2	6.00	172	6
Ethyl Formate	Ethyl Methanoate	109-94-4	$C_3H_6O_2$	74.0785	508.4	4.74	229	6
Methyl Acetate	Methyl Ethanoate	79-20-9	$C_3H_6O_2$	74.0785	506.5	4.750	228	6
Ethyl Acetate	Ethyl Ethanoate	141-78-6	$C_4H_8O_2$	88.1051	523.3	3.87	286	6
Propyl Acetate	Propyl Ethanoate	105-37-3	$C_5H_{10}O_2$	102.1317	549.7	3.36	345	6
Butyl Acetate	Butyl Ethanoate	123-86-4	$C_6H_{12}O_2$	116.1583	575.6	3.14	—	6
Dimethyl Ether (Methyl Ether)	Methoxymethane	115-10-6	C_2H_6O	46.0684	400.2	5.34	168	6
Ethyl Methyl Ether (Methyl Ethyl Ether)	Methoxyethane	540-67-0	C_3H_8O	60.0950	437.9	4.38	222	6
Ethyl tert-butyl Ether	2-Ethoxy-2-methyl Propane	637-92-3	$C_6H_{14}O$	102.1748	509.4	2.934	395	6
Diethyl Ether	Ethoxyethane (R-610)	60-29-7	$C_4H_{10}O$	74.1216	466.7	3.644	281	6

(*Contd.*)

Appendix III.2 (Contd.)

Compound	Systematic Name	CAS Reg. No.	Chemical Formula	Molar Mass M kg/kmol	Critical Temperature T_c K	Critical Pressure p_c MPa	Critical Volume V_c cm^3/mol	Ref.
Methyl *tert*-butyl Ether	2-Methoxy-2-methyl Propane	1634-04-4	$C_5H_{12}O$	88.1482	497.1	3.430	—	6
Phenol	Hydroxybenzene	108-95-2	C_6H_6O	94.1112	694.2	5.93	—	6
o-Cresol	2-Methylphenol	95-48-7	C_7H_8O	108.1378	697.6	4.17	—	6
m-Cresol	3-Methylphenol	108-39-4	C_7H_8O	108.1378	705.8	4.36	—	6
p-Cresol	4-Methylphenol	106-44-5	C_7H_8O	108.1378	704.6	4.07	—	6
Benzaldehyde	Phenylmethanal	100-52-7	C_7H_6O	106.1219	695	4.7	—	6
Ethylene Oxide (Oxirane)	1,2-Epoxyethane (Ethene Oxide)	75-21-8	C_2H_4O	44.0526	469	7.2	142	6
Propylene Oxide (Methyloxirane)	1,2-Epoxypropane	75-56-9	C_3H_6O	58.0791	485	5.2	190	6
Tetrahydrofuran (Oxolane) (Tetramethylene oxide) (Oxacyclopentane)	1,4-Epoxybutane	109-99-9	C_4H_8O	72.1057	540.5	5.19	224	6
Furan (Oxole)	Oxacyclopentadiene	110-00-9	C_4H_4O	68.0740	490.2	5.3	218	6
Furfural (Furfuraldehyde) (Furfurol)	2-Furancarboxaldehyde	98-01-1	$C_5H_4O_2$	96.0841	670	5.51	—	6
G. Organic Sulphur Compounds								
Dimethyl Sulphide	2-Thiapropane	75-18-3	C_2H_6S	62.1340	503	5.53	203.7	7
Ethyl Methyl Sulphide	2-Thiabutane	624-89-5	C_3H_8S	76.1606	533	4.25	—	7
Methyl Mercaptan	Methanethiol	74-93-1	CH_4S	48.1075	470	7.23	147	7
Ethyl Mercaptan	Ethanethiol	75-08-1	C_2H_6S	62.1340	499	5.49	207	7
Thiophene	Thiocyclopentadiene	110-02-1	C_4H_4S	84.1396	580	5.70	219	7

(Contd.)

Appendix III.2 *(Contd.)*

Compound	Systematic Name	CAS Reg. No.	Chemical Formula	Molar Mass M kg/kmol	Critical Temperature T_c K	Critical Pressure p_c MPa	Critical Volume V_c cm^3/mol	Ref.
H. Organic Compounds Containing Nitrogen								
Methyl Amine (R-630)	Methanamine (R-630)	74-89-5	CH_5N	31.0571	430.8	7.62	141	8
(Mono) Ethanol Amine	2-Aminoethanol	141-43-5	C_2H_7NO	61.0831	675	7.6	—	8
Ethyl Amine (R-631)	Ethanamine (R-631)	75-04-7	C_2H_7N	45.0837	456	5.6	180	8
n-Propyl Amine	1-Propanamine	107-10-8	C_3H_9N	59.1103	499	4.74	—	8
n-Butyl Amine	1-Butanamine	109-73-9	$C_4H_{11}N$	73.1368	531.9	4.20	—	8
Dimethyl Amine	N-Methylmethanamine	124-40-3	C_2H_7N	45.0837	437.2	5.34	304	8
Diethyl Amine	N-Ethylethanamine	109-89-7	$C_4H_{11}N$	73.1368	499.7	3.754	135	8
Hydrogen Cyanide (Hydrocyanic Acid)	Methanenitrile	74-90-8	CHN	27.0253	457	5.4		8
Acetonitrile (Methyl cyanide)	Ethanenitrile	75-05-8	C_2H_3N	41.0519	545.5	4.85	171	8
Acrylonitrile	Prop-2-enenitrile	107-13-1	C_3H_3N	53.0626	540	4.66	—	8
Cyanogen	Ethanedinitrile	460-19-5	C_2N_2	52.0348	400	6.0	—	8
Aniline	Benzenamine	62-53-3	C_6H_7N	93.1265	705	5.63	291	8
o-Toluidine (*o*-Methyl Aniline)	2-Methylbenzenamine	95-53-4	C_7H_9N	107.1531	717	4.7	346	8
m-Toluidine (*m*-Methyl Aniline)	3-Methylbenzenamine	108-44-1	C_7H_9N	107.1531	709	4.2	—	8
p-Toluidine (*p*-Methyl Aniline)	4-Methylbenzenamine	106-49-0	C_7H_9N	107.1531	667	2.4	—	8
Pyridine (Azine)	Azabenzene	110-86-1	C_5H_5N	79.0999	620.0	5.65	247	8

(Contd.)

Appendix III.2 (Contd.)

Compound	Systematic Name	CAS Reg. No.	Chemical Formula	Molar Mass M kg/kmol	Critical Temperature T_c K	Critical Pressure p_c MPa	Critical Volume V_c cm^3/mol	Ref.
I. Organic Compound Containing Halogens								
Chlorotrifluoromethane	R-13	75-72-9	$CClF_3$	104.4589	301.95	3.88	180	9
Dichlorodifluoromethane	R-12	75-71-8	CCl_2F_2	120.9135	385.0	4.13	214	9
Trichlorofluoromethane	R-11	75-69-4	CCl_3F	137.3681	471.1	4.48	248	9
Carbon Tetrachloride	Tetrachloromethane (R-10)	56-23-5	CCl_4	153.8227	556.3	4.54	276	9
Chlorodifluoromethane	R-22	75-45-6	$CHClF_2$	86.4684	369.25	4.99	165	9
Chloroform	Trichloromethane (R-20)	67-66-3	$CHCl_3$	119.3776	536.2	5.33	244	9
Fluoroform	Trifluoromethane (R-23)	75-46-7	CHF_3	70.0138	299.00	4.80	135	9
Methylene Chloride	Dichloromethane (R-30)	75-09-2	CH_2Cl_2	84.9326	508.0	6.35	—	9
Methylene Fluoride	Difluoromethane (R-32)	75-10-5	CH_2F_2	52.0234	351.25	5.783	122	9
Methyl Chloride	Chloromethane (R-40)	74-87-3	CH_3Cl	50.4875	416.25	6.68	140	9
Methyl Fluoride	Fluoromethane (R-41)	593-53-3	CH_3F	34.0329	317.4	5.87	109	9
1,1,1-Trichloroethane	Methyl Chloroform	71-55-6	$C_2H_3Cl_3$	133.4042	550	4.30	—	9
1,1,2-Tetrafluoroethane	R-134a	811-97-2	$C_2H_2F_4$	102.0309	374.18	4.055	199	9
1,1-Dichloro-2,2,2-Trifluoroethane	R-123	306-83-2	$C_2HCl_2F_3$	152.9305	456.85	3.670	277	9

(Contd.)

Appendix III.2 (*Contd.*)

Compound	Systematic Name	CAS Reg. No.	Chemical Formula	Molar Mass M kg/kmol	Critical Temperature T_c K	Critical Pressure p_c MPa	Critical Volume V_c cm^3/mol	Ref.
Ethylene Dichloride	1,2-Dichloroethane	107-06-2	$C_2H_4Cl_2$	98.9592	561.5	5.38	225	9
Ethylidene Chloride	1,1-Dichloroethane	75-34-3	$C_2H_4Cl_2$	98.9592	523.4	5.06	236	9
Ethyl Bromide	Bromoethane	74-96-4	C_2H_5Br	108.9651	504	5.8	214	9
Ethyl Chloride	Chloroethane	75-00-3	C_2H_5Cl	64.5141	460	5.2	—	9
Ethyl Fluoride	Fluoroethane (R-161)	353-36-6	C_2H_5F	48.0595	375.3	5.04	159	9
Bromobenzene	Phenyl bromide	108-86-1	C_6H_5Br	157.0079	670	—	—	9
Chlorobenzene	Phenyl Chloride	108-90-7	C_6H_5Cl	112.5569	633	4.53	308	9
Fluorobenzene	Phenyl fluoride	462-06-6	C_6H_5F	96.1023	560.1	4.55	268	9

Extracted and compiled from following references:

1. Ambrose D and Tsonopoulos, C; *J. Chem. Engg. Data*, Vol. 40, 1995, p. 531-546.
2. Daubert T E; *J. Chem. Engg. Data*, Vol. 41, 1996, p. 365-372.
3. Tsonopoulos, C and Ambrose, D; *J. Chem. Engg. Data*, Vol. 41, 1996, p. 645-656.
4. Tsonopoulos, C and Ambrose, D; *J. Chem. Engg. Data*, Vol. 40, 1995, p. 547-558.
5. Gude M and Teja, A S; *J. Chem. Engg. Data*, Vol. 40, 1995, p. 1025-1036.
6. Kudchadker, A P, Ambrose, D and Tsonopoulos, C; *J. Chem. Engg. Data*, Vol. 46, 2001, p. 457-479.
7. Tsonopoulos, C and Ambrose, D; *J. Chem. Engg. Data*, Vol. 46, 2001, p. 480-485.
8. Marsh, K N, Young, C L, Morton, D W; Ambrose, D. and Tsonopoulos, C; *J. Chem. Engg. Data*, Vol. 51, 2006, p. 305-314.
9. Marsh, K N, Abramson, A, Ambrose, D; Morton, D W; Nikitin, E. Tsonopoulos, C. and Yound, C L; *J. Chem. Engg. Data*, Vol. 52, 2007, p. 1509-1538.

(*Reproduced with the permission of the American Chemical Society, USA*)

Steam Tables

Notation

p = Absolute pressure in Torr, kPa or MPa
t = Saturation temperature in °C
T = Saturation temperature in K
v = Specific volume of superheated steam in m³/kg
v' = Specific volume of saturated or compressed water in m³/kg
v'' = Specific volume of saturated steam in m³/kg
h = Specific enthalpy of saturated or compressed water in kJ/kg
H = Specific enthalpy of saturated steam in kJ/kg
i = Specific enthalpy of superheated steam in kJ/kg
λ_v = Latent heat of vaporization of saturated water in kJ/kg
s = Specific entropy of superheated steam in kJ/(kg·K)
s' = Specific entropy of saturated or compressed water in kJ/(kg·K)
s'' = Specific entropy of saturated steam in kJ/(kg·K)

Table IV.1 Properties of Saturated Water and Saturated Steam Up to 1 Atmospheric Pressure

Pressure, p		Temperature		Specific volume, m³/kg		Specific Enthalpy, kJ/kg			Specific Entropy, kJ/(kg·K)		Pressure, p
kPa	Torr or mmHg	t °C	T K	v'	v''	h	H	λv	s'	s''	kPa
0.6108	4.6	0	273.15	0.001000 22	206.305	−0.042	2501.6	2501.6	−0.00015	9.15773	0.6108
0.6112	**4.6**	**0.01**	**273.16***	**0.001000 22**	**206.163**	**0**	**2501.6**	**2501.6**	**0**	**9.157 46**	**0.6112**
1.0	7.5	6.983	280.133	0.001000 07	129.209	29.335	2514.4	2485.0	0.10604	8.97667	1.0
1.5	11.3	13.036	286.186	0.001000 57	87.9821	54.715	2525.5	2470.7	0.19567	8.82883	1.5
2.0	15.0	17.513	290.663	0.001 001 24	67.0061	73.457	2533.6	2460.2	0.26065	8.72456	2.0
2.5	18.8	21.096	294.246	0.001001 96	54.2562	88.446	2540.2	2451.7	0.31191	8.64403	2.5
3.0	22.5	24.100	297.250	0.001002 66	45.6673	101.003	2545.6	2444.6	0.35436	8.578 48	3.0
3.166	**23.7**	**25.000**	**298.150**	**0.001002 89**	**43.4017**	**104.767**	**2547.3**	**2442.5**	**0.36701**	**8.55916**	**3.166**
3.5	26.3	26.694	299.844	0.001003 34	39.4787	111.845	2550.4	2438.5	0.39068	8.52322	3.5
4.0	30.0	28.983	302.133	0.001004 00	34.8022	121.412	2554.5	2433.1	0.42246	8.47548	4.0
4.5	33.8	31.03	304.180	0.001004 63	31.1408	129.988	2558.2	2428.2	0.45075	8.43347	4.5
5.0	37.5	32.90	306.050	0.001005 23	28.1944	137.772	2561.6	2423.8	0.47626	8.39596	5.0
5.5	41.3	34.61	307.760	0.001005 82	25.7707	144.908	2564.7	2419.8	0.49951	8.36210	5.5
6.0	45.0	36.18	309.330	0.001006 37	23.7410	151.502	2567.5	2416.0	0.52088	8.33124	6.0
6.5	48.8	37.65	310.800	0.00100691	22.0159	157.636	2570.2	2412.5	0.54066	8.30289	6.5
7.0	52.5	39.02	312.170	0.001 00743	20.5310	163.376	2572.6	2409.2	0.55909	8.27669	7.0
7.5	56.3	40.32	313.470	0.00100793	19.2391	168.771	2574.9	2406.2	0.57633	8.25233	7.5

(*Contd.*)

* reference state

Table IV.1 (Contd.)

Pressure, p		Temperature		Specific volume, m³/kg		Specific Enthalpy, kJ/kg			Specific Entropy, kJ/(kg·K)		Pressure, p
kPa	Torr or mmHg	t °C	T K	v'	v''	h	H	λ_v	s'	s''	kPa
8.0	60.0	41.53	314.680	0.00100842	18.1046	173.865	2577.1	2403.2	0.59255	8.22956	8.0
8.5	63.8	42.69	315.840	0.00100889	17.1001	178.691	2579.2	2400.5	0.60786	8.20821	8.5
9.0	67.5	43.79	316.940	0.00100935	16.2043	183.279	2581.1	2397.9	0.62235	8.18810	9.0
9.5	71.3	44.83	317.98	0.00100980	15.4003	187.652	2583.0	2395.3	0.63613	8.16909	9.5
10	75.0	45.83	318.98	0.00101023	14.6746	191.832	2584.8	2392.9	0.64925	8.15108	10
11	82.5	47.71	320.86	0.00101106	13.4161	199.680	2588.1	2388.4	0.67378	8.11766	11
12	90.0	49.45	322.60	0.00101186	12.3619	206.938	2591.2	2384.3	0.69634	8.08721	12
13	97.5	51.06	324.21	0.00101262	11.4657	213.695	2594.0	2380.3	0.71723	8.05924	13
14	105.0	52.57	325.72	0.00101334	10.6942	220.022	2596.7	2376.7	0.73669	8.03338	14
15	112.5	54.00	327.15	0.00101404	10.0228	225.973	2599.2	2373.2	0.75492	8.00933	15
16	120.0	55.34	328.49	0.00101471	9.43314	231.595	2601.6	2370.0	0.77207	7.98687	16
17	127.5	56.61	329.76	0.00101536	8.91095	236.925	2603.8	2366.9	0.78826	7.96580	17
18	135.0	57.83	330.98	0.00101599	8.44521	241.994	2605.9	2363.9	0.80360	7.94595	18
19	142.5	58.98	332.13	0.00101660	8.02716	246.829	2607.9	2361.1	0.81818	7.92720	19
20	150.0	60.06	333.24	0.00101719	7.64977	251.453	2609.9	2358.4	0.83207	7.90943	20
21	157.5	61.14	334.29	0.00101776	7.30732	255.884	2611.7	2355.8	0.84535	7.89254	21
22	165.0	62.16	335.31	0.00101832	6.99514	260.139	2613.5	2353.3	0.85805	7.87645	22
23	172.5	63.14	336.29	0.00101886	6.70934	264.234	2615.2	2350.9	0.87024	7.86108	23
24	180.0	64.08	337.23	0.00101939	6.44669	268.180	2616.8	2348.6	0.88196	7.84639	24
25	187.5	64.99	338.14	0.00101991	6.20447	271.990	2618.3	2346.4	0.89324	7.83230	25

(Contd.)

Table IV.1 (*Contd.*)

Pressure, p (kPa)	Torr or mmHg	Temperature t (°C)	Temperature T (K)	Specific volume, m³/kg v'	Specific volume, m³/kg v''	Specific Enthalpy, kJ/kg h	Specific Enthalpy, kJ/kg H	λ_v	Specific Entropy, kJ/(kg·K) s'	Specific Entropy, kJ/(kg·K) s''	Pressure, p (kPa)
26	195.0	65.87	339.02	0.00102041	5.98034	275.673	2619.9	2344.2	0.90411	7.81878	26
27	202.5	66.72	339.87	0.00102091	5.77235	279.238	2621.3	2342.1	0.91461	7.80578	27
28	210.0	67.55	340.70	0.00102139	5.57879	282.693	2622.7	2340.0	0.92476	7.79326	28
29	217.5	68.35	341.50	0.00102186	5.39820	286.045	2624.1	2338.1	0.93459	7.78118	29
30	225.0	69.12	342.27	0.00102232	5.22930	289.302	2625.4	2336.1	0.94411	7.76953	30
31	232.5	69.88	343.03	0.00102278	5.07098	292.468	2626.7	2334.3	0.95335	7.75826	31
32	240.0	70.61	343.76	0.00102322	4.92227	295.549	2628.0	2332.4	0.96232	7.74736	32
33	247.5	71.33	344.48	0.00102366	4.78232	298.550	2629.2	2330.6	0.97103	7.73679	33
34	255.0	72.03	345.18	0.00102408	4.65036	301.476	2630.4	2328.9	0.97952	7.72655	34
35	262.5	72.71	345.86	0.00102451	4.52571	304.330	2631.5	2327.2	0.98777	7.71661	35
36	270.0	73.37	346.52	0.00102492	4.40779	307.116	2632.6	2325.5	0.99582	7.70696	36
37	277.5	74.02	347.17	0.00102533	4.29605	309.838	2633.7	2323.9	1.00366	7.69757	37
38	285.0	74.66	347.81	0.00102573	4.19003	312.500	2634.8	2322.3	1.01132	7.68844	38
39	292.5	75.28	348.43	0.00102612	4.08928	315.103	2635.9	2320.8	1.01879	7.67955	39
40	300.0	75.89	349.04	0.00102651	3.99342	317.650	2636.9	2319.2	1.02610	7.67089	40
41	307.5	76.48	349.63	0.00102689	3.90210	320.145	2637.9	2317.7	1.03323	7.66245	41
42	315.0	77.06	350.21	0.00102726	3.81500	322.589	2638.9	2316.3	1.04022	7.65421	42
43	322.5	77.63	350.78	0.00102764	3.73183	324.985	2639.8	2314.8	1.04705	7.64618	43
44	330.0	78.19	351.34	0.00102800	3.65232	327.335	2640.7	2313.4	1.05374	7.63832	44
45	337.5	78.74	351.89	0.00102836	3.57625	329.640	2641.7	2312.0	1.06029	7.63065	45
46	345.0	79.28	352.43	0.00102872	3.50338	331.904	2642.6	2310.7	1.06672	7.62315	46

(*Contd.*)

Table IV.1 (Contd.)

Pressure, p	Pressure, p	Temperature	Temperature	Specific volume, m³/kg		Specific Enthalpy, kJ/kg			Specific Entropy, kJ/(kg·K)		Pressure, p
kPa	Torr or mmHg	t °C	T K	v'	v''	h	H	λ_v	s'	s''	kPa
47	352.5	79.81	352.96	0.001 029 07	3.433 52	334.126	2643.4	2309.3	1.073 02	7.615 82	47
48	360.0	80.33	353.48	0.001 029 41	3.366 49	336.309	2644.3	2308.0	1.079 19	7.608 64	48
49	367.5	80.84	353.99	0.001 029 76	3.302 10	338.455	2645.2	2306.7	1.085 26	7.601 61	49
50	375.0	81.35	354.50	0.001 030 09	3.240 22	340.564	2646.0	2305.4	1.091 21	7.594 72	50
52	390.0	82.33	355.48	0.001 030 76	3.123 38	344.679	2647.6	2302.9	1.102 79	7.581 37	52
54	405.0	83.27	356.42	0.001 031 40	3.014 94	348.665	2649.2	2300.5	1.113 99	7.568 52	54
56	420.0	84.19	357.34	0.001 032 04	2.914 01	352.529	2650.7	2298.2	1.124 81	7.556 15	56
58	435.0	85.09	358.24	0.001 032 66	2.819 84	356.280	2652.1	2295.9	1.135 29	7.544 22	58
60	450.0	85.95	359.10	0.001 033 26	2.731 75	359.925	2653.6	2293.6	1.145 44	7.532 70	60
62	465.0	86.80	359.95	0.001 033 86	2.649 18	363.471	2654.9	2291.5	1.155 30	7.521 56	62
64	480.0	87.62	360.77	0.001 034 44	2.571 62	366.923	2656.3	2289.4	1.164 87	7.510 79	64
66	495.0	88.42	361.57	0.001 035 01	2.498 61	370.286	2657.6	2287.3	1.174 18	7.500 35	66
68	510.0	89.20	362.35	0.001 035 57	2.429 76	373.566	2658.8	2285.3	1.183 24	7.490 22	68
70	525.0	89.96	363.11	0.001 036 12	2.364 73	376.768	2660.1	2283.3	1.192 05	7.480 40	70
72	540.0	90.70	363.85	0.001 036 66	2.303 20	379.894	2661.3	2281.4	1.200 65	7.470 85	72
74	555.0	91.43	364.58	0.001 037 19	2.244 90	382.949	2662.4	2279.5	1.209 03	7.461 57	74
76	570.0	92.14	365.29	0.001 037 71	2.189 57	385.937	2663.6	2277.6	1.217 21	7.452 54	76
78	585.0	92.83	365.98	0.001 038 23	2.136 99	388.860	2664.7	2275.8	1.225 20	7.443 75	78
80	600.0	93.51	366.66	0.001 038 74	2.086 96	391.722	2665.8	2274.0	1.233 01	7.435 19	80
82	615.0	94.18	367.33	0.001 039 23	2.039 30	394.526	2666.8	2272.3	1.240 65	7.426 84	82

(Contd.)

Table IV.1 (*Contd.*)

Pressure, p (kPa)	Pressure, p (Torr or mmHg)	Temperature t °C	Temperature T K	Specific volume, m³/kg v'	Specific volume, m³/kg v''	Specific Enthalpy, kJ/kg h	Specific Enthalpy, kJ/kg H	Specific Enthalpy, kJ/kg λ_v	Specific Entropy, kJ/(kg·K) s'	Specific Entropy, kJ/(kg·K) s''	Pressure, p (kPa)
84	630.1	94.83	367.98	0.001 039 73	1.993 83	397.274	2667.9	2270.6	1.248 12	7.418 69	84
86	645.1	95.47	368.62	0.001 040 21	1.950 41	399.969	2668.9	2268.9	1.255 43	7.410 74	86
88	660.1	96.10	369.25	0.001 040 69	1.908 91	402.613	2669.9	2267.3	1.262 59	7.402 97	88
90	675.1	96.71	369.86	0.001 041 16	1.869 19	405.207	2670.9	2265.6	1.269 60	7.395 38	90
92	690.1	97.32	370.47	0.001 041 62	1.831 15	407.755	2671.8	2264.0	1.276 48	7.387 96	92
94	705.1	97.91	371.06	0.001 042 08	1.794 67	410.257	2672.7	2262.5	1.283 22	7.380 70	94
96	720.1	98.49	371.64	0.001 042 53	1.759 67	412.716	2673.7	2260.9	1.289 84	7.373 59	96
98	735.1	99.07	372.22	0.001 042 98	1.726 05	415.133	2674.6	2259.4	1.296 33	7.366 63	98
100	750.1	99.63	372.79	0.001 043 42	1.693 73	417.510	2675.4	2257.9	1.302 71	7.359 82	100
101.325	**760.0**	**100.00**	**373.15**	**0.001 043 71**	**1.673 00**	**419.064**	**2676.0**	**2256.9**	**1.306 87**	**7.355 38**	**101.325**

Table IV.2 Properties of Saturated Water and Saturated Steam from 1 bar to Critical State

Pressure, p bar	Temperature t °C	Temperature T K	Specific volume, m³/kg v'	Specific volume, m³/kg v''	Specific Enthalpy, kJ/kg h	Specific Enthalpy, kJ/kg H	Specific Enthalpy, kJ/kg λ_v	Specific Entropy kJ/(kg·K) s'	Specific Entropy kJ/(kg·K) s''	Pressure, p bar
1.0	99.63	372.78	0.001 043 42	1.693 73	417.510	2675.4	2257.9	1.302 71	7.359 82	1.0
1.1	102.32	375.47	0.001 045 54	1.549 24	428.843	2679.6	2250.8	1.332 97	7.327 69	1.1
1.2	104.81	377.96	0.001 047 55	1.428 13	439.362	2683.4	2244.1	1.360 87	7.298 39	1.2
1.3	107.13	380.28	0.001 049 47	1.325 09	449.188	2687.0	2237.8	1.386 76	7.271 46	1.3
1.4	109.32	382.47	0.001 051 29	1.236 33	458.417	2690.3	2231.9	1.410 93	7.246 55	1.4
1.5	111.37	384.52	0.001 053 03	1.159 04	467.125	2693.4	2226.2	1.433 61	7.223 37	1.5
1.6	113.32	386.47	0.001 054 71	1.091 11	475.375	2696.2	2220.9	1.454 98	7.201 69	1.6
1.7	115.17	388.32	0.001 056 32	1.030 93	483.217	2699.0	2215.7	1.475 20	7.181 34	1.7
1.8	116.93	390.08	0.001 057 88	0.977 227	490.696	2701.5	2210.8	1.494 39	7.162 17	1.8
1.9	118.62	391.77	0.001 059 38	0.928 999	497.846	2704.0	2206.1	1.512 65	7.144 03	1.9
2.0	120.23	393.38	0.001 060 84	0.885 441	504.700	2706.3	2201.6	1.530 08	7.126 83	2.0
2.1	121.78	394.93	0.001 062 26	0.845 900	511.284	2708.5	2197.2	1.546 76	7.110 47	2.1
2.2	123.27	396.42	0.001 063 63	0.809 839	517.622	2710.6	2193.0	1.562 75	7.094 87	2.2
2.3	124.71	397.86	0.001 064 97	0.776 813	523.732	2712.6	2188.9	1.578 11	7.079 97	2.3
2.4	126.09	399.24	0.001 066 28	0.746 451	529.634	2714.5	2184.9	1.592 89	7.065 71	2.4
2.5	127.43	400.58	0.001 067 55	0.718 439	535.343	2716.4	2181.0	1.607 14	7.052 02	2.5
2.6	128.43	401.88	0.001 068 79	0.692 512	540.873	2718.2	2177.3	1.620 89	7.038 88	2.6
2.7	129.98	403.13	0.001 070 01	0.668 443	546.235	2719.7	2173.6	1.634 19	7.026 22	2.7
2.8	131.20	404.35	0.001 071 19	0.646 037	551.443	2721.5	2170.1	1.647 06	7.014 03	2.8
2.9	132.39	405.54	0.001 072 36	0.625 125	556.504	2723.1	2166.1	1.659 53	7.002 27	2.9

(Contd.)

Table IV.2   (*Contd.*)

Pressure, p bar	Temperature t °C	Temperature T K	Specific volume, m³/kg v'	Specific volume, m³/kg v''	Specific Enthalpy, kJ/kg h	Specific Enthalpy, kJ/kg H	Specific Enthalpy, kJ/kg λ_v	Specific Entropy kJ/(kg·K) s'	Specific Entropy kJ/(kg·K) s''	Pressure, p bar
3.0	133.54	406.69	0.001 073 50	0.605 562	561.429	2724.7	2163.2	1.671 64	6.990 90	3.0
3.1	134.66	407.81	0.001 074 62	0.587 219	566.226	2726.1	2159.9	1.683 39	6.979 90	3.1
3.2	135.75	408.90	0.001 075 72	0.569 985	570.902	2727.6	2156.7	1.694 81	6.969 25	3.2
3.3	136.82	409.97	0.001 076 79	0.553 761	575.464	2729.0	2453.5	1.705 93	6.958 93	3.3
3.4	137.86	411.01	0.001 077 85	0.538 459	579.918	2730.3	2150.4	1.716 75	6.948 91	3.4
3.5	138.87	412.02	0.001 078 90	0.524 003	584.270	2731.6	2147.4	1.727 30	6.939 18	3.5
3.6	139.86	413.01	0.001 079 92	0.510 323	588.525	2732.9	2144.4	1.737 59	6.929 72	3.6
3.7	140.83	413.98	0.001 080 93	0.497 357	592.688	2734.1	2141.4	1.747 63	6.920 52	3.7
3.8	141.78	414.93	0.001 081 92	0.485 051	596.764	2735.3	2138.6	1.757 44	6.911 56	3.8
3.9	142.71	415.86	0.001 082 90	0.473 355	600.757	2736.5	2135.7	1.767 03	6.902 83	3.9
4.0	143.62	416.77	0.001 083 87	0.462 224	604.670	2737.6	2133.0	1.776 40	6.894 33	4.0
4.1	144.52	417.67	0.001 084 82	0.451 618	608.507	2738.7	2130.2	1.785 57	6.886 02	4.1
4.2	145.39	418.54	0.001 085 75	0.441 500	612.272	2739.8	2127.5	1.794 55	6.877 92	4.2
4.3	146.25	419.40	0.001 086 68	0.431 836	615.967	2740.9	2124.9	1.803 34	6.870 00	4.3
4.4	147.09	420.24	0.001 087 59	0.422 597	619.596	2741.9	2122.3	1.811 96	6.862 26	4.4
4.5	147.92	421.07	0.001 088 49	0.413 754	623.161	2742.9	2119.7	1.820 41	6.854 70	4.5
4.6	148.73	421.88	0.001 089 38	0.405 283	626.665	2743.9	2117.2	1.828 70	6.847 30	4.6
4.7	149.53	422.68	0.001 090 26	0.397 160	630.111	2744.8	2114.7	1.836 83	6.840 05	4.7
4.8	150.31	423.46	0.001 091 13	0.389 364	633.499	2745.7	2112.2	1.844 82	6.832 95	4.8
4.9	151.08	424.23	0.001 091 99	0.381 875	636.833	2746.6	2109.8	1.852 66	6.826 00	4.9

(*Contd.*)

Table IV.2 (*Contd.*)

Pressure, p bar	Temperature t °C	Temperature T K	Specific volume, m^3/kg v'	Specific volume, m^3/kg v''	Specific Enthalpy, kJ/kg h	Specific Enthalpy, kJ/kg H	Specific Enthalpy, kJ/kg λ_v	Specific Entropy kJ/(kg·K) s'	Specific Entropy kJ/(kg·K) s''	Pressure, p bar
5.0	151.84	424.99	0.001 092 84	0.374 676	640.115	2747.5	2107.4	1.860 36	6.819 19	5.0
5.2	153.33	426.48	0.001 094 51	0.361 080	646.530	2749.3	2102.7	1.875 37	6.805 95	5.2
5.4	154.76	427.91	0.001 096 14	0.348 457	652.755	2750.9	2098.1	1.889 90	6.793 20	5.4
5.6	156.16	429.31	0.001 097 75	0.336 705	658.805	2752.5	2093.7	1.903 96	6.780 90	5.6
5.8	157.52	430.67	0.001 099 32	0.325 736	664.691	2754.0	2089.3	1.917 60	6.769 03	5.8
6.0	158.84	431.99	0.001 100 86	0.315 474	670.422	2755.5	2085.0	1.930 83	6.757 54	6.0
6.2	160.12	433.27	0.001 102 38	0.305 851	676.009	2756.9	2080.9	1.943 70	6.746 43	6.2
6.4	161.38	434.53	0.001 103 86	0.296 809	681.458	2758.2	2076.8	1.956 21	6.735 65	6.4
6.6	162.60	435.75	0.001 105 33	0.288 296	686.779	2759.5	2072.7	1.968 38	6.725 20	6.6
6.8	163.79	436.94	0.001 106 77	0.280 267	691.978	2760.8	2068.8	1.980 25	6.715 05	6.8
7.0	164.96	438.11	0.001 108 19	0.272 681	697.061	2762.0	2064.9	1.991 81	6.705 10	7.0
7.2	166.10	439.25	0.001 109 59	0.265 502	702.034	2763.1	2061.1	2.003 10	6.695 58	7.2
7.4	167.21	440.36	0.001 110 96	0.258 697	706.903	2764.3	2057.4	2.014 12	6.686 24	7.4
7.6	168.30	441.45	0.001 112 32	0.252 239	711.674	2765.4	2053.7	2.024 89	6.677 14	7.6
7.8	169.37	442.52	0.001 113 66	0.246 100	716.349	2766.4	2050.1	2.035 42	6.668 26	7.8
8.0	170.41	443.56	0.001 114 98	0.240 257	720.935	2767.5	2046.5	2.045 72	6.659 60	8.0
8.2	171.44	444.59	0.001 116 29	0.234 690	725.434	2768.5	2043.0	2.055 80	6.651 14	8.2
8.4	172.45	445.60	0.001 117 57	0.229 378	729.852	2769.4	2039.6	2.065 67	6.642 88	8.4
8.6	173.44	446.59	0.001 118 85	0.224 305	734.190	2770.4	2036.2	2.075 35	6.634 80	8.6
8.8	174.41	447.56	0.001 120 10	0.219 454	738.453	2771.3	2032.8	2.084 83	6.626 90	8.8

(*Contd.*)

Table IV.2 (*Contd.*)

Pressure, p bar	Temperature t °C	T K	Specific volume, m³/kg v'	v''	Specific Enthalpy, kJ/kg h	H	λ_v	Specific Entropy kJ/(kg·K) s'	s''	Pressure, p bar
9.0	175.36	448.51	0.001 121 35	0.214 812	742.644	2772.1	2029.5	2.094 14	6.619 17	9.0
9.2	176.29	449.44	0.001 122 58	0.210 364	746.764	2773.0	2026.2	2.103 27	6.611 60	9.2
9.4	177.21	450.36	0.001 123 79	0.206 099	750.819	2773.8	2023.0	2.112 23	6.604 19	9.4
9.6	178.12	451.27	0.001 125 00	0.202 006	754.809	2774.6	2019.8	2.121 03	6.596 92	9.6
9.8	179.01	452.16	0.001 126 19	0.198 073	758.737	2775.4	2016.7	2.129 67	6.589 80	9.8
10.0	179.88	453.03	0.001 127 37	0.194 293	762.605	2776.2	2013.6	2.138 17	6.582 81	10.0
10.5	182.02	455.17	0.001 130 26	0.185 450	772.029	2778.0	2006.0	2.158 80	6.565 90	10.5
11.0	184.07	457.22	0.001 133 09	0.177 384	781.124	2779.7	1998.5	2.178 61	6.549 73	11.0
11.5	186.05	459.20	0.001 135 86	0.169 995	789.917	2781.3	1991.3	2.197 68	6.534 24	11.5
12.0	187.96	461.11	0.001 138 58	0.163 200	798.430	2782.7	1984.3	2.216 06	6.519 36	12.0
12.5	189.81	462.96	0.001 141 24	0.156 931	806.685	2784.1	1977.4	2.233 80	6.505 05	12.5
13.0	191.61	464.76	0.001 143 85	0.151 127	814.700	2785.4	1970.7	2.250 95	6.491 26	13.0
13.5	193.35	466.50	0.001 146 41	0.145 738	822.491	2786.6	1964.1	2.267 56	6.477 95	13.5
14.0	195.04	468.19	0.001 148 93	0.140 721	830.073	2787.8	1957.7	2.283 66	6.465 09	14.0
14.5	196.69	469.84	0.001 151 41	0.136 038	837.460	2788.9	1951.4	2.299 29	6.452 65	14.5
15.0	198.29	471.44	0.001 153 86	0.131 656	844.663	2789.9	1945.2	2.314 47	6.440 59	15.0
15.5	199.85	473.00	0.001 156 26	0.127 547	851.693	2790.8	1939.2	2.329 24	6.428 89	15.5
16.0	201.37	474.52	0.001 158 64	0.123 686	858.561	2791.7	1933.2	2.343 61	6.417 53	16.0
16.5	202.86	476.01	0.001 160 98	0.120 051	865.275	2792.6	1927.3	2.357 62	6.406 48	16.5
17.0	204.31	477.46	0.001 163 29	0.116 623	871.843	2793.4	1921.5	2.371 27	6.395 74	17.0

(*Contd.*)

Table IV.2 *(Contd.)*

Pressure, p bar	Temperature t °C	Temperature T K	Specific volume, m³/kg v'	Specific volume, m³/kg v''	Specific Enthalpy, kJ/kg h	Specific Enthalpy, kJ/kg H	Specific Enthalpy, kJ/kg λ_v	Specific Entropy kJ/(kg·K) s'	Specific Entropy kJ/(kg·K) s''	Pressure, p bar
17.5	205.72	478.87	0.001 165 57	0.113 383	878.274	2794.1	1915.9	2.384 27	6.385 27	17.5
18.0	207.11	480.26	0.001 167 83	0.110 317	884.573	2794.8	1910.3	2.397 62	6.375 07	18.0
18.5	207.47	481.62	0.001 170 06	0.107 411	890.749	2795.5	1904.7	2.410 33	6.365 12	18.5
19.0	209.80	482.95	0.001 172 26	0.104 653	896.806	2796.1	1899.3	2.422 77	6.355 41	19.0
19.5	211.10	484.25	0.001 174 45	0.102 031	902.751	2796.7	1893.9	2.434 94	6.345 92	19.5
20.0	212.37	485.52	0.001 176 61	0.099 5361	908.588	2797.2	1888.6	2.446 86	6.336 65	20.0
21.0	214.85	488.00	0.001 180 86	0.094 8898	919.959	2798.2	1878.2	2.469 98	6.318 70	21.0
22.0	217.24	490.39	0.001 185 04	0.090 6516	930.953	2799.1	1868.1	2.492 21	6.301 48	22.0
23.0	219.55	492.70	0.001 189 15	0.086 7692	941.601	2799.8	1858.2	2.513 63	6.284 93	23.0
24.0	221.78	494.93	0.001 193 20	0.083 1994	951.929	2800.4	1848.5	2.534 30	6.268 99	24.0
25.0	223.94	497.09	0.001 197 18	0.079 9053	961.961	2800.9	1839.0	2.554 29	6.253 61	25.0
26.0	226.04	499.19	0.001 201 11	0.076 8560	971.719	2801.4	1829.6	2.573 64	6.238 74	26.0
27.0	228.07	501.22	0.001 204 98	0.074 0247	981.221	2801.7	1820.5	2.592 39	6.224 36	27.0
28.0	230.05	503.20	0.001 208 81	0.071 3887	990.494	2802.0	1811.5	2.610 60	6.210 41	28.0
29.0	231.97	505.12	0.001 212 60	0.068 9282	999.524	2802.2	1802.6	2.628 29	6.196 87	29.0
30.0	233.84	506.99	0.001 216 34	0.066 6261	1008.35	2802.3	1793.9	2.645 50	6.183 72	30.0
31.0	235.67	508.82	0.001 220 05	0.064 4674	1016.99	2802.3	1785.4	2.662 25	6.170 92	31.0
32.0	237.45	510.60	0.001 223 72	0.062 4389	1025.43	2802.3	1776.9	2.678 58	6.158 45	32.0
33.0	239.18	512.33	0.001 227 35	0.060 5290	1033.70	2802.3	1768.6	2.694 51	6.146 30	33.0
34.0	240.88	514.03	0.001 230 96	0.058 7276	1041.81	2802.1	1760.3	2.710 07	6.134 44	34.0

(Contd.)

Table IV.2 (*Contd.*)

Pressure, p bar	Temperature t °C	Temperature T K	Specific volume, m³/kg v'	Specific volume, m³/kg v''	Specific Enthalpy, kJ/kg h	Specific Enthalpy, kJ/kg H	Specific Enthalpy, kJ/kg λ_v	Specific Entropy kJ/(kg·K) s'	Specific Entropy kJ/(kg·K) s''	Pressure, p bar
35.0	242.54	515.69	0.001 234 54	0.057 0255	1049.76	2802.0	1752.2	2.725 27	6.122 85	35.0
36.0	244.16	517.31	0.001 238 09	0.055 4146	1057.55	2801.7	1744.2	2.740 13	6.111 52	36.0
37.0	245.75	518.90	0.001 241 62	0.053 8877	1065.21	2801.4	**1736.2**	2.754 67	6.100 43	37.0
38.0	247.31	520.46	0.001 245 12	0.052 4383	1072.73	2801.1	1728.4	2.768 90	6.089 58	38.0
39.0	248.84	521.99	0.001 248 60	0.051 0606	1080.13	2800.8	1720.6	2.782 85	6.078 94	39.0
40.0	250.33	523.48	0.001 252 06	0.049 7493	1087.40	2800.3	1712.9	2.796 52	6.068 51	40.0
42.0	253.24	526.39	0.001 258 93	0.047 3073	1101.60	2799.4	1697.8	2.823 10	6.048 22	42.0
44.0	256.05	529.20	0.001 265 73	0.045 0795	1115.38	2798.3	1682.9	2.848 71	6.028 64	44.0
46.0	258.75	531.90	0.001 272 47	0.043 0383	1128.76	2797.0	1668.3	2.873 46	6.009 69	46.0
48.0	261.37	534.52	0.001 279 17	0.041 1611	1141.78	2795.7	1653.9	2.897 40	5.991 33	48.0
50.0	263.91	537.06	0.001 285 82	0.039 4285	1154.47	2794.2	1639.7	2.920 60	5.973 49	50.0
52.0	266.37	539.52	0.001 292 44	0.037 8242	1166.85	2792.6	1625.7	2.943 12	5.956 14	52.0
54.0	268.76	541.91	0.001 299 03	0.036 3342	1178.94	2790.8	1611.9	2.965 01	5.939 23	54.0
56.0	271.09	544.24	0.001 305 59	0.034 9465	1190.77	2789.0	1598.2	2.986 31	5.922 72	56.0
58.0	273.35	546.50	0.001 312 14	0.033 6506	1202.35	2787.0	1584.7	3.007 06	5.906 58	58.0
60.0	275.55	548.70	0.001 318 68	0.032 4378	1213.69	2785.0	1571.3	3.027 30	5.890 79	60.0
65.0	280.82	553.97	0.001 334 99	0.029 7192	1241.14	2779.5	1538.4	3.075 87	5.852 65	65.0
70.0	285.79	558.94	0.001 351 32	0.027 3733	1267.41	2773.5	1506.0	3.121 89	5.816 16	70.0
75.0	290.50	563.65	0.001 367 72	0.025 3270	1292.69	2766.9	1474.2	3.165 71	5.781 05	75.0
80.0	294.97	568.12	0.001 384 24	0.023 5253	1317.10	2759.9	1442.8	3.207 62	5.747 10	80.0

(*Contd.*)

Table IV.2 (Contd.)

Pressure, p bar	Temperature t °C	T K	Specific volume, m³/kg v'	v''	Specific Enthalpy, kJ/kg h	H	λ_v	Specific Entropy kJ/(kg·K) s'	s''	Pressure, p bar
85.0	299.23	572.38	0.001 400 94	0.021 9258	1340.74	2752.5	1411.7	3.247 87	5.714 13	85.0
90.0	303.31	576.46	0.001 417 86	0.020 4953	1363.73	2744.6	1380.9	**3.286 66**	**5.682 01**	90.0
95.0	307.21	580.36	0.001 435 05	0.019 2076	1386.14	2736.4	1350.2	3.324 17	5.650 60	95.0
100.0	310.96	584.11	0.001 452 56	0.018 0413	1408.04	2727.7	1319.7	3.360 55	5.619 80	100.0
105.0	314.57	587.72	0.001 470 43	0.016 9790	1429.50	2718.7	1289.2	3.395 92	5.589 48	105.0
110.0	318.05	591.20	0.001 488 72	0.016 0062	1450.57	2709.3	1258.7	3.430 42	5.559 53	110.0
115.0	321.40	594.55	0.001 507 48	0.015 1109	1471.31	2699.5	1228.2	3.464 14	5.529 82	115.0
120.0	324.65	597.80	0.001 526 76	0.014 2830	1491.77	2689.2	1197.4	3.497 18	5.500 22	120.0
125.0	327.78	600.93	0.001 546 64	0.013 5141	1511.99	2678.3	1166.3	3.529 62	5.470 59	125.0
130.0	330.83	603.98	0.001 567 19	0.012 7970	1532.01	2667.0	1135.0	3.561 57	5.440 80	130.0
135.0	333.78	606.93	0.001 588 49	0.012 1256	1551.88	2655.0	1103.1	3.593 08	5.410 73	135.0
140.0	336.64	609.79	0.001 610 63	0.011 4950	1571.64	2642.4	1070.7	3.624 24	5.380 26	140.0
145.0	339.42	612.57	0.001 633 72	0.010 9010	1591.33	2629.0	1037.7	3.655 14	5.349 31	145.0
150.0	342.13	615.28	0.001 657 91	0.010 3402	1611.01	2615.0	1004.0	3.685 85	5.317 82	150.0
160.0	347.33	620.48	0.001 710 31	0.009 3075	1650.54	2584.9	934.3	3.747 10	5.253 14	160.0
170.0	352.26	625.41	0.001 76 96	0.008 3710	1691.7	2551.6	859.9	3.810 70	5.185 47	170.0
180.0	356.96	630.11	0.001 83 99	0.007 4977	1734.8	2513.9	779.1	3.876 54	5.112 77	180.0
190.0	361.43	634.58	0.001 92 60	0.006 6775	1778.7	2470.6	692.0	3.942 88	5.033 16	190.0
200.0	365.70	638.85	0.002 03 70	0.005 8765	1826.5	2418.3	591.9	4.014 87	4.941 20	200.0
210.0	369.78	642.93	0.002 20 15	0.005 0234	1886.2	2347.6	461.3	4.104 83	4.822 30	210.0
220.0	373.69	646.84	0.002 67 09	0.003 7265	2011.0	2195.4	184.4	4.294 51	4.579 57	220.0
221.7*	**374.15**	**647.30**	**0.003 17 00**	**0.003 1700**	**2107.4**	**2107.4**	**0.0**	**4.442 86**	**4.442 86**	**221.7**

* Represents critical point

Table IV.3 Properties of Superheated Steam

Pres., kPa (Torr) Sat. temp. °C Sat. temp. K	Parameter	Superheated steam temperature, °C (K)										
		100 (373.15)	120 (393.15)	140 (413.15)	160 (433.15)	180 (453.15)	200 (473.15)	220 (493.15)	240 (513.15)	260 (533.15)	280 (553.15)	300 (573.15)
1 (7.5) 6.983 280.133	v	172.187	181.421	190.655	199.888	209.120	218.352	227.584	236.815	246.046	255.277	264.508
	i	2688.6	2726.5	2764.6	2802.9	2841.4	2880.1	2919.0	2958.1	2997.4	3037.0	3076.8
	s	9.5136	9.6125	9.7070	9.7975	9.8843	9.9678	10.0484	10.1262	10.2014	10.2743	10.3450
2 (15) 17.513 290.663	v	86.080	90.700	95.319	99.936	104.554	109.170	113.787	118.403	123.019	127.635	132.251
	i	2688.5	2726.4	2764.5	2802.8	2841.3	2880.0	2918.9	2958.0	2997.4	3037.0	3076.8
	s	9.1934	9.2924	9.3870	9.4775	9.5643	9.6479	9.7284	9.8062	9.8814	9.9543	10.0251
3 (22.5) 24.100 297.250	v	57.378	60.460	63.540	66.619	69.698	72.777	75.855	78.932	82.010	85.088	88.165
	i	2688.4	2726.3	2764.5	2802.8	2841.3	2880.0	2918.9	2958.0	2997.4	3037.0	3076.8
	s	9.0060	9.1051	9.1997	9.2902	9.3771	9.4607	9.5412	9.6190	9.6943	9.7672	9.8379
4 (30.0) 28.983 302.133	v	43.027	45.339	47.650	49.961	52.270	54.580	56.889	59.197	61.506	63.814	66.122
	i	2688.3	2726.2	2764.4	2802.7	2841.2	2879.9	2918.8	2958.0	2997.3	3036.9	3076.8
	s	8.8730	8.9721	9.0668	9.1573	9.2443	9.3279	9.4084	9.4862	9.5615	9.6344	9.7051
5 (37.5) 32.90 306.05	v	34.417	36.267	38.117	39.966	41.814	43.661	45.509	47.356	49.203	51.050	52.896
	i	2688.1	2726.1	2764.3	2802.6	2841.2	2879.9	2918.8	2957.9	2997.3	3036.9	3076.7
	s	8.7698	8.8690	8.9636	9.0542	9.1412	9.2248	9.3054	9.3832	9.4584	9.5313	9.6021
6 (45.0) 36.18 309.33	v	28.676	30.219	31.761	33.302	34.843	36.383	37.922	39.462	41.001	42.540	44.079
	i	2688.0	2726.0	2764.2	2802.6	2841.1	2879.8	2918.8	2957.9	2997.3	3036.9	3076.7
	s	8.6854	8.7846	8.8793	8.9700	9.0569	9.1406	9.2212	9.2990	9.3742	9.4472	9.5179
8 (60.0) 41.53 314.68	v	21.501	22.659	23.816	24.973	26.129	27.284	28.439	29.594	30.749	31.903	33.058
	i	2687.8	2725.8	2764.1	2802.4	2841.0	2879.7	2918.7	2957.8	2997.2	3036.8	3076.7
	s	8.5521	8.6514	8.7463	8.8370	8.9240	9.0077	9.0883	9.1661	9.2414	9.3143	9.3851

(*Contd.*)

Table IV.3   (Contd.)

Pres., kPa (Torr) Sat. temp. °C Sat. temp. K	Para- meter	Superheated steam temperature, °C (K)										
		100 (373.15)	120 (393.15)	140 (413.15)	160 (433.15)	180 (453.15)	200 (473.15)	220 (493.15)	240 (513.15)	260 (533.15)	280 (553.15)	300 (573.15)
10(75.0) 45.83 318.98	v	17.195	18.123	19.050	19.975	20.900	21.825	22.750	23.674	24.598	25.521	26.445
	i	2687.5	2725.6	2763.9	2802.3	2840.9	2879.6	2918.6	2957.8	2997.2	3036.8	3076.6
	s	8.4486	8.5481	8.6430	8.7337	8.8208	8.9045	8.9852	9.0630	9.1383	9.2113	9.2820
20(150.0) 60.09 333.24	v	8.585	9.051	9.516	9.980	10.444	10.907	11.370	11.832	12.295	12.757	13.219
	i	2686.3	2724.6	2763.1	2801.6	2840.3	2879.2	2918.2	2957.4	2996.9	3036.5	3076.4
	s	8.1261	8.2262	8.3215	8.4127	8.5000	8.5839	8.6647	8.7426	8.8180	8.8910	8.9618
30(225.0) 69.12 342.27	v	5.714	6.027	6.338	6.648	6.958	7.268	7.577	7.885	8.194	8.502	8.811
	i	2685.1	2723.6	2762.3	2801.0	2839.8	2878.7	2917.8	2957.1	2996.6	3036.2	3076.1
	s	7.9363	8.0370	8.1329	8.2243	8.3119	8.3960	8.4769	8.5550	8.6305	8.7035	8.7744
40((300.0)) 75.89 349.04	v	4.279	4.515	4.749	4.982	5.215	5.448	5.680	5.912	6.144	6.375	6.606
	i	2683.8	2722.6	2761.4	2800.3	2839.2	2878.2	2917.4	2956.7	2996.3	3036.0	3075.9
	s	7.8009	7.9023	7.9985	8.0903	8.1782	8.2624	8.3435	8.4217	8.4973	8.5704	8.6413
50((375.0)) 81.35 354.5	v	3.418	3.607	3.796	3.983	4.170	4.356	4.542	4.728	4.913	5.099	5.284
	i	2682.6	2721.6	2760.6	2799.6	2838.6	2877.7	2917.0	2956.4	2995.9	3035.7	3075.7
	s	7.6953	7.7972	7.8940	7.9861	8.0742	8.1587	8.2399	8.3182	8.3939	8.4671	8.5380
60(450.0) 85.95 359.1	v	2.844	3.002	3.160	3.317	3.473	3.628	3.783	3.938	4.093	4.248	4.402
	i	2681.3	2720.6	2759.8	2798.9	2838.1	2877.3	2916.6	2956.0	2995.6	3035.4	3075.4
	s	7.6085	7.7111	7.8083	7.9008	7.9891	8.0738	8.1552	8.2336	8.3093	8.3826	8.4536
70((525)) 89.96 363.11	v	2.434	2.570	2.706	2.841	2.975	3.108	3.241	3.374	3.507	3.640	3.772
	i	2680.0	2719.6	2759.0	2798.2	2837.5	2876.8	2916.2	2955.7	2995.3	3035.2	3075.2
	s	7.5346	7.6379	7.7355	7.8284	7.9170	8.0019	8.0834	8.1619	8.2377	8.3111	8.3822

(Contd.)

Table IV.3 (Contd.)

Pres., kPa (Torr) Sat. temp. °C Sat. temp. K	Para-meter	Superheated steam temperature, °C (K)										
		100 (373.15)	120 (393.15)	140 (413.15)	160 (433.15)	180 (453.15)	200 (473.15)	220 (493.15)	240 (513.15)	260 (533.15)	280 (553.15)	300 (573.15)
80(600) 93.51 366.66	v	2.126	2.246	2.365	2.484	2.601	2.718	2.835	2.952	3.068	3.184	3.300
	i	2678.8	2718.6	2758.1	2797.5	2836.9	2876.3	2915.8	2955.3	2995.0	3034.9	3075.0
	s	7.4703	7.5742	7.6723	7.7655	7.8544	7.9395	8.0212	8.0998	8.1757	8.2491	8.3202
90(675.1) 96.71 369.86	v	1.887	1.994	2.101	2.206	2.311	2.415	2.519	2.623	2.726	2.829	2.933
	i	2677.5	2717.5	2757.3	2796.9	2836.4	2875.8	2915.4	2955.0	2994.7	3034.6	3074.7
	s	7.4132	7.5177	7.6164	7.7099	7.7991	7.8843	7.9662	8.0449	8.1209	8.1944	8.2656
100((750.1) 99.63 372.78	v	1.696	1.793	1.889	1.984	2.078	2.172	2.266	2.359	2.453	2.546	2.639
	i	2676.2	2716.5	2756.4	2796.2	2835.8	2875.4	2915.0	2954.6	2994.4	3034.4	3074.5
	s	7.3618	7.4670	7.5662	7.6601	7.7495	7.8349	7.9169	7.9958	8.0719	8.1454	8.2166
150(1125.1) 111.37 384.52	v	—	1.188	1.253	1.317	1.381	1.444	1.507	1.570	1.633	1.695	1.757
	i	—	2711.2	2752.2	2792.7	2832.9	2872.9	2912.9	2952.9	2992.9	3033.0	3073.3
	s	—	7.2693	7.3709	7.4667	7.5574	7.6439	7.7266	7.8061	7.8826	7.9565	8.0280
200(150.1) 120.23 400.58	v	—	—	0.9349	0.9840	1.032	1.080	1.128	1.175	1.222	1.269	1.316
	i	—	—	2747.8	2789.1	2830.0	2870.5	2910.8	2951.1	2991.4	3031.7	3072.1
	s	—	—	7.2298	7.3275	7.4196	7.5072	7.5907	7.6707	7.7477	7.8219	7.8937
250(1875.1) 127.43 400.58	v	—	—	0.7440	0.7840	0.8232	0.8620	0.9004	0.9385	0.9763	1.014	1.052
	i	—	—	2743.3	2785.5	2827.0	2868.0	2908.7	2949.3	2989.8	3030.3	3070.9
	s	—	—	7.1183	7.2179	7.3115	7.4001	7.4845	7.5651	7.6425	7.7171	7.7891
300(2250.2) 133.54 406.69	v	—	—	0.6167	0.6506	0.6837	0.7164	0.7486	0.7805	0.8123	0.8438	0.8753
	i	—	—	2738.8	2781.8	2824.0	2865.5	2906.6	2947.5	2988.2	3028.9	3069.7
	s	—	—	7.0254	7.1271	7.2222	7.3119	7.3971	7.4783	7.5562	7.6311	7.7034

(Contd.)

Table IV.3   (*Contd.*)

Pres., bar Sat. temp. °C Sat. temp. K	Para- meter	Superheated steam temperature, °C (K)										
		160 (433.15)	180 (453.15)	200 (473.15)	220 (493.15)	240 (513.15)	260 (533.15)	280 (553.15)	300 (573.15)	320 (593.15)	340 (613.15)	360 (633.15)
4 143.62 416.77	v	0.4837	0.5093	0.5343	0.5589	0.5831	0.6072	0.6311	0.6549	0.6785	0.7021	0.7256
	i	2774.2	2817.8	2860.4	2902.3	2943.9	2985.1	3026.2	3067.2	3108.3	3149.4	3190.6
	s	6.9805	7.0788	7.1708	7.2576	7.3402	7.4190	7.4947	7.5675	7.6379	7.7061	7.7723
4.5 147.92 421.07	v	0.4283	0.4514	0.4738	0.4958	0.5176	0.5391	0.5605	0.5817	0.6028	0.6238	0.6448
	i	2770.3	2814.6	2857.8	2900.2	2942.0	2983.5	3024.8	3066.0	3107.2	3148.4	3189.8
	s	6.9191	7.0191	7.1123	7.2000	7.2832	7.3625	7.4386	7.5117	7.5824	7.6507	7.7171
5 151.84 424.99	v	0.3835	0.4045	0.4250	0.4450	0.4647	0.4841	0.5034	0.5226	0.5416	0.5606	0.5795
	i	2766.4	2811.4	2855.1	2898.0	2940.1	2981.9	3023.4	3064.8	3106.1	3147.4	3188.8
	s	6.8631	9.9647	7.0592	7.1478	7.2317	7.3115	7.3879	7.4614	7.5322	7.6008	7.6673
5.5 155.47 428.62	v	0.3470	0.3664	0.3852	0.4036	0.4216	0.4394	0.4570	0.4745	0.4918	0.5091	0.5264
	i	2762.3	2808.1	2852.5	2895.7	2938.3	2980.3	3022.0	3063.5	3105.0	3146.4	3187.9
	s	6.8117	6.9151	7.0108	7.1004	7.1849	7.2653	7.3421	7.4158	4.4869	7.5556	7.6222
6 158.84 431.99	v	0.3165	0.3346	0.3520	0.3690	0.3857	0.4021	0.4183	0.4344	0.4504	0.4663	0.4821
	i	2758.2	2804.8	2849.7	2893.5	2936.4	2978.8	3020.6	3062.3	3103.9	3145.4	3187.0
	s	6.7640	6.8691	6.9662	7.0567	7.1419	7.2228	7.3000	7.3740	7.4454	7.5143	7.5810
6.5 161.99 435.14	v	—	0.3077	0.3240	0.3398	0.3553	0.3705	0.3856	0.4005	0.4153	0.4300	0.4446
	i	—	2801.5	2847.0	2891.2	2934.4	2977.0	3019.2	3061.0	3102.7	3144.4	3186.1
	s	—	6.8263	6.9247	7.0162	7.1021	7.1835	7.2611	7.3355	7.4070	7.4761	7.5431
7 164.96 438.11	v	—	0.2846	0.2999	0.3147	0.3292	0.3435	0.3575	0.3714	0.3852	0.3989	0.4125
	i	—	2798.0	2844.2	2888.9	2932.5	2975.4	3017.7	3059.8	3101.6	3143.4	3185.2
	s	—	6.7861	6.8859	6.9784	7.0651	7.1470	7.2250	7.2997	7.3715	7.4407	7.5078

(*Contd.*)

Table IV.3 (*Contd.*)

Pres., bar Sat. temp. °C Sat. temp. K	Para- meter	Superheated steam temperature, °C (K)										
		180 (453.15)	200 (473.15)	220 (493.15)	240 (513.15)	260 (533.15)	280 (553.15)	300 (573.15)	320 (593.15)	340 (613.15)	360 (633.15)	380 (653.15)
7.5 167.76 440.91	v	0.2646	0.2791	0.2930	0.3066	0.3200	0.3332	0.3462	0.3591	0.3719	0.3847	0.3974
	i	2794.6	2841.4	2886.6	2930.6	2973.7	3016.3	3058.5	3100.5	3142.4	3184.3	3226.2
	s	6.7482	6.8493	6.9429	7.0303	7.1128	7.1912	7.2662	7.3382	7.4077	7.4749	7.5401
8 170.41 443.56	v	0.2471	0.2608	0.2740	0.2869	0.2995	0.3119	0.3241	0.3363	0.3483	0.3603	0.3723
	i	2791.1	2838.6	2884.2	2928.6	2972.0	3014.9	3057.3	3099.4	3141.4	3183.4	3225.4
	s	6.7122	6.8148	6.9094	6.9976	7.0806	7.1595	7.2348	7.3070	7.3767	7.4441	7.5094
8.5 172.94 446.09	v	0.2316	0.2447	0.2572	0.2694	0.2814	0.2931	0.3047	0.3162	0.3275	0.3388	0.3501
	i	2787.5	2835.7	2881.9	2926.6	2970.4	3013.4	3056.0	3098.3	3140.4	3182.5	3224.6
	s	6.6780	6.7820	6.8777	6.9666	7.0503	7.1295	7.2051	7.2777	7.3475	7.4150	7.4805
9 175.36 448.51	v	0.2178	0.2303	0.2423	0.2539	0.2653	0.2764	0.2874	0.2983	0.3090	0.3197	0.3304
	i	2783.9	2832.7	2879.5	2924.6	2968.7	3012.0	3054.7	3097.1	3139.4	3181.5	3223.7
	s	6.6452	6.7508	6.8475	6.9373	7.0215	7.1012	7.1771	7.2499	7.3199	7.3876	7.4532
9.5 177.67 450.82	v	0.2055	0.2175	0.2290	0.2400	0.2509	0.2615	0.2719	0.2822	0.2925	0.3027	0.3128
	i	2780.2	2829.8	2877.0	2922.6	2967.0	3010.5	3053.4	3096.0	3138.4	3180.6	3222.9
	s	6.6137	6.7209	6.8187	6.9093	6.9941	7.0742	7.1505	7.2235	7.2938	7.3616	7.4273
10 179.88 453.03	v	0.1944	0.2059	0.2169	0.2276	0.2379	0.2480	0.2580	0.2678	0.2776	0.2873	0.2969
	i	2776.5	2826.8	2874.6	2920.6	2965.2	3009.0	3052.1	3094.9	3137.3	3179.7	3222.0
	s	6.5835	6.6922	6.7911	6.8825	6.9680	7.0485	7.1251	7.1984	7.2689	7.3368	7.4027
11 184.07 457.22	v	—	0.1859	0.1961	0.2060	0.2155	0.2248	0.2339	0.2429	0.2518	0.2607	0.2695
	i	—	2820.7	2869.6	2916.4	2961.8	3006.0	3049.5	3092.6	3135.3	3177.9	3220.3
	s	—	6.6379	6.7392	6.8323	6.9190	7.0005	7.0778	7.1516	7.2224	7.2907	7.3568

(*Contd.*)

Table IV.3 (*Contd.*)

Pres., bar Sat. temp. °C Sat. temp. K	Parameter	Superheated steam temperature, °C (K)										
		200 (473.15)	220 (493.15)	240 (513.15)	260 (533.15)	280 (553.15)	300 (573.15)	320 (593.15)	340 (613.15)	360 (633.15)	380 (653.15)	400 (673.15)
12 187.96 461.11	v	0.1692	0.1788	0.1879	0.1968	0.2054	0.2139	0.2222	0.2304	0.2386	0.2467	0.2547
	i	2814.4	2864.5	2912.2	2958.2	3003.0	3046.9	3090.3	3133.2	3176.0	3218.7	3261.3
	s	6.5872	6.6909	6.7858	6.8738	6.9562	7.0342	7.1085	7.1798	7.2484	7.3147	7.3790
13 191.61 464.76	v	0.1551	0.1641	0.1727	0.1810	0.1890	0.1969	0.2046	0.2123	0.2198	0.2273	0.2348
	i	2808.0	2859.3	2908.0	2954.7	3000.0	3044.3	3088.0	3131.2	3174.1	3217.0	3259.7
	s	6.5394	6.6457	6.7424	6.8316	6.9151	6.9938	7.0687	7.1404	7.2093	7.2759	7.3404
14 195.04 468.19	v	0.1429	0.1515	0.1596	0.1674	0.1749	0.1823	0.1896	0.1967	0.2038	0.2108	0.2177
	i	2801.4	2854.0	2903.6	2951.0	2996.9	3041.6	3085.6	3129.1	3172.3	3215.3	3258.2
	s	6.4941	6.6030	6.7016	6.7922	6.8766	6.9561	7.0315	7.1036	7.1729	7.2398	7.3045
15 198.29 471.44	v	0.1324	0.1406	0.1483	0.1556	0.1628	0.1697	0.1765	0.1832	0.1898	0.1964	0.2029
	i	2794.7	2848.6	2899.2	2947.3	2993.7	3038.9	3083.3	3127.0	3170.4	3213.5	3256.6
	s	6.4508	6.5624	6.6629	6.7550	6.8405	6.9207	6.9967	7.0693	7.1389	7.2060	7.2709
16 201.37 474.52	v	—	0.1310	0.1383	0.1453	0.1521	0.1587	0.1651	0.1714	0.1777	0.1838	0.1900
	i	—	2843.1	2894.7	2943.6	2990.6	3036.2	3080.9	3124.9	3168.5	3211.8	3255.0
	s	—	6.5237	6.6263	6.7198	6.8063	6.8873	6.9639	7.0369	7.1069	7.1743	7.2394
17 204.31 477.46	v	—	0.1225	0.1296	0.1362	0.1427	0.1489	0.1550	0.1610	0.1669	0.1728	0.1785
	i	—	2837.5	2890.1	2939.8	2987.4	3033.5	3078.5	3122.8	3166.6	3210.1	3253.5
	s	—	6.4866	6.5912	6.6863	6.7739	6.8557	6.9329	7.0064	7.0767	7.1444	7.2098
18 207.11 480.26	v	—	01150	0.1217	0.1282	0.1343	0.1402	0.1460	0.1517	0.1573	0.1629	0.1684
	i	—	2831.7	2885.4	2935.9	2984.1	3030.7	3076.1	3120.6	3164.7	3208.4	3251.9
	s	—	6.4509	6.5577	6.6543	6.7430	6.8257	6.9035	6.9774	7.0481	7.1160	7.1816

(*Contd.*)

Table IV.3 (Contd.)

Pres., bar Sat. temp. °C Sat. temp. K	Parameter	Superheated steam temperature, °C (K)									
		240 (513.15)	260 (533.15)	280 (533.15)	300 (373.15)	320 (393.15)	340 (613.15)	360 (633.15)	380 (653.15)	400 (673.15)	440 (713.15)
19 209.8 482.95	v	0.1147	0.1209	0.1268	0.1325	0.1380	0.1435	0.1488	0.1541	0.1593	0.1696
	i	2880.7	2932.0	2980.9	3027.9	3073.6	3118.5	3162.7	3206.6	3250.3	3337.4
	s	6.5254	6.6236	6.7135	6.7970	6.8755	6.9498	7.0209	7.0891	7.1550	7.2806
20 212.37 485.52	v	0.1084	0.1144	0.1200	0.1255	0.1308	0.1360	0.1411	0.1461	0.1511	0.1610
	i	2875.9	2928.1	2977.5	3025.0	3071.2	3116.3	3160.9	3204.9	3248.7	3336.0
	s	6.4943	6.5941	6.6852	6.7696	6.8487	6.9235	6.9950	7.0635	7.1295	7.2555
22 217.24 490.39	v	0.097 52	0.1031	0.1084	0.1134	0.1183	0.1231	0.1278	0.1324	0.1370	0.1460
	i	2866.0	2920.0	2970.8	3019.3	3066.2	3111.9	3156.9	3201.4	3245.5	3333.3
	s	6.4349	6.5382	6.6317	6.7179	6.7983	6.8742	6.9464	7.0155	7.0821	7.2088
24 221.78 494.93	v	0.088 39	0.093 67	0.098 63	0.1034	0.1079	0.1124	0.1167	0.1210	0.1252	0.1335
	i	2855.7	2911.6	2963.8	3013.4	3061.1	3107.5	3153.0	3197.8	3242.3	3330.6
	s	6.3788	6.4857	6.5818	6.6699	6.7517	6.8286	6.9016	6.9714	7.0384	7.1658
26 226.04 499.19	v	0.080 64	0.085 67	0.090 37	0.094 83	0.099 12	0.1033	0.1073	0.1113	0.1153	0.1230
	i	2845.2	2903.0	2956.7	3007.4	3056.0	3103.0	3149.0	3194.3	3239.0	3327.8
	s	6.3253	6.4360	6.5348	6.6249	6.7082	6.7862	6.8600	6.9304	6.9979	7.1260
28 230.05 503.2	v	0.073 97	0.78880	0.083 28	0.087 51	0.091 56	0.095 48	0.09929	0.1030	0.1067	0.1139
	i	2834.2	2894.2	2949.5	3001.3	3050.8	3098.5	3145.0	3190.7	3235.8	3325.1
	s	6.2738	6.3886	6.4903	6.5824	6.6672	6.7464	6.8210	6.8921	6.9601	7.0890
30 233.84 506.99	v	0.06816	0.07283	0.07712	0.08116	0.08500	0.08871	0.09232	0.09584	0.099 31	0.1061
	i	2822.9	2885.1	2942.0	2995.1	3045.4	3093.9	3140.9	3187.0	3232.5	3322.3
	s	6.2241	6.3432	6.4479	6.5422	6.6285	6.7088	6.7844	6.8561	6.9246	7.0543

(Contd.)

Table IV.3 (Contd.)

Pres., bar Sat. temp. °C Sat. temp. K	Para-meter	Superheated steam temperature, °C (K)									
		280 (553.15)	300 (573.15)	320 (593.15)	340 (613.15)	360 (633.15)	380 (653.15)	400 (673.15)	440 (713.15)	480 (753.15)	520 (793.15)
32 237.45 510.6	v	0.071 73	0.075 59	0.079 26	0.082 79	0.086 21	0.089 55	0.092 83	0.099 25	0.1055	0.1117
	i	2934.4	2988.7	3040.0	3089.2	3136.8	3183.4	3229.2	3319.5	3409.2	3498.8
	s	6.4072	6.5037	6.5917	6.6733	6.7497	6.8221	6.8912	7.0216	7.1439	7.2598
34 240.88 514.03	v	0.066 95	0.070 68	0.074 19	0.077 56	0.080 82	0.084 00	0.087 11	0.093 19	0.099 15	0.1050
	i	2926.2	2982.2	3034.5	3084.4	3132.7	3179.7	3225.9	3316.8	3406.8	3496.7
	s	6.3681	6.4669	6.5566	6.6394	6.7168	6.7899	6.8595	6.9907	7.1135	7.2299
36 244.16 517.31	v	0.062 70	0.066 30	0.069 68	0.072 91	0.076 03	0.079 06	0.082 02	0.087 81	0.093 47	0.099 03
	i	2918.6	2975.6	3028.9	3079.6	3128.4	3175.9	3222.5	3314.0	3404.4	3494.6
	s	6.3302	6.4315	6.5230	6.6070	6.6854	6.7592	6.8294	6.9614	7.0848	7.2015
38 247.31 520.46	v	0.058 88	0.062 37	0.065 64	0.068 75	0.071 74	0.074 64	0.077 47	0.083 00	0.088 38	0.093 67
	i	2910.4	2968.9	3023.3	3074.8	3124.2	3172.2	3219.1	3311.2	3402.0	3492.5
	s	6.2935	6.3973	6.4906	6.5760	6.6553	6.7299	6.8007	6.9336	7.0575	7.1746
40 250.33 523.48	v	0.055 44	0.058 83	0.062 00	0.06499	0.06787	0.070 66	0.073 38	0.07866	0.08381	0.088 86
	i	2902.0	2962.0	3017.5	3069.8	3119.9	3168.4	3215.7	3308.3	3399.6	3490.4
	s	6.2576	6.3642	6.4593	6.5461	6.6265	6.7019	6.7733	6.9069	7.0314	7.1489
42 253.24 526.39	v	0.052 31	0.055 62	0.058 70	0.06160	0.06437	0.06706	0.069 67	0.07474	0.079 67	0.084 50
	i	2893.5	2955.0	3011.6	3064.8	3115.5	3164.5	3212.3	3305.5	3397.1	3488.3
	s	6.2227	6.3320	6.4291	6.5173	6.5987	6.6749	6.7469	6.8815	7.0065	7.1244
44 256.05 529.2	v	0.049 46	0.052 70	0.055 69	0.058 50	0.06119	0.063 78	0.066 29	0.071 17	0.075 90	0.080 54
	i	2884.7	2947.8	3005.7	3059.7	3111.1	3160.6	3208.8	3302.6	3394.7	3486.2
	s	6.1884	6.3006	6.3998	6.4894	6.5719	6.6489	6.7216	6.8570	6.9826	7.1010

(Contd.)

Table IV.3 (*Contd.*)

Pres., bar / Sat. temp. °C / Sat. temp. K	Parameter	Superheated steam temperature, °C (K)									
		300 (573.15)	320 (593.15)	340 (613.15)	360 (633.15)	380 (653.15)	400 (673.15)	440 (713.15)	480 (753.15)	520 (793.15)	560 (833.15)
46 / 258.75 / 531.9	v	0.050 03	0.052 94	0.055 68	0.058 28	0.060 79	0.063 21	0.067 91	0.072 47	0.076 92	0.081 30
	i	2940.5	2999.6	3054.6	3106.7	3156.7	3205.3	3299.8	3392.3	3484.1	3575.8
	s	6.2700	6.3712	6.4624	6.5460	6.6239	6.6972	6.8335	6.9597	7.0784	7.1913
48 / 261.37 / 534.52	v	0.047 57	0.050 42	0.053 09	0.055 61	0.058 04	0.060 39	0.064 93	0.069 31	0.073 60	0.077 82
	i	2933.1	2993.4	3049.3	3102.2	3152.8	3201.8	3296.9	3389.8	3481.9	3573.9
	s	6.2399	6.3434	6.4362	6.5209	6.5996	6.6736	6.8108	6.9376	7.0568	7.1699
50 / 263.91 / 537.06	v	0.045 30	0.048 10	0.050 70	0.053 16	0.055 51	0.057 79	0.06218	0.006642	0.070 55	0.07461
	i	2925.5	2987.2	3044.1	3097.6	3148.8	3198.3	3294.0	3387.4	3479.8	3572.0
	s	6.2105	6.3163	6.4106	6.4966	6.5762	6.6508	6.7890	6.9164	7.0360	7.1494
54 / 268.76 / 541.91	v	0.041 25	0.043 95	0.046 44	0.048 78	0.051 02	0.053 17	0.05729	0.061 26	0.065 113	0.06891
	i	2909.8	2974.3	3033.3	3088.3	3140.7	3191.1	3288.2	3382.5	3475.6	3568.3
	s	6.1530	6.2636	6.3614	6.4498	6.5312	6.6072	6.7473	6.8760	6.9964	7.1105
58 / 273.35 / 546.5	v	0.037 74	0.040 36	0.04276	0.045 01	0.047 13	0.049 18	0.05308	0.056 82	0.06004 5	0.06400
	i	2893.5	2961.0	3022.2	3078.9	3132.4	3183.8	3282.3	3377.5	3471.3	3564.6
	s	6.0969	6.2128	6.3142	6.4052	6.4885	6.5660	6.7081	6.8381	6.9594	7.0741
62 / 277.70 / 550.85	v	0.034 65	0.037 22	0.039 55	0.04171	0.043 75	0.045 70	0.04941	0.05295	0.056 37	0.059 73
	i	2876.3	2947.3	3010.8	3069.2	3124.0	3176.4	3276.3	3372.5	3467.0	3560.8
	s	6.0418	6.1635	6.2688	6.3625	6.4478	6.5268	6.6710	6.8023	6.9245	7.0399
66 / 281.84 / 554.99	v	0.031 91	0.034 45	0.036 72	0.038 81	0.040 77	0.042 64	0.04618	0.049 54	0.05279	0.05597
	i	2858.3	2933.1	2999.0	3059.2	3115.5	3168.9	3270.3	3367.5	3462.7	3557.0
	s	5.9872	6.1154	6.2248	6.3214	6.4089	6.4894	6.6358	6.7684	6.8916	7.0076

(*Contd.*)

Table IV.3   (*Contd.*)

Pres., bar / Sat. temp. °C / Sat. temp. K	Para-meter	Superheated steam temperature, °C (K)										
		320 (593.15)	340 (613.15)	360 (633.15)	380 (653.15)	400 (673.15)	440 (713.15)	480 (753.15)	520 (793.15)	560 (833.15)	600 (873.15)	640 (913.15)
70 / 285.79 / 558.94	v	0.031 98	0.034 20	0.036 23	0.038 12	0.039 92	0.043 31	0.046 53	0.049 62	0.052 64	0.055 59	0.058 50
	i	2918.3	2987.0	3049.1	3106.7	3161.2	3264.2	3362.4	3458.3	3553.2	3647.9	3742.6
	s	6.0681	6.1820	6.2817	6.3714	6.4536	6.6022	6.7362	6.8603	6.9771	7.0880	7.1941
74 / 289.57 / 562.72	v	0.029 76	0.031 94	0.033 92	0.035 76	0.037 50	0.040 76	0.043 84	0.046 79	0.049 67	0.052 48	0.055 24
	i	2903.0	2974.6	3038.7	3097.8	3153.5	3258.0	3357.3	3454.0	3549.5	3644.5	3739.7
	s	6.0214	6.1402	6.2432	6.3351	6.4190	6.5700	6.7054	6.8305	6.9480	7.0594	7.1660
78 / 293.21 / 566.36	v	0.027 75	0.029 91	0.031 85	0.033 64	0.035 32	0.038 47	0.041 42	0.044 25	0.047 00	0.049 69	0.052 32
	i	2887.0	2961.8	3028.1	3088.8	3145.6	3251.8	3352.2	3449.6	3545.7	3641.2	3736.7
	s	5.9751	6.0992	6.2056	6.3000	6.3857	6.5390	6.6760	6.8021	6.9202	7.0322	7.1392
82 / 296.7 / 569.85	v	0.025 92	0.028 06	0.029 97	0.031 71	0.033 35	0.036 39	0.039 24	0.041 96	0.044 59	0.047 17	0.049 69
	i	2870.2	2948.6	3017.2	3079.5	3137.6	3245.5	3347.0	3445.2	3541.8	3637.9	3733.7
	s	5.9288	6.0588	6.1689	6.2659	6.3534	6.5092	6.6477	6.7748	6.8937	7.0062	7.1136
86 / 300.06 / 573.21	v	0.024 24	0.026 38	0.028 26	0.029 97	0.031 56	0.034 51	0.037 26	0.039 88	0.042 41	0.044 88	0.047 30
	i	2852.7	2935.0	3006.1	3070.1	3129.4	3239.1	3341.8	3440.8	3538.0	3634.5	3730.8
	s	5.8823	6.0189	6.1330	6.2326	6.3220	6.4804	6.6205	6.7486	6.8682	6.9813	7.0891
90 / 303.13 / 576.46	v	0.022 69	0.024 84	0.026 69	0.028 37	0.029 93	0.032 80	0.035 46	0.037 99	0.040 42	0.042 80	0.045 12
	i	2834.3	2920.9	2994.7	3060.5	3121.2	3232.7	3336.5	3436.3	3534.2	3631.1	3727.8
	s	5.8355	5.9792	6.0976	6.2000	6.2915	6.4525	6.5942	6.7233	6.8437	6.9574	7.0656
94 / 306.44 / 579.59	v	0.021 24	0.023 41	0.025 26	0.026 91	0.028 43	0.031 23	0.033 18	0.036 25	0.038 61	0.040 89	0.043 13
	i	2814.8	2906.3	2983.0	3050.7	3112.8	3226.2	3331.2	3431.9	3530.3	3627.8	3724.8
	s	5.7879	5.9397	6.0627	6.1631	6.2617	6.4254	6.5688	6.6990	6.8201	6.9343	7.0430
98 / 309.48 / 582.63	v	0.022 09	0.023 93	0.025 56	0.027 06	0.029 79	0.032 29	0.034 66	0.036 93	0.039 14	0.041 30	0.043 42
	i	2891.2	2970.9	3040.8	3104.2	3119.6	3325.9	3427.4	3526.5	3624.4	3721.8	3819.2
	s	5.9001	6.0282	6.1368	6.2325	6.3990	6.5441	6.6755	6.7974	6.9121	7.0213	7.1257

(*Contd.*)

Table IV.3 *(Contd.)*

Pres., bar / Sat. temp. °C / Sat. temp. K	Para-meter	Superheated steam temperature, °C (K)										
		340 (613.15)	360 (633.15)	380 (653.15)	400 (673.15)	440 (713.15)	480 (753.15)	520 (793.15)	560 (833.15)	600 (873.15)	640 (913.15)	680 (953.15)
100 310.96 584.11	v	0.021 47	0.023 31	0.024 93	0.026 41	0.029 11	0.031 58	0.033 91	0.03615	0.038 32	0.040 44	0.042 52
	i	2883.4	2964.8	3035.7	3099.9	3216.2	3323.2	3425.1	3524.5	3622.7	3720.4	3817.9
	s	5.8803	6.0110	6.1213	6.2182	6.3861	6.5321	6.6640	6.7863	6.9013	7.0107	7.1153
105 314.57 587.72	v	0.020 00	0.021 84	0.023 44	0.024 89	0.027 52	0.029 92	0.032 16	0.034 32	0.036 40	0.038 43	0.040 43
	i	2863.1	2949.1	3022.8	3089.0	3207.9	3316.4	3419.5	3519.7	3618.5	3716.6	3814.6
	s	5.8303	5.9684	6.0831	6.1829	6.3545	6.5027	6.6360	6.7593	6.8751	6.9850	7.0901
110 318.05 591.2	v	0.018 64	0.020 49	0.022 08	0.023 51	0.026 08	0.02840	0.030 58	0.032 65	0.034 66	0.036 61	0.038 52
	i	2841.7	2932.8	3009.6	3077.8	3199.4	3309.6	3413.8	3514.8	3614.2	3712.9	3811.3
	s	5.7797	5.9259	6.0454	6.1483	6.3238	6.4742	6.6091	6.7334	6.8499	6.9604	7.0659
115 321.40 cx594.55	v	0.017 38	0.019 26	0.020 84	0.022 25	0.02476	0.02702	0.02912	0.03113	0.033 06	0.03494	0.03678
	i	2819.0	2915.8	2996.0	3066.4	3190.7	3302.7	3408.1	3509.9	3609.9	3709.1	3808.0
	s	5.7279	5.8835	6.0082	6.1144	6.2939	6.4467	6.5830	6.7083	6.8256	6.9367	7.0427
120 324.65 597.8	v	0.016 19	0.018 11	0.019 69	0.02108	0.023 55	0.02575	0.02779	0.02973	0.031 60	0.033 42	0.035 519
	i	2794.7	2898.1	2982.0	3054.8	3182.0	3295.7	3402.3	3505.0	3605.7	3705.4	3804.7
	s	5.6747	5.8408	5.9712	6.0810	6.2647	6.4199	6.5578	6.6842	6.8022	6.9139	7.0203
125 327.78 600.93	v	0.015 08	0.017 04	0.018 63	0.020 01	0.02243	0.024 58	0.02657	0.02845	0.03026	0.03201	0.03373
	i	2768.7	2879.6	2967.6	3042.9	3173.1	3288.7	3396.5	3500.0	3601.4	3701.6	3801.3
	s	5.6195	5.7976	5.9345	6.0481	6.2362	6.3939	6.5334	6.6608	6.7796	6.8919	6.9987
130 330.83 603.98	v	0.014 01	0.016 04	0.01764	0.019 02	0.02140	0.023 50	0.023 50	0.02727	0.02902	0.030 72	0.032 37
	i	2740.6	2860.2	2952.7	3030.7	3164.1	3281.6	3390.6	3495.1	3597.1	3697.8	3798.0
	s	5.5618	5.7539	5.8979	6.0155	6.2082	6.3685	6.5096	6.6381	6.7577	6.8706	6.9779

(Contd.)

Table IV.3 (*Contd.*)

Pres., bar Sat. temp. °C Sat. temp. K	Parameter	Superheated steam temperature, °C (K)										
		340 (613.15)	360 (633.15)	380 (653.15)	400 (673.15)	440 (713.15)	480 (753.15)	520 (793.15)	560 (833.15)	600 (873.15)	640 (913.15)	680 (953.15)
135 333.78 606.93	v	0.012 99	0.015 10	0.016 72	0.018 09	0.020 44	0.022 50	0.024 39	0.026 17	0.027 87	0.029 52	0.031 12
	i	2709.9	2839.7	2937.3	3018.3	3155.0	3274.4	3384.7	3490.1	3592.8	3694.1	3794.7
	s	5.5007	5.7093	5.8612	5.9833	6.1808	6.3437	6.4865	6.6161	6.7365	6.8499	6.9578
140 336.64 609.79	v	0.0120 00	0.014 21	0.015 86	0.017 23	0.019 55	0.02157	0.02342	0.025 15	0.026 80	0.02840	0.029 96
	i	2675.7	2818.1	2921.4	3005.6	3145.0	3267.1	3378.8	3485.1	3588.5	3690.3	3791.3
	s	5.4348	5.6636	5.8243	5.9513	6.1538	6.3194	6.4639	6.5947	6.7159	6.8299	6.9382
145 339.42 612.57	v	0.011 00	0.013 37	0.01505	0.016 42	0.01872	0.02070	0.022 51	0.024 20	0.02581	0.027 37	0.028 88
	i	2635.8	2795.2	2904.9	2992.5	3136.4	3259.8	3372.8	3480.0	3584.1	3686.5	3788.0
	s	5.3603	5.6165	5.7872	5.9194	6.1272	6.2957	6.4419	6.5738	6.6959	6.8105	6.9193
150 342.13 615.28	v	—	0.012 56	0.01428	0.01566	0.017 94	0.01989	0.02166	0.023 31	0.02488	0.026 40	0.027 87
	i	—	2770.8	2887.7	2979.1	3126.9	3252.4	3366.8	3475.0	3579.8	3682.7	3784.7
	s	—	5.5677	5.7497	5.8876	6.1010	6.2724	6.4204	6.5535	6.6764	6.7917	6.9009
175 354.64 627.79	v	—	0.008 86	0.010 99	0.012 46	0.014 70	0.016 53	0.018 15	0.019 64	0.021 04	0.022 38	0.023 68
	i	—	2614.8	2789.4	2906.3	3077.2	3214.3	3336.0	3449.3	3557.8	3663.6	3767.9
	s	—	5.2791	5.5510	5.7274	5.9745	6.1617	6.3192	6.4586	6.5858	6.7042	6.8160
200 365.70 638.85	v	—	—	0.008 25	0.009 95	0.012 24	0.013 99	0.015 51	0.016 88	0.018 16	0.019 38	0.020 54
	i	—	—	2660.2	2820.5	3023.7	3174.4	3304.2	3423.0	3535.5	3644.3	3751.0
	s	—	—	5.3165	5.5585	5.8523	6.0581	6.2262	6.3724	6.5043	6.6261	6.7405

(Reproduced with the permission of *The Japan Society of Mechanical Engineers*, Japan from **1980 JSME Steam Tables in SI.**)
Note: Temperature scale refers to ITS-1968 scale.

Standard Enthalpies of Formation and of Combustion of Compounds

Appendix V.1 Standard Enthalpy of Formation of Inorganic Compounds

Substance	Formula	State	CAS Reg. No.	Molar mass M kg/kmol	ΔH_f^{o*}
Oxygen	O_2	g	7782-44-7	31.9988	0
Ozone	O_3	g	10028-15-6	47.9982	142.7
Hydrogen	H_2	g	1333-74-0	2.0159	0
Water	H_2O	g	7732-18-5	18.0153	−241.818
		l			−285.830
Hydrogen	H_2O_2	g	7722-84-1	34.0147	−136.31
peroxide		l			−187.78
		ao			−191.17
Fluorine	F_2	g	7782-41-4	37.9968	0
Hydrogen	HF	g	7664-39-3	20.0063	−271.1
fluoride		l			−299.78
		ai			−332.63
		ao			−320.08
Chlorine	Cl_2	g	7782-50-5	70.906	0
		ao			−23.4
Hydrogen chloride	HCl	g	7647-01-0	36.4609	−92.31
		ai			−167.16
Hypochlorous acid	HClO	g	7790-92-3	52.4603	−78.7
		ao			−120.9
Chlorine dioxide	ClO_2	g	10049-04-4	67.4518	102.5
Perchloric acid	$HClO_4$	l		100.4585	−40.58
		ai			−129.33

(Contd.)

${}^*\Delta H_f^0$ = Standard enthalpy of formation at 25°C (298.15 K) and 1 bar, kJ/mol

Appendix V.1   (*Contd.*)

Substance	Formula	State	CAS Reg. No.	Molar mass M kg/kmol	ΔH_f^o
Bromine	Br_2	g	7726-95-6	159.808	30.91
		l			0
		ao			−2.59
Hydrogen bromide	HBr	g	10035-10-6	80.9119	−36.40
		ai			−121.55
Bromine dioxide	BrO_2	c	67177-47-3	111.9028	48.5
Iodine	I_2	c	7553-56-2	253.8089	0
		g			62.44
		ao			22.6
Hydrogen Iodide	HI	g	10034-85-2	127.9124	26.48
		ai			−55.19
Iodic acid	HIO_3	c	—	175.9106	−230.1
		ao			−211.3
Sulphur	S	c (rhombic)	7704-34-9	32.065	0
		c (monoclinic)		32.065	0.33
		g			278.81
Sulphur (diatomic)	S_2	g	23550-45-0	64.13	128.37
Sulphur dioxide	SO_2	g	7446-09-5	64.0638	−296.83
		l			−320.5
		ao			−322.98
Sulphur trioxide	SO_3	g	7446-11-9		−395.72
		l			−441.04
		c			−454.51
Sulphuric acid	H_2SO_4	l	7664-93-9	98.0785	−813.99
		ai			−909.27
Hydrgen sulphide	H_2S	g	7783-06-4	34.0809	−20.63
		ao			−39.7
Thionyl chloride	$SOCl_2$	g	7719=09-7	118.9704	−212.5
		l			−245.6
Nitrogen	N_2	g	7727-37-9	28.0134	0
Nitrogen oxide	NO	g	10102-43-9	30.0061	90.25
Nitrogen dioxide	NO_2	g	10102-44-0	46.0055	33.18
Nitrous oxide	N_2O	g	10024-97-2	44.0128	82.05
		aq			56.1
(Di)nitrogen tetroxide	N_2O_4	g	10544-72-6	92.0110	9.16
		l			−19.50
(Di)nitrogen pentoxide	N_2O_5	g	10102-03-1	108.0104	11.3
		c			−43.1
Ammonia	NH_3	g	7664-41-7	17.0305	−46.11
		ao			−80.29
Hydrazine	N_2H_4	g	302-01-2	32.0452	95.40
		l			50.63
		ao			34.31
Nitrous acid	HNO_2	g (*cis*)	7782-77-6	47.0134	−77.99
		ao			−119.2

(*Contd.*)

Appendix V.1   (*Contd.*)

Substance	Formula	State	CAS Reg. No.	Molar mass M kg/kmol	ΔH_f^o
Nitric acid	HNO_3	g	7697-37-2	63.0128	−135.06
		l			−174.10
		ai			−207.36
Ammonium hydroxide	NH_4OH	l	1336-21-6	35.0458	−361.20
Ammonium nitrate	NH_4NO_3	c	6484-52-2	80.0434	−365.56
		ai			−339.87
Nitrosyl chloride	$NOCl$	g	2696-92-6	65.4591	51.71
Ammonium chloride	NH_4Cl	c	12125-02-9	53.4915	−314.43
		ai			−299.66
Ammonium bromide	NH_4Br	c	12124-97-9	97.9425	−270.83
		ai			−254.05
Ammonium iodide	NH_4I	c	12027-06-4	144.9430	−201.42
		ai			−187.69
Sulphamic acid	H_3NSO_3	c	5329-14-6	97.0937	−674.9
Ammonium hydrogen sulphate	NH_4HSO_4	c	7803-63-6	115.1090	−1026.96
		ai			−1019.85
Ammonium sulphate	$(NH_4)_2SO_4$	c	7783-20-2	132.1395	−1180.85
		ai			−1174.28
Phosphorous	P	white crystal	7723-14-0	30.9738	0
		red, triclinic		30.9738	−17.6
		black		30.9738	−39.3
		g			314.64
Phosphorous pentoxide	P_4O_{10}	c (hexagonal)	16752-60-6	283.8890	−2984.0
		amorphous		283.8890	−3042.0
		l			−1266.9
		ai			−1277.4
		ao			−1288.34
Phosphoric acid	H_3PO_4	c	7664-38-2	97.9952	−1279.0
		l			−1266.9
		ai			−1277.4
		ao			−1288.34
Phosphine	PH_3	g	7803-51-2	33.9976	5.4
		ao			−9.50
Metaphosphoric acid	HPO_3	c	10343-62-1	79.9799	−948.5
		aq			−977.0
Pyrophosphoric acid	$H_4P_2O_7$	c	2466=09-3	177.9791	−2241.0
		l			−2231.7
		ao			−2268.6
Ammonium dihydrogen phosphate	$NH_4H_2PO_4$	c	7722-76-1	115.0257	−1445.07
		ai			−1428.79
Ammonium (hydrogen) phosphate	$(NH_4)_2HPO_4$	c	—	132.0562	−1566.91
		ai			−1557.16
Ammonium phosphate	$(NH_4)_3PO_4$	c	—	149.0867	−1671.9
		ai			−1674.9
Boron	B	c	7440-42-8	10.811	0
		amorphous		10.811	3.8

(*Contd.*)

Appendix V.1 (*Contd.*)

Substance	Formula	State	CAS Reg. No.	Molar mass M kg/kmol	ΔH_f^o
Diborane	B_2H_6	g	19287-45-7	27.6696	35.6
Diboron	B_2O_3	c	1303-86-2	69.6202	−1272.77
trioxide		amorphous		69.6202	−1254.53
		g			−843.79
Boric acid	H_3BO_3	c	10043-35-3	61.8330	−1094.33
		g			−994.1
		ao			−1072.32
Silicon	Si	c	7440-21-3	28.0855	0
		amorphous		28.0855	4.2
		g			455.6
Silicon dioxide	SiO_2	c (α-quartz)	14808-60-7	60.0843	−910.94
		c (α-crysto-balite)			−909.48
		c (α-tridymite)			−909.06
		amorphous	7631-86-9		−903.49
		g			−322.0
		ai			−897.0
Silane	SiH_4	g	7803-62-5	32.1173	34.3
Disilane	Si_2H_6	g	1590-87-0	62.2186	80.3
Silicon	$SiCl_4$	g	10026-04-7	169.8975	−657.01
tetrachloride		l			−687.0
Sodium	Na	c	7440-23-5	22.9898	0
		g			107.32
Sodium acetate	$NaC_2H_3O_2$	c	127-09-3	82.0338	−708.81
		ai			−726.13
Sodium oxide	Na_2O	c	1313-59-3	61.9789	−414.22
		g			−35.6
Sodium	NaOH	c	1310-73-2	39.9971	−425.61
hydroxide		g			−207.1
		ai			−470.11
Sodium	NaF	c	7681-49-4	41.9882	−573.65
flouride		g			−291.2
		ai			−572.75
Sodium	NaCl	c	7647-14-5	58.4428	−411.15
chloride		g			−176.65
		ai			−407.27
Sodium	NaOCl	ai	—	74.4422	−347.3
hypochloride					
Sodium	$NaClO_3$	c	7775-09-9	106.4410	−365.77
chlorate		ai			−344.09
Sodium	NaBr	g	7647-15-6	102.8938	−143.1
bromide		ai			−361.67
Sodium	NaOBr	ai	—	118.8932	−334.3
hypobromide					
Sodium	$NaHCO_3$	c	—	84.0066	−950.81
bicarbonate		ai			−932.11
		ao			−943.9

(*Contd.*)

Appendix V.1   (*Contd.*)

Substance	Formula	State	CAS Reg. No.	Molar mass M kg/kmol	ΔH_f^o
Sodium carbonate	Na_2CO_3	c ai	497-19-8	105.9884	-1130.68 -1157.38
Sodium formate	$NaCHO_2$	c ai	141-53-7	68.0072	-666.5 -665.67
Sodium cyanide	$NaCN$	c (cubic) c (orthorhombic) g ai	143-33-9	49.0072 49.0072	-87.49 -90.75 109.0 - 89.5
Sodium sulphate	Na_2SO_4	c (orthorhombic) ai	7757-82-6	142.0421	-1387.08 -1389.51
Sodium sulphite	Na_2SO_3	c ai	7757-83-7	126.0427	-1100.8 -1115.87
Sodium sulphide	Na_2S	c ai	1313-82-2	78.0445	-364.8 -447.3
Sodium nitrite	$NaNO_2$	c ai	7632-00-0	68.9953	-358.65 -344.8
Sodium nitrate	$NaNO_3$	c ai	7631-99-4	84.9947	-467.85 -447.48
Sodium phosphate	Na_3PO_4	c ai	7601-54-9	163.9407	-1917.40 -1997.9
Sodium chromate	Na_2CrO_4	c ai	7775-11-3	161.9732	-1342.2 -1361.39
Sodium dichromate	$Na_2Cr_2O_7$	c ai	—	261.9675	-1978.6 -1970.7
Potassium	K	c g	7440=09-7	39.0983	0 89.24
Potassium oxide	K_2O	c g	12136-45-7	94.1960	-361.5 -63.0
Potassium hydroxide	KOH	c g ai	1310-58-3	56.1056	-424.76 -231.0 -482.37
Potassium fluoride	KF	c g ai	7789-23-3	58.0967	-567.27 -325.43 -585.01
Potassium chloride	KCl	c g ai	7447-40-7	74.5513	-436.75 -214.14 -419.53
Potassium bromide	KBr	c g ai	7758-02-3	119.0023	-393.80 -180.08 -373.92
Potassium iodide	KI	c g ai	7681-11-0	166.0028	-327.90 -125.5 -307.57
Potassium cyanide	KCN	c g ai	151-50-8	65.1157	-113.0 90.8 -101.7

(*Contd.*)

Appendix V.1 (*Contd.*)

Substance	Formula	State	CAS Reg. No.	Molar mass M kg/kmol	ΔH_f^o
Potassium chlorate	$KClO_3$	c ai	3811-04-9	122.5495	-397.73 -356.35
Potassium sulphide	K_2S	c ai	1312-73-8	110.2616	-380.7 -471.5
Potassium sulphate	K_2SO_4	c g ai	7778-80-5	174.2592	-1437.79 -1096.0 -1414.02
Potassium nitrate	KNO_3	c ai	7757-79-1	101.1032	-494.63 -459.74
Potassium carbonate	K_2CO_3	c ai	584-08-7	138.2055	-1151.02 -1182.90
Potassium bicarbonate	$KHCO_3$	c ai	—	100.1151	-963.2 -944.37
Potassium formate	KCO_2H	c ai	—	84.1157	-679.73 -677.93
Potassium acetate	$KC_2O_2H_3$	c ai	127-08-2	98.1423	-723.0 -738.39
Potassium phosphate	K_3PO_4	c ai	7778-53-2	212.2663	-1950.2 -2034.7
Potassium permanganate	$KMnO_4$	c ai	7722-64-7	158.0339	-837.2 -793.7
Potassium chromate	K_2CrO_4	c ai	7789-00-6	194.1903	-1403.7 -1385.91
Potassium dichromate	$K_2Cr_2O_7$	c ai	7778-50-9	294.1846	-2061.5 -1994.9
Carbon (graphite)	C	c	7782-42-5	12.0107	0
Carbon (diamond)	C	c	7782-40-3	12.0107	1.9
Carbon disulphide	CS_2	g l aq	75-15-0	76.1407	117.36 89.70 89.1
Carbon monoxide	CO	g ao	630-08-0	28.0101	-110.53 -120.96
Carbon dioxide	CO_2	g ao ai ao	124-38-9	44.0095	-393.51 -413.80 150.6 107.1
Calcium	Ca	c g	7440-70-2	40.078	0 178.2
Calcium oxide	CaO	c	1305-78-8	56.0774	-635.09
Calcium hydroxide	$Ca(OH)_2$	c g ai	1305-62-0	74.0927	-986.09 -544.0 -1002.82
Calcium fluoride	CaF_2	c g ai	7789-75-5	78.0748	-1219.6 -781.6 -1208.09

(*Contd.*)

Appendix V.1   (*Contd.*)

Substance	Formula	State	CAS Reg. No.	Molar mass M kg/kmol	ΔH_f^o
Calcium chloride	$CaCl_2$	c g ai	10043-52-4	110.9840	−795.8 −471.5 −877.13
Calcium phosphate	$Ca_3(PO_4)_2$	c (α-form) c (β-form) ai	10103-46-5	310.1767	−4109.9 −4120.8 −4183.2
Calcium carbonate	$CaCO_3$	c (calcite) c (aragonite) ai	471-34-1	100.0869 100.0869	−1206.92 −1207.13 −1219.97
Calcium carbide	CaC_2	c		64.0994	−59.8
Calcium sulphate	$CaSO_4$	c (anhydrite, insol.) c (soluble, α) c (soluble, β) ai	10101-41-4	136.1406 136.1406 136.1406	−1434.11 −1425.24 −1420.80 −1452.10
Magnesium	Mg	c g	7439-95-4	24.3050	0 147.70
Magnesium oxide	MgO	c (macro) c (micro) g	1309-48-4	40.3044	−601.70 −597.98 17.0
Magnesium hydroxide	$Mg(OH)_2$	c amorphous g ai	1309-42-8	58.3197 58.3197	−924.54 −920.5 −561.0 −926.84
Magnesium chloride	$MgCl_2$	c g ai	7786-30-3	95.2110	−641.32 −400.4 −801.15
Magnesium carbonate	$MgCO_3$	c	546-93-0	84.3139	−1095.8
Magnesium sulphate	$MgSO_4$	c ai ao	7487-88-9	120.3676	−1284.9 −1376.12 −1356.0
Iron	Fe	c g	7439-89-6	55.845	0 416.3
Iron oxide (hematite)	Fe_2O_3	c	1317-60-8	159.6882	−824.2
Ferric oxide (magnetite)	Fe_3O_4	c	1309-38-2	231.5326	−1118.4
Iron hydroxide	$Fe(OH)_2$	c g	18624-44-7	89.8597	−569.0 −372.0
Ferrous chloride	$FeCl_2$	c g ai	7758-94-3	126.751	−341.79 −148.5 −423.4

(*Contd.*)

Appendix V.1   *(Contd.)*

Substance	Formula	State	CAS Reg. No.	Molar mass M kg/kmol	ΔH_f^o
Ferric chloride	$FeCl_3$	c	7705-08-0	162.2040	−399.49
		g			−254.0
		ai			−550.2
Ferrous sulphate	$FeSO_4$	c	7720-78-7	151.9076	−928.4
		ai			−998.3
Ferric sulphate	$Fe_2(SO_4)_3$	c	10028-22-5	399.8778	−2581.5
		ai			−2825.0
Zinc Sulohate	$ZnSO_4$	c	7733-02-0	161.4716	−982.8
		ai			−1063.15
Copper Sulphate	$CuSO_4$	c	7758-98-7	159.6086	−771.36
		ai			−844.50
Nickel Sulphate	$NiSO_4$	c	7786-81-4	154.7560	−872.91
		ai			−963.2

State: c - crystal, g - gas, l - liquid,
ai - aqueous solution, ionised substance standard, $m^\ominus$ = 1 mol/kg
ao - aqueous soution, unionised substance standard, $m^\ominus$ = 1 mol/kg
aq - aqueous solution, concentration not specified

Reference: Wagman, D D, et al, The NBS Tables of Chemical Thermodynamic Properties, *Journal of Physical and Chemical Reference Data,* Vol. 11, Supplement 2, 1982.

Appendix V.2 Standard Enthalpies of Formation and Combustion of Organic Compounds

Common name	Systematic name	CAS Reg. No.	Chemical formula	Molar mass M kg/kmol	ΔH_f^{o1}	$-\Delta H_c^{o2}$ Gross	$-\Delta H_c^{o2}$ Net
A. Normal Alkanes							
Methane	Methane	74-82-8	CH_4,g	16.0425	-74.52	890.65	802.62
Ethane	Ethane	74-84-0	C_2H_6,g	30.0690	-83.82	1560.69	1428.64
			C_2H_6,l*		-93.46	1551.05	1419.00
Propane	Propane	74-98-6	C_3H_8,g	44.0956	-104.68	2219.17	2043.11
			C_3H_8,l*		-121.08	2202.77	2026.71
n-Butane	1-Butane	106-97-8	C_4H_{10},g*	58.1222	-125.79	2877.40	2657.32
			C_4H_{10},l		-147.53	2855.66	2635.58
n-Pentane	1-Pentane	109-66-0	C_5H_{12},g	72.1488	-146.76	3535.77	3271.67
			C_5H_{12},l		-173.49	3509.04	3244.94
n-Hexane	1-Hexane	110-54-3	C_6H_{14},g	86.1754	-166.92	4194.95	3886.84
			C_6H_{14},l		-198.66	4163.21	3855.10
n-Heptane	1-Heptane	142-82-5	C_7H_{16},g	100.2019	-187.65	4853.55	4501.46
			C_7H_{16},l		-224.22	4816.98	4464.89
n-Octane	1-Octane	111-65-9	C_8H_{18},g	114.2285	-208.82	5511.72	5115.62
			C_8H_{18},l		-250.29	5470.26	5074.15
n-Nonane	1-Nonane	111-84-2	C_9H_{20},g	128.2551	-228.74	6171.0	5730.9
			C_9H_{20},l		-275.18	6124.6	5684.5
n-Decane	1-Decane	124-18-5	$C_{10}H_{22}$,g	142.2817	-249.46	6829.7	6345.6
			$C_{10}H_{22}$,l		-300.83	6778.3	6294.2

(*Contd.*)

[1] ΔH_f^o = Standard enthalpy of formation at 25°C (298.15 K) and 1 bar, kJ/mol

[2] ΔH_c^o = Standard enthalpy t of combustion at 25°C (298.15 K) and 1 bar, kJ/mol

State: c - crystal, g - gas, l - liquid,

* at saturation pressure

Appendix V.2 *(Contd.)*

Common name	Systematic name	CAS Reg. No.	Chemical formula	Molar mass M kg/kmol	ΔH_f°	$-\Delta H_c^\circ$ Gross	$-\Delta H_c^\circ$ Net
B. Branched Alkanes and Cycloalkanes							
Isobutane	2-Methylpropane	75-28-5	C_4H_{10},g / C_4H_{10},l*	58.1222	−134.99 / −155.22	2868.20 / 2847.97	2648.12 / 2627.89
Isopentane	2-Methylbutane	78-78-4	C_5H_{12},g / C_5H_{12},l	72.1488	−153.70 / −178.89	3528.83 / 3503.64	3264.73 / 3239.54
Neopentane	2,2-Dimethylpropane	463-82-1	C_5H_{12},g* / C_5H_{12},l	72.1488	−167.92 / −190.31	3514.61 / 3492.22	3250.51 / 3228.12
Isohexane	2-Methylpentane	107-83-5	C_6H_{14},g / C_6H_{14},l	86.1754	−174.55 / −204.65	4187.32 / 4157.22	3879.21 / 3849.11
3-Methylpentane	3-Methylpentane	96-14-0	C_6H_{14},g / C_6H_{14},l	86.1754	−171.97 / −202.39	4189.90 / 4159.48	3881.79 / 3851.37
Neohexane	2,2-Dimethylbutane	75-83-2	C_6H_{14},g / C_6H_{14},l	86.1754	−184.68 / −212.66	4177.19 / 4149.21	3869.08 / 3841.10
Biisopropyl	2,3-Dimethylbutane	79-29-8	C_6H_{14},g / C_6H_{14},l	86.1754	−176.80 / −206.15	4185.07 / 4155.72	3876.96 / 3847.61
Cyclopropane	Trimethylene	75-19-4	C_3H_6,g / C_3H_6,l*	42.0797	53.3 / 34.51	2091.3 / 2073.2	1959.3 / 1941.2
Cyclobutane	Tetramethylene	287-23-0	C_4H_8,g / C_4H_8,l*	56.1063	22.7 / −0.3	2745.0 / 2721.1	2568.9 / 2545.0
Cyclopentane	Pentamethylene	287-92-3	C_5H_{10},g / C_5H_{10},l	70.1329	−77.1 / −105.8	3319.6 / 3290.9	3099.5 / 3070.8
Cyclohexane (Benzene Hydride)	Hexahydrobenzene	110-82-7	C_6H_{12},g / C_6H_{12},l	84.1595	−123.1 / −156.2	3952.9 / 3919.8	3688.9 / 3655.8
Styrene	Vinylbenzene	100-42-5	C_8H_8,g / C_8H_8,l	104.1491	147.36 / 103.89	4438.76 / 4395.29	4262.72 / 4219.25

(Contd.)

Appendix V.2   *(Contd.)*

Common name	Systematic name	CAS Reg. No.	Chemical formula	Molar mass M kg/kmol	ΔH_f^0	$-\Delta H_c^0$ Gross	$-\Delta H_c^0$ Net
C. Unsaturated Aliphatic Hydrocarbons							
Ethylene	Ethene	74-85-1	C_2H_4,g	28.0532	52.50	1411.2	1323.1
Allene	1,2-Propadiene	463-49-0	C_3H_4,g	40.0639	190.92	1944.35	1856.32
Propylene	Propene	115-07-1	C_3H_6,g*	42.0797	20.00	2058.0	1926.0
			C_3H_6,l		3.96	2042.0	1909.9
1-Butene	1-Butylene	106-98-9	C_4H_8,g*	56.1063	−0.54	2716.8	2540.8
(But-1-ene)			C_4H_8,l		−21.4	2696.0	2519.9
cis-But-2-ene	(Z)-But-2-ene	590-18-1	C_4H_8,g	56.1063	−7.40	2710.0	2533.9
			C_4H_8,l*		−29.9	2687.5	2511.4
trans-But-2-ene	(E)-But-2-ene	624-64-6	C_4H_8,g*	56.1063	−11.00	2706.4	2530.3
			C_4H_8,l		−33.0	2684.4	2508.3
Isobutene	2-Methyl-1-propene	115-11-7	C_4H_8,g	56.1063	−17.1	2700.3	2524.2
(Isobutylene)			C_4H_8,l*		−38.2	2679.2	2503.1
1,2-Butadiene	Methylallene	590-19-2	C_4H_6,g	54.0904	162.26	2593.79	2461.74
			C_4H_6,l		138.99	2570.52	2438.49
1,3-Butadiene	Divinyl	106-99-0	C_4H_6,g	54.0904	109.24	2541.74	2409.69
	(*trans*-Butadiene)		C_4H_6,l		87.19	2520.32	2388.31
α-Amylene	*n*-Pentene	109-67-1	C_5H_{10},g	70.1329	−21.3	3375.4	3155.3
	(Pent-1-ene)		C_5H_{10},l		−47.0	3349.7	3129.6
Cyclopropene	1-Cyclopropene	2781-85-3	C_3H_4,g	40.0639	277.1	2029.3	1941.3
			C_3H_4,l		258.8	2011.0	1923.0
Cyclobutene	1-Cyclobutene	822-35-5	C_4H_6,g	54.0904	156.7	2588.2	2456.2
			C_4H_6,l		133.4	2564.9	2432.9
Cyclopentene	1-Cyclopentene	142-29-0	C_5H_8,g	68.1170	33.9	3144.8	2968.7
			C_5H_8,l		4.3	3115.7	2939.6
Cyclohexene	1-Cyclohexene	110-83-8	C_6H_{10},g	82.1436	−4.9	3785.3	3565.2
(Benzene tetrahydride)			C_6H_{10},l		−38.4	3751.8	3531.8

(Contd.)

Appendix V.2 (*Contd.*)

Common name	Systematic name	CAS Reg. No.	Chemical formula	Molar mass M kg/kmol	ΔH°_f	$-\Delta H^\circ_c$ Gross	$-\Delta H^\circ_c$ Net
Acetylene	Ethyne	74-86-2	C_2H_2,g	26.0373	228.20	1301.0	1257.0
Methylacetylene (Allylene)	Propyne	74-99-7	C_3H_4,g	40.0639	184.51	1936.7	1848.7
Ethylacetylene (Ethylethyne)	But-1-yne	107-00-6	C_4H_6,g	54.0904	165.23	2596.8	2464.7
			C_4H_6,l*		141.9	2573.4	2441.4
D. Aromatic Hydrocarbons							
Anthracene	Paranaphthalene	120-12-7	$C_{14}H_{10}$,g	178.2292	227.69	7165.97	6945.91
			$C_{14}H_{10}$,c		129.20	7067.48	6847.43
Benzene	(6)Annulene	71-43-2	C_6H_6,g	78.1118	82.93	3301.5	3169.4
			C_6H_6,l		49.08	3267.6	3135.6
Toluene	Methylbenzene (Phenylmethane)	108-88-3	C_7H_8,g	92.1384	50.17	3948.1	3772.0
			C_7H_8,l		12.18	3910.1	3734.0
Ethylbenzene	Phenylethane	100-41-4	C_8H_{10},g	106.1650	29.92	4607.1	4387.1
			C_8H_{10},l		-12.34	4564.9	4344.8
o-Xylene	1,2-Dimethylbenzene	95-47-6	C_8H_{10},g	106.1650	19.08	4596.3	4376.2
			C_8H_{10},l		-24.35	4552.9	4332.8
m-Xylene	1,3-Dimethylbenzene	108-38-3	C_8H_{10},g	106.1650	17.32	4594.5	4374.5
			C_8H_{10},l		-25.35	4551.9	4331.8
p-Xylene	1,4-Dimethylbenzene	106-42-3	C_8H_{10},g	106.1650	18.03	4595.3	4375.2
			C_8H_{10},l		-25.35	4551.9	4331.8
			C_8H_{10},l		-24.35	4552.9	4332.8
Biphenyl	Diphenyl (Phenylbenzene)	92-52-4	$C_{12}H_{10}$,g	154.2078	181.4	6332.67	6112.62
			$C_{12}H_{10}$,l		116.0	6267.27	6047.22
			$C_{12}H_{10}$,c		99.4	6250.67	6030.62
Naphthalene	Naphthalene	91-20-3	$C_{10}H_8$,g	128.1705	150.58	5229.00	5052.95
			$C_{10}H_8$,c		78.53	5156.95	4980.90

(*Contd.*)

Appendix V.2 (*Contd.*)

Common name	Systematic name	CAS Reg. No.	Chemical formula	Molar mass M kg/kmol	ΔH°_f	$-\Delta H^\circ_c$ Gross	$-\Delta H^\circ_c$ Net
E. Organic Compounds Containing Carbon-Hydrogen-Oxygen							
Methanol	Methyl alcohol	67-56-1	CH_4O,g	32.0419	−200.94	764.23	676.21
			CH_4O,l		−238.91	726.26	638.24
			CH_4O,ao		−245.93	—	—
Ethanol	Ethyl alcohol	64-17-5	C_2H_6O,g	46.0684	−234.95	1409.56	1277.53
			C_2H_6O,l		−277.51	1367.00	1234.97
			C_2H_6O,ao		−288.3	—	—
n-Propanol (*n*-Propyl alcohol)	1-Propanol	71-23-8	C_3H_8O,g	60.0950	−255.20	2068.65	1892.61
			C_3H_8O,l		−302.70	2021.15	1845.11
Isopropanol (Isopropyl alcohol)	2-Propanol	67-63-0	C_3H_8O,g	60.0950	−272.29	2051.56	1875.52
			C_3H_8O,l		−317.90	2005.95	1829.91
n-Butanol (*n*-Butyl alcohol)	1-Butanol	71-36-3	$C_4H_{10}O$,g	74.1216	−274.60	2728.59	2508.54
			$C_4H_{10}O$,l		−326.60	2676.20	2456.15
Isobutanol (Isobutyl Alcohol)	2-Methyl-1-Propanol	78-83-1	$C_4H_{10}O$,g	74.1216	−282.92	2720.27	2500.22
			$C_4H_{10}O$,l		−334.09	2669.10	2449.05
sec-Butanol (*sec*-Butyl alcohol)	2-Butanol	78-92-2	$C_4H_{10}O$,g	74.1216	−292.88	2710.31	2490.26
			$C_4H_{10}O$,l		−342.50	2660.69	2440.64
tert-Butanol (*tert*-Butyl Alcohol)	2-Methyl-2-Propanol	75-65-0	$C_4H_{10}O$,g	74.1216	−312.46	2690.73	2470.68
			$C_4H_{10}O$,l		−359.24	2643.95	2423.90
			$C_4H_{10}O$,c		−365.89	2637.30	2417.25
n-Pentanol (*n*-Butylcarbinol)	*n*-Amyl alcohol	71-41-0	$C_5H_{12}O$,g	88.0948	−300.16	3382.37	3118.31
			$C_5H_{12}O$,l		−357.10	3325.43	3061.37
Ctclohexanol Hexahydrophenol (Hydroxycyclohexane)		108-93-0	$C_6H_{12}O$,g	100.1589	−286.2	3789.84	3525.78
			$C_6H_{12}O$,l		−348.2	3727.84	3463.78
Cyclohexanone	Cyclohexyl ketone	108-94-1	$C_6H_{10}O$,g	98.1430	−226.1	3564.11	3344.06
			$C_6H_{10}O$,l		−271.2	3519.01	3298.96
Phenol	Hydroxybenzene	108-95-2	C_6H_5OH,g	94.1112	−96.40	3122.15	2990.12
			C_6H_5OH,c		−166.65	3051.90	2919.87

(*Contd.*)

Appendix V.2 (Contd.)

Common name	Systematic name	CAS Reg. No.	Chemical formula	Molar mass M kg/kmol	ΔH°_f	$-\Delta H^\circ_c$ Gross	$-\Delta H^\circ_c$ Net
o-Cresol	o-Methylphenylol	95-48-7	C_7H_7OH,g	108.1378	-128.57	3769.32	2957.95
			C_7H_7OH,c		-204.60	3693.29	2881.92
m-Cresol	m-Methylphenol	108-39-4	C_7H_7OH,g	108.1378	-132.30	3765.59	2954.22
			C_7H_7OH,l		-194.01	3703.88	2892.51
p-Cresol	p-Methylphenol	106-44-5	C_7H_7OH,g	108.1378	-125.35	3772.54	2961.17
			C_7H_7OH,c		-199.28	3698.61	2887.24
1-Naphthol (α-Naphthol)	1-Naphthalenol	90-15-3	$C_{10}H_8O$,g	144.1699	-29.9	5048.52	4872.48
			$C_{10}H_8O$,c		-121.0	4957.42	4781.38
2-Naphthol (β-Naphthol)	2-Naphthalenol	135-19-3	$C_{10}H_8O$,g	144.1699	-30.0	5048.42	4872.38
			$C_{10}H_8O$,c		-124.2	4954.22	4778.18
Ethylene Glycol (Mono)ethylene Glycol	1,2-Ethanediol	107-21-1	$C_2H_6O_2$,g	62.0678	-389.0	1255.51	1123.48
			$C_2H_6O_2$,l		-455.7	1188.81	1056.78
1,2-Propylene Glycol	1,2-Propanediol	57-55-6	$C_3H_8O_2$,g	76.0944	-433.0	1890.85	1714.81
			$C_3H_8O_2$,l		-498.0	1825.85	1649.81
1,3-Propylene Glycol	1,3-Propanediol	504-63-2	$C_3H_8O_2$,g	76.0944	-409.0	1914.85	1738.81
			$C_3H_8O_2$,l		-482.0	1841.85	1665.81
Glycerine (Glycerol)	1,2,3-Propanetriol	56-81-5	$C_3H_8O_3$,g	92.0938	-582.7	1741.15	1565.11
			$C_3H_8O_3$,l		-668.5	1655.35	1479.31
Acetaldehyde	Ethanal	75-07-0	C_2H_4O,g	44.0526	-166.1	1192.58	1104.56
			C_2H_4O,l		-192.2	1166.48	1078.46
Propionaldehyde	Propanal	123-38-6	C_3H_6O,g	58.0791	-186.3	1851.72	1719.69
			C_3H_6O,l		-216.2	1821.82	1689.79
Acetone	2-Propanone	67-64-1	C_3H_6O,g	58.0791	-216.3	1821.72	1689.69
			C_3H_6O,l		-248.0	1790.02	1657.99
Camphor	2-Camphonone	76-22-2	$C_{10}H_{16}O$,g	152.2334	-267.5	5954.24	5602.16
			$C_{10}H_{16}O$,c		-319.4	5902.34	5550.26

(Contd.)

Appendix V.2   *(Contd.)*

Common name	Systematic name	CAS Reg. No.	Chemical formula	Molar mass M kg/kmol	ΔH°_f	$-\Delta H^\circ_c$ Gross	$-\Delta H^\circ_c$ Net
Methyl Ethyl Ketone	2-Butanone	78-93-3	C_4H_8O,g	72.1057	-239.0	2478.36	2302.32
			C_4H_8O,l		-273.5	2443.86	2267.82
Acetic Anhydride	Ethanoic Anhydride	108-24-7	$C_4H_6O_3$,g	102.0886	-572.5	1859.03	1727.00
			$C_4H_6O_3$,l		-624.4	1807.13	1675.10
Formaldehyde	Methanal	50-00-0	HCHO,g	30.0260	-108.6	570.74	526.73
			HCHO,aq		-170.7	—	—
Formic Acid	Methanoic Acid	64-18-6	CH_2O_2,g	46.0254	-378.8	300.54	256.53
			CH_2O_2,l		-424.8	254.54	210.53
Acetic Acid	Ethanoic Acid	64-19-7	$C_2H_4O_2$,g	60.0520	-432.6	926.08	838.06
			$C_2H_4O_2$,l		-484.2	874.48	786.46
Acrylic Acid	2-Propenoic Acid	79-10-7	$C_3H_4O_2$,g	72.0626	-322.6	1429.59	1341.57
			$C_3H_4O_2$,l		-383.8	1368.39	1280.37
Adipic Acvid	1,6-Hexanedioic acid	124-04-9	$C_6H_{10}O_4$,g	146.1412	-865.0	2925.21	2705.16
			$C_6H_{10}O_4$,c		-994.3	2795.91	2575.86
Propionic Acid	Propanoic Acid	79-09-4	$C_3H_6O_2$,g	74.0785	-452.8	1585.22	1453.19
			$C_3H_6O_2$,l		-507.8	1530.22	1398.19
n-Butyric Acid	Butanoic Acid	107-92-6	$C_4H_8O_2$,g	88.1051	-473.6	2243.76	2067.72
			$C_4H_8O_2$,l		-531.6	2185.76	2009.72
Citric Acid	1,2,3 Propanetricarboxylic Acid	77-92-9	$C_6H_8O_7$,c	192.1235	-1543.8	1960.58	1784.54
Oxalic Acid	Ethanedioic acid	144-62-7	$C_2H_2O_4$,g	90.0349	-723.7	349.15	305.14
			$C_2H_2O_4$,c		-821.7	251.15	207.14
Palmitic Acid	Hexadecanoic Acid	57-10-3	$C_{16}H_{32}O_2$,g	256.4241	-737.1	10132.34	9428.18
			$C_{16}H_{32}O_2$,l		-838.1	10031.34	9327.18
			$C_{16}H_{32}O_2$,c		-891.5	9977.94	9273.78
Salicylic Acid	2-Hydroxybenzoic acid	69-72-7	$C_7H_6O_3$,g	138.1207	-494.8	3117.26	2985.23
			$C_7H_6O_3$,c		-589.9	3022.16	2890.13

(Contd.)

Appendix V.2 (Contd.)

Common name	Systematic name	CAS Reg. No.	Chemical formula	Molar mass M kg/kmol	ΔH_f^0	$-\Delta H_c^0$ Gross	$-\Delta H_c^0$ Net
Stearic Acid	Octadecanoic Acid	57-11-4	$C_{18}H_{36}O_2,g$ $C_{18}H_{36}O_2,l$ $C_{18}H_{36}O_2,c$	284.4772	-781.2 -884.7 -947.7	11446.92 11343.42 11280.42	10654.74 10551.24 10488.24
Oleic Acid	(Z)-9-Octadecenoic Acid	112-80-1	$C_{18}H_{34}O_2,l$	282.4614	-764.8	11177.49	10429.32
o-Phthalic Acid	1,2-Benzenedicarboxylic Acid	88-99-3	$C_8H_6O_4,c$	166.1308	-782.0	3223.57	3091.54
m-Phthalic Acid	1,3-Benzenedicarboxylic Acid (Isophthalic Acid)	121-91-5	$C_8H_6O_4,g$ $C_8H_6O_4,c$	166.1308	-696.3 -803.0	3309.27 3202.57	3177.24 3070.54
p-Phthalic Acid	1,4-Benzenedicarboxylic Acid (Terephthalic Acid)	100-21-0	$C_8H_6O_4,g$ $C_8H_6O_4,c$	166.1308	-717.9 -816.1	3287.67 3189.47	3155.64 3057.44
Methyl Formate	Methyl Methanoate	107-31-3	$C_2H_4O_2,g$ $C_2H_4O_2,l$	60.0520	-352.4 -381.1	1006.28 977.58	918.26 889.56
Ethyl Formate	Ethyl Methanoate	109-94-4	$C_3H_6O_2,g$ $C_3H_6O_2,l$	74.0785	-388.3 -420.5	1649.72 1617.52	1517.69 1485.49
Methyl Acetate	Methyl Ethanoate	79-20-9	$C_3H_6O_2,g$ $C_3H_6O_2,l$	74.0785	-408.8 -441.4	1629.22 1596.62	1497.19 1464.59
Ethyl Acetate	Ethyl Ethanoate	141-78-6	$C_4H_8O_2,g$ $C_4H_8O_2,l$	88.1051	-444.5 -480.0	2272.86 2237.36	2096.82 2061.32
Propyl Acetate	Propyl Ethanoate	109-60-4	$C_5H_{10}O_2,g$ $C_5H_{10}O_2,l$	102.1317	-464.8 -504.4	2931.90 2892.30	2711.85 2672.25
Isopropyl Acetate	Isopropyl Ethanoate	108-21-4	$C_5H_{10}O_2,g$ $C_5H_{10}O_2,l$	102.1317	-481.7 -518.9	2915.00 2877.80	2694.95 2657.75
Methyl n-butanoate	Methyl n-butyrate	623-42-7	$C_5H_{10}O_2,g$ $C_5H_{10}O_2,l$	102.1317	-450.1 -490.0	2946.00 2906.70	2735.95 2686.65

(Contd.)

Appendix V.2 *(Contd.)*

Common name	Systematic name	CAS Reg. No.	Chemical formula	Molar mass M kg/kmol	ΔH°_f	$-\Delta H^\circ_c$ Gross	$-\Delta H^\circ_c$ Net
Butyl Acetate	Butyl Ethanoate	123-86-4	$C_6H_{12}O_2$,g $C_6H_{12}O_2$,l	116.1583	-485.3 -528.9	3590.74 3547.14	3326.68 3283.08
Dimethyl Ether (Methyl Ether)	Methoxymethane (Refrigerant E170)	115-10-6	C_2H_6O,g C_2H_6O,l*	46.0684	-184.0 -203.5	1460.51 1441.01	1328.48 1308.98
Ethyl Methyl Ether (Methyl Ethyl Ether)	Methoxyethane	540-67-0	C_3H_8O,g C_3H_8O,l*	60.0950	-216.4 -240.7	2107.45 2083.15	1931.41 1907.11
Ethyl *tert*-butyl Ether (ETBE)	2-Ethoxy-2-methyl Propane	637-92-3	$C_6H_{14}O$,g $C_6H_{14}O$,l	102.1748	-316.5 -351.6	4045.37 4010.27	3737.30 3702.20
Diethyl Ether	Ethoxyethane	60-29-7	$C_4H_{10}O$,g $C_4H_{10}O$,l	74.1216	-252.0 -279.2	2751.19 2723.99	2531.14 2503.94
Methyl *tert*-butyl Ether (MTBE)	2-Methoxy-2-methyl Propane	1634-04-4	$C_5H_{12}O$,g $C_5H_{12}O$,l	88.1482	-283.2 -313.6	3399.33 3368.93	3135.27 3104.87
Benzaldehyde	Phenylmethanal	100-52-7	C_7H_6O,g C_7H_6O,l	106.1219	-36.7 -87.0	3575.36 3525.06	3443.33 3393.03
Benzoic Acid	Benzenecarboxylic acid	65-85-0	$C_7H_6O_2$,g $C_7H_6O_2$,c	122.1213	-294.1 -384.8	3317.96 3227.26	3185.93 8095.23
Benzyl Alcohol	Benzenemethanol (α-Toluenol)	100-51-6	C_7H_8O,g C_7H_8O,l	108.1378	-100.4 -161.0	3797.49 3736.89	3621.45 3860.85
Benzyl Methyl Ketone (Phenylacetone)	1-Phenyl-2-propane	103-79-7	$C_9H_{10}O$,g $C_9H_{10}O$,l	134.1751	-100.7 -151.9	4870.04 4818.84	4649.99 4598.79
Ethylene Oxide (Oxirane)	1,2-Epoxyethane (Ethene Oxide)	75-21-8	C_2H_4O,g C_2H_4O,l	44.0526	-52.63 -77.4	1306.05 1281.32	1210.03 1193.30
α-*D*-Glucose	α-*D*-Glucopyranose	26655-34-5	$C_6H_{12}O_6$,c	180.1559	-1273.3	2802.74	2538.68
D-Fructose	β-*D*-Fructose	57-48-7	$C_6H_{12}O_6$,c	180.1559	-1265.6	2810.44	2546.38
D-Sucrose	β-*D*-Fructofuranosyl (α-*D*-Glucopyranoside)	57-50-1	$C_{12}H_{22}O_{11}$,c	342.2965	-2226.1	5640.15	5156.04

(Contd.)

Appendix V.2 (*Contd.*)

Common name	Systematic name	CAS Reg. No.	Chemical formula	Molar mass M kg/kmol	ΔH_f°	$-\Delta H_c^\circ$ Gross	$-\Delta H_c^\circ$ Net
Hydroquinone	1,4-Benzenediol	123-31-9	$C_6H_6O_2$,g	110.1106	−265.3	3239.08	3063.04
			$C_6H_6O_2$,c		−364.5	3139.88	2963.84
Propylene Oxide (Methyloxirane)	1,2-Epoxypropane (Propene Oxide)	75-56-9	C_3H_6O,g	58.0791	−93.73	1944.29	1812.26
			C_3H_6O,l		−121.63	1916.39	1784.36
Tetrahydrofuran (Oxolane) (Oxacyclopentane)	1,4-Epoxybutane	109-99-9	C_4H_8O,g	72.1057	−184.18	2533.18	2357.14
			C_4H_8O,l		−216.22	2501.14	2325.10
Furan (Oxole)	Oxacyclopentadiene	110-00-9	C_4H_4O,g	68.0740	−34.9	2110.80	2022.78
			C_4H_4O,l		−62.3	2083.40	1995.38
Furfural (Furfuraldehyde) (Furfurol)	2-Furancarboxaldehyde	98-01-1	$C_5H_4O_2$,g	96.0841	−151.0	2388.21	2300.19
			$C_5H_4O_2$,l,		−201.6	2337.61	2249.59
Resorcinol	1,3-Benzenediol	108-46-3	$C_6H_6O_2$,g	110.1106	−274.7	2943.85	2811.82
			$C_6H_6O_2$,c		−368.0	2850.55	2718.52

F. Organic Compounds Containing Nitrogen

Common name	Systematic name	CAS Reg. No.	Chemical formula	Molar mass M kg/kmol	ΔH_f°	$-\Delta H_c^\circ$ Gross	$-\Delta H_c^\circ$ Net
Acetamide	Ethanamide	60-35-5	C_2H_5NO,g	59.0672	−238.3	1263.30	1153.27
			C_2H_5NO,c		−317.0	1184.60	1074.57
Acetonitrile (Methyl Cyanide)	Ethanenitrile	75-05-8	C_2H_3N,g	41.05192	64.3	1280.07	1214.05
			C_2H_3N,l		31.4	1247.17	1181.15
Caprolactam	Hexahydro-2H-azepin-2-one	105-60-2	$C_6H_{11}NO$,g	113.1576	−239.6	3693.53	3451.47
			$C_6H_{11}NO$,c		−329.4	3603.73	3361.67
Methyl Amine	Methanamine	74-89-5	CH_5N,g	31.0571	−22.53	1085.56	975.53
			CH_5N,l		−47.27	1060.82	950.79
Cyanamide	Amidocyanogen	420-04-2	CH_2N_2,c	42.0400	58.8	738.14	694.13
Ethyl Amine	Ethanamine	75-04-7	C_2H_7N,g	45.0837	−47.47	1739.96	1585.92
			C_2H_7N,l		−74.13	1713.30	1559.26

(*Contd.*)

Appendix V.2 (*Contd.*)

Common name	Systematic name	CAS Reg. No.	Chemical formula	Molar mass M kg/kmol	ΔH°_{f}	$-\Delta H^{\circ}_{c}$ Gross	$-\Delta H^{\circ}_{c}$ Net
Dimethyl Amine	Methylmethanamine	124-40-3	C_2H_7N,g C_2H_7N,l	45.0837	-18.8 -42.6	1768.63 1744.83	1614.59 1590.79
n-Propyl Amine	1-Propanamine	107-10-8	C_3H_9N,g C_3H_9N,l	59.1103	-70.10 -101.47	2396.67 2365.30	2198.62 2167.25
n-Butyl Amine	1-Butanamine	109-73-9	$C_4H_{11}N$,g $C_4H_{11}N$,l	73.1368	-91.76 -127.6	3054.35 3018.51	2812.29 2776.45
Diethyl Amine	N-Ethylethanamine	109-89-7	$C_4H_{11}N$,g $C_4H_{11}N$,l	73.1368	-71.7 -103.2	3074.41 3042.91	2832.35 2800.85
Hydrogen Cyanide (Hydrocyanic Acid)	Methanenitrile	74-90-8	CHN,g CHN,l	27.0253	135.14 108.87	671.57 645.30	649.56 623.29
Acetamilide	N-Phenylacetamide	103-84-4	C_8H_9NO,g C_8H_9NO,c	135.1632	-128.9 -209.6	4305.42 4224.72	4107.37 4026.67
Acrylonitrile	Prop-2-enenitrile	107-13-1	C_3H_3N,g C_3H_3N,l	53.0626	180.6 147.1	1789.88 1756.38	1723.86 1690.36
Cyanogen (Oxalonitrile)	Ethanedinitrile	460-19-5	C_2N_2,g C_2N_2,l	52.0348	306.7 285.9	1093.72 1072.92	1093.72 1072.92
Aniline	Benzenamine	62-53-3	C_6H_7N,g C_6H_7N,l	93.1265	87.46 31.63	3448.97 3392.97	3294.93 3238.93
Glycine	Aminoacetic acid	56-40-6	$C_2H_5NO_2$,g $C_2H_5NO_2$,c	75.0666	-392.1 -528.5	1109.50 973.10	999.47 863.07
Nitrobenzene	Nitrobenzene	98-95-3	$C_6H_5NO_2$,g $C_6H_5NO_2$,l	123.1094	67.5 12.5	3143.14 3088.14	3033.11 2978.11
o-Nitrotoluene	1-Methyl-2-Nitrobenzene	88-72-2	$C_7H_7NO_2$,l	137.1360	-9.7	3745.28	3591.24
m-Nitrotoluene	1-Methyl-3-Nitrobenzene	99-08-1	$C_7H_7NO_2$,l	137.1360	-31.5	3723.48	3569.44
p-Nitrotoluene	1-Methyl-4-Nitrobenzene	99-99-0	$C_7H_7NO_2$,g $C_7H_7NO_2$,c	137.1360	31.0 -48.1	3785.98 3706.88	3631.94 3552.84

(*Contd.*)

Appendix V.2 *(Contd.)*

Common name	Systematic name	CAS Reg. No.	Chemical formula	Molar mass M kg/kmol	ΔH_f°	$-\Delta H_c^\circ$ Gross	$-\Delta H_c^\circ$ Net
o-Toluidine (*o*-Methyl Aniline)	2-Methylbenzenamine	95-53-4	C_7H_9N,g	107.1531	56.4	4097.21	3899.16
m-Toluidine (*m*-Methyl Aniline)	3-Methylbenzenamine	108-44-1	C_7H_9N,l C_7H_9N,g C_7H_9N,l	107.1531	-6.3 54.6 -8.1	4034.51 4095.41 4032.71	3836.46 3897.36 3834.66
p-Toluidine (*p*-Methyl Aniline)	4-Methylbenzenamine	106-49-0	C_7H_9N,g C_7H_9N,c	107.1531	55.3 -23.5	4096.11 4017.31	3898.06 3819.26
Pyridine (Azine)	Azabenzene	110-86-1	C_5H_5N,g C_5H_5N,l	79.0999	140.4 100.2	2822.53 2782.33	2712.50 2672.30
Benzamide	Benzoic acid amide	55-21-0	C_7H_7NO,c	121.1366	-202.6	3552.38	3398.34
Urea (Carbonyldiamide)	Carbonyldiamide (Carbonyldiamine)	57-13-6	CH_4N_2O,g CH_4N_2O,c	60.0553	-245.8 -333.51	719.37 631.66	631.35 543.64
Nitroglycerine	1,2,3-Propanetriol trinitrate	55-63-0	$C_3H_5N_3O_9$,g $C_3H_5N_3O_9$,l	227.0865	-270.9 -370.9	1624.21 1524.21	1514.18 1414.18
G. Organic Compounds Containing Halogens							
Chlorotrifluoromethane	Chlorotrifluoromethane	75-72-9	$CClF_3$,g	104.4589	-706.2	—	—
Dichlorodifluoromethane	Dichlorodifluoromethane	75-71-8	CCl_2F_2,g	120.9135	-477.4	—	—
Trichlorofluoromethane	Trichlorofluoromethane	75-69-4	CCl_3F,g CCl_3F,l	137.3681	-276.0 -301.33	—	—
Carbon Tetrachloride	Tetrachloromethane	56-23-5	CCl_4,g CCl_4,l	153.8227	-102.9 -135.44	—	—
Chlorodifluoromethane	Chlorodifluoromethane	75-45-6	$CHClF_2$,g	86.4684	-482.6	—	—
Chloroform	Trichloromethane	67-66-3	$CHCl_3$,g $CHCl_3$,l	119.3776	-103.14 -134.47	—	—
Fluoroform	Trifluoromethane	75-46-7	CHF_3,g	70.0138	-688.3	—	—

(Contd.)

Appendix V.2 (*Contd.*)

Common name	Systematic name	CAS Reg. No.	Chemical formula	Molar mass M kg/kmol	ΔH_f°	$-\Delta H_c^{\circ}$ Gross	$-\Delta H_c^{\circ}$ Net
Methylene Chloride	Dichloromethane	75-09-2	CH_2Cl_2,g CH_2Cl_2,l	84.9326	−92.47 −121.46	— —	— —
Methylene Fluoride	Difluoromethane	75-10-5	CH_2F_2,g	52.0234	−446.9	—	—
Methyl Bromide	Bromomethane	74-83-9	CH_3Br,g CH_3Br,l	94.9385	−35.1 −59.4	— —	— —
Methyl Chloride	Chloromethane	74-87-3	CH_3Cl,g CH_3Cl,l	50.4875	−80.83 −102.4	— —	— —
Methyl Iodide	Iodomethane	74-88-4	CH_3I,g CH_3I,l	141.9390	13.0 −15.5	— —	— —
1,1,1-Trichloroethane	Methyl Chloroform	71-55-6	$C_2H_3Cl_3$,g $C_2H_3Cl_3$,l	133.4042	−144.6 −177.4	— —	— —
1,1,2-Trichloroethane	Vinyl Trichloride	79-00-5	$C_2H_3Cl_3$,g $C_2H_3Cl_3$,l	133.4042	−151.2 −191.5	— —	— —
Ethylene Dichloride	1,2-Dichloroethane	107-06-2	$C_2H_4Cl_2$,g $C_2H_4Cl_2$,l	98.9592	−129.79 −165.23	— —	— —
Ethylidene Chloride	1,1-Dichloroethane	75-34-3	$C_2H_4Cl_2$,g $C_2H_4Cl_2$,l	98.9592	−129.41 −160.20	— —	— —
Ethyl Bromide	Bromoethane	74-96-4	C_2H_5Br,g C_2H_5Br,l	108.9651	−64.52 −92.01	— —	— —
Ethyl Chloride	Chloroethane	75-00-3	C_2H_5Cl,g C_2H_5Cl,l	64.5141	−112.17 −136.52	— —	— —
Ethyl Iodide	Iodoethane	75-03-6	C_2H_5I,g C_2H_5I,l	155.9656	−7.7 −40.2	— —	— —
Ethyl Fluoride	Fluoroethane	353-36-6	C_2H_5F,g	48.0595	−263.2	—	—

(*Contd.*)

Appendix V.2 *(Contd.)*

Common name	Systematic name	CAS Reg. No.	Chemical formula	Molar mass M kg/kmol	ΔH_f^0	$-\Delta H_c^0$ Gross	$-\Delta H_c^0$ Net
Phosgene	Carbonic dichloride	75-44-5	$COCl_2$,g	98.9161	−219.1	—	—
Bromobenzene	Phenyl bromide	108-86-1	C_6H_5Br,g	157.0079	105.4	—	—
			C_6H_5Br,l		60.9	—	—
Chlorobenzene	Phenyl Chloride	108-90-7	C_6H_5Cl,g	112.5569	52.0	—	—
			C_6H_5Cl,l		11.0	—	—
Fluorobenzene	Phenyl fluoride	462-06-6	C_6H_5F,g	96.1023	−116.0	—	—
			C_6H_5F,l		−150.6	—	—
Iodobenzene	Phenyl Iodide	591-50-4	C_6H_5I,g	204.0084	164.9	—	—
			C_6H_5I,l		117.2	—	—
Chloroacetic acid	Monochloroethanoic acid	79-11-8	$C_2H_3O_2Cl$,g	94.4970	−435.2	—	—
			$C_2H_3O_2Cl$,l		−479.8	—	—
			$C_2H_3O_2Cl$,c		−511.7	—	—
			$C_2H_2O_2Cl_2$,aq		−496.3	—	—
Dichloroacetic acid	Dichlorethanoic acid	79-43-6	$C_2H_2O_2Cl_2$,l	94.4970	−497.9	—	—
H. Organic Compounds Containing Sulphur							
Methyl mercaptan (Methyl thioalcohol)	Methanethiol	74-93-1	CH_4S,g	48.1075	−22.9	—	—
			CH_4S,l*		−46.7	—	—
Ethyl mercaptan (Ethyl thioalcohol)	Ethanethiol	75-08-1	C_2H_6S,g	62.1340	−46.3	—	—
			C_2H_6S,l		−73.6	—	—
n-Propyl mercaptan (1-Propylthiol)	1-Propanethiol	107-03-9	C_3H_8S,g	76.1606	−67.9	—	—
			C_3H_8S,l		−99.9	—	—

(Contd.)

Appendix V.2 (*Contd.*)

Common name	Systematic name	CAS Reg. No.	Chemical formula	Molar mass M kg/kmol	ΔH°_f	$-\Delta H^\circ_c$ Gross	$-\Delta H^\circ_c$ Net
Thiophene	Thiacyclopentadiene	110-02-1	C_4H_4S,g	84.1396	115.44	—	—
			C_4H_4S,l		80.71	—	—
Benzyl mercaptan	Benzenethiol	108-98-5	C_6H_6S,g	110.1768	112.4	—	—
			C_6H_6S,l		63.7	—	—
Thiourea	β-Thiopseudourea	62-56-6	CSN_2H_4,g	76.1209	22.9	—	—
			CSN_2H_4,c		-88.3	—	—

Extracted and compiled from following references:

1. TRC Thermodynamic Tables - Hydrocarbons and Non-hydrocarbons, Thermophysical Properties Division, National Institute of Standards and Technology (NIST), Bouldor, Colorado, USA, 2001.

2. Wagman, D D *et al*, The NBS Tables of Chemical Thermodynamic Properties, *J. Phys. Chem. Ref. Data*, Vol. 11, Supplement No. 2, 1982.

3. Pedley, J B, Naylor, R D, Kirby, S P; *Thermodyanmic Data of Organic Compounds*, 2nd Edition, Chapman and Hall, UK, 1986.

Index

29589744R00413

Made in the USA
Lexington, KY
31 January 2019